Production and Inventory Control Handbook

ALJIAN · *Purchasing Handbook*

AMERICAN SOCIETY OF TOOL AND MANUFACTURING ENGINEERS · *Manufacturing Planning and Estimating Handbook*

ARKIN · *Handbook of Sampling for Auditing and Accounting*

BAUMEISTER AND MARKS · *Standard Handbook for Mechanical Engineers*

BRADY · *Materials Handbook*

CONDON AND ODISHAW · *Handbook of Physics*

CONOVER · *Grounds Maintenance Handbook*

DICHTER · *Handbook of Consumer Motivations*

DUNN · *International Handbook of Advertising*

FACTORY MUTUAL ENGINEERING DIVISION · *Handbook of Industrial Loss Prevention*

FINK AND CARROLL · *Standard Handbook for Electrical Engineers*

GREENWALD · *McGraw-Hill Dictionary of Modern Economics*

HEYEL · *The Foreman's Handbook*

HUSKEY AND KORN · *Computer Handbook*

IRESON · *Reliability Handbook*

JURAN · *Quality Control Handbook*

KLERER AND KORN · *Digital Computer User's Handbook*

KORN AND KORN · *Mathematical Handbook for Scientists and Engineers*

LANGE · *Handbook of Chemistry*

LASSER · *Business Management Handbook*

LASSER · *Standard Handbook for Accountants*

MAGILL, HOLDEN, AND ACKLEY · *Air Pollution Handbook*

MANAS · *National Plumbing Code Handbook*

MARKUS · *Electronics and Nucleonics Dictionary*

MAYNARD · *Handbook of Business Administration*

MAYNARD · *Industrial Engineering Handbook*

MAYNARD · *Top Management Handbook*

MELCHER AND LARRICK · *Printing and Promotion Handbook*

MERRITT · *Building Construction Handbook*

MERRITT · *Standard Handbook for Civil Engineers*

MORROW · *Maintenance Engineering Handbook*

PERRY · *Engineering Manual*

ROSSNAGEL · *Handbook of Rigging*

SCHMIDT · *Construction Lending Guide*

STANIAR · *Plant Engineering Handbook*

STANLEY · *Handbook of International Marketing*

STEPHENSON · *Handbook of Public Relations*

STETKA · *NFPA Handbook of the National Electrical Code*

YODER, HENEMAN, TURNBULL, AND STONE · *Handbook of Personnel Management and Labor Relations*

Production and Inventory Control Handbook

**Prepared under the Supervision of
the Handbook Editorial Board of APICS —
American Production and Inventory Control Society**

JAMES H. GREENE, Ph.D.

EDITOR-IN-CHIEF

McGRAW-HILL BOOK COMPANY

New York   St. Louis   San Francisco   Düsseldorf   Johannesburg
Kuala Lumpur   London   Mexico   Montreal   New Delhi
Panama   Rio de Janeiro   Singapore   Sydney   Toronto

PRODUCTION AND INVENTORY CONTROL HANDBOOK

Library of Congress Catalog Card Number 79-76144

07-024332-8

67890 KPKP 79876

Editorial Board

Contributors

EMIL ALBERT *Manager, Production Planning and Procurement Department, The Adams and Westlake Company, Elkart, Indiana* (CHAPTERS 7 AND 14)

R. LEONARD ALLEN *Director of Inventory Control, Western Union Telegraph Company, New York, New York* (CHAPTERS 9 AND 21)

JOHN E. ANDERSON *Supervisor, Production and Inventory Control, Miles Laboratories, Inc., Elkhart, Indiana* (CHAPTER 14)

C. MARTIN ANTISDALE *Production Control Manager, Consolidated Diesel Electric Company, Old Greenwich, Connecticut* (CHAPTER 22)

H. DUANE APPLEQUIST *Corporation Coordinator, Work Scheduling and Control, The Standard Oil Company (Ohio), Cleveland, Ohio* (CHAPTER 9)

PAUL F. BACIGALUPO *Senior Systems Engineer, International Business Machines Corp., Waltham, Massachusetts* (CHAPTER 22)

ROBERT H. BAKER *Manager of Manufacturing, Decca Systems, Inc., Riverdale, Maryland* (CHAPTER 5)

E. ROBERT BARLOW *Vice President, Marketing, Rath and Strong, Inc., Boston, Massachusetts* (CHAPTER 4)

CLIFFORD M. BAUMBACK *Professor of Industrial Management, The University of Iowa, Iowa City, Iowa* (CHAPTERS 21 AND 23)

JAMES M. BECK *Manager of Research, Booz, Allen and Hamilton, Chicago, Illinois* (CHAPTER 2)

WALTER H. BEERS *Section Manager, Systems Analysis, McDonnell Aircraft Company, St. Louis, Missouri* (CHAPTER 24)

HENRY BENNETT *Manager, Materials Management, Miles Laboratories, Inc., West Haven, Connecticut* (CHAPTER 2)

W. NEIL BENTON *Vice President, Production, Booz, Allen and Hamilton, New York, New York* (CHAPTER 10)

RICHARD B. BLACK *Vice President, Finance and Operations, Maremont Corporation, Chicago, Illinois* (CHAPTER 10)

ROBERT G. BROWN *Industry Consultant, International Business Machines Corp., White Plains, New York* (CHAPTER 19)

BENJAMIN F. BUTTS *Principal, Management Consulting Service, Ernst and Ernst, Chicago, Illinois* (CHAPTER 3)

JOSEPH A. CARRANO   *Corporate Manager of Production Planning and Control, Hazeltine Corporation, Little Neck, New York* (CHAPTER 10)

M. A. CEPNIK   *Production Systems Planning Department, Chrysler Corporation, Highland Park, Michigan* (CHAPTER 24)

J. A. CHOBANIAN   *Corporate Control and Systems Engineer, J. I. Case Company, Racine, Wisconsin* (CHAPTER 17)

ROGER W. CHRISTIAN   *Modern Manufacturing, McGraw-Hill Publishing Company, New York, New York* (CHAPTER 30)

CALVIN WAYNE CHURCHMAN   *Production Planning Manager, Automatic Electric Company, Northlake, Illinois* (CHAPTER 14)

WALTER CLOUD   *Partner, Wright Associates, New York, New York* (CHAPTER 10)

ROBERT E. COLLINS   *Manager, Switchgear Production Control, Automatic Electric Company, Northlake, Illinois* (CHAPTER 12)

J. W. DENHAM, JR.   *Vice President, Distribution, Mattel, Inc., Hawthorne California* (CHAPTER 7)

JACK N. DURBEN   *Manager, Materials Control, Miles Laboratories, Inc., Elkhart, Indiana* (CHAPTER 14)

RICHARD E. EDGERTON   *Director of Management Information and Systems, Lansing General Hospitals, Lansing, Michigan* (CHAPTER 13)

JAY ELLISON   *Supervisor, Systems Analysis, McDonnell Douglas Corporation, St. Louis, Missouri* (CHAPTER 20)

NORBERT L. ENRICK   *Professor of Management and Production, College of Business Administration, Kent State University, Kent, Ohio* (CHAPTER 9)

EDWARD A. FAGYAL   *Director, Systems and Procedures, McDonnell Douglas Corporation, St. Louis, Missouri* (CHAPTER 24)

STUART FARRELL   *Director of Management Information Systems, Maritz, Inc., St. Louis, Missouri* (CHAPTER 20)

NORMAN E. FINCK   *President, GENOR Associates, Long Beach, California* (CHAPTER 13)

DONALD W. FOGARTY   *Professor, Department of Industrial Engineering, Saint Louis University, St. Louis, Missouri* (CHAPTERS 20 AND 22)

AARON GLICKSTEIN   *Director of Advanced System Design, Food Fair Stores, Inc., Philadelphia, Pennsylvania* (CHAPTER 26)

WALTER E. GODDARD, II   *Executive Vice President, Oliver Wight, Inc., Wilton Connecticut* (CHAPTER 30)

PHILIP GRABER   *Management Consulting Services, Ernst and Ernst, Chicago, Illinois* (CHAPTER 3)

E. V. GRIFFITH   *Program Administrator, International Business Machines Corp., White Plains, New York* (CHAPTER 23)

DONALD F. HESS   *Principal, Donald F. Hess Associates, Lancaster, Pennsylvania* (CHAPTERS 21 AND 23)

WILLIAM E. HOFFMAN   *Editor, Tooling and Production Magazine, Cleveland, Ohio* (CHAPTER 6)

PAUL J. HYMAN   *Assistant Staff Director, Materiel Management Systems Division, Office of the Assistant Secretary of Defense (Installations and Logistics), Washington, D. C.* (CHAPTER 18)

ROBERT L. JANSON *Works Manager, Baker Division, Otis Elevator Company, Cleveland, Ohio; Senior Consultant, Management Consulting Services, Ernst & Ernst, Cleveland, Ohio* (CHAPTER 11)

IRWIN JARETT *Chairman, Department of Accounting, Southern Illinois University, Edwardsville, Illinois* (CHAPTER 20)

R. C. JOHANSON *North Texas State University, Denton, Texas* (CHAPTER 2)

W. J. JONES *Dodge Manufacturing Company, Mishawaka, Indiana* (CHAPTER 15)

HENRY H. JORDAN, JR. *Associate, Wright Associates, New York, New York* (CHAPTER 10)

C. RAYMOND KENYON *Assistant Vice President, Lion Knitting Mills Company, Cleveland, Ohio* (CHAPTER 15)

SAUL KESSLER *Project Manager, Materials Management Systems, Western Union Telegraph, Co., New York* (CHAPTER 21)

ROBERT C. KLEKAMP *Assistant Professor of Management, Graduate School of Business, Xavier University, Cincinnati, Ohio and Vice President, W. G. Seinsheimer and Associates, Cincinnati, Ohio* (CHAPTER 10)

J. CLIFFORD KULICK *Manager of Manufacturing, Nixdorf-Krein Manufacturing Company, St. Louis, Missouri* (CHAPTER 10)

LAMONT LA ROBARDIER *Manager, Administrative Services Division, Arthur Andersen and Company, New York, New York* (CHAPTER 21)

STANLEY LARSON *Inventory Control and Systems, Cessna Aircraft Company, Wichita, Kansas* (CHAPTER 15)

ROGER W. M. LETTS *Manager, Operations Analysis, Lederle Laboratories, Pearl River, New York* (CHAPTER 23)

PHILIP A. LINK *Production Control Manager, Automatic Electric Company, Northlake, Illinois* (CHAPTER 12)

FRANK McCOARD *Director, Production Planning and Control Office (Retired), Ford Motor Company, Detroit, Michigan* (CHAPTER 1)

EUGENE R. MARSHALL *Department Chief, Planning Engineering and Standards Development, Western Electric Company, Inc., Indianapolis, Indiana* (CHAPTER 25)

JOHN R. MASON *Lybrand, Ross Brothers and Montgomery, New York, New York; Formerly, Staff, Management Research & Planning, Inc., Evanston, Illinois* (CHAPTER 15)

HAWLEY W. MERRIHEW *Senior Consultant, Management Sciences Division, H. B. Maynard and Company, Inc., Pittsburgh, Pennsylvania* (CHAPTER 29)

COLIN L. MOODIE *Associate Professor of Industrial Engineering, Purdue University, Lafayette, Indiana* (CHAPTER 13)

JAMES I. MORGAN *Staff Assistant, The Dow Chemical Company, Midland, Michigan* (CHAPTER 8)

C. J. MYERS *Supervisor, Materials Control, Dodge Manufacturing Corporation, Mishawaka, Indiana* (CHAPTER 14)

JOSEPH A. ORLICKY *Industrial Consultant, International Business Machines Corp., White Plains, New York* (CHAPTER 23)

GEORGE W. PLOSSL *Partner, Plossl and Wight Associates, Wilton, Connecticut* (CHAPTER 9)

H. W. POWELL *Vice President, Management Consulting, Executive Computer Leasing, Inc., Oakbrook, Illinois* (CHAPTER 16)

ARNOLD O. PUTNAM *President, Rath and Strong, Inc., Management Consultants, Boston, Massachusetts* (CHAPTERS 4 AND 13)

LARRY RITZMAN *Assistant Professor, College of Administrative Science, The Ohio State University, Columbus, Ohio* (CHAPTER 2)

STEPHEN D. ROBERTS *Assistant Professor, Department of Industrial and Systems Engineering, College of Engineering, University of Florida, Gainesville, Florida* (CHAPTER 27)

WALTER A. SADOWSKY *Technical Editor, Tooling and Production Magazine, Cleveland, Ohio* (CHAPTER 6)

ALBERT V. SANTORA *Associate Director Consulting Engineering, K. W. Tunnell Company, Inc., Norristown, Pennsylvania* (CHAPTER 5)

DONALD E. SCHECK *Assistant Professor, Department of Industrial and Systems Engineering, Ohio University, Athens, Ohio* (CHAPTERS 19 AND 13)

EDWIN SCHIES *Director of Production Control, Victor Business Machines Corp., Chicago, Illinois* (CHAPTER 6)

PAUL SCHNEIDER *Principal, A. T. Kearney and Company, Inc., Chicago, Illinois* (CHAPTER 23)

LEIGHTON F. SMITH *Management Consultant, Arthur Anderson and Company, Chicago, Illinois* (CHAPTER 23)

LEO A. SMITH *Assistant Professor, Industrial Engineering, Auburn University, Auburn, Alabama* (CHAPTER 10)

JAMES L. SOMERS *Coordinator, Manufacturing Production Control, Collins Radio Company, Cedar Rapids, Iowa* (CHAPTER 14)

J. L. SORENSEN *Management Consultant, Arthur Young and Company, Chicago, Illinois* (CHAPTER 23)

DAVID D. SWETT *Executive Vice President, Bruce Payne and Associates, Inc., New York, New York* (CHAPTER 10)

ROBERT E. THIELE, JR. *Senior Research Logician, The Dow Chemical Company, Midland, Michigan* (CHAPTER 8)

WARREN H. THOMAS *Associate Professor, Department of Industrial Engineering, State University of New York at Buffalo, Buffalo, New York* (CHAPTERS 13 AND 28)

GEORGE TROLLOPE *Director of Information Services, U.S. Electrical Motors, Milford, Connecticut* (CHAPTER 20)

KENNETH W. TUNNELL *President, K. W. Tunnell Company, Inc., Norristown, Pennsylvania* (CHAPTER 5)

ROBERT H. TURNER *Data Processing Manager, Taylor Corporation, Valley Forge, Pennsylvania* (CHAPTER 5)

ALFRED O. VALENTINE *Manager of Industrial Engineering, Philco-Ford Corporation, Communications and Electronics Division, Philadelphia, Pennsylvania* (CHAPTER 5)

ROSWELL W. VAN COTT *Manager, Materials, Winchester Western Division, Olin Mathieson Chemical Corporaton, New Haven, Connecticut* (CHAPTER 1)

JOHN VETERAN *Assistant to Vice President of Operations, Hewlett-Packard Company, Palo Alto, California* (CHAPTER 2)

WALTER H. WARRICK *Associate Professor, Operations Management, Northwestern University, Evanston, Illinois* (CHAPTER 15)

DENNIS B. WEBSTER *First Lieutenant, Ordnance Corps., U.S. Army Reserve, Aberdeen, Maryland* (CHAPTER 10)

T. G. WEEKS *Manager of Production Planning, Training and Research, Armstrong Cork Company, Lancaster, Pennsylvania* (CHAPTER 16)

R. E. WERNER *Supervisor, Divisional Systems, McDonnell Aircraft Company, St. Louis, Missouri* (CHAPTER 24)

OLIVER W. WIGHT *Partner, Plossl and Wight Associates, Wilton, Connecticut* (CHAPTERS 16, 17, AND 30)

J. C. ZIMMERMAN *Program Administrator, Manufacturing Industry Education, International Business Machines Corp., White Plains, New York* (CHAPTER 17)

R. ZWIERZYCKI *Director of Data Processing, McHenry County College, Crystal Lake, Illinois* (CHAPTER 26)

Foreword

Production and inventory control as it is known today is radically different from what it was just a few years ago. Even those persons who were actually engaged in it could not have foreseen changes. It seems safe to predict that production and inventory control concepts, techniques, and the manner of performing the function will be equally different in the near future. It is doubtful whether any other management field has seen the degree of change in objectives and techniques of operation since the end of World War II to the present. To be successful and even survive during this period, industry has met a series of different challenges.

During the first decade after the war, industry needed maximum production since there was an almost insatiable demand for products. The fundamental problem associated with production and inventory control centered around how to get more and more products out the door, not necessarily how to get them out more efficiently.

Cost was not the serious problem that it is today, for there was always somebody ready, willing, and able to buy the product as soon as it was available. Excess manufacturing costs were simply passed along to the buyer in the form of higher prices with not too much concern for the inevitable results.

In this environment the more successful production control practitioners were those who were extremely knowledgable in production and were above-average expeditors. They got the badly needed material produced and shipped. They were not concerned with the involved techniques of operation—they satisfied the industrial needs of the times.

The second decade after World War II has seen a reversal of this situation and with this a completely new series of objectives for the production and inventory control function to satisfy. We can identify two significant factors causing this change. First, supply caught up with demand and buyers were no longer lined up to buy the products as soon as they were available. Second, industry began to compete for the first time in a worldwide market. Low cost, high quality products were available in quantity and the inevitable happened.

Meeting this new kind of competition has become the number one industrial problem. Solution of the problem demanded more tightly controlled factories than ever before and the most efficient use of the basic manufacturing resources of men, money, and material. In most industries the production and inventory control function has been given the prime responsibility for achieving the necessary results.

It was but a relatively few years ago that practical computers became available for solving industry's many problems. The growth of computers as a management tool has continued at an almost unbelievable rate. This has complicated the production and inventory control scene by forcing new thinking, new concepts, and new approaches to problem-solving.

With the recent advent of successful and practical timesharing computers, the door has been opened for even small companies, companies who formerly could not economically justify computers of their own. The complicated production and inventory control system with its tremendous quantities of data is a natural for computerization. While many early attempts to use the computer for production control produced bitter results, others were most satisfactory despite all the problems of lack of experience and lack of understanding. The future trend will be to computerize more and more production and inventory control functions and to integrate them with other related management functions.

In today's highly sophisticated environment the more successful production control practitioners are a completely different breed than they once were. We see more all-round, systems-oriented, management-thinking individuals who have sufficient educational background to understand and use the new techniques and tools for achieving results necessary to solve today's problems. The challenges of the future will require even more from production control personnel.

It is because of these changes that the American Production and Inventory Control Society (APICS) undertook the task of developing this Handbook. APICS, founded by some twenty practioners in 1957, has devoted itself, first, to educating and training its members and second, to bringing an awareness of production and inventory control to general management and others not directly engaged in the field. There are now over 7,000 members in the society with chapters located throughout the world. The APICS membership includes most of industry's leading production and inventory control practitioners, many management consultants specializing in the field, as well as educators from leading colleges and universities.

The publication of this Handbook marks the completion of an effort that started with an idea several years ago and is the result of the efforts of many persons. It was felt that a handbook written primarily by APICS members would result in a practical and useful reference document.

APICS was fortunate to have as a member Dr. James H. Greene of Purdue University who was willing to serve as Editor-in-Chief of the Handbook. He has long been interested in the academic and practical applications of production and inventory control and has served as a consultant in various industrial plants to acquire firsthand knowledge of realworld problems. His choice as Editor-in-Chief is a most logical one and the members of the Society would like to take this opportunity to express appreciation for his dedicated effort.

APICS is proud to record that this Handbook is the work of over ninety contributors, most of whom are active members of the Society. To each contributor the Society owes a deep debt of gratitude for his long hours of work on the Handbook project.

There is one other group of APICS members whose dedicated efforts made this Handbook possible. This is the Handbook Editorial Board which was responsible for the important liaison work between the Society, the Editor-in-Chief, and the Chapter Editors. They met to plan the organization and emphasis of the book, reviewed the chapters and followed up with contributors to be sure that they met deadlines. This assignment was performed on a volunteer, nonpaying basis with a great expenditure of personal time. Little did we realize in early 1966 that they would serve for over three years. Yet, without exception the original members of the committee stayed with the project until it was successfully completed. The Society's sincere thanks and appreciation go to this group of dedicated people who performed this long, demanding assignment in a most satisfactory manner. They are appropriately recognized for their efforts on page v.

The Production and Inventory Control Handbook now joins the other educational publications of APICS, the *Production and Inventory Management Quarterly Journal*, and the *Annual Conference Proceedings*, in a continuing effort to bring the members, and other interested people, up-to-date material to help them perform at a higher level of efficiency. This objective will continue to be the prime objective of the Society in the future. It is with a great deal of pride that APICS brings you this Handbook.

Roswell W. Van Cott
Past President (1966)
American Production and
Inventory Control Society, Inc.

Preface

A handbook isn't just another book which you read and discard. It is a tool that has been carefully designed to help you be more productive. Like a tool it should never be more than a grasp away. It should always be near at hand to illustrate how others have solved the puzzling problem you are facing now. As a tool you will become familiar with it as time goes by, and you will come to trust and depend upon it. We hope that it will serve you not only today and tomorrow but for many years to come.

It was this philosophy that guided the organization and editing of the APICS Handbook. The organization of the Handbook is straightforward and without pretense. Each chapter of each section will lead you from the basic concepts to the present state of the art and beyond.

Section One introduces the basic concepts of production and inventory control. Management of the production and inventory control function is included in this section along with modern organizational theory and how it is applied in successful companies.

Section Two recognizes that production and inventory control activities support the profit-making objectives of the company and consequently must work closely with the customers, product developers, manufacturers, and practically all other functions of the complex organizational structure. This section considers the interrelationship of all the functions of the factory.

Section Three emphasizes planning for production control and includes forecasting product demand and how this demand is converted into short- and long-range planning. This section emphasizes manpower-planning in particular.

Section Four gets down to the details of operating the production control department, addressing itself to the work authorization, dispatching, and expediting techniques necessary for an efficient system.

Section Five covers the broad subject of inventory control. All levels of sophistication can be found in this section. In the first chapter is found the basic information needed to operate efficiently an inventory control department. The last part of the section includes some of the most advanced theory.

Section Six emphasizes the fact that every production control system should be constantly improved. Here are to be found the tools for designing a better system, whether it is a simple manual system, a card-data processing system, or a computer system.

Section Seven reinforces all of the other chapters. This section is for those who wish to learn about some of the quantitative tools or perhaps review what they have already learned. Here will be found a development of statistics from the very elementary to the advanced. The operations research techniques are included in one easily understood chapter. Production and inventory control has always made good use of nomographs, so a chapter on constructing these tools has been included.

Section Eight is the APICS–*Factory* report which will tell you how your company compares with similar companies.

This Handbook is the product of many outstanding people in the field. You are invited to use their experience and knowledge. As Editor-in-Chief, I am particularly grateful to the Chapter Editors and their many contributors.

Special recognition must be given to Roswell W. Van Cott, who as a past President of APICS had the foresight and wisdom to recognize the need for this Handbook. It was through his effort that the Handbook activities were put into motion. It was also through his foresight that the Editorial Board was selected—a group that has untiringly guided the development of the Handbook. I would like to express my sincere thanks to them for the many times they have come to my assistance.

I would like to thank the American Production and Inventory Control Society for supporting this project. In particular I would like to thank John M. Raymond, H. G. Callowhill, and Robert L. Smith, APICS Presidents, during the development of the Handbook. They have been more than considerate of the trials and tribulations of a handbook editor.

It would be impossible to thank the many secretaries who have contributed to this Handbook. I would like to express my gratitude to two of them who helped me personally in getting this Handbook to press: the late Mrs. Kathalene Groninger and Mrs. Emil Albert.

The Contributors and Editors recognize that production and inventory control is a dynamic field, subject to constant improvement. Consequently, the Handbook will require periodic updating. We will welcome your suggestions on how it may be improved to better serve you.

JAMES H. GREENE, PH.D.
Editor-in-Chief

Contents

Section Six   SYSTEMS FOR PRODUCTION AND INVENTORY CONTROL

Section Seven   TECHNIQUES AND TOOLS FOR PRODUCTION AND INVENTORY CONTROL

Section Eight   APICS-*FACTORY* REPORT

Index Follows Section Eight

Production and Inventory Control Handbook

Organization for Production and Inventory Control

Chapter **1**

Production and Inventory Concepts

EDITORS:

Roswell W. Van Cott *Manager, Materials, Winchester-Western Division, Olin Mathieson Chemical Corporation, New Haven, Connecticut*

Frank McCoard *Director, Production Planning and Control Office, Retired, Ford Motor Company, Detroit, Michigan*

CONTENTS

Although the term "production control" is relatively new in our business vocabulary, its objective and many of its fundamental methods are as old as organized production. When the Great Pyramid was built, some forgotten production control practitioner must have devised a timed plan for material supply, processing, and movement. He must also have followed up the execution of the plan, revised it because of failures of manpower, material supply, or equipment, and eventually delivered the finished product. So far as we know, the product was delivered in time to serve its planned purpose.

Production control exists in some form in every producing enterprise. The function as such may not appear as an entity on the organization chart; in fact there may not even be a formal organization chart. However, without some system of production control it would be impossible to produce and deliver a product within acceptable time limits.

There is little similarity between present production control techniques and those that were probably used in ancient Egypt, but the primary objective of production control has not changed. The primary objective is still to assure the availability of:

1. A specific product
2. In a specific quantity
3. At a specific time
4. At a specified place

The degree of production-cost economy with which production control attains this primary objective is this function's secondary but extremely important objective. Production control, to be worthy of its name, must attain this primary objective with the *efficient* use of materials, facilities, and transportation.

INVENTORY CONTROL

In manufacturing enterprises the functions associated with inventory control are, by definition, a vital part of production control. Therefore, the primary objective of inventory control is to support the attainment of the primary production control objective with the optimum investment in inventory.

Optimum inventory investment should not be confused with minimum inventory investment. Optimum investment may or may not be a minimum investment depending upon various factors. Subsequent sections of this handbook will deal in considerable detail with all phases of inventory control, both from managerial and technical viewpoints.

While this handbook is written primarily for manufacturing businesses, the various techniques for controlling inventory are the same regardless of the actual business involved and despite any differences that might exist in the primary objectives of any specific business. Inventory control techniques described in this handbook can be used by any enterprise where control of inventory is a critical managerial problem.

ACTIVITIES OF PRODUCTION CONTROL

It is apparent from an evaluation of this primary objective that production control does not conveniently fit into the sales, production, or finance boxes on the conventional organization chart since its functions clearly contain elements of all three. The organizational problems connected with production and inventory control are many and will be dealt with in detail in Chapter 3.

The principal activities of production control in attaining its objectives are:

1. Devising the production plans
2. Follow-up of the production plans and their execution
3. Physical movement of materials

DEVISING THE PRODUCTION PLANS

Depending upon the specific product being manufactured, the size and complexities of the operation involved, together with the management policies, production plans will be based on one of the following major planning base lines:

1. To assure the availability of a product for which a customer's order is already on hand
2. To assure the availability of a product in finished-product inventory before a customer's order is actually on hand, to meet a forecast of specific orders
3. To build an inventory of either finished product or semifinished product, in some stage of process, to meet a demand forecast but not expressed in terms of specific orders

In many companies it is necessary to use a combination of these planning base lines to achieve the objective with acceptable efficiency. For example, this would be true in those companies having multiproduct lines or other companies producing complex products made up of many subassemblies, where total production lead times are far in excess of acceptable product-order lead times. Each of these major planning base lines usually requires unique techniques, to develop plans properly. To be successful, a production control system, based on two or more planning base lines, must adequately recognize these differing techniques.

It must be recognized, however, that neither the planning base line used nor the techniques employed to develop the plan change any of the objectives in any way.

FOLLOW-UP OF PRODUCTION PLANS AND THEIR EXECUTION

Follow-up is an important aspect of any management-control activity. Unremitting follow-up is absolutely imperative to the successful production control operation—without such follow-up it's extremely doubtful that any plan will be successful. No matter how well the plan was originally conceived and developed, constant follow-up on all phases of the basic plan, and on the many events that affect the plan, is necessary to assure that even the base plan itself remains valid. Without constant follow-up to assure that each action necessary to complete the plan has been timely initiated and executed, no plan will ever be successful.

In practice this detailed follow-up is much more difficult—and much less glamorous—than is the planning itself. In addition, the techniques involved in follow-up are generally more personal and much less technical than are most production control techniques. However, to illustrate, if the proper engineering specifications are not obtained in time to procure the tools and/or the necessary raw materials required by plan, or if the tools and/or raw materials are not available at the time specified in the plan, etc., then obviously the objective cannot be met. While some mathematical techniques are now available to aid the practitioner in selecting the most critical follow-up areas, most follow-up activity is just pure hard-nosed work.

In any manufacturing enterprise the number of planned events that must be followed if the production control operations are to be effective are beyond simple description, and yet, the failure to meet on schedule any single event in the plan might jeopardize the success of the whole plan. It must also be recognized that any failure to perform the production plan on schedule must be considered a production control failure, even though such a failure might occur outside the organization designated as the production control organization.

The importance of follow-up is best illustrated by the fact that excellent production control follow-up frequently overcomes both mediocre planning and performance controls. In turn, the most excellent and sophisticated planning, without effective follow-up, is simply an interesting intellectual exercise.

Information of actual performance compared against the plan, recorded by the follow-up activity and fed back to the planning activity, becomes new input data to the whole production control system. Based on such up-to-the-minute feedback information, new plans may have to be developed if the objectives are to be met. Changes are common in any manufacturing activity, and constant change should be considered a normal part of any production control operation.

PHYSICAL MOVEMENT

Although physical movement of materials will, for convenience in sequence, be treated in this chapter as a supporting system rather than as a part of the primary production control system, this is not intended in any way to downgrade its importance. In the final analysis, all processing is essentially a materials-handling system through which materials pass on their way to conversion from a product of nature into a form usable by man. Material is not created by manufacture. It is simply extracted, combined, welded, bolted, or otherwise processed from one form to another through physical movement.

From a manufacturing production-control standpoint, physical movement is initiated by the creation of a demand which reflects itself in manufacturing activity in supplier plants, a transfer of this activity to your own plant, and finally the transfer of the product made by the plant involved to its customer. In recent years several different organizational concepts have been developed to solve and control this entire logistical problem better by assigning single-management responsibility to this whole area. While organizational concepts will be covered in detail in Chapters 2 and 3, it should be understood at this time that the entire logistical sequence of material is of prime concern in production control. Regardless of the organizational concept employed, the production control system will be the prime influence affecting physical movement, and the primary production control objective will remain unchanged.

THE SYSTEM

The system used to achieve the production control objective is an essential part of the overall system within a manufacturing company that has been described in some recent literature as the "logistics system." The logistics system is perhaps the prime system within the average manufacturing company, and it usually offers the most opportunities and advantages for computerizing because of the tremendous mass of operating data involved in the system—data which must be utilized constantly in decision making; data which is subject to continuous change and adjustment. However, whether the system utilizes the most modern computer concepts or a very simple handposted record, the system conponents may be broken down into two major categories:

1. The primary system
2. The supporting systems

Since achieving the production control objective depends upon data generated by the system, the manager charged with production control responsibility must also assume a degree of responsibility for the design and structure of the system itself. While this does not imply that the manager should be a systems engineer per se, it certainly does imply that he must at least specify what the system must accomplish, what information he needs from the system, and exactly when he needs it if he is to achieve the objective efficiently by the system. This responsibility cannot be delegated to the systems specialist.

It is not essential that the production control organization itself performs all the functions of the system. It *is* essential that all functions of the system be performed. For example, it is essential that a supplier designated by purchasing receive current specifications, quantity requirements, and delivery dates. Whether this information is furnished directly to the supplier from production control, or indirectly by production control via purchasing, is probably not essential to the satisfactory performance of the system.

THE PRIMARY SYSTEM

For ease of explanation the primary system can be divided into six recognizable major subsystems which will be outlined briefly. While the major system phases may not necessarily occur in the exact chronological order given below, they will occur at one or more stages in any successful production control system.

1. Translation of basic information concerning the product being manufactured into usable production and purchasing information. During this phase additional information which is needed in the purchasing and production control areas is developed and added to the available information concerning the product. This new information is, in turn, made a part of the basic-system data and becomes available for use in the development of the production plan once the demand requirements are known.

To illustrate, during this phase such things as supply sources may be developed, production information relative to where and how components will be used are determined and added to the basic-system data, etc. "Engineering information" in this frame of reference is used as a general term to define all engineering data. It may vary from a definite specification to a very general engineering description of procedures designed to produce a product having certain physical qualities. In all cases, however, the engineering information provided must be capable of translation into operating instructions for both production control and purchasing.

2. Determining the material requirements for a finished product. Customer orders or forecasts for the product are translated into material requirements for each step of the production process. These requirements would be expressed in terms common to the process stage specified for that specific production step. The term "materials" in this sense is used to describe inventory at

any stage of process other than the specified finished product itself. Simply, what are the material requirements at each point of manufacture necessary to meet the demand quantity of finished product?

The first stage of the finished-product-requirement conversion is *usually* based upon some form of demand forecast, since most manufacturing companies cannot plan their whole manufacturing cycle entirely upon receipt of firm customer orders. This is because the acceptable time for delivery of the finished product to satisfy a customer's order once it is received is generally much less than the actual total lead time that is necessary to procure and/or to make all the "materials" contained in the finished product.

Considerable care must be taken to properly identify those specific process points where material requirements are to be converted from actual customer orders or those where material conversion is to be made from forecasts of such orders. There are relatively few industries that are not obliged to start the original conversion of material requirements prior to the receipt of the actual customer orders.

This phase of the system is never static. The original material conversion is subject to constant modifications triggered by the feedback of actual data, and updated forecast information should constantly be injected into the development of material requirements. At any time, therefore, the material requirements are a mixture of forecasts both original and updated and actual customer requirements modified by the results of actual production.

3. Determination of the schedule time that each production or procurement quantity must be available at a specified point in the production process to assure availability of the finished product at the specified time. This is perhaps the most critical phase of the entire planning system, and the degree to which efficient use of materials, manpower, and facilities is achieved will depend upon scheduling decisions made at this step.

Later chapters in this handbook will deal in considerable detail with the techniques of determining scheduled dates. It is customary, in most systems, to first determine the date of final-product availability and by working from that date back into the process determine the latest "safe" date for material at each process step. This schedule is then modified through later feedback into the system of current sales, production, and forecast data.

4. Issue of orders to either outside suppliers or internal production facilities. The actual methods for accomplishing this phase of the system are dependent upon many diverse factors and vary according to the form of organization and the complexity of the involved manufacturing process. Regardless of the specific methods involved, however, the production control system must allow for the prompt issuance of these vital instructions in a form readily understood by either the outside supplier or internal production facilities.

The system, to adequately handle the complexities of the manufacturing situation, must allow for constant updating of lead-time requirements. Lead times constantly change as overall business conditions and machine technologies change. The successful system must be capable of reacting to these changes if materials are to be made available on time to satisfy the schedule.

5. The revision of the initial material requirements by the feedback of current information relative to receipt of customer orders, new forecasts of customer orders, losses of in-process material, variances between planned and actual material usage, or any other source affecting availability of material needed to satisfy demand.

The system must be structured to rapidly and accurately obtain all critical data affecting material requirements in a form for ready analysis and incorporation into new, updated requirements. This is a critical dimension for the system, and a quick and positive reaction to any change in material requirements for any reason is essential for the successful operation of any production control system.

6. Recording all materials going through the production process, comparing these actual events with the plan, and taking whatever action is necessary to make production coincide to the planned schedule.

It is not the purpose of this particular section of the handbook to describe just how this critical step is to be performed, but if the primary production control objectives are to be realized it is obvious that it is in this final step that the system will succeed or fail. The initial plan is just the start; production control must take whatever action necessary when events occur in the production process that prevent the plan from developing correctly.

If all such corrective action fails and the plan is not going to be met, it is production control's responsibility to advise management promptly as to the extent of the finished-product delay.

SUPPORTING SYSTEMS

There are several other systems within production control that act in support of the primary system. All these function with data supplied by the primary system, and in turn supply data to both the primary system and other supporting systems. All these supporting systems are essential to the successful functioning of the primary system. Four of the more important of these are as follows:

1. *Indirect-materials Systems:* The procurement and control, storage, and issuance of materials that are not a recognizable part of the product but that are essential for the manufacturing of the product. Examples of such materials are perishable tools, maintenance supplies, operating supplies, and the like. Usage of such materials may or may not bear any direct relationship to the rate of production.

2. *Material-storage Systems:* The control of materials into either the plant or internal storerooms, the storage and warehousing of such material, and its release to assembly and/or to shipping. This particular supporting system is perhaps the most neglected of all production control systems, for without adequate and acceptable performance in both the physical-handling and record-keeping functions of this supportng system, the primary system could not operate successfully.

3. *Outgoing-materials Systems:* The receipt and control of the finished product from production, the warehousing of the product, and shipment of the finished product to the customers. This might run the whole gamut from the proper recording and handling of a single item of finished product to be shipped against a specific customer order to a whole elaborate system of branch warehouses located in various geographical locations, with inventories to support orders of various finished products for many customers. At any rate, regardless of the size or complications involved, the system used to control this activity is a closely supporting system to the primary production control system.

4. *Materials-ordering System:* The development and monitoring of ordering quantities to optimize inventory investments. This would include the development and operational control of inventory economic order quantities in production, recognizing such things as the best machine efficiency, the cost of materials, the rate of usage, the cost of carrying inventory, etc. In the case of materials not directly related to production or identifiable with a finished product, the quantity to purchase is determined to maintain an inventory level that reflects

the best overall inventory investment. Decisions made here directly affect the primary system.

There are numerous other supporting systems affecting both directly and indirectly the operation of the primary system.

SYSTEMS DESIGN

In the past few years the whole subject of systems design, as it applies to the production and inventory control area, has been receiving considerable attention because of ever-increasing interest in the concept of completely integrated information systems or the *total system*. While progress to date in the operational development of such systems has been extremely slow, there is no longer any doubt that future systems development is going to be in this direction.

It is essential that the production and inventory control system be at least compatible with each of the other information systems in use within the company. Ideally it would be best that all such internal systems be completely integrated. The more integrated all systems become, the more it is possible to reduce serious time losses in production as well as excess costs involved in keeping and translating duplicate records.

The production control role in systems design is one of specifying *what* information the system must supply and *when* the objective is to be achieved. It plays a leading role in coordinating the development of more integrated and compatible records for all the related management functions. The systems expert is there to guide and to develop all the details as to how the system is to achieve its goal, but operating people must specify the goal.

Regardless of the methods employed in the mechanics of the system, there are some necessary guides for a well-designed production and inventory control system.

1. The system must not be any more complex than is essential to meet the basic objective.

Recognize the basic objective and organize a system to achieve it. Don't complicate the system with unessential, fancy gadgets, etc., and don't overcontrol the process. Overcontrol is not only more costly than undercontrol but also tends to stifle initiative and acceptance of responsibility, while the ingenuity of the personnel will usually compensate for undercontrol.

2. The system must be capable of quickly recognizing when actual events are not being realized in accordance with the approved plan.

Data being fed back into the system must be so structured that personnel operating the system can readily recognize potential problems in time to act to correct the situation or to upline the problem for management's attention. A system that simply records input data but does not allow for quick identification of problem areas will not achieve the objective.

3. The system must be designed so that the last acceptable data for each decision is clearly identified.

In the manufacturing process constant change is the rule rather than the exception. Therefore, decisions made before the last acceptable data for action are usually subject to additional change.

4. The system must allow for maximum speed in processing input, output, and feedback data, but such speeds should be governed by the ability of the system to absorb data.

While the speeds of present data processing and transmission are perhaps desirable, attempts to approach real time in the system may not be justified. There is, for example, no useful result achieved from the effort of giving a supplier daily changes resulting from changing demand if he manufactures and ships his product only once each month. Likewise, it seems pointless to transmit material receipts as they occur by the latest data transmission equipment if the computer system calls for a weekly batching of the information for a weekly computer update. Conversely, however, vital information cannot be left unprocessed.

5. Uniformity of systems is desirable for personnel training and for administrative control. However, care must be taken to assure that not too great a price is paid for the advantages of a uniform system.

Uniformity usually means that the product-identification system is the one required for the most complex item being manufactured or purchased. A bolt, for example, may be vital to the completion of a finished product, but it should not have the same importance as a complicated machined casting requiring many weeks for procurement and manufacture. The system should recognize the difference.

6. The operation of the system must be understood by management personnel who are not closely involved in production control.

Without this understanding the real and imagined complexities of the system, rather than the weaknesses in operating performances, will be blamed for all the delays, excessive production and transportation costs, and excessive and obsolete inventories. The necessity of management understanding the system cannot be minimized, and it is even more critical with advanced computer systems than in the less complex approaches to production control.

7. The system should be designed to provide information that is usable at the time it is provided.

There is little value in having information showing that something should not have been made or should not have been shipped. Hindsight is always blessed with 20/20 vision which is not true of foresight!

DATA PROCESSING AND TRANSMISSION

During the past few years the speed of processing, of input-output, and of feedback data has been greatly increased by the use of computers, transceivers, and related high-speed automatic or semiautomatic equipment. Sufficient volumes have now been written on this subject to perhaps create the feeling in some circles that a system does not offer adequate control without the use of such equipment. It is perhaps true that it would be impossible for some large manufacturers with complex and varied products to maintain their present production and deliveries without the use of such equipment. However, the systems outlined here and described in more detail in chapters to follow can and have been used successfully with manual records for data retrieval, desk calculators for processing, and mail or messenger for transmission. Although some of the particular techniques described in the following chapters do require electronic equipment, the principles can nearly always be adapted to slower methods when the need for maximum speed does not justify the costs. There is a tendency to forget that such mathematically oriented techniques as weighted, moving averages for forecasting and linear equations for facility requirements were successfully employed with manual records before the innovation of the computer. The equipment and applications should be selected to fit the job. It is no more sensible to drive tacks with a pile driver than it is to try to drive piles with a tack hammer.

It is generally true that speed of data processing increases the cost of the equipment. In addition to the equipment-cost factor, the accuracy required of input information increases with the speed of its processing and transmission. The degree of justifiable speed in data processing and transmission can be determined only by each company—depending upon the nature of its products and its competition.

Although the speed and sophistication of data processing and data-handling equipment have greatly increased during the past few years, there are still many problems in production and inventory control for which mathematical models could provide more efficient planning. There is reason to believe that more advanced equipment will be developed in the near future for those organizations whose problems justify the cost of more efficient equipment.

Regardless of the present and future speeds and capacities of electronic equipment and the conceptual know-how to support them, effective production and inventory control will always depend on *people*—people who not only know the basic systems, techniques, and mechanical aids for the job but also have sufficient understanding of the principles to successfully improvise when facility failure, manpower failure, and all the other imponderables of modern business require immediate decisions, with minimum information.

Chapter 2

Management of the Production Control Department

EDITORS:

Henry Bennett *Manager, Materials Management, Miles Laboratories, West Haven, Connecticut*

Dr. Larry Ritzman *Assistant Professor, College of Administrative Science, The Ohio State University, Columbus, Ohio*

CONTRIBUTORS:

Emil Albert *Manager, Production Planning and Procurement Department, The Adams and Westlake Company, Elkhart, Indiana*

James M. Beck *Manager, Management Information Services, U.S. Plumbing & Heating Group, American Standard, Inc., New York, N.Y.*

R. C. Johanson *North Texas State University, Denton, Texas*

John Veteran *Assistant to Vice President of Operations, Hewlett-Packard Company, Palo Alto, California*

CONTENTS

"**P**roduction and inventory management" may be defined as *the management of the time, place, and form utility of the elements of production, which is to have the right materials, manpower, and facilities at the right time, and in such a manner as to maximize the service to the consumer and to minimize the investment of the company.*

This chapter presents a background of the production and inventory control function along with basic organizational concepts relating to the function. Structures of typical production and inventory control organizations are compared.

The manpower requirements, with the many facets of recruiting, interviewing, and matching employees to the jobs, are included. Methods of payment and promotions are subjects of concern to the manager and are thus discussed in this chapter. Another topic is human relations, with the problems of motivation and communications. Of perhaps the greatest importance is the section on departmental efficiency.

DEVELOPMENT OF PRODUCTION CONTROL

The murky seas of time still cloud the origins of man, but recent excavations indicate he was around millions of years ago. These early men used tools, and in making tools the functions of design, materials procurement, and fabrication are involved. Since the better materials tend to be concentrated in only a few spots, the men controlling these sources were in a position to barter. Thus we have the beginning of trade. As the years passed, million upon million, man gradually learned to organize himself, his family, and his community. This stability aided in the distribution of the fruits of labor.

Successful trading is still based on products that fill a need at an acceptable price. The earliest products were probably materials of nature—flint, obsidian, mercury, hides, furs, etc. In the gathering and preparation of such products were the beginnings of modern inventory and production control.

Later, caravans and merchant ships required still more planning to assemble, transport, and deliver goods. Payment in goods preceded our monetary systems.

Military logistics furthered the art of procurement, supply, physical distribution, and related functions. The best-equipped and best-fed armies had an advantage. The use of metals in knives, swords, armor, guns, and cannons aided in setting the stage for the first industrial revolution. We are now in the midst of another industrial revolution, triggered by rapid scientific advancements in electronics, physics, mathematics, chemistry, and other sciences. This revolution has given birth to complex and costly products requiring a firm control of documentation, procurement, and flow of materials.

The founder of a small business is usually the man who does everything—inventory, foreman, purchaser, personnel expert, salesman, worker, and even accountant. As demand grows, the owner is forced to delegate. Production is placed under a foreman who controls the manufacturing operations. These include the supporting functions, such as planning, scheduling, quality control, equipment selection, coordination with marketing, etc.

As the level of business grows, the foreman's job of controlling these related functions becomes increasingly difficult. Either too little attention is paid to supporting functions, or too little is paid to actual production. Hot lists and rush jobs become a way of life.

Clearly the two areas have to be separated. A production and inventory control specialist is acquired and placed either under the foreman, or more likely under a new manager called a "manufacturing manager." Today's foremen usually concentrate on making the product and depend upon the efficient working of production and inventory control systems and procedures. Today the foreman has less knowledge of the supporting functions, and it is becoming increasingly difficult to keep him updated.

Production Control and the Economy. The accumulation and depletion of inventories has been acknowledged recently as a prime factor in the economic cycles of prosperity and recession. Cycles are triggered by the ebb and flow of demand for goods and services. Domestic and world events trigger a change in the psychological mood of businessmen and consumers which is translated into actions that affect inventories and production levels.

An overly optimistic analysis of market demands can inundate the business world with an avalanche of orders. Since productive capacity cannot fill all the demand, lead times are extended. This triggers still more orders. The end result is a buildup of unused inventory—unused because the capacity does not exist in the economy to consume it. Following this biased analysis of the market is a slump in labor efficiency caused by marginal workers, who are still in the learning phase. Then profits fall, material prices rise, returns on assets fall, money becomes scarce, and interest rates rise. Inevitably corrective forces come into play.

The emerging role of the government, following Keynesian theories, as a corrective agent cannot be underestimated. Its attempts to guide our economy have been both good and bad, but nevertheless the government will continue to be a very dominant factor in our economy.

The practice of economics is changing from an art to a science. Forecasts by economists at the present time vary widely, which illustrates the lack of a measurable cause-and-effect relationship among the economic variables. When a causative action can achieve a desired result, or when economic forces can be forecast accurately, the art will become subordinate to the science. The variables which affect the output of an economy are very complex and often intangible. We still have much to learn about predicting the reactions of the population to various stimuli, economic or otherwise.

Today's Manager. In the middle of this economic maelstrom stands the production and inventory control manager, playing a key role, but all too often caught in the surging tides without the ability to control the forces. Nevertheless, the production and inventory control managers must prepare themselves to be as effective as possible in their changing functions. Not only must external economic forces be more fully understood but also all operating systems and procedures of the firm must be studied and understood. The production and inventory control manager is often the first to know that systems are not working to peak efficiency—that there are areas of friction, lost energies, and failures. Tying independent functions together into an operating whole is one of his primary duties. To do this, he must be open-minded, a problem solver, a man who gets people working together, a planner, an economist. He must be conscious of costs, profits, and growth.

The second industrial revolution is still gathering steam. Products are more complex and production machinery is more automatic. Labor is becoming increasingly specialized in knowledge and the use of that knowledge. Today's industrial revolution is changing the administration of operating systems, and the total-systems concept is receiving increasing attention. Systems which crisscross old functional lines are being designed by well-rounded specialists capable of solving the needs of all departments involved. Organizational changes are taking place. "Coordination" is a key word.

The managements of companies know more about their operating systems. Top management is being educated through seminars, publications, and special schools. This is especially true with regard to computers and their impact on production and inventory control. It is imperative today to see and understand how all the gears of a business mesh and how they combine to achieve the final result—products for customers. The gears are operational systems and procedures—order processing, forecasting, planning, flow of parts and products, manufacturing cycles, costs, etc. There is no substitute for competence. First comes good personnel, then workable systems. There are still firms which fail because of lack of personnel with sufficient skills to control these interdependent systems and procedures.

Impact of the Computer. Computers have triggered the review and redesign of operating systems and management controls, as computers are revolutionizing product design and applications. Computers can aid in the accomplishment of production and inventory control functions, but first must come good systems design based on well-rounded knowledge and experience. The production and inventory control manager must have a working knowledge of operations research, systems analysis, computer hardware and software, economics, finance, and people. These are the tools he must work with to accomplish his functional duties as a cohesive force, welding manufacturing, marketing, and engineering together.

The effectiveness of any given production and inventory control system can be measured in terms such as profit, inventory turnover, back orders, cost as a percentage of shipments on schedule, and others. Computers don't assure these—better systems, ably administered, come first. Computers do have their place in speeding up manufacturing and reducing costs. The key lies in a critical analysis of all proposed computer applications. Will the costs be worth the results? Get costs and measure results. In this way one learns and the system will benefit. Don't believe all hardware salesmen but, since computers are here to stay, get all the aid available.

Recent Professional Developments. The professional aspects of production and inventory control are exemplified by the fine efforts of APICS—the American Production and Inventory Control Society. APICS chapters are a source of technical information which is made available through the interchange of ideas at regular monthly meetings. Quite a few chapters actually sponsor technical-training programs, especially where there is a university conveniently located within the chapter jurisdiction. The membership is dedicated to the attainment of a professional status, and its continuous efforts are likely to bring success. The society is constantly elevating the performance level of its members by making available technical data on a regular, published basis. Committees within the organization are establishing criteria for professionalism which define levels of performance and areas of endeavor, qualify their members, and hold out to them the highest goals of ethical and academic pursuits.

APICS was begun in Cleveland, Ohio, at a meeting in the Sheraton-Cleveland Hotel. This 1957 meeting sparked the beginning of the charter membership and the society has grown. Within 10 short years it had 110 active chapters and nearly 6,500 members.

ORGANIZATION CONCEPTS FOR MANAGEMENT

A manager plans the activities to be performed in his department, organizes the relationships among jobs, selects and trains employees, directs the work of subordinates, and compares actual results with those anticipated. These functions are common to all organizations and all levels in the organization structure.

No fundamental difference of purpose exists between this chapter and the other chapters of this handbook. All are directed toward the prediction and control of behavior. This chapter is unique in its emphasis—it focuses on the management of *human* behavior within *one* department: the production and inventory control department.

The content of the chapter is of necessity relatively qualitative. Defining, measuring, and understanding causal relationships among human variables presents more formidable problems than with nonhuman resources. Nonetheless, departmental success depends on how effectively the manager deals with these less tangible concepts and variables. Therefore this chapter discusses the planning procedure and how it applies to managing the production control function.

Planning is that phase of management which leads to change. It results in a sequence of predetermined steps of action which are well integrated and goal-directed. Planning is a mental activity, is purposive, is future oriented, and deals with facts and assumptions referred to as "planning premises." Plans take on several forms, including *objectives, policies, procedures, rules,* and *budgets.*

Objectives. The formulation of objectives as well as the means of achieving these ends is a planning process. Objectives specify those conditions which are preferred to the existing ones. They provide a sense of purpose and direction, supply standards of performance, and help link organizational subsystems.

Policies. Policies are general guidelines which act to channel the decision making and conduct of departmental employees. Policies possess a relatively permanent nature and spell out managerial desires for behavior of subordinates. Policies should allow some discretion on the part of subordinates, and excessive rigidity is to be avoided.

Policies cover many diverse areas. Examples are the adherence to lunch-break schedules, minimum educational requirements for various job classifications, encouragement of employee suggestions, and training provisions. They may be either *explicit* or *implicit.*

Managers are not in complete agreement that policies should always be stated explicitly. Many believe that it depends on the nature of the policy, with some policies being officially stated and others being implied. Whether a policy is explicit or implicit has much to do with the manner in which it is communicated. Other communication considerations are the size of the employee group, characteristics of the group, and characteristics of the manager.

Implicit policies exist without official communication or approval but nonetheless act as a guide to behavior. They originate in the manager's consistent patterns of behavior which filter down to lower organizational levels.

Policies vary as to their scope and importance, with the broader and more important policies being developed and administered at higher levels. Policies having a more limited coverage are administered from the lower levels of the organization. This pattern of policies integrated by their descending scope creates a hierarchy of policies analogous to the well-known pyramidal organization structure.

The advantages of policies are:

1. They avoid repeated analyses of courses of action, thereby allowing the manager to use his time more efficiently.

2. They assure a greater consistency in employee behavior.

The hierarchy of policies and the manner in which they are administered also have a material bearing on the "climate" existing within the department.

Procedures. Procedures are plans prescribing predetermined and standard methods of handling repetitive activities in the future. They are subordinate to policies and specify in detail the exact manner of accomplishing some activity, generally in chronological sequence. As is true with policies, they have a hierarchy of importance and are often specified explicitly in corporate or departmental manuals. Examples of procedures are the prescribed flow of forms and information for scheduling operations, the way candidates are to be selected and appraised for promotional purposes, the computations to be made in allocating work loads to various plants, and the manner in which departmental manpower requirements are to be reviewed.

Rules. Rules stipulate that a specific and definite action must be taken in a given situation. Rules, which are developed within the framework of existing policies, do not allow discretion as to how they are applied and are usually accompanied by specific penalities for rule violation.

Budgets. Budgets are plans which state in quantitative terms certain expected results. Their preparation is a basic planning device for anticipating future cash flows and expenses within the department. The budget acts as a control device after its implementation.

In review, one must be continually mindful of the separation of goals from objectives and objectives from policy. The achievement of goals will allow one to reach his objective, and the attainment of the several objectives allows one to follow policy.

Participation in a sport provides a good basis for comparison. *Policy* is to follow good sportsmanship and stimulate free competition within the guidelines of the game, whereas one *objective* is to win the game and this can only be accomplished through the attainment of *goals*—for instance, scoring points.

Steps in Planning. *Step 1. Problem Recognition.* Sensitivity to inadequacies in present conditions and to the desirability for change is an important characteristic of an effective planner. We are all exposed to unsolved problems and yet may not recognize them as such. Dissatisfaction with present conditions may arise out of the failure to meet existing objectives or the realization that the objectives themselves need modification.

Step 2. Problem Definition. A well-defined problem contributes materially to its ultimate solution. Problem definition also establishes the scope of the plan. If a problem is too narrowly defined, a suboptimal solution results. If the problem is stated too broadly, time and effort limitations may rule out a practical solution.

Step 3. Recognition of Organizational and Departmental Objectives. Problem solving cannot proceed without a clearly stated criterion of effectiveness against which alternative plans can be appraised. It is important that objectives be specific, operational, and well communicated to all managers who formulate basic or derivative plans.

Step 4. Obtaining and Employing Planning Premises. These can be in the form of forecast data, elements of higher-order policies, or segments of existing plans. Premises should be available for all factors having an important bearing on the plan. In terms of departmental manpower planning, for example, the manager must develop premises as to future work levels, company polices on internal versus external recruitment, anticipated turnover, and capabilities of present employees.

Step 5. Developing Alternative Courses of Action. Reduce the number to the most promising alternatives, evaluate these alternatives in terms of the objectives and planning premises, and finally select a particular plan for implementation. Probability theory as well as mathematical and computational techniques can be helpful in developing and evaluating alternatives. Nonetheless, these techniques are much more applicable when dealing with other than human resources. Quantitative and nonquantitative factors are to be balanced in the planning process.

Step 6. Developing Derivative Plans. The final-phase of planning is often necessary—developing derivative plans to achieve the initial plan. Making the basic plan, an end in itself, and developing new derivative plans create an integrated ends-means hierarchy. For example, the plan of assigning a task group to scheduling and expediting a particularly complex job would require derivative plans as to who is selected and the authority to be delegated to the group. Derivative plans may be the responsibility of the manager who constructed the basic plan or may be the responsibility of subordinates. This would depend on the extent of authority delegation within the department, the nature of the plan, and the extent to which participation is desired.

STRUCTURING THE ORGANIZATION

Organization, or more specifically *good* organization, is one of the most important points in determining the success or failure of an endeavor, and the production and inventory control department is no exception.

There are many types of structures dedicated to the production and inventory control function. The type varies from company to company and even from plant to plant in the same company. This is part of the problem and to overcome it requires a great deal of diligent effort by the manager of the production and inventory control organization.

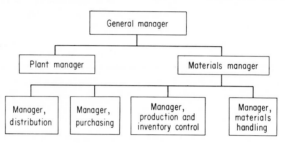

Fig. 1   Organization chart.

In one company organization, the production and inventory control function may be strictly clerical, completing only a portion of the true staff responsibility of the broad scope of production and inventory control (see Fig. 1). However, in another company producing similar product lines, the production and inventory control function may be performing all its classical staff functions and also some significant line responsibilities along with accountability (see Fig. 2). As is apparent, it is very difficult to outline a pat, inflexible series of steps involved in the organization, manning, staffing, and operation of a production and inventory control department. There are, however, basic steps which will almost become rules:

Step 1.   One of the first steps involved in organizing a production and inventory control department is to determine its interdepartmental reporting relationship. This will, in part, determine the level of authority for the function. After this has been accomplished, one needs to establish the functions to be performed within the department to attain the objectives which have been assigned.

These departmental functions are needed for estimating the volume and level of difficulty of the work which is likely to be performed.

Step 2.   In turn, preliminary intradepartmental organization charts with job levels, accountability, responsibility, and duties would be structured. It is important to point out here that several revisions and restructuring of responsibility and accountability are likely.

Step 3.   When the final organization is made firm, detailed job descriptions denoting manager duties and responsibilities, basic functions to be performed, reporting relationships (both superior and subordinate), and principal working relationships would be included. Those activities which are delegated would also be defined and should be separated into functions for which both the responsibility and accountability are delegated. Also included are those functions for which performance is expected although accountability is not delegated but is maintained at the next higher level of management.

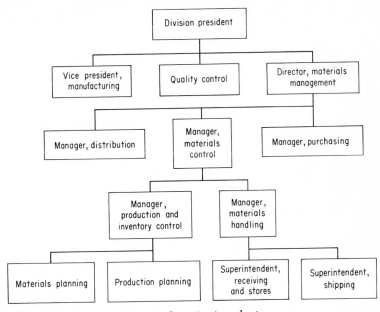

Fig. 2 Organization chart.

One will find that these steps of preplanning in organizing a department will:
1. Prevent overlapping and duplication of duties
2. Minimize staff-to-staff conflict regarding areas of responsibility
3. Provide for the most economical organization

MANPOWER REQUIREMENTS

Short- and long-range manpower requirements should be a part of the department head's continually updated review.

Initially a staff may be pared to meet the basic functions to be performed assuming that a relatively high level of talent is available for recruitment. It is also the responsibility, on a long-range basis, for the department head to have preplanned the replacement not only of himself but of the several levels of subordinates in his reporting structure.

Personnel Audit and Job Analysis. It can be quite helpful to have available a *personnel audit* on each individual in the department (see Fig. 3). This personnel audit should contain all pertinent information regarding the individual's goals, desires, interests, abilities, training, etc. When these data are matched accurately to a *job analysis,* one is much more likely to have a well-operating department and to maintain the long-range employment of his personnel.

The actual elements of the job analysis would be the *job description* and an *activity audit* for the specific duties to be performed on a day-to-day basis.

This should include the *job requirements,* duties, and often a brief description of the *working conditions* as well as the personal qualifications required to give the highest probability of success.

These job descriptions and specifications should be completed in detail and placed as well in the personal possession of each new employee as the department is staffed. In doing this, one often finds that the level of productivity falls well within the range that is expected.

Manpower Ratios. Manpower ratios and charts (Fig. 4) based on a sampling of existing production and inventory control departments in similar lines of manufacturing are often used. They are usually based on the number of production and inventory control people per dollar of sales volume or number of production employees.

Name _____   Title _____

Reports to _____   Title _____

Description of activities performed (list in order of importance)	Percent of time spent on activity	Documents used for activity	What procedure is used to gather this (performance) information	Objective	Classification of activity (1. doing, 2. planning, 3. both)

Fig. 3 Production and inventory control time and activity audit.

These charts are misused at times because the duties of a department may vary widely within the same industry. Therefore, the required number of employees would also be likely to vary. Many individuals may use this information when it supports their argument, but suppress it when it does not.

Internal Recruiting. The department manager must continually consider both short- and long-range requirements and objectives. It is generally accepted that where possible, recruitment of individuals from within the company is desirable. This is based on the premise that promotions stimulate higher productivity, creativity, competitive effort, morale, and other attributes. Some companies have a complete personnel profile (Fig. 5) on every employee within the organization listing all prior training he may have experienced. This profile is coded to reflect the degree of competence in new areas. These profiles also include personal data which is often correlated to long-term job requirements and may also include the employee's personal preference whether any specific skills are evident or not. It is well recognized that motivation as well as training play a strong part in success.

An internal recruiting system as described can produce some successful high-level top managers from some quite unexpected areas. It is important to note that the reputation of the system depends on the level of sophistication attained as well as its universal applications on a company-wide basis.

The most likely function to perform the activities described is the personnel

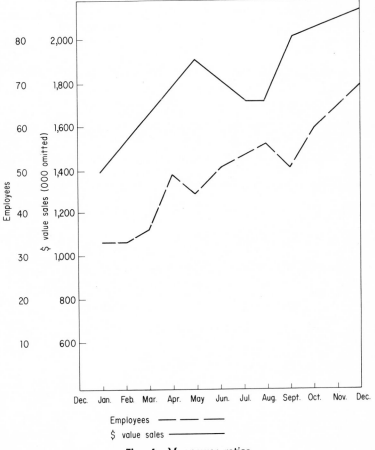

Fig. 4 Manpower ratios.

department. In the larger companies there is often a personnel specialist assigned strictly to the duties of maintaining an internal manpower inventory and selection system, which is run separately and parallel to the more familiar external recruitment and placement.

External Recruiting. Professional societies, employment agencies, consulting firms, and personal contacts may be the most likely sources of potential candidates for external recruitment.

High-level external recruitment presents difficulties within an organization, and it is quite difficult at times to escape the criticisms of the internal staff

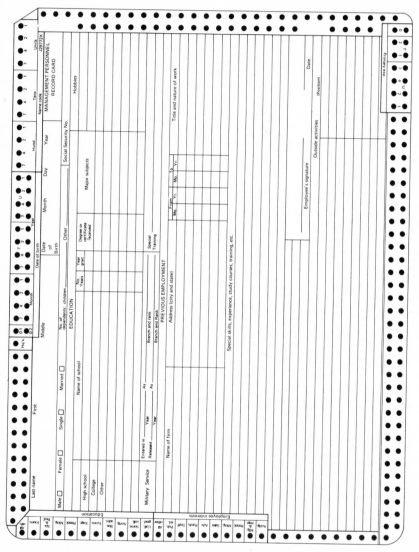

Fig. 5 Personnel profile.

2-12

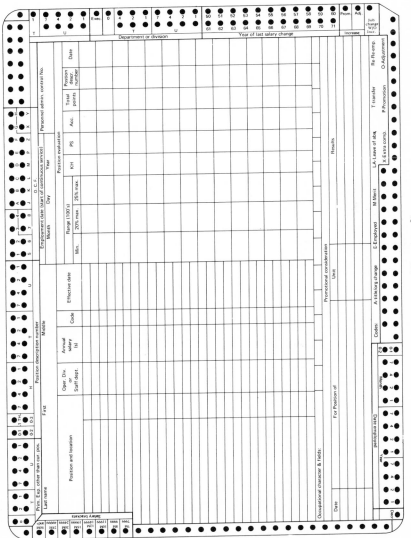

Fig. 5 (*Continued*)

and higher management. The lower levels of staff often cry that under these conditions they are not given the opportunity to advance and are being unjustifiably prevented from attaining higher levels of responsibility. The higher levels of management are just as critical of this situation, since it is often much

COMPREHENSIVE INTERVIEW GUIDE: CLERICAL APPLICANTS

Date _____

Applicant _____   Interviewer _____

This guide is an aid in obtaining complete information about the candidate. Along the left-hand side are a number of brief phrases to remind you of kinds of questions you should ask. You obviously should not ask them the way they are worded. The list of questions is not intended to be complete; you will probably want to ask some questions which are not in the list. (You should use the space on the right for notes.)

EDUCATION

— Complete H.S.? If not, why?

— H.S. program (College-
  General-Business)? Overall
  average? Courses liked least?
  Best? Why? Grades?

— School activities? Why enter?
  What did she get out of school?
  Goals?

— Consider college? Applied to
  any? Transcript sent? College
  Board Exams? Scholarship
  possibilities? Why no go?
  If no go, what study? Why?

— If applicant went to college,
  semesters completed? Major?
  Why no degree? How finance?

WORK HISTORY

— Specific duties of each job?
  What gained from jobs? What
  liked best about jobs? Least?
  Why? Relationship with supervisor?
  Coworkers? Promotions received?

— Attendance?

— How long at job? Why leave?
  More than one reason?

— Account for any time not
  mentioned on employment
  record.

Fig. 6 Standardized interview form.

more expensive to hire from an external source. Also, often the question is raised as to whether the proper talent was hired initially, reflecting on the judgment of the department administrator.

Interviewing the prospective staff candidate is one of the final and most critical steps in organizing the department. In order to compare objectively several competing candidates for the same position, it is important to maintain the same type of interview and apply a uniform technique for each successive candidate. In discussing this many otherwise successful managers violate a procedure designed to serve their best interests.

JOB EXPECTATIONS

— Why is she looking for work?
  What type of work interested in?
  Why our company?

— Salary requirements?

— How long does she plan to work?

SOCIAL

— What does she do in spare time?

— Membership in social organizations?
  How many? Offices? Elected or appointed?

— What type of group like best? Why?

— Friends working for the Company?

FAMILY AND HOME BACKGROUND

— Live with parents? If not, where?

— What does she do at home?

— What does she do with her money?

— Parents, brothers, sisters go
  to college? Complete?

— If single, marriage plans?
  Steady boyfriend? His ideas on
  marriage? His financial situation?

— If married, age when married?
  Plans for children?

— Husband's occupation? How long
  at job? Military status?
  Liability to transfer? Husband's
  education? Own or rent home?

— Transportation problems?

HEALTH

— How many days absent from
  school or work last year? Why?
  Any disabilities? Serious illness?

— Active in vigorous activities?

Fig. 6 *(Continued)*

Not only are there many types and styles of interviewing, but the techniques vary widely from individual to individual. Often a standardized interview form (Fig. 6) accompanying the standardized job-application form (Fig. 7) is very helpful, particularly if one is not conversant with the more professional aspects of interviewing techniques.

EVALUATION BY COMPREHENSIVE INTERVIEWER

Be sure you have obtained the reference information you want and have reviewed test scores before you make your evaluations.

Below are listed a number of activities which might be required of the applicant. First, check □ whether or not you like the applicant. Then check whether you Strongly Agree, Agree, Disagree, or Strongly Disagree that the applicant will do what is stated. If you did not get any information on which to base an evaluation, check the last column ("Didn't Cover").

	Strongly agree	Agree	Dis- agree	Strongly disagree	Didn't cover
* I like the applicant	□	□	□	□	□
THE APPLICANT WILL:					
1. Be able to get to the office easily	□	□	□	□	□
2. Accurately:					
a. Handle arithmetic problems	□	□	□	□	□
b. Type	□	□	□	□	□
c. Take and transcribe shorthand	□	□	□	□	□
d. File	□	□	□	□	□
3. Not have family problems which will interfere with work	□	□	□	□	□
4. Have a good attendance record	□	□	□	□	□
5. Be satisfied with our salary	□	□	□	□	□
6. Be easily handled (ie., supervised)	□	□	□	□	□
7. Get along well with coworkers	□	□	□	□	□
8. Produce more than the average employee	□	□	□	□	□
9. Be mature and businesslike	□	□	□	□	□
10. Work when supervisor leaves the room (dependable)	□	□	□	□	□
11. Not return to school	□	□	□	□	□
12. Not leave because of marriage or pregnancy in the next twelve months	□	□	□	□	□
13. Be challenged by and interested in the job for which she is being considered	□	□	□	□	□
14. Learn easily and quickly	□	□	□	□	□
15. _____	□	□	□	□	□
16. _____	□	□	□	□	□

Assuming that the applicant will perform as you have predicted above, will she be a good_____?
(Fill in position for which you are considering her.)

□ Definitely   □ Probably   □ Probably not   □ Definitely not

Comments:

Fig. 6   (*Continued*)

Many of the techniques are designed to find deficiencies in a particular job applicant and do very little to determine what his strong points are, for these are assumed to be accentuated by the training included in the job application.

An unfair comparison will exist between candidates available for an internal promotion and candidates being considered from an external source. This is obvious because in time one becomes well aware of the major and minor shortcomings of an individual within the organization. It is difficult to ascertain the undesirable qualities of an individual known for only a few brief hours. The person being interviewed is "on his best behavior," and if he is aware of his shortcomings, he is likely to suppress them.

EMPLOYMENT
APPLICATION

Aetna Life Insurance Company   The Aetna Casualty and Surety Company
The Standard Fire Insurance Company   Hartford, Connecticut 06115

An equal opportunity employer and a plans for progress company

Today's Date		
Month	Day	Year

Full name			
Miss / Mrs. / Mr.	Last	First	Middle

Present address ☐

Number and street	City or town	State

Permanent U.S. address (if different) ☐

Check address to which correspondence concerning this application should be sent.

*Date of birth	*Age	Telephone No.	Social Security No.
Month Day Year			/ /

For what type of position are you applying?	Salary expected
	$

EDUCATION

List all schools attended	Name and address of school	Dates From mo. yr.	Dates To mo. yr	Scho-lastic average	Did you grad-uate? Yes No	Year, or anticipated year, of graduation	Degree	High school course and/or college major
High/prep schools					☐ ☐			
					☐ ☐			
Colleges					☐ ☐			
					☐ ☐			
Other education					☐ ☐			

Circle quarter of class in which you stood: in high school: Top   2nd   3rd   Last;   In college: Top   2nd   3rd   Last

Do you plan to further your education?   ☐ Yes ☐ No   If so, when _____

How was your education financed? _____

ACTIVITIES

List organizations of which you have been, or are a member

(Do not list any organizations the name or nature of which would indicate your race, creed, color, national origin, or ancestry)

School (Scholastic, social, athletic, class, fraternity — Indicate whether high school or college)		Community and business (social, civic, political, professional)	
Organization	Position held	Organization	Position held

*The laws of many jurisdictions, including New York State, prohibit discrimination because of age. This information will not be used for purposes of discrimination.

Fig. 7 Standardized job-application form.

REFERENCES: The use of references is at times quite helpful, but they can also be misleading because of the "good guy" syndrome. The reference being contacted may be a close friend or would rather not be tagged with a negative appraisal. When references are used, the personnel department often requires "proof." There is usually a higher degree of reliability when references are checked on a confidential basis.

EMPLOYMENT RECORD

List all previous employment. Start with the most recent position in block no. 1 and work back
to least recent position. Identify part-time jobs with "P.T." and temporary jobs with "Temp."

Dates	1. From / to / Mo. Yr. Mo. Yr.	2. From / to / Mo. Yr. Mo. Yr.	3. From / to Mo. Yr. Mo. / Yr.
Employed by			
Address			
Duties performed			
Salary			
Reason for leaving			
Dates	4. From / to / Mo. Yr. Mo. Yr.	5. From / to / Mo. Yr. Mo. Yr.	6. From / to // Mo. Yr. Mo. Yr.
Employed by			
Address			
Duties performed			
Salary			
Reason for leaving			

If now employed, why do you desire to change?	If now employed, have you notified your present employer that you are seeking other work? ☐ Yes ☐ No
Were you ever discharged or asked to resign? ☐ Yes ☐ No If so, why?	In what office machines or clerical skills are you trained?
Why did you decide to apply for a position with us?	For what type of schedule are you available? ☐ Full time ☐ Part time ☐ Day ☐ Evening ☐ After school ☐ Summer
Give name of any employee by whom you are personally known.	
If hired, how many years do you expect to work for us?	Have you previously applied for a position with our companies? ☐ Yes ☐ No

U.S. MILITARY STATUS AND RECORD

Present Selective Service classification (if 1-Y or 4-F, please indicate reason).		If you have an incompleted military obligation, what are your plans for completing it?			
Branch of service	Active duty dates		Rank held		Type of duty
	From Mo./yr.	To Mo./yr.	Entry	Release	
What specialized training did you receive?				Type of discharge or separation	
Do you have a reserve obligation? ☐ Yes ☐ No If so, please describe					

Fig. 7   (*Continued*)

PERSONNEL TESTS: The extensive use of tests as a method of evaluating individuals has become quite popular over the last decades. Coefficients of correlation between the tests and the applicant's qualifications are said to be quite high by some of the more competent users. Other users cast doubt on some of the questionable test formats. The point to be made here is that valid and reliable personnel-evaluation tests are available. The reputation of a test is your best measure of selection. As with any standardized method used, one must remember that the entire purpose of a test is to assist in decision making.

PERSONAL

Height	Weight	Marital status
		☐ Single ☐ Engaged ☐ Married ☐ Divorced ☐ Separated ☐ Widowed

Have you ever been hospitalized, had any serious illnesses, or do you have any physical defects?
☐ Yes ☐ No   If so, describe

To what extent are you financially indebted?
$ To whom

Are you now receiving, or do you expect to receive, any income in the form of pension or disability payments from a previous employer, the Veterans Administration, or any federal or state program?

	If so, when did, or will, the payments begin?	How much do you, or will you, receive annually?
☐ Yes ☐ No		

Father's occupation	Mother's occupation

How many brothers have you?	Where are they employed?

How many sisters have you?	Where are they employed?

Date of your marriage	Is your husband or wife employed?
	☐ Yes ☐ No Where?

Maiden name	Husband's name

Married women give:

How many children have you?	Give age of each	No. of persons dependent on your earnings	Give relationship and age of each

With what part of the country are you most familiar?

If you desire to be located in any particular city or section of the country, please state preference and reason

Are you both willing and free to relocate if company needs require it?

Do you own your own home?	Is a position involving a considerable amount of overnight travel agreeable to you?
☐ Yes ☐ No	☐ Yes ☐ No

Have you ever been arrested?
☐ Yes ☐ No   If so, please explain

Have you had any motor vehicle accidents or violations?
☐ Yes ☐ No   If so, please explain

REFERENCES

Give names of three persons not related to you, who know you through school, business, or personal association.

Name	Business or profession	
	Street	City
Name	Business or profession	
	Street	City
Name	Business or profession	
	Street	City

(Please continue on next page and sign your name)

Fig. 7   (*Continued*)

The purpose of the test is not to *make* the decision but to *assist* when other factors contributing toward a conclusion are not available.

Various individuals react differently to an interview, so the interview may or may not reflect the true character of the individual.

INTERVIEWING: There is often a communication barrier in any conversation, and it is said that there are four versions of any conversation:

1. What you think you said
2. What you said
3. What the recipient heard
4. What the recipient thought you meant

ADDITIONAL INFORMATION

Please state any additional information which you feel would be helpful to us in considering your application with our companies. (Do not list any information the nature of which would indicate your race, creed, color, national origin, or ancestry.)

_____

_____

_____

_____

_____

_____

I certify that all the information I have given in this application is accurate and complete

Signed_____

COMPANY EMPLOYMENT RECORD

Status	Reg. No.	Date	Division	Salary	By	Category	If not salaried		Intv.
							Schedule	ED & ET	

Salary increase review at _____

Fig. 7   (*Continued*)

The ability to *communicate* is the one talent which separates man from other animals. Man is the only animal who has attained the skill to pass on the benefit of experience and amassed learning to succeeding generations by communications. Even with this advantage, we often neglect the development of this talent and consequently our communications are almost unintelligible. This is particularly true in the interview situation. A prospective job candidate seeking to please and impress an interviewer will seldom inform him that he does not understand the conversation.

MATCHING EMPLOYEE WITH JOB

Once the employee has been selected, groundwork should be laid by the manager to match the man to the job as well as the job to the man. In doing this the manager should recognize that there are essentially three elements to the manager's job:

1. That part of his job which is dictated by the system. These are functions which he must perform on a regular basis to "keep the wheels turning." These items often form that area of activity which an outsider views as the "managing" part of a job.

2. That part of his job that is dictated by a superior, such as special assignments, recommendations, and projects. These areas of performance bear indi-

rectly on the superior's immediate performance and constitute the area of work which can most directly affect the superior-subordinate relationship.

3. That area of a job which is dictated by a person himself. This is the creative aspect of management and the most fruitful area of performance for any management employee. It's that "little extra" that separates the leader from the follower, and is the characteristic most often found in top management men or those being groomed for such positions. It is these self-imposed accomplishments in which most managers take the highest degree of pride.

MANAGEMENT DIRECTION

Delegation is a talent required of all managers and must be included from the beginning during the design of the first tentative organization chart. It is often said that accountability and decision making should be delegated to a person at the lowest possible level of management. This will affect his training and will allow him to achieve and receive added responsibility.

THE EXCEPTIONS PRINCIPLE: A manager controls the actions of his subordinates to a considerable degree through policy formulation and the scope of the authority he delegates to them. In this way, the superior sets limits within which the subordinates act without further consultation. When a problem arises which is not routine and is outside the scope of a subordinate's authority, it is understood that he should refer the matter to his superior. If his superior does not have sufficient authority to decide, it is referred upward in the hierarchy to a manager having sufficient authority. This process is called the "exceptions principle." When followed correctly, the exceptions principle frees the manager from excess detail and from those decisions more efficiently made at lower levels. Similarly, it frees the subordinates from decisions best made at higher echelons.

The exceptions principle also can be applied to work done on the computer. If an activity or event is within an acceptable range determined in advance by the manager, it need not be called to his attention. If the activity exceeds the prescribed limits, he is informed so that he can decide how to bring it back within acceptable limits.

SPAN OF CONTROL: The span of control is the number of subordinates reporting to a manager. The concept associated with the span of a manager is that there is a limit to its size. When this limit is reached, it is wise to break up his group into subgroups. Decreasing the spans of control will increase the number of scalar levels required and could hinder effective communication between top and bottom organizational levels. On the other hand, the number of scalar levels can be decreased only by widening the spans of control. There is a limit to the degree the spans can be increased before impairing the manager's ability to coordinate his subordinates, even if he uses such techniques as assistants, staff organizations, and committees.

Maximum spans of control for various organizational levels have been suggested, although there is some question as to their validity. A better conclusion is that the limits are dependent on the manager's abilities, the types of activities to be managed, and the capabilities of his subordinates. Certainly an energetic and capable manager can tolerate a larger span than one possessing these qualities in a lesser degree. If the activities of subordinates are routine and change very little, a larger span is possible, particularly if the subordinates have been adequately trained. This is why larger spans of control tend to be found in the lower echelons of an organization. Finally, larger spans are justified if the subordinates are capable and willing to carry out their duties with little supervision.

EMPLOYEE CHARACTERISTICS: Managerial direction involves getting employees to accomplish *effectively* the tasks dictated, but the effectiveness of departmental employees depends on both their *ability* and *willingness* to contribute. The strength of these two employee characteristics depends on several determinants. These determinants may be grouped according to the degree of influence the manager has over them. There are at least six determinants over which the manager has little direct control:

1. One determinant is the number and quality of outside job alternatives perceived by the employee. If economic conditions are adverse or an employee's skills and experience are limited, he is likely to be very willing to contribute to his present organization.

2. Many of the employee's attitudes, beliefs, and values are formulated outside the work environment, yet they dramatically influence his on-the-job behavior.

3. The manager has but indirect control over group norms. It has long been known that the sanctions of "informal groups" exert enormous pressures on a member wishing to deviate from the norms of his group.

4. The emotional stabilities of subordinates set up constraints within which the manager must operate.

5. The degree to which a manager can enlarge a subordinate's job to allow greater "self-realization" is limited by economic necessities. Routine and uneventful jobs seldom evoke a strong loyalty and "moral commitment" on the part of an employee, yet the jobs must be done to achieve the economies of specialization.

6. The goals and expectations of employees as individuals and as a group are not under the complete control of a manager, yet the degree of compatibility of these goals with the realities of the work environment materially affects employee behavior and the willingness to contribute.

Do not conclude that the manager has no control over the above determinants. However, the determinants do act as constraints which must be recognized when dealing with subordinates. Furthermore, there are four categories of determinants over which the production and inventory control manager has considerable control:

1. One category has already been discussed—the plans, job activities, authority relationships, and job interrelationships formulated in earlier phases of the management process.

2. The payment and promotion systems of the department and the degree that these reward systems are linked operationally to effective behavior is one determinant.

3. Another is the training and development programs available to departmental employees.

4. The last consists of the interpersonal relationships the manager develops with his subordinates. More precisely it is his leadership style, his communication methods, and the manner in which he takes disciplinary action.

Different aspects of some of these determinants will be discussed in more detail, recognizing that few pat answers are available which apply to all situations. Although the progress in the "state of the art" has been extensive, there is considerable room for differences of opinion. A policy which "works" in one department, company, or geographical region may not work in another. Much depends on the precise nature of the situation.

PAYMENT SYSTEMS

Although much of the work of formulating and administering a payment system is performed by the personnel department, the production and inventory control

PRODUCTION AND INVENTORY CONTROL OPERATIONS

Job title: Manager of production and inventory control

Reports to: Vice president of manufacturing or director of materials management

Supervises: Supervisor of production planning
                     Supervisor of materials planning

BASIC FUNCTION:

Manage production and inventory control operations. Supervise the activities of production planning, materials planning, inventory, manpower planning, scheduling, and contract manufacturing. Administer production planning policy through the various production planning functions to achieve optimum results of production elements at minimum expense.

MAJOR DUTIES AND RESPONSIBILITIES:

1. Develop and institute production and inventory control programs, policies and plans for operations and implement systems that are approved and instituted.
2. Direct the preparation and issuance of production and inventory master plans and schedules.
3. Direct and administer the determination of production, material, and manpower required to meet the production plan. Secure approval of manpower strategy and implement manpower requirements with industrial relations.
4. Manage the planning and maintaining of the most favorable inventory levels of raw and packaging materials, work in process, and finished goods through direct supervision of the production planning supervisory functions.
5. Supervise the control of raw and packaging materials, work in process, and finished goods in regard to efficient plant operations and optimum investment.
6. Manage and direct the planning and scheduling functions for outside production approved contract manufacturers.
7. Participate in the development of manufacturing and inventory budgets.
8. Direct the maintenance of essential production and inventory control documents and files and prepare reports as required.
9. Review results against plans, report achievement activities, as well as take corrective action on plans as appropriate or required.
10. Approve inventory plans.
11. Perform special assignments as required.

PRINCIPAL WORKING RELATIONSHIPS:

1. Review production control plans, production schedules, and manpower plans with the manufacturing personnel.
2. Participate in problem-solving session with manufacturing personnel where production problems exist and vary actual output from plan.
3. Collaborate with the manufacturing director and quality control directors to schedule production in a manner so as to maintain established quality standards and to set up production plans on new products.
4. Review with corporate labor relations administrator the manufacturing manpower requirements.
5. Work with contract manufacturers in the administration of production and inventory control activities.
6. Work with corporate engineering and maintenance personnel in scheduling plant facilities for maintenance and installation of new equipment, etc.
7. Work with sales, marketing, and financial personnel to keep currently informed on sales and inventory needs in order to direct the logical modification of production plans to meet changing sales and inventory requirements with a minimum disruption to manufacturing.
8. Work with purchasing to achieve maximum efficient delivery of optimum-quality materials in economical increments.

Fig. 8 Job description.

manager plays an active role in its implementation within his department and is ultimately responsible for its success. Most payment systems are developed with formal, systematic procedures. As the nature of the jobs being considered becomes less routine and more creative, it becomes more difficult to follow formal payment-system procedures. Nonetheless, the approaches cited in the following paragraphs enjoy widespread application.

Most payment systems are developed using a two-step format: constructing the *job structure* which in turn provides the basis for the *rate structure*. Both steps require job information made available by *job analysis*. Data are collected on the nature of each job through observation, interviews, and questionnaires. The information collected is translated into a *job description* (Fig. 8), which typically has such headings as nature of the tasks, knowledge, education, skills, environmental conditions, and responsibilities.

The job structure is obtained through job evaluation. Jobs are weighted as to their relative importance to the company. There are four traditional approaches to job evaluation. The first two "rank" and "grade" methods are non-quantitative approaches which have simplicity as their main advantage.

Job	Rater A	Rater B	Rater C	Average	Final rank order
I	1	1	1	1	1
II	3	2	3	2.7	3
III	2	3	2	2.3	2

Fig. 9   Summary sheet for ranking method.

1. In the *rank method* (Fig. 9), as the name suggests, the rater simply ranks the jobs considering the "whole" job. At best, the rater has at his disposal the job description and some unweighted list of factors to use as a yardstick.

2. In the *grade method* (Fig. 10), the rater uses for his criteria descriptions of several job levels to which grades have been assigned. Using this scale as a guide, the rater then assigns a grade to each job. Two quantitative rating techniques are the point and factor-comparison methods.

3. The *point method* (Fig. 11), which is the most prevalent, breaks each job into *factors*. These factors are assigned weights according to their relative importance. Each factor is in turn broken down into several *degrees* which are assigned point values. A conventional point scale may consist of 10 to 15 factors, each of which has four or five degrees. When evaluating a job, the rater decides for each factor which of the degrees most closely approximates the job being rated. After all the job factors are rated, a total score is computed. This is the sum of the points for all the factors. The computed point total provides the desired basis for comparing one job with another.

4. The *factor-comparison method* (Fig. 12) compares key jobs with each other for each factor. The total job value is then calculated by apportioning among the factors the average current rate being paid. The scale so developed can then be employed to rate all jobs.

To complete the wage-payment system a job evaluation is made using one of these four techniques. In addition the wage rates being paid by other companies are obtained by wage surveys. From there a rate structure can be constructed which is reasonably consistent with the job structure and rates paid externally. The rate structure (Figs. 13 and 14) usually provides for a series

Grade	Description
1	Requires detailed and frequent instructions. The procedures to be followed must be specified in advance. Requires no contact with other employees or the public. No computational skills are required.
2	Performs routine work. Rather specific instructions must be followed, although can select own procedures in some instances. Requires use of reading, writing, adding, and subtracting.
3	Performs rather complex routine duties requiring considerable computational and verbal skill. Must be able to act in restricted field even on problems not previously encountered.
4	Encompasses a wider area of operation than grade 3 and requires much more contact with others. Position calls for technical training as well as wide general knowledge.

Fig. 10 Sample scale for grading method.

Job title_____

Factor	Degree	Points
Education required		
Experience required		
Initiative and judgment		
Supervision exercised		
Supervision required		
Mental effort		
Physical effort		
Complexity of tasks		
Working conditions		
Effect of error		
Personal contacts		

Date rated_____   Total points_____

Fig. 11 Rating sheet used for point method. This must be supplemented with detailed descriptions of each degree for each factor.

Key job	Factors					Present rates
	Responsibility	Mental	Skill	Physical	Wk cond.	
A	375	325	75	25	25	825
B	325	300	100	25	25	775
C	250	250	75	50	25	650
D	100	175	125	75	75	550
E	25	25	25	250	200	525
F	50	100	150	100	50	450
G	75	50	50	150	100	425
H	25	25	200	50	50	350

Fig. 12 Key-job data sheet for factor-comparison method.

of job classes to which each job is assigned. A base-rate curve and rate changes constitute the final rate structure.

The wage-payment system may or may not be augmented by a *group* or *individual* wage-incentive program. Wage incentives have been linked tradition- ally to direct labor where output is easily measured because jobs are well defined

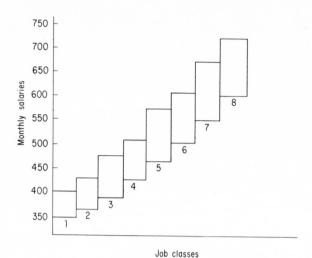

Job classes

Fig. 13 Example of a rate structure.

Dollars	Responsibility	Mental	Skill	Physical	Wk cond.
			Factors		
370	A				
350					
325	B	A			
300		B			
275					
250	C	C		E	
225					
200			H		E
175	D	D			
150			F	G	
125			D		
100		F	B	F	G
75	G		A	D	D
50	F	G	G	C	F
25	E	E	E	A	A

Fig. 14 Job comparison scale (derived from Fig. 13).

and standardized, the work cycle is short and repetitive, and the employee's output is proportional to the effort he expends. Most jobs within the production and inventory control department do not qualify on these counts, and therefore, traditional wage incentives are the exception rather than the rule. If an incentive program is deemed advisable, the production and inventory manager can select either a group or individual plan. The group plan is recommended when the work of the departmental employees is so interrelated as to place a premium on cooperative effort.

More common financial incentives for production and inventory control personnel include profit sharing (either cash or deferred distribution), stock-ownership plans, and fringe benefits. Found with increasing frequency are suggestion systems, merit bonuses, and vacation plans. Incentive compensation for supervisory positions is a controversial issue, although profit-sharing plans, factor-measurement systems, deferred compensation, and stock plans, are found in an increasing number of instances.

PROMOTION SYSTEMS

Promotion programs also include an appraisal of a person and his performance rather than a departmental position. Formal performance appraisals provide a source of information about the abilities and performance of an employee. Appraisals are sometimes used in conjunction with merit raises and employee-development plans, but are not always successful.

The major criticism of the current performance-appraisal techniques is their subjectivity. They are records of opinion which cannot be truly validated. Two raters can turn in substantially different and even conflicting appraisals of the same individual. Of course, some of the techniques are more subject to this weakness than others. Furthermore, the criticism seems to strengthen rather than weaken the case for a systematic appraisal system since *appraisal* is an unavoidable organizational activity.

Recent trends in promotion and appraisal are in the directions of:

1. Concentrating solely on performance rather than emphasizing capacity and personal characteristics

2. Development of direct measures of performance such as profit centers and setting specific goals to be achieved in future time periods

EMPLOYEE DEVELOPMENT AND TRAINING*

As with payment and promotion systems, the production and inventory control manager acts in conjunction with the personnel department in the activity of employee development and training. Advancements in learning theory promise more effective training and development programs, whether the objective is learning new techniques and factual concepts or new interpersonal skills and behavioral concepts.

The first logical step in training and development is an accurate assessment of who needs training and what sort of training is required. This information can be gathered from job analysis, performance appraisals, and the overall manpower analysis of the department. The second step is to decide on the content and format of the training program.

Perhaps the most effective programs provide active trainee participation, swift and accurate feedback of trainee progress, reinforcement of appropriate behavior, and application on the job of what has been learned. On the job is the most common training method. Within this method the following may be included:

1. Orientation training, which is a general introduction to the job and department policies

2. Job-instruction training (JIT), which is a detailed review demonstration of the job

3. Coaching

4. Job rotation

5. Assistantships, which are troubleshooting assignments

* The American Production and Inventory Control Society, Washington, D.C., has many training aids available.

The main drawback of on-the-job programs is the need for knowledgeable trainers and coaches possessing enough time to do an adequate job.

Other training methods can be grouped into off-the-job programs. They include:

1. Lectures such as university courses
2. Discussion groups, case studies, and role playing
3. Simulation and business games
4. Sensitivity training
5. Programmed instructions

The most appropriate technique should be chosen from these lists, depending on the needs of the trainee and the costs of the program. In any case, it is wise to follow up the training with a statistically valid evaluation of its effectiveness. Such an evaluation may take the form of tests, evaluations by the trainees, and observable behavior changes on the job. Good evaluation procedures require pretest and posttest data, preferably with the use of a control group.

EMPLOYEE APPRAISAL

Employee-development procedures have traditionally been accompanied by *appraisal interviews*. Following the completion of a performance evaluation, the manager should relay the results verbally to the subordinate as a matter of formal procedure. Research shows that these appraisal interviews often fail to achieve the expected results and are seldom conducted. The interviews often tend to become "tell and sell," one-directional dialogues which are not conducive to real behavior changes on the part of the subordinate.

Some researchers advocate, instead of problem-solving sessions, *target-setting* sessions, which are founded on mutual confidence. The subordinates, with the help of their supervisors, are encouraged to evaluate themselves and set their own goals for the next time period. These same researchers caution, however, that the evaluation approach must be consistent with the management philosophy and the climate of the organization. If management relies on the authority-obedience system, traditional evaluation methods should be retained.

HUMAN RELATIONS

Analyzed in the following sections will be four topics related to the manager's human relationships with his subordinates: motivation, leadership, communication, and discipline. Each of these activities plays an important role in creating conditions conducive to high employee effectiveness and morale.

Motivation. An employee is willing to contribute to his department only if he perceives that by doing so he gains more than he loses. This implies the need for a certain degree of congruency between individual and organizational goals. Understanding the goals of individual employees introduces the topic of motivation. The study of motivation begins with seeking out and cataloging the motivators of employees, so as to relate them to the reward system of the organization.

Perhaps the best of these cataloging schemes is referred to as the "needs hierarchy." Man is said to be a *wanting animal* always seeking to satisfy his needs. These needs exist in a hierarchy. As lower-level needs are satisfied, man turns his attention and energies to higher-level needs which become increasingly more difficult to satisfy. As man attempts to satisfy his needs, he is motivated. It is interesting that a satisfied need is no longer a motivator.

Physiological and safety needs comprise the first and basic level of needs as man seeks protection from danger and threats. Being in a somewhat dependent relationship, an employee responds favorably to managerial behavior that is consistent, fair, and does not cause an undue amount of fear of discharge. The all-important payment system relates to this basic level of needs.

The next level of the hierarchy consists of social needs. Man is a social animal and seeks a sense of belonging and acceptance. The prevalence of informal groups in the industrial setting gives adequate testimony to the social requirements of man. Managerial action thwarting an employee's social needs may lead to behavior detrimental to the organization. To the extent that an employee is a social man, the manager should be aware of his feelings and his need to belong.

The highest rung of the needs hierarchy encompasses egoistic and "self-actualizing" needs. Man seeks autonomy, self-respect, status, and the experience of continual self-development. The manager is no longer the motivator and controller. Instead, his role is to provide the framework and climate within which the employee's existing motivation and drives can be harnessed to serve organizational purposes.

Basing reward systems solely on one of these three simplified views of man's needs would be naïve. Man is too complex to be described adequately as striving solely for one level of needs. He is highly variable, capable of learning new motives and needs. The production and inventory control manager must therefore be a good diagnostician capable of detecting the differing and changing needs of each subordinate. The manager has at his disposal a repertory of behavior patterns so he can adjust to the needs of his employees. His behavior in motivating subordinates manifests itself along three dimensions: leadership, communication, and disciplinary practices.

Leadership. Theories of leadership are many and controversial. One of the first attempts to understand industrial leadership involved the observation of the *traits* of successful leaders. The search for a set of universal traits has not been successful, giving rise to advocates of *situational* leadership theory. This theory proposes that effective leadership roles and skills are unique to each situation. An effective leader with one group of employees may be ineffective with another group.

Of course, both trait and situational theories are oversimplifications. Many authorities now believe that both traits and situation must be included in a valid theory of leadership.

Leadershp behavior can be described in terms of a continuum extending between two opposite types of leadership—authoritarian and democratic styles. The pure authoritarian leader directs others in the form of orders, without letting them participate in the decision process. His supervision is close and he tends to be oriented solely to production requirements without considering the less obvious "people" problems of his actions. He enforces his decisions with threats, his formal authority, or the forcefulness of his personality.

The democratic leader, on the other hand, permits participation in the decision-making process and directs others through persuasion and example. He is apt to delegate more of his authority, giving his subordinates a greater chance for self-actualization.

There are many leadership styles on the continuum between these polar positions. For example, a manager may not allow participation but may attempt to "sell" his decision rather than rely on the authority of his position. He may invite employee suggestions before making his final decision. He may reach a tentative decision subject to revision after consulting his subordinates.

Research evidence generally favors a more democratic form of leadership.

Compared to a more truly authoritarian form, it seems to encourage more initiative, productive behavior, less dependency, and less resistance to changes on the part of subordinates.

Perhaps the safest conclusion is that effective leadership depends on three variables: the characteristics of the manager, the characteristics of his subordinates, and the nature of the situation. From the standpoint of employee characteristics a democratic style may be successful with one subordinate and viewed as a sign of weakness by another. A subordinate simply may not be capable of assuming a greater role in decision making or he may not be a "self-actualizing" man in terms of his job expectations.

Turning to the second variable—the manager's characteristics—we may find he is unable or unwilling to assume a democratic style. Delegating authority without continually looking over a subordinate's shoulder requires a capacity of trust and respect. It also involves a risk, since subordinates gain experience in managerial decision making and can become, in effect, competitors with the existing manager for higher positions in the corporate hierarchy.

The third variable—the situation—is also important. Often a decision must be made rapidly, ruling out participation. A subordinate's job may be so routine that his energies for achieving higher-level needs on the job have long since been invested in activities off the job. Finally, the climate set by top management may make a lower-level manager reluctant or even ineffective in pursuing a radically different leadership style.

Communication. The character and extent of boss-subordinate communications materially affect the ability and willingness of subordinates to make effective contributions. Interpersonal communications can be oral or written. Face-to-face oral communications have several advantages. It is possible to determine if the message is really understood, questions can be asked, and meanings can be clarified.

The complexity of the message and time constraints may necessitate written communications, which have the advantages of permanency, wide distribution, and careful formulation. Communication techniques other than face-to-face relationships between a manager and his subordinates include bulletin boards, meetings, conferences, suggestion systems, and company publications.

Transmitting messages which will be understood and acted upon depends on at least three variables: the direction of the message, the content of the message, and the structure of the communication nets. The direction of the message refers to whether it is sent upward, downward, or laterally. Delegation is an example of downward communication. It is the means by which superiors give their subordinates orders and needed information. Upward communication, one of the manager's most valuable sources of feedback information, exists primarily to the extent that he encourages it. Relating communication to styles, a democratic leader would be apt to encourage communication in both vertical directions, whereas the authoritarian leader would not be able to obtain accurate upward information.

The content of a message is also important. For example, a factual message lends itself much more easily to written communication than does one with emotional content. Laboratory experimentation shows some communication nets are more effective than others for varying purposes. The pyramid- or wheel-shaped network, for example, channels information to one person occupying a central control position (see Fig. 15a and b). These networks have been found to increase efficiency while lowering group-member satisfaction in routine, task-oriented situations. An all-channel network (Fig. 15c) is more suitable to nonroutine work demanding creativity and change.

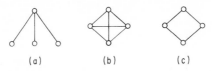

Fig. 15 Types of communication net-works: (a) pyramid; (b) all-channel; (c) wheel. (Only the all-channel has open two-way channels between all parties.)

The manager should be aware of barriers to effective communication. Blocking of the communication process can be caused by undue emphasis on "going through the channels," use of confusing and ambiguous language, and inadequate interpersonal relationships between the sender and the receiver.

DISCIPLINE

Despite the manager's best efforts in personal relationships, the need for disciplinary action sometimes arises. Discipline can, of course, serve constructive purposes and provide a certain measure of security for subordinates in establishing certain limits that must and will be enforced. Discipline is best when exercised immediately, consistently, impersonally, and with prior warning. The employee must be made aware that unacceptable behavior will be disciplined regardless of the offender. He must also be given forewarning as to the dividing line between acceptable and unacceptable behavior.

Perhaps the most challenging aspect of disciplinary action is making it an impersonal matter that does not permanently damage a manager's viable relationship with his subordinate. Only by impersonal disciplinary action will the manager continue to be viewed as a source of help and encouragement. Most disciplinary systems are progressive, beginning with oral warnings and discussions, restricted promotion opportunities, and written warnings. The more extreme forms of discipline such as transfers, demotions, or discharge are to be reserved for when all else fails.

MEASURING DEPARTMENTAL EFFICIENCY

When discussing the measurement of efficiency, care must be exercised to ascertain that the area being measured is clearly defined. In this section the subject of measurement is the production and inventory organization, not the manufacturing operation. The reader should keep this point clearly in mind when evaluating the following material for application.

While manufacturing efficiency is generally measured directly by comparing allowed time and actual time to establish a percent of efficiency, the measurement of efficiency of a support group like production and inventory control is generally based on the results achieved through other functions. In this sense, a systems approach is necessary in the evaluation because of joint and cross responsibility for the function of the enterprise. A further factor to clarify is that the concern here is with efficiency, which should not be confused with effectiveness. In any function, a given level of effectiveness is required. The level of efficiency attained must then be measured in relation to the desired effectiveness level.

Objectives of Efficiency Measurement. The primary objective in measuring departmental efficiency of the department head and the departmental policies is to improve departmental operations. This objective implies the necessity of combining the contributions of the various subelements of the department to achieve an overall measurement. In combining the contributions of subelements, problems generated from different data bases, tangible and intangible contributions, clerical errors, completeness of records and judgment factors must all be evaluated and weighted in their contribution to the overall efficiency measurement.

Control Devices. Control devices which might be used to establish measurement of departmental efficiency are listed below. They are based on the use of various cost data and statistical data generated in functions of the firm.

INVENTORY TURNOVER: Inventory turnover is calculated by comparing the amount of inventory used during a period to the average inventory on hand. In using this measurement, it is implied that the inventory is *active* inventory and that *stock outs* remain constant or do not occur. The important point to consider is that inventory turnover by itself is an incomplete measurement. It must be used in conjunction with established levels of customer service.

Units of measure require definition in using an inventory-turnover ratio. Before starting to use a turnover ratio, the user should determine operating criteria to include the following:

1. Is the computation of material used based strictly on out-of-pocket costs or are various inventory-carrying costs to be considered?

2. How is average inventory to be computed? Is it based on the average of beginning- or end-of-month inventory, or an average of the last x number of months, or some other approach?

CUSTOMER-SERVICE LEVEL: Use of this measurement considers the number of orders received, number of orders filled per schedule, and number of stock outs in relation to desired service levels.

QUEUE TIME: A measurement of the amount of time an order waits in queue preceding a given operation is an indication of the efficiency of scheduling. With queue time accounting for a large segment of total float time, reductions in queue time can have a major effect on the level of in-process inventories and manufacturing efficiency.

OTHER CONTROL DEVICES: Enumerated below are some other possible areas for efficiency measurement that might apply in specific circumstances.

1. Actual versus scheduled production
2. Actual versus scheduled deliveries
3. Clerical errors
4. Record accuracy
5. Standard versus actual production

Some of these measuring systems are the measurement of production facilities. However, since it is the responsibility of the production and inventory staff to achieve optimum scheduling of facilities to attain on-time delivery, these measuring devices can also be used as a basis of judgment for specific areas within production and inventory control as well as for the total operation.

Results of Efficiency Measurement. Efficiency measurement for a production and inventory control department is a source of many disagreements. These measurements can be both objective and subjective. Also it must be remembered that each separate increment in the total measurement system has its own coefficient of reliability. Job appraisals themselves may be used and actual performance measured against the content of the job description.

Budgetary control is also one of the better ways. A specific method of planning would be required to budget man-hours, work in process, and resultant finished goods. These would be measured according to how the actual performance deviated from the planned levels. This information is quite often reduced to graphical form and included in a monthly report which reflects the total departmental activity.

Discipline or action taken because of the deviations from planned results must be made with constraint and only after it has been established that the deviation was not caused by factors outside of the control of the individual.

Since the degree to which goals are achieved directly affects the attainment of the departmental objectives, it is obvious that a systems approach is necessary. The lack of a systems approach will result in increased costs and a reduction in departmental efficiency.

SUMMARY

This chapter has been directed toward organizational concepts, manpower requirements, and human relations necessary to achieve the goals of the production and inventory control function. Because inventory fluctuations have an effect on our economy, the need to achieve the goals of the organization is recognized as being of major importance.

To succeed in the operation of the department the manager must effectively plan the objectives, policies, procedures, rules, and budgets for his department. The planning function consists of a series of steps:

1. Problem recognition.
2. Problem definition
3. Recognition of organizational and departmental objectives
4. Establishment of planning premises
5. Development of alternative courses of action
6. Establishment of implementation plans

Whether these plans are stated explicitly or implicitly, they must be communicated effectively to the employees in the department.

In addition to planning, the manager must structure the organization. It is impossible to present a specific organizational plan for production and inventory control because of the diverse functions performed in various firms. Nevertheless, the manager should follow a few basic steps to develop a more efficient organization:

1. Determine interdepartmental reporting relationships.
2. Develop intradepartmental job levels, accountability, and responsibility.
3. Develop job descriptions.

The preceding steps of planning and organizing provide the necessary details to develop manpower requirements. The job descriptions and activity audits indicating job requirements and working conditions provide information to construct a job analysis to be matched with individual personnel audits.

Sources of manpower can be both internal and external. Objectively, the manager should look to the development of competent personnel internally. When it is necessary to recruit externally, the manager should be aware of the advantages and disadvantages of methods (references, tests, and interviews) used to evaluate the applicant. Analogous with determination of manpower requirements is the matching of the employee with the job.

The manager must recognize the three parts of his job:

1. That part dictated by the system
2. That part dictated by the superior
3. That part dictated by himself

Matching the employee with the job effectively contributes toward accomplishment of the managerial task by increasing the ability and willingness of the employee to contribute. Basically, the manager is confronted by the individual's hierarchy of needs. Extreme care must be exercised in attempting to categorize an individual's needs due to his constantly changing needs over the long and short term. Much has been written concerning the willingness of the employee to contribute, and the reader is directed to the Bibliography at the end of the chapter for a more extensive discussion.

One objective of the foregoing is to establish job structures and rate structures as the basis for payment plans. Job structures are obtained through job evaluations made by any of four approaches: the rank method, the grade method, the point method, and the factor-comparison method. The rate structure is the result of establishing money wages consistent with the job structure and competitive economic conditions.

Associated with the job- and rate-structure program is the area of promotion. It is generally assumed that a promotion is desired by individuals. This is not always correct, which presents a dilemma to the manager as he is faced with the problem of providing adequate compensation to satisfy and motivate the employees within the confines of a rate structure and organization plan.

The leadership style of the individual manager is a reflection of his basic characteristics. Consequently, the manager's style might range anywhere from an autocratic to a democratic approach. To further compound the complexity of the situation, the manager will usually find that he will need to use a different style when communicating with, training, directing, and disciplining different individuals.

An important function related to the management of the production and inventory control department is the measurement of departmental efficiency to improve departmental operations. Techniques available to the manager include inventory turnover, customer-service levels, queue time, plus extensive measures of direct operations as reflected in the production and inventory control program.

The preceding framework is provided as a starting point to assist the production and inventory control manager in the management of his department. Because of the human element it has not been possible to state specific solutions to specific problems. Hopefully, the material presented will provide guidelines to effectively improve the results of the manager's efforts.

BIBLIOGRAPHY

Argyris, Chris: *Integrating the Individual and the Organization,* John Wiley & Sons, Inc., New York, 1964.

Dale, Ernest: *Planning and Developing the Company Organization Structure,* American Management Association, New York, 1952.

Etzioni, Amitai: *Modern Organizations,* Prentice-Hall, Inc., Englewood Cliffs, N.J., 1964.

Koontz, Harold, and Cyril O'Donnell: *Principles of Management,* 4th ed., McGraw-Hill Book Company, New York, 1968.

Likert, R.: *New Patterns of Management,* McGraw-Hill Book Company, New York, 1961.

McFarland, Dalton E.: *Management Principles and Practices,* 2d ed., The Macmillan Company, 1964.

McGregor, Douglas: *The Human Side of Enterprise,* McGraw-Hill Book Company, New York, 1960.

March, J. G., and H. S. Simon: *Organizations,* John Wiley & Sons, Inc., New York, 1958.

Miller, David W., and Martin K. Starr: *Executive Decisions and Operations Research,* Prentice-Hall, Inc., Englewood Cliffs, N.J., 1960.

Schein, Edgar H.: *Organizational Psychology,* Prentice-Hall, Inc., Englewood Cliffs, N.J., 1965.

Chapter **3**

Organization Concepts for Production Control

EDITORS:

Benjamin F. Butts *Principal, Management Consulting Service, Ernst & Ernst, Chicago, Illinois*

Philip Graber *Management Consulting Services Staff, Ernst & Ernst, Chicago, Illinois*

CONTENTS

Discussions and analyses of industrial organizations presented in management literature take many forms and appear to have many diverse purposes. Some of these discuss principles of organizations and their application in the industrial context. Others present *new* concepts of organization and their proposed impact upon industrial life. Current discussion traces the impact of organizational structures on the employees' personalities.

To place the following discussion in the proper context, here in specific terms are the purpose and nature of this chapter:

1. A description of organizations as sets of relationships among individuals and work activities which are explicitly designed to accomplish goals.

2. The definition and description of organizational terminology and techniques.

3. A modern organizational concept—*organization as a total system*—which can effectively guide organizational planning in today's complex industrial environment.

4. A modern organizational tool—*management by objectives.*

5. The application of management by objectives to the opportunities and problems of the production and inventory control function.

Industrial enterprises must recognize and understand the nature and value of the organizations they establish and systematically plan organization structures and activities as they now plan their financial, production, sales, and distribution activities.

The concepts and tools described in this chapter can provide a set of explicit guidelines for the structuring and operation of the production and inventory control function. These guidelines are general enough to be utilized in many types of industrial organizations, but sufficiently specific to permit application to an organization problem by you, today.

ORGANIZATIONS: RELATIONSHIPS BETWEEN INDIVIDUALS AND WORK

An organization is formed when two or more people unite to achieve a common purpose or goal. The framework within which these people unite is the *organization* which is essential to their reaching common objectives. To successfully achieve the organization's objectives it is important to designate the people, the place they occupy, the range of authority, and the responsibility they exercise. Needed is a framework of relationships among people and the mechanisms through which they operate and coordinate their activities.

"Organizational design," as applied by the specialists, may be defined as breaking down broad and overwhelming tasks into manageable units with pinpointed responsibilities, while at the same time ensuring coordination of the work of the individuals involved.

Organization charts, with descriptions defining each position, provide a road map of the major features of an organization structure. In the ideal situation, organization charts assure that everyone knows the extent of his organizational position, his authority, and his accountability. Thus, theoretically, relationships among individuals and groups are clear.

Charts and position descriptions in themselves, however, provide only minimum help, except insofar as they are an aid to the memory and visualization. The charts and position descriptions do not solve the real problems of organization design such as: What is the best way of dividing the work to achieve the objectives and reduce conflicts among the organizational groups? Who should supervise whom and what should be the structure of the interrelationships? How much responsibility and authority should be allocated for each position? What form of organization will assure that each individual can utilize his powers to the fullest and to the maximum benefit of the organization? How can coordination for goal achievement be accomplished? How can the organization be changed? These are the important questions that should be asked about organizations, and effective methods for answering them will be presented in this chapter.

As an organization is started, one or two people have all the authority and assume all the responsibilities by force of circumstances, since the operations center around these one or two people. As expansion and growth continues this concentration of authority and responsibility becomes ineffective, and a formal framework of organization becomes necessary. Since all organizations are in the broadest sense dynamic within themselves, it is imperative that the organizational structure be reviewed constantly and modified as changes are required.

The restructuring and redefining of the organization, as changes require, can be based upon several methods. The most common approach might be referred to as the "classic approach," which is the grouping together of primary operating functions. The second approach might follow the traditional approach of the line and staff organization. Committee management has also been employed in solving the organizational problems. This effective approach of recent origin is finding growing acceptance because it defines the organization as a *total system* and structures the organization to fit the needs and requirements of the system. This view of organizations will be discussed later in this chapter.

DEFINITIONS OF ORGANIZATION CONCEPTS

There are a number of terms in management literature that may mean different things to different people. The behavioral and management scientists, like the data processing computer specialists, have developed a language of their own which intermingles old terms with new to define new concepts or to redefine old concepts and ideas. Three terms over which confusion exists are "administration," "management," and "organization." To a lesser degree, the terms "policies," "objectives," "authority," and "responsibility" also cause confusion.

Administration. "Administration" may be defined as the function within an organization which is concerned with establishing corporate policy. It is responsible for the coordination of such separate activities as finance, production, and distribution. It is also responsible for the definition of the goals and objectives of the organization and the ultimate control of the operations.

The administrative function includes the active planning, direction, coordination, and control of a business as a whole within the direction and scope of the basic policies established and the authority delegated by the board of directors. In other words, this function involves the determination of objectives, operating policies, and results.

Management. "Management" is the organizational function concerned with the execution of policy within the limits established by the administration and also the utilization of the organization and its personnel for the attainment of the objectives set before it.

Management can be seen as the function of *executive leadership*. It is the function of planning, organizing, and controlling the work of others. From the viewpoint of the production and inventory control practitioner, management would be separated into two caegories: *administrative management* and *operative management*. Administrative management is group-management oriented, while operative management performs management functions for the accomplishment of specific projects.

Organization. A definition frequently used states that *organization is people*. People do comprise an organization, but a number of people without organization would accomplish little. The more meaningful question is: What is effective organization? An effective organization is any group of people whose duties, responsibilities and interrelationships are clearly understood and who cooperate willingly under the direction of competent executive leadership in the efficient accomplishment of specific objectives.

Administration *determines* the organization and management *uses* it. Administration defines the goal; management strives toward it. Organization is the tool of management used to achieve the ends determined by administration. Organizing can be viewed as creating in advance of execution the basic conditions that are the prerequisite for the achievement of designated objectives.

Policies. "Policies" may be defined as a set of principles which members of the organization team use in reaching decisions for guiding their actions. Policies should set forth directions that decisions should take rather than be decisions themselves. Policies may be thought of as codes or general rules which state the established procedure to follow in recurring situations.

A policy is neither a plan nor a procedure but is used in the formulation of plans and procedures. It is a guide for the actions of the organization. A policy may be called a "statement of purpose." Definite and understandable terms or policy are prerequisite for the accomplishment of any objective. The body of principles and rules of action that serve as directives constitutes the policy. It guides the organization in achieving its objectives. From the production and inventory control viewpoint, policies should be set up by production executives as part of the managerial procedure for operating the plant to produce the product. Policies may be a statement of principle or a group of principles with supporting rules of action. Policies establish rules of action that govern the achievement of business objectives.

Companies generally operate on the basis of two types of policy: corporate and functional. Corporate policies are established by the board of directors and are the basis for broad objectives—the reason for the existence of the company. Functional policies provide the guides for carrying out divisional and departmental responsibilities.

There are six basic characteristics of good policies:
1. They tend to be broad.
2. They are current.
3. They are consistent.
4. They are complete.
5. They are inviolate.
6. They are in writing.

A typical corporate policy might read: "Manufacture a diversified line of products to provide continuing demand and to eliminate seasonality and the market fluctuations created by single product lines." On the other hand, typical manufacturing division corporate policy might read: "Manufacture products of quality to provide the greatest possible value from money expended." The broad corporate policy would immediately require the development of corporate objectives involving purchasing standards, raw-materials inspection and testing, quality control for in-process and finished goods, accounting controls for evaluating costs, equipment acquisition, and operator selection and training.

Objectives. "Objectives" may be defined as the *goals* for the organization as a whole, or for a particular group, or for an individual within an organization. Objectives are simply statements of what is expected from everyone involved in the organization and may subsequently provide a basis for measuring what has actually been achieved against these expectations. The systematic use of objectives throughout an entire organization is the basis for the current *management-by-objectives programs* that will be discussed in detail later.

Authority. It is necessary to grant the individual certain authority to carry out the responsibilities of the position defined by the organization structure for which the functions have been described by the policies and objectives. Authority is the right to command, to decide, and to act. No organization position can be established adequately unless it holds the necessary authority to carry out the assigned duties and responsibilities.

The principle that responsibility and authority should go hand in hand is well established and must be followed if the responsibilities of the job holder are to be achieved. This means that when responsibilities are assigned to a position, everyone should understand that the holder of the position also has the authority to carry out the duties of the position. Each day more and more companies are finding that the answer to the question of matching authority with responsibilities may be achieved by issuing *position descriptions*. Figure 1 is a typical position description which clearly defines the interrelationships of the activities, responsibilities, and authorities of the position.

Within a formal organization structure there are two types of authority—line and functional. We are most familiar with line authority from a manufacturing standpoint. Line authority gives an executive the right to give direct orders to subordinates. An executive with line authority controls his subordinates principally by discipline and decisions, or recommendations on compensation and promotion. The production control manager would have within his area of responsibility direct line authority over the personnel who report directly to him. The production control executive with line authority is concerned with determining the need, the time, and the place for action and issues direct orders within his department to line subordinates to get things done. It is this line authority that goes hand in hand with the responsibility. Figure 2 reflects a typical line organization with line authority extending directly from the president and general manager of the business down through the various levels of authority to the lowest operating level which has the basic primary objectives defined.

The concept of functional authority is more subtle than that of line authority and consequently is less widely understood and used. Understanding functional authority is of importance to the production and inventory control manager since he operates in this realm. Functional authority is sometimes referred to as "technical authority" because it is frequently based upon special knowledge or skill of activity. It is simply the right to see that activities carried on in other departments or other organizational units are conducted in accordance with the requirements of the unit having technical authority.

Functional authority has its origin in the specialized technical knowledge of the executive department or unit that exercises it. Just as line authority is

Title: Director of materials

Division: Materials   Date:_____

ORGANIZATION AND RELATIONSHIPS:

   The Director of materials reports to the president. He is responsible to him for the direction and coordination of all the activities in the company related to the flow of materials encompassing the functions of general traffic, general stores, purchasing, production and inventory control, and warehousing. He confers regularly with the president to receive direction relative to the objectives of the division and the plans of the company. In turn he provides the president with recommendations and reports concerning progress toward established materials-procurement and usage goals. He collaborates with the treasurer in the development and control of inventory budgets. He confers with the officer in charge in matters and plans relating to the operation of foreign subsidiaries. He confers with the production manager in matters relating to the manufacturing plans and operating controls. He confers with executives of the sales division relative to sales plans, forecasts, and other subjects of mutual interest. He consults with the vice president of industrial relations in matters relating to personnel policies. He directs the department heads under his jurisdiction, delegates responsibility to them, coordinates their activities, and counsels them on the various problems with which they are confronted. In turn he receives recommendations and advice from them in their mutual efforts to achieve divisional objectives and goals. He confers with suppliers, transportation, and shipping agencies and maintains contact with such trade and inventory associations as appear advisable for the better fulfillment of his role.

FUNCTION:

   Organize and direct the materials division encompassing general traffic, general stores, purchasing, production and inventory control, and warehousing; coordinate these activities to optimize the inventory investment which provides materials and parts to maintain high levels of customer service.

SPECIFIC DUTIES AND RESPONSIBILITIES:

   1. As approved, organize the division into operational units, delegate responsibilities, assign personnel to carry them out, and coordinate the activities of the division.
   2. Direct the development of purchasing policies and procedures through the director of purchases and his staff in the procurement of all materials, components, equipment, supplies, and services required by the company with the objective of obtaining the optimum price, quality, delivery, and services.

Fig. 1   Position description for director of materials.

3. Provide management with pertinent data concerning long-range availability and prices of materials and components.

4. See that maximum assistance is obtained from suppliers in the application of new and improved materials and processes to the company's products.

5. Provide for the continuation of a formal program of procurement value analysis to provide the company with materials and components possessing the maximum functional value at the lowest possible cost.

6. Direct the production and inventory control manager in the provision of materials and components to ensure the most efficient and economical utilization of manpower and manufacturing facilities through improved scheduling and inventory control techniques. Maintain balance between costs of acquisition and costs of possession of materials so as to minimize manpower fluctuations and maximize return on capital invested in inventories.

7. Provide a balanced inventory of service parts to assure the highest possible level of customer service which is economically sound.

8. Provide for the maintenance of inventories or the availability of materials and parts to fulfill the requirements of the company's subsidiaries and assure an uninterrupted flow of materials to meet their needs.

9. Direct the activities of warehousing, traffic, and general stores to assure the most economic and uninterrupted flow of inbound materials, their receipt and internal movement, storage and issuance, and subsequent outbound movement, storage and issuance, and subsequent outbound movement.

10. Develop, in collaboration with the treasurer's office, inventory budgets for the purpose of establishing acceptable inventory levels at varying levels of activity, upon which performance can be measured and operating controls effected.

11. Direct the efforts of the systems coordinator in provisioning for the maximum computerization of all clerical activities and the consolidation and refinement of clerical activities within the division.

12. Establish annual operating objectives and divisional goals with related performance indicators so that results may be appraised.

13. See that annual budget proposals of the various material division departments are prepared through subordinate managers, review and revise the proposals as situations warrant, check budget realization at regular intervals, and see that deviations therefrom are explained.

14. Administer established personnel policies with respect to both hourly and salaried employees within the division. Approve and process personnel actions involving appointments, transfers, promotions, reclassifications, rate increases, dismissals, etc., in accordance with established policy.

15. Provide for the continuing development and training of personnel within the division to assure maximum continuing growth and improvement in performance.

Fig. 1   (Continued)

a grant of *power*, functional authority is the authority of *knowledge*.   The holder of functional authority says if and when you do it, do it this way in accordance with this procedure or standard.   Production control departments typically assume functional authority when they direct the manufacturing effort in accordance with a planned production schedule.   Line executives help enforce functional authority by putting their line authority behind it.

As in the organization chart presented, the line authority, from the superintendent to the foreman, is behind the schedule to have its requirements attained. The president and general manager in this typical organization orders all line executives to follow and enforce the policies and procedures of the functional departments.   Thus, the functional departments are not merely advisory.   The production control department has its own authority which is backed by line authority.   Functional departments such as the production and inventory control department are therefore not the same as staff departments.   Production and inventory control should approach the job of enforcing the standards of the department, such as schedules, in a spirit of exercising authority, not just offering advice.

Functional departments, when effective, seldom need to resort to a show of authority.   The standards and schedules of the production control department must be useful, sensible, and persuasively presented to the line departments.   If

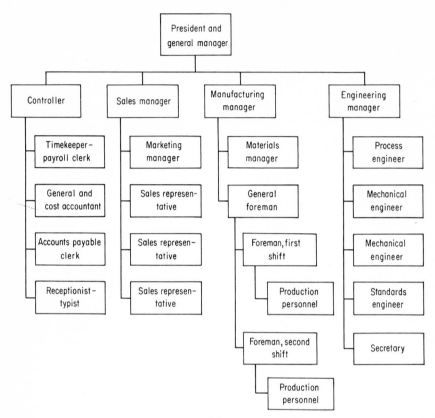

Fig. 2 Typical line organization.

the line department disagrees with the schedules of the production control department and the difference of opinion cannot be resolved, it is referred to the next highest common line superior. This system of checks and balances is an effective means of getting things done quickly and getting them done right. The production control manager as a functional executive with authority will also have line authority over the personnel in his own departments.

Responsibility. Responsibility is the obligation that an individual assumes when he accepts an assignment or a job. It is the obligation of the individual to properly perform the functions and duties that have been assigned to him in accordance with the direction given him. The right that corresponds to this obligation of responsibility is authority as previously noted. In an organizational sense responsibility is accountability for the performance of assigned duties. "Duties," as allotted to an individual, may be defined as the activities he is required to perform because of the place he occupies in the organization.

FORMS OF INDUSTRIAL ORGANIZATION STRUCTURE

Organizational theory writers are frequently confusing in their use of terms describing the forms of organization structure. Often the forms described are merely stages in the problem of differentiating and grouping functions within the organization.

There are only two basic forms of organization structure—line and staff. The structure of a particular company at any one time is a combination developed from these basic forms of organization. The term "functional organization" refers not to a basic structural form but merely to a certain type of relationship between line and staff responsibilities and authorities.

The line organization is the primary form of organization and in its simplest form is frequently referred to as the "military type" of organization. It is the hierarchy, or chain of functions and people with their responsibility and authority, that leads directly to the achievement of objectives. As a company grows and a greater division of labor and specialization is required, the line organization develops. The chain of responsibility and authority as illustrated in Fig. 2 is the primary chain of command. Authority is passed down from the president and general manager to the operating groups.

In the instance of the pure line organization, the foreman would be responsible for not only developing the techniques employed, but also formulating the work specifications, procuring materials, planning and scheduling the work load, and maintaining proper cost and production records.

There are few companies today operating with a pure line organization because of the problems associated with its rigidity and inflexibility and the need to bring technical understanding, knowledge, and experience into the activities.

Line and Staff Organizations. Reference has been made to functional authority and responsibility necessary because of the specialized knowledge of the functions involved. The line and staff plan of organization so common today developed through the recognition of the need for specialized functions. Assignments of specialized advisory and facilitation duties are made to staff individuals who give their attention solely to such work. This is the typical role of the production and inventory control department executive. In the line and staff organization, the line serves to maintain discipline and stability while the staff serves to furnish expert information.

CHARTING THE ORGANIZATION STRUCTURE

Organization charts can be of significant value as an effective means of portraying the organization structure. They frequently serve as a management tool in designing and structuring an organization to fit the needs of the company. However, the organization chart as an administrative tool is seldom used to its full potential. Practice shows that charts have a significant value not only in portraying the existing organization, but also in analyzing the organization, facilitating communication, and personnel administration. An organization chart can provide a clear and graphic picture of the existing organization structure. The organization chart is used primarily to reflect basic relationships and the grouping of positions and functions. An organization chart is not adaptable to defining responsibility and authority.

Essentially, the basic unit of the organization chart is the individual position. Each box of an organization chart represents and reflects one position. Grouping of boxes reflects the grouping of activities that make up departments or divisions, and an organization chart properly prepared reflects certain elementary relationships. It depicts who reports to whom and what direct relationship one position bears to another. A properly prepared organization chart can show duplicate and overlapping positions reflecting conditions where one man reports to two superiors, indicating conflicting administrative difficulty. Organization charts may reveal unbalanced organizations, and overextended spans of control are dramatically emphasized.

Types of Organization Charts. Organization charts have definite limitations when used for the wrong purpose or when attempts are made to expand their capabilities. They are current only on the date they are published, so in a dynamic, growing organization the maintenance of charts becomes a limiting factor. Various forms of dotted lines, symbols, and other devices have been used in an attempt to show informal relationships that exist between the roles of line and staff. These attempts are recognized as being limited.

Basic types of organization charts are used fairly universally. The company management may have previously determined the form of charting to be used; therefore, the departmental charts or divisional charts may well follow the pattern established for the overall company. The four major types are vertical organization charts (discussed previously), horizontal organization charts, functional organization charts, and replacement organization charts.

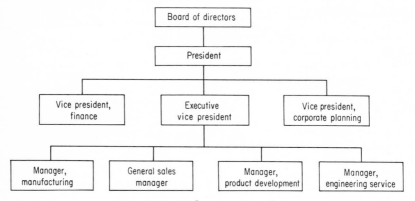

Fig. 3   Vertical-organization chart.

VERTICAL ORGANIZATION CHARTS: The vertical organization chart (Fig. 3) shows the organization structure in a schematic fashion. Such a chart is scalar in form, reflecting different levels of organization in a step arrangement showing individual positions and groups of positions. This chart is easy to read and understand, and it reflects the basic relationships between the superior and those he supervises, and among the managers of different organizational units. It is intended to reflect the flow of delegation downward in the organization but does not provide for a readily identified separation between line and staff.

HORIZONTAL ORGANIZATION CHARTS: The horizontal type reads from left to right rather than from the top to the bottom of the page. Although infrequently used, the horizontal chart may accommodate more positions than would be possible with the vertical chart. Another advantage is the tendency for the horizontal arrangement to minimize the importance of levels and the apparent conflicts between levels. There is no clear ascendancy reflected on the horizontal chart, and therefore there is less tendency to make erroneous inferences about differences in status and importance. The horizontal chart, however, is more difficult to read.

FUNCTIONAL ORGANIZATION CHARTS: The functional organization chart is a form of the basic vertical structural chart noted previously. Its purpose is to list the responsibilities for the functional groups identified as well as reflect the interrelationships. Figure 4 is a typical functional organization chart for the manufacturing activities of a job-shop manufacturer.

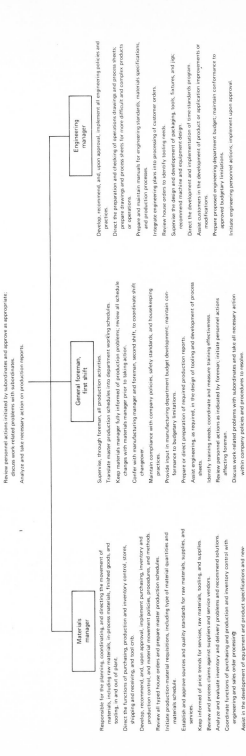

Manufacturing manager

Direct and coordinate all manufacturing activities, including materials management, production, and engineering.

Define and recommend manufacturing goals.

Develop, recommend, and, upon approval, implement plant operating policies, procedures, and practices.

Utilizing materials management concepts and personnel, ensure prompt and economical processing of production orders, receipt of scheduled materials, efficient production, and accurate and prompt engineering.

Establish and implement policies and practices regarding make or buy decisions for tooling and production items; refer extensive cost decisions to superior.

Make recommendations on major plant layout, design, or building alterations.

Maintain cost control, equipment, and personnel utilization programs to achieve optimization of profits and return on investment.

Direct implementation of time standards and rate-setting programs.

Review personnel actions initiated by subordinates and approve as appropriate; discuss work-related problems with subordinates.

Analyze and take necessary action on production reports.

Materials manager

Responsible for the planning, coordinating, and directing the movement of materials, including raw materials, in-process materials, finished goods, and tooling, in and out of plant.

Direct the functions of purchasing, production and inventory control, stores, shipping and receiving, and tool crib.

Develop, recommend, and, upon approval, implement purchasing, inventory and production control, and material movement policies, procedures, and methods.

Review all typed house orders and prepare master production schedules.

Initiate production-material requisitions, including type of material quantities and materials schedule.

Establish and approve sources and quality standards for raw materials, supplies, and services.

Keep informed of price trends for services, raw materials, tooling, and supplies.

Review and process claims against suppliers and service vendors.

Analyze and evaluate inventory and delivery problems and recommend solutions.

Coordinate functions of purchasing and production and inventory control with engineering and sales order processing.

Assist in the development of equipment and product specifications and new-material usage.

Assist sales department in the preparation of sales forecasts, providing information on production capacity, purchasing problems, and delivery schedules.

General foreman, first shift

Supervise, through foreman, all production activities.

Translate master production schedules into department working schedules.

Keep materials manager fully informed of production problems; review all schedule changes with materials manager prior to taking action.

Confer with manufacturing manager and foreman, second shift, to coordinate shift changeover.

Maintain compliance with company policies, safety standards, and housekeeping practices.

Provide input in manufacturing department budget development; maintain conformance to budgetary limitations.

Prepare or direct preparation of required production reports.

Assist engineering, as required, in the design of tooling and development of process sheets.

Identify training needs, coordinate and measure training effectiveness.

Review personnel actions as indicated by foreman; initiate personnel actions affecting foreman.

Discuss work-related problems with subordinates and take all necessary action within company policies and procedures to resolve.

Engineering manager

Develop, recommend, and, upon approval, implement all engineering policies and practices.

Direct the preparation and checking of operations drawings and process sheets; prepare drawings and process sheets for more difficult and complex products or operations.

Prepare and maintain manuals for engineering standards, materials specifications, and production processes.

Integrate engineering plans into processing of customer orders.

Review house orders to identify tooling needs.

Supervise the design and development of packaging, tools, fixtures, and jigs; recommend machine and equipment design.

Direct the development and implementation of time-standards program.

Assist customers in the development of product or application improvements or modifications.

Prepare proposed engineering department budget; maintain conformance to approved budgetary limitations.

Initiate engineering personnel actions; implement upon approval.

Fig. 4 Functional organization—manufacturing department.

REPLACEMENT ORGANIZATION CHARTS: A replacement organization chart is a specialized version of the structural organization chart which is used in management-and-development programs. It literally provides an inventory of management and outlines the planned progression training and replacement schedules for all the positions in the organization.

THE ORGANIZATION AS A TOTAL SYSTEM

The description of organizations as sets of relationships between individuals and work activities, definitions of organizational terminology and organization charts have been discussed. The question that must be answered now is: How do you design an effective organization for the production and inventory control function? The most effective procedure for this task is to view the industrial organization as a *total system.*

A "system" may be defined as a series of interrelated parts or activities that combine in a manner sufficient to achieve the objectives of the system. The systems concepts has had a long and fruitful history in the physical and social sciences and has been applied more recently in the management sciences. It has had success in these fields because it focuses the investigation on the significant parts of a problem.

Two important propositions flow from the systems concept:

1. Since the system is a series of interrelated parts or activities, a change in one of the parts or activities will create, in some degree, changes in all other parts of the system.

2. The system can be understood because the reasons for any given activity can be explained by examining the consequences or results of that activity. These results will be an accurate description of the system objectives.

It is important to point out that a system is a conceptual tool, not necessarily a physical reality in and of itself. For example, for some problems it is sufficient to define the manufacturing system as being composed only of the machinery and personnel engaged in the production of a company's product. For other types of problems, the manufacturing system would include purchasing, manufacturing, sales, and production and inventory control. The concept is in effect problem oriented and does not in itself demand specific techniques.

The implications of the second proposition should be further noted. In examining natural systems such as the physiology of the human body, the scientist has come to understand the functions of various physiological mechanisms by seeking the consequences of these mechanisms. In a like manner social scientists seeking an understanding of various social structures have successfully used this strategy of analysis. In a now-classic analysis it was shown that political machines exist because of their consequences—that they provide many "welfare-type" services to lower-income groups in return for voter allegiance. As federal, state, and local governments provide more of these services, the political machine loses much of its effectiveness.[1] Analytically, the important question is not what the political machine is, but rather what the organization does.

In dealing with man-made systems the consequences or objectives of the system can be specified by man. The proposition tells us that if the system is not working well, the first place to look is at the objectives of the system. It is usually found that the objectives of the system are either vague or conflicting, and on the basis of this knowledge, the system problem becomes quickly understood. The solution begins with a specific detailing of objectives and plans for achieving these objectives. The systems concept provides principles of application which suggest definite means for control.

Viewed as a system, the industrial organization can be defined in many appropriate ways depending on the problem at hand. For example, a data processing problem may require definition in terms of the information flow. The types of information required for the decision-making processes become the appropriate elements in the systems definition. In like manner, a financial problem may require a system definition in terms of cash flow.

For the problem we are concerned with here—the most effective organization of the production and inventory control function—we shall define the industrial organization as a system of industrial functions. We are concerned with the relationships of the production and inventory control function to the functions of manufacturing, sales, purchasing, engineering, finance, industrial relations, and research and development. These functions are interrelated so that changes in any one function will have effects on all other functions.

The appropriate place to begin an analysis of an industrial organization is to examine the results of the organization. These may be completely planned, rational, and effective for the organization as a total system. In this case they are usually referred to by all organization participants as "objectives." At the other extreme, they may be unplanned, irrational, and ineffectual for the organization. No matter what these results are called, detailed analysis usually finds that these activities are also objectives of the organization—poor objectives but nonetheless objectives.

Auxiliary Systems Concepts. The systems concept includes a set of auxiliary concepts that identify and describe the nature of systems. The six most important ones are input, process, output, feedback control, system objectives, and system goals.

The *input* function of a system provides it with operating material. This material may be raw goods in the manufacturing sense, information, or even ideas. It is this input upon which the system operates to achieve its objectives.

The system's *processes* are those activities which operate upon the input. These may be in the form of production processes, chemical processes, planning activities, scheduling, and processes of analysis, to name just a few.

The results of these processes are *output*. Output may be in the form of finished goods, completed services, or even validated hypotheses, as is the case in systems of scientific analysis.

The *feedback* function of a system compares the output with a specified criterion and provides for favorable changes in input, output, or even criteria if necessary.

The *objectives* of a system are the purposes for which the system has been designed. It is what the system is "shooting for." System objectives may be achieved in a variety of ways.

System *goals* are the constraints imposed upon the system. The goals of the system constrain the manner in which the objectives are achieved.

These auxiliary systems concepts may be used to describe a total system or subsystems within the total system. As one author has noted: "The total system bears the same relationship to its own objects and attributes as the subsystems do to their component elements. Thus the same set of terms may be used to describe very large, complex systems, or very small, simple systems."[2]

A manufacturing organization can be described visually using systems concepts as shown in Fig. 5 (p. 3–14).

Divided into subsystems this same manufacturing organization can be further described in terms of functional units. Figure 6 describes the organization in terms of functional-unit requirements. In this case the financial unit examines resources and sets financial-performance requirements which become the output of this unit. This output becomes the input for the sales organization which processes it and produces customer orders. These sales orders in turn become input to the engineering unit, the production and inventory control unit, and the purchasing unit. In like manner, the output from these units becomes input for other organizational units. Feedback is introduced to allow performance to be checked by the sales, financial, and production and inventory control units.

Some will undoubtedly feel that satisfactory input-output relationships have not been established for this organization and that more feedback relationships are necessary. Many organizations, however, are functioning today with the kind of relationships as shown.

Organization System versus Structure. The concept of an organization as a system differs considerably from that of an organization as a *structure*, which is a concept currently used by most industrial organizations. The difference can be seen by examining the accent given each of these concepts. An organization as a structure is concerned with functions, authority, reporting relationships, channels of communications, span of control, and informal organizations. This

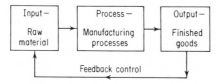

Fig. 5 Manufacturing organization.

line of analysis makes some important and at times critical assumptions, because certain elements are left unanalyzed and are taken as fact. Some of these elements are:

1. Organizational activities and procedures are assumed to be necessary and therefore functional.

2. No concept of dysfunctional or nonadaptive elements is introduced in the analysis.

3. No explicit consideration is given to alternative functions.

4. Motivation of personnel is assumed.

5. The possibility and necessity for change is not explicitly explored and provided for.

In contrast the concept of organization as a system focuses attention immediately upon the *objectives* of the total system and its many subsystems. It permits critical examination of the input of the system, the process by which this input is changed, and the output of the system as well as relating all these elements to the objectives of the total system. It focuses explicitly upon the manner in which organizational decisions are made and executed, and prescribes organizational designs in terms of these factors. The system concept is based upon only two assumptions:

1. All activities of the organization are interrelated.

2. The consequences of any particular form of organization are the objectives of the organization.

More important, however, the system concept permits examining the necessity of all activities, permitting consideration of alternative activities. It not only assumes that personnel "learn" to perform in various manners but also provides for the systematic consideration of change.

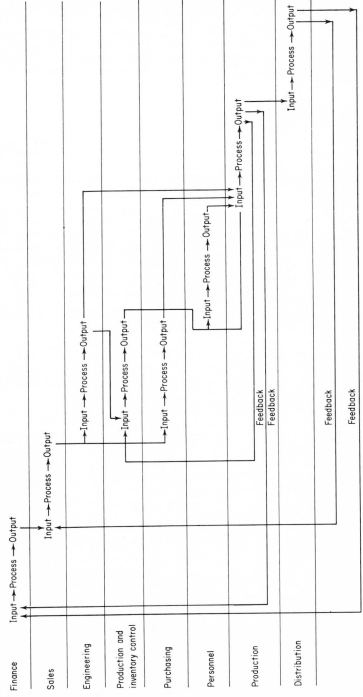

Fig. 6 Manufacturing organization.

3-15

MANAGEMENT BY OBJECTIVES

The concept of the organization as a system focuses, as shown, on the objectives of the system. How are organizational objectives achieved? Research evidence and practical experience strongly suggest that objectives are achieved by rewarding individuals for those activities that go into the achievement of objectives and by not rewarding activities which are unimportant for achieving established objectives. On the basis of this analysis the objectives of work-directed systems are those types and levels of activities that are rewarded by management and supervisory personnel. The form of these rewards may be financial, social, and status in nature. In all probability the rewards will be different for different individuals but contain elements of all three forms of rewards.

It is the objectives—those activities that will be rewarded—that define with what the system will be concerned and with what it will not be concerned, how the system will operate, and how the system should be structured.

The current emphasis on management by objectives appears to be a response to ideas set forth by the "management science" practitioners. The many techniques and investigative strategies embodied in cost effectiveness and operations research studies must begin with a specification, or at least an approximation, of what the system is supposed to achieve. Once this is established and validated, optimum or satisfactory solutions to problems can be found. Likewise the effective structuring of any organization and the functions within an organization require the explicit establishment of objectives for the total organization, the functional units within the organization, and the individual person within these functional units.

The objectives of the three organization levels appear sufficiently different and warrant separate labels.

1. "Organization objectives" are statements specifying what the organization as a unit wants to achieve over a particular time period.

2. In order to achieve these organization objectives, functional units, such as sales, manufacturing, production and inventory control, and so forth, will have to accomplish certain activities within a specified time period. These we shall refer to as "functional goals."

3. If functional goals are to be achieved, individuals in each functional unit will have to accomplish certain activities—again within specified time periods. These we shall refer to as individual "plans."

The distinguishing feature in these definitions is not the degree of specificity, but rather the organizational level involved.

Organizational objectives are always concerned with increasing profits, corporate growth, and share of markets. Functional-unit *goals* take the form of specifying what the unit will need to achieve for a particular period of time so the organization's objectives are achieved. For the sales department, this may mean establishing four new territories within the next 12 months. In the production and inventory control department, it may mean reducing the lead time from six to four weeks in the next six months so that the company's delivery position may be more competitive. Individual *plans* emphasize what each individual must accomplish so that the functional-unit's goals may be achieved. The sales manager may have to hire and train four new salesmen within the next six months. The inventory control manager may have to design and implement an improved work-flow or dispatch system to reduce queues within the next four months. The important point is that at all levels of the organization, *what* is to be achieved and *when* it is to be accomplished must be specified.[3]

As can be seen from this discussion, the establishment of corporate objectives is the beginning phase and the most important step in the structuring and staffing of any organization. For this reason it is important to explore, in some detail, the nature and process of establishing corporate objectives. Top management usually establishes two types of objectives: short-range and long-range. Short-range objectives usually cover a one-year period, while long-range objectives are usually concerned with a five-year or more time span. In terms of the commitment of corporate resources the short-range objectives play a significant role. It is these objectives which require the immediate attention of management and provide the basis for committing corporate talent and financial resources.

Long-range objectives, in contrast, can be altered on the basis of developing performance and economic fluctuations. These changes are less costly for the organization because relatively few resources are employed in seeking their achievement. From an organizational viewpoint, however, the establishment of long-range objectives is more important than the establishment of short-range objectives.

Designing organizations not only is a method of providing the most effective and efficient manner for carrying out work tasks, but also should provide for training personnel in skills and techniques necessary for achieving long-range objectives. Although these two purposes are not generally recognized by managements, their existence can be seen by the kinds of reshuffling of positions and personnel that usually accompany a change in top management.

Another type of conflict develops between functional-unit goals and long-range objectives. In many organizations staffed by qualified and ambitious personnel, the functional-unit goals may approximate an optimum utilization of unit resources. However, when these goals are placed in the context of the total system, they may provide the organization with achievements which are far less than optimum. For example, the sales department may seek a delivery-service level such that all orders are shipped on the requested dates without back orders, but the company may not be able to afford the investment in inventories necessary to attain this goal. This phenomenon, referred to as "sub-optimization," has significant implications for management.[4]

These examples focus attention upon one central point—the interrelationships among corporate objectives, functional-unit goals, and individual plans. It is because of these interrelationships that organizations of men produce so effectively. However, these interrelationships also provide the conditions that generate conflicts. For this reason, the establishment of corporate objectives and the review and approval of functional-unit goals must be accomplished by top management, which has the responsibility of maximizing the total corporate efforts.

THE SUBSYSTEM OF PRODUCTION AND INVENTORY CONTROL

The industrial function of production and inventory control can be conceived of as one subsystem within a total system of an industrial organization. Current industrial production and management practices have dictated standard functions and goals for the production and inventory control subsystem. The *APICS Dictionary of Production and Inventory Control Terms* defines the function of production control as "the function of directing or regulating the orderly movement of goods through the entire manufacturing cycle, from the requisitions of raw material to the delivery of the finished product, by means of the systematic release of subsidiary orders under a routine plan which utilizes the plant facilities most economically."[5]

In general the goals of the production and inventory control function are:
1. Customer service
2. Creating production efficiencies
3. Utilization of production capacity
4. Utilization of labor
5. Utilization of warehouse capacity
6. Control of raw or component-parts materials
7. Control of inventory investments

From a systems viewpoint the most striking feature of these goals is that many of them are shared by other subsystems within the organization. Customer service is a general goal of the sales department. Production efficiencies concern the manufacturing department, and in an indirect but not unimportant manner, the personnel department. The purchasing function has goals concerning raw materials and component parts, but inventory investments are also the obvious concern of the financial function.

The first question that must be answered in designing the production and inventory control organization is: What are the necessary relationships between this function and the other functions of the organization? This question can be answered most effectively by examinating corporate objectives and functional-unit goals. The reason for this comes from the logic and empirical nature of systems. The input of any system or subsystem can only be the result of:[6]
1. A previous process which is in line serially
2. A previous process, randomly generated
3. A process that is being reintroduced

These processes, as they operate in an industrial organization, appear to be the direct result of functional-unit goals. For example, a corporate objective is to achieve a sales increase of 20 percent over the next year. The sales department in setting its goals to achieve the corporate objectives may choose from several alternative approaches. They may decide to increase the advertising program by 10 percent, or hire two more salesmen either to increase the intensity of the sales efforts or to develop a new territory.

Let us examine the system effects of a sales department strategy which is to seek jobbing work which will supplement the anticipated growth in the sales of standard products and will also increase the utilization of specific manufacturing facilities. The consequences of this sales department goal will have a significant effect on the production control department part of the system. The input, feedback, and output systems may well require review, and the goals of the department will require reshaping as the random jobbing orders from the sales department arrive into the system. If the production control department sets a goal of reducing lead time to help increase sales, the production department's input would be quantitatively larger as a result of the previous process flowing serially from the stores department. The previous discussion shows the interrelationships of the functions' goals in meeting corporate objectives.

The production and inventory control function is essentially a planning, scheduling, and control function. The activities performed by this function are primarily paper-work activities, although the control element often requires that some department personnel be responsible for physically handling materials. This function can be diagramed as a system as shown in Figs. 7 and 8.

The importance of the production and inventory control function as a planning, scheduling, and control activity can be seen from these two figures. As a planning system the requirement for feedback is an integral part of the system. Output reports must not only be checked by this subsystem, but must also go to other subsystems such as sales, finance, and production for their use.

The production and inventory control's function of physically handling materials is usually much simpler. The raw material and component parts are received, stored, and delivered to the production facilities, produced, stored, and shipped to the customer. The material itself is not fed back to any element of *this* system, although within the production subsystem quality control checks may require that materials be reprocessed.

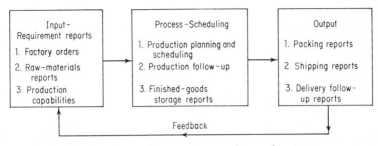

Fig. 7 Production and inventory control as a planning system.

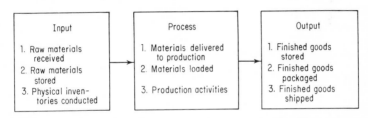

Fig. 8 Production and inventory control as a material-handling system.

The most effective manner for designing organizations is by continual reference to the objectives of the organization and the goals of the functional units. Assume, for example, some hypothetical goals for a production and inventory control unit under three different types of conditions:

1. A process-industry situation (Table 1)

TABLE 1 Relationship of Goals in Process-type Industries

Functions	Production and inventory control goals				
	Increase production 20% by next Jan. 19—	Reduce back orders 25% by next Jan. 19—	Evaluate entire shipping procedures by Sept. 19—	Establish automated inventory control system by Mar. 19—	Establish new storage facilities for product X by Sept. 19—
	(1)	(2)	(3)	(4)	(5)
Finance............	Yes	Yes		Yes	
Sales..............	Yes	Yes	Yes	Yes	Yes
Purchasing.........	Yes	Yes		Yes	Yes
Personnel..........	Yes				
Production.........	Yes	Yes	Yes		Yes
Engineering........	Yes	Yes		Yes	

2. A job-shop situation (Table 2)

3. A ship-from-stock situation (Table 3)

We are concerned first with how the production and inventory control unit should relate to other departments, and second with the internal organization of the unit itself.

Tables 1, 2, and 3 portray the relationships among a set of hypothetical goals of a production and inventory control group and other units of the organiza-

TABLE 2   Relationhip of Goals in Job-shop Industries

Functions	Production and inventory control goals				
	Increase production 20 % by next Jan. 19—	Reduce back orders 25 % by next Jan. 19—	Evaluate entire shipping procedures by Sept. 19—	Establish automated inventory control system by Mar. 19—	Establish new storage facilities for product X by Sept. 19—
	(1)	(2)	(3)	(4)	(5)
Finance............					
Sales..............	Yes	Yes	Yes	Yes	Yes
Purchasing..........	Yes		Yes		
Personnel..........	Yes	Yes			
Production.........	Yes	Yes			Yes
Engineering........	Yes	Yes			

TABLE 3   Relationship of Goals in Ship-from-stock Industries

Functions	Production and inventory control goals				
	Increase production 20 % by next Jan. 19—	Reduce back orders 25 % by next Jan. 19—	Evaluate entire shipping procedures by Sept. 19—	Establish automated inventory control system by Mar. 19—	Establish new storage facilities for product X by Sept. 19—
	(1)	(2)	(3)	(4)	(5)
Finance............	Yes	Yes	Yes	Yes	Yes
Sales..............	Yes	Yes	Yes	Yes	Yes
Purchasing..........	Yes	Yes		Yes	Yes
Personnel..........	Yes				
Production.........	Yes	Yes		Yes	Yes
Engineering........	Yes	Yes		Yes	

tion under three industrial situations. The goals are ranked across the top of the tables from 1 through 5 reflecting their order of importance. A "yes" at the intersection of a goal and a function signifies that the function has a primary interest in the achievement of the goal. A blank space indicates no primary interest in the goal.

As can be seen, the interests of other functional units in the activities of the production and inventory control function vary by industry situation. In process-type industries, for example, inventory investment is normally low, but under a goal of increased production, the financial department must know what the effect of this goal will be on inventory cost. In contrast, under the job-shop situation most inventory is purchased on the basis of order, and the financial unit has less concern with an inventory buildup, except for unexplained buildups of work-in-process inventories. In a like manner, goal 4, the establishment of an automated inventory control system, has little importance to the activities of the purchasing department in a job-shop situation, but has great impact on its activities in a ship-from-stock situation. The important point is that the necessary organizational relationships among the production and inventory control function and other units within the organization will vary on the basis of the established goals of all functional units.

TABLE 4 Relationship of Positions to the Achievement of Production and Inventory Control Goals (Under Two Assignment Situations)

Positions	Production and inventory control goals									
	Increase production 20% by next Jan. 19— (1)		Reduce back orders 25% by next Jan. 19— (2)		Evaluate entire shipping procedures by Sept. 19— (3)		Establish automated inventory control system by Mar. 19— (4)		Establish new storage facilities for product X by Sept. 19— (5)	
	A	B	A	B	A	B	A	B	A	B
Production control manager	1, 2, 3	1, 2	1, 2	1, 2	1, 2	1	1, 2	1	1, 2	1
Production scheduler	4	3	3, 4	3						
Receiving and stores foreman							3	2, 3	3	2, 3
Shipping foreman					3	2, 3				
Dispatcher	4	4	4	4			4		4	4
Receiving clerk										
Shipping clerk			4	4	4	4				
Stores clerk			4	4			4	4	4	4

This same form of analysis should be used in establishing the internal organization of the production and inventory control unit. Table 4 and Figs. 9 and 10 present this form of analysis.

Table 4 presents the production and inventory control goals as they have been assigned in two different manners, A and B, to typical positions in this function. Responsibility for goal achievement typically takes four separate forms:

1. Ultimate responsibility for achievement
2. Responsibility for developing individual plans to achieve goals
3. Responsibility for monitoring goal progress
4. Responsibility for actual implementation of plans

If the organization structure is to provide the proper conditions for goal achievement, two forms of relationships appear necessary. First, the position

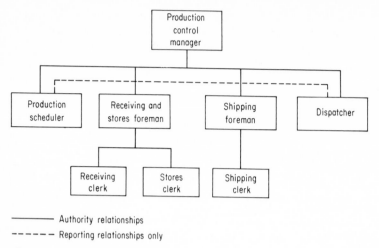

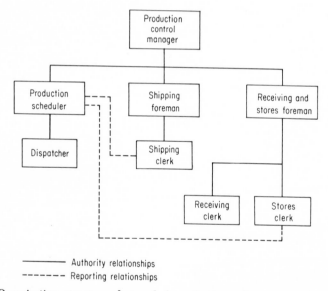

Fig. 9 Organization structures designed for effective achievement of goals—situation 1.

Fig. 10 Organization structure designed for effective achievement of goals—situation 2.

responsible for goal achievement must have direct authority over the positions responsible for developing the appropriate plans and monitoring the goal progress. Second, the position responsible for monitoring the goal progress must have a direct relationship, either authority or reporting, to the position responsible for implementation of plans.

Figures 9 and 10 portray the different structures that are generated from two different methods of assigning goal responsibilities within a production and inventory control group. These organization structures are not intended to describe a complete production and inventory control department but only to illustrate the point that department goals are a logical and effective criteria for organizing the department.

Three important points about this procedure should be pointed out:

1. The structure of any organization may change with the introduction of significantly different goals.

2. The reassignment of goal responsibilities may create the need for a new organizational arrangement.

3. The reporting or communication relationships, now commonly referred to as "informal organization," arise because they fulfill an organizational need and should be recognized as an integral element of organizations, and must be provided for in designing the organization.

ORGANIZATION INEFFICIENCIES

The system concept of an organization has focused the attention of researchers and practitioners on organizational inefficiencies. We have previously discussed one system of inefficiency—that of functional-unit optimization. Under this condition each subsystem optimizes in itself, but less than optimum efficiency is achieved by the total organization. A second condition exists in which each subsystem optimizes its activities, but does so on the basis of insufficient or

TABLE 5   Types of Organizational Problems and Solutions

Solutions	Problems		
	Subsystem optimization	Faulty communications	Faulty decision making
Centralized goal setting to achieve total-system optimums	Applicable solution	Applicable solution	Applicable solution
Change in organization structure and communication patterns	Not an applicable solution	Applicable solution	Not an applicable solution
Upgrade or replace decision maker	Not an applicable solution	Not an applicable solution	Applicable solution

inaccurate information concerning other subsystems goals. In this instance the problem is due to faulty communications. A third pattern of inefficiency has been isolated, in which the subsystems do not optimize their activities although they have access to all pertinent information. Technically this is caused by faulty decision making. In practical terms we refer to this type of inefficiency as "poor" management.[7]

In general, these patterns of inefficiencies within industrial organizations are caused by the increasing complexity of business activities. This increased complexity has generated problems which we have all experienced, such as increased paper work, bureaucratization, decentralization of decision making, and longer training periods, to name only a few. Table 5 presents the general types of solutions to these problems.

As can be seen from the table, there is only one general solution from a systems viewpoint suitable for all three of the general problems. This solution is the centralization of functional-unit goal setting to achieve the optimum utilization of the total-systems resources. Historically, industrial organizations have derived organizational solutions which do exactly this. They have created centralized management functions which balance the needs and resources of the various functional units. Functional-unit needs and resources are integrated with other units' needs and resources, at the top-management positions such as the vice president of manufacturing, engineering, and finance in multiplant operations or a vice president of operations in single-plant situations.

As manufacturing processes have become more complex, and concomitantly where the ratio of material dollars to total manufacturer's dollars has risen significantly, there has developed a need for further planning and control of material utilization. System theory suggests that material costs must be balanced with other elements and activities in the industrial organization. This will require increased control and coordination of the incoming flow of purchased materials with the manufacturing process.

The predicted organizational response to these conditions would be, and has been, the establishment of a new management concept, "materials management," with the position of "materials manager."

Materials management is that aspect of industrial management which is concerned with the activities involved in the acquisition and use of all materials employed in the production of a finished product. The scope of these activities is as broad as it is wide. They may include production and inventory control, purchasing, traffic, materials handling, and receiving. They may go so far as to include receiving-inspection within the broad scope of the materials management activity. "Materials management" can be defined as the planning, scheduling, procurement, and controlling of materials from the raw to the finished state in a manner consistent with optimum quality, quantity, cost, and utilization of facilities.

The requirements for timely and effective distribution of products have become vital in the competitive position of many companies. Consequently the need for coordinating all company distribution activities has given rise to the position of the "distribution manager." This distribution manager is basically responsible for meeting the needs of customers in the most economical manner available to the company. It is interesting and important to note that one of the reasons for the development of this position is that the concepts and tools needed to effectively coordinate distribution activities—the concepts and methods of management science—are now available.

From a system perspective the establishment of the distribution manager is an appropriate response to a given set of system conditions. As these conditions change, organizational responses in terms of new positions will probably be forthcoming. An approximate knowledge of what changes will occur in the supply and skill of labor, supply and cost of material, supply of capital and production costs, and developments in scientific methodology and information technology should enable one to predict the type of new industrial positions that will be forthcoming.

TRAINING FOR SYSTEM PERFORMANCE

A systematic consideration of the training needs and appropriate training techniques for the personnel involved in the production and inventory control function will be detailed in the following chapter.

However, introduced here is a concept that, while widely used in military organizations, is virtually unknown in industry—the concept of *team training*.

"Teams," as we are using the term here, are defined as ". . . human beings, work procedures, machines, and machine procedures as they interact in contributing to, or detracting from, the accomplishment of the defined goals of a system or subsystem."[8]

The concept of an organization as a system focuses attention upon the interrelationships of all organizational elements and their effect on organizational objectives and functional-unit goals.   If the organization is going to achieve its objectives, organizational participants must be trained to function as a total system of interacting participants and not as individuals.

This type of training is only applicable in certain types of organizational situations.   These are situations in which the organization is functioning under new circumstances, circumstances of crisis, or circumstances created by rapid internal or external changes.   It is applicable to those situations in which no standard operating procedures have been established, current job descriptions are meaningless, or corporate policies are not applicable.[9]   This type of training concerns itself with orienting all organizational participants toward organizational objectives and subsystem goals.   It stresses training the personnel to function as interdependent units, to identify, analyze, and correct errors in performance, to recognize when work loads are becoming so great as to create inefficiencies, and to understand and become familiar with the types of adjustments the system and subsystems can and should make.   Research evidence points out that organizations do make adjustments under stress.   These adjustments, however, are seldom the most effective adjustments at an individual and functional-unit level and are very often totally ineffective at the organization level.

We have stated both explicitly and by implication that the organization should be structured on the basis of organizational objectives and functional-unit goals. Further, when these objectives and goals change, as they must if the organization is to remain in existence, some changes in the organization structure will follow. Team training will provide organization participants with an understanding of these changes.   They will have been trained in functioning under changes and will be able to adapt quickly and effectively to these changes.

THE PRODUCTION AND INVENTORY CONTROL
ORGANIZATION: A FUNCTION OF TIME
AND CHANGE

It has been suggested that industrial organizations can be usefully viewed as a system of industrial functions and personnel relationships.   The logic and structure of this system is dictated by the organization's objectives and functional-group's goals within the organization.   This statement accurately reflects the findings of organizational research and experience, which have shown that organizational behavior is a function of its consequences and that these consequences are the objectives of the system and the system's participants.   These objectives may be very precise and known to all participants, or they may be general, vague, and even unknown to many participants.

These aspects of organizational behavior allow the development and meaningful implementation of a set of normative guides for structuring an organization which are embodied in the managerial system of "management by objectives." Management by objectives requires that specific organizational objectives be established, that specific functional-unit *goals* be developed which, when integrated, will achieve the total objectives, and in turn that individual plans be established to achieve functional-unit goals.

In effect, the consequences of individual and organizational behavior are specified, and individuals and functional units will be rewarded on the basis of achieving these consequences. Notice that it is not suggested that rewards be given on the basis of adequately performing position functions, but that they be given on the basis of achieving the specified consequences.

All organizations have mechanisms established to detect changes in both the external and internal environments in which the organization operates. In the industrial context these include market research departments, research and development, personnel, and long-range planning units. When changes occur in the organization's environment, or are created as in the case of research and development, this information is transmitted to the executive management group. This group decides what these changes mean to the organization and in what manner the organization should react to them.

The organizational mechanism for translating these decisions requires the establishment of new objectives, which in turn requires new goals and individual plans.

The most effective organization of a production and inventory control department is a function of time and the changing industrial conditions. One can and should expect that the organization and functions of production and inventory control will continue to undergo changes and that these changes will be, in their specifics, quite different for different companies and different industries. But then, is not this responsiveness to change a characteristic of every viable, effective professional group?

REFERENCES

1. Robert F. Merton, *Social Theory and Social Structure,* 2d ed., The Free Press of Glencoe, New York, 1957, pp. 73–75.
2. Stanford L. Optner, *Systems Analysis for Business and Industrial Problem Solving,* Prentice-Hall, Inc., Englewood Cliffs, N.J., 1965, p. 37.
3. For an excellent introduction to management by objectives, see George S. Odiorne, *Management by Objectives: A System of Managerial Leadership,* Pitman Publishing Corporation, New York, 1965.
4. For a discussion of this operations research concept from a management perspective, see Stanley Young, *Management: A Systems Analysis,* Scott, Foresman and Company, Chicago, 1966, p. 149.
5. *APICS Dictionary of Production and Inventory Control Terms,* published as *APICS Quarterly Bulletin,* vol. 4, no. 1, January, 1963.
6. Optner, *op. cit.,* p. 36.
7. For a mathematical description and analysis of these problems, see S. S. Sengupta and R. L. Ackoff, "Systems Theory from an Operations Research Point of View," *IEEE Transactions on Systems Science and Cybernetics,* vol. SSC-1, no. 1, pp. 9–13, November, 1965.
8. Robert Boguslaw and Elias H. Porter, "Team Functions and Training," in Robert M. Gagne (ed.), *Psychological Principles in System Development,* Holt, Rinehart and Winston, Inc., New York, 1962, p. 390.
9. For a detailed explanation of this concept, see *ibid.,* pp. 387–416.

BIBLIOGRAPHY

Beer, Stafford: *Cybernetics and Management,* John Wiley & Sons, Inc., New York, 1959.
Boguslaw, Robert, and Elias H. Porter: "Team Functions and Training," in Robert M. Gagne (ed.), *Psychological Principles in System Development,* Holt, Rinehart and Winston, Inc., New York, 1962.
Cleland, David F., and Wallace Munsey: "Who Works with Whom," *Harvard Business Review,* vol. 45, no. 5, September-October, 1967.

March, James G., and Herbert A. Simon: *Organizations,* John Wiley & Sons, Inc., York, 1958.

Merton, Robert K.: *Social Theory and Social Structure,* 2d ed., The Free Press of Glencoe, New York, 1957.

Odiorne, George S.: *Management by Objectives: A System of Managerial Leadership,* Pitman Publishing Corporation, New York, 1965.

Optner, Stanford L.: *Systems Analysis for Business and Industrial Problem Solving,* Prentice-Hall, Inc., Englewood Cliffs, N.J., 1965.

Pritzker, Robert A., and Robert A. Gring (eds.): *Modern Approaches to Production Planning and Control,* American Management Association, New York, 1960.

Roscoe, Edwin Scott: *Organization for Production: An Introduction to Industrial Management,* Richard D. Irwin, Inc., Homewood, Ill., 1959.

Rubenstein, Albert H., and Chadwick Hoberstroh (eds.): *Some Theories of Organization,* Richard D. Irwin, Inc., Homewood, Ill., 1960.

Sengupta, S. S., and R. L. Ackoff: "Systems Theory from an Operations Research Point of View," *IEEE Transactions on Systems Science and Cybernetics,* vol. SSC-1, no. 1, November, 1965.

Shuchman, Abe: *Scientific Decision Making in Business,* Holt, Rinehart and Winston, Inc., New York, 1963.

Staats, Arthur W.: *Human Learning,* Holt, Rinehart and Winston, Inc., New York, 1964.

Young, Stanley: *Management: A Systems Analysis,* Scott, Foresman and Company, Chicago, 1966.

Supporting Systems for Production and Inventory Control

Chapter 4

Customer Relations

EDITORS:

Arnold O. Putnam *President, Rath & Strong, Inc., Boston, Massachusetts*

E. Robert Barlow *Vice President, Marketing, Rath & Strong, Inc., Boston, Massachusetts*

CONTENTS

OVERVIEW OF CUSTOMER SERVICE

In the last analysis the objective of the inventory, production control, and distribution function is to get the right goods at the right place at the right time to maintain the desired level of customer service at minimum total cost. How this objective is carried out varies tremendously from industry to industry and even within each industry because of different needs. Before considering the relationship of inventory and production control to customer service, and specific functions of shipping, transportation, and warehousing, it seems best to consider some of the variables that make one industry different from another and the variations within each specific industry.

Type of Product. Products vary all the way from those that are standard and satisfy the needs of many customers to those that are completely special and have to be 100 percent back-ordered to meet requirements. Obviously the inventory, production, and distribution policies that are required to support these two different types of products are substantially different.

STANDARD PRODUCTS: Standard products are those that can be made to final, exact specifications for a multitude of customers against a forecast or rate of sale, and with relatively little risk in terms of obsolescence to the manufacturer. There may be random or trend variations in sales that require some longer or shorter inventory positions at certain periods of time, but for all practical purposes, obsolescence need not be considered too seriously. With standard-type products the main consideration is the amount of money invested in inventory related to the desired customer-service rate (see Chapters 16 to 17). Standard-type products, as we shall see later, lend themselves to less sophisticated inventory and production control systems. There are many managements that believe they have standard-type products but in fact the many sizes and/or colors may require broad support to meet specific customer demands.

STANDARD PLUS SPECIALS: There are many companies which are in the standard-plus-specials category. This means that many of the assemblies and components going into the particular end product may be made from a forecast of stock with relatively little risk of obsolescence and improved delivery performance and customer relations. In addition, there are special items that may be required. If these special features have sufficient volume in themselves, they can be made and attached at a final assembly—such as special seats in a new automobile. If the volume of the special is so small that it has to be made after the receipt of the order, it may be this which controls the lead time for delivery and customer service. Typical of this type of product would be a standard machine tool that needs a few specially made form tools before being shipped to the customer. The machine could be made for stock but would require this final bit of adaptation to satisfy the customer's requirements.

There are some types of standard parts that are handled in the standard-plus-special category but are really a refinement of the standard-type products. For example, in the oil-pumping equipment business it is frequently possible to assemble a pump from different-size A frames, reduction gears, motors, and level arms within 24 to 48 hours to produce a customer's unique order. This rapid delivery service is possible even though the exact combination has not been in stock as a *final* assembly. Sometimes the ability to adapt the product at the last moment to a customer's specific needs accomplishes the same purpose. If the special products have a substantially longer lead time than the standard products, it raises a question as to how far ahead the company should be in its standard production. The building of the *special* is the controlling factor in customer service. Inventory of *standards* should be maintained at a high enough level to assure that all the attention can be devoted to specials to meet lead-time schedules.

SPECIAL PRODUCTS: Special-type products are typical of those ordered on government contracts to support unique defense-weapon systems prior to production in mass quantities. In most of these cases a company can't risk production until the actual contract or order is received. Consequently the order is always in a back-order position, and good performance against schedule is necessary to satisfy the customer. In some cases plants have to combine products that are specials with those that are standard on common production facilities. Therefore, a universal type of production control system is necessary to keep these demands properly balanced and scheduled. Even for orders of special types, a company can protect itself by placing orders of intent with vendors to reserve certain types of standard raw materials, hardware, and component parts prior to the actual contract ordering. However, adequate escape clauses should be provided in the agreement in case the order doesn't materialize. Where there are common parts among a number of specials in a company's business, it may be possible to borrow back and forth between the projects in order to meet the lead-time commitments.

Spares or Repair-part Considerations. It may also be necessary to provide parts for repair or spares in addition to those going into the new products being furnished to the customer. Most companies do not reserve spare parts. This is because the reservation would be of short duration before being cleared by a shipment. Companies that do reserve spares may have difficulty in making the stock-room personnel respect the reservation if the spare and production items are in a combined storage area. Therefore some companies physically separate the spares stock and account for it separately. Such an approach theoretically requires more inventory for the same level of customer service, but it may be justified by the elimination of confusion. Where spares are stocked in more than one location, they are usually treated separately. An important part of customer relations is the maintenance of proper service and spare parts while the new-product customers are receiving their products satisfactorily. A failure to deliver promptly the spare or repair parts frequently leads to dissatisfaction and a loss of continuing business. Obviously, the more progressive industries give a tremendous amount of attention to continued customer satisfaction by prompt delivery of spares for service to maintain equipment in the field. Frequently, however, failure to supply spares and repair parts is not intentional but is rather the lack of detailed planning by the company involved. It does require special techniques to forecast many miscellaneous items with varying degrees of usage and wear-out rates if one is to effectively protect the customer and also supply parts for current production.

When the model is discontinued, there is the question of maintaining adequate supplies of parts for those that are likely to wear out. In many cases a company is happy to maintain adequate stocks as long as the usage or wear-out rate is high and the continued production of these spare items is a profitable venture. Unfortunately, in almost every situation, there are also those items that tend to malfunction only occasionally. In such cases the maintenance of adequate service stocks for customer satisfaction costs more money. Where a great number of parts and an extensive investment are involved, management is wise to make the proper balance of investment in inventory against the degree of risk of customer dissatisfaction.

Types of Service. In many industries the type of service is dictated historically by what has been established by competition and what the customers have been led to expect. However, there are some industries where there is a chance of varying the type of service within the particular industry itself. In other cases a combination of types of services is required to give satisfaction to the customers involved. Obviously for most consumer-goods items, we expect either to pick them up at retail stores or order them from a retail catalog. Rarely would we consider it advisable to order from the wholesale level or to wait any extended period of time for delivery. As items become more expensive, the question of where they may be purchased and at what cost becomes more important. As the volume increases for a particular type of product, the possibility arises of switching from a distributor who handles several different product lines to unique-product distributors. All these competitive and historical factors must be considered in the planning of the inventory, production, and distribution control systems if one is to be competitive by servicing the customer.

RETAIL SERVICE: While all of us are aware of the retail methods that bring products to us at the marketplace, few of us are aware of the various ways retail service is maintained and supported. In some types of business, the inventory at the final retail establishment is maintained on a unit basis. When sufficiently depleted, the reorder goes directly to the wholesaler or to the factory depending on the support network. In many cases inventory is not replenished by the buyer or the section manager except as the result of a periodic review unless the particular size or style happens to stock-out. Though this method is gradually being replaced, it is probably still the predominant method in many retail-type industries.

Another type of retail service is often maintained by the distributor or the manufacturer of the particular line. In this situation a *distributor's representative* goes to the retail establishment and reviews the adequacy of the stocks and orders those items that are too low for desired service. He writes up his recommended order, which is approved by the customer. In this way inventory levels are maintained at the desired level.

Retail businesses are exploring an automated type of inventory support. When the major packages are opened at the retail establishment, a punched information card is sent back to the distribution or manufacturing point and a resupply is sent forward more or less automatically.

These are some highlights of the types of service supporting the retail activities. All these should be considered in planning an efficient inventory, production, and distribution control system. By such a thorough approach, the optimum degree of customer service can be achieved at the right cost.

DISTRIBUTION SERVICE: *Distributors* backing up retailers frequently perform an important service when the product volume is considered insufficient to justify a unique supply system going directly from the producer to the ultimate retailer. The use of a distributor permits shipment combinations which would not be possible if the distributor did not exist. Thus, it may be possible for a manufacturer to save transportation costs by shipping a full truckload of a variety of his products to a distributor who is in turn supplying a number of retailers. The distributor may be able to combine the products of several manufacturers in one large shipment to a retailer, thus saving costs and time.

With the use of split shipments and because of the increased speed of transportation, the volume of products going directly from the factory to the ultimate retailer (bypassing the distributor) tends to be on the increase. On the other hand, one would be unwise not to consider carefully whether or not the distributor has an important role to play in customer service in each particular situation. Frequently it is a combination of direct shipments to the retailer in some areas and the use of distributors for others that makes the most efficient type of service.

WAREHOUSE SERVICE: There are some products, particularly semiconsumer-type products, for which the existence of warehouses for service and distribution to the customer is of considerable importance. Typical of this type of product might be industrial tools, some of which might be sold directly to factories and other to retailers who in turn sell to individuals. As we shall see in a later section, the consolidation of inventory into a smaller number of warehouses may permit a high degree of customer service at reduced inventory levels. In some cases warehouse personnel may be used to perform some repair work or make some final modifications of the product to make it satisfactory and acceptable to all the customers involved.

FACTORY SERVICE: There are a great many industries with either heavy or unique products requiring shipments to be made f.o.b. from the factory direct to the ultimate user without going through a distributor or a warehouse. Many of the OEM products (products supplied to original equipment manufacturers for incorporation into their products) are shipped from the factory to the OEM customers. These same products may be available to smaller users through distributors. Typical of the factory-f.o.b.-type shipments would be industrial equipment and machine tools. These products may have a back order ranging from one or two weeks to years depending on the lead time and engineering requirements of the specials in the products involved.

COMBINATION-SERVICE CONSIDERATIONS: As already pointed out, goods may require direct delivery in some cases. These same goods might also be sold through warehouses or distributors to other types of markets. This points out that there are a great many kinds of products that require more than one type of distribution to meet the total needs of the marketplace. The more combinations of different services required, the more complex the supporting system has to be to maintain the correct information and flow of goods. For example, when stock is not available at the warehouse or at the distribution point, it may be ordered automatically from the factory and sent directly to the retailer. In other cases the distributor or warehouse may handle only certain categories of orders such as small-volume and immediate-demand-type shipments, while the factory may be the sole source of supply for larger volumes or different types of products. In developing an information system for inventory, production, and distribution to supply these various customer needs, it is necessary to maintain a code to control the corresponding action and to modify these control codes with changing demands.

Competitive Factors. Regardless of the type of product involved in any particular distribution situation, management must appraise its position in relation to that of its competitors. Analysis shows that distribution patterns for industrial products are sometimes determined historically rather than logically. If the industry has traditionally been supplied by a large number of small manufacturers, customers may expect to receive shipments directly from the factory when ordering. If a few big factories are in the business, they may have numerous warehouses close to the customer making it necessary for other manufacturers to follow suit. Regardless of economic analysis management must always consider the position of the competitor.

SERVICE RATE FOR OFF-THE-SHELF SHIPMENTS: Retail outlets, warehouses, distributors, and the factory can each have a stock-item service rate to the next point in the delivery chain. These are calculated as a percentage of times the off-shelf items are not available (i.e., the factory may have a 5 percent stock-out rate to the region, the region 7 percent to the distributor, the distributor 3 percent to the retailer, and the retailer 1 percent to the customer).

If the various points in the distribution chain are all controlled by a single management, it is best to figure the effectiveness of the *system* rather than to rely on the off-the-shelf service at each particular point in the total distribution chain. The equal distribution of most of the stock in the areas closest to the point of retail sale always creates the possibility of extra cost of shipments between warehouses or a higher stock-out risk. Mathematically, it is better to hold a larger portion of the stock in a central or reserve warehouse if rapid transportation permits its distribution to support the random sales demands at the various outlying points.

Many textbooks indicate that the percent of the zero-stock balances is not the best indicator of service level. However, it is used frequently because it is the most convenient indicator to obtain. There is no real evidence that the number of zero balances indicates that the demand against these items will occur while there is zero stock. The actual number of demands against the zero balances and the period of time to fill orders is a more complete measure. However, there is evidence that the statistics can never be complete for this type of calculation. Once a supply system begins to fail, it may be that the number of successive demands will be limited by some customers turning toward other alternatives and therefore not showing the demand on the record. Regardless of the complexity of the calculations, as long as such calculations are approximate and consistent, they can guide management into thinking logically about their service rate in relationship to competition. Such indicators will probably be a substantial improvement over "seat-of-the-pants" controls existing in the past.

NORMAL TRANSIT TIME: Each industry has certain guidelines for shipping stock (and special) items. In recent years many industries have made a substantial improvement in the response rate for both stock and special items. A significant improvement has been a straightforward paper-work simplification of the order-entry procedures. The order is sent to the stock room and the shipping room with a minimum amount of delay. In some cases, data transmission networks between outlying regions and warehouses and the central factory or office have aided.

In many companies reduced inventories and improved inventory service at the final transfer point have resulted from using round-the-clock truck service or by using air freight. All the transit-time considerations have to come into the calculation in terms of meeting the competitive situation. In some cases reducing the transit time can offset the advantage of a larger number of warehouses that competitors use. (See Chapter 7.)

ORDER-ENTRY PROCEDURE

The relationship between the customer and the manufacturing organization typically starts when an order is received. Depending upon the type of product involved there may be some contact between the customer and the company prior to the order entry, but such contact is frequently on an exploratory basis. For the products that might be classified primarily as *special,* or in some cases *standard plus special,* there may be written quotations and perhaps letters of intent prior to the order itself. The quotation does not establish a commitment on the part of the customer, so usually it has no impact upon the manufacturing operation. Only when a quotation is accepted and the customer places an order does the commitment become firm on both sides.

The procedure followed for entering the order has considerable impact upon production control and scheduling as well as upon customer relations. In a computerized, integrated system, key information about the products required and the customer is captured at the order-entry stage. Recently the tendency has been to pass as much work as possible back to the salesman and sometimes to the customer. Again it depends upon the kind of products that are being handled as to how far back the paper work can be passed. If, for example, a company is making standard products which are sold to distributors, either wholesale or retail, it is frequently possible to leave an order form listing all the company's products with catalog numbers. The customer fills in the order form with the quantities of each product required. In some cases it may even be possible to have the customer order from a catalog or an order sheet by placing a number on punched tape. In such cases, or where key-punched cards are used, the order may go directly to the manufacturing company by telephone or telegraph lines. On the other hand, the customer may fill in a partially pre-prepared order sheet and mail it into the company. In many cases customers will also telephone in orders and an order clerk will fill in the form that ordinarily would be filled in by the customer.

When the order comes in on a form prepared by the customer or is telephoned in and prepared by the order clerk, perhaps on forms that are predesigned with numbers for product names, it typically will be scrutinized by an *order editor* and then entered in the system through prepared punch cards or punched tape. If the order has been received by telephone or telegraph, it may already be in the form of punched cards or tape. A hard copy may be generated for editing purposes at this time.

A variety of practices can be followed at the time the punched cards or tape are prepared. In almost all cases some hard copies will be generated. The order copy will vary with different products and the problems involved in generating at the same time invoices, shipping tickets, and bills of lading. If it is possible to ship the product out of stock or to send it as one shipment after manufacturing, it is desirable to prepare an invoice when the order is received. If there are split shipments, because of back ordering, it may be desirable to delay the preparation of invoices until a later time.

Products Shipped from Stock. If it is reasonably certain that shipment can be made immediately out of stock, the following procedure may be desirable. The order is checked first against the master customer file to verify the name and address and to obtain standard shipping instructions and any standard invoicing and discount instructions. It is then entered into the system by transfering the information to punched cards or tape. The orders are checked against the master inventory file to make sure there are products on hand. If all the required products can be filled from stock, the inventory will be reduced accordingly and picking tickets, shipping papers, and invoices prepared. The picking tickets and shipping papers will be sent to the warehouse. When the copies indicating that shipment has been made are returned to the accounting department, the invoices will be dispatched.

If on checking the orders against the inventory it is found not possible to ship some items, back orders will be prepared immediately. Only those items for which stock is available will be designated for picking and shipping, and invoices will be prepared for these items. Costume jewelry is a typical product that might be handled in this way. Orders are received, filled out of stock, and shipped by parcel post to the customer.

In some situations it may be that the products are available in the inventory, but the order must wait for several days before shipment because it is necessary to pool shipments into a single truck to get the most economical rate. In such cases inventory may have been reserved for a particular order that is held in the shipping room waiting for a truck before picking. Meanwhile, some other customer may require the same merchandise. In such a case, neither customer would get the merchandise immediately. The first would not because it was waiting for a truck; the second, because the computer indicated that no inventory was on hand. If a company such as a frozen foods company has many problems of this nature, it is probably better not to prepare invoices and deplete the inventory until the shipment has been made.

Although inventory records may be maintained on a computer, they may not be kept up to date, minute to minute, but handled on a batching basis. It may be possible under such circumstances for products to be depleted in a warehouse before they show up as out of stock on the computer record. If such a batching procedure is followed, it may be desirable to prepare the picking papers, but wait to prepare the invoices after evidence of shipment is received and then prepare the back orders.

Instead of using an order form that has been designed for easy key punching, a company warehousing a standard product may rely on a tub file of "product cards" for generating an order. When the customer's order is originated on his own form, order clerks select prepunched product cards and feed them into their data processing machine along with a prepunched header card containing the customer's name, address, and shipping instructions. Variable information is added to obtain hard copies of all the necessary forms for filling, shipping, and in some cases invoicing the order. Punched tape is generated so that the data can at the same time be fed into the computer in the same way as in the previous example.

Products Ordered in Advance. Sometimes companies in a seasonal business receive orders several months in advance of the time for shipment. In this situation it is desirable to not write the invoice until the shipment is made so that decisions on back orders versus cancellation of the balance of the order can be made properly. Many times if the order cannot be filled completely, no back order is made. The company waits until the customer decides whether he wishes to place another order.

Nonstandard Products. A somewhat different procedure is likely to be followed by companies making products that are not standard and therefore cannot be filled out of stock on hand. In many instances it may be necessary for an order to go first to engineering. In some cases the product is not completely designed at the order stage. The order may be a blanket order with the general magnitude of the expected price indicated, but the final price is dependent upon design and engineering costs. Or the price may be firm, but the specific components that will be required as attachments or integral parts of the product may require engineering decisions. In all cases where it is not possible to determine the precise nature of the product or the selling price, it is probably well to have orders cleared through engineering before data enters the system and starts influencing inventory and production scheduling. Only after engineering has determined precisely what is to be made to satisfy the order should the data enter the total system. For such products it is not unusual for partial shipments to be made. It is not desirable, therefore, to prepare an invoice at the time the rest of the documents are prepared.

In the case of parts which must be manufactured, the whole entry-order system becomes more intricate than in the case of standard products which can be shipped out of stock. The product that must be manufactured has a direct impact upon production, production planning, and scheduling as soon as it enters the system. The order data must be run against a master-parts file and against an open-order file as well as other manufacturing files in such cases.

Advising Customer. Whatever the nature of the product, the manner in which the order is entered and the immediate subsequent steps carried out have a vital impact upon customer relations. If the product can be shipped from stock, it is essential that the order processing be as fast as possible and the shipment be made to the customer quickly. If there is any delay that will ensue, it is essential that the customer be notified as to when he can expect to receive his order. This should be the case for a standard product which is temporarily out of stock as well as for a special product which must be manufactured. In each case the customer should be told when he can expect to receive his merchandise.

If the order is one that takes time to fill, the customer should not only be advised as to when he can expect the order but also at the time when the shipment is made. If a partial order is shipped and a back order is entered, the customer should be so advised. The invoices should be tied into the customer's order and to the shipments that have been made in such a way that the customer knows the charges exactly.

Automatic Replenishment. In most cases, the placing of an order is the first step in the process of getting merchandise to a customer. In some instances where customers maintain stocks of standard items, the order-entry system has been scrapped entirely in favor of automatic replenishment. In such cases, the *supplier* maintains a record of the customer's inventory. All withdrawals from the inventory are transmitted by telephone or telegraph line directly to the supplier's computer where they are recorded. Automatic reordering rules are programmed into the computer, and when the customer's inventory reaches the reorder point, an order is automatically generated and the customer's invenory is resupplied.

There are many such systems in existence, and the chances are that this type of relationship between customer and supplier will continue to expand. The relationship is extremely close in this kind of a situation. Nonetheless, it may be some time before most companies are able to tie in their customers' inventories with the computer at the source. Such companies may, however, be able to establish automatic reordering procedures for their own warehouse. For many manufacturers with extensive inventories located in warehouses or retail stores, the major customer is the warehouse organization. In such cases, it is desirable that procedures be established for *tracking* final demand. This final demand should be related to economic shipping quantities and economic manufacturing order quantities. Where final demand is tracked, procedures for producing the merchandise and resupplying the warehouses can be integrated in a manner to optimize cost for both the manufacturing and distributing organization.

INVENTORY'S ROLE IN CUSTOMER RELATIONS

Customer relations from the point of view of production planning and control involve:

1. Getting the order into the system as quickly and accurately as possible
2. Advising the customer of the action taken
3. Supplying the merchandise as quickly as possible

The first two involve the design of the order-entry system and the communication network. The third is related to the inventory maintained, production's response time (where applicable), and the efficiency of shipping.

The cost of shipping merchandise and the speed with which the customer must be supplied are usually functions of the location of the inventories relative to the customer's location. In some situations a customer expects to be supplied within a few hours or may even expect to be able to drive to the warehouse to pick up the merchandise. Where such service is required, it will be necessary to maintain inventory stocks close to the customer. This may dictate the use of distributors who in turn will maintain inventories, or it may mean an extensive network of branch warehouses.

The second important factor affecting the location of inventories is the cost of shipping the merchandise. Generally the larger the quantity of merchandise to be shipped to a particular place, the cheaper the shipping costs. For example, transportation cost for a barge load is cheaper than that for a railcar load, which is cheaper than a truckload, which is cheaper than a part of a truckload. All these are cheaper than railway express or parcel post. It is necessary, therefore, to determine whether it is cheaper to maintain a supply of merchandise in a warehouse in a particular location where sales are high and supply it by truck or railcar, or to incur high individual shipping costs and eliminate the cost of maintaining warehouses.

In the past it was the practice of many companies to maintain inventories in a number of private or public warehouses throughout the country. In recent years analysis of warehousing costs as compared with shipping costs has suggested that it is cheaper to cut down on the number of warehouse points. Two factors have influenced the trend in this direction:

1. A better understanding of the nature of the costs incurred, particularly the cost of maintaining the extra safety stock required for multiple warehouse locations
2. Faster transportation by truck and plane

Stock-out Policy and Safety Stocks. A company's relationship to its customers depends upon the kinds of products it makes. If the company is making special products, which must be engineered, the customer will not expect rapid delivery. The customer knows that the articles must be manufactured specially, and he is prepared to wait. For standard products the customer expects to obtain quick service. Degrees of variation between the completely standard product and the special product have many implications in terms of customer service. A company must, therefore, consider the impact on its customer relations if it is unable to supply its products quickly at all times. In some cases a company knows that a stock out will not mean a lost sale because the customer will be willing to wait for the item to be shipped. In other cases, the sale will be lost and the customer will go elsewhere for merchandise. If stock outs occur frequently, the company may lose not only the sale but also the customer, because it has become undependable as a supplier of merchandise.

Companies have found it difficult to apply a cost to a stock out because they are not sure that the stock out means a lost sale or the loss of a customer. It

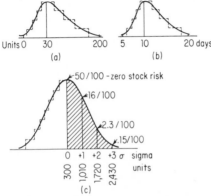

Fig. 1 Safety stocks at various risks: (A) sales per day; (B) days to replenish; (C) combined variations. (*From Arnold O. Putnam, E. Robert Barlow, and Gabriel N. Stilion, Unified Operations Management, McGraw-Hill Book Company, New York, 1963, p. 218.*)

is possible, in most cases, to put a cost on *preventing* stock outs. It is possible to determine how much safety stock is required to provide various degrees of protection against stock outs. We know the average daily usage of a product, the variation in usage per day, the average amount of time it takes to replace stock in a warehouse, and the variation around the average replacement time.

Let us assume that warehoused television sets cost $160 per unit and sell for $200, returning a profit of $40. Let us also assume average sales of 30 units per day with an average of 10 days to replace the stock after an order is issued. The variation in sales per day is shown on graph A of Fig. 1. Graph B shows the variation in time to replenish, and graph C represents the combined variation, i.e., the variation in number of units required to cover orders during a replenishment period. It will be noted that a handy phenomenon of real life is that the two somewhat skewed distributions, A and B, combine to make one which is adequately represented by the well-known bell-shaped normal curve.

The histograms A and B are constructed by taking actual samples from historical data. Each X represents a reading in the appropriate value range shown on the horizontal axis. The average sales per day multiplied by the average lead time (30 × 10) equals the average usage during the 10-day replenishment period. The histogram C is calculated by considering the possibility of variations in both sales and lead time. It shows the probable variation in sales during a replenishment period. The graph C is obtained by considering the interaction of the quantities in graphs A and B.

By definition, one-half of the time sales or lead time will be less than average, so a reorder point of 300 would provide inventory during this 50 percent of the time. One-half of the time the combination of sales or replenishment time will be greater than "average" so, unless the reorder point is raised above 300, stock outs will occur 50 percent of the time. It can be seen from the normal curve that the probability of stock out is reduced substantially by raising the reorder point from 300 to 1,010, providing a safety stock of 710 units. A safety stock of 710 is the statistician's 1 standard deviation (called "sigma") for this particular case. At the 1-sigma point the normal curve has its point of inflection; that is, it stops curving downward and starts to flatten. Each equal increment of safety stock beyond 1 sigma gives less additional protection to the company than the previous increment. Table 1 shows what happens in the example under discussion.

TABLE 1   Cost of Stock-out Protection*

Reorder point................	300	1,010	1,720	2,430	3,140
Standard deviations...........	......	+1	+2	+3	+4
Stock-out risk................	50%	16.6%	2.3%	0.1%	0.003%
Average monthly demand.......	600	600	600	600	600
Lost sales....................	300	100	14	0.6	0.018
Lost profit...................	$12,000	$4,000	$560	$24	$1
Incremental:					
Gain.......................	......	$8,000	$3,440	$536	$23
Inventory investment........	......	$113,600	$113,600	$113,600	$113,600
Return:					
Monthly....................	......	7.05%	3.03%	0.47%	0.02%
Annual.....................	......	85%	36%	6%	0.2%

* From Arnold O. Putnam, E. Robert Barlow, Gabriel N. Stilian, *Unified Operations Management*, McGraw-Hill Book Company, New York, 1963, p. 218.

This example is designed to dramatize the small return on excessive investments in safety stocks. While many companies have product lines which cost much less per unit, the cumulative effect can be similar to that shown above. This example has assumed that sales are lost if there is a stock out. It is possible that the customer will wait and that the business will not be lost. An example of this type, however, gives an indication of the cost of providing safety stock against stock out and gives the sales manager a basis for making judgments about how much protection he needs to maintain good customer relations.

Undoubtedly a sales manager would decide that the same rules did not apply to all products. For products where the marginal contribution to profits is high, more protection may be desired because the cost of stock outs in terms of lost sales would be greater than for products with a relatively low contribution. A variety of other factors may also enter into the situation. For example, if there is a good backup stock in a central warehouse or at the plant, it may be possible to supply merchandise to a customer very quickly by air but with an increased transportation cost to the company. If an analysis of customer's requirements indicates that rapid air shipment will be equally satisfactory as the alternative to supplying out of a local warehouse, the cost of protection against stock outs compared to cost of premium transportation can be weighed. To take advantage of premium transportation, it is essential that backup stocks be available.

Backup Stocks Improve Customer Relations.   It can be demonstrated that, to give the same degree of protection, less safety stock must be maintained in one location than when several locations are used.   Four warehouses (Fig. 2) with a safety stock of 40 units each (for a total of 160 units) would give the same assurance as one warehouse with 80.   This assumes that the same items are involved and there is no inventory-time loss due to transportation.   This can be seen clearly if 100 items are stored in one location and airmailed as compared to having one 1 item in 100 different places.   A second demand in each place will cause a stock out, while it will take 101 demands on central to produce a stock out.   The statistical formula for handling variation is $\sqrt{a^2 + b^2 + c^2 + d^2} \ldots$

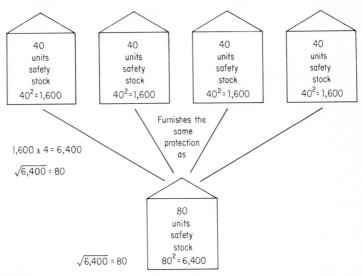

Fig. 2   Safety stock required for different number of warehouses.   (*From a Practical Approach to Scientific Inventory Management, 2d ed., Rath and Strong, Inc., Boston, 1961.*)

This fact can be used to reduce safety stock in any warehouse as long as merchandise can be shipped quickly from the central warehouse.   The total of safety stock required to give protection to customers will be reduced with either a central warehouse or backup point at the factory.

Companies with a central warehouse and an extensive branch-warehousing system are likely to find that the major demands upon manufacturing and production control come from replenishing their own distribution system.   The factory would be faced with large and infrequent demands if manufacturing did not track their customer demands at the point they first hit the system but waited until demand was placed upon the factory by the central warehouse.   Data representing demand by the central warehouse upon the factory would give an entirely false picture of the real demand.   In the typical situation, the central warehouse would show little usage for two months, then a large order would occur followed by no usage, etc.   The actual demand for the product as represented by customers' orders at the branch warehouses might indicate quite a regular and predictable demand. It is essential, therefore, that manufacturing track customer demand rather than replenishment demand for the central warehouse.

Some companies with large warehouse systems also supply customers directly. In this situation it is not uncommon for production control to give priority to a customer's order. The production control people are likely to state that the warehouse-system orders represent no particular customer and there is no real pressure put upon them by outsiders to get the orders out. Therefore, customers who have placed orders directly and who are likely to be putting pressure on production control for delivery get preference. The distribution people quickly become aware of the situation and are likely to place orders sooner because they fear a long lead time. The net result is an increase in a backlog of orders.

If the distribution system is ordering sensibly according to a well-designed formula, it should be treated on an equal basis with customers ordering directly. Presumably warehouses have been set up to provide good service to customers on products that they are expected to need. If the production control group fails to give the warehouse organization good service, the customers in turn will not get the service for which the system was designed. What production control needs is a system that will track demand at the consumer level and translate this demand into manufacturing orders in a way that provides the most economical service to the company and to the customer. This can be provided by the critical-ratio system for distribution.

Critical Ratio for Distribution.[1] A variation of the critical-ratio technique now widely used in manufacturing operations can be applied to reduce distribution costs and improve service. Daily warehouse usages at all points are provided to the manufacturing organization through telecommunications and with the help of a computer give the needed shipping quantities.

Each day, or less frequently if desirable, information on usage and inventory levels at all points in the system will be subjected to predetermined computer formulas which will indicate the item and quantities to be shipped to each distribution point. Some of the assumptions implicit in the application of critical-ratio techniques to distribution are:

1. The priority ranking for shipping each item from one point to the next can be expressed mathematically considering the risk of running out of stock before the regular shipment is received.

2. The amount of each item to be shipped can be determined initially by economics related to order cost versus inventory level.

3. The initial economic order shipment (EOS) can be decreased mathematically if conditions indicate that the backup stock should be used sparingly.

4. The safety stock at both the distribution point and the factory can be raised or lowered to balance performance (service level) against investment.

The first step in the analysis is to determine the expected amount of merchandise to be supplied customers from a particular warehouse during the year. This can be translated into truckloads or freight-car loads. Total number of truckloads per year can be expressed as number of truckloads per month or per week. We can assume that the cheapest method of shipping would be to send all merchandise to the warehouse from the central warehouse or the plant in truck loads. The schedule for trucks going to the warehouse can then be worked out.

Assume that in a particular analysis it was discovered that the optimum number of truckloads was about 50 per year or 1 per week, and all items on the truck should be for at least one week's supply to eliminate the need to ship the next truck early or result in a stock out. If we divide the available quantity (i.e., the on-hand less safety stock) by the smoothed usage at a warehouse, we get the best estimate of anticipated stock of each item in terms of *days of supply* (DS). Thus, *on-hand* (OH) minus *safety stock* (SS) divided by smoothed usage (Sm) equals DS. The days of supply divided by lead time (LT) plus the lead time remaining (LTR) provide a priority ratio of need (i.e., DS divided by LT plus LTR equals *critical ratio*).

If the days of supply do not cover the lead time remaining, we anticipate a stock out before the next shipment. If we don't put the item on the next shipment, then the days of supply must cover the lead time also. Thus any item with a critical ratio less than 1.0 should be shipped on the immediate trip, but if the critical ratio is greater than 1.0, forecast indicates the item can be deferred until the next economical trip. Thus a computer program is designed to make the above calculations on each item and provide reports that list line items in order of their criticalness.

For the normal shipment of an item from backup stock, the shipping quantity should never be less than the usage during the lead time. On the other hand, if every item of a large multiproduct inventory had to be shipped every trip, the paper work plus the cost of picking and putting away would be excessive.

The economic-order-quantity formula can be applied in a modified form to balance the cost involved. Thus

$$\text{EOS} = \sqrt{\frac{2uo}{ic}}$$

where u = usage during period

o = variable cost of ordering, including paper work, picking, counting, receiving, and storing

i = carrying charges expressed as a percentage in a time period equivalent to the usage period

c = the direct cost effect on the inventory level per unit involved

The cost value involved here requires specific analysis of what happens in each individual case, as it could range from the full manufacturing cost of the item for the period to an amount as low as the added value created by the transportation commitment.

Another important factor in the situation is related to reducing the amount of each shipment if the stock availability at the higher level is threatened during the lead time remaining before the next replenishment. The availability can be calculated. First the days of supply is obtained by dividing the on-hand inventory at the central or backup point by the smoothed usage for that specific stream of goods. The days of supply divided by the lead time remaining to replenish the central stock gives the *index of criticality*. If this index is less than 1.0, all shipments of that item would be reduced to the index level, i.e., a 5 index equals 50 percent of the EOS. Expressed in a formula, the on-hand central supply divided by the smoothed-usage total equals days of supply (DS). The critical ratio equals DS/LTR (lead time remaining for supply from factory). The procedure prevents a common distribution problem of shipping too much of some items to branch warehouses in one week which will result in stock outs caused by demands from other branch warehouses in the next week. The controls should also minimize the cost of any warehouse shipments to cover imbalances.

The critical ratio of all items could be calculated daily and ranked according to criticality. All items with a critical ratio of less than 1 would have to be shipped on the next truck that is going. If all such items did not represent a full truckload, then the next items on the critical list would be selected and shipped. With such a system it should be possible to reduce the inventories in the distribution system significantly and maintain stock out at any risk level desired.

The system would not only undertake to keep the branch warehouses supplied, but would provide for the resupply by production control of the backup warehouse.

SUMMARY

As suggested at the beginning of this chapter, good customer relations can only exist if customers obtain the products they want at the times they require them. While the sales department is responsible for direct contacts with customers, the maintenance of good customer service requires smooth functioning of a variety of operations, including order entry, production control, inventory control, warehousing, and shipping. The definition of adequate customer service will differ from company to company depending upon the nature of the products and competitive situation. The requirements vary from providing the customer with the product immediately out of warehouse stock for standard products to delivery in months or years for special products built to customer specifications.

There are opportunities for utilizing new statistical techniques and computer assistance to cut costs and improve service for almost every variation of product and customer requirements. These opportunities can be seized best by first determining the desired level of customer service and then tracing through the whole system from inventory to final shipment to determine the needs at each stage, the alternatives available, and the relative cost-service advantages.

REFERENCE

1. From Arnold O. Putnam, "Managing Distribution and Inventories for Profit and Reliable Customer Service," *APICS Quarterly Bulletin,* vol. 6, no. 4, October, 1965.

Chapter 5

Product and Process Information

EDITOR:

Kenneth W. Tunnell *President, K. W. Tunnell Co., Inc., Norristown, Pennsylvania*

CONTRIBUTORS:

Robert H. Baker *Manager of Manufacturing, Decca Systems Inc., Riverdale, Maryland*

Albert V. Santora *Senior Staff Consultant, K. W. Tunnell Co., Inc., Norristown, Pennsylvania*

Alfred O. Valentine *Manager of Industrial Engineering, Philco-Ford Corporation, Communications and Electronics Division, Philadelphia, Pennsylvania*

Robert H. Turner *Data Processing Manager, Taylor Corporation, Valley Forge, Pennsylvania*

CONTENTS

Product and process data are an essential foundation upon which every production and inventory control system is constructed. These files of relatively static information, currently and accurately maintained, are positively required in order for a production control system to function effectively. The data are used not only in systems design, but in day-to-day operations for analysis and decision making.

This chapter is devoted to identifying various types of product and process information and to reviewing various critical techniques which production and inventory control personnel will find applicable in working with this data.

THE IMPORTANCE OF PRODUCT AND PROCESS DEFINITION

Every manufacturing concern is faced with the critically important task of currently defining its product. The complexity of the task varies considerably from company to company depending upon the product, the nature of the manufacturing resources, and the management policies. For example, a chemical firm producing 25 standard-blend items will have a much different product-definition requirement than a power transmission manufacturer producing 2,000 standard and 1,500 nonstandard items of chain and sprockets.

Most industrial firms are neither standard-product manufacturers nor custom-products manufacturers. Today most firms produce a range of *standard* products and also produce both a *modified-standard* product and *nonstandard* products, both of which are to a customer's specifications. There are relatively few mass producers of standard end-item products—even the automotive industry manufactures a standard product where standard-stock subassemblies are processed through final assembly and controlled by detail schedules and releases of customer-dealer requirements.

In today's competitive business world each business must carefully assess its product definition and determine critically, "What business are we in?" Often, analysis will show that the current product line, listed in catalogs and advertising, is neither the most profitable nor composed of the items which will best utilize the labor, material, equipment, and technological resources available at the factory.

STANDARD-PRODUCTS PROGRAM

One prominent United States manufacturer of process instrumentation and equipment determined that current product definition was unsatisfactory and that rapid analysis was required. A *standard-products program* was established with the necessary program task force and steering committee.

Program Objectives. The objective of the standard-products program is to establish all policies, plans, systems, and procedures to identify, market, manufacture, distribute, and control the "standard products" offered for sale.

Program Scope. The program deals with the answers to the following seven questions:

1. What products, by definition, are to be considered "standard" products?
2. Are these products to be purchased from outside suppliers or manufactured, and if manufactured, at what facility?
3. Where and by what decision rules are the functions of the production planning and inventory control to be performed?
4. Where and by what decision rules are the standard-stock items to be distributed and stocked?
5. How can the standard products be produced and sold more economically, thus improving their contribution to profit?

6. Can the basic designs be improved and/or standarized to provide a better product at lower costs?

7. How can improved product-line management be accomplished?

Product definition in the final analysis is really the task of establishing and maintaining the factory common language for product-oriented communications. Ideally, there should be one description or numerical identification of the product end item for use by marketing for catalogs and promotion brochures, accounting for standard-cost and job-cost files, and manufacturing for bill-of-material files and customer-order preparation.

PRODUCT DEFINITION, CODING, AND CLASSIFICATION

All products must be accurately and precisely defined from the product end-item level down to part and raw-material levels (see Fig. 1).

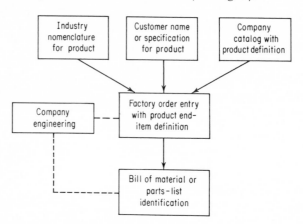

Fig. 1   Product-definition level.

"Product end items" are defined as those items which are typically shipped to customers, as distinguished from either accessories or spare parts.

The production and inventory control manager will often find that one of his most vital tasks is this product structuring.

The following kinds of data are typically required for adequate product definition:

Part Number.   A numerical or alphanumeric grouping of characters which is unique to a particular purchased or manufactured item.   The part number can be significant, semisignificant, or nonsignificant.

Description.   A noun phrase with appropriate dimensions which serves to give a language definition to the product.

Stock Code.   A digital coding which indicates if the item is:

1. Standard stock
2. Standard nonstock
3. Nonstandard-nonstock

ABC Code.   The coding which results from usage value analysis of inventory items.

Inventory Code.   The coding which designates the relative inventory level of an item.

Procurement Code. The coding which indicates the procurement policy for the item.

Examples of product-item coding are shown below. Naturally, these codes may be revised, replaced, or substituted from business to business.

Code Identification	Legend
ABC Code	
1	A items
2	B items
3	C items
4	No-usage items
5	Nonevaluated
Stock Code	
1	Standard-stock materials forecast
2	Standard nonstock
3	Nonstandard
4	Standard products
5	Old products phasing out
6	New products phasing in
7	Standard-stock marketing forecast
Procurement Code	
1	Make complete
2	Buy complete
3	Make or buy complete
4	Purchased semifinished
5	Make and send out for further processing
Inventory Code	
0	Raw material
1	Semifinished parts
2	Subassemblies
3	Finished goods
4	Finished parts
5	Expense material

As indicated previously, product-structure definition is typically accomplished by use of bills of material. These lists indicate the detail parts and subassemblies required in order to manufacture the product and often will show the relationship between the various levels of assembly in the product. This coding is called "level coding" and is required for net-requirements planning.

PRODUCTION INFORMATION AND THE MANUFACTURING PLAN

The critical requirement for this information is the same for the stock-product or the made-to-order-product manufacturer. For the stock-product manufacturer labor, material, and other production resources will be planned in accordance with forecasted product requirements. This forecasting will be accomplished by the marketing and the manufacturing departments. From the forecasted product sales a manufacturing plan will be developed which is called a "master schedule." All too often the marketing function will forecast in terms of product groups, leaving it to manufacturing to further define the detailed product items.

In companies fabricating products to order, the product definition typically will be just as stringent, but will require engineering effort for the individual order before the bills of material can be made available to manufacturing. In these companies the allocation of manufacturing resources and development of the manufacturing plan will relate to the current backlog and mix of business. Nevertheless, adequate product definition is just as vital.

Spare-parts and assemblies production assume major significance in many industries. For one major engine manufacturer in the United States, spare parts represent almost 30 percent of the total sales volume. In such a situation, obviously, the product structure for all spare-parts items, including packaging and instruction data, is of extreme importance.

PROCESS DEFINITION AND PRODUCTION SCHEDULING

The vital nature of process definition is easily recalled when we consider how often it is said of an unsuccessful production control manager, "He doesn't understand the process here at our factory," or "He doesn't have experience in an industry such as ours." This negative approach to the need for process definition quickly illustrates its importance. It is not possible to schedule, plan, and control a plant facility unless there is specific process definition. It is true that in many smaller plants, the process knowledge is maintained in unwritten form by the production manager. The very existence of the master schedule, loading, detail schedule, and dispatching system elements of an entire production control system is dependent on this process definition.

VARIOUS TYPES OF PRODUCT INFORMATION

Product definition is absolutely essential to the effective operation of any production control function. The definition of product to be manufactured or procured must encompass:

1. Final end-item description
2. Composition and configuration

The documents that will interpret product-design concepts into meaningful information used in orderly planning for manufacture of the product are:

1. Drawings
2. Parts lists or bills of material
3. Specifications
4. Data lists
5. Recipes
6. Formulas
7. Batch ingredients, etc.

All the information contained in the various documents defining a given product should be organized and controlled so as to assure that each of the required elements of product definition is contained in a vehicle of communication. This vehicle in many plants is the bill of materials with related drawings.

A typical bill of material* is shown as Fig. 2. This document has been printed by automatic data processing equipment and is representative of the use of product master files. In this case the basic engineering bill of material was released and was keypunched; thus, every detail part and subassembly had all static product information available for rapid machine processing and reporting. Bills of material, where-used files, and similar documents can be produced. Note the kind of information which was stored:

Part number
Description

---

* See Chapter 17 for further information regarding the bill of material.

Quantity per assembly
Next higher assembly
Quantity per end item
Level code

Responsibility for Product Information. The responsibility for the release of product information in both process and fabrication or assembly industries falls to the engineering function.

This, of course, varies in other types of manufacturing operations as follows: in the style-goods business (decals, cards, etc.), the product release is made by the art department; in the garment industry, product release is accomplished directly by manufacturing in accordance with specifications established by marketing or by a design function; in the pharmaceutical industry, the laboratory is responsible for the development of product specifications.

BILL OF MATERIAL

Part number	Description	Quantity per assembly	Next assembly number	Quantity	Level code
99209K01	9450				
92182A05	SCREEN	2	99209K01	2	1
94866A32	SHIELDOLOAD END	2	99209K01	2	1
94866A33	SHIELDOLINE END	2	99209K01	2	1
99005A00	ARMATURE	2	99209K01	2	1
99018A00	LOAD TERM	1	99209K01	1	1
99018B00	LOAD TERM	1	99209K01	1	1
99167A00	ARC RUNNER	2	99209K01	2	1
99170A00	TRIPPER BAR RET	1	99209K01	1	1
99184A00	SHIELD	2	99209K01	2	1
99185A00	SHIELD	2	99209K01	2	1
99224A00	COVER	1	99209K01	1	1
99275A00	MAGNET	2	99209K01	2	1
99359A00	ARMATURE RET	2	99209K01	1	1
99399A00	ARMATURE SPRING	1	99209K01	1	1
99401A00	CALIB SCREW	2	99209K01	2	1
99423A00	UNDERWRITERS LAB	1	99209K01	1	1
99424A00	E RING	2	99209K01	2	1
301027B02	SCREWORET	2	99209K01	2	1
301027E04	SCREWS	2	99209K01	2	1
201027E05	SCREW	2	99209K01	2	1

Fig. 2   Bill of material.

Due to the potentially great impact of new products on current manufacturing operation, it is necessary that close coordination exist on a continuing basis between design engineering, manufacturing, and production control.   In both the mass production or flow type of factory and the job or make-to-order factory new products will be introduced into the existing product line requiring special efforts.

New-product Release.   In the production of any new model, after final drawings have been approved, a definite system for engineering releases is necessary to inform all functional departments of standard data.   This data is then used with the issued drawing as authorization for requisitioning material, writing of operation sheets from which tool design and tool production begins according to standard procedures, procurement of special patterns, dies, and molds, and as a record of design progress leading toward release for initial production.   This system should be used in conjunction with existing control plans in the engineering, industrial engineering, and production control departments and will serve to coordinate all departments by supplying standard information.

The production control planning which relates to new-product introduction can most effectively be accomplished by one man or a staff group specifically charged with the responsibility for this activity. The complexity of the planning and coordination is extensive and dictates that this be a centralized responsibility.

The new-product introduction checklist shown in Fig. 3 and the engineering-

	Begin	Complete	Man-hours	By
Part A. Design				
1. Obtain development authorization				Engineering
				Sales
				Planning
2. Obtain marketing authorization				Engineering
				Sales
3. Prepare manufacturing drawings				Engineering
				Drafting
				Planning
4. Interim planning and cost estimating				Planning
				Cost
				Engineering
5. Make necessary drawing revisions and				Drafting
subassembly drawings				Engineering
				Planning
6. Manufacture samples				Model shop
7. Test samples				Engineering test
8. Release design and specifications				Line engineer
Part B. Planning				
1. Final planning				Planning
2. Issue tracings				Drafting
3. Establish standard costs				Cost
4. Review and approve				Products task force
5. Establish packing method and label design				Engineering
				Planning
Part C. Tooling and production				Sales
1. Plant equipment appropriation				Planning
2. Tool drafting				Planning
3. Order tools				Planning
4. Tool and equipment procurement				Planning
5. Approve one part from each major tool				Planning
(prior to production release)				Engineering
6. Order material for units including				Production
packing material				
7. Release production schedule				Production
8. Produce at planned rate				Production

Fig. 3 New-product introduction information.

release form shown in Fig. 4 are helpful forms for the production control planner in coordinating this new-product function.

The engineering-release form contains all the essential information required when a new or existing item is released. After the initial design has been approved and the drawing signed by the chief engineer, heads of design engineering, and drafting, prints are issued to the industrial engineering department and the shop superintendent for review, suggestions, and approval. The prints are to be returned to the head of design engineering within 48 hours. After final design has been determined, drawn up, and approved by the chief engineer, the engineering-release form is issued. One copy is sent to industrial engineering as an aid in tool control, special procurement problems involving patterns, molds, dies, etc., and also authorization to write and issue the original operations sheet. One copy is sent to production control as authorization to initiate the requisitions for material according to anticipated production schedules.

It should be noted at this point that the ability to read drawings will be of considerable benefit to a production control management and staff, although not mandatory. Often, judgements relating to the lead times, capacity, resource allocation, and raw-material availability will be greatly speeded by this ability.

```
┌─────────────────────────────────────────────────────────────────────────┐
│ Release No. _____  ENGINEERING RELEASE    Part no._____   │
│ Supersedes  _____  Date_____    Assembly no. _____  │
│ Machine no. _____       Part name_____  │
│ Quantity per assembly_____    Assembly name _____  │
│ Drawing date_____        Prints issued _____  │
│ Material specifications _____  │
├──────────────────────┬──────────────────────────┬───────────────────────┤
│     Raw material     │      Purchased part       │       Casting         │
│ New_____ Active___ │ New_____ Active_____ │ Pat. no. _____ │
│ No. _____  │ Vendor _____ │ Est. weight _____ │
│ Size_____  │ No. and spec. _____ │ _____  │
├──────────────────────┴──────────────────────────┴───────────────────────┤
│ Field replacement _____ Ref. dwg. change no._____ │
│                                 Supersedes drawing_____  │
│ Remarks _____  │
│         _____  │
│         _____  │
├──────────────────────┬───────────────────────────────────────────────────┤
│ Issued by            │ Approved by                                        │
└──────────────────────┴───────────────────────────────────────────────────┘
```

Fig. 4   Engineering-release form.

VARIOUS TYPES OF PROCESS INFORMATION

Process definition is a "must" for the effective production and inventory control system; however, this process information can vary tremendously depending upon the size and nature of the business, the product, and the organization established or required to produce it.

The complexity of a business is determined by a number of factors. Listed below are some of the factors which can create great differences in operating characteristics and the techniques of planning and control.

1. Number of products manufactured or processed
2. Number of parts in product
3. Number of operations or processes on a part
4. Difficulty of operations or processes on a part
5. Number and complexity of tooling or equipment required
6. Size or length of production runs

Relatively little production planning and control is required in a one-process industry such as a chemical operation where the process and its required equipment are defined and developed in detail by qualified engineering personnel prior to even the construction of the facility and where control is almost entirely a matter of equipment performance and maintenance.

Most other types of industrial and service operations require a greater amount of planning and control of their operations on a continuing and effective basis. Many of these other types have what we may call "processes"—even though they are not entirely comparable to the chemical process—and the old adage remains true: "Control the process and you control what comes out of it."

Process information and definition are what permit or determine effective control to be established and maintained.   Our position here will be to illustrate the major types of process information that are applicable to the greater majority of operations with little or minor modification.

Probably the first bit of process information required by production and inventory control is the delineation of which items to make and which to buy.   This information is derived from a make-versus-buy analysis which is normally based on pure economic evaluation.

Information based on the analysis is best posted to the bill of materials where it remains readily available for everyday use and provides an easy means of implementation for further analysis and comparison as future needs may warrant.

TREDOR CORP.				OPERATION SHEET—ROUTE CARD					Sheet of		
Part or assembly No. (1)	Rev. (2)	Next assembly (5)	Rev. (6)	Latest ECN & date (4)	Card (18)	Rev. & date (19)	Engineer (20)	Part or assembly No (1)			Rev. (2)
Part or assembly description (3)				Product identification & description (7)				W/O or acct No. (21)		Order Quantity (22)	
Material description (8)				Material code (9)		Quantity for each (10)		Econ. lot size (17)		Actual lot size (23)	
								Lot number (24)		Due date (25)	
								Issue date (26)		Start date (28)	
Work ctr.	Optn. No.	Operation description			Tool No. & description	S.U. hours	Hours ea.	Labor — Date sched. comp.	Material — Optr. No.	Overhead — Quantity produced — Good Rwk. Scrap QC Sig.	
(11)	(12)	(13)			(14)	(15)	(16)	– – – (27) (29)	(30)		
								– – –		(31) (32) (33) (34)	
								– – –			
								– – –			
								– – –			
								– – –			
								– – –			
								– – –			
								– – –			
								– – –			
								– – –			
								– – –			
								– – –			

Fig. 5   Operation-sheet route card.

Operation Sheet.   Undoubtedly the most helpful and important of all process information is the operation sheet.   This is also known as the "process sheet," "routing sheet," and "route and tool sheet."

A typical example of manufacturing-information documentation is illustrated in Fig. 5.   This particular example indicates consideration for the basic information requirements not only for manufacturing but also for scheduling, loading, material control, quality control, and cost accounting.   In addition, it recognizes system needs, as it is adaptable to either manual or machine systems and provides identification and separation of both the fixed standard information and the variable lot information.

The originator, working from the blueprint, provides the following information (see reference numbers on figure):

1. Part or assembly number

2. Latest revision, issue, or modification number of the drawing

3. Part of assembly description

4. Latest engineering-change notice (ECN) and date of effectivity or issue

This change should normally be the one that authorized the latest revision; however, in an engineering-change procedure that accumulates changes to a specific number prior to actually making a drawing change or revision, or where engineering documentation traditionally maintains a time lag which is later than manufacturing or production requirements, this information must be provided on a current basis.

5. Next assembly

6. Next assembly revision number

These items permit proper explosion of the bill of materials and the creation of the where-used file in addition to assisting in material movement and control.

7. End-product identification and description

8. Material description

9. Material code

10. Quantity for each

11. Work center or machine

12. Operation number

13. Operation description

14. Tool number and description

15. Estimated or standard setup hours

16. Estimated or standard each-piece hours

17. Economic lot size

18. Route-card or operation-sheet revision

19. Date of card revision

20. Signature or initials of originator

These, then, are the information items which are typically fixed or standard for any part or assembly regardless of the specific order or lot size which is authorized in the future.

When a work order is issued the production control department adds the variable information as follows:

21. Work order or account number

22. Order quantity

23. Actual lot size

24. Lot number

Items 23 and 24 permit the optimum scheduling of quantities by economical lots, balancing the requirements of this order with other scheduled requirements through the operation, and also control and status by lot.

25. Due date—to stores or for shipment

26. Issue date—when order is issued by production control

27. Date scheduled—used where milestone scheduled dates are used in a longer process or between varying cost or work centers within the manufacturing cycle

28. Start date—which indicates when the job is actually issued by the dispatcher or physically started in the manufacturing process

This variable information which is specific to the order or lot is added to the reproducible master as a strip or overlay on the right side of the double line by any one of several methods available. This permits reproduction of the operation sheets for the operating people, the route card which accompanies the work, a copy for scheduling and one for material control, and also a copy to the cost department.

The copy to scheduling enables them to use the right-hand columns for extension of the indicated setup and each-piece times for machine or work-center loading.

When each operation has been completed the operator provides the following:

29. Date completed
30. Operator number

Quality control or inspection provides information on the route card, in-process by operation if required, as follows:

31. Good pieces produced
32. Rejected pieces which require rework
33. Rejected pieces which cannot be reworked
34. Initials or stamp of inspector or quality control engineer

This permits yield identification at any point in the process and also permits control of scrap, rework, and partial makeup work orders through the means of subsidiary control procedures for these items.

The cost department uses their copy to fill in the following information:

35. Labor costs
36. Material costs
37. Overhead costs

This permits the cost department to price out the actual process information and to have available a valid cost for each item or assembly in the same manner of breakdown that is common between manufacturing and production control.

Flow Process Chart. The flow process chart is a graphic presentation of the sequence of operations, transportations, delays, and storages occurring during a process. The material flow process chart presents the process in terms of the events which occur to the material such as the distance moved and the time required to move it.

In practice today the flow process chart is used to improve the present process method and flow, or it precedes the operation sheet and route card by analyzing and evaluating process flow alternatives of which the most desirable is then incorporated as the standard in the operation or process sheet. It is this information that is then given to production control.

In most manufacturing operations today one of the major objectives is control through the scheduling and building by levels, i.e., parts, subassemblies, assemblies, final assembly. One distinct advantage resulting from this improved control is a substantial reduction in work-in-process inventory. In order to effectively perform this function production control must have valid information from which to generate workable and attainable schedules for these levels.

The first requirement within this objective is the information needed to gather together from stores all the material that is fabricated or assembled at an operation or work station. These are commonly known as "material pulls."

The bill of materials, primarily a major input of product information, can, with planned modification, also become an important part of process information as the "pull sheet." In properly idented form, not only can a copy of it be used to accumulate the parts in the stock room for issue to manufacturing, but the actual disbursement of parts can be recorded on the same basic document and then used to post against stock-room inventories to maintain current stock status.

The use of the bill of materials as a pull sheet provides an important advantage to the control function through the continuing maintenance of the integrity of the product content which is to be processed.

In operations where this is not used, a separate document must be provided to the stock room indicating what is to be pulled and how many of each for a particular subassembly or assembly.

The second requirement, that of "kitting," also requires that information be provided to the stock room so that they can properly package or bin the material for most effective transportation and optimum utilization at the work station.

Ideally, this material should be kitted or positioned into the bins or holders in exactly the way they will be used during the processing. Therefore, kit sheets or bin sheets will have to be furnished identifying the containers, the specific item which is to be placed in them, and the work station to which they will be delivered.

In the electrical equipment and electronic industries an important item of many subassembly and assembly kits is wire of various kinds. Wherever possible wire should be prepared in advance of use by cutting to length, stripping, and tinning.

Whether this is done by production personnel and then returned to stock for kitting or whether it is performed within the stock room as a service function, a wire-run list must be provided to identify the wire as to specification, length, and number of each required.

Tools, fixtures, and gauges are other items which must be provided at the time kits are issued to production. This information is provided on the operation sheets although the tools are normally issued in kit form from the tool crib or are available as needed in the production area.

Any changes in either the total manufacturing-cycle time or its individual processing or material-handling cycles should be forwarded to production control for their cognizance and inclusion in their scheduling procedure.

RESPONSIBILITY FOR PROCESS DEFINITION

The responsibility for process definition, like the process information itself, varies widely according to the nature of the business and its complexity. In addition, the degree of management sophistication, the recognition and use of advanced management techniques, and the possible information requirements of customers (government agencies, etc.) will vary considerably.

In the smaller operations one will generally find that individuals have multiple responsibilities. Relationships and procedures are, more often than not, handled on a day-to-day basis in an informal manner. The strongest and most knowledgeable individuals tend to accept more responsibility, and the organizational structure and responsibilities usually evolve from this effect.

In the larger operations organizational tasks and responsibilities are more formalized, and procedures are generally clearly defined.

Although these two extremes appear to be widely divergent, there is a common ground which we shall attempt to interpret as the area of responsibility for process definition.

In the past several decades we have become accustomed to hearing about methods engineers, process engineers, production engineers, manufacturing engineers, and industrial engineers. Each company has its own job titles for these people who provide the technical and professional assistance to manufacturing and processing.

Formal definitions have been developed and written to describe the responsibilities and activities of these people and their function in the organization. These definitions are readily available for reference, so it appears redundant to quote them here.

Many of these titles or terms have been considered synonomous and have been used interchangeably during this time. Many of the functions and responsibilities in the definitions are common amongst them, and the obvious overlapping has done little to clarify or standardize this area. However, the concept of industrial engineering, as presented in the definition of the American Institute of Industrial Engineers, is by far the broadest, and in fact, represents the increasing trend of common usage in industry today.

As an illustration let us look at an organization chart of an industrial engineering department showing an extremely simplified functional breakdown. The functional breakdown presented in Fig. 6 is typical of the division of responsibility and activity in an average operation today. As our process-information requirements must come from all the major sections of an organization such as this, we propose to use the term "industrial engineering" as the source responsibility for process information.

Although product information ostensibly ends with the release to production of a clean set of drawings and bill of material with an appropriate procedure for information flow pertaining to engineering changes, this does not necessarily mean that the process-information responsibility begins at that point.

The most effective planning by industrial engineering is the preplanning effort which takes place prior to the actual release to production. This is a preventive type of activity which has as its objective the prevention of excess costs rather than the correction or reduction of them after they have been put into production.

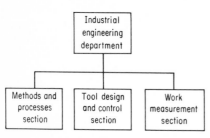

Fig. 6 Organization of industrial engineering department.

This entails a review of the preliminary bill of material with preliminary make-or-buy evaluation to reduce the paper-work procedural lead time after release. When this information is promptly provided, it means that material control can better do its job of providing the material in time to meet the schedules.

When drawings are released, they are reviewed in detail for completeness and manufacturing feasibility. Operation sheets are made for each part or assembly defining the material requirements, the work center or equipment to be used, the method and sequence to be followed, the tools specified and authorized, and the estimated or standard performance times applied. This comprises the major process information that is provided to production control by one source document.

Industrial engineering defines the workplace layout and develops the visual aids and instruction sheets which in turn provide production control with the basic information required for kitting, as outlined previously.

Therefore, we can say that, in most operations, the responsibility for providing process information lies with an industrial engineering capability, whether large or small, whether formal or informal, whether called by this term or one synonymous with it.

RELATIONSHIPS WITH ENGINEERING AND INDUSTRIAL ENGINEERING

Relationships of the production control department with other departments within the internal structure of an organization will vary widely from one industry to the next. Often there will be some major difference in the relationships between the production control department and other departments from one company to the next, even though both companies are producing, marketing, and distributing the same or similar products.   These differences usually occur as a result of *specific management philosophies* relating to sales, manufacturing, engineering, or general administration of the company.   Even more important to production control personnel is the specific management philosophy which defines and delegates the responsibilities, duties, and authority of the production control department.

The difference in relationships can be readily recognized where the *product* varies.   An equally important difference can be found in the types or methods of manufacture: job or intermittant manufacture, or process type of manufacture. Each of these types of manufacturing activity will provide major changes in relationships and organization, which are further compounded by product, market, distribution methods, technological advances and changes, and management philosophy.

In summary, relationships between production control and design or industrial engineering departments can vary from one company to the next depending upon three major elements:

1. Product or industry
2. Specific management philosophy
3. Type of manufacturing activity

For example, we can expect that there is a considerable difference in relationships in a plant producing six or seven guidance systems for space vehicles and a plant producing hundreds of thousands of 12- by 18-inch United States flags.   The complexity of product definition and change control can create a mass of interaction of data and communication for the guidance-system manufacturer and relatively little for the flag manufacturer.   In the first case, production control might have heavy responsibilities for engineering-change control and/or configuration management throughout the entire life of the project including engineering and production phases.   In the case of producing United States flags, one can expect that during the production cycle little, if any, chance will exist for change of product design.   Changes in flag material or changes in staff and ornament design or material can be expected; these changes must be scheduled and released in coordination with production control master and detail schedules.

Thus, major differences in nature and volume of communications and data flow do exist in the two plants described above.   However, we still do see some basic similarity of relationships of engineering and industrial engineering with production and inventory control.

The essence of the engineering–industrial engineering relationship with production control is that the engineering function typically must define mechanical chemical, electrical, etc. characteristics of the item to be manufactured, while the industrial engineering function typically must define what manufacturing processes, equipment, and facilities will be used.   Thus, engineering specifies the "what," while industrial engineering specifies the "how" and the "where."

It is recognized that in process-type manufacturing operations the engineering department may play the major role in specifying the manufacturing techniques.

Listed below are some of the documents and services production control must get from engineering and industrial engineering.   Although the list is not all-inclusive and does not attempt to cover all industries, it does list the basic items provided by engineering and industrial engineering.

From engineering:

1. Design documentation (drawings)
2. Advance-order lists

3. Project schedules
4. Release schedules
5. Drawing-number control
6. Model-number control
7. Part-number control
8. Material specifications
9. Bills of material
10. Product specifications
11. Engineering shop orders
12. Engineering-change orders
13. Standardization
14. Numerical control data
15. Handbook and instruction manual
16. Process specification
17. Technical assistance

From industrial engineering:

1. Project schedules
2. Release schedules
3. Design review
4. Facilities planning
5. Plant layout
6. Manufacturing philosophy
7. Operation sheets
8. Time standards
9. Methods
10. Tool planning
11. Tool schedules
12. Assembly-kit lists
13. Make-or-buy determinations
14. Numerical control data
15. Process specification
16. Technical assistance

Production control is a vital link in a chain of events that must take place between design completion and the time when the finished product is packaged and shipped to its destination. Therefore, it is essential that production control understand its role in monitoring engineering data as it is released. Engineering data and its control is, of course, a responsibility of the engineering department. However, it is important that schedules of release and the controls of changes be monitored closely by production control to ensure that information relating to manufacturing and procurement are clear and that duplication is guarded against. Inventories, lead times, customer delivery dates, and manufacturing facilities are all considerations which are affected by design engineering and industrial engineering.

Production control participates in the development of policy, procedure forms, reports, etc., utilized by engineering and industrial engineering departments which shall be used as basic data for procurement and manufacturing. A continuing communication between engineering and production control is essential to be certain that all the requirements of manufacturing are considered in the scheduling and documentation of engineering data.

PROJECT SCHEDULES

Production control is responsible for schedule development and monitoring of schedules to ensure that deliveries are made in accordance with promises to customers and established management policy on customer service.

Master scheduling and project scheduling are discussed in detail in other chapters of this handbook; therefore, for purposes of this discussion we shall address ourselves to the point of relationships.

It is important that, at the outset of every project, engineering and industrial engineering responsibilities be defined. The definition of these activities should include start and completion dates for each activity. These dates must then

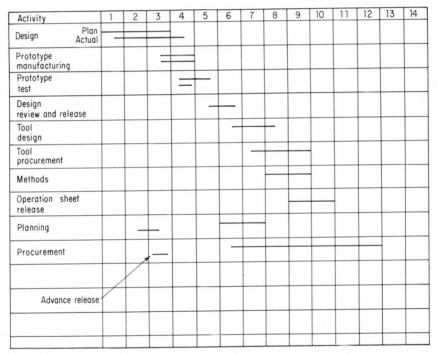

Fig. 7 Project schedule and progress report.

be monitored and shipping dates rescheduled. Far too often as a result of not defining the engineering activity and applying necessary follow-up, the manufacturing and procurement lead time are compressed to a point of excessive cost and almost impossible recovery-schedule conditions. Even a simple bar chart can be effective if properly administrated.

Use of PERT (program evaluation and review techniques), covered in detail elsewhere in this handbook, will provide effective control and monitoring of scheduled activity.

Figure 7 shows a simple bar-chart-type project schedule and progress report.

ENGINEERING-CHANGE SYSTEMS

Engineering changes to current models of product are essential to progress. The development and incorporation of changes in design can, and do, affect the marketability and profit contribution of a product. New products are very often old products which have been continually changed over the product life cycle.

Design changes and/or engineering documentation changes occur for many reasons, all of which, when properly administered, make for an improved product. Changes often reflect market or customer requirements and in general represent the manufacturer's concept of "a better mouse trap." Marketing and sales groups often play a major role in the announcement of major model changes which they frequently treat as a new-product release.

The finished-goods inventories in warehouses and on dealers' shelves can become obsolete upon the announcement of a major model change. Moreover, sudden dips in order entry of the current model could affect factory inventories severely and at great cost. Therefore, engineering change in many cases must be planned carefully, and inventory strategy, including factory inventories, must be considered in the timing of product-change release to the marketplace.

Frequently, slow-moving products can be "turned around" and sales improved through a model-design change. While sales and marketing groups are prone to quick announcements in such cases, inventory strategies must be carefully worked out. Detail factory-cost analysis must be made before we can "abandon ship."

Many changes in design are forced upon the factory, sometimes *before* and many times *after* a product has reached the marketplace. These changes are more plentiful in more complex products and in the early stages of production than in less complex products and in the later stages of production. Changes forced upon the factory are usually those dealing with function, customer specifications, and occasionally, safety. It is not uncommon in certain product lines to test and inspect prior to shipment and have the product reported as "dead on arrival" when examined by the customer. A minor change in dimensions or specifications makes the product functional again. These are the kinds of changes that are mandatory and must be incorporated at the production line at once.

Frequently, sales-oriented managers request that changes be incorporated into the product at once for reasons which are nonfunctional. "Competitive position" is the more frequently used term. This term may be translated to mean that, "Our competitor has better features in his similar but better model this year." We may also translate the term to mean that, "A change will give us something better than our competitor, and thus, better position in the marketplace."

Careful analysis of inventories, lead times, and production schedules must be made before making the decision to change. Usually this kind of decision must be made at a high level of management.

Many changes in decision are incorporated for purposes of cost reduction. These changes are very often initiated at the manufacturing stage and sometimes are initiated at the suggestion of a supplier or vendor.

There are still other changes which are considered minor or routine and may involve simple changes in hardware or drafting corrections, sometimes spelling corrections to a drawing or parts list. These may not affect "form, fit, or function" of the product and may not affect inventories. Therefore, simple changes of this type can be incorporated at once.

Regardless of the type or kind of change in design or engineering documentation, an orderly method or system of recording and communication must be developed and implemented. A method of change-analysis approval, incorporation, and control must be devised and this procedure adhered to. Means of monitoring and checking the system must be developed. Finally, the system must respond rapidly and must be capable of reflecting the good judgment of the people working with it.

An understanding of the impact of change is essential prior to development of engineering-change systems. Depending upon the kind and type of engineering change contemplated, varying effects upon the entire organization will take place. A whole series of events and activity resembling a chain reaction evolves.

The greatest impact of engineering change will be felt in the production and inventory control function. Determinations of inventory quantities and values including finished goods, work in process, finished parts, and raw materials must be made. Further determinations must be made as to disposition of parts changed or deleted.

Parts, materials, or assemblies must be scrapped or reworked. Therefore, production control must be certain that all parts, material, or assemblies to be changed or deleted are accumulated from various parts of the manufacturing departments, stores, and subcontractors. Rework or scrap orders must be published and distributed. Perhaps the most critical part of the entire procedure is to ascertain that all parts or subassemblies that are to be changed have, indeed, been accumulated and changed. Failure to accomplish this task effectively may result in old parts or subassemblies being assembled into the final assembly. If the nature of the change will permit the assembly of these parts, then the consequence may be a malfunction at test or inspection of the product.

Schedules must be redeveloped for current orders, and changes in customer or warehouse delivery must be communicated to the sales department. The redevelopment of new schedules will require research and follow-up of engineering, tooling, standards, methods, and procurement lead times.

Machine loads and schedules must be reviewed and adjusted. Rework orders will require new schedules.

Drawings, shop orders, and manufacturing specifications, including operation sheets, must be physically accumulated and destroyed or changed. Consideration for parts changed which are used on other products is an important one. Should the engineering change require a deletion of the part from one product and not from others, then the accumulation of physical parts is more complex. Then only a partial amount of the parts in the manufacturing area will have to be removed to stores or disposition areas. Should a change be required where rework can be performed, instead of scrap or deletion, then production control must be certain that the part number is changed. This kind of situation can be somewhat of a problem if the new part and the old part are similar, since there can be a good possibility of mixing the two parts in stores or in manufacturing areas of the plant. This problem can be avoided by good part-numbering and identification plans.

Production control must also make certain that the new change has been analyzed in inventory control. Frequently the addition of a part to a model will change the inventory class of the part. If as a result of a change the anticipated usage of a part is increased substantially, then the part may move from a C classification to a B classification, or from a B class to an A class. Likewise the deletion of a part from a model may change the class of the part from A to B or from B to C.

Where-used File. The utilization of the "where-used file" can simplify the determination of where a part is used. The where-used file is a file of all part numbers used in manufacturing. The end-product number is posted along with the quantity per unit for each product model. This file must be corrected or updated each time an engineering change is published.

The where-used file can be a computer-produced record or a simple card file organized by part-number numerical order. The use of the where-used file can eliminate the burdensome task of searching through all bills of material to determine the use of a part.

Finally, production control must determine the effectivity date of the change. The effectivity date is the date, lot number, or serial number that the change was incorporated into the product. The effectivity date is determined from schedule and lead-time information which has been confirmed by manufacturing, procurement, engineering, and industrial engineering. The effectivity date may then be transmitted to all concerned, including engineering, quality control, configuration control, and the customer through the sales department or contract administration. The effectivity date may sometimes be published and distributed to repair depots and/or service centers. Many government contracts make effectivity dates mandatory.

Although all changes do not have the same impact upon an organization, all changes will have some impact. The following is a checklist of items or documents that may be affected by engineering change. The checklist is not intended to be all-inclusive. It is prepared to demonstrate the volume of activities affected by engineering change in product design or documentation. The production control department should prepare its own checklist tailored to its own product line and organization.

CHECKLIST OF ITEMS AFFECTED BY ENGINEERING CHANGE:

I. Inventories
  A. Finished goods
    1. Warehouse
    2. Distribution
    3. Dealers
  B. Work in process
    1. Major assembly
    2. Subassembly
    3. Parts making
      a. Manufacturing
      b. Subcontract
  C. Finished parts
    1. Stores
    2. Assembly area
    3. Repair depots
    4. Warehouse
    5. Open orders with suppliers
  D. Raw materials
    1. Stores
    2. In process
    3. Open order with suppliers
II. Industrial engineering
  A. Tooling
    1. In process
    2. Design lead time
    3. Tool-making lead time
      a. Materials
        (1) Stores
        (2) Open order or lead time
  B. Operation sheets
  C. Time standards
  D. Audiovisual production aids
  E. Make or buy
  F. Assembly-kit lists

III. Production control
   A. Production schedules
   B. Lead time
      1. Engineering
      2. Tooling
      3. Methods, standards, kitting
      4. Procurement
   C. Shop and machine loading
   D. Interchangeability and substitutions
   E. Classification of inventory
   F. Effectivity date
   G. Disposition of goods deleted or changed
   H. Rework orders
   I. Disposition of drawings, shop orders, etc.
   J. Where-used file
   K. Inventory class
   L. Economic-order-quantity change
IV. Cost estimating and accounting
   A. Prices
      1. Customer open orders
      2. Open proposals
      3. Future proposals
   B. Cost
      1. Change of cost of product
      2. Obsolete parts and material
      3. Tooling
         a. Capital investment
      4. Scrap
   C. Engineering
      1. Design
      2. Drafting
      3. Clerical
V. Engineering
   A. Drawings
   B. Bills of material
   C. Parts lists
   D. Product specifications
   E. Where-used file
   F. Handbook and instruction manual
   G. Schematics
   H. Customer requirements
VI. Sales
   A. Catalogs
   B. Price lists
   C. Handbook and instruction manuals
   D. Spare-parts provisioning
   E. Service centers and repair depots
   F. Products in the field (customers, dealers, etc.)
   G. Customer requirements and specifications

It is obvious that engineering changes can indeed present a burdensome task to the entire manufacturing organization. There is always cost involved in design change, although the type and kind of change will dictate the order of magnitude. Therefore, the basic step in organizing for an engineering-change control system is to develop a strategy or policy for evaluation of changes.

POLICY DEVELOPMENT: Developing a policy will depend very largely upon specific product lines and methods of sales and distribution. The relationship of manufacturing the product and its final delivery to the customer is important to the policy. The answers to these questions will classify the problem to start with:

1. Is the product manufactured to stock?
2. Is the product distributed through warehouses and dealers?
3. Is the product manufactured to stock and shipped directly from factory to customer?
4. Is the product a standard item which is modified to customer specifications?
5. Is the product manufactured completely to customer specifications?
6. Is the product a commercial item or manufactured under government contract?

More than one of these questions can be answered affirmatively in most cases. Moreover, in most plants the questions above can be answered differently for various product lines. A standard engineering-change control system must apply to all product lines. Where a product is manufactured repetitively, regardless of whether or not the method is considered mass production, many changes can be incorporated in future production lots as opposed to the current production lot. The manufacturing group will hope for no changes at all during a production run. Although it is desirable to "freeze design" during a production run, it is not always attainable. Every effort must be made, however, to minimize changes during a production run. Mandatory changes are the only changes that should be incorporated during a production run. Mandatory changes are those required for function or customer requirement, which will sometimes include essential quality and reliability improvement. All other changes should be incorporated in subsequent production runs.

Engineering-change Considerations. Although we know that to "freeze design" can result in a "freeze in sales," we must be prepared to weigh the costs of change against market probabilities. The total impact of change upon the factory and customer deliveries must be measured.

These questions should be answered prior to approval of a change:

1. Is the change at all necessary?
2. What are the total costs of change?
3. Can the change be incorporated in the next or subsequent runs?
4. Will the change halt production? How long?
5. Will schedules and customer delivery be jeopardized?
6. Have inventory positions been analyzed?
7. If the change is requested for purposes of improving manufacturing methods, can the "ease of manufacture" counterbalance the costs of change and schedule jeopardy?

Engineering-change Classifications. Engineering changes should be classified or coded to indicate the extent and significance of change. An example of such a classification of change is shown below, using U.S. Air Force-Navy Aeronautical Bulletin 445.

CLASS I DEVIATION: Any change affecting fit, form, or function of an item or more specifically affecting one or more of the following configuration features:

1. Contract specifications, price, weight, delivery, or schedule
2. Contract reliability and/or maintainability
3. Interchangeability
4. Electrical interference to communications equipment or electromagnetic radiation hazards.
5. Safety, performance, or durability
6. AGE/SE, trainers, training devices, or GFE

CLASS II VARIATIONS: Any change not falling within the class I category. Changes may be further classified to indicate incorporation policy.

Example 1

Mandatory: Must be incorporated into current production run
Routine: Incorporate in the next production run

Example 2

Class A: Incorporate into all products including units in the field through Revision AA1
Class B: Incorporate into all unpacked units including units in assembly and subassembly
Class C: Incorporate into all unassembled units
Class D: Incorporate next time ordered

Example 3

Class A: Scrap
Class B: Rework
Class C: Use up current materials
Class D: Next time ordered

Design-review Procedure. Engineering design or documentation changes will occur more frequently in the early stages of production. Figure 8 shows a schematic of this procedure. It is not uncommon in some industries to anticipate these changes and to accept the problem. Many manufacturing companies are organized to maintain special areas where reasonably short runs are made as production pilot runs. During this stage of development, design and manufacturing methods can be tested and changes made at will. This pilot run can serve as the final design review before establishment of a base-line configuration. The policy provides for any change to be made during the pilot production run which culminates in a complete design review and implementation of all changes. This point is frequently referred to as "base-line design" or "configuration." After the establishment of base-line design only mandatory changes affecting function and/or customer requirements may be incorporated.

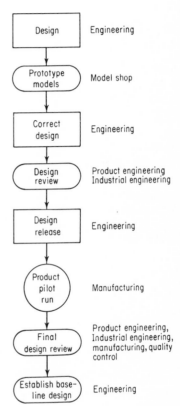

Fig. 8 Pilot run and final-design review procedure.

Engineering changes can be requested from any department within the company and frequently from suppliers or vendors. The request for change is usually a printed form which also serves as an engineering-change notice when properly approved. Engineering-change requests (ECR) are sometimes referred to as "engineering-change proposals" (ECP). Engineering-change notices (ECN) are sometimes referred to as "engineering-change order" (ECO) or "engineering-change authority" (ECA).

An ECR (request) must have proper approvals and then an ECN (notice) is initiated. Frequently the same form with multicopies is used as the ECR and converted upon approval to an ECN. ECNs and ECRs must be numbered and logged for control. Should a request be rejected for any reason, the requester will be notified and given an opportunity to represent his request at a higher level of management.

Figure 9 illustrates the format for a multipart ECO system, while Fig. 10

can be used both as an ECR and subsequently as an ECN. Figure 11 is an engineering authorization which is used for new-product release and engineering-change order (ECO).

Sample Engineering-change Procedure (Abbreviated)

1. Purpose: To provide a procedure for processing and controlling engineering changes.
2. Scope: This procedure applies to all engineering changes and includes the procedure for requesting engineering changes.
3. Definitions:
   A. *Document* is any drawing, parts list, or product specification used to define a product.
   B. *Deviation Class I change* is any change affecting fit, form, or function specifically affecting one or more of the following configuration features:
      (1) Specifications, price, weight delivery, or schedule
      (2) Reliability and/or maintainability
      (3) Interchangeability
      (4) Safety, performance, or durability
   C. *Variation Class II changes* are all other changes not classified as Class I.

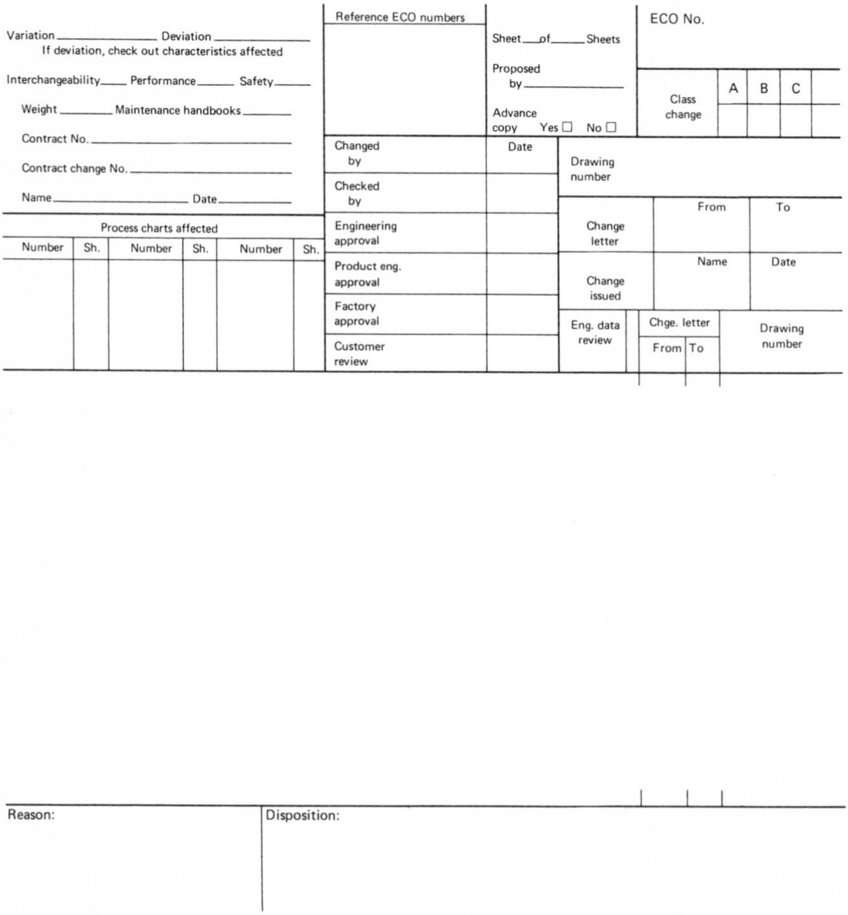

Fig. 9 Multipart ECO system.

☐ Engineering change request
☐ Engineering change notice
   CM No. _____
   Engineering change No. _____
   Project No. _____
   Sheet ____ of ____

☐ Class I (deviation)
☐ Class II (variation)

Dwg. No.

Drawing No. _____ Unit No. _____ Present revision _____

Rev.

Title _____

Reason for change	Type of Change	Effectivity	Material disposition
☐ Error	☐ Mandatory	☐ Immediate	☐ None
☐ Additional information	☐ Elective	☐ Next time ordered	☐ Use up stock
☐ Design improvement	☐ Routine	☐ (See remarks)	☐ Order as required
☐ Vendor required	☐ Emergency		☐ Scrap
☐ Customer required			☐ Rework
☐ Latest process			☐ Use elsewhere
☐ Clarification			☐ (See remarks)
☐ Cost reduction			
☐ (See remarks)			

Description of change   From   To

Remarks

Change requested by _____

Date originated _____

Effective date _____

Change rejected by _____

Reason _____

_____

Approved by	Date
Department head	
Project engineer	
Manufacturing engineer	
Director of engineering	
Quality control	
Government agency	

Draftsman _____ Drafting supervisor _____ Checker _____
Date _____ Date _____ Date _____

Fig. 10 ECR, ECN.

D. *Mandatory changes* are those necessary to the function and operation of the product or specifically required by the customer. Mandatory changes must be incorporated in current production runs.

E. *Routine changes* are those that do not affect function or operation necessarily and can be incorporated in the next or subsequent production runs. These changes can include those intended for cost reduction, product improvement, ease of manufacture, and quality improvement, etc.

F. *Engineering-change request* (ECR) is the form used for officially requesting a change.

G. *Engineering-change notice* (ECN) is the authorization for changing engineering documents.

4. ECR
   A. Any department may initiate an engineering-change request. The ECR form
      must be filled out.
      1. Drawing number
      2. Title
      3. Reason for change
      4. Effectivity date
      5. Sign

Used on:	Drawing No._____
	Rev_____
Title:	

DESIGN ENGINEERING

1. Classification

    ☐ Class I   ☐ New part   ☐ New assemblies
    ☐ Class II - Revision requiring no disposition of parts or assemblies
    ☐ Class III - Change to be made as soon as practical
            ☐ Balancing of parts required
    ☐ Class IV - Change to be effective immediately
           Completed parts   Completed assemblies

           ☐ Use as is   ☐ Use as is
           ☐ Alter or scrap   ☐ Alter or scrap

2. The following parts are affected by the above change:

   _____   _____   _____   _____   _____

3. Type of change   (Give description and reason of change, special instructions, etc.)
           ☐ Design   ☐ Cost reduction
           ☐ Shop request   ☐ Sales request   S.O._____

      Description:_____

      Reason: _____

Prepared by_____ Date_____ Approved by_____ Date_____

PRODUCTION ENGINEER

1. Estimated monthly requirement _____

2. Tooling information
    ☐ Tooling required   ☐ New   ☐ Alteration
    ☐ Tooling is available   ☐ Temporary   ☐ Permanent
    ☐ Tooling is not required
    Remarks:_____

                Approved by_____ Date_____

METHODS DEPARTMENT

1. Source   5.   Special instructions
    ☐ Purchase part
    ☐ Shop part
2. Required tools
    ☐ Alteration   Date available_____
    ☐ New   Date available_____
3. Stock status
    Completed parts
    ☐ Use as is
    ☐ Alter or scrap
    Completed assemblies
    ☐ Use as is
    ☐ Alter or scrap
4. Material
    ☐ Standard
    ☐ Special

              Prepared by:_____
                  Date:_____

Fig. 11 Engineering authorization for production release.

B. Department head must approve and sign ECR.

C. Forward ECR to change control administrator (CCA).

D. The control administrator will check the ECR and classify the change.

E. The ECR shall be forwarded to the project engineer for disposition.

   1. If the request is rejected, the ECR with the engineer's reason for rejection will be returned to the requester via the change control administrator.

   2. If the request is approved, copies of the ECR are distributed to industrial engineering, production and inventory control, quality control, and the CCA.

F. Industrial engineering will review the ECR and evaluate costs, schedules, and technical feasibility. Considerations for cost shall include capital investment required, tooling, facility change, methods, etc. These costs and considerations shall be defined and recommendations indicated.

   1. Copies of the ECR shall be forwarded to the CCA and the cost accounting and cost estimating group.

G. Production and inventory control will review the ECR and evaluate costs, schedules, and lead times. Cost considerations will include all inventories affected. Effect of change upon current schedules will be evaluated and effectivity dates developed. All considerations and recommendations will be indicated and copies forwarded to the CCA and the cost accounting and estimating.

H. Quality control will review the ECR and evaluate costs, schedules, and quality considerations. Recommendations will be indicated and copies forwarded to the CCA and the cost accounting and cost estimating group.

I. Cost accounting and cost estimating will review ECR's received from industrial engineering, production and inventory control and quality control and will prepare a report and recommendation considering total cost of change. Cost consideration will include all inventories, capital investment, tooling, etc. The summary report will reflect new pricing and consideration for open orders and proposals and will be forwarded to the engineering department with copies of ECR from industrial engineering, quality control, and production and inventory control.

J. The engineering department will evaluate the cost and pricing reports along with recommendations from quality control, production and inventory control, and industrial engineering and will approve or reject the ECR.

   1. The controller and marketing department will be consulted.

   2. If the request is now rejected, the requester will also be so advised.

K. Engineering will assign an ECN number to the ECR and forward to the CCA.

L. The CCA will record the ECN number and release to drafting and engineering for processing.

   1. Copies of ECNs will be distributed to departments concerned (production control, manufacturing inspection, quality control, engineering, industrial engineering, etc.).

5. ECN

A. Production and inventory control upon receipt of the ECN will:

   1. Issue appropriate "stop-work orders."

   2. Physically accumulate parts-materials drawing-shop orders, assembly-work orders for scrap rework, or other dispositions.

   3. Prepare inventory reports for accounting "write off."

   4. Place new orders or rework orders for items changed.

   5. Determine availability schedules for materials components, etc.

   6. Develop schedules and effectivity dates (adjust master schedules).

   7. Communicate dates to sales.

   8. Determine extent of tooling changes and obtain schedules.

   9. Provide new machine loads as required.

   10. Adjust inventory records including planned available balances.

   11. Adjust where-used file.

   12. Adjust interchangeability and substitution files.

   13. Adjust inventory classification files.

   14. Adjust EOQ determinations.

   15. Establish follow-up dispatch plans.

B. Industrial engineering upon receipt of the ECN will:

   1. Evaluate tool changes and establish tool schedules.

2. Prepare necessary tool "stop-work orders."
3. Design new tools or changes.
4. Evaluate, change, or establish new methods and operation sheets.
5. Evaluate time-standard changes and implement new standards as required.
6. Determine make-or-buy policy as required.

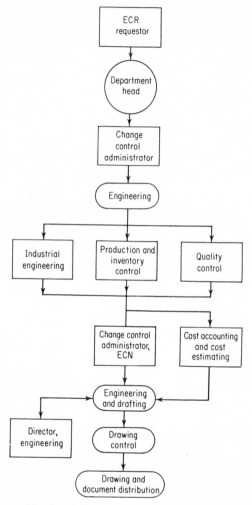

Fig. 12 Simplified flow chart, engineering-change system.

7. Review and correct assembly-kit lists.
8. Change audio-visual aids as required.

PRINT-CONTROL SYSTEMS AND DATA CONTROL

Control of engineering-print files is seldom a production control responsibility. However, it is extremely important to production control that the integrity of these files be maintained. Obviously, the higher the incidence of engineering change in a company, the more the maintenance of drawing files is a problem.

Most companies operate under one of two basic philosophies of making engineering prints available for manufacturing:

1. One centralized print file exists for the entire company. As new shop orders are prepared and released to manufacture, part, or assembly items, the engineering department runs off a new copy of the latest revision of the print from the tracing in the engineering file. Thus, each shop order has new drawings. After the completion of each order, the old drawings are destroyed.

2. A centralized file is maintained by engineering, but there are one or more shop files (maintained either by engineering or shop clerical personnel). As revisions are made to the drawings, these are filed in the shop print files. New drawings are not issued with each order.

Production control must assure itself that manufacturing personnel do in fact get current drawings in order to avoid costly rework, obsolescence, and schedule delays.

"Data control" is the term commonly associated with careful auditing of input and other file data used in the production control system. The responsibility for editing this data will vary. The requirement for maximum accuracy and timely receipt of the transaction and file data cannot be overemphasized.

In many companies using automatic or electronic data processing equipment, the production control organization has instituted a data-control function. The prime purpose of data control is to coordinate with engineering and industrial engineering in the release and revision of product-oriented data (bills of material) used in the structuring of product files of static data.

Regardless of the organizational group functionally responsible for data control and audit, the production control department must play the role of "devils advocate" in order to fulfill its basic mission.

VALUE ANALYSIS AND ITS IMPORTANCE TO PRODUCTION CONTROL

Value analysis or value engineering is a relatively new management strategy. The technique was conceived and formalized by Lawrence D. Miles in the late 1940s as part of an operations-research assignment at General Electric in Schenectady. Since its introduction, its techniques have been developed, expanded, and refined, making it a popular management tool.

The success of value analysis (VA) or value engineering (VE) becomes apparent when it is recognized that:

1. Most major companies, the federal government, and more than a dozen states have active and formal programs with VA or VE departments and staffs.

2. The Society of American Value Engineers (SAVE) has grown substantially since its founding and has a membership of 2,500 engineers and analysts.

3. The Department of Defense regularly includes payment and bonus provisions in all major contracts for value-engineering effort.

4. The strategy is being employed in Europe and Asia.

What Is Value Analysis or Value Engineering? The terms are frequently used synonymously; however, "value engineering" generally refers to the broad field because those engaged in the activity are frequently engineers. The term "value analysis" refers to the strategy or techniques employed.

The "analysis technique" may be defined simply as a formal strategy which identifies unnecessary costs that do not add value and which develops equivalent performance with lower cost.

Those not familiar with value engineering frequently think of the technique as a glamorized type of cost reduction. The strategy does, in fact, result in major cost reductions but differs substantially from typical cost-reduction programs. Traditional cost-reduction and work-simplification programs are company oriented and focus on method and process to achieve economy of manufacture. Value engineering is customer oriented and considers the basic requirements for the product or service. Further, it identifies costs that do not contribute quality or life to the product or process and stimulates design as well as method and process changes.

Function and Value. Consider a typical tie clasp in terms of value, function, and cost. The clasp was probably purchased for approximately $1.00 and serves the purpose or function of holding one's tie in place. A paper clip will perform the same "hold tie" function at a cost of one penny. The difference in cost (99 cents) is what is paid for a secondary function of appearance. The 1-cent cost for a paper clip represents "use value." It is based on the performance or service that is performed for the function of holding one's tie. The 99 cents extra for the clasp represents "esteem value." It is based on the aesthetic or appearance functions of the clasp. We make many similar purchases in our lives and never give them much thought; however, in industry primary function and use value become important. It is not desirable to pay for unnecessary functions that produce high cost and low use value. Value-engineering techniques require that functions, both primary and secondary, be isolated, enabling the analyst to seek more cost-effective designs or services.

Value-engineering changes do not degrade the product. Many changes result in improved product-quality performance and/or service. A study conducted by the American Ordinance Association in 1963 on a sampling of over a 100 value-engineering-change proposals indicated that the average VE change improves performance. Among the factors evaluated were reliability, maintainability, quality, human factors, weight, parts availability, etc.

Reasons for Poor Value. Whenever we or our customers pay for features, appearance items, or services that are not required, we are not getting the best value. There are many reasons for poor value, including:

1. *Habits and Attitudes.* We are indeed creatures of habit and automatically for many reasons tend to reject change.

2. *Lack of Time.* While a crash program may be justified, the decisions or designs made, or the materials used, frequently reflect the lack of time. Unfortunately, it may later be impractical or too costly to correct poor judgments.

3. *Fear of Personal Loss.* Often decisions are based on what is expected and not what is right for the product, customer, or plant.

4. *Lack of Ideas.* Frequently, a time-tested method, design, or process is considered without thought; newer, better technologies are not given consideration.

5. *Wrong Beliefs.* People do not always know the capabilities of a material, product, technique, or process. On the basis of a single bad experience, we may erroneously reject an idea or application that is much more cost effective.

6. *Lack of Information.* As a result of poor communication or because of habits or attitudes, the decision makers are not always given the information to make the best decision.

The VE Job Plan. The VE approach uses a formal definitive job plan. The job plan follows the patterns of problem solving that are frequently referred to as the "scientific method." Essentially, information is obtained, solutions are developed, tested, and refined, until a selection is made or an action is taken.

Most companies having VE programs use either a five- or six-phase value-analysis job plan. There are five phases in the Philco-Ford job plan. These include information, speculation, evaluation, planning, and reporting phases.

Some companies expand the first phase into a preparation and information phase, or expand the last phase into reporting and execution phases, and have a six-phase job plan. It is necessary that whenever a value analysis is performed by an individual or team, the job plan be followed in detail if maximum results are to be obtained.

1. *Information Phase.* This is the phase when all facts concerning the product or service must be obtained. During this phase, key questions must be asked and answered, such as: "What is it? What does it do? What does it cost?" It is necessary to completely understand as much about the product, part, or process as possible. In particular, emphasis should be placed on the functions intended and required for the product or service and functions for the various subparts or services.

2. *Speculation Phase.* This is perhaps one of the most interesting phases for those performing the analysis. The analysts attempt to brainstorm other approaches to satisfy the function at lower cost.

3. *Evaluation Phase.* This phase is the screening phase, the ideas conceived in the speculation phase are expanded upon and improved. It is during this phase that specialists are used to provide information and assistance. Vendors are called upon to review ideas and present new or revised concepts.

4. *Planning Phase.* This is the phase to develop final cost data, to finalize alternatives, and to make final decisions on the alternatives. It is during this phase that costs are reviewed and savings are calculated.

5. *Reporting Phase.* This is the selling phase, and one of the hardest. It is necessary that the results of the analysis be clearly presented to the decision makers for their understanding and approval. Special preprinted forms may be used to assist both those making the evaluation and those approving it. If the reporting phase has been conducted properly, and those at the working level and line jobs are sold on the idea, implementation follows easily.

VA is not limited primarily to fabricated- or assembled-item redesign. Many outstanding savings are made with applications of the technique in other areas. The summary below illustrates the flexibility and scope of the technique.

It should be noted that normal cost reduction would not have uncovered all the savings that were developed by using the value-analysis strategy. In each case, when function was emphasized, the range of possible solutions was substantially broadened, allowing the analyst to develop solutions that were not only unique but resulted in substantial cost savings and good value.

Example 1
Problem: Make design changes to reduce the construction cost on a large garage for a trucking firm.
Function: Protect trucks, later changed to park trucks.
General Explanations and Solutions: Company management had plans drawn to construct a large garage complex for its truck fleet. The value analyst pointed out that trucks were on the road an average of 20 out of 24 hours. What was really required was a large parking area and a small maintenance building.

Example 2
Problem: Reduce the number of guards by combining entrances to classified areas.
Function: Monitor doors.
General Explanations and Solutions: It was impossible to reduce the number of entrances to the classified areas. However, it was found that each guard could monitor and control two entrance doors by using closed circuit TV and electric door locks.

Example 3
Problem: Reduce the manufacturing cost of gasoline tanks for landing craft.
Function: Hold gasoline.
General Explanations and Solutions: The initial design was inherently very costly. It

was discovered that standard 55-gallon steel drums could be easily modified, coated, and used.

Example 4

Problem: Reduce the manufacturing cost of an oil dipstick.

Function: Measure oil.

General Explanations and Solutions: It was discovered that a standard dipstick that was produced in large volume could be purchased and used. The use of standard hardware always results in substantial cost reductions.

Functions of a VE Department. A value engineering department, regardless of size, must provide the following functions in order to be effective:

1. Provide training for personnel in all departments, and particularly the engineering, manufacturing, and materials operations.

2. Install, monitor, and publicize plant-wide programs that ensure participation and activity at all levels. In order to maintain plant-wide interest, it is necessary that individual and department results be publicized. In some plants, department goals are established and individual or group awards given for outstanding results.

3. Lead VA reviews on special projects, as well as programs that need special boosts to achieve cost targets. Frequently, because of competition or the opportunity for potential business, a special effort is made to reduce the cost or improve the performance of a product. In order to accomplish this, teams are organized to perform value-analysis studies on the product, assemblies, and parts.

4. It is also desirable that special support be provided to the purchasing department to assist vendors in establishing programs.

5. In industries engaged in contracts with the Department of Defense, the VE or VA department will normally have a key role in developing VA proposals as well as processing VA studies.

How Training Programs Are Conducted. VE training programs can play a major role in improving a company's competitive position by getting the operating departments and individuals in the departments to:

1. Think in terms of function and value.

2. Be aware of VA techniques that result in improving product cost.

In order to accomplish this training, special value-engineering seminars are held with personnel at all levels. The engineering (design, manufacturing, process, etc.), as well as procurement and manufacturing departments are heavily represented at the sessions. Several types of programs are conducted, from short (several hours to one day) orientation sessions for the management levels to one- to three-week working-training sessions for the worker levels. An active VE or VA department would attempt to train at least 10 percent of the professional work force each year.

The working-training programs are split into lectures and laboratory sessions, with considerable emphasis on group participation. During the laboratory phases, the class is separated into small four- to six-man teams. The teams, then working with different hardware items that were produced in the plant, are led through the five- or six-step VA job plan. The various phases are scheduled to permit the presentation phase to be the concluding session of the training program.

It can be expected that savings developed as a result of the analysis performed during the training program will cover the cost of the training session. This includes the instructor's and participants' salaries, as well as miscellaneous material costs associated with a program of this type.

Reducing the Cost of Change. In any cost-reduction computation, implementation costs must be considered. In addition to inventory, tooling, material, and equipment costs, engineering, drafting, and testing costs are generally incurred whenever design or process changes are made. Frequently, these implementation costs are so high that excellent ideas must be abandoned. In order to minimize this, it is desirable that value-engineering effort be applied during the early stages of any design program. Figure 13 illustrates the effect of savings and implementation costs.

Special Value-engineering Techniques. A successful value-analysis effort will require the application of several VA techniques. An experienced analyst will be able to select and apply those techniques that will produce good results. Inexperienced analysts will also produce good savings but will have to work harder in order to discern the appropriate technique for the circumstances. The most important techniques that are employed include:

1. *Evaluation by Comparison.* The analyst compares the cost of a device or service with costs of similar commonplace items or services. Comparisons of this type highlight high-cost items and indicate alternative approaches. As an example, the high cost of special latches on electronic enclosures when compared to kitchen-cabinet hardware has stimulated many design changes.

2. *ABC Cost-visability Technique.* When analyzing components that make up a device or looking at annual costs, the ABC inventory control technique is employed. In order to conserve value-engineering effort, summaries of the various component or service costs that identify the areas of high total cost (unit cost multiplied by usage) are made. The largest potential savings are obviously in the high-cost areas. These are the areas on which the analyst will obviously want to concentrate his efforts for maximum results.

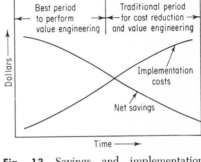

Fig. 13 Savings and implementation costs. (Note: Continuous changes in design, material, and process technologies will result in the net-savings curve becoming asymptotic.)

3. *Checklist Technique.* Value analysts and departments frequently utilize checklists during several phases of the job plan. These lists stimulate thought and ensure thoroughness. During the information phase, a list that assists the analyst in obtaining all the pertinent facts concerning the product is used. Typical questions include those relative to the design, materials used, function of product and subparts, manufacturing techniques used, special requirements, etc. During the speculation phase, an idea-stimulation listing is frequently used by the analysts to develop alternative approaches.

4. *Use of Industry Specialists.* It is sometimes very desirable and necessary to consult with industry specialists, particularly during the evaluation and planning phases of the job plan. While a good analyst is well versed in design and manufacturing technologies, he is not as technically proficient as an engineer who has devoted several years to problem solving and working in the technology. Therefore, when a new approach is to be considered, it is foolhardy to rely on anything less than expert advice and assistance.

5. *Brainstorming.* This technique produces very unique, as well as exceptionally large, cost reductions because it encourages the analysts to consider many

alternative solutions. The technique requires that those involved collectively make a listing of possible solutions or alternatives. Initially, no attempt is made to evaluate ideas, but rather each idea is used to stimulate others until perhaps 50 or 60 ideas have been listed. At that point, all the ideas are reviewed and sorted. Those with the greatest potential are given further consideration.

6. *Tolerance and Finish Review.* It is very productive to review tolerance and finish requirements on a product and its subparts. Frequently, in order to be safe, the engineer will automatically specify unrealistically tight tolerances or machined finishes that are unnecessary. In other instances, plating and/or surface preparation and painting requirements are found to be excessive or unrealistic for the application. Reductions in tolerance and finish requirements frequently reduce product costs by as much as 25 percent.

7. *Vendor-assistance Requests.* An effective way to reduce vendor costs is to allow each vendor to critique your product designs. Who can better suggest design changes to reduce the cost of a casting or molded product than the vendor? He is aware of the yield percentages and finishing costs associated with the design. Frequently it is possible to make simple changes that drastically reduce the cost and have no effect on the part's function. Whenever a product is reviewed, the vendors that make the major components should be requested to critique the designs for costs reduction.

8. *Consideration of Supplier's Standards.* A standard product or even a modified standard is much less costly than a special design. Whenever a product uses special screws, nuts, fasteners, knobs, etc., special emphasis should be placed on finding standard alternatives. Standard hardware is inherently less costly because of the volume production.

The Value-engineering Organization. A typical value-engineering organization will consist of a supervisor or manager and three or four engineers or analysts. However, depending on company size, successful VE operations may be as small as one man working part time. One well-qualified engineer will be more effective than several inexperienced men. Rarely are there more than 10 engineers or analysts in a department.

Conclusions and Relationship to Production Control. Value engineering is an effective strategy that can provide significant real savings with minor expenditures. The proper use of its techniques results in the elimination of unnecessary costs and ultimate improvement in a company's competitive position.

Most VE or VA departments report ratios of annual department budgets to implemented savings of 10:1 to 15:1. As with any technique or strategy, it is necessary that competent professionals be trained and qualified in its use.

In typical business operations the production control department will not be called upon to organize or administer a value-engineering program. Often materials managers or production control managers will be requested to supply members of specific VA task groups. Materials managers should constantly strive to get their purchasing departments to insist upon vendor VE projects.

Value engineering can greatly reduce the costs of manufacturing or procuring an item, thus leading to reduced investment in finished-stock and/or work-in-process inventories. In addition, lead time often can be substantially cut.

Value engineering is an exciting technique which can greatly benefit the production and inventory control manager in the performance of his job.

STANDARDIZATION PROGRAMS

The production control manager can benefit from product- and part-standardization programs in the same fashion as from a value-engineering program.

Often an invaluable service can be provided for design engineering departments by the production control department working in conjunction with the data processing department. By the development of bill-of-material master files, a where-used report can be prepared. This analysis can be used in conjunction with a report which is called the "part or product listing by commodity group" with as many logical subgroupings as the data will readily facilitate.

These two reports will serve as the media from which a standardization program can begin. It is not uncommon, for example, to find that due to the lack of a disciplined part-number assignment system, the lack of a where-used file, and the lack of part listings by commodity group, the design engineers in a company are using 16 types of $\frac{1}{4}$-inch lockwashers or 18 types of a resistor with the same value.

The impact of a standardization program on the inventory, procurement, and product costs can be most significant.

PART-NUMBERING SYSTEMS

As volumes of communication grow and with the ever-increasing complexity of reporting business activities, the importance of proper part numbering or coding is great.

The choice of the proper part-numbering system involves not only coding for identifying the item, but also coding to facilitate automatic or electronic data processing operations which, in turn, will prepare required reports.

Part numbering is an extremely complex task which, for successful completion, demands full cognizance of the factors involved. Everyone in business today appears to have an opinion on part numbering; all too often these opinions are erroneous and uninformed.

Typically, part numbering should take into consideration the following elements:

1. Expandability of categories
2. Flexibility for new items in the file
3. Ability to be sorted into required categories or field
4. Minimum number of characters consistent with the overall requirements
5. Easy assignment (convenience)

There is tremendous reliance on proper part-numbering systems in the automatic data processing groups, where in many cases their overall operating effectiveness can be directly related to good or bad part-numbering systems. Any system which has been allowed to degenerate to being a combination of several systems, or a significant system which has been allowed to outgrow its significance, or any system which is controlled by fuzzy procedures can tend to be inefficient and extremely costly. This is true not only from the standpoint of wasted effort on the part of operating personnel, but also because of the ever-present possibility of misinterpretation which leads to duplicate and/or wrong materials being procured, manufactured, or shipped. Estimates have been made that in some large organizations the correction of a single part number throughout the corporate structure, when an error has been made, can rise well above the $10,000 level. Obviously it pays to establish and strictly maintain a part-numbering system.

Types of Part-numbering Systems. SIGNIFICANT: All characters in the numbering system represent a dimension, weight, or any other factor. (See Fig. 14.)

SEMISIGNIFICANT: Some of the fields in the numbering system represent a group or another factor. (See Fig. 15.)

NONSIGNIFICANT: None of the numbers assigned have any significance. This is sometimes called the "sequence method" of part numbering. There is no classification of groups. (See Fig. 16.)

The selection of a numbering system is governed primarily by the type and variety of products manufactured by the organization employing the system. In some organizations where there is a limited product line, or where classification is vital, the use of a fully significant numbering system might well be practical. As an example, a company that produces tubing only could well allow two or three digits to represent the material, and the remaining portion of the part number to indicate various inside and outside diameters. To further expand on this, it would even be possible to add several more digits to denote the length of the item.

Still working with the example above, the tubing manufacturer if he expands his product line into various shapes such as squares, oblongs, rods, and perhaps

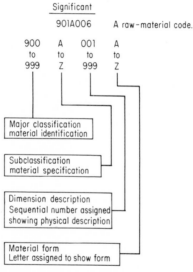

Fig. 14 Significant-code systems. In this code, each of the four fields of data is meaningful and provides a reference for item analysis.

adds various threading or punchings, it is easy to see how these unforeseen conditions could possibly strain even the best significant part-numbering system.

Many users of significant systems further complicate their use by inserting alphabetic characters to expand the range of what can be represented. This leads to a whole new variety of problems, the most serious of which is the extreme difficulty of communicating the proper character orally. How many times have each of us in telephone conversations had to elaborate and repeat, trying to understand or make understood the characters E, B, D, and T. It is also very easy to mistake characters or numbers and/or other letters in hand-written forms or on fuzzy or smudged carbon on shop work papers. Most manufacturers find the rigidity and limits imposed by the significant system to be unacceptable, and therefore, the nonsignificant types of systems are more commonplace.

Listed below are five points that show the practicality of using a nonsignificant system:

1. A nonsignificant system functions independently of classifications and standards. Any or all may be updated, revised, or changed, as circumstances dictate.

2. A nonsignificant numbering system, of any number of digits, can identify more parts with more flexibility than any significant system.

3. A single nonsignificant system can cover all types of numbering, including standard hardware and all product classes, where a significant system could possibly cause dual systems and/or repetition.

4. Sheer volume alone defeats the one prime advantage of a significant system, which would be operating people memorizing the meanings of the part numbers.

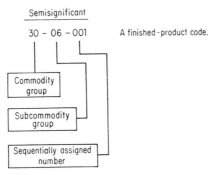

Fig. 15 Semisignificant code. In this semisignificant product code, there are three fields of data. Some 60 commodity numbers were assigned to the products with up to 99 possible subgroupings within each commodity group. Numbers are assigned sequentially to individual items within each subcommodity group.

5. A nonsignificant system cannot run out of numbers or break down through diversification of new products, sizes, finishes, materials, etc.

Before further discussing a totally nonsignificant system, we should look at a compromise where we can make use of a small portion of a significant system. If only one, two, or three digits of a part number are made significant, we would not totally destroy the five points of a nonsignificant system, and by representing such things as major product lines and/or classes of products we can eliminate additional labor of preparing summaries and/or segregating special areas.

Nonsignificant

86007   A finished-part code

Fig. 16 Nonsignificant code. In this coding system as each new item is catalogued, the next number sequentially is assigned. There is no ability to analyze or sort the items.

In utilizing the semisignificant approach we shall have to expand what is basically a nonsignificant number by the additional semisignificant digits, but often this cost is outweighed by its usefulness and better acceptance of the operating people to this type of a system. Care must be taken that when introducing a limited amount of significants into a system, to cater to a particular need, it does not open the door to a rash of additional suffixes, prefixes, letters, etc., which if adopted would tend to contradict its worth and would lead right back to an unwieldy significant number with all its inherent deficiencies.

Once a particular part-numbering system is chosen, care should be taken that the procedures governing its use are clear and concise and enforced. The administration of the system should rest with one group to preclude any chance of error. If the need arises for assignment of part numbers at remote locations, the administrating group could assign a block, insisting upon proper feedback for the maintenance of the central control.

In summation regarding part-numbering systems and their control, before any decisions are made establishing a system, use a checklist and/or decision table containing such information as answers to the following:

1. Is a part-number system needed?
2. Why?
3. What are the objectives?
4. What are the steps of structuring to reach the objectives?
5. Will it serve all areas?
6. Is it manageable?
7. Is it documented?
8. Has responsibility for its performance been delegated?

SUMMARY

The adequacy of product and process definition is a vital factor in the operation of a production control system. The production control department does not in either case create the basic data, but cannot successfully fulfill its mission without the information.

It is necessary for production control to coordinate and/or establish the scheduling of new-product releases and to insist on a discipline system for engineering changes.

A harmonious and close-working relationship is required with not only engineering and industrial engineering but also the manufacturing function in order to achieve required customer-service levels.

Chapter **6**

Facilities for Production

EDITOR:

William E. Hoffman *Editor, Tooling and Production Magazine, Cleveland, Ohio*

CONTRIBUTORS:

Walter A. Sadowsky *Technical Editor, Tooling and Production Magazine, Cleveland, Ohio*

Edwin Schies *Director, Production Control, Victor Business Machines Group, Chicago, Illinois*

CONTENTS

ORGANIZATION AND MANAGEMENT
OF FACTORY FACILITIES

Determination of machining operations should be made to produce most efficient flow of work. While sequential descriptions may be similar for different plants, production methods can vary widely. It depends on the size of the company (capital available) and/or production quantities required. However, any plant involved with long production runs should work toward an automation system.

Work Flow Between Operations. DEPARTMENTAL FLOW: Small plants equipped only with standard machines usually segregate their machinery in departments by type of process performed. Workpieces are routed from the drilling department to the lathe department, to the grinder department, etc. This system permits great flexibility where many different products are involved. Work flow is not apt to be held up in case of breakdown in any machine because the operation may be easily shifted to another machine.

Since related machines are located in the same area, duplication of tooling is greatly reduced. Ready accessibility of tooling permits faster setups, and specialization of work gives operators and setup men higher skills on particular machines. Close proximity of similar machines results in greater work-handling efficiency when secondary operations are required.

Toolroom or research and development work should never be mixed with production jobs. A slowed-down production line can be very costly. However, experimental or short-run precision work may be done in the toolroom to take advantage of operator skill and machine tool quality.

IN-LINE PRODUCTION: One-of-a-kind or family parts may be run on special and standard machines that are "permanently" set up. The special may consist of a single, long transfer line (Fig. 1) on which parts are loaded in a row. Individual machine units are located on one or both sides of the line, and they

Fig. 1 Transfer machine. Automobile cylinder blocks are machined on this 25-station Greenlee automatic transfer machine.

perform many operations as the parts are automatically conveyed from station to station. Machining of automobile cylinder blocks is an example.

Standard machines may be laid out in line to perform a large variety of operations by setting them in proper sequence. Operations may start with stamping and progress through stages of welding, assembly, and painting. Manufacturing of refrigerators is one example.

SINGLE UNIT: SEVERAL FUNCTIONS: Several operations may be combined into one compact machine such as an indexing machine or a numerically controlled (NC) machining center. While the indexing machine is intended for high production machining of same or similar parts, the NC machine's purpose is to machine virtually any part in small production lots.

Production costs are lowered because both machines take the place of several machines. Some reasons for lowered costs are that less facility space is required, only one operator is needed instead of several, and there are fewer inspection points.

How to Quickly Get into Production. Preparation is the key to quickly getting into production. It should begin when justification for the new machine has been made or upon receipt of the work order.

The process engineering department is responsible for planning manufacturing procedures. It determines operation sequence and provides route sheets for the machine shop. Route sheets give all machining data including type of tooling to use for the specific job.

Facilities preparation involves making room for the equipment in the proper space, possibly constructing a base, and arranging for electrical and other utility installation. Supervisory personnel in the maintenance department should be notified of changes well in advance so they can order necessary materials.

Backup equipment, such as modern cutting tools, toolholders, jigs, fixtures, and inspection devices, should be made or purchased in time to permit checking of all tools and devices before going into production.

The personnel department should be alerted so that it can furnish a qualified operator for the new machine. Whether he is a new man or a present employee, chances are that he will need some instruction in setup and operation. Prior training at the builder's plant would be most advisable in some situations because the operator could go right into production after the installation of the machine.

Raw stock should be made available before delivery of the machine to ensure having proper material to work with. If stock will consist of new forgings or castings, sufficient time should be allowed to make dies and patterns. These have to be checked out. And again, if the workpiece is new, sample parts should be made on other available equipment so that they can be quality-approved before the machine is installed.

If the delivery schedule on the parts is tight, it might be a good idea to make a short production run of the parts on other available equipment so that they can be quality-approved before the machine is installed. This might also be a good idea to get a head start while setting up the new machine. If it is not possible to make the parts except with the incoming machine, the machine's builder may be requested to make a short production run before delivery of the machine. This also serves to check that the machine will function as required, and it will provide a fully equipped unit ready to go into production on delivery.

Scheduling for Manufacturing Facilities. Many small plants start in business without a formal scheduling program. Orders are processed to the machine shop merely by sending a part print to the foreman. The number of pieces required are scrawled on the print, or sometimes are written on an accompanying order sheet. It doesn't take days or weeks for paper work or other communications to travel from office to office because the owner himself usually delivers the order to the shop. When jobs pile up, the small flexible work force is put on overtime.

Efficiency in such a plant is high. It could operate in this manner indefinitely as long as it remained small and it didn't bite off more than it could chew. However, once it expands and takes on a wider variety of jobs, more complex workpieces, and larger quantities, some engineered planning will be required. Separate schedules will need to be written to plan the whole company operation on a long-term basis and to cover day-to-day detailed production procedures.

Both types of schedules will need much the same information. In fact schedules of immediate manufacturing considerations are blended with data on long-range work to provide an overall plant-wide schedule. Estimates have to be made to determine times required for setups and production. Material costs and delivery dates are noted, machine tool selections are made, and tooling costs are estimated.

After original schedules are complete and jobs are in production, the planning paperwork should be updated to record changes and additions. Perhaps a job was reprocessed to another higher- or lower-priced machine, material or dimensional specifications were changed, machine breakdown occurred, cutting-tool life was not as anticipated, time-study readings were off, etc. Costs can thus be broken down to specific areas to provide a truer picture for future estimations.

In large companies paper work can become a problem when thousands of parts need to be processed. Between the initial sales order and final shipping of the part, excessive paper work (especially in processing through the offices)

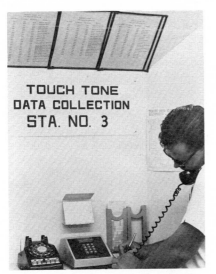 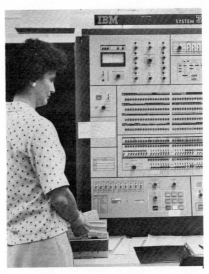

Fig. 2 Computer-telephone system. Combination computer-telephone system responds verbally to telephone questions. Computer is an IBM 360-50 model. (*From American Machinist Magazine, Jan.* 15, 1968, p. 106.)

can bog down the job to a crawl and increase cost sufficiently to make the effort unprofitable.

One company involved in the manufacture of aerospace parts employs a combination telephone-computer system to schedule and control production. The sophisticated system, located at Rohr Corporation's Chula Vista and Riverside, California plants, keeps track of 40,000 to 50,000 different parts in various stages of production.[1] Although the two plants are widely separated and some of the production parts have to travel back and forth, the inherent speeds of the telephone and computer (see Fig. 2) permit a smooth flow of work between plants.

Conventional electronic data processing can also cut office work time from days or weeks to minutes or hours. Flow charts, such as PERT and CPM, can be invaluable when one is trying to visually schedule and evaluate the progress of complex products. However, flow charts themselves can become entangled if they are made all-inclusive. Complexity can be avoided by making up two or more charts to cover different aspects of manufacturing.

Project size and high computer costs need not be limiting factors when contemplating PERT and CPM scheduling techniques. Smaller projects can also be controlled by employing an inexpensive pocket-sized, circular slide rule, which performs all the basic PERT-CPM computations.

This device, the Pert-O-Graph computer (Fig. 3), comes in a kit along with a handbook and explanatory guide. A simple, three-step sequence operates

Fig. 3 Pert-O-Graph. Planning networks can be set up quickly without electronic computers with a simple slide-rule device. (*Courtesy of James Halcomb Associates, Sunnyvale, Calif.*)

the "instrument": set the index, move the "hairline" to the desired circular scale, then read the answer directly.

One of the most difficult predictions to make in manufacturing is the delivery date. There are so many variables involved, it would take a whole book to offer solutions. Each new job presents fresh problems. Generally, it can be suggested that playing it safe or allowing too much time to meet deliveries results in excessive production costs and reduced profit. On the other hand, it may be wise to allow time cushions between certain operations when experience has shown that problems are likely to arise.

Organized Maintenance Keeps Production Flowing. While new machines are made to require less operator attention, their complexity requires closer observation to ensure continuous production. Not only should the machine-repair mechanic be skilled in fixing a malfunctioning machine, but he should also be familiar with preventive maintenance.

During his rounds with the oil can, the mechanic should be looking and listening for telltale signs of deterioration. For instance, a quick analysis of a strange noise in the gearbox can be made by placing a screwdriver point against the box and pressing an ear on the handle end. This stethoscopic effect amplifies the sound within the gearbox to provide an instant diagnosis.

It would be nice to solve all maintenance problems so easily, but sometimes the nature of the trouble can be complex. A numerically controlled machine, for instance, may be down due to an electronic or hydraulic cause, and a specialist is required to repair it. If the machine is a new type, it would be best to call in the manufacturer's service representative. If the machine is not covered by a warranty, it may be expensive to rely on the manufacturer for all repairs. Therefore, it is wise to send the company electrician or repairman to the machine manufacturer's plant for instruction.

Some companies maintain charts on which repair data are kept. Recorded are hours of operation, hours of downtime (specified as to reason), nature of breakdown and date, and name of repairman. From such a chart, determination can readily be made as to frequency of breakdowns and patterns. This information can then be used to take immediate action or to set up a procedure for preventive maintenance.

For example, when the same component shows a record of periodic breakdown or wears out rapidly, either it may be replaced with a product of superior quality or, if a better product is not available, it may be replaced before it causes downtime. To avoid delays and to keep the machine running productively, it would be necessary to carry spare parts in inventory. And if at all possible, replacements and repairs should be made during nonproductive hours— at night or on weekends.

One disadvantage of automation equipment and combined-operations machines is that a breakdown stops all functions. On the other hand, when a standard machine breaks down, the parts may be rerouted to a similar machine or temporarily shipped to a neighboring job shop to perform the single operation. Incidentally, it would pay to have a list of reliable shops for use in emergencies—to assist during breakdowns or to meet tight delivery dates.

Tips on How to Reduce Costs. There are thousands of ways to cut down on or even to eliminate some manufacturing costs. Management is aware of many cost-saving devices and uses them. After all, its main purpose for planning revolves around the efficiency factor. However, since there are so many bases to cover between the engineering department and the production floor, the following suggestions are provided to serve as a checklist for further efficiency:

Make sure the draftsman puts all machining dimensions on the workpiece drawing. It's cheaper and more accurate to use calculators in the engineering department than to have the machinist figure out dimensions with pencil and paper.

Ensure that blueprints can be easily read by the machinist. Production profits go down the drain when an expensive machine is idled while the operator tries to decipher a drawing.

Check part drawings for excessively close tolerance dimensions. Question to determine absolute need. Looser tolerances will reduce cost of manufacturing.

Employ simplified (but easy to understand) drawing methods, and use tabulated drawings for similar parts.

Where tabulations are not possible on complex part or assembly drawings, make similar drawings by reproducing the original on sepia paper (or other types) and make changes to suit new design.

Retain a simple engineering-changes and drawing system and ensure that the machine shop notifies the engineering department of changes it instigates.

Do not have a designer check his own work. The tendency is to repeat one's mistakes. Employ a checker.

Install a make-or-buy committee, and check local job shops to see if they can produce the part cheaper.

When designing jigs and fixtures, foolproof them so that a part can't be inserted the wrong way.

Fig. 4 Combined tapping and stamping. Tapping unit is incorporated into a progressive die to eliminate a second operation. Cold-form taps are hydraulically driven and heads are moved to the work with compressed air. (*Made by Laughter Corp.*)

If jigs or fixtures are to be used for second-operation work, design them to check critical machining dimensions of previous operations.

Design jigs and fixtures so that they can be used with other similar jobs.

For higher production jobs, consider designing a double fixture or indexing table so that parts can be loaded while machining is being performed.

Specify standard materials in standard sizes whenever possible.

Maintain a training program for both draftsmen and machinists.

Make operator motion-economy studies.

Install mechanical or air-clamping devices on production machines.

If production quantity is large, investigate feasibility of using special high production equipment.

Look for ways to combine operations. For instance, tapping can be performed in process with a stamping operation (Fig. 4).

Machine the workpiece only to drawing specifications.   Don't give away closer tolerances or better finishes than asked for.

Investigate methods to speed material handling.   Consider conveyors, chutes, magazines, transfer mechanisms, and other feeding systems.

Institute a preventive maintenance program.

Keep informed on latest processes and products by reading technical journals and by attending seminars, technical society meetings, and trade shows.

Use an employee suggestion system.

Provide good working conditions in the shop, especially proper lighting.   An operator shouldn't have to take a workpiece to the light in order to check it.

Fig. 5 Tool tray. Tool tray that is attached to this Bridgeport milling machine keeps tools handy for the operator.

Use unskilled labor for most automatic operations and for simple loading and unloading of parts into jigs and fixtures.

Maintain close records on all machinery downtime so that recurring problems can be evaluated and corrected.

Give the quality control department authority to stop production when quality of workpiece does not meet specifications.

Inspection tools should be checked at specified intervals, depending on amount and type of use to which they are subjected.

Eliminate or reduce delays of any type.   Operators lined up at the tool crib means that expensive machinery is idle.

Keep sharpened replacement cutting tools at the production machine.   Holding devices are commercially available (see Fig. 5).

See that machines are kept free of chips.   Use automatic chip conveyors where practical.

Add tooling accessories such as tracer attachments, multiple-spindle drilling heads, gun-drilling devices, quick-release chucks, quick-acting vises, in-process hole deburrers, mist spray coolers, digital readouts for lathe and mill, air-operated rotary tables, lead screw tappers, etc.

Investigate modern metalworking processes for production purposes.   Many are out of the laboratory stage.   Production successes are being achieved with the following: electrical discharge machining, electrolytic grinding, electrochemical machining, electromagnetic forming, explosive forming and cladding, electron-beam welding, laser welding and machining, hydroforming, ultrasonic machining, machining with ceramic and diamond cutting tools, NC machining, etc.

Why Buy that Machine?   Machine tool purchase orders are placed either to prepare for future business or to fill an immediate need. Justification may come through an extensive study involving several engineers, or the decision may be reached when a shop foreman threatens to resign—he wants a new machine to meet increasing production requirements. In both cases, the question is asked: "Which one should we buy?"

The field can be narrowed somewhat by first recognizing individual requirements.

1. Will production consist of short runs or long runs?

2. Do workpieces require precision machining or are loose dimensional tolerances permissible?

3. Is the versatility of standard machinery a must, or is uninterrupted continuity of production flow paramount?

4. What is the shape, size, and hardness of the workpiece?

5. What process will be used (drilling, turning, milling, grinding, etc.)?

6. Finally, what size budget is there with which to shop?

Actual choice may subsequently boil down to the following detailed considerations (not necessarily in order of importance):

1. Cost—compared with competitors' models

2. Productivity—meets or surpasses requirements

3. Versatility—can be easily set up to run different jobs

4. Automatic operation—either mechanical or by NC

5. Accuracy and reliability—dimensional tolerances come out consistently precise

6. Longevity—will hold up over many years of pounding with minimum maintenance

7. Latest model—has extra capabilities and available accessories for possible future use

COST: While new machines are intended to bring savings and increased profit, they will also cost money. In addition to initial investment, there are fixed costs and operating costs. Initial costs may include those for installation, tooling, and accessories. Fixed costs may be incurred through interest payments, depreciation, and insurance. Operation of the machine will result in costs for labor, power, maintenance, and replacement of worn tooling. Comparing projected production increases expected from the new machine against all its costs will determine amount of profit that can be hoped for from its purchase. Thus, although cost is an important factor, high production operational features of the new machine can outweigh price.

PRODUCTIVITY: Workpiece shape and quantity requirements usually determine the type of equipment that is needed to produce the part economically. To machine parts made from bar stock, for instance, if production runs are low and many setups are required, a turret lathe would be ideal. However, the same parts on high production runs would be more profitably machined on an automatic screw machine. Even more economic production can be achieved if production quantity warrants a cold-heading operation.

VERSATILITY: Standard machines should be used for all short production runs. Flexibility of these machines permits quick and easy changeovers from one part to another. Versatility is, of course, aided by extras that the manufacturer either builds into the machine or has available as attachments. These consist of higher power, wide variation in speeds and feeds, automatic functions, and tooling accessories.

AUTOMATIC OPERATION: Machine tools have been designed for various types of automatic operation. One of the oldest systems is in the screw machine which has a mechanical system of cams. Many thousands of parts can be repetitively machined from automatically fed bar stock. This machine can be reset to make any number of different parts within the capacity of its spindle.

Special single-purpose machines are used for extremely long-run jobs, such as are common in the automotive industry. These machines can be set up

Fig. 6 Tape-controlled machine. Tape-controlled work center automatically machines four sides in one loading. Tool changer of this Ex-Cell-O machine has a 32-tool storage library.

in an automation line to function in process with other machines, or they can be operated as single automation units by combining with loading mechanisms, such as vibrating hoppers.

The newest and hottest automatic equipment is the numerically controlled machine. After loading the workpiece on the machine's table, the operator presses a button and then watches as the machine performs its machining operations (Fig. 6). If the machine is equipped with a tool changer, the operator may witness 75 or more operations without lifting a finger. And if the machine is of the "machining center" type, the operator will see the machine perform numerous operations that would be done conventionally by several manually operated machine tools. Because all machining functions are specified and controlled by the engineering department on a reel of tape, the NC machine in effect is operated by management.

For long-run jobs of relative simplicity, standard automatic machines would be best. However, for the versatility required to produce complex parts (especially with contoured shapes) in short runs with assured accuracy, the NC machine is economically justified.

ACCURACY AND RELIABILITY: End use of a workpiece should determine the accuracy required in its manufacture. It is obvious that a child's toy wagon would not require precision machine tools to produce. On the other hand, components that go into a space missile cannot be made with enough precision. In between these extremes there are numerous products with varying degrees of accuracy requirements. An important consideration when ordering a production machine is that it not exceed accuracy capability for the specific product it is intended to produce. The extra cost of a sophisticated machine may make the difference between profit and loss in production.

However, when repeatability of close tolerances is required, it pays to go overboard on precision machinery. Machine tool manufacturers themselves are the biggest advocates of this philosophy. Instead of using conventional production machines to manufacture their products, many employ high-precision jig borers in their production lines. These machines assure them of reliable accuracy from part to part.

LONGEVITY: While machine tool builders do not as a rule offer guarantees on their products, there are good service arrangements from most companies. In fact, builders try to reduce the necessity of service by recommending the machine model to fit the job. Their engineers will gladly work with prospective purchasers to determine horsepower and other requirements. This advance communication between builder (or distributor) and customer can eliminate many possible problems.

When properly used and maintained, machine tools give many years of top performance.

LATEST MODEL: Many machines simply will not wear out. However, they can become obsolete; and for this reason careful thought should be given to possible future needs when investigating new machines. Some questions to consider:

Can product configuration change to necessitate a larger machine?

Can product dimensional tolerances change to require higher machining accuracy?

Is spindle speed sufficient to permit eventual use of ceramic cutting tools?

What accessories are available?

Can the machine accept a tracer attachment?

Can the machine be easily retrofitted to numerical control?

Machine Tool Replacement Decisions. A general rule cannot be laid down as to the best time to replace a machine. By running a machine hard and beyond its capacity a plant can sometimes realize sufficient production profit to compensate for the machine's short life. On the other hand, a machine that is "babied" will last indefinitely, and the curse here is that the machine can rumble along years after it is obsolete. Since new equipment is usually more productive than the old, it would pay to consider periodic replacement in order to stay competitive.

Various procedures are employed to analyze need for new machinery—for reliance on a shop foreman's common sense to results obtained from complex mathematical formulas. Since foremen are human and fallible, most companies take a more or less scientific approach when evaluating machine replacement.

Whatever the method employed, financial values are a big factor in arriving at answers. While there may be 50 or more cost considerations, the basic study will revolve around either the annual cost, present worth, or rate of return.

ANNUAL COST: This payoff-period method is a common rule of thumb used by engineers. Investment cost is divided by annual earning to arrive at amount of time needed to break even. Thus we learn how long it will take to get the money back into working capital.

However, the assumption that a machine is likely to be the best buy if it pays for itself rapidly can be a mistake. The method may indicate purchase of an inferior machine which will pay for itself in one year, but which can break down after 18 months. On the other hand, a better machine may take two years to pay off, but it will continue to be productive. And when the time arrives for replacement, it will have more trade-in value.

Being easy to work with, the annual-cost method can provide a quick answer to whether or not a projected new machine will provide a high profit or a loss.[2]

PRESENT WORTH: This method consists of arriving at the present worth of alternatives by calculating expenditures of each, both in equal service. An old machine and a new machine are compared for yearly operating expense, selling price after specified time, price of new machine, repair payments of old machine, and interest charges to pay for a new machine. After totaling costs of each alternative, results are compared to determine present worth.[3]

RATE OF RETURN: Conventional accounting practice may be used to estimate return on investment, which is the interest rate at which the money returned (discounted to the present) equals the investment's cost. An estimate is made on the amount of money the machine tool will bring in every year, including the final year when it is traded in. An interest rate is used to discount the annual returns to make them add up to the original cost of the machine.[4]

MAPI SYSTEM: A more complicated method of determining when a machine can be replaced is the Machinery and Allied Products Institute formula. Called MAPI after the institute's initials, the method defines the old machine as the "defender" and the new machine as the "challenger." More than 20 factors are considered and tabulated on MAPI work sheets. These permit finding and comparing the sum of operating inferiority and capital cost of the present machine with that of the proposed new machine. Solutions consider present conditions or those that will exist no longer than one year into the future.[5]

TOOLING FOR PRODUCTION

Standard Tooling. Use the correct tool for the given task. Many of the factors affecting choice of machines to operate at a good profit also relate to tool selection. The right tool for the right job can mean a lot. Certainly, all operations are affected by the tools. All that the machine does must be done through the tools. If a machine is versatile, tooling can make it even more versatile. If it's a good producer, it needs good tools to retain its efficiency and low-cost operation. Its accuracy and reliability are lost without dependable tools. Finally, automatic operation and longevity depend on proper setup with suitable tools. The tools, then, are the "hands" of the machine.

The term "tooling" refers to all segments of the setup. It includes cutting tools, toolholders, workpiece holders, dies, templates, and gauges. The tools contact and alter the workpiece. They may add or remove material, or they may reshape existing material. They may simply rotate the workpiece. The machine provides power and alignment; the tooling does the rest.

Workholding devices are divided into two groups: those for flat irregular workpieces and those for round workpieces, including gears, splines, squares, and hexagonal bar stock. The holders for flat material include pump jigs, vises, special vise jaws, V blocks, angle plates, magnetic chucks, vacuum chucks, electrostatic chucks, etc. For round workpieces, there are jawed chucks, arbors, mandrels, solid arbors, straight mandrels, split collets and bushings, self-actuating wedge cam and wedge rollers, face-driving centers, etc.

Toolholders include drill chucks, collets, sleeves, drivers, tool bit holders, adapters, arbors, and retainers.

Where do you get all this standard tooling? Standard tools and fixtures can be purchased, or they can be made in the shop from readily available plans and templates. A look at the tool catalog from any large manufacturer shows hundreds of tools and should give you an idea of what is available before going to special tooling.

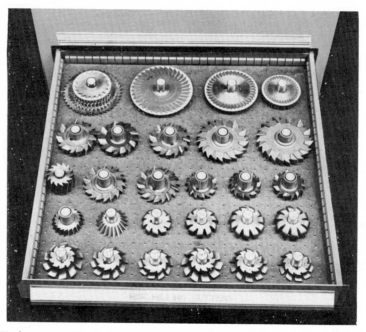

Fig. 7 Tool storage. Neatly kept cutters are easily accessible and free from damaging contact with one another. (*Courtesy of Vidmar Division Volkert Stampings.*)

How many tools to get? Of course, a few all-purpose tools may do many jobs with a minimum degree of efficiency, but greater efficiency is likely to result if you can afford to have a variety of standard tools. Your operators can then choose the most efficient tool for a particular job. Skill is a factor, and the small job shop may have an advantage here, because the workers will tend to be more skilled. They will need to use more imagination to make all sorts of "special" tooling out of standard tools. They can do a superlative job if you give them a wide variety of standard tools to build with.

Storage space need not be a problem, and it is important to remember that production is increased by having the right tool on hand when it's needed. Having men standing around the tool crib waiting for a tool is bad business. It's cheaper to invest in more tools and modern, space-saving storage facilities (see Fig. 7). Tools stored systematically not only save time in dispensing but also permit quick inventory taking at any time.

Another way some companies save on waiting-around time is to provide operators and toolmakers with their own individual set of frequently used tools.   Most
commonly provided are lathe tool bits and drill sets (Fig. 8).

Holders are the basic elements of tooling.   They can be permanent or adjustable, and there are holders for holders.   Simple holders require the operator
to tap the cutting tool with a hammer to line it up.   More sophisticated holders
use a dial for precise micrometer adjustment (Fig. 9).   The hammered device
is economical if tolerances are liberal and readjustment not too frequent.   But
the tapping takes skill, so you may have to pay a highly trained man to do a
low-tolerance job.

Fig. 8 Drill sets. Drill sets kept in
machinist's toolbox save back-and-forth
steps to tool crib.

Fig. 9 Toolholder. Preset dimensions
can be determined by first taking a practice cut and then measuring it. (*Courtesy of DeVlieg Machine Co.*)

The ultimate in operator ease for handling tools comes when using preset
tools.   Here, the operator simply inserts the cutting tip and shank in the holder
(Fig. 10).   The tool is preset in the shank, and once the holder is adjusted
to the spindle, tools can be replaced with no further adjustments in the setup.
In another form of presetting, most ganged tools are preset one with another.

Special Tooling.   To summarize the tooling discussion so far, there are three
sources: commercial, regular, and special.   Commercial or standard tooling, discussed above, is found in vendor catalogs—and there's a lot to choose from.
Once your shop is established, you will have many standard components available in the tool crib.   Commercial tooling is usually listed in standard sizes
specified by various engineering societies and organizations or by the tooling
manufacturer.   This includes everything from grinding wheels and cutting tips,
to mills, burrs, reamers, drills, taps, jigs, collets, and chucks.

Regular tooling that is "standard" to one company is found in that company's toolroom standards book. It's for the company's own use, though it could become standard as others find use for it. It can be made by batch production in the company toolroom, or contracted outside the shop. It may be used

Fig. 10 Preset tools. Presetting provides the ability to readily replace worn tools and resume the machining operation with a minimum of downtime. (*Courtesy of DeVlieg Machine Co.*)

for several products in the company's line, and it may be stocked in the crib for many years. Thus, it has some of the advantages of standard or commercial tooling, though it may not be mass produced. It costs more than standard, and the production line may have to wait for it to be made during model changes.

Special tooling is usually that tooling built for one product only. It cannot be avoided if the product requires tooling of unusual size or shape. Only one set of specialized tooling is built except where high production requirements necessitate more. It usually is expensive, but it can save money and often is the only answer. For example, you can make one special setup where several different cuts would be made at one time.

Special tooling is not stocked in the crib, though it may be assembled from standard components. This assembly requires high skill and lots of time. The special tooling is not pretested, and so costly delays may result in tryout stages. Alterations may be required. The complexity involved sometimes prevents even the most skilled engineers and designers from making it right the first time. Try to avoid specials. Closer cooperation between various engineering groups in a plant might well reduce the need for special tooling.

In summary, here are the advantages of using standard tooling:

1. It's mass produced and thus low in cost. The same tool made in the toolroom would be many times more costly.

2. Each piece will be useful for many jobs, not just one or two.

3. It's easy to set up. Its design has evolved through long, hard experience with several types of special tools for the same job.

4. The manufacturers are specialists, thus designing best quality.

5. It's readily available from the vendor, warehouse, or tool crib. Some can even be kept with the machine.

6. The toolroom is free for more essential jobs.

7. Design time is reduced or eliminated.

8. In large plants, great quantities of commercial tooling may be kept in inventory, thus reducing delays in changeover or start of production.

9. Repair and maintenance are easier.

Cutting Tools. The type of cutting tool depends on the machine, the length of the production run, the nature of the toolholder, and the type of material and shape to be machined. One way to purchase it is to get bids. Give the tool company a sample of the workpiece you want to produce, or provide a drawing of it. Tell the toolmaker the accuracy required and how long a run is anticipated.

A basic way to save money is to preserve the tools in stock by regrinding or resharpening them. But it must be done frequently. Tools last longer if they are ground before they get dull. When a tool is kept sharp, it cuts rapidly and efficiently at all times. It requires a very small amount of regrinding, so many resharpenings are possible. On the other hand, if it gets dull, it pulls hard in the machine and makes a rough cut.

If regrinding is too expensive or requires too many highly skilled men, you may want to try throwaway cutting tools (see Fig. 11). As you might guess, they are thrown away when dull, requiring no maintenance. The toolholder is simplified, built of a hard steel alloy. A high-speed or carbide-insert cutting point is held by a clamping method.

The main saving of throwaway tools is time. Time to change or reset tools is cut to seconds. And there is a tendency to operate machines at maximum output, rather than try to minimize tool wear. In short, tool cost may be high using throwaways, but overall production increase and elimination of regrinding time make the overall cost lower. In one comparison, tool cost per hour was ten times higher, but overall production-cost was 70 percent.

Fig. 11 Throwaway cutting tools. This Kennametal carbide insert is indexable so that it can machine from each corner before it is completely worn and subsequently discarded.

Forecasting for Tooling Needs. Most small plants that operate on the job-shop level play it by ear when it comes to purchasing new equipment. When they get too far behind in production, they go shopping for a new machine and more tooling. This is not really efficient because delivery dates have fallen behind and orders are lost. These plants could do much better if they knew in advance the type and quantity of work to expect in the months or years ahead.

Not only would such forecasting of sales permit sufficient time to shop for equipment, but also management would have time to consider other, more efficient processes should projected production requirements warrant it. Large companies generally recognize this potential of sales forecasting and employ it.

Tool and machinery requirements can be determined by translating forecasts into work load. The amount and type of work anticipated will thus have a bearing on choice of equipment.

ORDERING, STOCKING, AND MAINTAINING PRODUCTION TOOLING

Determining the need and methods required to order new or repair tooling is explained below. The methods and procedures required to maintain tooling in usable condition and the storing and issuing of these tools is covered in detail.

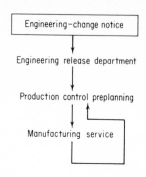

Engineering–change notice

↓

Engineering release department

↓

Production control preplanning

↓

Manufacturing service

CHANGE ☒AUTHORIZATION ☒ENGINEERING

		CHANGE NO. X-245	DATE 2-19-

☒MAJOR ☐MINOR ☐RECORD ☐EMERGENCY ☐NORMAL | CHANGE ANALYSIS DATE BY

PART NAME DRIVE CRANK | PART NO. 12340

INTERCHANGEABILITY ☒OLD ☒NEW ☒PRESENT | ☐BUY ☒MAKE

URGENCY: NEW PRODUCTION MUST CONFORM.

DESCRIPTION OF CHANGE | CHANGE LETTER FROM TO
| LAYOUT ISSUE FROM TO

NEW PART

REASON FOR CHANGE

NEW PART REQUIRED TO IMPROVE
FUNCTION OF DRIVE CRANK MECHANISM

MATERIAL | ☐COIL STOCK ☐STRIP STOCK

TEMPER SHEAR WIDTH | STOCK THICKNESS PITCH

LBS PER "M" PIECES BLANKS PER FOOT OF LENGTH | WT. PER STRIP LBS.

☐FROM STRIP TO COIL ☐FROM COIL TO STRIP

TOOL AND GAGE NUMBERS AFFECTED	TOOL REC. CARD		DISPOSITION		TOOL PROD. ORDER NO.	NEW	CHANGE	REMARKS
	ADD	REMOVE	DISCARD	SCRAP				

REMARKS

CHANGE TO
BECOME EFFECTIVE ☐WHEN PRACTICAL ☒IMMEDIATELY ☐WITH NEXT PURCHASE ☐PRODUCTION CONFORMS
☐OTHER · SEE PAGE

DISPOSITION OF PARTS IN STOCK: ☐REWORK ☐USE UP ☐SCRAP

DISTRIBUTION	AUTH.	REPORT	PRINT	LAYOUT	DISPOSITION	USE UP	REWORK	HOLD	DISCARD	SCHEDULE	START	FINISH	FINISHED
PREPLANNING					MATERIAL					PROCESSING			
PROCESSING					VENDOR PARTS IN PROCESS					TOOL DESIGN			
PURCHASING					VICTOR PARTS IN PROCESS					TOOL MANUFACTURING			
PRODUCTION CONT.					PARTS IN STOCK					METHODS & STNDS.			
QUALITY CONTROL					NEXT ASSEMBLIES					PURCHASING			
RESEARCH					OTHER ASSEMBLIES					PRODUCTION CONT.			
TOOL STORES					TOOLS								
					GAGES								
SERVICE DEPT.					PREPARED BY DAK			REQUESTED BY KLR		APPROVED BY			
SPEC. MACH. DEPT.													
COST DEPT.										RKV			
WORK SIMP. PROGRAM					DATE 2-19-			DATE 2-18-		DATE 2-19-			

Fig. 12 Engineering-change notice.

Ordering New Tools. The research engineer routes new-part drawings to the factory product engineering department. The product engineer reviews part prints and questions obvious discrepancies with the research engineer. The engineering release section assigns part numbers to the blueprints and originates an engineering-change-notice release form (see Fig. 12) along with the new-part print. Changes to existing part numbers can be issued in the same manner using the engineering-change-notice form documenting the details of the change being made.

The engineering-change-notice release, along with the part print, is routed to the production control preplanning coordinating section. An individual record is originated for each part number appearing on an engineering-change notice for purposes of control and coordination. The part number, drawing letter,

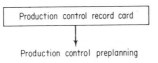

Production control preplanning

PART NO. 12340	DWG. LETTER NONE		CHG. NOTICE NO. X-245	DATE 2-19-
DEPARTMENTAL PROGRESS	DATE		URGENCY _____	
	TO	FROM	☐ PRESENT	
PROCESS DEPT.	2-19-		☒ NEW	
METHODS & STDS.			☐ OPTIONAL	
QUALITY ASSURANCE			TOOL DUE	
SERVICE DEPT.			☐ BUY	
PURCHASING			☒ MAKE	
COST DEPT.				
			REMARKS	
FINAL RELEASE DATE				

Fig. 13 Individual-part number record.

engineering-change-notice number, date received, and spaces assigned to control flow of necessary data are shown on this form. One card for each part number makes it possible to know if any overlap of changes occur on existing or new parts (see Fig. 13).

The engineering-change notice and the new part prints are now routed to the industrial engineering department, process engineering section.

The process engineer develops a process or routing layout which shows the necessary details required to produce the part (Fig. 14).

The tool designer develops necessary tool drawings and determines estimated cost.

The tool engineer assigns a number to the tool and originates a form inserting the details on the form indicating what is required to produce the new tool. The form can be called a "tool production order," or TPO (Fig. 15). The TPO shows the estimated cost and other required data.

Authorized signatures are applied to the TPO, namely those of the process engineering manager and the industrial engineering director. Then the TPO, engineering-change notice, process layout, part drawing, and tool drawing package is returned to the production control preplanning section.

The preplanning section assigns delivery dates for tooling after determining whether to "buy or make." The buy-or-make decision depends on the toolroom load, the machine tools available to make the tool, and the estimated purchase cost versus the manufactured tool cost.

TPOs are used as the authority to place purchase orders with acceptable suppliers.

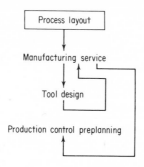

Fig. 14 Processing layout.

Manufactured TPOs are sent to the toolroom with the target dates inserted by the preplanning coordinating section. Weekly or monthly reports are originated by the preplanning section reflecting outstanding purchased and manufactured TPOs. The purchasing department reviews these reports and inserts updated promised dates on delivery of the tools and returns them to the preplanning coordinating section. The toolroom foreman reviews the manufactured TPO recap and indicates, based on capacity, promised dates opposite each tool in his possession.

The toolroom backlog is reviewed weekly, and if it appears that overtime can handle the requirements, recommendation is made to do this. Another alternative would be to subcontract any overload.

The methods and standards section assigns to the process layout time standards to each direct-labor operation.

The quality control section inserts inspection information on the master process layout.

The preplanning section maintains current-activity data on those tools which are purchased and those which are manufactured.

Repair Orders for Tooling. A shop foreman, setup man, floor inspector, toolroom foreman, or toolmaker can be given the authority to request tool repair orders. When it is evident that a tool does not produce acceptable parts, a tool-repair-order form is originated and attached to the tool, which is then sent to the toolroom. (Fig. 16). Necessary repairs are made to the tool, which is then inspected, tried out, and if accepted, sent into the tool store department.

The setup man, in some instances, will check with a toolmaker troubleshooter when setting up a tool which is identified with a caution tag attached originally by the toolmaker or tool inspector. This precaution helps minimize machine and tool damage.

Inspection of Tooling. Tools are inspected after each production run to determine if grinding or other work is required to make the tool usable and available for the next production run. Inspection of tooling occurs after a new tool has been completed or an existing tool has been changed or repaired.

A tool inspection report is originated by the tool inspection department for all tools which clear the tool inspection department (Fig. 17).

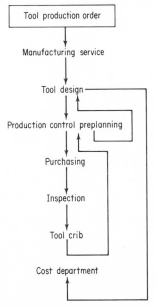

Fig. 15 Tool production order (TPO).

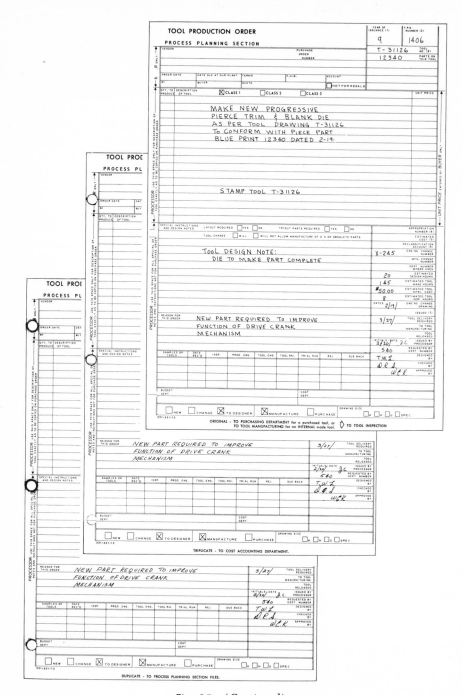

Fig. 15 (*Continued*)

New, changed, and repaired tools are tried out functionally and the piece part is dimensionally checked to assure that the tool produces acceptable parts.

Ordering and Requisitioning Standard Tools and Perishable Supplies. The control and availability of standard tools and perishable supplies is done via safety stocks or constant review of the item's activity. In most cases, these items are considered "shelf items" and normally are made available within a matter of days. On those items which require longer lead time, the inventory-record card is watched very closely by the tool-crib supervisor and the inventory is replenished based on turnover.

Fig. 16 Tool repair order.

When it becomes necessary to replenish inventory, a traveling requisition form can be used on those items which are repetitive or a purchase requisition form can be originated and sent to the purchasing department representative for actual order placement.

Periodic audits should be made of those standard tools and supplies which show little or no turnover activity.

Storing Tools. Tools, fixtures, gauges, production supplies, etc., must be physically controlled through a stock-room facility. Bins should be identified by alpha or numeric code to make possible the location of tools, etc., upon demand.

An inventory-record card is originated for each tool, fixture, or perishable supply (Fig. 18). The receipts, withdrawals, on-order, and on-hand data are shown on this card.

"Tool numbers" or perishable-supplies descriptions must have separate locator cards originated in the tool stores department. These can be 3- by 5-inch cards (Fig. 19).

A tool number or description plus the bin location is the only basic data needed, but if desired, the name of the supplier may be included on the locator card.

A tool-crib supervisor must have the proper storage space located adjacent to toolroom and/or factory manufacturing area.

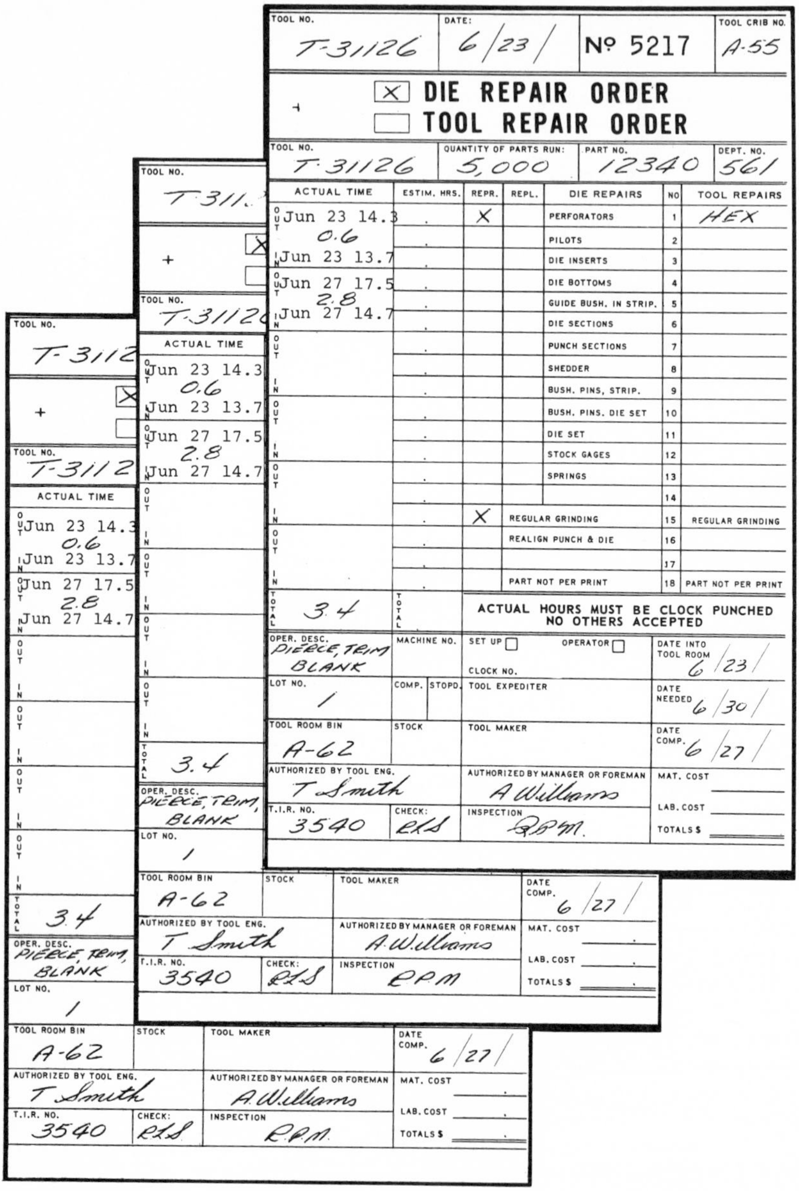

TOOL NO. T-31126 | DATE: 6/23/ | № 5217 | TOOL CRIB NO. A-55

☒ DIE REPAIR ORDER
☐ TOOL REPAIR ORDER

TOOL NO. T-31126 | QUANTITY OF PARTS RUN: 5,000 | PART NO. 12340 | DEPT. NO. 561

ACTUAL TIME	ESTIM. HRS.	REPR.	REPL.	DIE REPAIRS	NO	TOOL REPAIRS
OUT Jun 23 14.3	.	X		PERFORATORS	1	HEX
0.6	.			PILOTS	2	
IN Jun 23 13.7	.			DIE INSERTS	3	
OUT Jun 27 17.5	.			DIE BOTTOMS	4	
2.8 IN Jun 27 14.7	.			GUIDE BUSH. IN STRIP.	5	
	.			DIE SECTIONS	6	
OUT	.			PUNCH SECTIONS	7	
	.			SHEDDER	8	
IN	.			BUSH. PINS, STRIP.	9	
OUT	.			BUSH. PINS, DIE SET	10	
	.			DIE SET	11	
IN	.			STOCK GAGES	12	
OUT	.			SPRINGS	13	
	.				14	
IN	.	X		REGULAR GRINDING	15	REGULAR GRINDING
OUT	.			REALIGN PUNCH & DIE	16	
	.				17	
IN	.			PART NOT PER PRINT	18	PART NOT PER PRINT
TOTAL 3.4	TOTAL			ACTUAL HOURS MUST BE CLOCK PUNCHED NO OTHERS ACCEPTED		

OPER. DESC. PIERCE, TRIM BLANK | MACHINE NO. | SET UP ☐ OPERATOR ☐ CLOCK NO. | DATE INTO TOOL ROOM 6/23/

LOT NO. 1 | COMP. | STOPD. | TOOL EXPEDITER | DATE NEEDED 6/30/

TOOL ROOM BIN A-62 | STOCK | TOOL MAKER | DATE COMP. 6/27/

AUTHORIZED BY TOOL ENG. T Smith | AUTHORIZED BY MANAGER OR FOREMAN A Williams | MAT. COST

T.I.R. NO. 3540 | CHECK: RLS | INSPECTION RPM. | LAB. COST | TOTALS $

Fig. 16 (*Continued*)

Tool-crib Controls. Tools, fixtures, gauges, and production supplies can be withdrawn from stock through the use of three different methods:

1. *Tool-loan-order forms* (*Fig. 20*), *originated in triplicate, showing:*
   a. Tool number
   b. Bin number
   c. Quantity requested

d. Date requested
e. Department number
f. Clock number
g. Requisitioner's signature
The original copy is retained by the requisitioner.

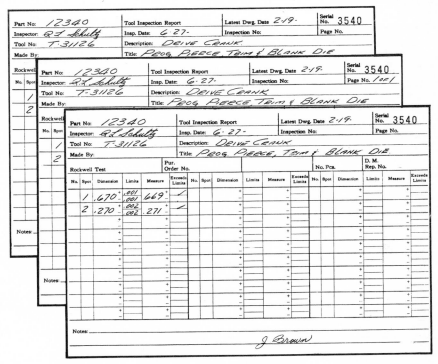

Fig. 17 Inspection report.

The second copy is filed onto a clipboard or in a file drawer by the tool-crib attendant in *department-number* order sequence. This will make it possible to determine at any time the tooling charged out to any one department.

The third copy is placed in the bin space where the tool was physically located.

When the tool is returned to the bin location, the three copies of the tool loan order are matched and destroyed. One copy may be retained if historical information is desirable.

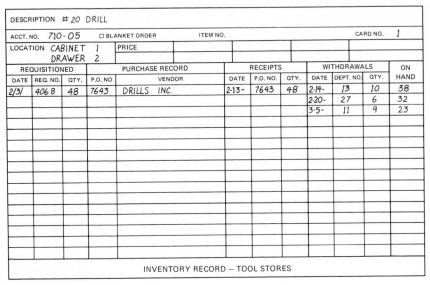

DESCRIPTION # 20 DRILL

ACCT. NO. 710-05 □ BLANKET ORDER   ITEM NO.   CARD NO. 1

LOCATION CABINET 1   PRICE
         DRAWER 2

REQUISITIONED			PURCHASE RECORD		RECEIPTS			WITHDRAWALS			ON HAND
DATE	REQ. NO.	QTY.	P.O. NO	VENDOR	DATE	P.O. NO.	QTY.	DATE	DEPT. NO.	QTY.	
2/3/	406 B	48	7643	DRILLS INC.	2-13-	7643	48	2-14-	13	10	38
								2-20-	27	6	32
								3-5-	11	9	23

INVENTORY RECORD — TOOL STORES

Fig. 18 Tool inventory-record card.

DESCRIPTION PROG. PIERCE, TRIM & BLANK DIE   TOOL NO. T-31126

LOCATION A55

PART NO S   12340   DEPT. USED 561

RELEASE DATE 3-28-

SUPER DIE INC.   T.P.O. NO. 1406   P.O. NO.

REMARKS

TOOL RECORD

Fig. 19 Locator card.

Tool loan order → Tool crib → Tool maker or Shop foreman or Setup man

TOOL LOAN ORDER   No. **15321**

Clock No. *2011*   Bin No. *A-55*

Dept. *12*   Date *6-20*

QUAN.	SIZE	KIND OF TOOL
1		

WORKMAN...
If lost it wi...
Keep this s...
Then exchar...

Signed...
This Tool (...

TOOL LOAN ORDER   No. **15321**

Clock No. *2011*   Bin No. *A-55*

Dept. *12*   Date *6-20*

QUAN.	SIZE	KIND OF TOOL
1		

WORKMAN...
If lost it wi...
Keep this s...
Then exchar...

Signed...
This Tool (...

TOOL LOAN ORDER   No. **15321**

Clock No. *2011*   Bin No. *A-55*

Dept. *12*   Date *6-20*

QUAN.	SIZE	KIND OF TOOL
1		*T-31126*

WORKMAN NOTE: This tool is in your charge until it is returned.
If lost it will be charged to you.
Keep this slip until tool is returned.
Then exchange it for receipted slip.

Signed *Richard Frank*
This Tool Order is for one item only.

Fig. 20 Tool loan order.

This form is used only when the company has assigned numbers to the tool, fixture, riveting blocks, guages, etc.

2. *Supply requisition* (Fig. 21): Only one copy of this form is necessary in most systems. Perishable tools, such as drills, batteries, wrenches, rags, etc., are withdrawn through the use of this form. These items *do not* carry a company-assigned part number and are not normally returned to the tool crib for repeated use.

Supply requisition
↓
Shop personnel
↓
Shop foreman
↓
Tool crib

SUPPLY REQUISITION			NO.	
DATE _I-16-_			DEPT. NO. __25__	
QUANTITY	STOCK, TOOL OR FORM NO.	DESCRIPTION	UNIT COST	TOTAL
12		#20 HIGH SPEED STEEL DRILLS		
REQUISITIONED BY _William Brown_		APPROVED _Dan Kuhlin_		

Fig. 21 Supply requisition.

3. *Toolmaker brass check:* Tools, fixtures, etc., can also be withdrawn from the tool crib by having a toolmaker present an identification marker in the form of a brass check with his identification number stamped thereon.

The brass check is placed by the tool-crib attendant in the location where the tool is normally stored until the tool is returned, at which time the brass check is returned to the toolmaker.

Tool engineering, in conjunction with the toolroom foreman, makes a determination possible of the amount of tool life available after each production run. A record is maintained in the tool engineering or toolroom department of the number of pieces produced by each tool (Fig. 22). An individual record card is maintained for this purpose, and the quantity produced is inserted after each run and accumulated.

Estimated tool life is used to project the number of months or years a tool can continue to supply the production demand. New TPOs must be originated far enough in advance to allow ample lead time to purchase or make replacement tooling before current tooling is beyond repair.

Scheduling Tools for Production Runs.   The tool-loan-order form can be originated by a production control dispatcher, foreman, setup man, or toolmaker.

The dispatcher assigns part order to lathes, mills, punch presses, etc., after assurance that necessary tooling is available.   Tools are withdrawn from tool

Tool design
or
Tool room

TOOL HISTORY RECORD										TOOL NUMBER T- 31126	
DESCRIPTION OF TOOL PROG. PIERCE TRIM & BLANK			ACCEPTED VARIANCE FROM TOOL AND/OR PRODUCTION DESIGN							AUTHORIZED BY	
PART NO'S. OF PARTS PRODUCED BY THIS TOOL 12340										DRAWING SIZE H	
										TOOL MFG. HOURS OR COST	
DATE T.P.O. ISSUED 2-20-	T.P.O. AND/OR P.O. NO. 1406	DATE RELEASED FOR PROD'N. 4-1-		MAXIMUM POTENTIAL PRODUCTION DESIGNED INTO TOOL 2,000,000				MAXIMUM QUANTITY PRODUCTION SHOP IS PERMITTED TO RUN 60,000			
PRODUCTION ACTIVITY							MAINTENANCE ACTIVITY				
DATE	PARTS MANUFACTURED	MACH. NO.	LOT NO.	QUANTITY	SETUP MAN NO.	EST. REP.HRS.	ACTUAL REP. HRS.	ENG. OR MFG. CHANGE NO. EST.HRS.	TOOL DISPOSITION BY	MAINTENANCE REQUIREMENTS - REMARKS	
4-1	12340	62	1	50,000	6						
6-23	12340	13	1	5,000	13		3.4			REPAIR HEX PERFORATOR	

Fig. 22   Tool history card.

crib and routed to specific machines in the factory to arrive prior to the completion of the job currently running in that machine.   Necessary raw materials or semicompleted parts are also requested at the same time and should arrive at the machine with the tool.

Tools must be kept in good condition at all times.

Summary.   In summary, it can be said that the ordering, stocking, and maintenance of tooling can be accomplished through simple, workable, and understandable systems and procedures.   It is suggested that time be taken to analyze your objective and then apply common sense and assign competent people to the task.

REFERENCES

1. H. Goodell, "Scheduling with a Computer," *American Machinist,* Jan. 15, 1968.
2. A chart showing the type of data that may be included in a comparison study is shown in *An Introduction of Material Handling,* Published and Authored by The Material Handling Institute, Inc., Pittsburgh, Pa., 1966, p. 20.
3. Examples that illustrate simple computations are found in H. B. Maynard (ed.), *Industrial Engineering Handbook,* McGraw-Hill Book Company, New York, 1956, p. 7–86.
4. An easy and practical method for finding rate of return may be found in B. T. Fullerton, *Machine Replacement for the Shop Manager,* Huebner Publications, Inc., Cleveland, 1965, Chapter VI, p. 41.
5. Details of the MAPI approach can be found in G. Terborgh, *Dynamic Equipment Policy,* Port City Press, Inc., Baltimore, 1949.

BIBLIOGRAPHY

Brierley, R. G., anl H. J. Siekmann: *Machining Principles and Cost Control,* McGraw-Hill Book Company, New York, 1964.

Carroll, Phil: *Practical Production and Inventory Control,* McGraw-Hill Book Company, New York, 1966.

Eary, D. F., and G. E. Johnson: *Process Engineering for Manufacturing,* Prentice-Hall, Inc., Englewood Cliffs, N.J., 1962.

Fullerton, B.: *Machine Replacement for the Shop Manager,* Huebner Publications, Inc., Cleveland.

Koepke, C. A. *Plant Production Control,* John Wiley & Sons, Inc., New York, 1941.

MacNiece, E. H.: *Production Forecasting, Planning, and Control,* 2d ed., John Wiley & Sons, Inc., New York, 1957.

Maynard, H. B. (ed.): *Industrial Engineering Handbook,* 2d ed., McGraw-Hill Book Company, New York, 1963.

Niedzwiedzki, A.: *Manual of Machinability and Tool Evaluation,* Huebner Publications, Inc., Cleveland, 1960.

Parsons, C. W. S.: *Estimating Machining Costs,* McGraw-Hill Book Company, New York, 1957.

Reinfeld, N. V.: *Production Control,* Prentice-Hall, Inc., Englewood Cliffs, N.J., 1959.

Rusinoff, S. E.: *Manufacturing Processes,* American Technical Society, Chicago, 1948.

Varnum, E. C. : "Algebraic Model Helps Decide Machine Tool Replacements," *Tooling and Production,* vol. 23, no. 9, December, 1957.

Wage, H. W.: *Manufacturing Engineering,* McGraw-Hill Book Company, New York, 1963.

Walker, W. F.: *Engineering Productivity,* Chemical Publishing Company, Inc., New York, 1964, vol. 1.

Chapter **7**

Transportation and Physical Distribution

EDITORS:

J. W. Denham, Jr. *Vice President, Distribution, Mattel, Inc., Hawthorne, California*

Emil Albert *Manager, Production Planning and Procurement Department, The Adams and Westlake Company, Elkhart, Indiana*

CONTENTS

Distribution in industrial firms in the United States is most frequently defined by naming several functional departments which exist in the majority of manufacturing firms. These departments, if grouped under one organization heading, are frequently defined as "distribution." The functional areas most frequently included under this heading are:

Inventory management
Customer-order processing
Transportation management
Warehousing and shipping

In some organizations, distribution has been expanded to include the complete production planning function involving materials planning, plant scheduling, receiving, stores, and purchasing.

Marketing and manufacturing are the primary communications and information interfaces within the organization. The primary role of the distribution function is to support the activities associated with marketing and manufacturing.

Regardless of the specific functional areas which are defined as the distribution function in any one manufacturing organization, the real importance of distribution in any organization is the emphasis and importance placed on the distribution concept. This concept relates to management's objectives and goals for planning and controlling all the costs associated with inventory levels and the movement of inventory to the ultimate consumer. The objective in every industrial firm is to carry out the goals and directives of management.

The purpose of this chapter is to discuss the *distribution system* in terms of:

1. The decision-making environment
2. Costs for decision making
3. Distribution models
4. Modes of transportation
5. Correlation of transportation and inventory control

DECISION-MAKING ENVIRONMENT

Only by the study of the environment and the interrelationships among the distribution functions and other organization functions can a rational basis for effective management be established. To establish an effective distribution system, the multiple-decision loops and the interrelationships that generate activities within the organization must be understood and executed effectively. Decisions made within the distribution function must be measured in terms of the impact on the entire organization and the influence these decisions have on the organization's primary objective.

The different emphasis on distribution decision making in industries depends upon the importance placed on controlling and reducing the cycle time from customer order to product delivery, and the inherent inventory risks. The extremes of emphasis include heavy industry at one end, where products are manufactured to specific engineering designs requiring lengthy lead times, to the opposite end involving consumer-product industries manufacturing goods for impulse purchases. The reaction time for customer requirements in these two extreme cases may justify quite different organization structures and responsibilities for the individual functional areas involved.

The consumer-oriented company must react quickly to changes. There are usually many substitutes available, and the superiority of one product over another may not be clearly identifiable. In many cases, consumer products are manufactured continuously or at least on certain production lines. The ability to rapidly adjust to changing conditions is of primary importance to ensure that the product is available in the marketplace.

The industrial product may have a clear-cut technical difference from similar or substitute products. The importance of coordinating all functions involved to minimize the cycle time between customer order and delivery will probably not be critical. The organization which is oriented to consumer-type products will probably place more emphasis on the distribution concept. By contrasting the above two extremes, clear delineations for coordination, planning, and control can be made.

Policy Decisions. The policy decisions related to the distribution concept include two broad areas, those which are related to customer service and those which are related to costs associated with inventory. All policies related to customer service concern the capabilities of the firm to respond to customer orders in the minimum amount of time or at a time specified by the customer.

Control over transportation routing frequently determines the transit time of a product from seller to buyer. A company policy regarding who has the pre-rogative to select the carriers is a major one controlling the total time required for delivery of product and therefore affects customer service. Frequently these decisions are based on the competitive environment of the company and industrial practices concerning who will bear the burden of transportation costs.

Utilization of field warehouses to provide reduced delivery time is a traditional method for providing service in many industries. This is a method which is usually accepted by many firms within the same industry. Warehousing is one of the most expensive ways for an industrial firm to improve its service to customers.

Additional risks include increased complexity in inventory control and increased costs associated with additional warehousing. Because they are the most difficult to manage, inventories are the primary internal policy subject related to customer service within the distribution functions. The risks related to potential stock outs versus the additional inventory burden associated with minimizing product stock outs, are one of the most frequently studied and complex policy areas in the firm. Determining inventory levels is extremely complex because it in-volves not only the inventory outlay in finished products but also the inventories of work in process, stores, and vendor commitments which have not yet been produced.

Reducing order-processing-cycle time is a major way for reducing the order-delivery cycle. This is one of the least costly methods for reducing the total delivery time of a product to a customer because it basically involves clerical functions and data processing operations.

The policies regarding transit time, order-processing time, field warehousing, and inventory levels are all interrelated variables which in the aggregate deter-mine the total time required to deliver a product. The trade-offs among these four elements for reducing customer-order delivery time must be properly evalu-ated in an economic analysis to determine whether improving the efficiency of any one element is worth the value received.

Timing of Decisions. There are several areas of planning where decisions must be made well in advance of the action to be taken. For example, seasonal fluctuation in product demand is a factor which must be considered if the busi-ness is to take full advantage of its potential. The failure to adequately plan or compensate for seasonal fluctuations in demand and materials could cause interruptions in production and also stock-out conditions in the distribution channels.

Long lead times are usually required to make significant production-capacity increases or decreases. Planned changes in the demand pattern resulting from the introduction of new products or the promotion of existing products require planning for a specific time period or completion date. Failure to consider all the significant variables required to support the distribution of a new product or the promotion of an existing product can be one of the most expensive failures by the distribution function. This is particularly true of products which have seasonal demands or demand concentrated into short time periods on a cyclical basis.

The above refers primarily to lost profit opportunities. The following is re-lated to cost-avoidance decisions which can be generated within the distribution functions. The planning of inventory when anticipating a changing of material costs can be an important way of reducing cost and should be done within the distribution function in conjunction with purchasing. The purchasing of materials in economic ordering and shipping quantities is a traditional example where coordination reduces cost. Advantage can be taken of these potential

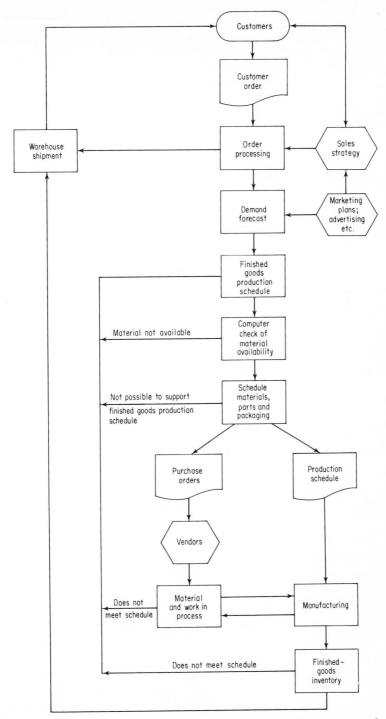

Fig. 1 Schematic model of interrelationships (marketing, distribution, and manu-facturing).

cost-avoidance decisions only if adequate planning and forecasting is provided for inventory of finished goods, components, and materials. Comprehensive planning in the form of a forecast, both for the end product and all related aspects of product capabilities, is fundamental to all other planning.

System and Information. Complete and timely information are the most important factors affecting the distribution function's efficiency and cost. As indicated in Fig. 1, the key source of all information coming into the distribution system is the customer's order. The method in which this information is *exploded* into inventory requirements, production plans, production schedules, material requirements, purchasing, and forecasting is fundamental to the effectiveness of the entire system and its ability to respond efficiently to the demands of the customers.

Once the primary decisions within planning have been developed and communicated, the basic distribution function becomes one of control—minimizing the impact of deviations from plan. Adherence to the production schedule is of paramount importance in carrying out all other plans. The failure to adhere to production schedules may cause dramatic changes and diseconomies in many related functions. The importance of control depends on the nature of the business and its ability to respond and compensate for failure to meet production schedules.

Vendor performance in supporting the materials inventory plan is a primary control point. *Vendor evaluation* can provide indications of future production problems when shipping schedules are not adhered to. Inbound transportation and outbound transportation time must be controlled if full advantage is to be made of improvements established in other parts of the company. These are frequently overlooked and left uncontrolled. For example, a significant expenditure may be considered for reducing the amount of changeover time for a production line by two or three days to improve customer service. It is frequently possible to gain this time with rigid control and enforcement of efficiencies in shipping, order processing, and transportation.

Frequently overlooked is the control of the number of errors that develop in the information system used for forecasting, production scheduling, and material control. A system which is properly designed will indicate potential problems resulting from errors which "creep" into information systems. It is very difficult to determine where and how to detect the errors in a system. This can be done only by rigid analysis and constant control over the information within the system.

In all the functional areas the planning and implementation of plans should be carried out to complement the objectives of the marketing organization. Failure to orient the response of the above system to the requirements of the marketing organization will inhibit and reduce the full potential of marketing goals and objectives. This is not to say that the system should be responsive to marketing objectives at any cost. However, it is incumbent on the distribution system to respond to marketing objectives whenever it is in the best interest of the company.

DISTRIBUTION COSTS

Distribution decisions may be made using mathematical models as discussed in this handbook or by some less analytical, intuitive technique. Regardless of the method used, some information about costs must be available. The following is a discussion of these costs.

Inventory Costs. The traditional costs associated with inventory are interest on invested capital, storage, obsolescence, and product deterioration. These costs occur at all levels of inventory activity from raw materials to finished goods. However, the two most expensive elements of inventory, with the highest risk, are the costs of lost sales by not having inventory when it's required, and the loss through technological obsolescence or price obsolescence caused by competitive products. The system must be capable of minimizing all major inventory risks.

The reaction time of a control system generating sales forecasts, production schedules, and inventory decisions is a primary determinant in the cost of inventory because of the risks inherent in the delay in responding to product demand. The traditional inventory costs are in many cases not the primary determinant of inventory levels. This is because the environment in the marketplace, the competition from other products, and the unwillingness of management to assume risks in many cases will be more important than the combination of interest, obsolescence, and storage costs which are traditionally used to calculate inventory costs.

Transportation Costs. Transportation costs are primarily a function of four basic elements: the distance a shipment must travel, the weight of the shipment, the nature or type of product, and the mode of transportation utilized.

Generally, transportation costs, regardless of the size of shipment or the nature of the product, increase at a decreasing rate as the distance becomes greater. For example, the per-mile costs of transportation will generally be higher on a shipment being transported 50 miles than it will be for a shipment being transported 200 miles. The important thing is that although the four elements mentioned above determine the basic transportation costs, there are many variables included in the actual shipping cost.

Because transportation rates are negotiable and the volume of traffic moving between any two given points has an influence on the general cost level, it is very unwise to generalize on the specific transportation costs of any commodity between two given points without an analysis of all the available alternatives.

Shipping and Warehousing Costs. Warehousing makes it possible to have whatever is being stored available for future use or utility. It is also a function which is frequently used to create equilibrium between productive capacity and consumer demand. Warehousing only adds value to the product by making it available for future use.

Only under unusual economic conditions is it more desirable to warehouse a product than it is to move an item to the next step closer to the final consumer. A majority of products remain in storage most of their life cycle. The actual processing or manufacturing time required for materials to be changed into products is relatively small compared to the amount of time products or materials remain in storage. Products, their component parts, and materials are generally stored in several places between the raw-material stage and the finished-product stage. For example, paper products which are ultimately used as packaging for milk containers begin with logs which are stored prior to processing through lumber mills; the logs are then ground into pulp and the pulp processed into rolls of paper which are stored. The paper product is processed for assembly into a milk carton and then stored. The carton material is transported to the filling operation, where it is stored briefly before filling. After the carton is filled it is moved to the retail outlet and stored until sold. The container is then moved to the customer's refrigerator for storage prior to consumption.

Storage throughout the above system has several characteristics which are common to many systems requiring warehousing. It is necessary to provide assurance of supply for the next process or event. The nonavailability of product in any one of the succeeding steps would mean serious economic loss to the operation. Storage and warehousing costs are built into the price of the product as it moves to the next stage in the system. Storage itself does not improve the intrinsic value of the product.

One characteristic of storage which should be important to the cost-oriented manager is that by its very nature storage and warehousing is not a primary function; it therefore does not always attract attention of progressive management. This situation frequently results in inefficient warehouse operations.

There are five major cost elements which constitute the operating costs of a warehouse or storage facility:

1. Labor
2. Management, including staff functions such as industrial engineering, operations research, data processing, etc.
3. Facility cost, including interest on investment and taxes
4. Equipment, including mobile equipment plus stationary equipment
5. Maintenance: both facilities and equipment

The primary cost elements of warehousing relate to utilization of the cubic capacity of the facility, particularly if the floor space is a limiting factor. Efficient labor utilization is a second critical problem area to solve. Warehousing operations are frequently subject to rapidly changing levels of activity. This characteristic prevents any incentive for achieving high efficiency levels. It is difficult to maintain discipline when there is frequently not enough work to keep the entire labor force busy for extended time periods. Management finds it difficult to sustain efficient operations under this type of erratic change in activity. The current trends to resolve this type of problem include automating warehouse operations, increasing the warehouse capacity, or removing bottlenecks from existing operations. Careful planning and simulation of automated warehouse operations are frequently not sufficient to avoid protracted start-ups and long, costly "break-in" periods.

The distance traveled when a sequence of items must be placed into storage or withdrawn from storage must also be considered in labor costs. These operations are all controllable and measurable.

The cost of managing the warehouse will vary with the span of control established for first-line supervision and the amount of staff services used. Staff services may include industrial engineering, operations research analysts, and data processing. The larger the warehouse, the more potential use there is for these types of staff services. There are no significant efficiency ratios for the cost of warehouse management because the cost must be placed in context of the results obtained. It should be sufficient to say that the addition of staff services or additional management to a warehouse operation should be used only for the purpose of achieving measurable and justifiable increase in operating effectiveness.

Facility costs are frequently a result of policies beyond the control of the warehouse manager. However, as much influence as possible should be exerted by the operating management. The warehouse facility must be planned to accomplish a specific purpose. For example, the warehouse may be designed to receive and store materials during the next five years. In this case, adequate forecast must be made concerning such things as how many receiving doors will be required for the differences in volume, number of materials, and parts received.

Order-processing Costs. Processing customer orders should accomplish two essential functions for the firm. Assimilating the customer requirements into a data form that can be used for shipping the product to the customer is the number-one function. The simultaneous capturing of data to be used for sales forecasting, market analysis, and market planning is the second important use of customer-order processing.

Current levels of marketing and sales management proficiency usually require the analysis and summary of customers orders and shipping information into several levels. The systems of exploding comprehensive sales and marketing information are the fastest-growing trends related to order processing. These systems usually have three primary inputs of information:

1. Customer orders
2. Current production and inventory information
3. Shipping information

The order-processing system in a company utilizing a computer should consider the following operations to be performed within the framework of the order-processing system:

1. Preparation of customer order for shipment
2. Collect, store, and process sales statistics
3. Generate sales forecasts
4. Collect current production and inventory information
5. Serve as a data base for production scheduling and inventory planning

All these functions require a considerable amount of data handling and data processing. This is the crux of an effective order-processing system. It is not the single function of preparing shipping orders from customer orders that makes this function so important. It is the related functions that can be processed concurrently to make this one of the key operating systems within today's business operation.

Very often, the customer-order-processing computer programs are so integrated with other functions that it becomes impossible to clearly separate them to determine what the cost of each activity is. The cost of performing a fully integrated customer-order-processing system, including the elements previously discussed, will depend on the following:

1. The number and types of customers.
2. The number of products or stock numbers.
3. The number of exceptions to "normal" order processing.
4. Efficiency of the computer program and system.
5. The computer equipment utilized.
6. The number and variety of such qualifications as sales terms, price discounts, volume discounts, etc.
7. The length of the order-processing and shipping cycle. The longer the customer order is held prior to shipment, the more costly it becomes to store and maintain this item.

Another important aspect is the "opportunity cost" phase of the function—that is, the cost of *not* processing customer orders in the most efficient manner possible in order to achieve more favorable results in other areas of the company. For example, it is not uncommon to require three to four days before shipment can take place after the order is received.

Under almost any circumstances it is possible to perform this cycle in a maximum of 24 hours with the proper system and computing equipment. The advantage of reducing this time must be balanced against the cost of improving other functional systems which would help perform the minimum cycle time.

The order-processing system is the basic source of all marketing and sales information by customer, products, and geographical areas. It has an additional importance because there are many alternative ways of processing customer orders to obtain this type of information in an efficient manner. Therefore, the feasible alternatives must be evaluated to achieve a high degree of efficiency.

Production Scheduling Costs. The nature of production scheduling costs makes it difficult to compare good versus poor performance. The essence of efficient production scheduling is choosing the best alternative available under given conditions of productive capacity, demand, and material availability. Poor timing of production scheduling decisions can generate major inefficiencies and excessive costs in the system. Failure to start or reduce production at the optimum time can create serious negative economic effects. The failure to minimize the number of production schedule changes can create production losses. Serious labor problems can result from ineffective production scheduling which does not consider the consequences of labor-force fluctuations. The failure to evaluate alternatives, such as the increasing production capacity versus producing on an overtime or premium basis, is the source of many major production scheduling costs.

The production scheduling cost elements are related to the number of products to be produced, the similarity of the products, the commonality of parts and components within the products, the continuity of production, the efficiency of the production line, and the frequency of change in the product line.

DISTRIBUTION MODELS

A model is a thing used to represent something else. The important thing about a model which represents something else is how *valid* is the representation. One very realistic model which can be found in every grade school is a physical representation of the sun's solar system. This type of model has several characteristics which differ from the type used to describe business relationships. The physical model of the solar system has a limited number of relationships for observation so that certain ones are readily understood. A static model is unsatisfactory if it is necessary to understand dynamic relationships. With the large number of variables which may exist in business it is not always possible to comprehend the dynamics of the relationships without developing a complex mathematical model.

Distribution models will correspond with "the real world" only in terms of the information they provide. The relationships and dynamics which take place in the real business function will be represented or quantified by a mathematical formula or algorithm. The mathematics is only a short-cut method to indicate or measure relationships that are being emulated.

The number of significant relationships which a model must represent will determine the design complexity of the model. The number of relationships will also determine the difficulty of testing the model for its correspondence to the real world. Distribution models are primarily used to determine complex cost relationships. For example, the interrelationships among the economics of production, inventory costs, stock-out costs, and transportation costs under given demand conditions could provide the basis for a complex model. The specific objectives of a model must be defined and conditions established which will permit adequate testing of the model's validity.

Distribution models may be helpful to a manager by defining or identifying problems. Aiding the manager to test several alternatives and determine the best course of action is another important use for models. The results from a given set of problem conditions can also be predicted or simulated by models.

Models can assist in predicting the results of decisions or conditions without actually carrying out the real situation. From this point of view, it is less expensive to test the results of decisions with a model than to risk the costly implementation. Testing decisions or determining alternative courses of action can be less expensive and take less time by utilizing a model. The purpose of a business or distribution model is to augment decision making and reduce the risk of operating.

The objective of a model must be defined in order to begin its proper development. The model's objective may change or be modified during its development or during its testing. The primary reason for establishing the objective of the model first is to determine the major parameters that will assist in controlling the subject to be studied. A too general and broad explanation of the model's objective can lead to a significant amount of unnecessary development time because of the many aspects of a business problem which can be explored. Specific objectives must be defined to eliminate the loss of development time on tangential aspects of the problem. How accurately the model must correspond with the execution of the real event is the second important determination in the development period. The number of variables which are to be considered must be identified before serious development can be initiated. For example, if a production schedule model is to be developed, some of the variables to be considered are:

Overtime
Additional production shifts
Tooling capacities
Production-line capacity
Availability of labor
Length of production run

All these variables must be considered even though it may not be necessary to build them into the model because they may prove to be trivial. Generally, the more variables considered, the longer it takes to compute the results. The number of variables will also influence the amount of time required to program and develop the model. In many cases it may be impractical to determine the impact a specific variable will have on the results of the model. Usually, the more realism desired in the model, the larger the number of variables which will be considered.

The calculation and measurement of the results of the interaction between two or more variables is the major purpose of the model. The usual method is to develop a mathematical algorithm which represents the real-world activities that must be represented by the model.

Once the model has been developed to quantify the interactions among variables, data must be gathered to be used as input for testing the model. This latter is an important phase in model development. Failure to perform adequate tests and evaluations of the effect of the major variables will inevitably cause severe restrictions in the confidence that can be placed in the model.

Time required to develop the model depends on the experience of the personnel working and the interest on the part of the management in the project. Although it is impossible to predict the amount of time required for model development and computer programming, it is safe to say that a minimum of 50 percent of the total time—from initiation to completion—will be spent in model development rather than programming. The remainder of the time will probably be consumed in programming and testing the model. These time estimates assume that it is not possible to utilize "canned" programs or previously programmed techniques such as linear programming.

Linear Programming.   Linear programming is one of the most frequently used "instruments of economic logic." The methods for solving linear-programming problems are described in numerous texts and journals and also in Chapters 13 and 26 of this handbook. This section will not discuss methods of solution. The purpose of this section will be to specify problem areas where linear-programming models can be applied.

Linear programming is a method which allocates limited resources. The technique provides optimum distribution of limited resources. Linear-programming models have been useful in the following types of situations:

1. The problem is to minimize the total transportation cost for distributing products from several origins to several market areas. At the same time, the demand in each market area must be satisfied. This problem has very limited use, since it deals only with one cost element of the total distribution problem and does not consider many other significant costs or the profit ramifications of the problem situation.

2. An expansion of the foregoing problem could include the production cost plus inventory and other distribution costs. The inclusion of these costs will provide a more comprehensive statement of the problem situation. Their inclusion will also improve the probability of being able to maximize profit or minimize cost.

3. If several producing points are involved in the above problem, and there are no restraints placed on the minimum level of production activity which must take place at any specific producing point, drastic shifts in total production volume of a specific producing point may be recommended in the optimum solution to the problem. A typical situation involves several producing plants, some of which are higher-cost production points than others. When considering only product costs, it may be determined by the linear-programming model that the high-cost producing point should be eliminated while adding additional hours of overtime, or additional shifts, or production at the lowest-cost production points.

4. In the same manner that production is allocated from producing points for markets, a similar type of application involves the allocation of limited materials into several products which have commmon material requirements. The objective is to maximize the profit that can be made by allocating a limited amount of materials to products which require varying amounts of the limited materials and have different profit margins. Another similar problem area involves optimizing profits by minimizing distribution costs of a limited mix of products into several market areas, each market area having a peculiar mix.

Heuristic Models. A heuristic model is valuable for simulating or conducting empirical studies which are unproved or incapable of proof. Many distribution problems fall in the category "incapable of proof" because there are so many variables which are not stable enough to be quantified at the time the problem solution is desired. The objective of the model might be to develop the best cost alternatives among several production schedules which have the highest probability of satisfying an uncertain demand. The model developed would attempt to determine the lowest-cost schedule among thousands of possibilities. The model would work by continuously developing feasible schedules and selecting from among these the lowest-cost schedule.

The minimum-cost schedules derived from this model may not be acceptable to management because they may require drastic or sudden changes in production levels or inventory risk. Although certain policies are built into the model, it may not always be possible to develop an acceptable low-cost production schedule for management from a model of this type because all conditions cannot be anticipated at the time the model is developed. If this type of situation should occur, it is easy enough for management to disregard a minimum-cost schedule which conflicts with operating policies.

The problem would be to develop minimum-cost production plans to meet an unpredictable seasonal demand. A computer-oriented model would be developed to generate an array of minimum-cost production plans. This model recognizes the probabilistic nature of demand and also practical considerations of assembly-line rates, learning, lead times, etc.

Model Limitations. Distribution models generally involve so many important variables that it is difficult to understand their dynamic relationships. Understanding the relationships is essential to good decision making and may be difficult without constructing some form of model. The scientist has worked for many years with models to crystallize his understanding of problems. Although management decisions involve extremely complex relationships among many variables, utilization of models for understanding the problems has been very limited.

Even though understanding the problem and its complex variables is essential, it does not guarantee that good decisions can or will be made. Experience in dealing with models to recognize good decisions or solutions is important. Many models will only provide management with experience of how to recognize *poor* solutions or decisions. In some cases, a model's major contribution will be to eliminate solutions which are not feasible and thereby provide management with alternatives, any one of which may not be significantly better than the other. Therefore, it is important for management to practice thinking through solutions as they relate to specific problems.

The development of a model frequently requires a complement of personnel including systems analysts, programmers, functional operating supervisors, and management. In almost all cases, a computer is necessary to operate a comprehensive model. Depending on the complexity of the particular model, the personnel can be involved for several weeks, several months, or more than a year. If the model is to be developed, tested, and implemented, a considerable amount of time, effort and cost must be expected to achieve success. Even after a model has been developed, it is very likely that a substantial amount of computer-program maintenance will be required. Changing environmental factors will influence the validity of the solutions developed from the model and will necessitate additional programming and system work.

New insight into improving standards and measurement of performance against these standards can be derived from models. Frequently, standards and performance measurements are made within the confines of specific functional activities. This is very difficult to do and it is therefore seldom accomplished. It is therefore important to evaluate the interface activities of functions. In some cases, it is possible to gain new insight into measuring interface effectiveness by utilizing models. In cases where this can be accomplished, the establishment of performance standards and their measurement can provide significant contributions to good management.

TRANSPORTATION MODES

The production and inventory control manager must be concerned with his firm's place in the sequence of manufacturing if he is to relate properly the selection of a transportation mode with storage facilities, economic order quantities, lead times, and reorder points. Position of the firm in the sequence of manufacturing refers to whether it operates as an extractor, refiner, fabricator, assembler, distributor, or any combination of these.

The type and quantity of product to be moved in and out of a facility must be matched with the operating attributes and characteristics of the various modes of transportation. Normally, a shipper would not attempt to move a large volume of grain by air freight because the shipping costs, volume of freight, and schedules are not compatible with the operation of a milling facility. By the same token, complete exclusion of air freight is not recommended as specific conditions could justify the use of air freight to meet emergency conditions.

It is not possible to review all the various manufacturing and distribution facilities just to list their specific transportation needs. This will be left to the reader. It is suggested that the following factors be considered:

1. Volume of material to be moved
2. Ratio of freight cost to total cost of the product
3. Need for continuous flow of material; i.e., whether a constant material flow is necessary to feed a processing operation (refinery), or an intermittent flow will suffice to feed a job shop
4. Effect of external conditions such as weather
5. Effect of government traffic regulations
6. Operating-cost characteristics of the transportation mode

In addition there are usually special aspects that apply in individual cases.

Characteristics of Transportation Modes. The following tables set down the operating characteristics of the basic transportation modes. These characteristics should be matched with the needs of the specific facility.

PHYSICAL CHARACTERISTICS:

A. *Railroads*
　　1. Integrated single system.
　　2. Carload and train principle.
　　3. Rail-flanged wheel-guidance system.
　　4. High-ton movement per horsepower.
　　5. Limited rail network serving major commercial centers.

B. *Motor Carriers*
　　1. Single-movement unit with exception of semitrailers and doubles.
　　2. Flexibility of route over all highways and most roads.
　　3. Guidance is roadway; driver relatively less safe enroute.
　　4. Flexible terminal location.
　　5. System is facilitated by interstate highway developments.

C. *Pipelines*
　　1. Closed, guided system with no flexibility of route.
　　2. Route and capacity is limited to pipe diameter and pressure.
　　3. Fixed facilities with fixed propulsion united (pumping stations).
　　4. Low propulsive force required to maintain low speeds of 2 to 3 miles per hour.
　　5. Storage tanks are needed at terminals for continuous operation.
　　6. Routes are one directional.

D. *Air Carriers*
　　1. Discrete single-movement unit, heavier than air.
　　2. Flexible "roadway," yet is required to transit within FAA-controlled airways.
　　3. Requires great stability and critical weight and balance.
　　4. High-skill pilot guidance required.
　　5. Terminals are fixed.

E. *Water Carriers*
　　1. Single-movement unit on ocean; multiple units used with barges and tug for inland carriers.
　　2. Routes are limited by waterways, canals, and locks.
　　3. Needs stability and trim for correct buoyancy.
　　4. Navigational-skill guidance is important.
　　5. Limited to fixed terminals.

6. Shipments cover large point-to-point volumes requiring sizable terminal and interconnecting facilities.
7. Low power requirement per tons carried.

ECONOMIC CHARACTERISTICS:

A. *Railroads*
1. Purchases and maintains its own right of way.
2. High fixed cost, low variable cost structure.
3. Declining unit-cost industry.
4. Operates on little or no subsidies.
5. Needs volume over long distances for economy of scale operations.

B. *Motor Carriers*
1. Operation is high variable, low fixed cost, out-of-pocket cost industry.
2. Economical in short haul.
3. Requires small investment to enter business.
4. Pays use tax for highways but does not own the roadway.
5. No direct subsidy from government.
6. Operates favorably in the distribution phase of logistics.

C. *Pipelines*
1. High fixed costs to variable with very little out-of-pocket costs.
2. Declining unit-cost industry up to the route capacity.
3. No subsidies are provided.
4. System owns and maintains its own "right-of-way" or roadway.
5. Costs are a function of system size and utilization.

D. *Air Carriers*
1. No "roadway" cost, nor terminal expense of owning runway and landing facility exists.
2. Subsidy through promotion by the federal government.
3. Relatively high fixed and high variable cost with declining unit cost up to plane capacity.
4. More economical in long-haul operation.
5. High cost of aircraft and resultant high cost of idle equipment.

E. *Water Carriers*
1. No "roadway" cost but high terminal cost, including stevedoring, dockage, and wharfage.
2. Ocean carriers are subsidized on selected trade routes by Federal Maritime Commission.
3. High fixed cost and a declining unit cost up to ship capacity.
4. Requires high volume point to point for economies of scale.
5. High daily demurrage cost for ship delay (about $3,000 per day).

SERVICE CHARACTERISTICS:

A. *Railroads*
1. Overall speed slow but has express service.
2. Incomplete as to delivery (terminal to terminal).
3. Generally low rates on carload lots.
4. Adaptability to varying loads and volume and all types of material somewhat limited.
5. Best in raw-material transport rather than finished products.
6. Rough handling and slow, especially on less-than-carload freight.
7. Reliable service, little affected by weather.

B. *Motor Carriers*
1. Flexible and responsive to customer-service needs.
2. Provides door-to-door service, thus low packing costs.
3. Lower rates for short haul are offered.

4. Safer handling for finished goods and fragile items is provided.
5. Size and weight limitations are a handicap.
6. Service is affected by weather.
7. Acts as delivery agent for other modes, due to flexibility from terminal to customer.
8. Speed of service is relatively good, fewer transfer delays exist.

C. *Pipelines*
1. Slow speed but very continuous flow.
2. Lowest-cost carrier.
3. Limited in commodity range to gases, liquids, and solids movable in slurries.
4. Great quantities are moved over time.
5. Very dependable and not affected by weather.

D. *Air Carriers*
1. Low weight capacity available per unit.
2. High speeds from terminal to terminal but is incomplete from and to terminals.
3. Costly service. but low packaging requirements counterbalance cost.
4. Long-haul advantage exists.
5. Rate advantages to largest cities exists.
6. Favorable for high-value and perishable products.
7. Luxury passenger accommodations are available.
8. Extensively affected by weather.

E. *Water Carriers*
1. Overall speed is slow.
2. Needs volume (200 to 500 tons) for port calls.
3. Service is incomplete from and to terminals.
4. Handling damage and pilferage are high.
5. Seasonal service exists on inland waters and some ocean areas.
6. High-capacity carrier.
7. Loading and unloading performed for carriers by stevedores.

INTERNAL CHARACTERISTICS:

A. *Railroads*
1. An oligopolistic industry which is difficult or impossible for competition to enter.
2. Operation is by ICC regulation as a public utility serving public convenience and necessity, including the operation of unprofitable runs.
3. Organizations are large and highly departmentalized.
4. Extensive capitalization required.
5. Most railroads are considered to have conservative management.

B. *Motor Carriers*
1. Extreme competition exists from many small firms.
2. Common and contract carriers are for hire, but most carriers are private.
3. Ease of entrance into and exit from business exists.
4. Many specialized carriers (by type of commodity) exist.
5. Profit margins for most carriers is small.
6. Many carriers operate as exempt commodity carriers.

C. *Pipelines*
1. Oligopolistic and is owned by petroleum companies with minor exceptions.
2. System is ICC-controlled as common carrier.
3. Little labor is required to operate system.
4. Product commingling problems.

     5. Railroads with existing right-of-ways are entering pipeline business.
     6. Cooperation by producers in use of pipelines is required.
     7. Pipeline types are crude-oil gathering, crude-oil trunk, and product lines.
  D. *Air Carriers*
     1. System is oligopolistic.
     2. Classes of carriers are divided as to trunk, feeder, and all-freight.
     3. Continual changes in equipment are made in a "keep up with the Joneses" race.
     4. Lines have progressive, innovative management.
     5. Companies are becoming large.
  E. *Water Carriers*
     1. System is oligopolistic.
     2. Some ships are privately owned and operated.
     3. Organizations vary as to types of water carriers, foreign trade, inland water, Great Lakes.
     4. Foreign trade is organized under rate conferences.

EXTERNAL CHARACTERISTICS:
A. *Railroads*
     1. All railroads are under economic regulation of ICC. All are common carriers.
     2. Negotiation of labor contracts is with *strong* brotherhoods of railroad workers.
     3. Markets are moving and diversifying away from railheads.
     4. Serious competition exists with trucking industry.
     5. Public environment presently is favorable to mergers, etc.
     6. Current demand for speed in passenger transportation cannot be satisfied.
B. *Motor Carriers*
     1. ICC regulation over common and contract carriers only concerns economic regulation.
     2. State safety and weight regulation exists over all carriers. Many states have differing regulations.
     3. Regulations are difficult to enforce.
     4. System is favored by market segmentation and diversification and by suburbanization and interurbia complexes.
     5. Affected by strong central labor control of teamsters.
C. *Pipelines*
     1. System operates in a very select market using specialized service.
     2. ICC-regulated as common carrier.
     3. Natural-gas lines are regulated by Federal Power Commission.
     4. Competition is from railroads and water carriers.
D. *Air Carriers*
     1. System is affected by national prestige and defense consideration.
     2. CAB regulates and promotes; FAA administers policies and safety.
     3. There is a marketing emphasis on lowering inventories and utilizing premium transportation such as air.
     4. International influence exists including State Department control from IATA agreements.
     5. Market demand for speed in passenger transport field is high and increasing.
E. *Water Carriers*
     1. ICC controls inland and lake carriers.
     2. FMC and MA controls foreign trade.

3. FMC promotes ocean shipping through subsidies.
4. High competition exists with foreign flags.
5. High cost of United States labor in shipbuilding, stevedoring, and sea-going trades is a detriment.
6. United States Army engineers maintain inland waterways.
7. United States Coast Guard controls safety-at-sea requirements.

TECHNICAL ASPECTS:

A. *Railroads*
   1. Power units are nearly all diesel.
   2. Trend is to specialized equipment: damage-free cars, large-door box-cars, tri-level auto carriers.
   3. Some automated roadways and classification yards are being built for trailer-on-flatcar equipment and railhead yards for trailers (piggyvilles).
   4. Unit train capability is being extended.

B. *Motor Carriers*
   1. A variety of specialized equipment exists.
   2. Central dispatching communication for improved control is being used.
   3. Sleeper cabs for long hauls are used.
   4. Advances in extent and design for roadways and interstate systems are being made.
   5. Improvements in safety engineering.

C. *Pipelines*
   1. System is protected underground.
   2. There are more miles of pipelines than rails (third most extensive carrier).
   3. System has automated metering and valve monitoring for product control and is most highly automated of all carriers.

D. *Air Carriers*
   1. High-performance jet aircraft are used in all services.
   2. Automated baggage and freight handling exists at most terminals.
   3. Ground control and airborne safety devices.
   4. Specialized cargo planes, swing-tail, roll-on, etc., have been developed.
   5. Unitization of operations in minimizing ground time for cargo operations is used.

E. *Water Carriers*
   1. Large self-sustaining high-speed United States flag vessels are under development.
   2. Specialized ships for containers, heavy lift, roll-on, roll-off are in use.
   3. Specialized terminals for buck loading and container loading are being developed.
   4. Specialized and diversified barges, yet integrated for common tow are in use.

FUTURE OUTLOOK:

A. *Railroads*
   1. High-speed rapid transit systems for urban needs are being developed.
   2. More diversification through owning subsidiary truckers, pipelines, and barges for complete service is being enlarged.
   3. Trend to cost-of-service pricing policy by ICC will favor rails in economic advantages areas of long hauls and volume needs.
   4. Containerization interlink with foreign trade ships is being developed.
   5. There is little chance of gaining lost share of transport market.

B. *Motor Carriers*
   1. More short hauling with interurbia self-sufficiency will develop.

    2. Truckers are becoming bigger firms, buying up little ones.

    3. Future problems in traffic congestion will increase.

    4. Trend will be toward more uniform state regulations.

    5. More door-to-door service will be demanded in finished goods.

    6. ICC reviews and tightening of regulations will be a result of urban thinking.

    7. Legislature.

C. *Pipelines*

    1. Product diversification in pipelines will result with lower-cost cleaning operations.

    2. More solids such as woodchips and coal will be handled in slurries.

    3. More railroads will enter the pipeline business as more depreciated tanker cars are retired.

D. *Air Carriers*

    1. Automated air controlling for approaches to congested areas is used.

    2. Larger and faster aircraft will be developed.

    3. More helicopter service as terminals move out.

    4. Lower rates will be applied for deferred air freight.

    5. More businesses will utilize their own aircraft.

    6. Trend may change from speed to economy.

E. *Water Carriers*

    1. Increased intercoastal and coastwide shipping, with containers, in rate competition with railroads is projected.

    2. Hydrofoils for luxury passenger service are under development.

    3. Nuclear power usage.

    4. Automated controls on ships for crew reduction.

    5. Mode integration with rails and trucks through containerization.

Transportation Rates. Transportation rates have been under varying degrees of government regulation since 1887. Currently rates and regulations are pointing toward the establishment of a national transportation policy. It is not the objective here to review the extensive government regulations and rate-making structure, but rather to make the reader aware of the various aspects of rate making and regulation as they effect production and inventory control.

RATE SYSTEMS: There are two general rate systems. First are those rates which diminish with distance so that average cost per mile is less for long distances than short distances. A second rate system is based on *blanket rates* which combine a group of delivery points under one rate.

All these rate systems consist of two portions: the line-haul part and the accessorial part. The calculation of the line-haul part is based on four approaches:

1. Class rates which have a basic rate plus allowances for special conditions of the commodity being shipped

2. Exception rates which are adjustments to class rates for special privileges to the shipper and consignee

3. Commodity rates which are established for high-volume commodities under special routes over extended periods of time

4. All-commodity rates (freight of all kinds) which are rates established to cover bulk shipments of heterogeneous products

The second portion of the rate system involves those costs necessary to provide the line-haul service. Involved are terminal costs, clerical costs, fixed costs, demurrage charges, etc.

ADDITIONAL SERVICES: There are a number of services available which the shipper might find advantageous. Among these are:

1. Diversion and reconsignment which allows the shipper to change destination and consignee while the shipment is in transit.

2. Transit privileges which allow the shipper to unload, process, and reload a shipment between shipping point and destination. In this case, a shipment is handled at a rate below that which would apply if two separate shipments were made. The objective is to allow processing of material between the shipping point and destination and still provide the shipper with a cost structure competitive with processors situated at either terminal.

3. Stop-off privileges which allow the shipper to either load or unload between the shipping point and destination at a rate lower than that which would apply if separate shipments were made.

Documentation of Shipments. The basic document used as evidence of shipment is the bill of lading (Fig. 2). The bill of lading serves three functions: (1) as a receipt for the material, (2) as a contract for carriage, and (3) as evidence of title. The bill of lading can be basically either a nonnegotiable straight bill of lading assigned to a specific entity or an order bill of lading which can be bought and sold. Of course, the bill of lading is not the only document involved in transportation, but it is the basic document involved. For details in handling shipping documents, the reader is referred to the Bibliography at the end of the chapter for specific details covering specific types of shipments.

CORRELATION OF TRANSPORTATION AND INVENTORY CONTROL

Basic and advanced approaches to the development of economic order quantities and reorder points are covered in Chapters 14 and 16. Transportation costs and modes of transportation are directly involved in various aspects of these formulations. These effects should be carefully investigated and correlated before arbitrarily using the formula.

Transit Time. Although each mode of transportation has different speeds of movement, the factors that are important to the practitioner are total door-to-door time and consistency of schedule.

In the development of lead times, a factor for transit time is included which covers door-to-door service. The stress is on door-to-door service as a product in transit processes neither time nor place utility as far as the user is concerned. Therefore, the transit time is a summation of movements, storages, transfers, etc., from the time the material leaves the shippers' plant until it reaches the users' plant.

Consistency of schedules determines the extent to which transit time has to be adjusted to allow for a safety factor. A product which can be moved between two points with a high degree of consistency by a low-cost mode in four days, for example, may be more advantageous than a higher-cost mode which might be able to move the material in only one day but at much lower assurance of consistently delivering in one day. A sampling of transit times required by the various modes should be made to establish a probability distribution showing the expected delivery (see Chapter 28). From this distribution, probabilities can be established to indicate with what assurance the shipper can expect to realize delivery in a certain number of days. Table 1 is a hypothetical example. In this example, the customer using rail freight would have to allow 3.1 days' transit time in his formulation.

He would only have to allow two days if he shipped by air freight. A very important point here is the determination of the assurance level. In the case of rail freight, the receiver would have to allow three days to assure himself that he would have material in his facility 90 percent of the time. He would also have to allow three days to have a 90 percent assurance level when using

† The fibre boxes used for this shipment conform to the specifications set forth in the box maker's certificate thereon, and all other requirements of Consolidated Freight Classification.

†Shipper's imprint in lieu of stamp; not a part of bill of lading approved by the Interstate Commerce Commission.

(Uniform Domestic Straight Bill of Lading, adopted by Carriers in Official, Southern, Western and Illinois Classification territories, Mar. 15, 1922, as amended Aug. 1, 1930, and June 15, 1941.)

UNIFORM STRAIGHT BILL OF LADING
ORIGINAL — NOT NEGOTIABLE

Shipper's No. ______

COMPANY Agent's No. ______

RECEIVED, subject to the classifications and tariffs in effect on the date of the issue of this Bill of Lading,

At SO. BEND, IND., / CHICAGO, ILL., / ELKHART, IND., ______ 19____ FROM **THE ADAMS & WESTLAKE COMPANY**

the property described below, in apparent good order, except as noted (contents and condition of contents of packages unknown), marked, consigned, and destined as indicated below, which said company (the word company being understood throughout this contract as meaning any person or corporation in possession of the property under the contract) agrees to carry to its usual place of delivery at said destination, if on its own road or its own water line, otherwise to deliver to another carrier on the route to said destination. It is mutually agreed, as to each carrier of all or any of said property over all or any portion of said route to destination, and as to each party at any time interested in all or any of said property, that every service to be performed hereunder shall be subject to all the conditions not prohibited by law, whether printed or written, herein contained, including the conditions on back hereof, which are hereby agreed to by the shipper and accepted for himself and his assigns.

(Mail or street address of consignee—For purposes of notification only.)

Consigned to ______

Destination ______ State of ______ County of ______

Route ______

Delivering Carrier ______ Car Initial ______ Car No. ______

NO. OF PACKAGES								
Boxes	Ctns.	Crates	Bdls.	Pallets	Kind of Package, Description of Articles, Special Marks, and Exceptions	*WEIGHT (Sb. to Cr.)	Class or Rate	Ck. Col.
					Window Shades, N.O.I.B.N.			
					Shade Fixtures Rollers			
					Sash R. R. or Bus			
					Sash Parts or Window Frame Parts Rwy. Car or Motor Bus			
					Rubber Packing			
					Weather Strips			
					Steel or Alum. Brass Moulding, Finished			
					Vestibule Diaphragms			
					R. R. Car Parts, Steel, Painted			
					Brass - Bronze - I. or S. Hardware N. O. S.			
					Locks or Lock Sets N. O. I. B. N.			
					Iron or Lavatory Basins Steel (Bowls)			
					Metal Lanterns N.O.I.B.N. Oil - Elect.			
					Oil-Elec. Lamps, N.O.I.B.N. Without Glass Globes or Shades			
					Aluminum or Alum. and Iron or Steel Combined Sash			
					Lamp or Lantern Fixtures (Parts) N.O.I.B.N.			
					Lantern Globes other than Mica			
					Glass Lamp Chimneys, Not Cut			
					Lamp Lenses, N.O.I.B.N. Cast or Moulded, Not Ground			
					Aluminum Junction Boxes or Cabinets, without Fittings			
					Railway Passenger Car Parcel Racks, S.U., K.D.			
					Frames or Holders, Price Card, Steel and Glass Comb.			
					Switch Targets, Rwy. Track - I. or S.			
					Spray Cans Brass or Tin			
					Mercury Switches or Relays			
					Doors, Alum. or Alum. & Iron Combined, S. U.			
					Door Frames, K. D., Not Assembled			

Subject to Section 7 of Conditions of applicable bill of lading, if this shipment is to be delivered to the consignee without recourse on the consignor, the consignor shall sign the following statement:
The carrier shall not make delivery of this shipment without payment of freight and all other lawful charges.

______ (Signature of consignor)

If charges are to be prepaid, write or stamp here, "To be Prepaid."

Received $ ______ to apply in prepayment of the charges on the property described hereon.

______ Agent or Cashier.

Per ______ (The signature here acknowledges only the amount prepaid.)

Charges advanced: $ ______

†Shop Order P. A. No.

*If the shipment moves between two ports by a carrier by water, the law requires that the bill of lading shall state whether it is carrier's or shipper's weight. NOTE—Where the rate is dependent on value, shippers are required to state specifically in writing the agreed or declared value of the property. The agreed or declared value of the property is hereby specifically stated by the shipper to be not exceeding ______ per ______

THE ADAMS & WESTLAKE COMPANY, Shipper, Per ______ Agent ______ Per ______

Permanent post-office address of shipper: ELKHART, INDIANA, U.S.A.
Form W. R. 117 UARCO INCORPORATED

Fig. 2 Bill of lading. (*Courtesy of The Adams & Westlake Company, Elkhart, Ind.*)

air freight. Therefore, from an assurance level standpoint he would have to allow three days in both cases and would be penalized by the higher cost of air freight without receiving any benefit from it.

COST OF PRODUCT: The cost of a product includes, in general terms, the cost to fabricate and the cost to distribute. Usually the closer the product moves to the ultimate consumer, the greater the amount of transportation cost it has. A product when first extracted from nature has a negligible amount of transportation cost. From this point on the basic material cost is the same, but at each successive move, labor and transportation costs are added so that total transportation costs in the product continually increase. In Table 2, again using hypothetical figures, as the product moves further down the distribution channel, transportation costs take on greater importance. This indicates the need to carefully select a transportation mode to reduce the cost of the product.

TABLE 1   Shipper Assurance

Days required for delivery	Rail freight		Air freight	
	P	$P \times$ days	P	$P \times$ days
1	0	0	0.40	0.40
2	0	0	0.30	0.60
3	0.90	2.70	0.20	0.60
4	0.10	0.40	0.10	0.40
Expected delivery	...	3.10 days	...	2.00 days

TABLE 2   Transportation Costs

Product state	Cumulative cost			Cumulative total cost
	Material	Labor	Transportation	
Bauxite ore..............	0.05	0.02	0.01	0.08
Alumina................	0.05	0.05	0.05	0.15
Pig....................	0.05	0.08	0.07	0.20
Mill product............	0.05	0.11	0.09	0.25

Size of Shipment. Correlation of mathematical economic order quantities (EOQs) must be made with the standard transportation quantities. If an EOQ is close to the most economical transportation quantity, an adjustment is probably in order to bring the two quantities in line. The extent to which the quantities are adjusted will be determined by trading off increased inventory carrying costs against reduced transportation costs.

Terminal Location Factors. It is not our purpose at this point to investigate the theory of location. This material is adequately covered by Mossman and Morton[1] and Hesket, Ivie, and Glaskowsky.[2] Rather, we wish to evaluate the factors that affect consumer location, plant and warehouse locations, and transportation modes to determine relationships which affect the production and inventory control function.

Recommended locations are determined by factors of transportation costs, labor costs, and operating costs in the selected area. As costs and demand are not equal at various locations, determination of the least-cost location becomes a matter of cost trade-offs between the cost factors involved.

DEMAND CONSIDERATIONS: In selecting a region in which to locate a warehouse or plant, of primary concern is demand for the product. Unless an adequate demand exists or can be developed, no amount of production and inventory control techniques will provide an adequate profit on operations. The considerations to be made in regard to demand are:

1. Overall population concentration of the market area. In effect, what overall market might be expected in the market area of the firm?

2. Expected growth of the market area. An area which at present does not generate a large enough market may, in the very near future, be large enough if the growth rate is sufficient.

3. Regional development expected. Political boundaries generally do not agree with boundaries of economic regions which are areas that generate substantial intraregional trading. Changes in political boundaries and policies may open markets. An example would be opening of Windsor, Ontario, markets to Detroit business and vice versa if changes were made in United States-Canadian trade relations.

4. The type of product manufactured. If a homogeneous product is furnished, competition will tend to limit the market area and demand as a substitute product will be readily available. If the product is a heterogeneous product, the market area will tend to be larger and may even be on a national scale.

PRODUCTION-FACILITY CONSIDERATIONS: Considerations necessary in determining the adequacy of a site for a production facility include:

1. Economies of scale in plant size. Each type of manufacturing operation has a size of plant which is most economical to operate. Location selection must then consider the production capacity of the facility and the demand in the area. If the facility's output exceeds the demand of the area, location determination should be tempered to include supplying a second market area or operating at less than optimum production as economic conditions dictate.

2. Area operating costs. Each area will usually have variations in costs peculiar to that area. Careful evaluation of all costs must be made to determine what peculiar costs exist. As an example, water supply and drainage problems might exist in a specific area, fire protection may be inadequate, etc.

3. Labor costs and supply. This item in general is self-explanatory. Care should be taken to be sure correct costs are established and that just straight hourly costs are not used. The important cost is the cost per item produced. A number of companies have been misled into moving into new areas where lower hourly costs existed but output was relatively lower; hence per-unit costs actually rose.

4. Product weight gain versus weight loss. In general a product which experiences a weight gain should be produced near the market. An example is the bottling of soft drinks in which the major weight item in the product is water generally always available near the market. Likewise, a weight-losing product would generally be produced near the source of supply. Many extracting-type industries fall into this category.

TRANSPORTATION-FACILITY CONSIDERATIONS: Detailed attributes of transportation modes are outlined elsewhere in this chapter. At this time we only wish to enumerate some general areas of consideration.

1. *Problem of Unbalanced Flow.* Generally the volume flow of traffic between two points will not be in balance. This fact may be advantageous to a producer if his material can be moved in the low-volume direction at a low freight rate. An example of the advantageous arrangement would be:

a. Move a weight-losing raw material away from the market to a highly efficient and economical labor market.

b. Send the finished goods back to the original market and other markets at regular rates. This proposal might have a lower overall cost than producing the finished goods in the original market.

2. *Effect of Shipment Size.* This factor determines both the mode and size of shipment. The shipment size, of course, can vary from barge loads, shiploads, etc., down to less-than-carload or -truckload quantities or parcel post and United Parcel Service-size cartons. The selection of the most economical method of transportation will limit plant-site selections to those which can be served by the mode selected. The necessity to transfer shipments from one transportation mode to another should also be avoided to reduce transportation costs and time.

3. *Designation of Special-purpose Transportation Equipment.* A number of pieces of special-purpose transportation equipment have been developed. These do have an advantage of reducing transportation costs when they are in use. They also have a disadvantage of increasing fixed costs when they are purchased. A decision to use special-purpose equipment should be made after doing a cost study involving a trade-off between reduced transportation costs and increased fixed costs.

Included in this same area is consideration of the purchase versus the hiring of transportation equipment. In many cases the shipper can realize savings by purchasing his own equipment. The same reasoning applies as above. If equipment is purchased, fixed costs are increased. This could be an extensive drain on resources if the equipment is not kept in use most of the time. The purchase decision should be based on an engineering economic study to determine the best approach.

METHODS FOR DETERMINING TERMINAL LOCATIONS: The reasons for establishing a terminal location include:

1. Meeting the production function of the facility
2. Acting as a break-bulk and reassembly point where large homogeneous shipments are re-sorted into smaller heterogeneous shipments
3. Service as a dual interface between the supplier and production function on one side and the production function and customer on the other

All these criteria should be considered within the parameters and objectives of the firm.

Two general techniques, as outlined below, can be used to attempt to solve the locational problem. Both techniques have shortcomings and both are based on simplifying assumptions as noted. As of now, there is no technique available to handle a locational problem in a manner which considers all the possible location combinations and other variables. Practical solutions today are somewhat less than optimum. Use of the following techniques within the confines of their parameters and assumptions will give acceptable but not necessarily optimum solutions.

1. *Graphic Solution.* The graphic solution is based on determining the geographical point where the total ton-per-mile cost of inputs and outputs counterbalance. This technique is based on a number of simplifying assumptions, including:

a. That freight rates are linear
b. That sources of supply are fixed as to volume and price
c. That markets are fixed

In other words, the situation is considered static. The user is cautioned to review his situation in light of the assumptions before attempting to apply this model.

The application of the model is quite simple. (For complete details as to the model, see Smykay, Bowersox, and Mossman.[3]) The first step (Fig. 3) is to locate the sources of supply and market in relation to the x and y axes of the first quadrant. Distance is measured in miles, quantity in a unit of weight measure, and cost in dollars. The solution becomes a matter of mathematically solving for x and y in relation to the total ton-per-mile cost of all material to be moved in and out of a facility. This solution will indicate the point where, based on the assumption, a plant should be located to achieve the lowest total transportation costs.

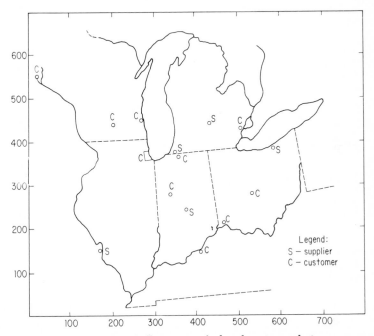

Fig. 3 Graphical illustration of plant-location technique.

As was previously indicated, the solution will probably not be an optimum solution because of the assumptions and parameters. The initial solution will probably be in the middle of a lake or field where transportation facilities are not available. The solution will then have to be modified to the closest terminal which has the necessary site facilities.

2. *Linear-programming Solution.* Linear programming (for details on how to apply linear programming, see Chapter 13) can be used to evaluate preselected sites under much the same conditions as the graphic solution. The important point to remember when applying this technique is that locations have to be preselected, after which transportation costs, volume markets, and suppliers can be selected. The optimum solutions, under the given conditions, can then be determined. Next, a new model must be established with new locations, volume, markets, and suppliers. Again the optimum solution is found by applying linear-programming techniques. This new solution is compared to the original solution, and the most economical solution is selected. This procedure is continued until all the desired locations are evaluated.

Linear programming, like the graphic method, does not necessarily select the optimum solution. It does select the best solution out of the proposed locations. Achieving an optimum solution or even an acceptable solution will depend on the ability of the model builder to design an efficient system to start with.

SUMMARY

Distribution is most frequently defined by the several functional departments:
Inventory management
Customer-order processing
Transportation management
Warehouse and shipping
In some organizations distribution is expanded to include production planning, materials planning, plant scheduling, receiving stores, and purchasing.

Only by the study of the environment can the relationships among the distribution functions and other organization functions be fully understood.

The policy decisions related to the distribution concept include two broad areas, those which are related to customer service and those which are related to costs associated with inventory. Complete and timely information are essential for adequate control.

REFERENCES

1. Frank H. Mossman, and Newton Morton, *Logistics of Distribution Systems*, Allyn and Bacon, Inc., Boston, 1965.
2. J. L. Hesket, Robert M. Ivie, and Nicholas A. Glaskowsky, Jr., *Business Logistics*, The Ronald Press Company, New York, 1964.
3. Edward W. Smykay, Donald J. Bowersox, and Frank H. Mossman, *Physical Distribution Management*, The Macmillan Company, New York, 1961.

BIBLIOGRAPHY

Ammer, Dean S.: *Materials Management*, Richard D. Irwin, Inc., Homewood, Ill., 1962.
Bowersox, Donald J.: *Food Distribution Center Location: Technique and Procedure*, Bureau of Business and Economic Research, Michigan State University, East Lansing, Mich., 1962.
Hay, William W.: *An Introduction to Transportation Engineering*, John Wiley & Sons, Inc., New York, 1961.
Hesket, J. L., Robert M. Ivie, and Nicholas A. Glaskowsky, Jr.: *Business Logistics*, The Ronald Press Company, New York, 1964.
Lochlin, D. Phillip: *Economics of Transportation*, Richard D. Irwin, Inc., Homewood, Ill., 1960.
Mossman, Frank H., and Newton Morton: *Logistics of Distribution Systems*, Allyn and Bacon, Inc., Boston, 1965.
Smykay, Edward W., Donald J. Bowersox, and Frank H. Mossman: *Physical Distribution Management*, The Macmillan Company, New York, 1961.
Taft, Charles A.: *Management of Traffic and Physical Distribution*, Richard D. Irwin, Inc., Homewood, Ill., 1964.

Section Three

Planning for Production Control

Chapter **8**

Forecasting

EDITORS:

James I. Morgan *Staff Assistant, The Dow Chemical Company, Midland, Michigan*

Robert E. Thiele, Jr. *Senior Research Logician, The Dow Chemical Company, Midland, Michigan*

CONTENTS

Effective planning for production and inventory control requires some means for resolving the uncertainty of the future. A necessary part of this resolution is some guess, estimate, prediction, forecast, or whatever else you may call it, of the future. The term "forecasting" will be used here to characterize the mechanism of arriving at measures for planning the future.

Before we get our hopes too high, it is important to realize that we cannot resolve all the uncertainty of the future. We can only attempt to reduce some of it. Also, let's realize that there is no forecasting mechanism which will be suitable for all situations. This chapter makes no pretense of presenting a general-purpose forecasting procedure.

CONSIDERATIONS IN FORECASTING

Realizing that we must forecast to plan, what do we need to know about forecasting? Of interest are the more obvious questions of why, what, and how; but also involved are such questions as how frequently, what time horizon, how precisely, and what is a good forecast.

Why Forecast? The question of why is simply answered by: *To plan the future.* A basic axiom of planning is that it cannot be done without some forecast of the future.

What to Forecast? As to what to forecast, a concise answer is: *Everything we need to know to plan the future.* This covers such things as product demands and supplies, costs, prices, and lead times. In this chapter we shall not attempt to discuss all these things; rather we shall limit ourselves to the key factor in most production and inventory control systems—the demand for an item. In any case, it is generally not feasible nor economical to forecast everything in actual situations.

In every system, there is an uncontrollable *triggering event* whose magnitude determines what happens in the rest of the system. In an inventory system or a production scheduling system, the triggering event is the demand for an item. The better we are able to determine future levels of this demand, the better we should be able to control the system, and consequently, the better we should be able to maximize the system's effectiveness. Thus, *demand for a physical product is the thing which triggers our system.* The better we can estimate this demand, the better we should be able to plan.

Under the question of *what,* the problems of item mix are important. Few companies use one raw material or supply item or have just one product to distribute. Therefore, many items may have to be forecast. A difficulty in many situations is that it may be hard to define an item and hence to determine what items to forecast. How we distinguish or delineate an item largely depends upon what we are trying to plan. In other words, we must answer: *What is the purpose of the forecast?*

If we are planning how much stock to carry, we must do our planning at the finest distinction by which a customer requires an item. If the customer wants a particular size, package, color, formulation, physical property, or finishing, we must stock his needs if we are to get his business. In some cases, it may be possible to substitute an item with similar attributes (retail stores seem to be best able to get away with this), but this is an exception rather than the rule.

The lowest common denominator by which we distinguish one stock item from another is commonly called the "stock-keeping unit," or SKU. Effective planning of inventory stock levels must be done through forecasts of each SKU. Unfortunately, when possible combinations of attributes are considered, the number of SKUs increases enormously, thus creating special forecasting problems.

On the other hand, if we are planning new or leased physical facilities months to years in the future, we seldom need detailed SKU forecasts. We are more interested in aggregate rather than individual movements—the degree of aggregation depending upon our needs. Product obsolescence, in many cases, may make it foolish to attempt long-term forecasting on an SKU basis.

Another consideration on what to forecast is location or geographical area. Seldom in physical distribution systems do we distribute through one location; hence the need for area forecasts. How the area is delineated depends again on the purpose of the forecast. The possibility of transshipment when one area is short of a given item adds another complexity. And needless to say, adding geography to product definition increases by severalfold the number of items which must be forecasted.

Another aspect of *what* we are forecasting is the time period. We generally think of demand per time; hence we have to determine the time period. Because we can readily convert from one time basis to another, the time period is not so critical as product mix or geographical considerations. It is important to keep in mind, however, that if the time period is repetitive (that is, we are not making a one-time estimation), then we have what is called a "time series." In such a series, the demand can take on different values in successive and equal time periods. A vast collection of methods for time-series analysis has been developed, several of which will be given in this chapter.

How to Forecast? Now the big question: *How?* Here we are interested in such things as:

What are the different methods?

Which are the practical methods?

How are these methods applied?

What are the limitations of each method?

Unfortunately there are probably as many methods—and then some—as there are people who forecast. Many of the methods are valuable in certain situations; however, as yet, no foolproof methodology has been developed.

The ideal way to estimate future demand for a product is to first determine the customers, their uses for the product, how much they will need for each use, how and when each customer will order the material, and any other relevant information, and then develop a computational system or mathematical model which will relate the demand to the factors. Because of the vast number of factors and interrelationships, a complete model is seldom, if ever, possible. Approximate models, however, have been developed and used in many practical situations.

A difficulty with models of this type is that they must be developed for a specific situation and as such may be time consuming to develop and to use and hence expensive. Of course, if possible benefits outweigh costs, then they are desirable. The development of these models (so-called operations research models) is a field in itself and beyond the scope of this chapter.

An excellent example of an operations research type of forecasting model is one which the United States government is using to forecast weather for up to two weeks in advance. The model is composed of formulas which dynamically simulate the forces of the atmosphere and the oceans. The complexity of the model is such that a 24-hour forecast requires 10 billion computer instructions and 14 hours of computing time using one of the largest computers available.

Because of the difficulty of developing more complete models, it is necessary to rely on other, less scientific means of estimation. Later in this chapter we shall attempt to answer the questions we have posed above. First, let's answer some other questions.

Distinctions between Forecasting Methods. One important question is: *Are there different types of forecasts?* Most certainly there are some distinctions which should be mentioned.

FORECASTS OR PREDICTIONS: In estimating demand it is helpful to consder two classes of factors which generate the future. One class contains the factors which have generated the demand in the past; the other class contains the factors which influence demand for the first time. R. G. Brown refers to estimates of the first class as "forecasts" and to estimates of the second class as "predictions."[1]

By examining the past, we should be able to get a feel for the effects of factors of the first class. The statistical tools of *time-series analysis* provide one means of anticipating the future on the basis of the past. These techniques assume that relationships which held in the past will continue to hold in the future. Anticipating the effects of the second class of factors is not readily handled by statistical means. Here, knowledge, experience, judgment, and intuition are important in making predictions. The past is generally the first place we look when we want to know the future. A good forecasting technique should effectively use the past provided that the past has meaning to the future.

SINGLE POINT OR FREQUENCY DISTRIBUTION: A forecast may be strictly a one-value estimation or it may be one or more values in which some frequency distribution is involved. Chapters 27 and 28 discuss the principles behind frequency distributions, and so we shall not go into them here. A later section of this chapter further discusses the use of distributions. As Brown in Chapter 19 of this handbook mentions, "a single-valued forecast is generally unsatisfactory in inventory control work." Some kind of a frequency distribution is called for, even though this may be nothing but an estimate of the highest and lowest values that a demand may take in a time period. When a range is given, it is assumed that the actual value will fall with equal frequency anyplace between the high and the low point of the range. This is referred to as a "uniform distribution."

Related to the problem of a single-value versus a frequency-distribution forecast is the distinction which must be made between discrete and continuous values. Chapters 27 and 28 elaborate on this distinction.

In many cases, a helpful estimate may be obtained by "bounding," that is, estimating the highest and/or lowest value that the forecast value might reasonably be.

REPETITIVE OR ONE TIME: Another distinction is whether the forecast is made for a single situation or whether it is to be made over and over again. The techniques used in either case can vary. Time-series analysis becomes more important with repetitive situations. Repetitive situations are usually better structured than one-time situations and thus are more amenable to mathematical treatment.

QUANTITATIVE OR QUALITATIVE: A qualitative estimation states whether the value is expected to go up or down. A quantitative estimation states an amount. In many cases, a mere qualitative estimation of direction is as desirable as an estimation of magnitude. Qualitative techniques are usually easier to carry out and are generally more successful. In production planning and inventory work, however, we need quantitative estimations.

LONG RANGE OR SHORT RANGE: These types of estimation are relative to each other. The relativeness depends upon the nature of the variable. For instance, an estimate of sales for one year in advance would be considered short range, whereas an estimation of the operation of a particular machine for one year would be considered long range. The techniques of estimation used in both cases are usually different. The long-range estimations are generally less scientific.

HUNCH OR SCIENTIFIC: The distinction here is one of degree. A hunch estimation gives values based solely on intuition or other unscientific characteristics. When a good amount of judgment and experience form part of the hunch, the estimates may be good. They may even be better than scientific estimates. The scientific estimation involves a more organized study of the factors involved. It attempts to determine the factors which affect the variable, how the factors affect the variable, and how these relationships change with time. It attempts to completely explain the variable. Ideally, it is the only sound method. Because of the complexity of the factors involved, the lack of scientific methodology, and/or time and expense, it is seldom possible to make a complete scientific model to estimate the variable. As a result, a scientific study may not always be successful. It is the ideal, however.

Outline of Methods. It seems safe to say that with all these distinctions there must be many forecast methods. Indeed there are. In fact, the literature on forecasting methods is so voluminous that it is hopeless to try to survey all the methods in this chapter. No doubt we have omitted many successful techniques. Even when forecasters agree on a forecast, they are apt to reach common conclusions for different reasons. Even when forecasters are right, they are frequently right because of reasons or conditions they did not anticipate.

The following outline summarizes the spectrum of forecasting techniques. The distinctions mentioned above may be found in these techniques.

I. Unscientific techniques
   A. Guesses
   B. Hunches based upon intuition
   C. Hunches based upon experience, judgment, and commonsense reasoning
II. Quasi-scientific techniques
   A. Intrinsic
      1. Persistence: The same value which occurred last period will occur next period.
      2. Trajectory: The trend of the past data is fitted to a mathematical curve by means of least squares or other techniques. It is assumed that future values will follow the same trend. The trends may be short or long range.
      3. Cyclical: These techniques are similar to trajectory except that cycles are examined and are assumed to hold for future periods. The values for future periods are correlated to values in a previous cycle. The cycles may be seasonal, business, etc. The use of the value for same period last year fits into this category.
      4. Use of averages
         a. The arithmetic average of all past data gives the estimate for the next period.
         b. The arithmetic average of most recent data gives the estimate. Data may be over a finite number of most recent periods (moving average) or a fixed period such as last year.
         c. A weighted average of all or part of past data gives the estimate. Exponential smoothing fits into this category.
      5. Correlative: An estimate is developed from an autocorrelation function which relates estimate to finite number of preceding values.
      6. Random: A probability distribution is obtained from past data or assumed by subjective means. Estimates of future values are obtained by Monte Carlo methods. The probability may be the variation from one period to the next, the variation from the average, the variation from trend, the variation from a cycle, etc. Coin tossing might be used to predict either an upward or downward change.

7. Studies of previous forecasts: These techniques involve obtaining relationships between the actual values and the values estimated from some method. These relationships are then used to adjust future values estimated by this method. These techniques are often valuable in removing bias or accounting for factors which the given method has omitted. Many so-called adaptive methods fall into this category.

B. Extrinsic
   1. Correlative
      a. Leading time series: A time series of an index or some factor may be affected by the same components which affect the value being studied. A mathematic equation relates the estimate to past values of leading time series.
      b. Analogue: The characteristics of some other factor may be such that it can be used to estimate the value under study. These techniques are especially valuable when no historical data is available.
   2. Causation
      a. Leading time series: These techniques are the same as 1(a) except that the factors are related causally.
      b. Comparative pressures: A ratio or difference may reach a specified value which may be an indication that a change is imminent which will affect the value estimated.
C. Combinations: Weighted or unweighted averages of any of the above unscientific and quasi-scientific estimates. Opinion polls and surveys are estimates of this type. The classical analyses of time series fall into this category.
III. Scientific: Methodology which develops a scientific model that relates the estimate to all factors influencing it. Causal relationships are quantitatively enumerated.

The technique which is used in a particular situation depends upon many factors. One is the ability to interpret the factors influencing the variable in question. Available historical data and what data can be generated are also important. The time available to make studies is another.

Later sections of this chapter will introduce some of the more practical techniques in production and inventory control and summarize an approach to undertaking a forecasting problem. First, however, let's answer some further questions.

How Frequently to Forecast? There is no pat answer to the question of how frequently to forecast. In repetitive situations, two possibilities present themselves: on some periodic basis or whenever some new historical data are available. Often new data are available periodically (such as monthly demand recaps) so that these possibilities may be identical.

In real-time control systems, it is frequently desirable to make a forecast whenever a new demand (new history) is received. Thus, an item is looked at only when some new action transpires. (The term "transaction" is often used to describe systems of this type.) These systems generally have to have some periodic means of "cleaning out" dead items, however.

With periodic systems, a balance must be made between the benefits of a new forecast and the cost of obtaining it. Because a forecast is by nature inaccurate, it is often of little benefit to update a forecast just because new data are available, especially when the new forecasts may be expensive to obtain. Quite often forecasts for monthly planning made quarterly or even yearly are satisfactory. Such tools as ABC (item-volume) analysis can be helpful in determining how frequently to forecast (often for A items, less often for C items).

An important factor with using past data is how current are the data. Information systems may give a lag between the transaction and its recording in the data bank where it is available for use in making forecasts. Time is necessary to assemble, condition, and aggregate data. This information lead time can fail to pick up marked changes in demand which may make forecasts (based on "old" data) unreliable. Often, the information lead time can be overcome with a costlier information system. Nevertheless, the cost of the information system must be balanced against the benefits received.

What Time Horizon to Forecast? The time horizon to forecast is dependent upon the reason for forecasting. Unless seasonality or supply capacity is important, inventory control forecasts generally are short term—one period in the future. Production planning forecasts, especially when supply constraints or seasonality are present, may be over a longer term—say months for the coming year. Facilities planning forecasts are of even longer term—say 5 to 10 years in the future. Some techniques are generally better for short-term forecasting (moving average), others for medium-term (seasonality adjustments to averages), and others for longer-term (trend lines). Forecasts for all time horizons do require judgment, with judgment perhaps being the most critical to longer-term forecasts.

How Precisely to Forecast? Important to the question of precision is the value of an item. With a high-value item, such as a jet or ocean vessel, it is fairly important to be precise in demand forecasts; however, with nail demand, precision isn't too important (unless, of course, your entire business is distributing nails). Such tools as ABC (item-volume) analysis can be helpful in determining how precisely to forecast. (Concentrate on the big items with more sophisticated methods—use less-sophisticated methods on the small.)

What Is a Good Forecast? An important consideration is how to determine if a forecast is any good, or what makes one forecast technique better than another. It is not possible to give pat answers here. The answer depends upon what we are forecasting. In general, however, the factors of error and bias are important.

A difficulty with error is that there are several ways of measuring it. Examples are sum of deviations, average (mean), absolute deviation, standard deviation of errors, and percentage of demand variation explained by a functional equation. It may be necessary to consider several of these measurements when selecting the best forecasting technique.

The problem of bias (whether the demand is actually consistently higher or lower than the forecast) is often overlooked. One reason is that there is no generally accepted measurement of bias. You can have low error, but high bias. In some cases, such as inventory control, bias is important. In other cases it is not.

The best test of a forecast technique is to try it out on history. This may not be possible if reliable past data are not available. If the forecast mechanism depends upon history and if data are available, then it is good practice to develop forecast mechanisms on the first half of available history and test them on the second half. Simple enough, but it seems as if few forecasters bother with this simple test.

A major difficulty with using history is that the demand history we have is generally sales or shipment history rather than demand. This history reflects not what was actually demanded, but what was shipped. It fails to consider lost demand because of product unavailability, delayed shipments, substituted product, or transshipments.

This lack of correspondence of shipments with demand is a major problem in inventory forecasting. Modern electronic data processing systems will help alleviate this problem, as they will allow us to store more historical information such as date requested, date promised, and date shipped. However, it won't be until we have customers' computers ordering upon suppliers' computers that we may be able to solve this problem.

PRACTICAL METHODS WITH APPLICATIONS AND LIMITATIONS

Depending on the intended use, a forecast usually can be made in a variety of ways. The following sections cover the two general categories—moving average and equation fitting—which have found widest application in production and inventory control. These methods utilize historical data. They are based on the assumption that the past history of a time series is rich in information concerning its future behavior. History tends to repeat itself in that patterns observed in the past may recur in the future. By careful analysis of the past, one can observe these patterns and thus predict the future. These are methods for forecasting the expected (most likely) value of the time series. A glossary of the symbols used in describing the methods is given at the end of the chapter.

MOVING AVERAGES

Many common forecasting methods come under the general category of moving averages. These techniques *average* or *smooth* past data in some way.

Simple Averages. If historical data is the basis for a demand forecast, a simple forecast is to take the actual demand from the preceding period. Since most time series experience variations in demand (often called "noise" or "disturbance"), better estimates are generally possible by smoothing the history through averaging. In mathematical terms, the simple average of demand for two months (which we shall designate by the symbols 1 and 2) is given by

$$A = \frac{X_1 + X_2}{2}$$

where X_1 = sales in period 1
X_2 = sales in period 2
A = two-month average demand

For example, if the demand in period 1 was 100 ($X_1 = 100$) and the demand in period 2 was 150 ($X_2 = 150$), then the two-month average is

$$A = \frac{100 + 150}{2} = 125$$

The general formula for calculating an average of N periods (where $N = 12$ for a 12-month average, for example) is

$$A = \frac{X_1 + X_2 + \cdots + X_N}{N} \tag{1}$$

Mathematically, the average is expressed more succinctly by use of a summation sign

$$A = \frac{\sum_{i=1}^{N} X_i}{N}$$

In this case the index i takes values which increase going back in time.

This method is commonly applied by taking an average over some fixed period. For example, the average monthly sales for last year might be the forecast for each month of the current year.

Because of its ease of understanding and application, this method is used often. Its major difficulty is its slower response to demand pattern changes.

Simple Moving Averages. Contrasted with a fixed-period average is a moving average in which the average is taken over a period which changes with time. For instance, the forecast for a given month would be the average monthly sales over the immediately preceding 12 months rather than the 12 of last year. This moving of the base period makes the forecast respond more rapidly to demand than with the simple fixed-period forecasts.

In mathematical terms, a moving average forecast for an arbitrary time period $(t + 1)$ based on history through time t would be

$$F_{t+1} = A_t = \frac{X_t + X_{t-1} + \cdots + X_{t-N+2} + X_{t-N+1}}{N}$$

$$= \frac{\sum_{i=t-N+1}^{t} X_i}{N} \tag{2}$$

where A_t = average through period t
F_{t+1} = forecast for period $t + 1$
X_t = sales in time period t
X_{t-1} = sales in time period $t - 1$

In this symbolism, the values of the index i increase with time. In practice, the starting point is the last current moving average. Hence the calculation is

$$A_t = A_{t-1} - \frac{X_{t-N}}{N} + \frac{X_t}{N} = A_{t-1} + \frac{X_t - X_{t-N}}{N} \tag{3}$$

There are two types of moving averages. The formula above is based on a trailing moving average. For analytical purposes, such as correlating one time series with another, centered moving averages are often used. In this type of average the referenced time period is the middle period of the average. For instance, the formula for a three-month centered average is

$$A_t = \frac{X_{t+1} + X_t + X_{t-1}}{3}$$

Special adjustments are needed for centered moving averages for even-numbered periods.

By definition, centered moving averages can't be used for direct forecasting unless the forecasted time series is related to the averaged series by a lagged relationship.

For a stationary series (i.e., no significant trend up or down over time), a long-term moving average would give best results. Here a 12-, 15-, or even 18-month trailing moving average would be used. Examples of products suitable to this approach might be commodities such as caustic soda, flour, or washing-machine assembly parts.

On the other hand, if sharp changes in demand level are to be expected, short-term moving averages will better detect these changes. Three-month moving averages might better be used for products such as popular phonograph records, books, or dye (color) stocks. An extreme example would be the weather which, it is said, is best predicted with a one-day moving average (i.e., the weather tomorrow will be the same as today).

Weighted Moving Averages. The averages discussed so far give equal weights to the historical data. For instance, Eq. (2) could be written

$$A_t = \frac{1}{N} X_t + \frac{1}{N} X_{t-1} + \cdots + \frac{1}{N} X_{t-N+1}$$

where $1/N$ is the weight given to each value.

The sum of the weights is 1. With this type of mechanism, each past period is assumed to be equally important. In many situations, especially if the time series is not stationary, it may be desirable to give more weight to most-recent data. For instance the formula

$$A_t = 0.7X_t + 0.3X_{t-1}$$

might be used to make a weighted forecast based on two periods of history. In this case, more weight is given to X_t, the more recent history.

The corresponding unweighted (or in reality, the equally weighted) forecast would be

$$A_t = 0.5X_t + 0.5X_{t-1}$$

In more general terms, the forecast formula can be written as

$$A_t = \alpha X_t + (1 - \alpha)X_{t-1} \tag{4}$$

where α is a weighting factor.

For N periods, the general equation is

$$A_t = w_t X_t + w_{t-1}X_{t-1} + \cdots + w_{t-N+1}X_{t-N+1} \tag{5}$$

where w_t is a weighting factor for time t and

$$w_t + w_{t-1} + \cdots + w_{t-N+1} = 1$$

Weighted moving averages have been extensively used in inventory forecasting. The multiplicity of possible formulas which can be used is subject to the forecast designer's imagination.

A particular type of weighted moving average, exponential smoothing, has found extensive use in inventory applications with a huge body of literature being developed about it. It is discussed in detail in a later section.

Seasonality Factors. Where seasonality can be reasonably measured, better forecasts generally are possible by including factors which adjust for it. For series with regular, repetitive variations over L periods ($L = 12$ for seasonal monthly data), a seasonal multiplier or factor can be used in an equation such as

$$\text{SF}_{t+1} = F_{t+1}S_{t+1}$$

where SF_{t+1} = seasonally adjusted forecast
F_{t+1} = unadjusted forecast
S_{t+1} = seasonal multiplication factor

Forecasts can also be adjusted by an additive factor:

$$\text{SF}_{t+1} = F_{t+1} + S_{t+1}$$

where S_{t+1} is the seasonal additive factor.

There are several methods for determining a seasonal adjustment factor. The most common method for determining a multiplication factor is to take the ratio of the actual demand in the corresponding period of the last cycle to the average demand over the cycle.   That is,

$$S_{t+1} = \frac{X_{t+1-L}}{SA}$$

where X_{t+1-L} = demand in period $t + 1 - L$
$\quad\ \ SA$ = average demand
$\quad\ \ \ L$ = cycle period

The value of SA can be determined from Eqs. (1) or (2).

A seasonal factor obtained in this way is simply one estimate of the seasonality.   The seasonal factor itself can be forecast by averaging methods.

A major problem with the use of seasonal factors is that several cycles of history are needed to get meaningful estimates.   Further, the use of seasonality factors increases the amount of data handling and calculations.   Further, the existence of trend, other cyclical factors, and random factors can complicate the determination of seasonal factors.   Therefore, it is important to ascertain that seasonality really exists and that the use of seasonality forecasts will significantly improve the forecasts.   The data-handling problems can be alleviated somewhat if the seasonality factors apply to several contiguous periods, i.e., a quarterly factor for monthly forecasts.   Subjective estimates often overexaggerate the magnitude of seasonality.   Also what appears to be seasonality may actually be induced by control mechanisms.   See Harrison[2] for a discusssion of seasonality in forecasting and some methods for making seasonal estimates.   There are several methods of testing the significance of seasonality, of which the analysis of variance is the most common (see Chapter 28).

Of course, the simplest seasonal forecast is

$$F_{t+1} = X_{t+1-L}$$

That is, the forecast is the actual demand for the same period in the last cycle.

Census Method II.   The ultimate in sophistication in the use of moving-average techniques is Census Method II.   This method was developed by the U.S. Bureau of the Census to forecast economic time series.   It is often called the "Shiskin decomposition method" (for Julius Shiskin, the Bureau statistician responsible for its development).   This method was an outgrowth of Census Method I which was the computerization of standard methods of time-series analysis.   For details of time-series analysis methods, see Croxton and Cowden.[3] Method II takes fuller advantage of the capabilities of the electronic computer, adding many adjustments and other features.   The method would be literally infeasible to do without a computer.

The method is quite complex as far as the number of steps required.   We shall not attempt to give a detailed presentation here.   McLaughlin[4] gives a detailed discussion.   In any case, packages for executing the method are available on a number of computer systems and have been widely used.   Thus the user is spared the necessity of doing the multitudinous calculations.

Basically, the method assumes a demand series D as composed of four components:

$$D = T \times C \times S \times I$$

where T = trend component
$\quad\ \ C$ = cyclical component
$\quad\ \ S$ = seasonal component
$\quad\ \ \ I$ = irregular component

It decomposes the series into three components:

$$D = TC \times S \times I$$

where TC is the combined effect of trend and cycle components. The components are estimated as follows:

1. Estimate TC component via a moving average of D.
2. Estimate SI as ratio of D to TC.
3. Adjust SI for extreme points (find extreme points and round by moving average).
4. Estimate S by an averaging of SI.
5. Estimate TCI by ratio of D to S.
6. Estimate I by ratio of TCI to TC.

Several of these steps are repeated more than once for refinements.

Forecasts F then are based on

$$F = TC \times S$$

with I giving a measure of variation.

Because of the heavy computer requirements, the method is generally not suited for SKU forecasting. A certain amount of aggregation is usually desirable when using the method. It is also limited to products with a fair amount of history (six to seven years of monthly data). Its principal uses in production and inventory planning are in monthly forecasting for a seasonal major product over the coming year and in analyzing trend and seasonal factors for use in other forecasting methods. For the analysis of time-series data with regard to seasonal, trend-cycle, and irregular components, probably no better system exists.

Exponential Smoothing. The use of exponential smoothing in inventory forecasting was introduced by Brown.[1] This method combines the moving-average features with minimal data storage requirements.

BASIC MODEL: Basically, exponential smoothing is a moving average in which different weights are given to past data. The weights are set so that they decrease as they go back in time. Thus greater significance is given to more recent history. (By contrast, the average monthly demand for the past 12 months would be a 12-month trailing moving average with equal weights given to each of the 12 months.)

In order to forecast using this method, we first need some past knowledge of our system. Assume an average of past values which can be used as the forecast for the current period. For illustrative purposes, let this average be 100. Now assume that we experience a demand of 120 in the current period and we are interested in calculating a new average which can be used as a forecast for next period. We want to take advantage of our latest experience to make our new forecast. Since 120 is higher than 100, we logically want to make our forecast higher than 100. The question is how much higher. In other words, how much weight do we want to give to our new experience? Exponential smoothing makes a forecast by saying that we want to add to (subtract from) our previous forecast a fraction of the amount by which the demand this period exceeds (is below) the previous forecast. That is,

New forecast = old forecast + α(new demand − old forecast)

where α (Greek letter "alpha") is an arbitrary smoothing constant between 0 and 1. Its value depends upon how much weight we want to give to our new experience—the higher the value, the greater the weight. If alpha were

1, we would give all our weight to the latest value while ignoring the old average. If alpha were 0, we would ignore the latest value. If we took alpha as 0.25, then the new forecast in our example would be

$$\text{New forecast} = 100 + 0.25(120 - 100)$$
$$= 105$$

Mathematically, the relationship is

$$F_{t+1} = A_t = A_{t-1} + \alpha(X_t - A_{t-1}) \tag{6}$$

where F_{t+1} = forecast for next period $t + 1$

A_t = exponentially smoothed average through period t

A_{t-1} = exponentially smoothed average through $t - 1$ (previously calculated average)

X_t = actual demand in current period t

α = smoothing constant ($0 \leq \alpha \leq 1$)

The preceding relation can be rearranged to give

$$A_t = \alpha X_t + (1 - \alpha)A_{t-1} \tag{7}$$

which is the basic equation of simple exponential smoothing. We then can take this value of A_t as the old average in the calculation for the next time period. That is,

$$A_{t+1} = \alpha X_{t+1} + (1 - \alpha)A_t$$

Thus, one of the principal advantages of a simple exponential smoothing over other types of moving averages is that only two values have to be carried from period to period. To make a forecast for the next period, all that is necessary is the value for α (the smoothing constant), the more recent data point, and the last forecast.

When Eq. (7) is applied successively backward in time to some initial average A_0, the exponential smoothing model becomes

$$A_t = \alpha X_t + \alpha\beta X_{t-1} + \alpha\beta^2 X_{t-2} + \cdots + \alpha\beta^{t-1}X_1 + \beta^t A_0 \tag{8}$$

where $\beta = (1 - \alpha)$. The "exponential" part of the name is derived from the exponents of β. Since α is less than 1, the coefficients of the past-demand terms decrease going back in time. It can also be shown that the coefficients sum to 1 so that the model is a weighted moving average.

Another way of looking at exponential smoothing is as follows. Suppose that just before the current data point became available, a catastrophe in the data storage system left us with only the current average, A_{t-1}. One proposal for obtaining a forecast for the next period might be to assume that the data point N periods ago was A_{t-1}. That is, $X_{t-N} = A_{t-1}$ in Eq. (3). The current average then becomes

$$A_t = A_{t-1} - \frac{A_{t-1}}{N} + \frac{X_t}{N}$$

or

$$A_t = \frac{1}{N} X_t + \left(1 - \frac{1}{N}\right) A_{t-1} \tag{9}$$

If $1/N$ is replaced by α and $1 - 1/N$ by $1 - \alpha$, the calculation then becomes

$$A_t = \alpha X_t + (1 - \alpha)A_{t-1}$$

which is Eq. (7). Note that this equation is equivalent to Eq. (4) with

$$A_{t-1} = X_{t-1}$$

As we can see from Eq. (9), the weighting or smoothing factor α is related to N, the number of periods in a moving average. Since the relationship is inverse ($\alpha \sim 1/N$) small α values should be used where large N values are effective. The two systems would be exactly equivalent except for the fact that where data points are eliminated from consideration after N periods in moving-average calculations, they are theoretically never "forgotten" in exponential-smoothing calculations. Brown[1] relates α and N by

$$\alpha = \frac{2}{N+1} \tag{10}$$

Hence where the data points in a 12-month moving average would all be weighted $\frac{1}{12}$, or 0.0833, for 12 past periods (and 0 for anything older than that), an equivalent exponential-smoothing system in the sense of average age of data would have a smoothing constant of $2/(12+1) = 0.154$. The weights in Eq. (8) would be 0.154, 0.130, 0.110, 0.0932, etc., decreasing exponentially. (An earlier name, "exponentially weighted moving averages," expresses this more precisely at the expense of being wordier.) Figure 1 illustrates the weights for some representative smoothing constants.

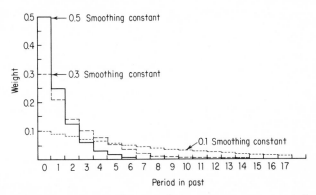

Fig. 1 Exponential-smoothing weights: weights given to previous periods for different smoothing constants.

Another way of understanding the significance of the smoothing constant is to compare what proportion of the total weight is given to a specific number of periods. A value of 0.5 gives over 90 percent of the total weight to data from the last 4 periods, whereas a value of 0.1 gives the same proportion of weight to data from the last 22 periods.

The necessary information to start such an exponential-smoothing forecasting system includes:

1. Some initial estimate (X_0) of the level (usually an average of historical data)

2. A value for the smoothing constant α

Because of the difficulty of choosing alpha and because of the possibility that varying values of alpha may be appropriate at different times, several methods have been developed which allow alpha to change based on certain criteria. Some of these methods are discussed in a later section.

The initial estimate can be one data point or an average. Because of decreasing weights, the influence of the initial estimate on the forecast decreases with time; therefore, the initial choice is not overly critical.

One way of starting a system is to assume an alpha of 1 for the first period (all the weight is applied to the only piece of history—the single bit of history is the forecast), an alpha of $\frac{1}{2}$ after the second period, an alpha of $\frac{1}{3}$ after the third period, and so on until the alpha is no longer greater than the long-term desired smoothing constant. In mathematical terms,

$$\alpha = 1/N \qquad \text{if } \alpha > \alpha' \qquad \text{else } \alpha = \alpha'$$

where N = number of periods of history
α' = long-term (steady-state) smoothing constant

This method does require carrying over an additional piece of data—the number of periods of history, N.

In a manner analogous to how the length of time included in the moving average varies with the series type, the smoothing constant in exponential smoothing also varies with series type. For a relatively stationary series, α could range from 0.1 to 0.15, corresponding to 18 to 12 period moving averages, while for series with sharp level changes, α may vary from 0.2 to 0.5, equivalent to 9 to 3 period moving averages. Figure 2 is a nomograph which can be used to test the significance of alpha. Lacking any other information, an alpha of 0.1 is a reasonable choice for a reasonably stable series, whereas a value of 0.2 is a good starter for an uncertain series. For a series with wide fluctuations, epitomized by alternating high and low values, a smaller alpha (0.05 to 0.1) is generally a good selection. Likewise, a low alpha is usually best for so-called lumpy demand—many periods with zero demands. Higher values of alpha are generally best when short runs (trends or cycles) are possible.

Smaller alphas are usually more appropriate with shorter time periods (day or weeks, compared to quarters or years) because they have relatively greater fluctuations than longer periods. Likewise individual SKUs may have greater relative fluctuations than aggregate items and therefore call for smaller smoothing constants.

Figure 3 shows the response of the simple exponential-smoothing model to several standardized inputs. The *impulse* might represent the effect of random noise. The simple model reacts proportionally to α in the next period and then resumes tracking the true value. The *step* illustrates a basic nonstationary series. The simple model's speed of response is directly proportional to the value of alpha. In the case of *ramp* or trend, the simple model eventually has the correct slope, but *always* lags the true value, the lag being inversely proportional to alpha.

MULTIPLE EXPONENTIAL SMOOTHING: Because of the lag inherent in simple exponential smoothing, higher-order models have been developed and used. The basic equation of multiple exponential smoothing is

$$A_t{}^n = \alpha A_t{}^{n-1} + (1 - \alpha)A_{t-1}{}^n \tag{11}$$

where $A_t{}^n$ = nth-order smoothed averaged. In the equation, the n is a designator of the order rather than a power term. The A's are a function of the demand X with

$$A_t{}^0 = X_t$$

by definition.

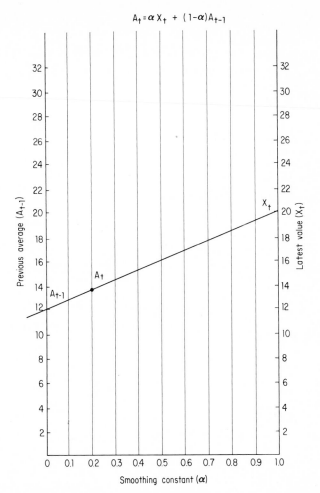

$$A_t = \alpha X_t + (1-\alpha)A_{t-1}$$

Fig. 2 Exponential-smoothing nomograph (graph to determine *new* average for different smoothing constants). Procedure: Locate X_t and A_{t-1} on respective axes. Draw line connecting these points. Read A_t on vertical scale as intersection of drawn line with vertical line for desired smoothing constant.

Thus, the first three orders of exponential smoothing are

$$A'_t = \alpha X_t + (1 - \alpha)A'_{t-1} \tag{12}$$
$$A''_t = \alpha A'_t + (1 - \alpha)A''_{t-1} \tag{13}$$
$$A'''_t = \alpha A''_t + (1 - \alpha)A'''_{t-1} \tag{14}$$

where the prime sign is used to indicate the order of smoothing. Orders higher than three have found little practical use. Brown[5] covers higher-order smoothing in more detail, giving the background for the equations. Double smoothing would be used where a trend is believed to exist, whereas triple smoothing would be used where the trend changes with time.

A double-smoothed forecast consists of two components:

$$F_{t+1} = A_t + R_t$$

where A_t = average demand at period t

R_t = trend at period t

The components are estimated from

$$A_t = 2A'_t - A''_t$$
$$R_t = A''_t - A''_{t-1}$$

where A'_t and A''_t are determined by Eqs. (12) and (13) respectively. The forecast, by substitution, is then

$$F_{t+1} = 2A'_t - A''_{t-1} \qquad (15)$$

Hence in order to forecast by double exponential smoothing, three values must be carried from month to month: the smoothing constant and the single- and double-smoothed averages, A' and A''.

The equation for forecasting more than one period in advance is

$$F_{t+u} = A_t + uR_t$$

where u is the lead time of the forecast.

Double smoothing, at the expense of having extra calculation and data storage requirements, gives more response to demand changes than single smoothing.

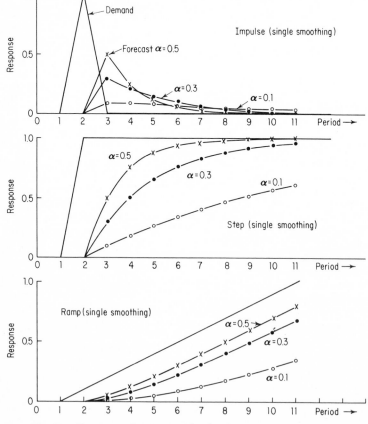

Fig. 3. Response of exponential smoothing to standard inputs.

There is a lag; however, its magnitude decreases with time under steady-state conditions. Because of the greater response, smaller values of alpha give the same significance to history. For instance, a smoothing constant of 0.1 with double smoothing is approximately equivalent to an alpha of 0.2 with single smoothing.

WINTER'S MODIFIED MODEL: In an attempt to account for seasonality and trend while still using relatively simple exponential-smoothing techniques, a model was proposed by Winters.[6] It consists of a multiplicative seasonality factor and an additive trend factor, each smoothed separately. Its form is

$$F_{t+1} = A_t = \alpha \frac{X_t}{S_{t-L}} + (1 - \alpha)(A_{t-1} + R_{t-1}) \tag{16}$$

where S_{t-L} = seasonal factor
R_{t-1} = trend factor

The trend factor is updated by

$$R_t = \delta(A_t - A_{t-1}) + (1 - \delta)R_{t-1} \tag{17}$$

where δ = smoothing constant $(0 \leq \delta \leq 1)$.

The seasonal factor is updated by

$$S_t = \gamma \frac{X_t}{A_t} + (1 - \gamma)S_{t-L} \tag{18}$$

where γ = smoothing constant $(0 \leq \gamma \leq 1)$.

The forecast for u periods in the future is then

$$F_{t+u} = (F_t + uR_t)S_{t-L+u} \tag{19}$$

One of the advantages of using seasonal and trend factors in an exponential-smoothing model is that forecasts can be made for months beyond the current forecasts.

With this model, the problem of choosing a smoothing factor is threefold, since theoretically values for α, δ, and γ must be selected. In practice, however, since trend and seasonality are not subject to step changes very often, smoothing factors between 0.1 and 0.2 are often assigned based on experience.

A careful examination of the exponential model and its response to various inputs leads to the notion that if somehow α could be adjusted or updated, the model might track more closely the underlying series to be forecast. Several directions have been followed in research on this problem.

BROWN'S GENERAL MODELS: Brown[5] has proposed many exponential-smoothing models, including polynominals, exponentials, sinusoids, sums, and products of such functions. In summary, the models are exponential smoothing based on "discounted multiple regression"; the effect of using them approximates moving the time-axis origin to the most recent data point. While elegant mathematically, these models require more storage and manipulation for each series than may be desired for inventory systems.

Brown's basic trend correction model is

$$F_{t+u} = A_t + uR_t$$

where $A_t = A_{t-1} + R_{t-1} + \alpha(2 - \alpha)(X_t - F_t)$
$R_t = R_{t-1} + \alpha^2(X_t - F_t)$

He recommends a smoothing constant of 0.05. Chapter 19 presents some of the elementary concepts of his approach.

ERROR STATISTICS: In order to test how well a particular model is predicting the series, several statistics based on the error

$$e_t = X_t - F_t \tag{20}$$

can be used. One statistic is the sum of forecast errors:

$$E_t = \sum_{i=1}^{t} e_i \tag{21}$$

$$= e_t + E_{t-1}$$

Another statistic is the standard deviation of the forecast error over a period of time. Its calculation is

$$SE = \left(\sum_{i=1}^{N} e_i^2 / N \right)^{0.5}$$

This measurement can be used to test the effectiveness of a forecasting scheme. For instance, it could be used as a test for determining the "best" (on the basis of lowest resulting SE) smoothing constant in exponential smoothing. A difficulty with this use is that generally a plot of SE versus the smoothing constant gives a curve with a flat minimum (see Fig. 4). As a result, it is difficult, by this approach alone, to justify that one smoothing constant is significantly better than another. Other error measures include sum of absolute errors [Σ abs(e)], sum of squared errors (Σ e^2), average error (Σ e/N), relative error [$\Sigma(e/X)$], and unexplained variation (SE$^2/\sigma^2$).

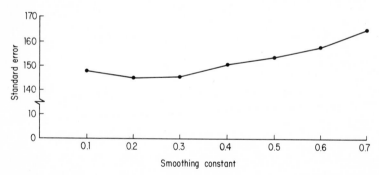

Fig. 4 Error related to smoothing constant (based on a 36-period test of actual product).

In exponential smoothing, a useful statistic is the mean absolute deviation (MAD), which is defined as the smoothed absolute value of the error. Its calculation is

$$P_t = \eta \text{ abs}(e_t) + (1 - \eta)P_{t-1} \tag{22}$$

where P_t = mean absolute deviation at period t
η = smoothing constant ($0 \leq \eta \leq 1$)
abs(e_t) = absolute value of e_t

In most practical systems, $\eta \approx 0.1$ (assuming no radical swings in absolute deviation).

Another related statistic is the smoothed average deviation (SAD), called Q here. It is calculated similarly as

$$Q_t = \eta e_t + (1 - \eta)Q_{t-1} \tag{23}$$

Here again a practical value η is 0.1.

In measuring the suitability of a particular model to a particular time series in a multiple forecasting environment, the assumption is made that the errors actually are random values, normally distributed with zero mean. If this assumption is granted, then something like "control limits" could be estimated for these errors. In order to do this, some measure of how the system is following or tracking the actual data is needed. Since, if the above assumption is made, P can be shown to approximate (or at least be proportional to) SE, it could be included as one factor in such a tracking signal. Now if the random-error assumption is correct, the sum of such errors, E_t, should also oscillate around zero. If, however, some change has occurred in the basic character of the series, E_t will accumulate above or below zero. Therefore the ratio

$$\text{TS}_t = E_t / P_t \tag{24}$$

should remain inside of the limits. This ratio is commonly called a "tracking signal." The most commonly used control-limit values are ± 4.0. If TS passes these limits for, say, two consecutive periods, E is reset to zero. If, within some short period (say, six time units), the same control value is again violated, this is a good indication the basic series has undergone a change in character. If no further violations are observed in this period, it is assumed that some short-term aberration affected the series.

In a similar way, the tracking signal could be calculated by

$$\text{TS}_t = Q_t / P_t \tag{25}$$

Here the theoretical limit of the ratio is ± 1.0. The approximate ± 2 "sigma" tracking-signal limit is

$$\text{TSL} = \frac{2.4\eta}{[\eta(2 - \eta)]^{0.5}} \tag{26}$$

For $\eta = 0.1$, this is ± 0.55. A similar control-by-exception system to that above would serve to warn of changes in the characteristics of the series.

ADAPTIVE MODELS: In recent years, research in exponential-smoothing forecasting systems has led to the development of models in which the smoothing factor is not constant, but is adjusted based on current performance of the model. Some representative adaptive systems that have been used in actual situations are discussed here.

1. *Trigg and Leach Modification.* A simple modification of single smoothing has been proposed by Trigg and Leach.[7] They point out that since the Q/P (SAD/MAD) ratio has limits of ± 1.0, its absolute value could be used directly as an adaptive α. In their evaluation of the response of such a system, they show good results for step and ramp functions. The response, or rather overreaction, to impulses suggests that this method should not be used where large random fluctuation may be encountered. They also suggest that because of the magnification of effect, an adaptive α such as this be used only in the equation for single exponential smoothing.

2. *Burgess Model.* In a recent paper, Burgess[8] proposes the use of a second-order model with seasonality factors and an adaptive smoothing constant deter-

mined by statistical tests. The basic formula for a next-period forecast is

$$F_{t+1} = S_{t+1-L}(A_t + R_t) \tag{27}$$

with the formula for u periods in the future as

$$F_{t+u} = S_{t+u-L}(A_t + uR_t)$$

The smoothing constant is obtained by the following logic: The mean absolute deviation P_t, the smoothed absolute deviation Q_t, the tracking signal TS_t, and the tracking-signal limit TSL are calculated using Eqs. (22), (23), (25), and (26), respectively. A parameter H is calculated from

$$H = \frac{1 - \alpha}{\alpha}$$

where α is the previous smoothing constant. If the tracking signal is greater than the tracking-signal limit [abs$(TS_t) > $ TSL], then set $H = H - r$, or else set $H = H + 1$. In mathematical terms,

$$H = \begin{cases} H - r & \text{if abs}(TS_t) > \text{TSL} \\ H + 1 & \text{otherwise} \end{cases}$$

The parameter r is a reduction factor set high (i.e., $r = 10$) for a fast response to control-limit breakthroughs and low (i.e., $r = 2$) for slow reaction. The smoothing constant is then calculated from

$$\alpha = \frac{1}{H + 1}$$

To keep the value of the smoothing constant within a reasonable range, limits are set on the values H can take. For instance, to keep α within the range of 0.05 and 0.5, the maximum and minimum values of H would be 19 and 1, respectively.

With this approach to changing alpha each period, a high value such as 0.5 can be used as the initial value (using 0.5 as the starting value, H can be interpreted as the count of the number of periods since forecasting commenced). As the series shows more stability, the value of alpha is automatically reduced. Unless some deviation occurs which throws the smoothed forecast errors out of a control limit, the value of alpha will reach a steady-state value of the lower limit.

The value of A_t in Eq. (27) is then obtained as follows. The single-smoothed average is calculated by

$$A_t' = \alpha \frac{X_t}{S_{t-L}} + (1 - \alpha)A_{t-1}'$$

The double-smoothed average, A_{t-1}'' is calculated by Eq. (13). A current trend estimate is calculated by

$$T_t = \frac{A_t' - A_t''}{H}$$

A trend signal is calculated by

$$RS_t = \text{abs} \frac{(T_t)}{P_t}$$

A trend-control limit is given by

$$TL_t = 0.625k\alpha^{1.5}$$

where k is a factor to give the desired level of probability significance. (It is analogous to $k = 3$ sigma limits in quality control.) If the mean value of the trend signal is within the trend-control limit, then the average in the forecast equation is the single-smoothed average; otherwise it is the double-smoothed forecast of Eq. (15). That is,

$$A_t = \begin{cases} A'_t & \text{if } RS_t < TL_t \\ 2A'_t - A''_t & \text{otherwise} \end{cases}$$

The trend component R_t in the forecast equation is determined from the conditions

$$R_t = \begin{cases} 0 & \text{if } RS_t < TL_t \\ T_t & \text{otherwise} \end{cases}$$

Likewise, a significance level can be placed on the seasonality factor. A seasonality limit is given by

$$SL_t = \frac{\psi \text{abs}(X_t/A_t - S_{t-L})}{S_{t-L} + (1 - \psi)SL_{t-1}}$$

where ψ is a smoothing constant for which Burgess suggests a value of 0.3. If the limit is greater than 1, then seasonality is not significant and therefore no seasonal adjustment is made. The seasonal factor S_t is calculated by Eq. (18).

In mathematical terms,

$$S_t = \begin{cases} 1.0 & \text{if } SL_t > 1.0 \\ S_t & \text{otherwise} \end{cases}$$

This model overcomes many of the difficulties with simple exponential smoothing at the expense of being complex and requiring more data storage. The values of Q, P, α, A', A'', SL, and S must be carried over from period to period for each item as compared with just A and α for single smoothing; therefore, the user must carefully judge whether this violation of the "principle of parsimonious parameterization" produces significantly better forecasts.

3. *Dudman Model.* Starting with Winter's model as a basis, Dudman[9] has developed a model which automatically adjusts smoothing constant, trend, and seasonality.

The smoothing constant is determined from a ratio of an autocovariance estimate to a variance estimate. That is,

$$\alpha = \frac{W_t}{V_t(1 + \xi)}$$

where W_t = autocovariance estimate
$\quad\quad V_t$ = variance estimate
$\quad\quad \xi$ = factor to dampen effect of autocorrelation

The variance estimates are

$$W_t = \rho e_t e_{t-1} + (1 - \rho)W_{t-1}$$
$$V_t = \rho e_{t-1}^2 + (1 - \rho)V_{t-1}$$

where the e's are the appropriate forecast errors and ρ is a smoothing constant.

The current average and trend equations are respectively

$$A_t = A_{t-1} + R_{t-1} + \alpha e_t$$
$$R_t = \delta(A_t - A_{t-1}) + (1 - \delta)R_{t-1}$$
$$\quad = R_{t-1} + \alpha \delta e_t$$

The seasonal factor for the current period j of the cycle is updated by

$$S_{j,t} = \gamma \frac{C_t}{A_{t-1} + R_{t-1}} + S_{j,t-1}$$

where $S_{j,t}$ is the seasonal factor for cycle period j calculated at the time t. The seasonal factors (a total of $L - 1$) for other than period j are normalized by the relationship

$$S_{i,t} = \frac{S_{i,t-1} (L - S_{j,t})}{L - S_{j,t-1}}$$

so that the summation of the factors over the cycle time L is equal to L.

The forecast is

$$F_{t+u} = (A_t + uR_t)S_{t+u,t}$$

Dudman recommends values of 0.15, 0.15, and 0.20 for δ, ξ, and γ, respectively. She also proposes that during the course of a cycle, the sum of the absolute deviations be calculated for the case where seasonal factors are used and also for the case where the seasonal factors all have the value 1.0. If at the end of a cycle the former is less than 85 percent of the latter, then the seasonal factors are used over the next cycle; otherwise they are not.

EQUATION FITTING

Up to this point the methods presented have smoothed or averaged out the random factors in a series of historical data points. In some cases, this may be taken care of in another way. For instance, if only annual data are available, the monthly fluctuations for a year are essentially absorbed in the single yearly value. For very new (or fast-decaying) products, the random fluctuations may be less important.

For series where some pattern seems to emerge from the randomness of the data, a correlation of the data either with time, with past values of the series, or with some other series may yield a mathematical curve or relationship which can be used for forecasting by extrapolation. The most commonly used statistical approach to curve fitting involves correlation or regression by maximum-likelihood criterion. Chapter 28 covers the subject in more detail and so we discuss it only briefly here. A more detailed presentation is given by Wolberg.[10]

Curves fitted by maximum-likelihood regression have the property of "least squares." The fundamental concept of least squares involves selecting the coefficients of an equation so that the sum of the squares of the deviations of the calculated values from the data points is minimized.

Mathematically, minimize

$$\sum_{i=1}^{N} (X_i - Y_i)^2$$

where X_i = actual value in period i ($i = 1, 2, \ldots, N$)
Y_i = value calculated by fitted equation

In the symbolism of this section, we shall use Y to represent a value obtained by a curve fit. Thus, the forecast would be

$$F_t = Y_t$$

where F_t = forecast for period t.

Intrinsic Factors. Two types of intrinsic curve fitting are commonly used. In one type, autocorrelation, the predicted value is related to past values of the series. In the other, the predicted value is related to time. Least-square methods are most commonly used to fit these types of curves; however, other techniques are also used and some are mentioned here. Regression-analysis computer packages are common now, thus freeing the forecaster from the drudgery of making calculations.

AUTOCORRELATION: The basic concept of autocorrelation is to correlate a current value of a time series to previous values. This approach can be used if a time series is influenced by recent past values. The most obvious relationship of this type would be $Y_{t+1} = X_t$, i.e., the forecast is the last value of the series. Other common relationships are

$$Y_{t+1} = X_t + a$$
$$Y_{t+1} = aX_t$$
$$Y_{t+1} = a_0 + a_1X_t$$
$$Y_{t+1} = a_0 + a_1X_t + a_2X_{t-1}$$

The general linear-coefficient equation is

$$Y_{t+1} = a_0 + \sum_{i=1}^{M} a_i X_{t+1-i} \tag{28}$$

where M = the number of past-value terms.

The coefficients may be obtained by the linear multiple-regression techniques of Chapter 28. Meaningful correlations can be obtained only if M (number of terms in the equation) is less than N (number of historical data values used).

Seasonality can be introduced into an autocorrelation function by having one of the terms include the corresponding value from the previous cycle.

TIME-DEPENDENT CORRELATIONS: The spectrum of possible models in which a time series can be related to time is limited by the forecaster's ability to formulate the model and solve for its coefficients. We shall discuss only some of the more common models.

1. *Linear.* The most familiar model is the linear or straight-line model:

$$Y_t = a + bt \tag{29}$$

In this equation, the coefficient b represents the linear trend. The coefficient a is a position coefficient. Figure 13 in Chapter 19 gives a plot of this model. For the determination of coefficients a and b, the data X_t for periods 1 to N are required. The equations for determining the coefficients are

$$a = A \times S1 - B \times S2$$
$$b = -B \times S1 + C \times S2$$

where $A = 2(2N + 1)/[N(N - 1)]$
$\quad\quad B = 6/[N(N - 1)]$
$\quad\quad C = 12/[N(N^2 - 1)]$

$$S1 = \sum_{i=1}^{N} X_i$$

$$S2 = \sum_{i=1}^{N} iX_i$$

X_i = given data for period i ($i = 1$ for oldest observation)
N = number of values of data

This model may also be used if the data can be transformed into a linear form. For instance, if

$$X'_i = f(X_i)$$

where f is some mathematical operation such as taking a logarithm, then the X'_i can be substituted for X_i in the above equations.

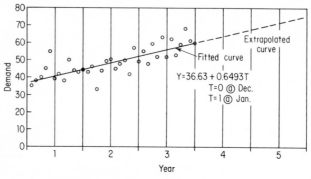

Fig. 5 Extrapolation of fitted linear curve.

With this model, projections can be made by extrapolating the model in time beyond the given data set. Care must be taken in this extrapolation, however, because the confidence interval widens as the curve projects in time. Figure 5 is an example of a fitted curve which is projected in time.

2. *Polynomials.* Polynomials in time are sometimes helpful but are much more sensitive to minor fluctuations in the data. The general equation is

$$Y_t = a_0 + \sum_{i=1}^{M} a_i t^i \tag{30}$$

where M = number of time-dependent terms. If $M = 1$, then the linear equation of the previous section results. If $M = 2$, then a second-order equation of the form $Y = a_0 + a_1 t + a_2 t^2$ results. The second-degree equation can be used if there is an acceleration in the trend.

The coefficients of each term can be determined by the linear multiple-regression techniques of Chapter 28. Note that the term "linear" here refers to the coefficients and not the time variables.

Care must be taken in using these equations as they can give very extreme forecasts in long-range projections. Their use should be based on a thorough appraisal of the past data and should comprise very short-term forecasts at most.

3. *Sinusoids.* Equations such as

$$Y_t = a \sin (\omega t) + b \cos (\omega t) \qquad (31)$$

are referred to as "sinusoids" since they involve sine functions. They can be used to represent cyclic or recurrent patterns when these appear to be the dominant factor. The parameter ω gives the period of the cycle. Regression analysis of Y_t with sin (ωt) and cos (ωt) yields the coefficients a and b.

4. *Exponential Curves.* One family of commonly used curves involves the use of the exponential function, exp. The most common equation is

$$Y_t = a \exp (bt) \qquad (32)$$

where a and b are coefficients and exp represents the exponential-function base (exp = 2.71828). This equation assumes that the series is growing at a constant rate exp $(b) -1$. For a growing series b will be positive; for a decaying series, negative. The coefficient a is a location parameter.

The equation may be linearized by the natural logarithm transformation

$$\log (Y_t) = \log (a) + bt$$

Hence the formulas for the linear model may be used to obtain a fit by substituting log (X_i) for X_i. The resulting coefficients are log (a) and (b). Figure 6 is an example of a fitted curve.

This curve can also be expressed by

$$Y_t = aB^t$$

where $B = \exp (b)$. The linearization form is then

$$\log (Y_t) = \log (a) + t \log (B)$$

5. *S-type Growth Curves.* A family of curves has the characteristic that the rate of change is a prime characteristic of the curve. The increment of growth declines with time approaching zero as a limit. These curves are sometimes referred to "S curves" because they usually start with a small slope (when plotted on constant scale paper), sweep upward in mid-area, and flatten out as they approach a maximum value. Their first stage represents a period of experimentation, the second stage represents the rapid exploitation of the product, and the third stage represents the leveling off of growth with the saturation of demand. They are also sometimes referred to as "asymptotic" growth curves because each approaches an upper limit.

The two most common types of S curves are the *Gompertz* curve (see Fig. 7)

$$Y_t = ka^{b^t} \qquad (33)$$

and the *Pearl-Reed* or logistics curve

$$Y_t = \frac{1}{k + ab^t} \qquad (34)$$

For the Gompertz, k is the upper limit. For the logistics, the upper limit is $1/k$. Their main difference is the point of inflection, the Gompertz reaching the inflection earlier.

Since neither of these curves can be linearized directly, they cannot be solved

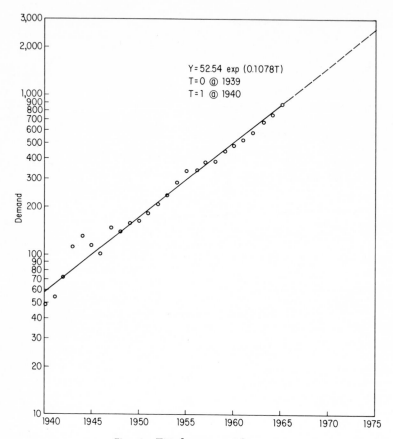

Fig. 6 Fitted exponential curve.

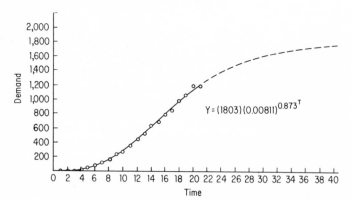

Fig. 7 Fitted Gompertz curve.

directly by linear-regression techniques. One approach to solution involves split-ting the historical data of N values into three equal parts and taking partial totals of an appropriate function of the data. For the Gompertz, the function is the natural logarithm

$$S1 = \sum_{i=1}^{N1} \log (X_i) \qquad S2 = \sum_{i=N1+1}^{N2} \log (X_i) \qquad S3 = \sum_{i=N2+1}^{N} \log (X_i)$$

where $N1 = N/3$ and $N2 = 2N/3$. For the logistics, the function is the reciprocal $(1/X_i)$.

The coefficients for the Gompertz can then be obtained by solving the following equations:

$$b^{N1} = \frac{S3 - S2}{S2 - S1}$$

$$\log (a) = \frac{(S2 - S1)(b - 1)}{(b)(b^{N1} - 1)^2}$$

$$\log (k) = \frac{S1 \times S3 - (S2)^2}{(S1 + S3 - 2 \times S2)N^1}$$

For the logistics, a and k are substituted for $\log a$ and $\log k$ respectively in the above equations.

Another approach for determining the Gompertz curve coefficients is to first transform the equation to the form

$$\log (Y_t) = \log (k) + b^t \log (a)$$

Then select an arbitrary value of b (some value between 0 and 1) and take a regression between $\log Y_t$ and b^t calculating the sum of squares of the residuals or errors. Repeat using other values of b until a value is obtained which gives the lowest sum-of-squares values. The values of k and a are coefficients obtained by this regression.

For the Pearl-Reed model, first transform the equation to

$$\log \left(\frac{1 - kY_t}{Y_t} \right) = \log (a) + t \log (b)$$

Then select a value of k (on approximate upper bound on k is the reciprocal of the highest data value) and take a regression of the left-hand term of the equation versus t. Repeat the iterative process with different values of k until no significant reduction in the sum of squares of the residuals is obtained.

Care must be taken in the use of these curves. Data should include history of the item from its inception. There should be reason to believe the growth rate is decreasing with time and that the series is apt to reach a saturation point. For a fuller discussion of the use and fitting of these curves, see Croxton and Cowden.[3]

USE OF REGRESSION MODELS: Some points need to be emphasized on the use of a fitted curve, particularly in regard to data selection and model projection.

A careful perusal of the time-series data before the regression analysis may eliminate causes of later difficulty. When examining a rough plot of the data to determine a fitting model, extraneous data should be removed or else smoothed. Such data might be early information with an obviously different trend or individual points which are evidently random impulses. This "hand smoothing" will precondition the data for better use of regression analysis. (Fur-ther discussion is given later in this chapter.)

The base period (time span on which the regression is based) of the historical data can have a major influence on the coefficient obtained. The inclusion of one additional data value may give quite different coefficients if that data point is unusually high or low. To get away from the ambiguity of base-period selection, although not necessarily away from the problems, a moving base-period fit can be used. For example, a regression may be done each period using the last 12 periods as the base period.

When projecting regression models into the future as a forecast mechanism, two major factors should be considered in regard to the confidence placed in the extrapolated points. First, how good is the model at fitting the past? This can be judged by measures such as the explained variation, sum of absolute errors, sum of squared errors, and percent deviation. Even if the correlation is excellent, extrapolation of the fit is into an area of widening confidence limits (see Fig. 8). A second factor to consider is the relationship of the forecast

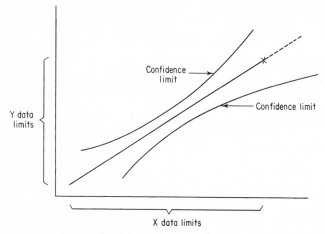

Fig. 8 Confidence limits of fitted curve.

extrapolation period to the base period. Intuitively, you would not project more than one period if you only had two periods' data. (Hopefully, you would not project anything at all!) Similarly, if you have a model which gives a good fit for a long period of time (60 to 96 periods) you should be able to project it for 6 to 12 periods with a reasonable amount of confidence. You may be more confident still if you had used 48 periods (of 60) to build the model and had gotten good results predicting the remaining 12 points of the history.

In using curves, especially growth curves, for longer-range forecasting, it is helpful to compare the curve for an item with the curve for the set of which the item is a part—for instance, comparing the curve of apples and the curve for fruit. It is quite possible to fit curves in which the growth of apples is greater than the growth of fruit so that in some future period the forecast demand for apples is greater than the forecast demand for fruit. Judgment is continually called for in forecasting.

The discussion so far has assumed, for the most part, the use of linear-regression techniques in curve fitting. This approach uses a least-squares criterion. This criterion may not necessarily be the best criterion. For one thing, least-squares fits may give undue weight to freak values. As a result, a number of other mathematical approaches to curve fitting are becoming increasingly used. Two of these approaches come under the headings of linear programming and nonlinear programming.

LINEAR-PROGRAMMING CURVE FITTING: Recently, much interest has been generated in the use of linear programming to fit linear-coefficient curves by criteria other than least squares. Linear-programming techniques are well developed, and computer packages are readily available. The trick is to formulate the criterion and its restrictions in such a way that a standard linear-programming algorithm can be used to determine the coefficients.

One criterion amenable to this approach is the minimization of the sum of absolute errors. To use this criterion for the linear curve $Y = a + bt$, each historical value is assumed to be determined by

$$X_i = a + (b - c)i + d_i - g_i$$

where a, b, c, d, and g are coefficients. The latter two coefficients represent the error and thus are different for each period. The doubling of the coefficients (b and c) is necessary because of the nonnegativity constraint in linear programming. If only positive coefficients are desired, the c would be removed. A similar argument explains the double error terms, d_i and g_i. In both cases, only one coefficient will be greater than zero for any solution.

The linear-programming model is then

$$\text{Minimize} \quad \sum_{i=1}^{N} (g_i + d_i)$$

subject to the above set of equations and to all coefficients being greater than or equal to zero.

Another criterion is to minimize the maximum deviation (minimax). The objective here is to minimize d subject to all coefficients being greater than or equal to zero, where d is the maximum deviation. The equations for the linear curve are

$$X_i = a + (b - c)i + d - f_i$$
$$X_i = a + (b - c)i - d + g_i$$

Again, double coefficients are necessary where both positive and negative coefficients are possible. Also note the necessity for doubling the number of equations (data sets) to allow for a negative maximum deviation. The particular nature of this criterion calls for extra judgment in the use of curves derived from it for forecasting.

Another feature of regression by linear programming is the ability to add constraints to any variable. As already noted, the coefficients can be selectively limited to positive values. In addition, the coefficient values may be bounded, the regression line may be forced through the origin (0,0) by elimination of the free term (a), or any other constraint of the variables which can be expressed as a linear inequality may be used. This makes the two regression schemes based on linear programming very flexible indeed. The main difficulty with using linear programming is the complexity of the calculations, making a computer a necessity. Klein[11] and Bracken and McCormick[12] give a more detailed discussion on curve fitting by linear programming.

NONLINEAR-PROGRAMMING CURVE FITTING: For the fitting of curves in which the coefficients are nonlinear and also for cases where a nonlinear criterion is used, several nonlinear-programming techniques have been used. See Bracken and McCormick,[12] Wilde and Beightler,[13] and Draper and Smith[14] for an introductory discussion. Nonlinear techniques are more complicated mathematically and are not as "standardized" as linear programming; therefore, we shall not delve into them here.

Extrinsic Factors. Almost every time series is influenced by other factors, although it may not be known exactly how. The most rigorous model (mathematically speaking) would be the causative-factor type in which relationships between the forecast variable and the extrinsic factors are explicitly spelled out. Construction of such a model would involve examining the system for the true underlying causes for demand and then building equations composed of the relationships between the forecast variable and the causative factors. Such models may be involved and relatively expensive; consequently, the value of the resulting forecast would have to justify the effort.

For cases where explicit causative models are not feasible, and for cases where causal relationships are believed to exist but their exact nature is not known, correlation techniques are commonly used to fit forecasting equations. The techniques are used also to relate time series where "nonsense" correlations exist. That is, two series may react similarly, but there is no logical explanation as to why.

While these correlations are relatively easy to make using computers, they are sensitive to the fact that relationships may change. They should be periodically reevaluated to see if the relationships are still valid.

CORRELATIONS: Extrinsic correlation techniques utilize past relationships between the forecast variable and one or more extrinsic factors. A simple example is the fitting of the curve

$$Y_t = a + bZ_t$$

by least-squares techniques. Here Z_t is the value of an extrinsic time series for period t. For this equation, the equations to determine the parameters are

$$a = \frac{(\Sigma Z^2)(\Sigma X) - (\Sigma Z)(\Sigma ZX)}{(N)(\Sigma Z^2) - (\Sigma Z)^2}$$

$$b = \frac{\Sigma X - Na}{\Sigma Z}$$

where the summations are over periods 1 to N. The value of the variable Z_t may be smoothed or adjusted before the fit is made.

Any number of extrinsic variables could be included in the equation. Likewise, more than one term could be included for each variable (a variable could have both a linear and a second-order term). A problem with using this approach is determining which variables and which terms to include. Stepwise regression techniques which selectively analyze the significance of each term are helpful in determining which factors and terms to include in the equation. Methods for fitting multiple-variable and multiple-term equations are discussed in Chapter 28.

The equation above assumes that forecast-period values of the extrinsic factor are available. This situation is generally not possible; nevertheless, forecasted values, with their increased uncertainties, are often available. In this latter situation, however, the correlations should be made using the historical forecasts rather than the actual values.

LEADING SERIES: Rather than making correlations between coincident periods, forecast correlations may be made between the forecast variable and a past-period value of the extrinsic variable, such as

$$Y_t = a + bZ_{t-3}$$

This type of correlation is called a "leading-series correlation." As with the equations mentioned in the preceding section, multiple variables and terms may be included in the equation. Both current and leading variables may be included in the same equation.

With this type of correlation, the problem is thus the quest for "leading" series. The U.S. Department of Commerce has extensively studied time series which affect the national economy in its search for leading series. Its *BCD* (*Business Cycle Developments*) series are even grouped into leading, roughly coincident, and lagging sets relative to the national economy. Data for the history of the sets are available, and a monthly magazine called *BCD* is prepared under the direction of Julius Shiskin (developer of the major moving-average time-series decomposition techniques). The basic series and over 300 component series are discussed and explained in the magazine.

IMPLEMENTING A FORECAST

This chapter has introduced the problems of forecasting, presented points which should be considered in forecasting, and outlined some of the different methods. We have discussed some of the more practical methods with some mention of how they are applied and their limitations. In this section, we shall expand on these latter two subjects as we concern ourselves with the problems of implementing a forecasting procedure.

In approaching a forecasting problem, the reader must answer the questions stated in the beginning of this chapter. In answering the question *how*, he must be aware of the distinctions mentioned in the beginning of the chapter. He must ask what part subjective factors will play in the forecast. He must ascertain what part history will play in deciding the forecasting mechanism.

Influence of Subjective Factors. There is no such thing as a completely objective means of determining a forecast. No matter how sophisticated the statistics and mathematics involved in a forecasting scheme, there is much subjective judgment in determining which model or equation to use, which variables should be a part of the model, and what data should be used in determining the model coefficients.

One question which should be answered is whether a scientific or quasi-scientific method should be used at all in preference to a nonscientific method. In many cases, this question is answered by the huge volume of forecasts which must be made. In other cases, a scientific forecast can be used as a "check" on a nonscientific forecast, and vice versa as no scientific forecast should be accepted blindly without some subjective reasoning.

One of the most intriguing areas of forecasting is how to combine subjective considerations (such as special knowledge about a new customer) with a scientific forecast. Often this can be done by building into a forecasting system an additive special-knowledge factor. For example.

$$F^* = F + \text{SK}$$

where F^* = forecast after special knowledge
  F = forecast before special knowledge
  SK = special-knowledge factor

There is danger, however, in overdoing special knowledge, especially when forecast deviations are a part of the forecast system. This danger can be overcome, for example, by including the special-knowledge factor if the factor is, say, greater than some measure of the forecast error. For example,

$$\text{if } SK > (k \times SE) \qquad \begin{cases} \text{then } F^* = F + SK \\ \text{else } F^* = F \end{cases}$$

where SE = the standard deviation of the forecast error
k = control factor (such as 1.5)

One practical example of how a statistical forecast can be combined with a nonstatistical prediction is to see if the single-value prediction falls within plus or minus some control limits (in the quality control sense) of the single-value statistical forecast. The control limits would be some measure of the forecast error, which would be based on history. If the prediction fell outside the control limits, the person making the prediction would be asked to reevaluate his estimate.

One way of combining statistical and nonstatistical forecasting is to take a weighted average of the two, the weighting factors giving a measure of how much confidence is placed in each of the methods.

Use of Statistical Distributions. An important question is whether the forecast is single-valued or described by a distribution. The use of the latter is becoming more common because of the realization that

1. Single-valued forecasts are limited in trying to describe an event which is not known with certainty.

2. Inventory control methods have shown how measurements of uncertainty are vital in determining such things as safety stocks.

3. Business has become sophisticated in the use of quantitative methods.

Subjective methods can be used in obtaining distributions (this is indeed a necessity if no history exists). However, history is often of more value in determining the distribution than in determining the single-point expected value estimate. Forecasting systems in which the single-point estimate is obtained by subjective judgment and the distribution is obtained from statistical analysis of history are quite common.

A difficulty with multipoint or distribution estimates is that more data are involved, thus making the job of forecasting and the job of bookkeeping more difficult. Thus the benefits of the more detailed forecasts must be balanced against the costs of obtaining them.

One approach to determining a probability distribution of a sales estimate is given by this example. The customers or users are enumerated and three estimates of their requirements are made—an expected maximum (optimistic), the most likely, and an expected minimum (pessimistic). A model is constructed in which these values are parameters to an assumed distribution such as beta, uniform, or triangular. Using Monte Carlo simulation, a number of forecasts are made which are then fitted to a distribution.

Use of History. Even if an item's history is not used in developing the forecasting technique, its study is important in giving insight into the item's demand characteristics and in understanding the factors influencing the item's demand.

In determining the importance of history in influencing the item's future demand, consideration must be given to what internal factors are at work trying to change the history. There may be factors such as sales promotions, product improvements, introductions of competitive products, developments of new uses, and the like which are under the control of the forecasting organization and

TABLE 1   Data for Analysis

As given		Sequenced				
Period	Demand	Demand	Frequency	Cumulative frequency	Cumulative proportion	Cumulative percentage
1	11	10	0	0	0	0
2	18	11	1	1	0.1	10
3	15	12	2	3	0.3	30
4	19	13	1	4	0.4	40
5	13	14	0	4	0.4	40
6	12	15	3	7	0.7	70
7	15	16	1	8	0.8	80
8	15	17	0	8	0.8	80
9	12	18	1	9	0.9	90
10	16	19	1	10	1.0	100
		20	0	10	1.0	100

which the organization is trying to exploit. Change is inherent in business, and the forecaster must be cognizant of efforts effecting this change.

After deciding that history is to be a part of a forecast, the question arises as to how to analyze it. The following approach can be used. (A computer program could be written to do the same analysis described here and more.) If there is much data, the question of how much to use arises. Generally it is best to use as much as possible, discarding some of it as the analysis proceeds. The general problem is not enough data rather than too much. The amount of data is especially important in fitting curves by regression analysis as the results may be very sensitive to the period of fit.

Table 1 gives some data which will be analyzed for illustrative purposes.

A. *The data should be plotted on coordinate graph paper in time sequence.* This assumes data are given in demand units per time period. The time period should correspond to the forecast period. Special graph papers are available which have a time axis. See Fig. 9 for a scatter diagram of the data of Table 1.

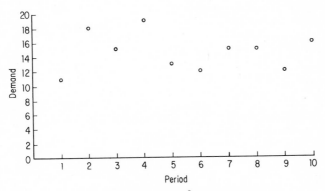

Fig. 9   Scatter diagram.

Scaling of the vertical axis is important, as it may affect the data interpretations. The zero value should be included, at least on the initial graph.

Points to observe are:
1. Do values tend to follow either an upward or a downward trend? If so, can a line or curve be drawn through the data points to represent the trend? The slope of the line can indicate whether the trend is significant enough to be considered further. If the variation of data points about the fitted line is high (especially in relationship to the trend), then the use of a mathematically fitted curve may not be of much value in developing a forecast mechanism. If the fitted line is a straight line, then a linear model may be the best fit. If the line is a curve, some other equation might be appropriate and the use of curve-fitting techniques may find a mathematical curve which gives a reasonable fit.
2. Are the data such that later values are a multiple of 10 or 100 of earlier values? If so, an exponential growth curve may exist, in which case the plot should be made also on a graph paper whose vertical axis has a logarithmic scale. (This growth in the series might be obvious from the data, in which case the plot can be made initially on semilog paper.)
3. Is there much variation about the average or trend line? This gives a measure of the noise which the forecast method should reduce. What is the magnitude and significance of this variation in relationship to the average?
4. Are there extreme values which can be explained by unusual circumstances? These values ("outliers") might be eliminated from further analysis or else smoothed (averaged) in some way.
5. Do the data run in cycles? If so, do these cycles have a common periodicity? Is there seasonality?
6. Do the data appear to be one "population" or several? That is, are there breaks in the data (such as a sudden jump or step, or a change in trend)? If so, perhaps only the latest "population" (set of data) should be analyzed. If there are trends, seasonality, or other measurable factors affecting the demand, then measures of these factors should be obtained (such as determining the trend from a fit of a linear curve, or determining seasonality by some measure). The Shiskin method, if available, is most helpful at this stage. The data should then be adjusted by these measures before the following steps are done. In practice, these adjustments would be part of the forecasting mechanism. Step B below should be done with both unadjusted and adjusted data to see what effects the adjustments have had. The significance of the adjustments can be measured by comparing the adjusted variance against the unadjusted variance.

Sometimes the data should be adjusted before analysis. For instance, the variation in the number of working days in a month may be significant enough to warrant adjustment, although this factor may be considered in the seasonal factor. Likewise, strikes or other shutdowns may be significant.

B. *Common statistical averages should be taken.* These include the average (mean):

$$\mu = \frac{\sum\limits_{i=1}^{N} X_i}{N}$$

the variance:

$$V = \frac{\sum\limits_{i=1}^{N} (X_i - \mu)^2}{N}$$

the standard deviation:

$$\sigma = \sqrt{V}$$

and the range:

$$RG = X_{\max} - X_{\min}$$

where the X values are the highest and lowest, respectively.

The variance can also be calculated from

$$V = \frac{\displaystyle\sum_{i=1}^{N} (X_i)^2}{N} - \mu^2$$

that is, mean of the squares minus the square of the mean.

Note that the above formula gives the variance of the given data. If the given data are considered as a sample of the general population of data, then the following formulas should be used if the sample size N is small:

$$V = \frac{\displaystyle\sum_{i=1}^{N} (X_i - \mu)^2}{N - 1} = \frac{N \displaystyle\sum_{i=1}^{N} (X_i)^2 - \left(\displaystyle\sum_{i=1}^{N} X_i \right)^2}{N(N - 1)}$$

If the sample size N is small, ≤ 10, then the sample standard deviation can be approximated by

$$\sigma = \frac{RG}{\sqrt{N}}$$

The graph of Fig. 10 can also be used in roughly determining the standard deviation for monthly data.

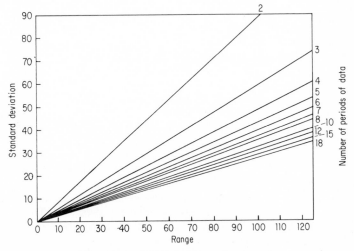

Fig. 10 Standard deviation from range.

C. *A histogram of demand variation should be made.* Figure 11 is an example. The data are broken down into classes. The frequency with which the data fall within each class is tabulated and plotted. If the data are discrete rather than continuous (such as some small number of orders per day), then each demand level (number of orders) would be a class.

Points to observe are:

1. Is the frequency uniformly distributed between the highest and lowest value? If so, a uniform distribution may describe the demand.

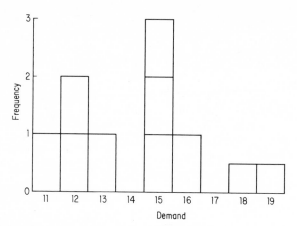

Fig. 11 Histogram.

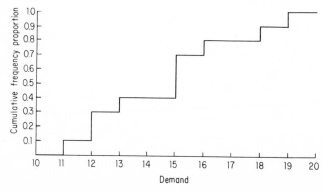

Fig. 12 Cumulative frequency plot.

2. Does the frequency peak near the center? If so, a symmetrical distribution, such as a normal distribution, may describe the demand.
3. Does the frequency peak, but not near the center? If so, the distribution is biased and some unsymmetrical distribution, such as lognormal, may describe the demand.
4. Are data discrete with the mean approximately equal to the variance? Then the Poisson distribution may describe the demand. To use this distribution there should be some logical justification for the arrival of demand orders being independent of one another.

D. *A cumulative frequency-proportion plot should be made.* See Fig. 12

for a plot on rectangular paper. The cumulative plot aids testing of whether a distribution follows certain special mathematical functions. Special graph papers are available to test plots against normal and lognormal distributions. The cumulative frequency plot is also valuable for giving measures as "what proportion of the time periods will the demand be over a given amount." If random sampling is done using Monte Carlo methods, then the cumulative frequency plot is needed to give the demand corresponding to a selected random number.

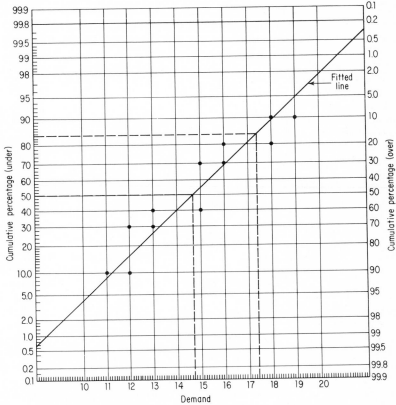

Fitted mean (50% line)=14.7
Fitted std. dev. (84% line - 50% line)=17.4 -14.7 = 2.7

Fig. 13 Cumulative frequency plot on normal-probability paper.

Figure 13 is an example of a cumulative frequency plot of the given data on normal probability paper. An "eyeball" straight line has been drawn through the plotted points. The intersection of the line with the 0.50 point on the vertical axis gives the "fitted" estimate of the mean. The intersection of the line with the 0.84 point* gives the 1-standard-deviation intersection. The fitted standard deviation is then determined by

$$\sigma = 0.84 \text{ intersection} - 0.50 \text{ intersection}$$

* The cumulative probability at 1 standard deviation above the mean is 0.8413. See Table A in Chapter 28.

Similarly an estimate of the standard deviation can be obtained from the 0.16-point intersection. If the fitted straight line gives a reasonable fit to the plotted points, and the fitted mean and standard deviation approximate the calculated values, then the normal distribution can be assumed to approximate the given data.

The normal distribution is frequently used to approximate the distribution of demand data primarily because it is relatively easily understood and the mathematics and tables for its use are well developed. In practice, few demand populations are "normal"; nevertheless, the normal distribution is used because no other distribution gives a reasonable fit.

One difficulty with using a normal distribution is that it allows demand to fall below zero, a situation which is usually unrealistic.

The lognormal distribution is sometimes used in preference to the normal distribution because it has no below-zero values; however, the mathematics for using it are more complicated.

The analysis of history using these steps can give some feel for whether there are patterns which can be used in a forecasting procedure. This analysis can give some feel as to whether there might be other extrinsic factors (such as national economy) to which the given time series can be related by correlation analysis. This analysis of extrinsic relationships is generally not worth the effort with individual stockkeeping units, but is often extremely valuable for forecasting a business for longer-term planning. When combined with subjective estimation of the factors difficult or impossible to determine from history (such as new markets), this analysis can tell whether curve fitting and/or correlative relationships are significant enough to be used.

In initial explorations of a variable, the elementary plotting of points is very useful. It is preferred over sophisticated mathematical methods unless the researcher has some a priori basis for choosing a specific method.

Use of Sophisticated Methods. Unsophisticated methods fail to furnish a clear explanation of phenomena under investigation; nevertheless, they are desirable in a "first look" at a problem. Even sophisticated models will yield unreliable results if employed without careful planning, without understanding the phenomena, and without understanding the technique of analysis.

A look at the management science literature on forecasting—especially some of it on exponential smoothing—may give one the impression that the management scientists feel compelled to increase the complexity of all models on the assumption that intricacy and sophistication are correlated with usefulness. This premise is valid for some systems; nevertheless, the simpler approaches will frequently serve as well or almost as well. Elaborate models are worthwhile only if they have been adequately researched.

Choice of Method. The requirements of a good forecasting method are:

1. It should state use for which intended.
2. It should state assumptions.
3. It should not be too restrictive.
4. It should state possible range of error.
5. It should be easy to understand.
6. It should have a mechanism for showing when it is out of balance and provide a means for rectifying this situation.
7. *It should work.*

In choosing among the methods described, the following points need consideration in addition to which method gives the best forecast:

1. Amount of calculations
2. Amount of storage

3. Hand versus machine calculations
4. Ability to initiate system
5. Ability to "tune up" system
6. Ability to maintain system

The amount of calculations and amount of storage affect whether calculations are by hand or machine or some combination of the two. Hand calculations can make use of nomographs and tables. Many machines, from desk calculator to on-line computer, are available.

Timeliness of the forecast is important in choosing whether a computer is to be used. Batch processing of data by computer may require only seconds of actual computer time but may require lengthy periods to condition data for the computer and to get the results back from the computer.

The various methods have their advantages and disadvantages. The simple-average model doesn't react to changes. Simple moving-average methods require considerable data storage, but don't readily react to changes, and have the problem of choosing the length of the average. Basic exponential smoothing has low data storage, reacts to changes although with a lag, and has the problem of choosing a smoothing constant. Adaptive exponential-smoothing models correct somewhat for the problems of lag and the choice of smoothing constant, but they are more complex and require more calculations. They tend to be heuristic or pseudo-statistical. Exponential smoothing is generally more suitable to stockkeeping-unit forecasts than for aggregate-item forecasts.

In general, curve-fitting methods are used for longer-range forecasts. Curves are more apt to be fitted to yearly rather than weekly or monthly data because of the increased randomness which tends to appear in shorter periods. Fitted curves can, of course, be adjusted by seasonal factors.

Intrinsic correlation models require much data storage, may require frequent extensive calculations, and have the problems of choice of curve (model), selection of period over which to fit data, and selection of fitting criterion. Extrinsic correlation models may improve forecasts over intrinsic forecasts by relationships with causative factors. However, the problems exist of which factors to include and whether the relationships will continue to hold.

When many items are forecast at the same time, consideration must be given to whether the same method is used for all items or different methods are used for various classes of items. The concept of ABC analysis is important in answering this question. Even when the same method is used for many items, questions arise as to whether each item will have its own parameters in its equations or whether some parameters can be used over many items. For instance, a common seasonality factor may be used for many items. Or with exponential smoothing, the same smoothing constant may be used over many items.

In general, the average methods are more applicable when many items are to be forecast routinely, whereas the curve fitting are more appropriate when a single occasional forecast is to be made.

The ultimate criterion as to which is the best forecasting technique or which is the best parameter in a forecasting model should be not which technique or parameter gives the best forecast by some error criteria, but rather which technique or parameter minimizes the cost associated with production and inventory planning and control. These costs include not only inventory, production, and customer-service costs, but also system costs—the costs of forecasting. The costs of forecasting include the cost in developing, testing, and selling the technique, the cost of using, and the cost of maintaining. The cost versus the value of the forecast is often overlooked, but it is extremely important.

Use of a Computer. Electronic computers have been used both for routine forecasting and for testing forecasting methods. One recent advance has been the development of forecasting modules which can be built into inventory control and production scheduling systems. These modules eliminate the need for reprogramming the forecasting model every time a control system is developed.

The other progression has been the development of computer program packages which permit the forecaster to try out different methods on historical data. Most computer manufacturers and software companies offer these packages, and many companies now have developed their own. These programs permit the forecaster to very rapidly simulate how well a given technique works with actual data.

The computer does have some very definite advantages. It has tremendous calculation and storage capabilities which

1. Save processing time over hand calculations
2. Facilitate the use of methods otherwise impractical
3. Allow the handling of many items

The computer can give fancy printouts including graphical output. On the other hand, the use of computers can be costly, and many forecasting methods can tax the capabilities of a computer—especially when many items are forecast. With computers, human judgment is not a part of the calculations, thus causing forecasting to be "automatic." There is no forecasting method that can effectively handle all contingencies, and the intervention of human judgment is often extremely valuable.

Another difficulty with using computers is that people tend to ignore the fact that some mathematical method is used in developing a computer-derived forecast. They become result rather than method oriented. Because they don't have to perform the calculations themselves, they often don't understand the method. More important, they may not understand the limitations of the method and thus the limitations of the results. Finally, the results from a computer are dependent upon the input data with the GIGO (Garbage In, Garbage Out) principle in effect. Conditioning sales history by computer can be an extremely difficult job.

Summary. The following points summarize the factors to consider in the search for techniques.

1. There are no infallible ways to forecast the future. *No* technique works for all situations, and more than one technique may satisfactorily work for a given situation.

2. A forecast should recognize that there is no certainty. Therefore, a forecast is expected to be wrong—"to forecast is to be wrong." Even though there is this uncertainty, we nevertheless should use good methods.

3. Conditions change so that we must have some way of adapting our forecasts to these changes.

4. Even though many of the forecasting techniques may be quite scientifically sound, there is much judgment in:

    a. Use of techniques
    b. What data to use
    c. How data is conditioned

The forecaster is more important than the method.

5. The forecaster should not be technique oriented.
6. Precision is seldom important in a forecast.
7. Elements which determine the best method include:

    Purpose
    Money—potential benefit
    Timeliness

GLOSSARY OF SYMBOLS

The following is a list of the mathematical symbols used in this chapter, with a brief definition of each. Indexes, coefficients in equations, and intermediate values used in simplifying formulas are not included.

Symbol	Definition
A	Average demand
A_t	An average demand as of time period t
A'_t	Single-smoothed average for period t
A''_t	Double-smoothed average for period t
A'''_t	Triple-smoothed average for period t
C	Cyclical component in a time series
D	Demand in a time series
e_t	Forecast error for period t
E_t	Sum of forecast errors through period t
F	Forecast of time series
F_t	Forecast demand for period t
F^*	Special-knowledge adjusted forecast
I	Irregular component in time series
k	Safety or significance control factor
L	Time periods in cycle
M	Number of terms in equations
N	Number of periods in history
P_t	Mean absolute deviation (MAD) at period t
Q_t	Smoothed average deviation (SAD) at period t
r	Reduction factor
R_t	Trend at period t
RG	Range
RS_t	Trend signal at period t
S	Seasonal component in time series
S_t	Seasonal adjustment factor for period t
SA	Average demand over a cycle
SE	Standard deviation of forecast error
SF_t	Seasonally adjusted forecast for period t
SK	Special-knowledge factor
SL_t	Seasonality limit for period t
t	Time period
T	Trend component in time series
T_t	Trend estimate for period t
TL_t	Trend-control limit at period t
TS_t	Tracking signal at period t
TSL	Tracking-signal limit
u	Lead time of forecast (periods)
V	Variance
V_t	Variance estimate at period t
w_t	Weighting factor for period t
W_t	Autocovariance estimate at period t
X_t	Actual demand in period t
X'_t	Transformed demand in period t
Y_t	A demand for period t estimated by a curve
Z_t	Value of external factor in period t
α	Demand smoothing constant
α'	Long-term demand smoothing constant
β	Complement of demand smoothing constant ($= 1 - \alpha$)

γ Seasonality smoothing constant
δ Trend smoothing constant
η Error smoothing constant
μ Mean
ξ Autocorrelation damping factor
ρ Variance smoothing constant
σ Standard deviation
ψ Seasonality limit smoothing constant
ω Cycle period in sinusoidal functions

REFERENCES

1. R. G. Brown, *Statistical Forecasting for Inventory Control*, McGraw-Hill Book Company, New York, 1959.
2. P. J. Harrison, "Short-term Sales Forecasting," *Applied Statistics*, vol. 14, pp. 102–139, 1965.
3. F. E. Croxton and D. J. Cowden, *Applied General Statistics*, 2d ed., Prentice-Hall, Inc., Englewood Cliffs, N.J., 1955.
4. R. L. McLaughlin, *Time Series Forecasting*, American Marketing Association, Chicago, 1962.
5. R. G. Brown, *Smoothing, Forecasting, and Prediction of Discrete Time Series*, Prentice-Hall, Inc., Englewood Cliffs, N.J., 1963.
6. P. R. Winters, "Forecasting Sales by Exponentially Weighted Moving Averages," *Management Science*, vol. 6, pp. 324–342, March, 1960.
7. D. W. Trigg and A. G. Leach, "Exponential Smoothing with an Adaptive Response Rate," *Operational Research Quarterly*, vol. 18, pp. 53–59, March, 1967.
8. J. T. Burgess, "Adaptive Forecasting," paper presented at 13th annual meeting of The Institute of Management Science, Philadelphia, Pa., September, 1966.
9. R. S. Dudman, "Forecasting with Three-factor Adaptive Smoothing," paper presented at 13th annual meeting of The Institute of Management Science, Philadelphia, Pa., September, 1966.
10. J. R. Wolberg, *Prediction Analysis*, D. Van Nostrand Company, Inc., Princeton, N.J., 1967.
11. M. Klein, "Rational Approximation via Minimax Linear Programming Regression," *Proc. 23rd Nat'l Conf. of the Association for Computer Machinery*, Brandon Systems Press, Princeton, N.J., 1968, pp. 79–84.
12. J. Bracken and G. P. McCormick, *Selected Applications of Nonlinear Programming*, John Wiley & Sons, Inc., New York, 1968.
13. D. J. Wilde and C. S. Beightler, *Foundations of Optimization*, Prentice-Hall, Inc., Englewood Cliffs, N.J., 1967.
14. N. P. Draper and H. Smith, *Applied Regression Analysis*, John Wiley & Sons, Inc., New York, 1967.

BIBLIOGRAPHY

Box, G. E. P., and G. M. Jenkins: *Time Series Analysis, Forecasting and Control*, Holden Day, Inc., San Francisco, 1969.
Montgomery, D. C.: "An Introduction to Short Term Forecasting," *The Journal of Industrial Engineering*, vol. 19, pp. 500–504, 1968.
Murdick, R. G., and A. E. Schaefer: *Sales Forecasting for Lower Costs and Higher Profits*, Prentice-Hall, Inc., Englewood Cliffs, N.J. 1967.
Parzen, E.: *Empirical Time Series Analysis*, Holden Day, Inc., San Francisco, 1970.
Spencer, Clark, and Hoguet, *Business and Economic Forecasting*, Richard D. Irwin, Inc., Homewood, Ill., 1961.
Techniques for Forecasting Product Demand, American Institute of Certified Public Accountants, New York, 1968.

Chapter **9**

Short-range Planning[*]

EDITOR:

George W. Plössl   *Partner, Plossl & Wight Associates, Wilton, Connecticut*

CONTRIBUTORS:

R. Leonard Allen   *Production and Inventory Control Specialist, American-Standard, New York, New York*

H. Duane Applequist   *Corporation Coordinator, Work Scheduling and Control, The Standard Oil Co. (Ohio), Cleveland, Ohio*

Dr. Norbert L. Enrick   *Professor of Management and Production, College of Business Administration, Kent State University, Kent, Ohio*

Dr. Donald E. Scheck   *Professor of Industrial Engineering, Ohio University, Athens, Ohio*

[*] Some material in this chapter adapted from G. W. Plossl and O. W. Wight, *Production and Inventory Control: Principles and Techniques,* © 1967. Adapted by permission of Prentice-Hall, Inc., Englewood Cliffs, New Jersey.

CONTENTS

Short-range planning covers the function of setting limits or levels of production capacity for future manufacturing operations, considering both the forecast demand to be satisfied and the facilities (men, machines, money, materials) available and needed to satisfy it.

Product-demand forecasting is covered in Chapter 8; product and process information in Chapter 5. This chapter covers planning and scheduling principles and techniques, including necessary information on costs involved, management policies required, and practical examples of effective techniques.

Short-range planning usually covers one-year periods but may involve two- or three-year periods to ensure smooth transition between present and future operations involving new plant or equipment.

NEED FOR CAPACITY PLANNING

Good customer service requires enough plant capacity to produce the product demanded within allowable lead times, without excessive inventory and with economical plant operation at rates as level as possible. Capacity planning attempts to *reconcile these three conflicting objectives* within limits established by management policy. Alternate production plans show management the effects of different policies and activities on customer service, inventory investment, and plant operation, providing guides to decisions on such variables as forecast errors, seasonal inventory buildups, stable employment levels, etc.

In a manufacturing business, inventories exist either as a result of or to support production. Total inventories can be controlled only when total production is controlled. Finished inventory will increase only when production exceeds demand and decrease only when demand exceeds production. The production plan shows planned totals of demand and production, and the inventory resulting. Actual totals are then compared to the plan so that necessary replanning or corrective action can be taken to meet changing conditions in time to be effective.

Inventory control systems, by themselves, will not release work at level rates or in amounts equal to the capacity of a replenishing facility (plant or vendor) to handle the work. A production plan is necessary to establish this capacity and to link the *input* control system (inventory control and scheduling) with the *output* control system (dispatching and expediting). The production plan sets the rates at which detailed inventory control and scheduling techniques release work. It provides control limits to show when actual total output is too low or too high.

Product-group forecasts are generally more accurate than individual-item forecasts over planning periods of one-quarter, one-half, or one year. Production plans utilize this characteristic of forecasting to best advantage, basing planning and control of capacity on group demand. Individual-item forecasts are used only to help select the mix of specific items to schedule into production at the planned rate.

Production control activities (machine loading, dispatching, and expediting) are simpler, less expensive, and more effective when work-in-process levels (backlogs) are reduced. Lead times are also shorter and less variable. Backlogs cannot be controlled without effective production planning.

PLANNING PRODUCTION CAPACITY

Few companies have perfect forecasts, so any successful system must be capable of coping with an imperfect one. This can be done if two basic forecast characteristics are understood and applied:

1. Forecast accuracy is a function of *time*. The farther it goes into the future, the less likely a forecast is to be accurate.

2. Forecast accuracy is a function of the *number of items in the group*. The larger the product group, the more accurate the forecast is likely to be.

Production plans should be made using the *broadest possible product groups that go through similar manufacturing operations*. Production plans establish production rates for operations, while individual manufacturing orders are scheduled to the planned rate at the last moment based on the latest requirements—whether generated by an order-point or materials-planning system.

Choosing meaningful groups requires a thorough knowledge of the plant's manufacturing processes. These groupings are seldom the same ones used by the marketing department or the inventory control system. The groups must be meaningful in terms of demand on the manufacturing facilities. Even a crude production plan is far better than no plan at all, since it provides:

1. A means of *planning* production rates
2. A means of *controlling* production rates to meet the plan
3. A means of *regulating* the rate of *release* of work to the plant in order to control the level of work in process

The Dictionary of Production and Inventory Control Terms defines "production planning" as "the function of setting the limits or levels of manufacturing operations in the future."

A good production plan is a projection of the level of production required for a specific production facility, but it is not a firm commitment for the individual items to be made within the plan. It establishes the framework within which inventory control techniques will operate. It sets the rate at which orders must be generated to feed the plant.

Experience has shown that introducing a production plan for companies without one is usually the most significant and rewarding systems revision. Companies with seasonal production are especially vulnerable to high costs and inefficient operations when they lack effective production planning. The production plan lays out in advance the program for building inventory ahead of the peak selling season and permits charting a course against which actual performance can be measured.

Without a production plan, it is typical for management to become alarmed by the inventory buildup ahead of the peak season because they lack the specific information as to the level of inventory needed. Too frequently, the reaction is to cut back production rates just before the peak season, and then to react at considerable expense to increase production again when sales pick up and the inventory disappears. With a production plan, the inventory buildup can be compared regularly to the planned levels, and the question of too high or too low can be decided in time for corrective action to be effective.

Making the Production Plan. Two basic principles must be observed:

1. The production plan should cover product families or groups processed by common manufacturing facilities. Forecasts used for production planning must be for these product groups and *not* for product groups that have meaning only to the sales department.

2. The production plan should be expressed in the simplest terms meaningful to plant operating people. The measures of production should be *pieces, hours,* etc.

The steps involved in making a production plan are:

1. Determine the period to be covered by the production plan. Many companies make a general, overall monthly production plan, one year in advance. This is used to establish overall inventory-production policy and as a basis for checking equipment-capacity requirements. They then make a detailed weekly plan covering each quarter which is used to plan and stabilize manpower requirements.

2. Establish the base inventory level. This is the sum of the reserve stocks plus one-half the order quantities for all the items in the product group when an order-point system is being used, and is the average on-hand inventory needed to meet the customer-service level set by management policy.

3. Spread the sales forecast over the planning period. This should take into account regular cycles or peaks produced by promotions, stocking new warehouses, etc.

4. Determine the total inventory for the product group at the beginning of the planning period. This is usually the net inventory available for new business, but may also include items manufactured for sale to customers but not yet packed or delivered to warehouses.

5. Set the desired inventory level at the end of the period. This is the

base inventory level plus inventory added to cover plant shutdowns, seasonal peaks, or other requirements.

6. Calculate the change in inventory level during the planning period. This is the difference between beginning and ending inventories.

7. Calculate the total production required for the planning period. This is the total sales forecast plus or minus any change in the inventory level.

8. Spread the total production over the period as desired. This should consider holidays or other lost production and the time required to increase or decrease production rates from present levels.

The weekly production rate can be calculated by using this simple formula:

$$R = \frac{D - S + \Sigma F}{N}$$

where R = weekly production rate to achieve level production over the planning period, units/week

D = desired total inventory at the end of the planning period, units

S = actual total starting inventory, units

ΣF = total sales forecast for the planning period, units

N = number of weeks in the planning period

Example Assume for a product line of stamped ashtrays:

1. Actual starting inventory equals 130,000 units
2. Desired inventory at the end of the planning period equals 130,000 units
3. Total sales forecast equals 140,000 units
4. Five weeks in the planning period

Then

$$R = \frac{D - S + \Sigma F}{N} = \frac{130m - 130m + 140m}{5}$$

$$R = 28,000 \text{ units/week}$$

Table 1 shows the weekly production plan that would result. The starting inventory and the desired inventory at the end of the planning period are identical. In this special case, the total production is equal to the sales forecast. The production plan has two lines for each week, *planned* and *actual*. During October, actual sales, production, and inventory will be posted against the plan in order to track and control the production rate.

TABLE 1 Weekly Production Plan for October

All stamped ashtrays (figures in units)

Week date		Sales	Production	Inventory
Start				130,000
10/3	Planned	20,000	28,000	138,000
	Actual			
10/10	Planned	25,000	28,000	141,000
	Actual			
10/17	Planned	30,000	28,000	139,000
	Actual			
10/24	Planned	30,000	28,000	137,000
	Actual			
10/31	Planned	35,000	28,000	130,000
	Actual			

The production plan also regulates the flow of orders into the plant.   Table 2 shows a weekly *starting schedule* for the ashtrays covered by the production plan.   Of 50 different types of stamped ashtrays in the group only 7 will be started through production during the week of October 3.   These have the lowest inventories and are *at* or *near* their order points.   The total of all seven items scheduled is equal to the planned production rate.

Many companies that do not use production plans have all the information and are comparing performance against plans—but are doing this separately for sales, production, and inventory data.   Most marketing and sales departments compare actual sales against forecasts.   Financial people track the actual inventory level against the data on which budgets of profit have been based.   The production control manager or plant manager compares production against *planned* production rates.

TABLE 2   Weekly Starting Schedule

Stamped ashtrays	
Week of 10/3	
Item	**Quantity**
2" round	14,000
2¼" round	2,000
3" round	5,000
4" round	3,000
6" oval	1,500
3" hex	1,500
5" hex	1,000
Total	28,000

Manufacturing control decisions can be made best when all three factors— sales, production, and inventory—are viewed together.   It would be wrong to insist that a plant meet a planned increase in production rate if sales were not up to forecast and inventory were higher than planned.   On the other hand, if production were up to the planned rate, but sales were exceeding the forecast, causing inventory to drop below the planned level, the manufacturing rates would obviously have to be increased.   Looking at the three factors together in a production plan is the first and basic step to establishing a sound production control system.

Examples of Simple Production Plans.   Table 3 shows a production plan by month for all stamped ashtrays for one year.   Production is at a level rate to satisfy the sales forecast and to reduce the inventory from 150,000 units at the beginning of the planned period to approximately 130,000 units for one year later.   The calculations are:

1. Cumulative sales forecast for the year equals 1,456,000 pieces
2. Inventory change equals −20,000 pieces (from 150,000 to 130,000)
3. Required production equals 1,436,000 pieces
4. Weekly production rate (50 weeks) equals 28,700 pieces per week

After the vacation shutdown period in July, the inventory will be below the base inventory level until December.   Consequently, service at that time will probably be poorer than desired.   The production planner should call this to the attention of management.   It results from holding a level production rate through the year.   Two alternatives are available: either run at a higher level during the early part of the year (so that the inventory at the end of July is equal to 130,000 units) and then reduce production during August to hit the year-end inventory goal, or set a higher target inventory than the base level of 130,000 for the end of December and maintain production at a level rate throughout the year.

For example, if it were decided to set the production level high enough so that the July-end inventory was equal to the base level of 130,000, approximately 500 more units per week would have to be manufactured. If the production level remained unchanged for the balance of the year and the sales forecast

TABLE 3   Yearly Production Plan

All stamped ashtrays
(all figures in thousands)

| Month | | Wk. | Sales | | Production | | Inventory* Dec. 31 |
			Month	Cumul.	Month	Cumul.	150 M
Jan.	Planned Actual	5	140	140	144	144	154
Feb.	Planned Actual	4	112	252	115	259	157
Mar.	Planned Actual	4	112	364	115	374	160
Apr.	Planned Actual	4	112	476	115	489	163
May	Planned Actual	5	140	616	144	633	167
June	Planned Actual	4	112	728	115	748	170
July	Planned Actual	2†	112	840	57	805	115
Aug.	Planned Actual	5	140	980	144	949	119
Sept.	Planned Actual	4	112	1,092	115	1,064	122
Oct.	Planned Actual	5	140	1,232	144	1,208	126
Nov.	Planned Actual	4	112	1,344	115	1,323	129
Dec.	Planned Actual	4	112	1,456	115	1,438	132

*Base inventory level (1/2 order quantities plus reserve stock = 130 M)
†Vacation shutdown = 2 weeks

were accurate, the year-end inventory would be 157,000 units (500 per week times 50 weeks, plus 132,000) instead of 132,000 as previously planned.

The Seasonal Production Plan. When making a seasonal production plan, three alternatives are available:

1. Hold a level production rate at the expense of carrying high inventories.

2. Hold inventories down by varying the production rate to meet the seasonal sales requirements.

3. Some combination of these two extremes, with changes in the production rate to minimize excess inventory and meet the seasonal requirements.

Table 4 shows a yearly production plan for all-steel-cartridge, automotive-type filters. It covers a selling year from October 1 to September 30. The production and inventory are planned to meet the seasonal demand pattern which starts from a low in December, increases to a peak in August, and then drops back to another low. It measures inventory, sales, and production in terms of *labor-hours,* meaningful for this large and mixed product group where some individual products take far longer to manufacture than others.

Several possible yearly production plans are illustrated:

Plan 1 (Table 4) attempts to maintain production level throughout the year. Inventory from January through June is quite high.

TABLE 4   Yearly Production Plan 1

			Sales		Production		Inventory* (Sept. 30 1,200)	Remarks
Month		Wk.	Month	Cumul.	Month	Cumul.		
Oct.	Planned Actual	5	800	800	1,120	1,120	1,520	Prod. = 224/wk
Nov.	Planned Actual	4	600	1,400	896	2,016	1,816	
Dec.	Planned Actual	4	500	1,900	896	2,912	2,212	
Jan.	Planned Actual	5	1,000	2,900	1,120	4,032	2,332	
Feb.	Planned Actual	4	800	3,700	896	4,928	2,428	
Mar.	Planned Actual	4	800	4,500	896	5,824	2,524	
Apr.	Planned Actual	4	900	5,400	896	6,720	2,520	
May	Planned Actual	5	1,200	6,600	1,120	7,840	2,440	
June	Planned Actual	4	1,000	7,600	896	8,736	2,336	
July	Planned Actual	2†	1,000	8,600	448	9,184	1,784	
Aug.	Planned Actual	5	1,500	10,100	1,120	10,304	1,404	
Sept.	Planned Actual	4	900	11,000	896	11,200	1,400	

All-steel-cartridge automotive-type filters
(all figures in thousands of hours of labor)

*Base inventory level = 1,400 M hours.
†Vacation shutdown = 2 weeks.

Plan 2 (Table 5) changes the production level four times but maintains a much lower level of inventory.

Plan 3 (Table 6) varies the production level twice during the year and arrives at a level of inventory that is a compromise between the first two plans. The summary, Table 7, based on costs assumed, shows plan 3 giving the lowest total cost.

A seasonal production plan attempts to balance inventory investment against the cost of changing the production level. The costs needed to solve this planning problem are not readily available but can frequently be estimated with some confidence. Primary factors are overtime, hiring, training, and layoff. Other real costs are more nebulous. Training new employees or low morale of workers facing layoff reduces quality, with higher scrap and rework losses. Frequent layoffs give a company a poor reputation in the labor market and make it difficult to hire and keep high-caliber workers.

Production-rate changes, particularly increases, are very difficult to accomplish as scheduled. New employees are not able to produce at desired rates for varying periods, and some are never able to attain minimum rates and must be replaced. Parts-production increases must precede assembly-rate increases.

TABLE 5   Yearly Production Plan 2

All-steel-cartridge automotive-type filters
(all figures in thousands of hours of labor)

Month		Wk.	Sales Month	Sales Cumul.	Production Month	Production Cumul.	Inventory* (Sept. 30 1,200)	Remarks
Oct.	Planned	5	800	800	805	805	1,205	Prod. = 161/wk
	Actual							
Nov.	Planned	4	600	1,400	645	1,450	1,250	
	Actual							
Dec.	Planned	4	500	1,900	645	2,095	1,395	
	Actual							
Jan.	Planned	5	1,000	2,900	1,000	3,095	1,395	Prod. = 200/wk
	Actual							
Feb.	Planned	4	800	3,700	800	3,895	1,395	
	Actual							
Mar.	Planned	4	800	4,500	800	4,695	1,395	
	Actual							
Apr.	Planned	4	900	5,400	950	5,645	1,445	Prod. = 238/wk
	Actual							
May	Planned	5	1,200	6,600	1,190	6,835	1,435	
	Actual							
June	Planned	4	1,000	7,600	950	7,785	1,385	
	Actual							
July	Planned	2†	1,000	8,600	620	8,405	1,005	Prod. = 309/wk
	Actual							
Aug.	Planned	5	1,500	10,100	1,550	9,955	1,055	
	Actual							
Sept.	Planned	4	900	11,000	1,240	11,195	1,395	
	Actual							

*Base inventory level = 1,400 M hours.
†Vacation shutdown = 2 weeks.

TABLE 6   Yearly Production Plan 3

All-steel-cartridge automotive-type filters
(all figures in thousands of hours of labor)

Month		Wk.	Sales Month	Sales Cumul.	Production Month	Production Cumul.	Inventory* (Sept. 30 1,200)	Remarks
Oct.	Planned	5	800	800	975	975	1,375	Prod. = 195/wk
	Actual							
Nov.	Planned	4	600	1,400	780	1,755	1,555	
	Actual							
Dec.	Planned	4	500	1,900	780	2,535	1,835	
	Actual							
Jan.	Planned	5	1,000	2,900	975	3,510	1,810	
	Actual							
Feb.	Planned	4	800	3,700	780	4,290	1,790	
	Actual							
Mar.	Planned	4	800	4,500	780	5,070	1,770	
	Actual							
Apr.	Planned	4	900	5,400	780	5,850	1,650	
	Actual							
May	Planned	5	1,200	6,600	975	6,825	1,425	
	Actual							
June	Planned	4	1,000	7,600	1,272	8,097	1,697	Prod. = 318/wk
	Actual							
July	Planned	2†	1,000	8,600	636	8,733	1,333	
	Actual							
Aug.	Planned	5	1,500	10,100	1,590	10,323	1,423	
	Actual							
Sept.	Planned	4	900	11,000	1,272	11.595	1,795	
	Actual							

*Base inventory level = 1,400 M hours.
†Vacation shutdown = 2 weeks.

Manufacturing foremen are usually reluctant to add people until they "can see the parts there to work on."

Plans 2 and 3 require far more capacity to handle the peak production than does plan 1. This may be close to or even beyond the maximum capacity of the plant and equipment available. Production is at a high rate going into the slow selling season in plan 3. Unless sales are considerably higher next year, another change in production level may be required sooner in plan 3 than in plan 1. This may make plan 1 potentially the lowest-cost plan.

Other considerations when making production plans are:

1. There is a definite period of time required to change production levels.

TABLE 7   Summary—Production Plans 1, 2, and 3

All-steel-cartridge automotive-type filters

Prod. plan	Avg. inv. level (M hours)	Avg. inv. (M $)*	Avg. inv. carry. cost†	Changes in prod. level	Cost of changes††	Total cost (M $)
Plan 1	2,060	8,240	1,648	1	150	1,798
Plan 2	1,313	5,252	1,050	4	600	1,650
Plan 3	1,622	6,488	1,298	2	300	1,598

* At $400 per labor hour.
† At 20%.
†† At $150M per change.

The new production rate must be given to the plant soon enough for it to react.

2. The number of holidays during the year may be a substantial factor affecting the level of inventory. Setting a daily production rate and using actual working days in the plan will handle this.

3. Many people have three-week or even four-week vacations. June through August is likely to be a period of slack production, and it is important to pinpoint just where lost production will occur during this period.

4. Overtime work is expensive, but in some circumstances is more desirable than adding people. A rule of thumb used by many practitioners is *never to plan* to use overtime. Then overtime provides flexibility in meeeting unexpected surges in sales or overcoming losses in production caused by equipment breakdowns or similar failures. Planned overtime is much easier to start than to stop.

5. Seasonal production plans attempt to store production *labor* and *machine-hours* in the cheapest form.

Changing the Plan. Production plans are frequently made on a monthly basis for the year and on a weekly basis for each quarter. *How often should they be changed?* The objective is to change production plans only when necessary. It is extremely important to determine ahead of time what circumstances will require a change in the production level. As will be shown later, rules can be established for determining when to change production plans.

APPLICATIONS OF PRODUCTION PLANNING

A production plan should be made for each major manufacturing area. If it is desirable to run two subareas at different production rates, two production plans—one for each submanufacturing area—should be established. One facility feeding subassemblies into an intermediate inventory ahead of an assembly department would require a separate production plan from that made for the assembly operations.

A production plan in a make-to-stock plant will be illustrated for a company manufacturing a line of kitchen mixers, marketed in 20 different models, each made up of a motor, gears, bowls, beaters, and other miscellaneous castings and small parts. The general process flow is shown in Fig. 1.

Production plans should be made for:

1. *Finished Goods.* Separate production plans for the high-speed assembly line for high-volume items and the small-lot assembly line for the slow movers.

2. *Finished-component Stores.* Separate production plans for motor manufacturing, gear and small-parts machining, and castings machining.

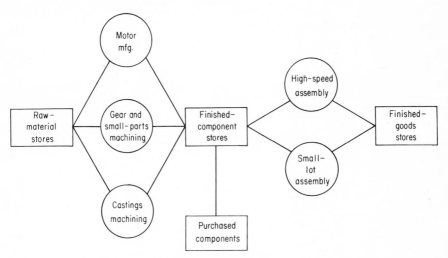

Fig. 1 General process flow—kitchen mixer line.

3. *Purchased Components.* A production plan could be developed for purchased components if desired, to regulate their flow into finished-component stores, and also for other groups of raw materials.

The production plan in each case would be for the *total* production expressed in understandable terms for each facility, using the simplest terms that are meaningful to manufacturing people. In motor manufacturing, for example, it would probably be in *number of motors.* Parts going through the gear and small-parts machining department would have wide variations in labor content, and measuring production in pieces would not be so meaningful. In this case, the total production plan would use *standard hours.*

One of the best methods for determining "meaningful terms" is to talk to the foreman about changing production levels—what personnel changes would he have to make if the number of *pieces* on the production schedule were increased? If this term is meaningless to him and he requires *hours,* which are much harder to provide, the added work is usually justified to ensure getting action in the plant.

Table 8 shows a production plan for one-quarter of a year for the final assembly area where all 20 models of mixers are put together. The sales forecast for the family is 2,000 units per week, the starting actual inventory is 10,100 pieces of all models, and the desired total inventory at the end of the quarter is 14,000 pieces.

Finished-goods inventory will be increased from the base level of 10,100 pieces (required to ensure giving 98 percent service) by two-weeks' supply (4,000 pieces), in anticipation of the annual vacation shutdown. The plan shows that a production rate of 2,300 units is needed to meet the demand and build up the inventory.

TABLE 8   Production Plan—20 Models of Kitchen Mixers
           All Data in Thousands of Pieces

2nd qtr. week no.		Sales forecast		Production		Inventory
		Weekly	Cumulative	Weekly	Cumulative	
First qtr.	Planned		26.0		26.0	10.1
	Actual		24.0		24.0	10.1
14	Planned	2.0	26.0	2.3	26.3	10.4
	Actual					
15	Planned	2.0	28.0	2.3	28.6	10.7
	Actual					
16	Planned	2.0	30.0	2.3	30.9	11.0
	Actual					
17	Planned	2.0	32.0	2.3	33.2	11.3
	Actual					
18	Planned	2.0	34.0	2.3	35.5	11.6
	Actual					
19	Planned	2.0	36.0	2.3	37.8	11.9
	Actual					
20	Planned	2.0	38.0	2.3	40.1	12.2
	Actual					
21	Planned	2.0	40.0	2.3	42.4	12.5
	Actual					
22	Planned	2.0	42.0	2.3	44.7	12.8
	Actual					
23	Planned	2.0	44.0	2.3	47.0	13.1
	Actual					
24	Planned	2.0	46.0	2.3	49.3	13.4
	Actual					
25	Planned	2.0	48.0	2.3	51.6	13.7
	Actual					
26	Planned	2.0	50.0	2.3	53.9	14.0
	Actual					

No provision has been made for holidays; it has been assumed that an *average* weekly rate of 2,300 mixers is required. If any weeks are short of working days, production in other weeks will have to exceed the average to meet the quarterly total of 29,900.

Cumulative sales and production figures are also shown in the plan. These permit comparison of actual sales and production against planned values and against one another over the period. The plan shows that 26,000 mixers were to be produced and sold in the first quarter. Actual sales were below forecast but were equal to the 24,000 mixers actually produced, and the inventory goal was met.

The plan shows that the marketing department has not decided to change the weekly forecast of 2,000 mixers because of the lower sales rate in the first quarter. They do not believe the first-quarter deficit of 2,000 mixers will be made up, and the second-quarter plan therefore starts with a cumulative sales figure of 24,000. Had they anticipated overcoming this deficit *in addition* to selling 26,000 mixers in the second quarter, the weekly sales rate in the plan would have been 2,150 pieces (26,000 plus 2,000 divided by 13 weeks).

Actual total sales and production for the first quarter become the starting figures for the second-quarter plan. Using these figures takes care of production deficits in the preceding quarter. The development of the weekly rates in making the new plan should be based on the desired inventory level at the end of the quarter and the expected total demand.

In making a production plan for finished goods in a make-to-stock plant, the service-versus-investment chart is valuable. It establishes the *base inventory level* at which the production plans aim. The service-versus-investment chart is based upon average demand during the year. Where demand varies greatly, the reserve stock required for a particular service level will also vary. Where there is a wide variation, the service-versus-investment chart should be based upon demand experienced at the time the inventory reaches its low point when there is no anticipation inventory on hand to assist the normal reserve stock in giving customer service, such as occurred in the seasonal plans for ashtrays in

TABLE 9 Quarterly Production Plan—Functional Department In Machine-hours

Week ending		Orders		Production		Component stockroom inventory
		Weekly	Cumulative	Weekly	Cumulative	
4/7	Planned	2,800	64,190	4,300	55,390	12,820
	Actual	2,750	64,200	5,100	55,390	13,670
4/14	Planned	2,800	66,990	4,300	59,690	14,320
	Actual	3,400	67,600	7,580	62,970	17,850
4/21	Planned	2,800	69,790	4,300	63,990	15,820
	Actual	3,260	70,860	4,490	67,460	19,080
6/30	Planned	2,800	97,790	4,300	106,990	30,820
	Actual					

Table 3. Such alternatives can be evaluated better if a definite measure of the effect on customer service can be obtained.

Functional Departments. Departments performing basic starting operations on raw materials or castings, such as the motor manufacturing or general machining departments for mixers, are usually more difficult to control. Using only inventory control and backlog measuring techniques (such as machine loading), the resulting erratic rate of order input causes excessive and variable lead times and results in very slow reaction to changes in the total demand caused by increasing or decreasing business. The same principle of establishing a planned level of operation of these departments and then scheduling to meet this plan can reduce the lead time for components, level out manufacturing operations, and reduce reaction time to such changes.

A production plan for a functional department can be set up by converting the sales forecast for finished goods into *hours of machining* requirements (see Table 9). Incoming orders for finished products are also converted into hours of machining in order to compare actual against planned demand. Production levels and component inventories are expressed in the same terms.

The inventory targets of such plans are the base inventory levels of the group of parts. These are the average inventories of purchased items equal to the reserve stock plus one-half the order quantity, for each item. For manufactured items, targets are derived from totals obtained by simulation or calculations based on the materials plan. Having a production plan for each major facility makes it possible to plan for different production rates when it is necessary to increase parts-inventory levels and to prepare for reduced production if factory equipment is being rearranged or if a key piece of equipment is to be shut down for overhaul.

The timing of changes in production levels is very important. Assembly rates cannot be increased and sustained until production rates of components are increased. Any change in production levels which requires hiring and training people will require a considerable period of time to accomplish. In a complex factory, production rates have to be increased successively through a sequence of departments. The production plan makes it possible to accomplish such changes on an orderly basis with a minimum of lost time.

For service departments such as painting or plating, production rates for significant equipment groups can be planned—recognizing that it is not always possible to precisely control the flow of material into these departments since it comes from many other departments. The scheduled input of orders into source departments should be balanced as closely as possible to meet the planned production rates in service departments. A very few of the products going through the service department will generate the bulk of the man-hours required within the department. Controlling the input of only these items can effectively level the production rate, reduce the work in process, and consequently reduce lead time.

Purchased Materials. Establishing a production rate and scheduling orders to meet this planned rate can also apply to purchased parts, particularly when such orders comprise a large portion of the vendor's business. Changes in the rate of orders flowing to him will generate severe ups and downs in his activity level and result in widely varying procurement lead times for his customers. The fact that this is "his problem" does not lessen its effect on his customers' inventories. By giving him a production plan from which to work and by scheduling the mix of individual items to meet this production plan, lead times can be reduced and stabilized. As each mix schedule is issued, a review of the status of both new orders and previous orders should be made.

Make-to-order Plants. Production planning is more difficult to apply in a make-to-order plant where a customer's order must be on hand before the finished product is started. Most such plants assume that they can only plan from customer-order backlogs using these backlogs as make-to-stock plants use finished-goods inventories. This assumption ignores a basic forecast characteristic—large groups of items can be forecast with some accuracy, even where individual items cannot.

The definitions of manufacturing groups are not as readily apparent as they are in a make-to-stock plant. Nevertheless, there are usually groups of like products that go through similar manufacturing facilities which can be identified if the ultimate purpose of *planning the rate of production* is kept in mind. Even if the groups so identified do not account for the full load on the facilities, preparing a production plan for even a portion of the capacity is far better than doing no planning, and almost invariably justifies the cost.

Table 10 shows an example of a paper-manufacturing company making a variety of grades of paper. Incoming orders for coarse paper have been reviewed for a 10-week period, not by individual items, but totals in terms meaningful to production (in this case, production-hours). The forecast based on previous history was approximately 200 hours per week. Cumulative sales deviated between plus one week (195 hours) and minus one-tenth of a week (20 hours) of production. This determines how much unreleased-order backlog is necessary. Table 10 indicates that one week of backlog will normally keep production going at a fairly level rate. Based on this, whenever the total backlog is greater than one week of work at the planned rate, the production level will have to be increased.

Once a planned weekly production rate has been determined, a schedule can be made out on a weekly basis, specifying individual items. Where possible, reduce the scheduling cycle to less than one week. For example, the plant rate might be 200 hours' worth of coarse paper the following week, yet detailed orders for individual sizes would be issued only for the first two or three days. Orders coming in during the early part of the week would then be used to fill in the schedule for the balance of the week.

Most make-to-order plants have customers who place repeat orders for some regularly scheduled items. These can be used as buffers to absorb the ups and downs in incoming business for a product group. When total orders fall below the anticipated rate, these regularly scheduled items can be run at higher

TABLE 10 Incoming Orders for All Coarse Papers In Production-hours

Forecast = 200 hours/week

Week	Orders	Cumulative orders	Cumulative forecast	Deviation
1	210	210	200	+ 10
2	220	430	400	+ 30
3	150	580	600	− 20
4	230	810	800	+ 10
5	300	1,110	1,000	+ 110
6	270	1,380	1,200	+ 180
7	215	1,595	1,400	+ 195
8	180	1,775	1,600	+ 175
9	140	1,915	1,800	+ 115
10	210	2,125	2,000	+ 125

than the normal rate in order to make up the deficit in production. This approach reduces the amount of backlog required and results in reduced lead times and better customer service, which pay for the extra effort required.

Practical Considerations. Many plants produce both make-to-order and make-to-stock products. Their production plan can allow a portion of the total man-hours each week for special-order items, but the ups and downs inevitable in their incoming-order rate can be handled by scheduling more or less of the make-to-stock items.

Production plans in any business must allow for rework and scrap. This can be done by adding capacity to cover scrap and rework or providing additional man-load above that required to meet the planned rate.

The production rate of feeder or secondary operations supporting the main assembly and manufacturing area should be planned in addition to the total production of the primary operations. Using this total plan for the primary areas, the components that go into secondary facilities should be reviewed on a regular basis and scheduled into the machine groups to meet the planned production rate. This review will be facilitated if the parts are listed together according to the machine groups which process them and if the order quantities are expressed in machine-hours. If the components in the groups are ordered by different individuals, each person can be assigned a quota of machine-hours against which he must release orders in each period. The total of these quotas will, of course, equal the planned total for the machine group.

Graphical Techniques. Some practitioners prefer graphical planning techniques. Figure 2 is a graph of the monthly production plan for the filters shown previously in Table 4. The production plan shows generally that, during the early part of the year, production exceeds sales, and consequently, inventory builds up. It is reduced during the peak selling season (May through September) when sales exceed production. Because the plan is based on a shop calendar with two 4-week months and one 5-week month in every quarter, the graph of this production plan indicates that the production rate is erratic when, in fact, it is level at 228,000 hours per week.

The time scale could be made *weeks* or *days* or *four-week periods* to eliminate the distortion. Another approach would be to plot sales and production cumulatively as shown in Fig. 3. The spacings for the months have been adjusted

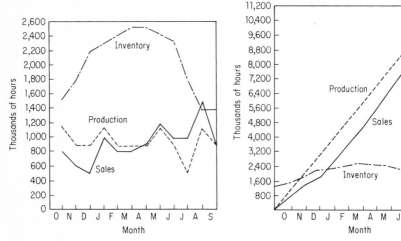

Fig. 2 Graphical production plan—all-steel-cartridge automotive-type filters.

Fig. 3 Graphical cumulative production plan—all-steel-cartridge automotive-type filters.

to be proportional to the number of production weeks available in each month. Consequently, the cumulative production total shows as a straight line, which is of more value in planning and following production than Fig. 2. Figure 3 also shows that inventory will be built up during the early part of the year, but that as the sales and production cumulative lines "close the gap," inventory will be reduced.

Graphical production plans require more work to prepare, and study is required to understand them. They can become extremely complex, particularly when actual data are plotted against the planned data, one of the most important uses of the production plan.

Many practitioners feel that graphical techniques have been somewhat overemphasized in business literature and fail exactly where they should succeed: *conveying the picture rapidly.* The people who are to take action to correct deviations from plan want information in terms of hours, men, pieces, tons, etc. They must translate the graph into numbers in order to determine the degree of action that is required. Running both techniques concurrently and presenting the information in both forms to management can determine which form is most readily understood—graphical or numerical plans.

Product lines that have a similar process flow exist far more often than is usually recognized. Capacity at critical operations in the sequence can be established by a production plan, and individual products can then be scheduled at the planned rate using the technique of *line balancing*. Line balancing is a technique to avoid overloading one operation in a sequence through which many products are passing. The product mix is fed in so as to achieve a balance among product groups which place widely variable demand on operations. If, for example, two major product groups went through a sequence of operations, and one of the groups required twice the amount of milling, it would be foolish to schedule an extraordinarily large quantity of this product in any week. Balanced loading aims at releasing work so that it flows through the operations rather than getting "bottlenecked."

Tying the Plan and Budget Together. Production control personnel and accounting personnel present information to management. Both use cost data, and therefore it is important that they present information on similar bases. The accounting department should be familiar with the production plans and know how to convert these plans into dollars so that the accounting budget figures are based on the same anticipated sales, production, and inventory figures as the production control budgets. As the ability to design and implement integrated control systems develops, production planning and control systems will merge with financial planning and control systems. Until then, the production control executive must work closely with the financial executive so that both systems present consistent information.

CONTROLLING PRODUCTION CAPACITY

Fluctuations in production level compared with fluctuations in demand show that most manufacturing executives tend to wait too long before deciding to change production levels, and then overreact when they do change. The root of this problem is usually the information—or lack of it—on which they base their decisions. The manufacturing executive, basing this decision on uncertain information (i.e., forecasts), is uncertain whether or not a change is necessary. If no one has established what size inventory deficit or overstock justifies a change in production rate, the decision is postponed while changes in demand accumulate—building up to a genuine crisis which then forces a decision. In a make-to-stock company the inventory may decline far below the level required to give good customer service; in a make-to-order company the delivery lead times quoted to customers may lengthen until they are no longer competitive. A good production control system should focus attention on the decisions that must be made, the alternatives that exist (often unpleasant), and the consequences of not making the decision.

Control over any function requires:

1. A *norm* or plan against which to measure to determine whether the function is "on target"

2. Some *tolerance limits,* so that the system does not react to random variations, but will recognize trends and call for corrective action

3. *Feedback,* so that actual performance can be compared against plan

4. *Corrective action* to get back on plan when deviations occur

In production planning, the *norm* is the production plan and the *tolerance limits* are based on measurement of the probable error in the forecast on which the plan was based. The *feedback* consists of reporting actual production rates for the same production facilities covered by the plan, and *corrective actions* include hiring, layoff, overtime, subcontracting work, etc.

Using a Production Plan to Control Production Rates. The production plan minimizes overcompensation for business changes by requiring that production change *only enough during the planned period* to get the inventory back to the planned level. Table 11 shows a production plan for a make-to-stock company with actual activity for the month of July posted against the plan. The base inventory level required to give the desired level of customer service was equal to 1,400 units.

TABLE 11   Make-to-stock Production Plan

Month	Sales			Production		Inv.	Remarks
	Week	Month	Cumulative	Month	Cumulative		
July							
Planned	2	1,000	8,600	448	9,184	1,784	
Actual		1,120	9,400	470	9,600	1,400	
August							
Planned	5	1,500	10,100	1,120	10,304	1,404	
Actual							
Sept.							
Planned	4	900	11,000	896	11,200	1,400	
Actual							

In July cumulative production totals were ahead of plan but sales were even further ahead, so that the inventory is at the base level of 1,400 units. If this is to be maintained during the month of August, production will have to be 1,500 units instead of the 1,120 units previously planned. Two alternatives are available:

1. To go below the base inventory level and have customer service deteriorate
2. To change the production rate (although this change may only last a short time)

It is possible to make a production plan that includes *stabilization stock* to reduce the probability of having to change the plan too frequently. How much stabilization stock must be included in order to accomplish the purpose without excessive amounts of inventory? This problem is analogous to that of determining the amount of reserve stock to carry for an item in order to reduce the possibility of a stock out.

**TABLE 12   Incoming Business—Turret Lathes
In Hours**

Forecast = 1,000 hours
per week

Week	Incoming business
5/1	1,400
5/8	700
5/15	920
5/22	700
5/29	850
6/5	1,060
6/12	425
6/19	950
6/26	1,300
7/3	1,060
7/24	856
7/31	502

This problem occurs also in a make-to-order business. Table 12 shows incoming business stated in machine-hours for a group of turret lathes. The forecast was 1,000 hours per week; sales have varied widely for the period shown. One way to handle this incoming business would be to change production weekly to meet incoming sales rates; when production levels can be changed cheaply and easily, this will give the best customer service. However, changing production levels in most plants is neither cheap nor easy and incurs extra costs due to overtime, hiring, training, lost production, and higher scrap rates from inexperienced operators.

TABLE 13   Weighted-average Forecast, Incoming Business—Turret Lathes
In Hours

New forecast = W x incoming business + $(1-W)$ x old forecast
Using weighting factors $W = 0.2$
$1-W = 0.8$

Week	Incoming business	0.2 x incoming business	Old forecast	0.8 x old forecast	New forecast
5/1	1,400	280	1,000	800	1,080
5/8	700	140	1,080	865	1,005
5/15	920	185	1,005	805	990
5/22	700	140	990	791	931
5/29	850	170	931	745	915
6/5	1,060	212	915	731	943
6/12	425	85	943	755	840
6/19	950	190	840	672	862
6/26	1,300	260	862	690	950
7/3	1,060	212	950	760	972
7/24	856	170	972	778	948
7/31	502	-------	948	-------	-------

If exponential-smoothing forecasting (see Chapter 8) were applied to this particular set of data, a regular weekly updated forecast could be maintained as in Table 13. This forecast could be the production rate for the following week, if fairly small changes in production were easy and inexpensive to make. Using the weighted-average forecast would reduce the weekly high rate from 1,400 to 1,080 hours and increase the low from 425 to 840 hours. From almost 1,000 hours (a high of 1,400 to a low of 425 hours), use of the weighted-average technique reduces the production variation to just over 200 hours. However, this approach will require some order backlogs, because full fluctuations in incoming orders are *not* passed back to production, but are partially absorbed in order backlogs.

TABLE 14   Mean Absolute Deviation of Incoming Business—Turret Lathes
In Hours

Week	Incoming	Forecast	Deviation
5/1	1,400	1,000	400
5/8	700	1,080	380
5/15	920	1,005	85
5/22	700	990	290
5/29	850	931	81
		Total	1,236

MAD = 1,236/5 = 247

If such backlogs are to be used to stabilize production, how much backlog must be maintained? In a previous example, this decision was made roughly by observing deviations from the forecast of incoming-business hours (Table 12). A more accurate method is to use the normal distribution (see Chapter 27) to analyze the variations in incoming business. Table 14 shows this analysis

TABLE 15   Table of Safety Factors for Normal Distribution Plus and Minus Variations

Probable percent of occurrences	Standard deviation	Mean absolute deviation
0.00	0.00	0.00
25.00	0.67	0.84
30.00	0.84	1.05
34.13	1.00	1.25
35.00	1.04	1.30
39.44	1.25	1.56
40.00	1.28	1.60
43.32	1.50	1.88
44.00	1.56	1.95
44.52	1.60	2.00
45.00	1.65	2.06
46.00	1.75	2.19
47.00	1.88	2.35
47.72	2.00	2.50
48.00	2.05	2.56
48.61	2.20	2.75
49.00	2.33	2.91
49.18	2.40	3.00
49.38	2.50	3.13
49.50	2.57	3.20
49.60	2.65	3.31
49.70	2.75	3.44
49.80	2.88	3.60
49.86	3.00	3.75
49.90	3.09	3.85
49.93	3.20	4.00
49.99	4.00	5.00

TABLE 16   Backlog Hours with Level Production—Turret Lathes

Week	Incoming business	Production	Backlog hours
6/5	1,060	900	617*
6/12	425	900	142
6/19	950	900	192
6/26	1,300	900	592
7/3	1,060	900	752
7/24	856	900	708
7/31	502	900	310

*2.5 x 247 (MAD) = 617.

of the first five weeks of incoming business. The individual weekly deviations are calculated, and the mean absolute deviation (MAD) is found to be 247 hours. Reserve stocks of product inventory must protect only against *excessive* demand during the lead time. Since demand during the lead time will be *less* than the forecast approximately half of the time, no reserve stock will be needed to give 50 percent customer service. In determining the backlog needed to stabilize manufacturing operations, however, a different approach must be used, since backlogs will decrease when incoming business is less than anticipated and will increase when it is higher. While only plus variations must be accounted for in setting reserve-stock levels, both plus and minus variations must be used in determining backlog requirements for a production plan. Table 15 is the table of safety factors for both plus and minus variations with a normal distribution.

Table 16 shows the results of level production, with backlogs starting at 617 hours ($2\frac{1}{2}$ mean absolute deviations) in the week of June 5. It shows that $2\frac{1}{2}$ mean absolute deviations should protect against running out of orders for more than $47\frac{1}{2}$ percent of the minus fluctuations in incoming business. Starting with the backlog of 617 hours and a production rate of 900 hours equal to the forecasted average incoming business, the backlog would go below 617 hours whenever incoming business was less than the forecasted production rate. Since incoming business should be lower than forecast only 50 percent of the time, over $47\frac{1}{2}$ percent protection should provide for fairly stable production without running out of orders frequently.

Incoming business will be above forecast 50 percent of the time, and backlogs will increase at such times. An additional 617 hours will include more than

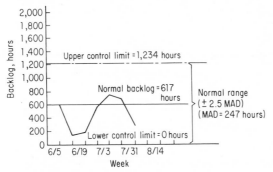

Fig. 4 Turret lathe backlog control chart.

$47\frac{1}{2}$ percent of the times when incoming business is higher than forecast. The backlog could then go as low as zero (at which point production should be decreased). Figure 4 shows the turret lathe backlog graphically and shows the upper and lower control limits to indicate when to change production rates.

This backlog of hours is called "stabilization stock." Table 17 shows the amount of stabilization stock required for various numbers of production-level changes during the year. If it is desired to change production only once during the year, the fraction of weeks without change should be $\frac{49}{50}$ or 98 percent. This 98 percent (±49 percent) stabilization should require ±2.91 MAD according to Table 16, or 1,440 hours of stabilization stock. If more frequent changes can be tolerated, less stabilization stock will be required, as shown. The choice of the particular number of changes depends on the economics of carrying the extra stabilization inventory versus the costs of changing the production rate.

Value of Decision Rules. Decision rules have great practical value in industry. Established decision rules help manufacturing management avoid postponing decisions until a crisis has occurred. Rather than having management teams spend a great deal of time each week deciding whether the present situation really justifies a change in the production rate, the decision as to *what justifies a change* should be made once. From then on, the weekly discussions can be concerned with the action to be taken to accomplish the change necessary.

Whenever decision rules have been applied, the results have almost always been good. The actual decision rule is probably secondary in importance to having a rational approach to the control of the production level. Application of this technique will not eliminate the ups and downs in the business cycle, but decision rules can be of great value in measuring and coping with these changes in activity in the most effective and economical manner.

Controlling Purchased Material. A purchased-material production plan includes meaningful groups of purchased items. All components of a particular assembly can be grouped together and then broken down into subgroups obtained from particular vendors. Looking at the total purchased inventory in relation to the total rate of use can give a quick overall control that cannot be attained by reviewing individual orders for items in that group.

Meaningful totals must be used in these purchasing plans; the most meaningful total is usually dollars. Making a purchasing plan starts by determining the number of components needed to meet a planned production rate, and then extending each of the individual-component inventories and purchase commit-

TABLE 17   Stabilization Stock versus Production-level Changes

Production changes per year	Fraction of weeks without a change	Percent of weeks without a change	No. MAD* ± required (MAD = 247 hours)	Stabilization stock, hours
1	49/50 =	98	2.91	1,440
2	48/50 =	96	2.56	1,265
4	46/50 =	92	2.19	1,080
6	44/50 =	88	1.95	964
8	42/50 =	84	1.74	860
10	40/50 =	80	1.60	790
12	38/50 =	76	1.48	730
14	36/50 =	72	1.36	670
16	34/50 =	68	1.25	617
18	32/50 =	64	1.15	568
20	30/50 =	60	1.05	519

*From Table 15

ments by the unit cost so that a meaningful total in dollars will result. In other respects, the purchasing plan is identical to the production plan, and its use as a control instrument is exactly the same.

The purchasing plan is a striking example of the similarity between the planning and controlling of production and using financial budgets. In fact, if the accounting system were able to give cost information within 24 to 48 hours after activities occurred, the production control system could be tied right into it.

COSTS INVOLVED

Evaluating alternatives in planning and controlling capacity involves three groups of costs:

1. Inventory-carrying costs
2. Customer-service costs
3. Production-rate-changes costs

Costs of carrying additional inventories of finished products in a make-to-stock company must be balanced against those associated with poorer customer service if stock outs occur.

Inventory costs must also be weighed against the costs of varying production rates to meet seasonal or random-demand fluctuations in make-to-stock firms.

In make-to-order companies the expense of changing production rates must be compared to costs associated with lost orders when unfilled-order backlogs become excessive.

Specific values of these costs are difficult, often impossible, to determine with confidence. Standard cost-accounting systems do not develop such costs. Their value varies with time, changes in management policy, different products, and many factors unrelated to the decisions involved in planning and scheduling production.

Inventory-carrying Costs. Factors included in inventory-carrying costs are cost of money invested, obsolescence, deterioration, shrinkage or loss, taxes, insurance, space charges, and handling costs. Values used range from 15 to 30 percent but may be as high as 100 percent in style, seasonal, or short shelf-life items. While there is obviously some specific cost resulting from carrying inventory, it is equally obvious that no single "magic number" will represent this cost for a variety of items over a period of changing policies and objectives. It should be reevaluated for each major study.

Customer-service Costs. These include cancelled or lost orders, both current and future, expediting costs, extra freight, more expensive substitutes, and special handling charges. These costs are the most difficult to evaluate. Decisions are better and, at least, more consistent if an effort is made to assign some value to customer-service costs. Typical is assigning a very high value to this to reflect a policy of "never out of stock" of a specific product.

Production-rate-changes Costs. These are comprised of overtime, hiring, laying off, training, extra outside-material procurement, temporary labor premiums, and increased scrap and rework costs. Some of these can be closely estimated. Difficult to evaluate and rarely included are values reflecting a company's policy of maintaining "stable employment," which could be handled, like "never being out of stock," by using a very high cost.

APPLICATIONS OF LINEAR-PROGRAMMING TECHNIQUES

Linear-programming applications can be classified as:

1. *The Diet Problem.* Determine the most economical blend of components in human or animal food, fertilizer, metal, or petroleum refining.

2. *The Product-mix Problem.* Determine the most profitable mix of products to be marketed when total output is limited by raw-material or component availability or production capacity.

3. *The Distribution Problem.* Determine the most economical method of supplying several destinations from several sources with different production and transportation costs.

4. *The Machine-loading Problem.* Determine the most economical distribution of several jobs among several machines when each job cannot be assigned to its most efficient machine without limiting total production.

5. *The Stock-cutting Problem.* Obtain maximum utilization of raw material or available packing space.

6. *The Production-scheduling Problem.* Minimize production and related costs under conditions of limited capacity with a variety of possible schedules.

Linear programming can be used to obtain optimum answers to problems in which:

1. An objective such as profit, cost, time, or quantity is to be minimized or maximized and can be expressed as a linear function of the other elements of the problem.

2. There are restrictions on the extent the objective can be attained. These limitations can be represented by a system of linear equalities or inequalities.

Although it yields numerical solutions defined as "optimum," the assumptions made are rarely evident to the nonmathematical practitioner. In few real-life problems are the variables linearly related over any practical range. The method also becomes more cumbersome as the number of variables increases; few real problems involve a convenient number. Where properly applied, however, the technique has real power to show how sensitive the "optimum" solution is to changes in the major variables, proving which are truly significant in controlling the activity studied.

LINEAR-DECISION RULES

The alternative ways to schedule production to meet fluctuating demand are:

1. Vary production to match the demand. The variation can be obtained by:
  a. Adding people to the productive force or laying them off
  b. Working short shifts or overtime to vary the work hours of a constant labor force
  c. Subcontracting work to outside companies
  d. Some combination of a, b, and/or c

2. Hold production constant and let inventories of products take care of demand fluctuations.

3. Hold production constant and let backlogs of unfilled customers' orders take care of the fluctuations.

4. Some combination of 1, 2, and/or 3.

Each of these major and subalternatives has costs associated with it. The problem of selecting that combination of alternatives which results in the lowest total cost of operations with relatively unknown future demand and performance is a formidable task. *Linear-decision rules* have been developed which give *optimal* solutions to this problem for certain well-defined assumptions about the related costs. An example will illustrate the form and use of a simple linear-decision rule.

Company A manufactures glue using a semicontinuous process. Regular payroll costs are known, as are overtime premium payments. The costs associated with hiring and laying off employees are shown in Table 18.

TABLE 18 Costs of Hiring and Laying Off, Company "A" Linear-decision Rule

No. men* per month	Total cost
1	$ 150
2	400
3	700
4	1,000
5	1,500
6	2,000
8	2,800
10	4,000
12	5,000
15	7,000
20	10,000
25	$13,500

*Net additions to (hired) or reductions from
(laid off) the work force during the month.

TABLE 19 Inventory Carrying Costs, Company "A" Linear-decision Rule

Net inventory thousands of gallons	Monthly cost
−200	$7,000
−150	5,000
−100	3,500
− 50	2,250
0	1,600
50	1,000
100	600
150	400
200	450
250	800
300	1,250
350	1,900
400	2,800
450	4,000
500	$6,000

Inventory-carrying costs are also studied and are determined to be as shown in Table 19. Negative inventory (back orders) is believed to be very undesirable, and high costs are associated with being out of stock.

An operations research team developed two equations[1] which are intended to yield minimum cost decisions on manpower and production rates for the glue company. These are:

$$M_{Jan} = 2.09 + 0.743 M_{Dec} - 0.010 I_{Dec} + \left\{ \begin{array}{l} 0.0101 D_{Jan} \\ +0.0088 D_{Feb} \\ +0.0071 D_{Mar} \\ +0.0054 D_{Apr} \\ +0.0042 D_{May} \\ +0.0031 D_{June} \\ +0.0023 D_{July} \\ +0.0016 D_{Aug} \\ +0.0012 D_{Sept} \\ +0.0009 D_{Oct} \\ +0.0006 D_{Nov} \\ +0.0005 D_{Dec} \end{array} \right.$$

$$P_{Jan} = 153 + 0.993 M_{Dec} - 0.464 I_{Dec} + \left\{ \begin{array}{l} 0.463 D_{Jan} \\ +0.234 D_{Feb} \\ +0.111 D_{Mar} \\ +0.046 D_{Apr} \\ +0.013 D_{May} \\ -0.002 D_{June} \\ -0.008 D_{July} \\ -0.010 D_{Aug} \\ -0.009 D_{Sept} \\ -0.008 D_{Oct} \\ -0.007 D_{Nov} \\ -0.005 D_{Dec} \end{array} \right.$$

where M = man-load, number of men employed
I = inventory, gallons of glue in thousands
D = forecasted demand, gallons ordered in thousands
P = production, gallons of glue in thousands

Using these two equations, simple calculations each month will determine the most economical man-load and production rate for the following month, based on forecasts of demand for the next 12 months. For example, suppose that the data at the end of December were

$$\text{Man-load} = M_{Dec} = 80 \text{ men}$$

$$\text{Inventory} = I_{Dec} = 300,000 \text{ gallons}$$

Demand (in gallons) for the next year is forecast as

$$D_{Jan} = 380,000 \qquad D_{July} = 565,000$$
$$D_{Feb} = 370,000 \qquad D_{Aug} = 430,000$$
$$D_{Mar} = 528,000 \qquad D_{Sept} = 360,000$$
$$D_{Apr} = 720,000 \qquad D_{Oct} = 750,000$$
$$D_{May} = 420,000 \qquad D_{Nov} = 683,000$$
$$D_{June} = 800,000 \qquad D_{Dec} = 546,000$$

Solving the two equations for January operating data gives

$$\text{Man-load} = M_{Jan} = 82 \text{ men (2 more than December)}$$

$$\text{Production} = P_{Jan} = 426,000 \text{ gallons}$$

The inventory will increase by the difference between production and demand $(426,000 - 380,000 = 46,000 \text{ gallons})$. The planned inventory at the end of January will then be $300,000 + 46,000 = 346,000$ gallons. This can be calculated in one step using the equation

$$I_{Jan} = I_{Dec} + P_{Jan} - D_{Jan}$$

Some interesting observations can be made about the application of such equations to the real business world:

1. A practical management would want to test their effectiveness by simulating what would have happened if the equations had been used in the past and comparing against actual results.

2. Because of the complexity of the mathematical derivations, it is not possible to determine the effect on the decisions of changes in costs without deriving new equations. This would require the services of the operations research team each time it had to be done.

3. Factors which were not included in the original derivation might become important, and it may be difficult or impossible to include them in new equations.

4. The equations assume a specific amount of production per worker. The actual number of people employed or the hours worked would have to be increased if this productivity were not met.

Linear-decision rules have real potential for assisting management to control production-level changes on a rational basis. The great danger is in assuming that management can be relinquished to such rules and that they can handle all significant changes which may occur—they cannot! Applied properly, linear decision rules result in improved control over production levels when compared to intuitive or irrational approaches. Results would certainly be more stable and consistent as long as no major variations occurred in the factors which affect the basic assumptions used in the derivation of the equations.

Decision Rules and Reaction Time. The application of decision rules assumes that production rates can be changed rapidly. In many real-life situations, this is not the case. It may take a considerable period of time to hire and train new people.

Reaction time is that time elapsed from the moment it is decided to change production levels until the production rates have either increased or decreased. A rigorous calculation of stabilization-stock levels would include some inventory to cover deviations from forecast during this period. The calculation of this quantity of *reaction reserves* involves the calculation of anticipated forecast error *over the reaction time*. This is the same as developing reserve stock, when the forecast error is calculated over a weekly time period and must be converted to forecast error over the lead-time period.

Practical Considerations. In applying decision rules, some practical considerations are as follows.

1. *Seasonal Production.* During the inventory-building season, the actual inventory can vary from the planned level by as much as a month's supply without causing any immediate problems as long as corrective action can be taken in time to meet the target set for the end of the peak selling season. It is often practical to maintain a monthly production plan during the inventory-building period, and then switch over to a weekly production plan during the peak selling season.

2. *Inertia in Changing Production.* There is a tendency in most plants for production levels to have tremendous inertia. This is the very reason for having decision rules—delays in changing the production rate can make the amount of change required so large as to be almost impossible to attain in the time available. This inertia exists when the production rate is cut back as well as when it is increased. Companies with incentive systems often find that they can produce as much after a reduction in hours because the workers increase their pace in order to earn their normal wage even though hours have been shortened.

3. *Average Production Rates.* Line manufacturing people tend to look at planned production rates as ceilings rather than as averages. Production losses caused by holidays, unexpected equipment breakdowns, absenteeism, etc., tend to be overlooked. Close attention to the cumulative production totals on the production plan will avoid serious effects resulting from the sum of many small losses.

4. *Sequence of Changes.* In manufacturing assemblies such as the kitchen mixers, any change in the assembly production rate can only be made in the proper time sequence, following changes in plans to purchase raw materials, manufacture components, and put together subassemblies. Decreases in the production rate, on the other hand, can be instituted simultaneously at all stages of production.

5. *Overtime versus Increased Work Force.* The real question is, "Will the production increase be of a long enough duration to justify hiring people—or should it be handled with overtime?" The answer to this question can be obtained by developing the costs of overtime versus the costs of increasing production to the new level and bringing it back down again. This must be handled with the practical recognition that there might be other considerations—such as the company's reputation for employment stability—that should be considered. As with any decision alternatives, the proper approach is to gather the best available cost information, show the probable cost of the alternatives, point out the intangibles involved in the alternatives, and finally, assist management in making a decision.

6. *Simulation.* Statistics and mathematics[2] have real application in industry, but should not be adopted with blind faith. The production control manager

should simulate, using past history, experiment with these techniques, and see what would have happened if they had been in practice in the past. He can then evaluate these results and advise management as to what to expect before applying any type of decision rule.

CONTROLLING INPUT: SCHEDULING

Control of input to manufacturing facilities must be a function of both inventory controls and available capacity if work in process, backlogs, and lead time are to be controlled. Input control can be broken down into:

1. Selecting the right orders based either on the materials control system or customer orders to meet the planned production rates

2. Scheduling—assigning desired starting and/or completion dates to operations on each order

3. Loading—comparing the hours required for each operation with the hours available in each work center in the time period scheduled.

When better input control is achieved, less time and effort are required for job location, expediting, and dispatching, but more important, positive benefits will be obtained through getting more jobs completed on schedule.

Selecting the Input. Once a production level is established, schedulers must feed in the right items at the rate needed to meet the planned production level. A desire to ensure meeting required dates by "getting jobs started as early as possible" actually works against achieving the desired result.

An inventory control system in a manufacturing company will generate random peaks and troughs of shop orders, and the flow of these orders must be regulated in order to control work-in-process levels. Some examples follow, showing how this control over input can be accomplished.

Table 20 shows a simple production plan for a company making several models of lamps. This production plan is used to control the assembly operation, and calls for level production over a five-week period and a reduction of inventory to the base level.

**TABLE 20   Production Plan—All Models of Lamps
In Pieces**

		Sales	Production	Inventory
Week 8 (actual starting inventory)				22,000
Week 9	Planned	5,200	6,000	22,800
	Actual			
Week 10	Planned	6,200	6,000	22,600
	Actual			
Week 11	Planned	6,200	6,000	22,400
	Actual			
Week 12	Planned	7,200	6,000	21,200
	Actual			
Week 13	Planned	7,200	6,000	20,000*
	Actual			

*Base inventory level.

Table 21 shows the weekly production scheduling report for the lamps included in the production plan of Table 20. It shows data on incoming business for each item, net stock available, the amount currently on order with the factory, and the order point and economic ordering quantities. Exponential smoothing (see Chapter 8) has been used to update a weekly weighted average of incoming business to serve as a forecast of demand for each item, so that the latest sales trends can be identified. The order point itself has been recalculated

each week for the new demand forecast, using an updated calculation of the
mean absolute deviation to revise the reserve stock. The total inventory (the
sum of available and on order) and the order point are both expressed as
weeks of stock by dividing them by the latest forecast of incoming business.

The total inventories of lamps shown on the production scheduling report
in Table 21 are above their order points. This is normal when inventories

**TABLE 21   Weekly Production Scheduling Report
In Pieces**

Lamp No.	Weekly incoming business	Year to date incoming business	Net stock available	Factory order	Order point	Weekly weighted average incoming business	Total weeks of stock	Order point expressed as weeks of stock	Economic ordering quantity
7W	341	17,933	1,739	3,078	2,730	485	10	5.6	2,250
7D	288	9,837	1,224	832	1,436	274	7	5.2	1,500
9W	894	35,329	4,007	1,956	4,242	924	6	4.5	2,000
9D	251	10,120	2,189	662	1,386	259	11	5.3	1,500
9P	1,187	46,690	8,371	-------	6,250	1,290	6	4.8	2,500
11D	1,332	47,078	2,844	7,050	6,768	1,345	7	5.0	2,500
11P	598	21,896	778	3,302	3,346	639	6	5.2	2.000

are being built up in anticipation of seasonal sales or a vacation shutdown. To
choose the proper items to be scheduled in order to meet the planned production
rate of 6,000 lamps per week, the scheduler may select those lamps closest
to their order points—those with the lowest total weeks of stock—and schedule
them so that inventories are kept in balance. Three items have a six-week
inventory level: the no. 11P (pin-up lamp) which is closer to its order point
than any other, the no. 9P (pin-up lamp), and the no. 9W (wall lamp). Scheduling these would release a total of 6,500 lamps for assembly production. The
scheduler would compensate for the small excess in succeeding starting schedules.

**TABLE 22   Ranked Weekly Production Scheduling Report
In Pieces**

Lamp No.	Weekly incoming business	Year to date incoming business	Net stock available	Factory order	Order point	Weekly weighted average incoming business	Total weeks of stock	Order point expressed as weeks of stock	Economic ordering quantity
11P	598	21,896	778	3,302	3,346	639	6	5.2	2,000
9P	1187	46,690	8,371	-----	6,250	1,290	6	4.8	2,500
9W	894	35,329	4,007	1,956	4,242	924	6	4.5	2,000
7D	288	9,837	1,224	832	1,436	274	7	5.2	1,500
11D	1332	47,078	2,844	7,050	6,768	1,345	7	5.0	2,500
7W	341	17,933	1,739	3,078	2,730	485	10	5.6	2,250
9D	251	10,120	2,189	662	1,386	259	11	5.3	1,500

Used this way, the production scheduling report also eliminates the need
to recalculate order points when building up inventory levels in anticipation
of high sales or low production. The production plan indicates the rates needed
to raise the inventory, and the scheduling report shows which items to select
to meet the planned production rate.

Table 22 shows a ranked weekly production scheduling report with the items
arranged in order of increasing total weeks of stock and decreasing order-point
weeks. If there is a large number of items involved and a computer is available
to do the sorting, this type of ranking can speed up the work of preparing
a schedule and eliminate errors.

Other factors must often be considered when preparing schedules. When
scheduling a press department, a screw machine department, or a line of extrusion
presses, the ability of the department to perform the required number of setups

is as important as its total of available machine-hours. For this situation, a periodic review of all the parts made in the department (using a scheduling report such as Table 23) will make it possible to schedule to both a total of machine-hours and a limiting maximum number of setups.

First, a target of hours must be set, based on the forecasted rate of usage of all the parts, adding or deducting the effects of any desired changes in

TABLE 23   Weekly Schedule Review—Turret Lathes

Week ending _____ 12-10 _____

Week No. _____ 48 _____   _70_ planned weekly schedule hours

Dept _____ 84 _____   _10_ maximum setup hours

Machine center _____ #1700   _110_ total hours in machine center

Part No.	A B C	Description	Used on	Annual use	Week No. of next planned order release	Order qty.	Order qty. cost	Order qty. hours	Setup hours
21	A	2d—spindle	A motor	3,000	47	200	1,222	22	5
30	A	Upr. spg. carr.	A motor	6,000	48	700	281	31	3
59	A	Piston	A motor	6,000	3	400	298	31	2
64	B	Lwr. spg. carr.	A motor	6,000	50	1,000	235	40	3
18	C	Pack washer	Gear box	1,000	51	500	41	12.5	2
27	B	Roller	Gear box	2,400	51	400	138	20	2
29	C	Spg. guide	Coupling	200	50	500	25	50	3
34	C	Adj. screw	Coupling	2,400	50	2,300	85	77	3
54	C	Ball seat	Emerg. relse.	275	50	150	37	30	2
55	C	Spg. plug	Coupling	275	51	250	29	25	3
56	C	Floor plate	B motor	92	2	100	82	9	3
46	C	No. 3—1st, No. 5—2d — lens holder	Control box	850	49	450	131	15	5

inventory levels of these parts. This is identical to preparing a production plan using hours of machining time. Next, a maximum limit is established for setups, based on the number of setup men available or the number of machine-hours which can be devoted to setting up without cutting into needed capacity for making parts.

Using Table 23, suppose a review of the report indicates that components 21, 30, and 46 should be started in the next week. If he were to schedule

TABLE 24   Schedule A

Component	Order quantity hours	Setup hours
21	22	5
30	31	3
46	15	5
Totals	68	13

these the scheduler would release 68 hours of machine-running time and 13 hours of setup as shown in Table 24. He would be close to the planned weekly schedule of 70 total hours, but he would have exceeded the maximum of 10 setup hours and the shop could not meet this schedule.

By reviewing other items in the group near their release dates, he would find that component 27 would soon have to be reordered. Substituting this for component 46, which is in better condition than either 21 or 30, his schedule would be as shown in Table 25. This would be practical for the shop. He would then have to be sure to schedule component 46 the following week, and might even have to expedite subsequent operations on this part to cut the normal lead time and get it in stock on time.

TABLE 25 Schedule B

Component	Order quantity hours	Setup hours
21	22	5
30	31	3
27	20	2
Totals	73	10

Scheduling Sequenced Operations. Many intermittent, semiprocess, and even so-called job shops have a definable flow of work through the plant. In this type plant, control can be improved by having the scheduler look beyond the first operation to subsequent operations which are critical because of limited capacity or inflexibility. Releasing work into a starting operation that will be backlogged later is self-defeating.

In many plants, it is practical to generate a weekly schedule and then release

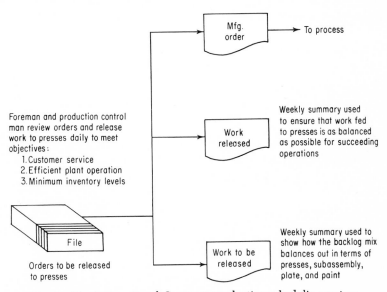

Fig. 5 The Pattern Panel Company production scheduling system.

work to the plant on a daily basis. Every day, a day's work can be released for the first operation which is also a day's work for later critical operations. For example, the general sequence of operations for the Pattern Panel Company making control-panel housings is:

1. Shear—press department
2. Blank—press department
3. Pierce—press department

4. De-burr—subassembly department
5. Insert bushings—subassembly department
6. Subassemble fasteners—subassembly department
7. Plate or paint—finishing department
8. Inspect—quality control department
9. Pack—shipping department

The scheduler, following the system shown in Fig. 5, releases a balanced load each week. Their emphasis is on rapid flow. They receive many individual orders, most requiring fairly short processing times. Table 26 shows the weekly release summary used.

For each major load center, the production planner has a target number of cumulative hours to be released per week. He and the foreman review daily the orders ahead of the press department and try to select orders within the capacity of subsequent departments. The planner would try to release orders totaling as near 240 hours as possible to the press department, without exceeding 120 hours in the subassembly department, 80 hours in plating, or 40 hours in the painting department.

An adjunct to the weekly release summary is a weekly analysis of orders

TABLE 26 Pattern Panel Company Weekly
Release Summary

Load center	Hours released	Weekly capacity
		Week No. 14
Press department	20 48 108 168 180	240 hours
Subassembly	40 60 105 115	120 hours
Plate	8 11 24 28	80 hours
Paint	10 18 36	40 hours

to be released showing how much work they will generate for the press, subassembly, plating, and painting departments. A temporary drop-off in plating because of the mix of make-to-order business can be offset by generating more make-to-stock orders that will help level the load on the plating facility. This "input load balancing" is a most effective technique for controlling semiprocess flow operations processing make-to-order and make-to-stock products.

Table 27 shows this type of load balancing for a series of three of the most critical operations in a metal-fabricating plant: the second, eighth, and tenth operations. Adequate average capacity is available at each operation, but releasing orders into production at random will cause temporary overloads and underloads on the factory floor. Orders are rechecked weekly to put them in proper priority (alphabetically—order A being highest, etc.). These orders, in a "hold for release" file, are reviewed weekly by a planner to get the needed orders into process while generating the best balanced load on the facilities.

Schedule 1 containing orders A, B, C, D, E, and F into process would generate overloads at operations 2 and 8 over the 10 percent excess allowed. Removing job F (which has low priority and high hours in operations 2 and 8) and adding jobs H, J, and K results in a better-balanced schedule within the 10 percent allowance for over- or underloads. Job G will generate the same unbalanced conditions that job F did. Jobs F and G will have a very high priority on next week's schedule. This approach avoids releasing work to a starting operation that will simply get bogged down at a succeeding operation.

Although it is covered in detail in a later chapter, use of load-balancing techniques has been shown here in the simplest form as applied to scheduling. Where more than two operations have to be balanced, the calculations can become very tedious. With a computer, this logic can be programmed and the computer be made to select the optimum starting schedule.

TABLE 27 Balancing Input for Sequenced Operations

	Running time in hours		
	Operation 2	Operation 8	Operation 10
Job A	-------	2.22	3.99
Job B	2.76	4.96	6.00
Job C	-------	-------	6.75
Job D	0.63	0.50	1.30
Job E	8.75	7.80	8.75
Job F	13.52	11.84	12.64
Job G	7.64	6.56	7.24
Job H	1.46	-------	3.26
Job J	2.52	2.00	5.20
Job K	4.38	4.44	8.04
Job L	7.38	8.00	14.00
Job M	16.90	13.80	13.40

Schedule 1 = Jobs   A, B, C, D, E, F
Schedule 2 = Jobs   A, B, C, D, E, H, J, K

	Operation 2 20 hours/ week	Operation 8 20 hours/ week	Operation 10 40 hours/ week
Planned cap.			
Schedule 1	25.66	27.32	39.43
Schedule 2	20.50	21.92	43.29

Principles of Scheduling

1. Select the input to meet the planned production rate. *If the plant is not actually producing to meet this plan, the amount of work released into starting operations should not exceed actual capacity.*

2. Keep backlogs off the shop floor wherever possible because they:
   a. Are more difficult to control
   b. Make engineering changes more expensive to implement
   c. Generate more expediting
   d. Create physical problems (newer jobs pile up in front of old work that gets pushed back into corners)

3. Sequence orders based on latest requirements rather than required dates established when the order was first released. The computer (which can compare changing inventory requirements for many items with production requirements) and the introduction of such techniques as *critical ratio* (described in Chapter 4) make it possible to review and revise desired schedule dates periodically.

4. Schedule only items the factory can make. Planners or schedulers should keep on their desks all orders for which raw material, components, tools, or other necessary materials are not available. This will clearly define where the basic problem lies in getting work completed. There are some exceptions to this rule. Where a finished product takes three weeks to assemble and the missing component is one added at the last operation, assembly orders can be issued if the scheduler is confident that the missing component will be available when needed. In the drug, electronic, and similar industries it is sometimes

impossible to determine before a schedule is released whether the product can actually be produced.

5. Schedule to a short cycle (weekly or even daily). This not only helps to get the latest and most accurate requirement dates on the orders scheduled, but it also assists in controlling the orders flowing through the factory.

An interesting fallacy that has gained wide recognition is that the schedule period must equal the lead time. Even in the extreme example of a company with a nine-month lead time required for a sequence of 50 different operations, someone must make a decision practically on a daily basis as to which items will be started in the first operation. A firm nine-month *starting* schedule is *not* required. A weekly starting schedule based on the latest available information on customer requirements, inventory status, and plant work load is practical and effective.

SCHEDULING TECHNIQUES

Frequently, even stock chasing doesn't begin until jobs have failed to meet their shipping date. A better approach is to establish schedule dates by operations and to review jobs that are due to ship this week and next week as well as those that are past due, to determine what problems are causing delays. Table 28 shows this type of *production schedule review*. This can be very

TABLE 28   Production Schedule Review

Customer	S.O.	Past due	This week	Next week	Nearest lot		Next lot		Remarks
					Loc.	Qty.	Loc.	Qty.	
Stalco	17,624	577			D-32	1,150	....	....	Will ship next week
Chambers	11,318			40	D-40	94	....	....	On salvage (?)
Trild Inc.	10,628		1,100		D-29	1,000	....	N.A.	Call complete
Morton	10,959		1,780	2,500	D-32	5,200	....	....	Balance 6,040 stock
Padsing	11,003		7,000		D-22	7,500	....	....	O.K.
Pennbush	11,004			20,000	D-22	10,750	D-2	10,750	Will ship 10M, balance 3/26
Stalco	11,008			7,000	D-40	8,240	....	....	O.K.

effective if used in conjunction with an operations scheduling system to detect delays. The sales department can then be informed which jobs will be shipped on time and which won't, providing them with the means of telling the customer ahead of time if his job will not be shipped as promised.

Operation Scheduling. Table 29 lists the steps in operations scheduling. The first is to provide data for the scheduling system (which must include the operations sequence or factory routing). Table 30 is a typical manufacturing order, including the operation sequence and showing the setup hours and running time required. Running hours have been calculated by multiplying the quantity on the order (expressed in thousands) by the time figure shown in the column headed "Running hours/1,000." This order is designed to travel with the work through the factory so that the operator can note his time and quantities directly on it. In some companies, this operation sequence is maintained on a master form which can be reproduced when repetitive orders for the same product are run. In others, this type of routing is maintained in a deck of punched cards or in a computer tape or disk file. When the manufacturing order is printed out, a punched card is made for each operation, to be used by the machine operator to report his time. The traveling order by itself does not

TABLE 29 Scheduling Steps

1. Provide data
   - A. Operation sequences
   - B Standards, engineered or estimated
2. Develop system
   - A. Shop calendar
   - B. Scheduling rules
3. Choose scheduling method
   - A. Back scheduling
   - B. Forward scheduling
4. Schedule
   - A. Multiply order quantity by time per operation
   - B. Add transit time
   - C. Add allowance for delays

TABLE 30 Typical Manufacturing Order

Part name	Drawing No.	Used on	Date	Order	Qty.
Pinion spindle	E-17352	Frame assembly E-oo14	wk. 21	2,950	5,000

Material	Remarks
Steel bar stock–0.500" Spec. A-407	Note thread is left-hand

Dept.	Mach. group	Op. No.	Operation description	Set-up hr	Run hr/ 1,000	Run hr this lot	Man No.	Qty. comp.	Qty. scrap	Qty. salv.	Insp.
040	Truck	01	Draw bar stock from stores								
517	14	02	Make pinion spindle on screw machine	14.5	3.1	15.5					
319	18	03	Mill slot to B/P	1.3	9.5	47.5					
771	42	04	Tumble for burrs			2.0					
624	06	05	Drill hole for pin	0.2	4.0	20.0					
771	40	06	Degrease			0.5					
771	43	07	Plate – dull zinc			4.7					
009	04	08	Inspect			AQC 403					
040	Truck	09	Deliver to stock			—					

usually provide the means to report an operator's time and quantity to the timekeeping department.

Time standards, either engineered or estimated, are essential to any scheduling system. Since there will always be orders for new items that have to be scheduled into production before engineering standards have been developed, some means of estimating these standards in either the industrial engineering or the

JUNE

Wk No.	Sun.	Mon.	Tues.	Wed.	Thurs.	Fri.	Sat.
22	May 24	25 347	26 348	27 349	28 350	29	30
23	31	June 1 351	2 352	3 353	4 354	5 355	6
24	7	8 356	9 357	10 358	11 359	12 360	13
25	14	15 361	16 362	17 363	18 364	19 365	20
26	21	22 366	23 367	24 368	25 369	26 370	27

JULY

Wk No.	Sun.	Mon.	Tues.	Wed.	Thurs.	Fri.	Sat.
27	June 28	29 371	30 372	July 1 373	2 374	3	4
28	5	6 375	7 376	8 377	9 378	10 379	11
*29	12	13	14	15	16	17	18
*30	19	20	21	22	23	24	25

AUGUST

Wk No.	Sun.	Mon.	Tues.	Wed.	Thurs.	Fri.	Sat.
31	July 26	27 380	28 381	29 382	30 383	31 384	Aug. 1
32	2	3 385	4 386	5 387	6 388	7 389	8
33	9	10 390	11 391	12 392	13 393	14 394	15
34	16	17 395	18 396	19 397	20 398	21 399	22

*Vacation weeks are subject to change.

Fig. 6 Shop calendar.

production control department is necessary.   Accuracy is not vital, but consistency is important.

Figure 6 shows a shop calendar used by many companies on which each *working day* is numbered consecutively—in some cases, the consecutive numbering covers a period of four years.   This enables the scheduler to establish dates without correcting for weekends, plant shutdown periods, or holidays.

Some simple scheduling rules are shown in Table 31.   These are oversimplified but illustrate the type of rules which must be developed before scheduling can begin.

TABLE 31   Simple Scheduling Rules

1. Multiply hours per thousand pieces by number of thousands on order.

2. Round up to nearest 16-hour day (two shifts) and express time in days, round down to nearest day when excess hours are less than 10 percent of total, minimum one day for operation.

3. Allow 5 days to withdraw stock from stockroom.

4. Allow 1 day between successive operations within the same department.

5. Allow 3 days between successive operations in different departments.

6. Allow 1 day for inspection.

7. Allow 1 day to get material into stockroom.

8. Allow 2 extra weeks for screw-machine parts.

TABLE 32   Block Scheduling Rules

1. Allow 1 week for releasing order and drawing material from storeroom.

2. Allow 6 weeks for screw machine operations.

3. Allow 1 day for each 400 pieces in the milling department; round upward to next full week.

4. Allow 1 week for drilling and tapping, burring and similar operations using minor equipment.

5. When operations are especially short, combine within the same week.

6. Allow 1 week for inspection and delivery of completed material.

Block Scheduling.   Many companies use general rules such as the block-scheduling rules shown in Table 32 to estimate the amount of time required for each part.   These save computation time, but usually result in extremely long lead times.

Table 33 shows two ways of scheduling the manufacturing order shown previously in Table 30; both cases show backward scheduling from the required date (week 51 or day 445).   Block scheduling with completion dates by week numbers results in a total of 14 weeks' lead time.

Operation time scheduling requires 44 working days, or about nine weeks to complete.   In the computation the transit time is added to the next operation. For example, operation 7 must be completed on day 440 in order to allow three days' transit time and one day of running time at operation 8.   Transit time is used to cover the following elements:

1. Time waiting to be picked up for movement out of the department—*wait time*

2. Time actually in transit—*move time*

3. Time waiting to be started at the next machine center—*queue time*

Setup time has also been taken into account. For example, in operation 02 one extra operating day is included because of the setup time required on the screw machine.

Backward and Forward Scheduling. There are two principal scheduling methods:

1. *Backward Scheduling.* Starting with the date on which the order is required to be completed, calculating backward to determine the proper release date for the order. This assumes that the finished date is known and computes start dates.

TABLE 33   Scheduling

Operation No.	Block scheduling		Operation time scheduling	
	Time allowed	Week	Time allowed	Day
Release date		37		402
01	1 week	38	5 days	407
02	6 weeks	44	12 days $T^* = 3$ days	419
03	3 weeks	47	3 days $T = 3$ days	425
04	1 week	48	1 day $T = 3$ days	429
05	1 week	49	2 days $T = 3$ days	434
06	⎱ 1 week	50	1 day $T = 1$ day	438
07	⎰		1 day $T = 3$ days	440
08	⎱ 1 week	51	1 day	444
09	⎰		1 day	445
Date required		Week 51		Day 445

*T = transit time.

2. *Forward Scheduling.* Starting with either today's date or the first open time at the first operation, computing the schedule date for each operation to determine the completion date.

Forward scheduling is most frequently used in companies such as paper and steel mills, where the product is bulky but requires few components. The scheduler will probably check the customer's order, and if the requested date and the required date are far enough away, he will not schedule the order until he must. In effect, he is really combining backward scheduling with forward scheduling.

Backward scheduling is typically used where components being manufactured to go into an assembled product have different lead times. After determining the required schedule dates for major subassemblies, the scheduler uses these as the required dates for each component and works backward to determine the proper release date for each component manufacturing order.

Sequencing Similar Orders. Substantial advantages can be gained by processing similar orders in their proper sequence:

1. Setup times on screw machines, punch presses, etc. can be reduced by running families of parts which require only minor changes to convert the setup.

2. Cleanout and changeover times can be reduced by running lighter-colored batches of paints, chemicals, etc., before darker ones.

3. Raw material can be saved by combining corrugated box sizes, textile patterns, etc., when cutting from continuous sheets.

Inventory records are coded to identify all members of the significant families or preferred sequences. Listings can be used for periodic review to ensure consideration of all items in the groups. The family or group can be considered as one item when determining (economic) order quantities. The total for the family is then distributed among its members so that all will run out or reach the reorder point at about the same time and the family will again be ready for processing.[3]

Short-interval Scheduling.[4] Productivity of clerical activities can be improved 30 to 50 percent through the allocation, assignment, and control of work in small increments. Short-interval scheduling has been applied also to maintenance, mail rooms, tool and die making, construction, and similar nonstandardized activities. Other advantages include improved control of backlogs, better attention to job priorities, earlier detection and identification of problems, more equitable work distribution, and improved discipline.

The system can be applied to short, repetitive operations reasonably uniform and constant in work content. Since the supervisor handles and distributes all work at frequent intervals and maintains the necessary control records, he must remain in his department almost constantly.

The essential steps in short-interval scheduling are:

1. Reduce volume fluctuations by regulating all work coming into this system, control backlogs by dispatching only the planned amounts of work, and regulate the sequence of processing.

2. Provide for handling nonroutine or exceptional work outside the system.

3. Identify all operations and change the sequence to get the best possible work flow.

4. Improve methods and layout to get the best possible performance.

5. Estimate or measure all operation times.

6. Determine the capacity of each work center and provide adequate, flexible staffing.

7. Determine the overall timetable for the entire process.

8. Determine the time interval for dispatching batches of work.

9. Establish one or more dispatching points under a supervisor to release work in the proper amounts, time, and order.

10. Follow work in process to see that the schedule is being met.

Forecasting and planning for work expected and manpower required for a future time period is necessary. Long-range forecasts by management provide overall man-load and space and equipment requirements. Short-range forecasts by the supervisor provide the basis for day-by-day assignment and control of work using the batch or tally systems. For project work, it is normal to plan three months ahead week by week.

Short-interval scheduling relies heavily on adequate work-measurement techniques. Precise work measurement is not necessary. The supervisor should know or develop the level of performance he can expect from his people with the standards available.

Management should receive regular reports highlighting present performance and trends. Periodic audits of the system should be made by an independent function (systems department or controller's auditor) to be sure that the system is being used properly, that standards are up to date, and that service is adequate.

There are three types of short-interval scheduling systems in use:

1. Batch
2. Tally
3. Project

Each type provides the supervisor knowledge of work input, work assigned to each employee, progress of each employee against the schedule, completion time of work assignments, current backlog of work, and employee performance against standards.

Differences between the three types occur in length of scheduling increment, homogeneity of tasks to be performed, relative location of individual work stations, responsibility for recording work done, and degree of built-in control.

The *batch* system is the most positive. It includes, for each work center and work input station, means for distributing batches of work to the employees,

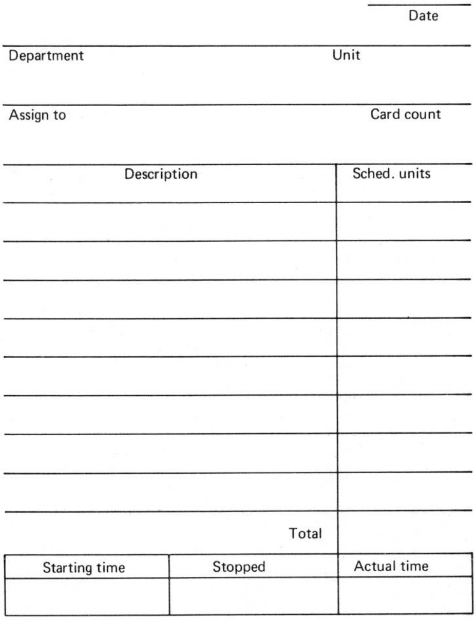

		Date
Department		Unit
Assign to		Card count
Description		Sched. units
	Total	

Starting time	Stopped	Actual time

Fig. 7 Batch ticket. (*From The Standard Oil Company, Cleveland, Ohio.*)

keeping track of work assignments and completion, and moving completed work to its next work center. At the input station, the work scheduler sorts incoming work into convenient homogeneous batches approximating one hour of work. He attaches a batch ticket as in Fig. 7, indicating to whom the work has been assigned and the number of units of work included. Batches are stored in trays or bins to be distributed in the desired priority. The employee initials the ticket and indicates the time he completed the work.

The sign-out sheet, in Fig. 8, shows the department's planned production target for the day. This provides a measure against which the supervisor can compare overall actual performance and also indicates trouble spots developing either externally or internally. The supervisor notes the number of units of work assigned to each employee. At the end of each time period, he can determine incomplete assignments and can distribute additional batches. The employees do not have to worry about work priority and can also be shown that work is being distributed fairly. As work batches are completed, the time period is noted on the sign-out sheet and the employee credited.

The *tally* system is used where employees work in scattered areas and/or where the work does not lend itself readily to batching. The work may go directly to the employee or it may be received into an input station, sorted,

Department ____________ Division ____________ Unit ____________ Supervisor ____________ Date ____________

Forecast and daily plan comparison

Starting carryover	Plan	Act.	Hours received	Plan	Act.	Planned production	Plan	Act.	Ending carryover	Plan	Act.	Percent productivity	Plan	Act.	Hours required	Plan	Act.	Hours available	Plan	Act.	Out hours	Plan	Act.

Name	Asgm't		Diff.		Diff.		Diff.		Diff.		Diff.		Diff.		Diff.		Diff.	C/O	Comp.	Prod.
	Assg'd																			
	Sched.																			
	Actual																			
	Assg'd																			
	Sched.																			
	Actual																			
	Assg'd																			
	Sched.																			
	Actual																			
	Assg'd																			
	Sched.																			
	Actual																			
	Assg'd																			
	Sched.																			
	Actual																			
	Assg'd																			
	Sched.																			
	Actual																			
	Assg'd																			
	Sched.																			
	Actual																			
	Assg'd																			
	Sched.																			
	Actual																			
	Assg'd																			
	Sched.																			
	Actual																			
	Assg'd																			
	Sched.																			
	Actual																			
	Assg'd																			
	Sched.																			
	Actual																			
	Assg'd																			
	Sched.																			
	Actual																			
		Totals																C/O	Comp.	Prod.
Actual																				
Plan																		Tot. Plan		
Cumulative difference																				

Fig. 8 Sign-out sheet. (*From The Standard Oil Company, Cleveland, Ohio.*)

and distributed. The supervisor controls the distribution of work to the individual employees. The backlog is kept at the work input station where the supervisor may determine its quantity and assign priority. Unlike the batch system, the tally system requires that the supervisor review work accomplished during the day at the individual work stations. The tally system takes more diligent supervision. Spot checks of employees' tally sheets over long periods have revealed that actual productivity is often 10 to 15 percent less than that reported.

The *project* system is used for controlling the work of professional staff personnel including engineers, accountants, researchers, etc., and focuses on the major phases of the project set up to accomplish specific objectives. One day each week the individual and his supervisor review progress of work against the previous week's schedule, including project hours to date, hours remaining, and whether or not the project is on schedule. They plan the hours to be spent on each project and other activities during the coming week. As the week progresses, the employee records the actual time spent each day on each project and other activities. His supervisor periodically checks progress against the plan.

Line of Balance (LOB). This is a manual, graphical technique for planning, scheduling, and monitoring progress of simple to complex projects (see Chapter 13). These may be products assembled over a moderate time period against a firm schedule, a development program for a complex assembly, or a research and engineering project. The project is represented by a network showing the relationship in time among the various milestones (such as receipt of finished components, completion of testing, etc.) making up the project.

The discipline required to set up the chart can help to ensure thorough planning. The schedule of critical activities can be developed accurately (depending on accuracy of data on required lead times) and actual progress monitored. The technique permits showing simultaneously on one chart:

1. Source of each component element (purchase, manufacture, assembly, test, etc.)

2. Sequence of assembly, including subassembly, testing, inspection, packaging, shipping, and such related activities

3. Comparison of scheduled versus actual finished-product deliveries

4. Comparison of scheduled versus actual component-element completions showing present and potential shortages or delays.

The technique is expensive to set up, increasingly so as the number of components and control points increases. It is inflexible and expensive to revise with schedule changes, variations in elements, or revisions in elemental lead times. Analysis of project status requires accumulating data on all elements simultaneously.

LOB is a network planning technique similar to PERT, CPS, CPM, precedence lists, etc., but lacking their flexibility, versatility, and scope. A Gantt chart should be considered before applying LOB; it will be considerably less expensive and may produce equal results.

LOB has been most frequently applied to complex assemblies built for the United States Navy, whose contracts usually require using the chart to report status to government inspectors. Commerical and industrial applications of LOB as an operating technique are extremely rare. Here materials planning (see Chapters 13 and 19) finds almost universal application in planning, scheduling, and controlling production of complex, assembled products.

An LOB chart consists of three sections—the production plan, the objective chart, and the progress chart (Fig. 9). The lower half is the production plan. Inaccuracies in it will be reflected throughout the LOB chart, It is a "key"

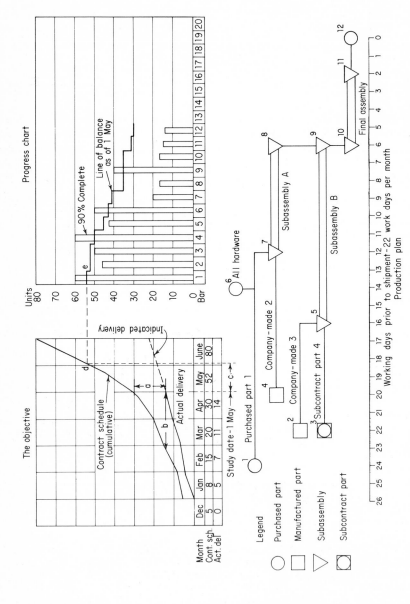

Fig. 9 Sample line-of-balance chart. (*Adapted from Line of Balance Technology, Special Projects Office, Department of the Navy, NAVEXOS p. 1851, rev. 4-62.*)

components product tree with time represented on the horizontal axis. The length of each product-tree bar denotes lead time required to produce one "batch" of that component or assembly; the overall product-structure length is the total product lead time. For example, purchased part 1 requires 12 working days lead time (24 minus 12) and total product lead time is 24 days.

First, select those components (from the bill of material) or events (from the route or process sheets) whose timely completion is important to the project. Relatively unimportant components are lumped together ("All Hardware"). Second, obtain or estimate lead times for each "batch" of the selected key components; these should be the most likely time, inclusive of processing, movement, and waiting time. Finally, draw the chart starting from the right with the completion day, week, or month as zero and working to the left, "branching out" as assemblies become subassemblies, and subassemblies become components. Connect all component horizontal lead-time bars with a vertical line where subassembly or assembly occurs, forming an interconnected network. Select a time scale in units suitable for effective monitoring.

Mark the *start* of each key component or event line with a control-point number, commencing from the top left and moving to the bottom right. Intermediate events should be given a number only if they are to be monitored. Always number the completion of the project. Symbols indicating the type of component (raw material, purchased part, manufactured part, subassembly, etc.) are helpful, and color coding increases the ease of interpretation. Descriptions of components or events can be shown on the chart. Selection of key components and events, assignment of control-point numbers, and use of descriptions must be dictated by the economics of over- or undercontrolling project progress.

The completed production plan could be used like a Gantt chart for monitoring the project by assigning specific dates to the horizontal time scale and recording actual progress on individual bars of the chart where few or no partial lots of the total order are expected at any control point. Where individual lots are scheduled over several periods, the Gantt chart is difficult to adapt and the LOB progress chart makes possible recording control-point completion status against schedule.

The upper left portion of the figure is the *objective chart*. It is the cumulative contract delivery schedule plotted vertically against time plotted horizontally. The cumulative actual delivery schedule is plotted as the project progresses. The horizontal axis is divided into time intervals most closely approximating the delivery schedule. Frequently, both scheduled and actual deliveries in each interval are posted below this axis as a summary of project status. The vertical axis shows units of delivered end product.

The functions of the objective chart are:

1. To show the quantity of end product ahead of or behind schedule by the vertical gap between the two curves (*a*) and by the scheduled and actual totals summarized below the horizontal axis.

2. To show the number of time periods ahead of or behind schedule by the horizontal gap between the two curves (*b*).

3. To indicate the production rates by the slopes of the lines. Extending the actual line ahead on its historical trend can yield estimates of future production.

4. To provide the basis for drawing the "line of balance" on the progress chart where control-point completion status is measured.

The upper right portion of the figure is the *progress chart*. The length of the vertical bars represents the actual quantity of end-product sets of each component or event completed at the study date. The bars are numbered horizontally for each control point on the production plan. The vertical scale shows end-product sets (more than one component may be required per end product). The progress chart shares this scale with the objective chart. The length of the bars increases as progress occurs at each control point. The most important benefit is the measurement of control-point status against plan and is obtained by striking the "line of balance"—the minimum quantity of each control-point element required to support the end-product delivery schedule as of the study date.

To strike the line of balance:

1. Start with the study date (May 1 on the horizontal axis of the objective chart) and mark off to the right (c for control-point 1) the number of lead-time periods required for each control point in advance of end-product completion. This lead-time information is obtained from the production plan. For example, control-points 8, 9, and 10 must be completed six working days in advance of shipment; control-point 3, two months in advance, and so on.

2. Draw a vertical dashed line from the lead-time termination until it intersects the cumulative delivery schedule as at d.

3. From the point of intersection draw a horizontal dashed line to the corresponding control-point bar on the progress chart, e. This is the "balance quantity" or minimum control-point quantity required to support the end-product delivery schedule.

4. Repeat this procedure for all control points on the production plan.

5. Join the balance quantities to form one staircase-type line of balance across the progress chart.

Bars above the line indicate control points ahead of schedule. Those ending below the line show control points short of quantities required.

The LOB chart is read as a book—from upper left to lower right. First, the objective chart is checked; if the schedule is being properly met no further reading is required. If the program is significantly behind schedule, the progress chart is checked to determine the control points that are behind schedule. As completion of some control points is dependent upon earlier control points, the true problem control point(s) must be located by referring to the production plan.

The chart also shows: (1) the amount of off-schedule deliveries in units and periods of time, (2) the indicated future deliveries based on actual delivery-curve trend, and (3) whether off-schedule or imbalance is caused by a common source type such as subcontracted or raw materials.

SCHEDULING ASSEMBLIES

Two factors vital in scheduling assembly operations are *component availability* and *assembly-capacity rates*. Parts flow must support assembly rates. Where components are common to many products, the order-point–order-quantity inventory control system (see Chapters 14, 16, and 19) is generally used. When unique to one product, a part in a complex assembly of many components with different lead times should be controlled by a materials plan.

Scheduled assembly rates can be held close to actual capacity since component availability is known. Staging or laying out sets of parts in advance of assembly should be held to a minimum. Increasing these advance supplies as a means of gaining information sooner on shortages is poor practice because:

1. Component inventories will be increased.
2. More space will be occupied.

3. Additional records of shortages in each kit will be required.

4. Components in short supply will become more critical.

5. Record errors increase through shifting components from one layout to another.

6. Stock-room work load increases.

7. Control of assembly priorities diminishes.

Scheduled assembly work should equal available capacity. Capacity usually varies with mix of individual products requiring different assembly times. *Line balancing* (see Chapter 13) is used to develop schedules of balanced loads of available capacity, utilizing the line flexibility by shifting work among work stations for economical assembly.

Meeting the planned assembly rate, the finished-goods inventory control system can be used to indicate specific items to be scheduled to:

1. Produce a balanced inventory (equal week's supply of all items)

2. Build up specific products for sales promotions

3. Minimize capital investment in seasonal products

4. Store hours of labor or machine time expected to become critical

TABLE 34   Loading Steps

1. Choose load centers
A.   Department
B.   Group
C.   Machine or work station
2. Develop efficiency factors by load center
3. Choose loading method
A.   To "infinite" capacity
B.   To "finite" capacity
C.   Combination
4. Load scheduled orders into load centers
5. Unload "completed" hours

MACHINE LOADING

As Table 34 shows, the first step in machine loading is to choose the load centers. Some companies load by department only if all the machines in a department are interchangeable. When different machine centers within the department have different capabilities (as in a general machining department), the technique is to break the machines down into similar machine groups. All 24-inch boring mills, for example, might be included in the same group if jobs are interchangeable among the machines. In some instances—for example, a screw machine with a milling cutter attachment but otherwise identical with other machines in the group—coding should be set up so that an individual machine can be singled out if a job can be done only on it. Group as many machines together as possible, since this will reduce the work and tend to stabilize the load.

One of the most important steps is to develop *efficiency factors* by load centers. A load center with two men is capable of 80 hours of production per week, but actual output might be considerably less than 80 hours if time is spent on setup work and indirect activity. If they are working on incentive, however, they could be turning out more than 80 "standard hours" of production.

The next step is to choose the actual loading method. This may be *loading to infinite capacity* if the load is shown in the week in which it should ideally fall, without regard to the capacity to handle all the work. If the department were loaded only according to its present capacity (*loading to finite capacity*), scheduling could not be done in one continuous calculation. Each scheduling step would involve checking the machine-load to see if there were sufficient capacity available in the week in which the work was required. Loading to finite capacity by operation is more complex than infinite-capacity loading. Any plant activity that does not go according to schedule will require that the load be recalculated and loads will now fall in different time periods. Finite-capacity loading also requires that the scheduler establish priority for loading the jobs.

In practice, finite-capacity loading by itself is unsatisfactory, since it assumes that present capacity is all that is available and does not show the time period in which overloads will occur if an attempt is made to meet desirable schedules. Without the latter information, action cannot be taken to improve the plant's performance in meeting customer requirements.

A good machine-loading system involves a combination of both techniques. Orders are first scheduled and loaded to infinite capacity to see where overloads will occur, then rescheduled to level the load based on available capacity *after* corrective actions have been taken wherever possible.

The last step is selection of the *unloading* technique. Manual systems may require shortcuts such as considering a job to be completed when the first lot of pieces is reported. This saves posting many partial lots and recalculating load balances, but the load is always understated by the number of hours remaining on jobs unloaded. Another shortcut relieves the load only when the last lot is completed, giving a load constantly overstated by the hours completed but not removed.

The numbers of hours to be unloaded must equal the number of hours loaded for each job. For example, if 12 "standard hours" have been loaded and the job is completed in 9 actual hours, 12 hours must be relieved from the load.

A machine-load, based on actual work orders released, is a good short-term technique for highlighting underloads or overloads on work centers and showing the need for overtime, temporary transfers, subcontracting, or other short-range adjustments. It is seldom adequate for long-term capacity planning.

An effective production capacity plan must extend far enough into the future to cover the time required for hiring and training needed production and service employees, obtaining necessary equipment and materials, and *operating long enough* at higher capacity to be worthwhile. The backlog of open orders in the machine-load rarely covers this much lead time.

Several companies have successfully used *simulated* machine-loads over longer planning periods to assist capacity planning. Forecasts of individual finished products to be manufactured during this period can be exploded into detailed requirements of production-hours on each major work center. While actual production of individual items can be expected to vary greatly from such long-range forecasts, increases in one item will tend to be offset by decreases in another, and the aggregate hours will be reasonably accurate. Machine loads based on these aggregate hours will indicate developing trends toward underload or overload and will give dependable data on *average* capacity required to meet the forecasted demand on manufacturing facilities.

REFERENCES

1. Charles C. Holt, Franco Modigliani, John F. Muth, and Herbert A. Simon, *Planning Production, Inventories, and Work Force,* Prentice-Hall, Inc., Englewood Cliffs, N.J., 1960.

2. Richard I. Levin and C. A. Kirkpatrick, *Quantitative Approaches to Management*, McGraw-Hill Book Company, New York, 1965.
3. George W. Plossl and Oliver W. Wight, *Production and Inventory Control: Principles and Techniques*, Prentice-Hall, Inc., Englewood Cliffs, N.J., 1967, Chapters 7 and 8.
4. Raymond J. Behan, *Cost Reduction Through Short Interval Scheduling*, Prentice Hall, Englewood Cliffs, N.J., 1969.

BIBLIOGRAPHY

Applequist, H. D.: "Short Interval Scheduling Systems," *Proceedings of Eighth Annual Conference*, American Institute of Industrial Engineers, Detroit Chapter, Apr. 1, 1965.
Enrick, Norbert L.: *"Management Operations Research,* Holt, Rinehart and Winston, Inc., New York, 1965.
Line of Balance Technology, Special Projects Office, Department of the Navy, NAVEXOS p. 1851 (rev. 4–62).
Magee, John F., and David M. Boodman: *Production Planning and Inventory Control* 2d ed., McGraw-Hill Book Company, New York, 1967.
Putnam, Arnold O., E. Robert Barlow, and Gabriel N. Stilian: *Unified Operations Management*, McGraw-Hill Book Company, New York, 1963.

Chapter 10

Manpower Management

EDITOR:

Henry H. Jordan, Jr. *Management Consultant, Wright Associates, New York, New York*

ASSISTANT EDITOR:

Joseph A. Carrano *Corporate Manager of Production Planning and Control, Hazeltine Corporation, Little Neck, New York*

CONTRIBUTORS:

W. Neil Benton *Vice President, Production, Booz, Allen & Hamilton, New York, New York*

Richard B. Black *Vice President, Finance and Operations, Maremont Corporation, Chicago, Illinois*

Walter Cloud *Partner, Wright Associates, New York, New York*

Dr. Robert C. Klekamp *Assistant Professor of Management, Graduate School of Business, Xavier University, Cincinnati, Ohio; Vice President, W. G. Seinsheimer and Associates, Cincinnati, Ohio*

J. Clifford Kulick *Manager of Manufacturing, Nixdorf-Krein Manufacturing Company, St. Louis, Missouri*

Leo A. Smith *Assistant Professor, Industrial Engineering, Auburn University, Auburn, Alabama*

David D. Swett *Executive Vice President, Bruce Payne & Associates, Inc., New York, New York*

Dennis B. Webster *First Lieutenant, Ordance Corps, U.S. Army Reserve, Aberdeen, Maryland*

CONTENTS

HUMAN-RESOURCES CONCEPT

To gain an insight into the human-resources concept one must look to the manner in which history has treated man. We find man in the role of inventor, soldier, discoverer, statesman, farmer, churchman—in short, every one of a myriad panorama of occupations he found necessary or expedient to engage in to cope with his environment. If the subject at hand is the history of art, one traces perhaps the evolution of a particular school. In political history, the framework of study is perhaps the degree of self-rule that existed in various cultures. Religious history in various cultures may be explored by examining the nature of the deity of each. In short, each area of historical investigation is done within some pertinent construct that gives a sense of order to research. The history of man as a resource can best be understood if each culture is viewed as a man-tool system. In other words, the productive capacity of a culture tends to depend upon how man relates to his tools, and how the man and his tools are used by his particular culture.

Early History. The earliest history of productive man emphasizes survival. In other words, the entire man-tool system of early civilizations seemed to be largely preoccupied with the maintenance and preservation of life. The physiological needs were so overwhelming that little psychic energy was available to improve the man-tool system.

Those civilizations that finally realized the recurring benefit of even minute improvements in their man-tool systems began to advance. The relationship between conception, improvement, increased productivity, and hence more time for further conceptual development was realized. This early period, however, seemed to emphasize the total of mass effectiveness of man-tool systems. Civilizations were characterized by the results of the mass applications of labor. The pyramids of Egypt are noted for, among other things, the fantastic use of mass manpower in their construction. The cities of the Aztec civilization appear to be notable if only for the fact that they were products of a civilization that knew little of tools. In short, the early history of productive man emphasized the effect of the application of a mass of manpower in the utilization of the man-tool system. The results were impressive, but so were the costs of human resources.

Industrial Revolution. With the dawn of the industrial revolution, however, the man-tool system became a man-machine system, and we began to look to the economists rather than the historians for a picture of man-the-producer. The total system became further differentiated by the economists into the three agents of production—land, capital, and labor. Adam Smith published his pioneering work, *An Inquiry into the Nature and Causes of the Wealth of Nations,* in 1776.[1] In developing an economic system, Smith placed great emphasis not upon labor as a mass but rather upon the importance of individual skill and ability. Smith did recognize all three productive agents, but hoped to explain the dynamics of an economic development through improvement in the effectiveness of the individual as a producer.

The economists that followed Smith were not as kind to man-the-producer. Malthus dealt with labor, but in terms of its propensity to consume the available food.[2] Ricardo's *Principles of Political Economy and Taxation*[3] based the theory of value upon labor costs but, like Alfred Marshall,[4,5] Joseph Schumpeter,[6,7] Thorstein Veblen,[8] and even Keynes,[9] Ricardo treated man-the-producer as an economic entity. These economists saw man as responsive to the demands of the market. If the market did not need his skill, they saw him moving to a more favorable market or acquiring a new skill. They saw him seeking to acquire skills and talent that might lead to higher-paying jobs. These assumptions were at best extremely crude models of individual behavior. World War II economists began incorporating the findings of the psychologists into their models and shed a new light upon the theme that began with Smith, i.e., the vast importance of the individual in any economic system.

Industrial Engineering. The next discipline to *focus* upon man was industrial engineering. The advent of Taylorism *centered* attention upon labor as a tremendous lever in the total productivity picture. It *directed* attention, however, not upon the mass of labor but upon the utilization of individual skills. It differentiated the skills and attempted to combine each with the environmental factors that existed so that the total system maximized productivity. Controversy has raged over Taylor's humanism or lack thereof. Be this as it may, one could little doubt the effectiveness of his approach to man-the-producer as a potent factor in the search for increased productivity. Taylorism brought with it a drastic change in the concepts of both labor and the managerial process. The very basis for Taylor's system was the premise that every aspect in which man related to his machine must be planned. Here we have the philosophical embryo of what we today call "production control," i.e., the preplanning of

Product	January	February		Monday			Tuesday		
				1	2	3	1	2	3
A345	300	195		4	3	3	3	3	2
B721	120	50		1	3	2	4	2	0
R211	160	0		6	4	2	3	3	3
T491	94	250		6	8	0	4	3	1

Fig. 1   Master schedule.

Master Schedule.   The focal point of manpower planning and control is the master schedule (see Fig. 1), which indicates the number of units of product(s) to be manufactured during specific time periods to meet customer requirements and hence company goals.   With the knowledge of what is to be manufactured and when it is to be completed, the function of manpower planning and control actively begins.

With the master schedule determining the manpower requirements, consideration needs to be given to the numerous factors that directly or indirectly affect the master schedule and hence all manpower planning and control.   These input factors are shown in the schematic in Fig. 2, along with the actions that follow as a result of the master schedule.

The factors of manpower capacity, customer order/forecast, standing or firm orders, and product-line mix which directly affect the master schedule and hence manpower planning and control are discussed below.

Manpower Capacity.   The term "capacity" may refer to *available* capacity or *demanded* capacity.   The former relates to the availability of such resources as manpower and equipment under normal operating conditions.   Demanded capacity refers to the translation of customer-order–forecast requirements into needed manpower, equipment, and other production resources.   Manpower planning and control requires the comparison and adjustment of demanded manpower capacity to available manpower capacity.

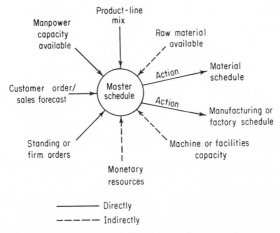

Fig. 2   Master-schedule input and output factors.

Available manpower capacity is rarely constant. For example, the addition of five assemblers to the work force increases available capacity. Moreover, it may be difficult to determine quantitatively the output of these five new workers. Similarly, the addition of a new machine tool with its associated manning will increase the available manpower capacity. But for manpower planning purposes that portion of the increased available capacity that must be compared with the demanded capacity may be difficult to measure. Here a pertinent factor in the dynamics of available manpower capacity is the increased proficiency a worker may attain by repetition of work process. This change may be quantified by use of the "learning curve" technique discussed in a later section.

In determining available manpower capacity it is important to determine the quality as well as the quantity of the various categories of skills available. Consideration of the level or grade of skill within each category is also important. The quality as well as quantity of available manpower capacity is particularly important when high-cost, high-skill levels are required. For example, if the manpower planners utilize semiskilled workers when the demanded capacity requires high-skilled workers, high costs can result from poor-quality performance and low output per worker. Conversely, if higher-skilled workers are used on lower-skilled tasks, the cost of production will increase.

The elastic nature of available manpower capacity permits its adjustment to demanded manpower capacity by such methods as:

1. Working overtime
2. Adding a second or third shift
3. Hiring new employees
4. Laying off employees
5. Reducing the work week
6. Adding new equipment
7. Disposing of surplus equipment
8. Leasing additional warehouse space
9. Increasing subcontracting
10. Making more and subcontracting less

For good manpower planning and control it is essential to know what the available manpower capacity will be over the planning period. This requires continual assessment of the change in quantity and quality of workers, as well as equipment changes with their accompanying new manpower requirements. For instance, older equipment may require three operators, while newer equipment will produce the same quantity and quality with only one operator.

Customer Order/Sales Forecast. In the absence of firm customer orders, the planning of manpower is based on a forecast of sales. Where there are a number of products, the number of units in each line of the mix should be specified. After the required number of units is determined, it is compared with the inventory forecast for the period during which delivery will be made. The difference between the number of units in inventory and the ordered forecasted number establishes the number to be produced. Manpower needs are based on the quantity to be produced in each line of the product mix. This may be done in accordance with the loading methods described in a later section.

When manpower planning is based on forecast in lieu of firm customer orders, it is important that the planner have an understanding of forecasting techniques. There are numerous methods of preparing forecasts. The various methods used will produce forecasts of differing accuracies. The intent is to use the method that produces the most consistently accurate forecast results. Use of forecasts presupposes that the user acknowledges them as imperfect attempts to determine the future, with their accompanying pitfalls and inaccuracies. A few of the forecasting methods used include forecasts made by the sales force, market surveys of new or untried products, regression or correlation analysis, projection of past trends into the future, or simply maintaining the status quo and following the same practices as used in the prior time period.

Cyclical and Seasonal Considerations. Cyclical or seasonal demands on capacity resulting from customer-order forecast requirements compel the manager to make a choice. The choice is between a stable work force with fluctuating inventories and a fluctuating work force with relatively fixed inventory. Where companies face cyclical or seasonal demands for their finished product, manpower policy must be coordinated with inventory policy. The fluctuations may fit the seasons, such as toy manufacturing with Christmas, or fit the business cycles, such as auto manufacturing and other consumer durables. In many instances company personnel policies or difficult recruiting requirements and associated heavy costs of layoffs and hiring may dictate planning for a level work force and fluctuating inventories.

In deciding whether to level production and hence manpower as opposed to minimizing inventory, a quantitative study should be made. The nature

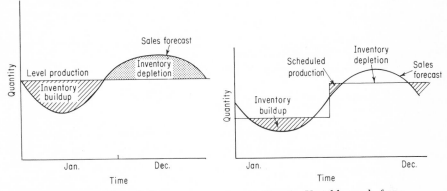

Fig. 3 Level work force.   **Fig. 4** Variable work force.

of future customer orders should be determined from one or more of the forecast methods previously mentioned. In Fig. 3, a graphic presentation of the forecast indicates the nature of the fluctuations. Superimposed on the forecast is a horizontal or leveling line that provides the same production quantity over the period of the forecast, but without the peaks and troughs. Production planned on the leveling method minimizes manpower fluctuations but accentuates inventory accumulation as shown by the crosshatched area. The minimum manpower costs resulting from a constant level of production must be balanced against the increased cost of carrying inventory during the periods of slack customer demand. The decision of manpower versus inventories may be made by comparing the relevant costs of each course of action and weighing these against the satisfaction of customer requirements and the associated "goodwill."

Another approach may be employed where a trained labor force is readily available, or the labor skill required is low resulting in low training costs. As shown in Fig. 4, the production level is changed in a step manner to closely approach customer demand. With each increase in production, additions would be made to the work force. Conversely each decline would result in layoffs, shorter work weeks, or other decreases in man-hours of available capacity.

Product-line Mix. In determining manpower requirements it is important to distinguish between the different product lines made in the same plant. This is especially important since different products typically vary with respect to their contribution to profit, their manpower requirements, and material content. For manpower planning purposes it is often necessary to consider each product in the mix as a separate entity and plan accordingly.

Hopefully, the mix selected will be one providing the greatest profit at the time. But when the number of products is large or the customer demands change month to month, the problem of planning becomes more complex. This requires adjustments such as additional shifts, overtime, layoffs, and other situations resulting from a fluctuating work load.

The problem of product mix is accentuated when the customer order/forecast demands more capacity than is available. For instance, product-line A demands 60 percent of the available capacity, product-line B 30 percent, and product-line C 35 percent. Since demanded capacity is 125 percent, the products can't be produced with the existing available capacity. A number of methods may be used to expand the available manpower capacity: by additional shifts, overtime, subcontracting, adding permanent workers, hiring temporary help and many others. An alternative to expanding available capacity to equal or exceed demanded capacity is to delay or stretch out customer order/forecast requirements and load the available capacity primarily with the higher-profit products and load the balance of the available capacity with product lines in descending order of profit contribution. Serious consideration must also be given to customer satisfaction and future product potential.

Standing Orders or Firm Business. An aid in manpower planning is the existence of standing orders or firm business. It enables the planners to assign manpower on a continuing basis to a core of work that is of a relatively permanent nature. Unlike other customer orders that may fluctuate, firm business is considered consistent and predictable with respect to quantity. Manpower may be allocated to this core of firm business with additional orders layered on this core. This enables planning for a basically permanent work force to handle the firm business with the concentration of manpower planning in the area of exception, the area of other-than-firm business. Surges in the nonfirm-business area may be handled with overtime, temporary additional shifts, temporary additions to the work force, or other short-range actions.

Control of Manpower. The control of manpower focuses on the manpower plan designed to meet customer requirements. The element of control involves monitoring or measuring the actual occurrences and comparing them with the earlier-created manpower plan. Manpower planning and control forms a portion of a total management-information system designed to serve the entire organization. The manpower control elements senses all deviations from the manpower plan and takes corrective action. Deviations result in most situations because of the inability to look into the future and predict with accuracy future events. Inherent in planning is the necessity to predict and prepare a manpower plan under conditions of great uncertainty. Control requires the corrective action necessary to bring manpower requirements in line with the present situation.

Numerous methods of reporting and measuring are used to compare the actual with the plan to aid in corrective action. As part of an overall management-information system, reports are prepared on the present manpower by number of employees, number of absentees, layoffs, transfers, new hires, and also by skill, type, and level.

Numerous measures of efficiency and productivity are also used. A common measure is output per unit of manpower. It may be dollars or units of output per man-hour, man-day, man-month, man-year, or any other useful measure of man-time. Other useful ratios are the number of direct to indirect man-hours, direct-labor man-hours to idle man-hours, direct-labor man-hours to machine-hour time, overtime hours to straight-time hours, piece-rate workers to day workers. Each ratio serves as a means of comparing the actual with the planned or expected. Corrective action may be taken to bring performance back within expected values. Without the comparison with a plan or norm there would be no knowledge of the efficient use of manpower.

The corrective action to bring actual performance in line with the plan may require resorting to overtime, an additional shift, subcontracting the work, or addition of workers to the work force on at least a temporary basis. There may be situations where manpower is reduced because performance exceeds the plan. Another alternative is to change the plan, provided enough flexibility exists to permit meeting delivery commitments to the customer. Still another alternative is to use a manpower pool that has been created to move into work centers that fall behind schedule.

Long-range Manpower Planning. Although most manpower planning is of necessity short range, long-range manpower planning is equally important. Long-range planning is a necessity in conditions where demand for skilled labor will increase but the available supply is constant or decreasing. In this case the long-range plan may require upgrading existing manpower through various training programs. For instance, there may be apprentice programs to supply skilled toolmakers or machinists, formal on-the-job training programs, technical-school programs, tuition-refund plans for part-time technical-training courses. Another approach to long-range manpower planning is the relocation of the plant to an area with a surplus of the type of labor required.

Long-range manpower planning should be an integral part of any company's long-range plan extending more than one year into the future.

MANPOWER LOADING

The loading phase is the initial planning phase between the master schedule, developed from the sales forecast or customer order, and other manufacturing or factory schedules (see Fig. 5). This is the critical period for the production

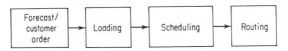

Fig. 5 Order-processing sequence.

planner, since it precedes the commitment to deliver a product of given quality and quantity at a specific time.

Manpower loading is the assignment of work to manpower categories such as work centers or machine centers, but without specifying the sequence, start, or completion date. Scheduling as opposed to loading is concerned with the sequence, start, or completion. Loading, which precedes scheduling, contributes to increasing the accuracy of production schedules. In many cases loading is combined with the scheduling and routing activities.

Planning the Load. The accumulation of information and the calculation of the load begins in the process planning stage with the planner. The planner takes the information received in the form of the shop drawings and the bill of materials and creates the process sheet (see Figs. 6, 7, and 8). The process sheet indicates the work necessary to convert raw material into the finished product by utilizing manpower and equipment. It lists the steps to be followed and the equipment and tooling required. Most important it states the work center or machine center requiring manpower and the hours of manpower required. At this point, time, the common denominator of loading, first appears. With a knowledge of the products the customer requires, the process sheet indicating the type of manpower required, and the man-hours necessary to manufacture the product, manpower loading begins. It involves the matching of

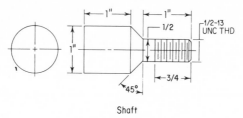

Shaft

Fig. 6 Shop drawing.

Item description	Specifications	No. units
Shaft	$2\frac{1}{4}'' \times 13''$ CF R114 BAR	1

Fig. 7 Bill of material.

Operation number	Description of operation	Machine center or work center number	Gauges, fixtures, tools	Setup hours	Total hours
001	Cut to length on power saw	21-4	....	0.0	0.3
010	Center	30-7	....	0.0	0.2
015	Turn on lathe	30-7	921Y	0.3	1.1
025	Mill threads	40-8	346D	0.4	0.9
035	Bench work—file, burr	10-1	....	0.0	1.0
075	Inspect	90-			

Fig. 8 Process sheet.

available manpower capacity with the required manpower capacity indicated by the process sheet together with the forecast or customer order. The quality of manpower loading is only as good as the quality of the process sheets, forecasts, or other information used to determine the available manpower capacity and required manpower capacity.

Manpower loading is valuable to the decision maker in assisting him to determine whether to increase or decrease manpower, change the skill level, work overtime, add another shift, maintain the status quo, or seek other possible manpower alternatives. Such manpower decisions are made with a knowledge of

Time now
Capacity
Week 1   Week 2   Week 3
0%   100% 0%   100% 0%   100%

Work center A	/////////	///Man-hours/// /////
Work center B	////////	//////// /////
Work center C	/////	///// /////////

Fig. 9   Period loading.

the product mix, available plant and equipment capacity, and customer demand and its fluctuations.

Graphic Loading Techniques.   The actual comparison of available manpower capacity and required capacity can be done by various techniques, e.g., graphically—utilizing bar-type load charts, the application of electronic data processing equipment, or posting to records or reports.   The most widely used technique is the use of bar-type load charts.   The primary forms of bar-chart-type loading are period loading and cumulative loading.

PERIOD LOADING: The available manpower is represented by a convenient measure of time, such as the week.   The required manpower capacity is then loaded into the "blocked out" periods of time, as in Fig. 9.   In this example each period is one week.   Each week in turn graphically represents 100 percent of the available manpower capacity.

A visual comparison is made between the available man-hours in the period and the required man-hours to meet customer commitments.   The intent is to load each period to an established limit while still maintaining the flow from one work center to the next in a coordinated fashion.   The number of periods loaded would depend on the duration of the manufacturing cycle of the product and the degree of accuracy in forecasting required manpower capacity.

The loading may be done continuously on a "rolling" basis of extending one period into the future as an equal period of time passes.   Another approach is to do it periodically as the forecasted work load dictates.   Since loading is a first approximation for scheduling purposes, no attempt is made to establish the sequence, starting, or completion of the work.

CUMULATIVE LOADING: The second form of bar-chart loading is the cumulative loading method.   Unlike the period loading method, the required man-hours of load are merely added to the existing work load at each work center.   There is no attempt to load by period of time.

In the example in Fig. 10, the horizontal scale is man-hours.   A visual comparison of work center B with work center C shows a relative overload at C and underload at B assuming each has available equal capacity.   Since balance

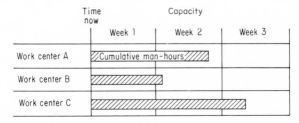

Fig. 10   Cumulative loading.

is desired, the overload and underload conditions are brought to the attention of the production planner. To further aid the production planner, various refinements may be made in the bar-type charts such as superimposing on the present existing chart the load conditions last week or last month. Wall boards and other graphic devices are commercially available to provide bar-type load display (see Chapter 21).

The advantages of the bar-type load charts are:
1. Simplicity and ease of understanding
2. Opportunity to use lower-paid clerical personnel
3. Promotion of management by exception
4. Relative low cost of loading system

The disadvantages include:
1. Oversimplifies and disguises possible problem areas
2. May fail to provide the level of detailed information necessary to determine courses of action
3. Lacks ability to indicate the interdependency and effect that a load at one work center will have on another work center

Alternative Loading Methods. Other methods of manpower loading used are the analytical method, the standard-volume method, and the critical-operation method.

ANALYTICAL METHOD: The analytical method involves a detailed analysis of all the subassemblies and component parts that make up the finished product specified in the forecast or customer order. This requires breaking down the product into all its parts and determining the man-hours required by type or work center.

The basic information would come from process sheets (see Fig. 8), planning standards, planning-time estimates, or cost accounting data. The usual form of the data would be man-hours, although man-days, man-weeks, man-months, or labor dollars by skill or work area are also used. Cost accounting may maintain cost data by assigning certain homogeneous production areas the title of a specific work center to facilitate data gathering and information handling.

The resulting compilation of the total man-hours required to manufacture the specified product provides an accurate estimate of the manpower load for a future period. This future manpower load or required capacity is compared with the available manpower capacity. The comparison aids the decision maker in determining whether to add to the work force, add a second or third shift, work overtime, lay off workers, or plan other courses of action. All this is done as far in advance of the actual work performance as possible.

The use of the analytical method coupled with bar-chart-type loading enables a comparison of available manpower capacity and demanded manpower capacity. As a result action may be taken to cut back on manpower, work overtime, increase the work force, or select other alternatives. All courses of action are made considering the production environment, possible product-mix changes, rush orders, volume changes, and other typical changes.

STANDARD-VOLUME METHOD: Another method of loading is the standard-volume method, which is an approximation of the analytical method. This loading technique is quicker and less costly, but also less precise than the analytical method. A summary is prepared of the man-hours required to make what is called a "standard volume" or a predetermined amount of production of each product in the product mix. This standard volume or unit of production becomes a bench mark against which various levels of production are compared. The man-hours for the standard volume would be derived from planning standards or planning-time estimates.

The approximation of actual load is determined by multiplying the man-hours for the standard volume by the number of units of standard volume that make up the customer order or forecast. The comparison of this demanded manpower capacity with the available capacity, perhaps using bar-type load charts, indicates the need for an increase or decrease in manpower to meet the customer order or forecast. This quick and inexpensive method provides a readily available means of determining manpower requirements.

CRITICAL-OPERATION METHOD: This is a subjective method as opposed to the above-mentioned objective methods. It is based on the fact that many companies have one or more manufacturing operations that control or limit all other operations in the manufacturing cycle. For example, a critical operation may be the painting operation which acts as a bottleneck in the process. Based on past experience, each order of over 500 units will in a given time period require increased overtime in the painting operation to meet commitments.

A review of performance of the production process reveals the critical operations. A list of these provides a checklist of possible manpower problem areas. Operating by the principle of management by exception, it may be possible to closely monitor only the critical operations and still meet all manpower needs. This assumes that the noncritical operations will possess sufficient manpower so that an overload will not occur. Thus the available capacity is compared with the required capacity for only the critical operations. All decisions to increase or decrease manpower center about the critical operations.

This method permits manpower loading without resorting to either the analytical or standard-volume methods. While it is the least precise method of manpower loading, it may also be used as an initial approach in conjunction with the analytical or standard-volume methods.

Statistical Load Control. This is a tool for management that enables a more precise control of the load without the problems created by changing capacity when it is unnecessary (overcontrol) or delaying changes when they are urgently needed (undercontrol). Statistical load control quantifies many of the decision points that are normally handled by intuition. It uses the same mathematical concepts as the statistical technology of quality control. It is based on the fact that variations occur and that no two things are ever exactly alike.

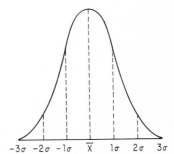

$-3\sigma \quad -2\sigma \quad -1\sigma \quad \overline{X} \quad 1\sigma \quad 2\sigma \quad 3\sigma$

Fig. 11 Standard deviations and the normal curve.

Where chance is given full play, these variations will fall into a pattern called the "normal frequency distribution" or "bell-shaped" curve.

The "standard deviation" (σ) is used as the measure of spread for most industrial frequency distributions. The relationship of standard deviations to the normal curve is shown in Fig. 11. It is to be noted that plus or minus 3 standard deviations ($\pm 3\sigma$) covers 99.73 percent of all occurrences, $\pm 2\sigma$ covers 95.45 percent, and $\pm 1\sigma$ covers 68.27 percent of all occurrences.

CONTROL CHARTS: A control chart is used to establish standards of expected normal variation due to chance causes. This range of chance variations is expressed as plus and minus 3 standard deviations, i.e., $\overline{X} \pm 3\sigma$. When a variance occurs that falls outside -3σ to $+3\sigma$, the variation indicates that something has changed due to assignable causes and not chance. The process is then considered to be out of control and in need of corrective action.

Using a base period of time and determining the load at stated intervals during the period, the arithmetic mean load ($\overline{X}$) and standard deviation (σ) are computed in days, weeks, or months of load. A control chart is constructed as shown in Fig. 12.

This means that by establishing control limits, all loads that fall between the upper and lower control limits are considered normal load conditions resulting from chance variations and do not require changes in manpower capacity. If they fall outside of the control limits, the pattern of business has changed and management is alerted to adjust manpower levels. The decision must be made then to increase or decrease capacity or maintain the status quo. To account for cyclical or seasonal fluctuations, the responsible manpower loading personnel may construct a series of statistical control charts for unusual but predictable conditions.

This statistical tool tells the decision maker that the load is out of control or in control in accordance with previously established limits.

Theoretical Manpower versus Actual Manpower. In manpower loading, the difference between the theoretical manpower load and actual manpower load must be understood. In theory, a normal work week of 40 hours provides 40 man-hours for loading purposes. In actual practice, however, the manpower available for loading will be considerably less than the 40 theoretical man-hours.

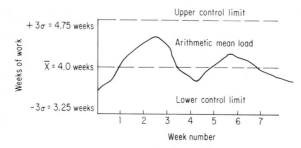

Fig. 12 Control chart for loading.

There is also a difference between "standard" predetermined hours and the man-hours actually required. The reason is that standard hours do not consider all the variables of the production process. Some of the variables are the efficiency of the individual worker, absenteeism, and unexpected idle time due to lack of tools or material. Therefore, a job requiring 20 standard hours could take more than 20 man-hours to complete, considering the variables that may actually occur.

Two approaches may be used in determining the actual man-hours available for loading. The first approach is to begin with standard hours and subtract those factors not originally considered. A simpler approach is to begin with the theoretical man-hours and subtract all factors such as rate of absenteeism; time for rest periods and personal time; time lost due to lack of tools, material, or supervision; and efficiency level of workers. The net number of man-hours will be a realistic or actual figure for loading purposes.

Direct and Indirect Labor. Most methods of manpower loading deal almost exclusively with direct labor. It is recognized that loading for indirect labor is also necessary for good manpower management. This is because of the increase in indirect workers with a relative decrease in direct-labor workers. Increased mechanization and automation have been major causes of this relative increase in indirect workers. The large, more costly automated machine tools require fewer machine operators, but require more indirect workers such as maintenance men and numerical-control equipment programmers.

The most widely used method of indirect-labor loading is the method whereby a ratio of indirect-labor manpower to direct labor is derived. The history of the production process may indicate that 15 indirect-labor personnel are required to support 10 direct-labor personnel for a certain function. The ratio of 1.5 indirect to 1 direct is established. Whenever the available manpower capacity is compared with the demanded manpower capacity, the factor of 1.5:1 is applied to properly consider the indirect labor required.

A more analytical method requires a study of all indirect-labor jobs and the factors that affect them. Factors such as the number of direct-labor manufacturing personnel, floor area of plant, quantity of components bought and made, and number of process and design changes are related to the existing indirect-labor jobs. A numerical ratio is developed, such as 50 indirect-labor people required per 1,000 purchased parts or 120 indirect-labor people per 1,000 square feet of area. This numerical ratio is then applied, where the future number of purchased parts can be multiplied by the numerical ratio to determine the number of indirect-labor personnel required. Similarly, this may be done for all factors that are isolated as having a direct relationship to the number of indirect-labor personnel.

WORK SIMPLIFICATION

Work simplification with its inevitable slogan "Work smarter, not harder" has pretty well pervaded every nook and cranny in industry. Supervisors have been trained, workers have been trained, management has been exposed. The impact upon American industry of these programs has been profound. Like drops of water eroding a stone, productivity has been improved, industry has learned to take a questioning look at how it does things, and people have actually become conscious of the importance of methods upon productivity and costs.

This is not to say that much does not need to be done. There are no methods anywhere that cannot be improved. There is no job that cannot be still further simplified. Many very common individual practices are inefficient partly as a result of obsolete plants, designed when labor was so cheap that a few dozen material handlers more or less did not make a real difference. In other cases people have just been doing things in the same old way for so long that it has become *the* way and no one ever questions it any more. It is this questioning approach that is the key to work simplification.

The importance of work simplification, in its broadest sense, cannot be overemphasized. It is the key to the total productivity and standard of living of an entire country. Politicians and statesmen refer to rich countries and poor countries. To us there are no rich or poor countries, only productive ones and nonproductive ones. For what a country has is nothing more or less than the sum total of what it produces. A country is a rich country when its people work effectively and are productive. It is poor when they are not.

Work simplification means different things to different industries since it is shaped and determined by the nature of the problems involved. In the following section we shall point out how work simplification can be approached in some typical situations and how the industry affects the approach.

Approaches to Work Simplification. ELIMINATION OF WORK: The simplest work of all is no work. Therefore, the initial question is: Can the job be entirely eliminated? The ways of eliminating operations take many forms. Reports which are of doubtful value can simply be discontinued. A polishing or grinding operation may be discontinued if analysis indicates that a less finished surface is acceptable.

COMBINING OPERATIONS: The second question is: Can an operation be combined with another operation, making one operation out of two? For example, a slitting operation may be eliminated by attaching an electric knife to a prior operation, thereby combining the slitting with a drying operation with considerable savings as the result.

PROCESS IMPROVEMENT: The third question must be: Can a better, less expensive process be substituted for the one in question? We are now in an area of practically endless possibilities. Can hand-typed labels be abandoned in favor of Addressograph plates? Can Addressograph plates be eliminated and replaced by computor-produced labels? Can ingot molding be replaced by continuous casting? Can a crane transport rather than a truck? Under this heading comes the whole gamut of technological, computor-oriented work-simplification ideas which have had such a profound impact recently on American industry.

OPERATION IMPROVEMENT: Lastly, improvements can be made to operations while still utilizing existing processes and equipment. These are some of the things to look for:

What are we really trying to accomplish by the operation? What is the heart of the matter and the really essential elements? Are we assemblying parts, cutting metal? Typically, this is the *do* of the operation, the one completely essential aspect which cannot be further eliminated. This we now must accomplish in the most effective way possible.

What about the workplace layout? Are all the needed parts as close to the central assembly point as possible? Are we using a full three-dimensional work area or are we limited to a plane? Are fixtures at the proper height relative to parts and the operator's position?

The transport of objects or parts does not add to their value. Transport merely takes time and adds cost without value and therefore should be reduced to the irreducible minimum by every known means.

The most frequently used parts and tools should be closest. The least frequently used can be further away. Try different combinations and test total transport time for complete assemblies. Select that method which moves things the least.

Are both hands used effectively or is it a one-handed operation? Good workplace design results in hand and eye movements which are opposite and symmetrical. Both hands are used simultaneously moving in opposite directions. The feet or knees can be used to activate switches or clamps, freeing hands for more useful purposes. One of the differences between a home and industrial sewing machine is that with the industrial model the operator uses feet and knees to every advantage while the household model requires many hand operations.

Does the hand serve as a holding device when it could be used better for manipulation? An activated clamp or fixture holds parts more securely and two of them may well enable the operator to engage in two-handed assembly with an increase in output.

How is the finished part disposed of? Is it drop delivered or hand delivered? This is clearly related to transport.

Can basic types of manipulation be simplified by the use of prepositioning or holding devices or the design of storage bins? It is much simpler to grasp a tool, for example, that is being held in nearly a *use* position than it is to hunt for the correct tool.

Can devices be employed which will preposition parts such as vibrators and feeders? These are often used to sort and align parts and deliver them to assembly positions where they can be used with a minimum of effort.

Example of a Method Study. This example, drawn from industry, describes the same product being produced displaying four different stages in methods evolution:

First, there was the one-handed bench assembly with the parts delivered in the usual way. The operator simply picked up parts and assembled them one to the other, located the screwdriver on the bench and went to work.

Next, someone had worked out a classical two-handed bench-assembly problem. The parts were arranged organ-bank fashion in tiers above *two* holding fixtures. The screwdrivers, now two of them, were hanging prepositioned, ready for immediate use. A foot-operated drop delivery emptied the fixture after each assembly. It was a good workmanlike job.

Next, there was an assembly conveyor with parts held in a movable fixture which marched by each work station with military precision. Operators now became specialists in placing a given part or operating the screwdriver which was never relinquished even for a moment. Operators, because they now dealt with just a few parts, got them by handfuls. It was very efficient arrangement and took less space than the individual workbenches. The integrated assembly line, which transported, assembled, and added the package as well, was a distinct improvement.

But the ultimate had still not been reached. Over in one corner a mechanic assembled with three machines. The assembly process was now completely automatic. Parts fed into hoppers were prepositioned by vibration. A ring of carriers passed each part feeder and picked up the part. A screwdriver untouched by human hands gave the final tightening to a predetermined, unvarying torque. Finally, the completed assembly, still untouched by human hands, flipped out of its holder and was conveyed to the packing line. One service attendant could run a dozen such machines and labor cost approached absolute zero, but not so other costs. The machines, of course, were expensive to build and even more so to design. But the product, blessed with nationwide distribution and near-universal acceptance, could sustain the development effort. This was work simplification to the nth degree.

The above illustration characterizes the full scope of work simplification. The evolutionary stage to which any particular operation is developed, of course, depends upon rather precise economic considerations. How much can be saved per piece? How many pieces are produced per year? How many years of life will the product have? These elementary considerations determine whether the operation ever gets out of the one-handed stage, and many truthfully should not.

Analysis Aids. There are a number of graphical charting techniques which can aid the work-simplification analyst in determining when he might initiate process or operation improvements. These techniques are useful for initially designing work methods as well as when evaluating the existing methods for possible improvement. Examples of the use of these charts are given at great length in many texts concerned with methods analysis and time study, and therefore they are only briefly mentioned here.

PROCESS CHARTS: Process charts are used to present a clear picture of the sequence of events constituting a particular activity or process. Given this picture it is often easy to see where potential improvements can be made. Process charts may be one of two types:

Man-process charts display the activities that an individual worker performs as he goes through a cycle of the production process.

Material-process charts display the sequence of steps or activities that a unit or lot of material goes through as it flows through the process.

The two types of charts should not be combined, as to do so would only confuse the analyst. An example of a process chart is shown in Fig. 13. In utilizing the chart one describes in the sequence of its occurrence each operation, transportation, inspection, delay, and storage activity that occurs within the process and records the time for that particular activity and/or the distance moved. Having completed the chart, one can analyze each step in the process for possible

Identification	Symbols			
Process name __Toy__	◯ Operation	Summary	Present method	Proposed method
__barn panel__	⇨ Transportation	No. of operations	8	
Department __12__	☐ Inspection	No. of transpor- tations	4	
Charted by __G.A. Smith__	◖ Delay	Distance traveled	1407 ft	
Date __1 December 1968__	▽ Storage	Total time	168.40/panel	

Details of (present ~~proposed~~) method	Activity symbol	Time in minutes	Distance in feet	Details of (present ~~proposed~~) method	Activity symbol	Time in minutes	Distance in feet
Hard board in				Panels to assembly	⇨	0.04	800
storage in 4' x 8' sheets	▽			department storage			
Hard board loaded on				Panels in storage			
hand truck	◯	0.05/panel		awaiting assembly	▽		
Hard board to rough							
out	⇨	0.01/panel	367				
Hard board awaiting rough							
out	◖	40.00					
Rough out roof and							
side panels	◯	0.78/panel					
Panels loaded on							
hand truck	◯	0.03/panel					
Panels to finish out	⇨	0.01/panel	30				
Panels awaiting finish							
out	◖	67.00					
Finish out panels	◯	1.83/panel					
Inspect	☐	0.10/panel					
Panels loaded on							
hand truck	◯	0.03/panel					
Panels to paint shop	⇨	0.07/panel	210				
Panels waiting to							
enter paint shop	◖	37.00					
Roof panels loading							
on paint rack 1,		0.07/panel					
side panels on rack 2	◯	0.63/panel					
Paint panels and dry	◯	20.00					
Unload panels from							
paint racks to truck	◯	0.35					

Fig. 13   Process chart.

improvement or compare each step against the corresponding step in a proposed method. The activity symbols commonly used in process charting are shown in the figure.

OPERATION CHARTS: Operation charts (see Fig. 14) differ from process charts only in that they refer to a particular operation within the process as opposed to the total process itself. Their purpose is to present a detailed description of the activities of the worker's hands as he performs the task, and for this reason they are often called "right- and left-hand" charts. As is the case with process charts, operation charts present a clear picture of what occurs and thus aid the analyst in finding possible areas for improvement. Generally activity times are not included in this analysis, since it is the motions of the worker as he performs the task that are being studied and not the time for the task's performance.

ACTIVITY CHARTS: When a production activity is accomplished by two or more men working together or by one or more men working with one or more machines, it is often helpful to chart the activity of each member of the production

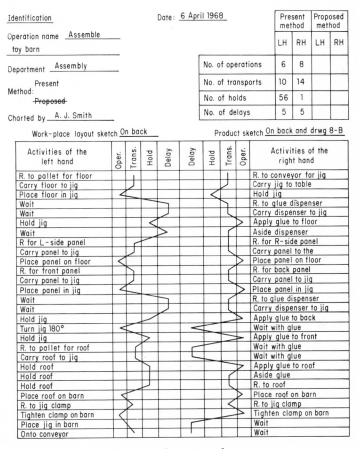

Fig. 14 Operation chart.

group against a time scale so that a clear picture is obtained for the amount of productive and idle time pertaining to each. Given this picture it is often possible to determine how the work may be rearranged or redistributed to maximize the total amount of productive time occurring in each work cycle. Such charts, known as "activity charts" (Fig. 15), are also referred to as "man-machine charts," since a common application is in studying the activities of a worker and the machine or machines he is operating. In constructing activity charts it is important that one or more work cycles be charted so that the entire operation can be viewed and analyzed in the correct perspective.

Identification _____

Activity charted ____Rough cut of 20 pigs for toy barn on pattern lathe_____

Chart of (present ~~proposed~~) method

Charted by ___C. D. Smith_____

Date ____22 August 1968_____

Activity of __Man__		Time in Minutes		Activity of __Pattern lathe__
Secure blank from stock rack and place in lathe	1.8	1	2.6	Idle
Set tracer arm at start of pattern	0.6	2		
Start lathe	0.2			
Inspect pigs cut on previous cycle	0.9	3		Cut 20 pigs on blank and run until automatic cutoff
Place bar of pigs on pallet	0.6	4	2.6	
Idle	1.10	5		
Secure blank from stock and place in lathe	1.8	6 7	2.6	Idle
Set tracer arm at start of pattern	0.6			
Start lathe	0.2	8		
Inspect pigs cut on previous cycle	0.9			Cut 20 pigs on blank and run until automatic cutoff
Place bar of pigs on pallet	0.6	9	2.6	
Idle	1.10	10		
		11		

Fig. 15 Activity chart.

TECHNIQUES OF WORK MEASUREMENT

To be proficient in planning and controlling efficient production and inventory facilities, it is of the utmost importance to be able to schedule and evaluate plant operations. This can be accomplished only through the use of accurate time estimates. Thus it becomes important to be able to know how to construct these time measurements and to realize the strengths and weaknesses of these aids.

There are two basic uses of time estimates—planning and evaluation. The planning estimate is used for such objectives as scheduling production and delivery dates, planning personnel requirements, planning for the arrival of incoming materials, and estimating costs. The evaluation estimate is used for such purposes as a basis for wage-incentive plans or standard-cost systems. For these reasons the planning estimate may be referred to as a "forecast" and the evaluation estimate may be called a "standard."

With all these different uses for time estimates, it is easy to see that any one measurement technique may not meet all the objectives required for each of the estimates. Various applications may require different accuracies in the estimates, and it is important to be able to select the tool that satisfies the intended need.

A number of techniques have been developed because of the various objectives involved in the setting of time estimates and the conditions surrounding the task. Methods are available that give highly accurate estimates for cases where precision is required, and others give crude approximations where only "ballpark" figures are desired. The most common methods are discussed below. (Note of caution: It is assumed that whenever a technique is to be used to set a time standard, a thorough methods analysis has preceded the application of the technique.)

Estimates Based on Past Experience. This technique of obtaining time estimates is often used in practice but rarely advocated in texts. Certainly this method should not be employed unless time, resources, or needs will not permit any other technique to be used, or unless the estimates need to be little more than approximate figures. Sometimes, however, even mindful of these limitations, this technique may be the only way to obtain an estimate for an operation that has never been performed.

In the application of this procedure, past performances of similar jobs are often kept in the same file. Whenever an estimate of a particular task is needed, performance measures are available for reference for that or similar jobs. If a number of performance measures are available for the same task, an average or some other method of combining may be used, perhaps with some changes made based on modifications of other variables in the task. If no past records are available, an estimate of the time necessary for the task under consideration is often made by individuals familiar with the task such as foremen or production personnel. Several of these people may discuss the task and arrive at a valued judgement, or one individual may estimate the time himself.

Estimates from past experience should not be used for a critical, short-range purpose such as wage payments, but they may be very effective for highly repetitive, moderate, or long-range tasks, such as the PERT estimates in the Polaris Development Program, if the personnel are experienced and no better technique is available.

Stopwatch Time Study. Of all the procedures for obtaining time estimates, one of the most common and accurate methods is that of stopwatch time study. Time study was originated by Frederick W. Taylor in the machine shop of Midvale Steel Company around 1881, but Ralph M. Barnes is also often given credit for being a pioneer in the full development of this tool of management.

The objective of a time study is to develop a *standard time* for a particular task. "Standard time" in this instance conveys a special meaning and is defined as the amount of time (usually expressed in minutes per part) required to perform a task by a person possessing a moderate degree of skill, using a prescribed method, and working at a pace that will cause no harmful effects to the individual (usually referred to as a "normal pace").

To obtain a standard time, therefore, it is not simply a matter of going out on the production floor and timing a worker performing the task. First, one must have some idea of what normal pace consists of in order to arrive at a *performance rating* for the worker. In rating an individual's performance, one judges his performance, percentagewise, in regard to the expected performance of a trained individual working at the company's specified normal pace. For example, if an individual is judged to be working at only 80 percent of normal, his rating would be 0.80; if he is working 20 percent higher than normal, his rating would be 1.20. (Note, however, that the performance rating evaluates the worker's performance both in terms of speed and skill, as contrasted to pace rating which judges an individual's performance only in terms of speed.)

Also, tasks are not generally timed for a whole day; therefore, there are other variables that have to be considered in the estimate, such as personal needs and delays inherent in the task. The standard time allotted for a task must reflect the inclusion of these unavoidable delays and worker's needs that may be unrelated to the task.

The equipment that a time-study analyst uses frequently consists only of a clipboard to which a decimal stopwatch and data sheets are attached. For the study the analyst places himself in a position not distracting to the worker

Study No. 10045   STOP–WATCH OBSERVATIONS   Time began 1:30 Time ended 2:00
Production during study

No.	Description	R*	T	R	T	R	T	R	T	R	T	R	T	R	T	R	T	R	T	R	T	Ave. elem. time	Rating	Normal time	Allow	Std. time
1	Reach for assembled part and box- place box at side of paper and the part in the paper	120	03	100	21	110	38	100	56	120	74	100	92	100	12	100	35	100	52	80	72					
			3		4		4		3		3		3		5		3		3		4					
2	Wrap part	120	07	100	25	110	43	100	61	120	79	100	96	100	17	100	39	100	57	80	76					
			4		4		5		5		5		4		5		4		5		4					
3	Reach for box; Place wrapped part in individual box	120	11	100	29	110	47	100	64	120	83	100	99	100	23	100	43	100	61	80	79					
			4		4		4		3		4		3		6		4		4		3					
4	Close lid and aside individual box to carton	120	17	100	34	110	53	100	71	120	39	100	07	100	32	100	49	100	68	80	86					
			6		5		6		7		6		8		9		6		7		7					

Standard time – minutes/piece

Foreign elements

	Total	Average (hundreds of minutes)	Average rating	Normal time
Element 1	35	35/10 = 3.50	1.03	.0361
Element 2	45	45/10 = 4.50	1.03	.0464
Element 3	39	39/10 = 3.90	1.03	.0402
Element 4	67	67/10 = 6.70	1.03	.0690
				.1917 total normal time

Standard time = normal time + (normal time x allowances)
minutes/part

= .1917 + (.1917 x .12)

= 0.2147 minute/part

Details of allowances —

Minimum delay   2%
Personal   4%
Fatigue   5%
Cleanup   1%
12%

* R = rating, T = time.

Fig. 16   Stopwatch observation sheet.

where he can readily observe both the individual performing the task and his watch and board. Although there are many variations in the method of conducting a time study (see Fig. 16), one accepted procedure will be presented.

Step 1. Observe and record job conditions. The analyst should observe the job for a time and then discuss the task with both foreman and workers. He should become as familiar with the task as if he were going to perform it himself. All conditions surrounding the task should be recorded in a neat, orderly, and systematic manner so that the job could be reconstructed if the need arose.

Step 2. Establish the elements of the job. For repetitive tasks the job is broken into "timetable" elements, and the description of the elements may be prepared on the data sheets before the study begins. Elements should have definite beginning and ending points. Machine elements should be separated from worker-controlled elements.   For nonrepetitive tasks, the job is still broken into elements, but the elements may be longer and not as easily anticipated as with the repetitive tasks.   This may necessitate doing a "write as you go" type of study.   Nonproductive and productive work should be separated.

Step 3.   Time the elements.   A number of observations should be recorded

TIME-STUDY SHEET

Operation	Packing ball-stud scope mount		Oper. No.	46
Mach. type	None	Mach. No.		Dept.	Final assembly
Part name	Ball-stud scope mount	Part No.	1440	Operator	John Steele
Study No.	10045	Analyst	James Smith	Date	12/4/69

Elem No.	Left-hand description	Right-hand description	Machine element	Speed	Feed	Std. time
1	Reach for assembled part, grasp, and return, placing part on stack of tissue paper	Reach for individual box, grasp, and return, placing box at right side of tissue paper				
2	Wrap part in paper	Using the thumb, separate two layers of the paper and wrap the part				
3	Reach, grasp, and hold box	Reach, grasp, and hold box; transfer to the left hand and release; reach and grasp part, move part to box, position and place wrapped part in box				
4	Release and return, alternately aside individual box to carton, position and place box in carton	Close lid; alternately aside individual box to carton, position, and place box in carton				

| Standard production—pieces/hour | | Standard time —minutes/piece |
| Sketch of work place | | Setup, tools, jigs, fixtures, gauges — |

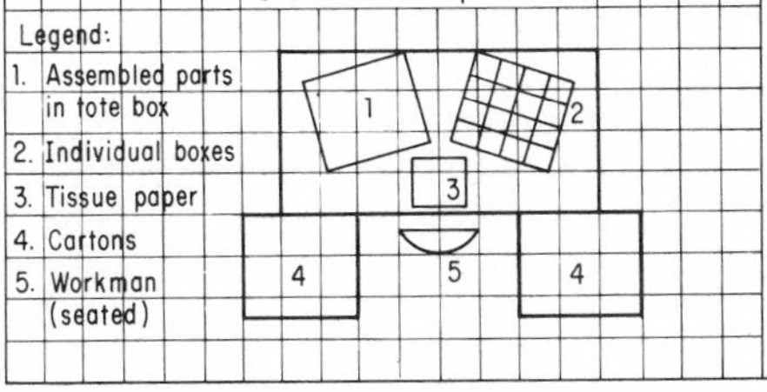

Legend:
1. Assembled parts in tote box
2. Individual boxes
3. Tissue paper
4. Cartons
5. Workman (seated)

Fig. 16   (*Continued*)

for each of the elements.   During these observations the analyst should judge and record the worker's performance rating.   For highly repetitive tasks one rating may apply to an entire cycle, but for long or nonrepetitive tasks a rating is generally applied to each element studied.

This step of the procedure is a sampling technique, and as such, enough samples must be taken to represent the population.   Determining the number of samples to take is a statistical problem, but recognized texts dealing with management or industrial engineering practices give procedures, tables, or charts which can be used to determine the number of readings required for a desired level of accuracy.

Step 4. Determine the normal time. Depending on how the rating procedure was performed in step 3 (by element or cycle), the ratings should be multiplied by the recorded time to calculate the *normal time* required for the task. If a rating was given for each element, the procedure should be to first normalize each element by multiplying the element's recorded time by its rating, and secondly to add together all elements for the task to obtain total normal time for the task. If a rating was given for each cycle only, the procedure would be to add up the recorded times for all elements of the task and then normalize the total recorded task time by multiplying the total recorded time by its rating.

Step 5. Determine the standard time. Using the normal time developed in step 4, allowances (usually expressed as a percent of normal time) for rests, personal delays, and unavoidable delays are added to increase the normal time to the standard time for the task. The standard time is the estimate that is often used for scheduling and incentive pay plans. A problem encountered in using standard times for scheduling purposes will be discussed later.

To recapitulate, the method and equations used to obtain the standard time from the recorded times of a task are:

1. Recorded time × rating = normal time
2. Normal time + (normal time × allowances) = standard time

Work Sampling. Work sampling, sometimes called "ratio delay," is another method of direct observation for estimating the time to perform a task using a sampling procedure. It can be used to develop allowances used in time studies or to determine standard times for jobs.

Work sampling has the advantages over other types of work measurement of being inexpensive, requiring little training for the observers, using no timing device, collecting data in simple terms, and simultaneously including many men and machines in the data collection process. A high degree of accuracy may be obtained using work sampling. In fact, it may sometimes be more accurate than methods using continuous observation.

The simplest work-sampling study consists of using a number of randomly selected observations and noting whether the individual on the task under study is either working or not, and if he is working, a judged performance index is noted. The observations, therefore, are dichotomous, and will follow a binomial distribution. Frequently a normal approximation to the binomial can be used and normal-curve tables are searched to find the required number of observations for a desired level of accuracy. Any good reference text dealing with management or industrial engineering practices will give procedures or tables and charts which explain how to calculate the required number of observations.

The standard time for a job may be calculated in the following manner:

$$\begin{array}{l}\text{Standard time} \\ \text{(time units/part)}\end{array} = \frac{\begin{array}{c}\text{total time} \\ \text{(time units)}\end{array} \times \begin{array}{c}\text{working time} \\ \text{(percent)}\end{array} \times \begin{array}{c}\text{performance index} \\ \text{(percent)}\end{array}}{\text{total number of pieces produced}} + \begin{array}{c}\text{allowances} \\ \text{(time units/piece)}\end{array}$$

Of the estimates that are needed to determine the standard time, only the percentage of working time and performance index must be provided by the work-sampling study. The total time can be found on company time-card records. The total number of parts produced can be obtained from production records. Allowances are the result of company-union negotiations or past practices and are readily available.

The stepwise procedure of determining a standard time for a task is as follows:

Step 1. Select the task or tasks to be studied. From past records, if available, estimate the percentage of working time that can be expected to be observed on the task. For this percentage approximate the number of observations required for the desired accuracy level.

Step 2. For the tasks to be studied, divide the working time on each task into time increments, usually minutes, and number them consecutively. Using a random-number table, select the instants that an observation should be taken by choosing random numbers that correspond to the numbered time increments over the range of working times. The period of the sampling study should be long enough to allow the workers to become accustomed to the observer's presence and therefore less likely to feign activity for his benefit and bias the results.

Step 3. Begin making the observations as determined in step 2. Periodically check the percentages of working and idle times and recalculate the number of readings that should be obtained.

Step 4. Continue to collect data until the desired number of observations have been obtained. Calculate the standard time, using the equation given above.

Predetermined Motion-Time Systems. The use of predetermined motion-time systems to calculate a time estimate is one of the most refined techniques of work measurement. As opposed to the techniques of time study or standard data, the time units are *basic motions* of much shorter duration in a predetermined motion-time analysis.

There have been a number of predetermined motion-time systems formulated since the early 1940s. They are available under such names as "methods time measurement" (MTM), "motion-time analysis" (MTA), "work factor plan" (WF), "motor-time standards" (MTS), and "basic motion-time study" (BMT). Generally for these systems the times associated with the basic motions have been normalized, but no allowances have been added.

The basic motions contained within a predetermined motion-time system are very small elements upon which extensive time data have been collected and analyzed by such techniques as time study and motion-picture analysis. To estimate a time for a task requires that the job be synthesized from the basic motions and the times accumulated for each of the motions included. Allowances are then added to determine the *standard time* for the task. In this manner the methods and times for jobs can be specified even before the job is actually performed by an operator. The application of this technique necessitates the use of a well-trained analyst.

Standard Data. In the process of time studying a number of similar tasks, it may become obvious that there are elements common to many jobs. If these elements are identical for each task, the time values obtained could be collected from all the jobs studied and averaged for a more accurate estimate than could be obtained from just the study of one of the tasks. This is exactly how standard data, or elemental times, are developed. Data on elements common to a family of jobs are gathered from which standard times may be synthesized for other tasks containing these elements. In effect it is a form of a predetermined time system, but the elements are not as minuscule and are generally developed within the framework of one plant's operations. However, some industries, such as the metalworking industry, have developed standard data for industry-wide use.

Three types of elements are generally encountered when compiling standard data: (1) elements which are identical from job to job, (2) elements which are similar in nature but the times vary due to differences in a particular variable (size, weight, etc.) involved in the task, and (3) elements whose times are controlled by the physical or technical characteristics of the material and process, such as machining process time in a metal-removing task.

Elements of the first type are easy to handle. To ensure that a representative time is obtained, a sufficient number of them are collected and averaged together. Elements of the second type are a little more difficult. Sufficient studies will have to be taken to ascertain the relationship between the varying characteristic of the element and the performance time in order to develop a series of time values that vary with the characteristic. Elements in the third group can generally be calculated from physical data, such as from the feeds, speeds, depth of cut, etc., in the machining task discussed above.

Problems in Using Work-measurement Techniques for Production Control. A basic problem exists in using these methods of work measurement for production control. Except for the *past-experience* method these techniques are most frequently used in determining standard times for incentive-pay systems. Time estimates for production control are also needed for planning and scheduling purposes. An incentive-pay system is generally set up so that an average-skilled employee working at a normal pace will earn 25 to 30 percent incentive pay, i.e., will be performing the task in 25 to 30 percent less time than the standard allows. This means that if the standard time is used for scheduling purposes, the jobs will be completed on the average in 25 to 30 percent less time than the schedule permits and will greatly increase the likelihood of creating idle time on production facilities.

Before standard times are used for scheduling, therefore, the times should be adjusted to account for this discrepancy. This can be done separately by jobs if it is known who the workers will be and their average performance indices, or by departments by using an average factor that would account for the differences between the standard and expected times. Sometimes, however, this difference is ignored, the attitude being that the scheduling plan is so loose that this additional error will make little difference in the plan's overall effectiveness.

THE PRODUCTION-PROGRESS FUNCTION

Anyone who has performed a repetitive task, whether it was simple, involving the performance of only a few operations, or complex, requiring many operations, probably noticed that he became more proficient as the frequency increased. That is, he "learned" the task as he gained experience with it. The scale upon which task proficiency was measured might have been based on any number of criteria, such as time to perform the task, accuracy of performing the task, or cost of performing the task. Nevertheless, the relationship between the proficiency measure and the number of times the task was performed probably appeared as shown in Fig. 17. In the typical learning curve, task proficiency is shown to be low initially, to increase rapidly as the task is repeated the

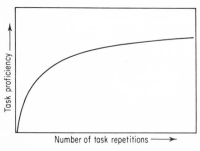

Fig. 17 Typical learning curve.

first few times, and to continue to increase but at a slower and slower rate as the number of task repetitions becomes greater and greater. The learning curve thus is typically exponential in nature and can be represented by an equation of the form

$$Y = KX^n$$

where Y = the proficiency measure
   K = a constant
   X = the cumulative number of task repetitions
   n = the exponent of the curve

The phenomenon of the learning curve is familiar to individuals within the production planning and control organization concerned with the management of direct labor. It has long been recognized that human learning must be accounted for when setting time standards for manual operations, and one must be careful not to assign a new employee to a paced task where the pace has been set based on fully learned performance.

Human learning is not the only type of learning that should concern the production planning and control organization, however, because production processes, in the aggregate, also are subject to the phenomenon of learning. Just as human performance tends to improve as individuals repeat tasks, so also does the performance of complete production processes tend to show improvement as time passes and manufacturing continues. This process improvement manifests itself as a decrease in the number of man-hours required to produce a unit of product. Although a large part of the improvement is the result of direct-labor learning, a significant contribution to the total is made by improvement in supporting operations. For this reason when reference is made to total-process learning the phenomenon is sometimes referred to as "the time-reduction curve," "the experience curve," "the startup curve," "the production-acceleration curve," or "the production-progress function." The term "production-progress function" shall be used here as it seems to be gaining wide acceptability.

A number of factors contribute to the ability of a manufacturing process to improve. If a large amount of effective engineering effort is expended prior to production initiation on the problems of product design, tooling and equipment selection, work-methods design, and personnel selection and training, then the opportunity for learning, or improvement, is reduced. Once production has begun, advances in the state of the art, tooling and work-methods changes, quality improvements resulting in less scrap, rework, and inspection, effective work-simplification programs, and human performance learning will all enhance the ability of the process to improve. It is imperative that individuals using the production-progress function as a planning tool understand that many factors contribute to the improvement phenomenon.

Development of the Curve. The production-progress function was first used for production planning purposes in the airframe industry during the 1940s. The form of the equation used to model the improvement phenomenon was a negative exponential rather than the positive one given above, since the variable of interest was the number of man-hours required to produce each airframe. A variation of the original model commonly used today is

$$Y = KX^{-n}$$

where Y = the cumulative average man-hours per unit after X number of units have been produced
   K = the number of man-hours required to build the first unit
   X = the cumulative number of units produced
   n = the exponent of the curve

The curve is shown plotted in Fig. 18. It should be pointed out that in some applications of the progress function Y is defined as the actual number of man-hours required to build a unit after X number of units have been produced rather than as the cumulative average man-hours per unit. The definition of Y which should be used in any particular situation will depend on the situation itself; cumulative average man-hours will be used here since its use is perhaps most common.

The model has the characteristic of describing constant percentage reductions. Each time the cumulative production is increased by a constant percentage, the cumulative average man-hours per unit is decreased by a constant percentage. This characteristic can be illustrated as follows. Take any two points in production, say, X_1 and X_2 where X_2 is greater than X_1. Define the ratio of X_2 to X_1 as the production ratio and call this quantity C. Application of the model indicates that the cumulative average man-hours per unit at X_1 is $Y_1 = KX_1^{-n}$ and similarly at X_2 it is $Y_2 = KX_2^{-n}$. Next form the ratio of Y_2 to Y_1:

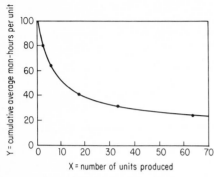

Fig. 18   The production-progress function.

$$\frac{Y_2}{Y_1} = \frac{KX_2^{-n}}{KX_1^{-n}} = \frac{X_2^{-n}}{X_1^{-n}} = \left(\frac{X_2}{X_1}\right)^{-n} = C^{-n}$$

Since Y_2 is less than Y_1, the quantity C^{-n} lies between 0 and 1. Rearranging the previous equation, one finds that $Y_2 = Y_1 C^{-n}$. From this it can be seen that if the production ratio between any two points in production is a constant, C, then the cumulative average man-hours per unit at the second point will be a constant (C^{-n}) percentage of what it was at the first point.

In practice the production ratio usually chosen is $C = 2$. Thus each time production is doubled the cumulative average man-hours per unit is reduced to 2^{-n} percent of its previous value. Values of the exponent n for various percent curves can be calculated quickly. For example, if when production doubled the cumulative average time was reduced to 80 percent of its previous figure, one has $Y_2 = Y_1 (0.80)$ or $C^{-n} = 0.80$. Since $C = 2$, one thus has $2^{-n} = 0.80$ and the value of n is easily found to be 0.322. Values of n for several learning percentages are presented below for ready reference. It should be noted that a learning percentage of P percent implies that when production doubles the cumulative average man-hours per unit is reduced to P percent of its initial value; it is not reduced by P percent.

Learning Percentage	Value of n
95	0.074
90	0.152
85	0.234
80	0.322
75	0.415
70	0.515
65	0.622

The value of the constant K was defined earlier to be the number of man-hours required to manufacture the first production unit. This result is obtained in the following manner. Let Y_1 equal the cumulative average man-hours per unit after the first unit has been produced, that is, at $X = 1$. Note that the cumulative average time is equal to the unit production time when only one unit has been produced. Application of the model illustrates that K is equal to Y_1, which is the unit production time of the first unit.

$$Y = KX^{-n}$$
$$Y_1 = K(1)^{-n} = K$$

Example The production-progress function can be applied as in the following situation. A firm has recently accepted a contract to build twenty 35-foot boats for a sport-fishing charter outfit operating throughout the Caribbean. The first two boats have been completed, taking 7,000 and 4,900 man-hours, respectively. Estimate how many man-hours will be required to produce all 20 boats and how many boats will be completed before the man-hour requirement per boat is 3,000 hours or less.

In approaching this problem one must first determine the percent learning that is in effect so that one may know what value of the exponent n to use in the progress-function equation. Since production has doubled from unit 1 to unit 2, the correct learning percentage can be determined by forming the ratio of the cumulative average time at unit 2 to the cumulative average time at unit 1.

Y_1 = the cumulative average time at the first unit = 7,000 man-hours
Y_2 = the cumulative average time after the second unit = $(7,000 + 4,900)/2 = 5,950$ man-hours

$$\frac{Y_2}{Y_1} = \frac{5,950}{7,000} = 0.85$$

Thus the cumulative average time after unit 2 has been produced is 85 percent of what it was at unit 1, and the correct value of n is found in the table to be 0.234.

The total number of man-hours required for all 20 boats can now be estimated. The total time required at any point in production is equal to the cumulative average time at that point multiplied by the number of units produced. Thus

$$T = \text{total time} = YX$$
$$T = (KX^{-n})(X)$$
$$= KX^{(1-n)}$$

The total time for all 20 boats is therefore found as follows:

$$T = \text{time for 20 boats} = K(20)^{(1-n)}$$
$$= 7,000(20)^{(0.766)}.$$

This equation can be solved either directly if one has a slide rule available or by converting to logarithms. Solution by logarithms is perhaps more accurate and is used here.

$$T = KX^{(1-n)}$$
$$\text{Log } T = \log K + (1 - n)(\log X)$$
$$= \log 7,000 + (0.766)(\log 20)$$
$$= 3.84510 + 0.766(1.30103)$$
$$= 3.84510 + 0.99659$$
$$= 4.84169$$
$$= 69,454 \text{ man-hours}$$

To find the production unit on which the time per boat goes below 3,000 man-hours, one must again use the total-time equation. The unit time for any particular unit X can be found by subtracting the total time at unit $X - 1$ from the total time at unit X. That is, unit time for $X = T_X - T_{X-1}$. In order to find the point in production where the unit time is equal to some specified number of hours, in this case 3,000, one must first guess at the point and then make successive unit-time calculations until he has found the desired point in production. This procedure is illustrated below where the initial guess was that the unit time would be less than or equal to 3,000 hours on unit 12.

$$T = KX^{(1-n)} = 7,000(X)^{0.766}$$

Unit No.	Total Time	Difference = Unit Time
11	43,830	.....
12	46,990	3,130
13	49,890	2,900

Thus the unit time goes below 3,000 man-hours on unit 13.

An aid in obtaining a close initial guess is to take the first derivative of T with respect to X and solve for the value of X for which the derivative is equal to the desired number of hours. For the current example the calculations would have been as follows:

$$\frac{dT}{dX} = (1 - n)KX^{-n}$$

$$= \text{estimate of the number of man-hours required per unit}$$

$$3,000 = (1 - 0.234)(7,000)(X)^{-n}$$

$$= (0.766)(7,000)(X)^{-n}$$

$$= 5,362(X)^{-n}$$

$$\text{Log } 3,000 = \log 5,362 - 0.234(\log X)$$

$$3.47712 = 3.72933 - 0.234(\log X)$$

$$\text{Log } X = (3.47712 - 3.72933)/(-0.234)$$

$$= 1.07782$$

$$X = 11.96 = 12$$

This method does not give an exact answer because X is a discrete rather than a continuous variable, but it becomes an increasingly better estimate as X increases, since the progress curve becomes flatter with increasing X.

The preceding example has demonstrated the type of planning information that one can obtain through application of the production-progress function. Such information can be useful in scheduling production, estimating delivery dates, estimating production budgets, and performing break-even analyses as well as estimating man-hour requirements. The user may wish to actually draw the progress curve for his particular process so that he may refer to it readily. This can be done rather quickly by calculating only a few points on the curve as follows:

Point in Production	Cumulative Average Man-Hours
Unit 1	$Y_1 = K$
Unit 2	$Y_2 = K(\% \text{ learning})$
Unit 4	$Y_4 = K(\% \text{ learning})^2$
Unit 8	$Y_8 = K(\% \text{ learning})^3$
Unit 16	$Y_{16} = K(\% \text{ learning})^4$
etc.	etc.

and drawing the curve through these points. It should be pointed out that if the progress curve is plotted on log-log coordinate paper, the resulting curve will be linear with slope equal to $-n$. Many persons may find the linear curve easier to interpret than the exponential one, and it is suggested that one at least consider using it.

For the example problem the progress curve can be plotted from the following data:

Point in Production	Cumulative Average Man-Hours
Unit 1	$Y_1 = K = 7,000$
Unit 2	$Y_2 = K(0.85) = 5,950$
Unit 4	$Y_4 = K(0.85)^2 = 5,058$
Unit 8	$Y_8 = K(0.85)^3 = 4,299$
Unit 16	$Y_{16} = K(0.85)^4 = 3,654$

The curve is shown plotted on log-log coordinates in Fig. 19.

Some Cautions in Applying the Production-progress Function. Probably the greatest problem that confronts the potential user of the production progress function is estimation of the correct value of the exponent n to use in the calculations. One common application error is to assume that an n value which has been found to be appropriate for one industry or one class of products will be appropriate for use in other industries or for other products. All too often the airframe industry's characteristic improvement of 20 percent with its corresponding n value of 0.322 has been carried over to other applications with no justification for doing so. There are several procedures that one can apply in estimating the value of n to use in any particular situation. A few are given below with the caution that each has its limitations and potential sources for error.

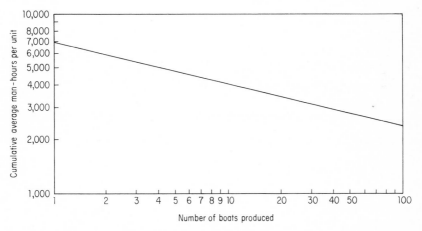

Fig. 19 The production-progress function, log-log scale.

1. Assume n will be the same as for previous applications within the same industry.

2. Assume n will be the same as for previous applications with the same or a similar product.

3. *a.* Evaluate the status of production variables that affect the ability of the process to improve.

    b. Compare the current status of these variables with that existing during previous production of a similar product.

    c. Knowing n from the previous production situations, estimate the new n by comparison of (*a*) and (*b*).

4. Wait until two or four units have been produced and estimate n from these data as was done in the application example.

Even if one has been able to obtain a good estimate of n, there are several additional application errors that he must guard against. If one is using elemental time data in calculating the expected value of K so as to use the model before production begins, he must know if the elemental data applies to a learned or unlearned process. If it came from a learned process, the user should perhaps inflate his estimate of K as determined by the elemental data. One must not forget that the improvement percentage applies to the aggregate production process and that the same percentage may not apply to individual components of the process. Nor must one assume that multishift situations will give the same results as single-shift operations when determining the value of X to use in the model calculations. Finally, one must not ignore the effects of labor-force changes, production interruptions, or new-equipment installations, as these may result in a period of either relearning or unusually accelerated learning. If one will be careful in estimating the values of n and K and keep in mind the various factors that can affect his production-progress calculations so as not to apply the model blindly, he should be able to obtain reliable information for planning purposes through its application.

MAKE-OR-BUY ANALYSIS

The decision to make or buy is based on two basic considerations which are separate and distinct and should be kept completely independent. These are reduced costs and additional capacity.

Reduced-cost Consideration. If the supplier and the prime contractor company have nearly equivalent capabilities in terms of manufacturing processes, it is rarely cheaper to buy than make. This may seem heretical to many accountants or purchasing executives, but it can be demonstrated that it is so. The key factor, of course, is identification of fixed versus variable costs. Most large companies have high fixed costs as a result of rental or depreciation of equipment, salaries, taxes, and the like.

Make-or-buy decisions should be made on the basis of variable or incremental costs. In other words, you must ask, "How much extra will it cost to produce the units in question?" never, "What is the unit cost of producing the parts including full burden, administrative costs, and overhead?"

Innumerable times one hears the phrase, "We can buy them much cheaper than we can make them," which may be true in a strict accounting sense. The following example will, however, serve to illustrate the principle involved. An article or part can be manufactured as follows:

Direct materials	$0.80
Direct labor	0.10
Factory overhead—fixed	0.40
Factory overhead—variable	0.05
General and administrative	0.60
Total factory cost	$1.95

The purchasing agent may easily locate a supplier who will furnish the part for $1.50. The vendor, while paying the same or even more for direct labor and materials and variable overhead ($0.95) can make a profit, since his fixed costs may be much less due to limited overhead, general, and administrative expenses. The purchaser, however, may not be maximizing his profits at this price because his fixed costs are going on anyway.

Capacity Balance. Many firms purchase parts they could make themselves, on the basis of balancing out their plant capacity. Cost is a factor here and also profit, but the decision is based on utilization of capacity in a long-term sense rather than a simple unit-cost concept. Firms know they must maintain a high utilization of equipment if they are to keep costs low. Idle plant and equipment can be very costly. Therefore, where demand varies, wise management staffs and equips to a minimum point and absorbs fluctuations through purchase of fabricated parts. This is an intelligent approach and is a real cost saver for a variety of reasons:

1. It cuts down on training costs for new employees—employees who produce the most scrap and are the least productive.

2. It permits maximum output with minimum investment.

3. It enables the plant to run with stable work force and stable output.

4. It reduces overtime.

The ability to level production by purchasing parts depends upon a company's ability to project production ahead and predict shop loads accurately. The steps in this process are as follows:

1. Establish sales forecast or production needs for a period well in advance of purchase lead times.

2. Reduce sales and production forecasts to requirements for specific items of manufacture.

3. Use accurate work standards to project hours of work for each machine center of the plant.

4. Compare work loads for each section with optimum, stable levels desired for plant operations.

5. Contract with suppliers to furnish all parts which would create excessive work loads.

6. Schedule and maintain machine loads for each machine center to dovetail with receipts of purchased parts.

Other considerations in conjunction with make-or-buy decisions are quality control requirements and diversification of supply to protect plant assembly schedules.

Quality Control. The production of parts adhering to exact specifications requires time and organization. This should be seriously considered in make-or-buy decisions. A company may have gained a high degree of skill and in-plant experience which permits manufacturing parts easily to exact specifications. A supplier, if he has not made a similar part, may have difficulty initially in meeting specifications. It takes time to develop skills.

Diversification of Supply. Protection of assembly schedules through multiple sources can be a factor in the make-or-buy decision. Suppliers may be shut down by strikes over which a customer has no control. This dictates more than one supplier of critical parts, or splitting the requirements between the customer's own plant and a supplier. This may require some extra tooling, but may be less costly than a production stoppage.

MULTIPLE SHIFTS AND OVERTIME CONSIDERATIONS

The question of whether to operate on a multiple-shift basis, to work overtime, or to expand single-shift operations is primarily an economic one. However, there are many other considerations, such as availability of labor, equipment, and supervision.

On the one hand there are series of continuous process-type operations such as in steel mills, refineries, and power plants where there is rarely any alternative to a full three-shift, seven-days-a-week operation. Such operations are much more costly to shut down than they are to run on a continuous basis, and everyone who works in these industries accepts this as a way of life and adapts to it.

On the other hand there are a few traditionally one-shift operations where no one would even consider working more than one shift. One of these is in garment plants where the sewing machine operator has her own machine which she has coddled, adjusted, and possibly cursed at until it does everything just the way she wants it to—it "feels" right to her. No one else can run this machine and only certain mechanics are allowed to "lay" a screwdriver on it. That some stranger would come in and actually touch *her* machine at night is unthinkable.

In between these two extremes there is a large body of industry where shift operations as conditions change may or may not be necessary and advisable. Some of the factors and conditions governing these decisions are discussed below.

Cost of Capital Investment. Where the cost of capital equipment is high, there are economic reasons why it must be operated at the highest possible degree of utilization. Textile factories are an example of this heavy investment in capital equipment.

The economics are simple. The depreciation costs are fixed, since the equipment will likely be obsolete in 5 to 10 years. With total fixed costs amounting to 30 to 40 percent on some operations, the equipment must operate at no less than 24 hours per day since dropping two shifts will increase fixed costs to 40 to 50 percent.

Aside from the depreciation which must be carefully and accurately taken into consideration for cost purposes, there is, of course, the original cost of equipment acquisition. No one could afford to purchase three times as much equipment for a single-shift operation as his competitor is using on a three-shift basis. On the other hand, there are those operators, usually small, who have an abundance of fully depreciated equipment and therefore are not affected by original cost.

Availability of Equipment. When companies are forced to expand production on relatively short notice, they often cannot get additional equipment quickly enough. Therefore, they have no alternative but to run a second shift. This situation is frequently encountered when a single, specialized piece of equipment constitutes a bottleneck. Basically this is a shortterm problem, since in the long run additional equipment can be procured if warranted by other considerations.

Availability of Personnel. The availability of personnel may also affect decisions on shift operation and sometimes can work either way. At times people may be available for first-shift work but not for second or third shifts. On the other hand there may be people available for second or third shifts but not the first. In this latter category are many people working at a second job, students who attend classes during the day, mothers who cannot leave their children except when their husbands or some other person who works days are available.

Availability of Supervision. Many times it is possible to recruit personnel for second- and third-shift work if adequate supervision can be provided for them. Where the technical qualifications required of supervision are high, this can be difficult.

Quality and Performance by Shifts Compared. This is a question which has been answered two ways. There are plants and companies in which the performance both as to quantity and quality is always higher on the second than on the first shift. Various explanations have been advanced for this, and it has been said—facetiously, of course—that things are better on the second and third shifts because there are not so many members of management around to bother the workers. Strange as this may seem, there are good reasons why it is so in many instances:

The average experience may be higher on the later shifts if the company makes a practice of training on the first shift and putting more experienced workers on night.

Obviously there are cases where the reverse is true and the new employees are all concentrated on the second shift.

Second-shift workers may be more professional in their approach to the job.

Especially in banks where clearing activities are usually done at night to reduce float time, the best workers and highest performances tend to be at night.

There actually may be fewer distractions at night so workers can concentrate on the job at hand.

The second shift may not be loaded as fully, either by having a smaller work force or smaller load per work station; accordingly, there are fewer bottlenecks and problem areas.

LINE BALANCING

The line-balancing term is used on assembly-line operations where a crew of persons performs sequential operations. The objective of the balancing effort is to distribute the work as evenly as possible for maximum output and economy.

In actual practice there are many kinds of line balancing, or rather the line-balancing principle may be applied to a number of varied operations. For this reason there are actually several different approaches to line balancing, each being applicable to the particular set of conditions.

To balance lines effectively, good, reliable predetermined time data should be available. A great deal of line balancing has been done without this very valuable and flexible aid, using direct time studies. The problem, however, with using direct time studies is that when making changes and testing different line balances, one does not always have the time-study element for the particular configuration desired. Therefore, the method must be actually performed by someone, and new time studies must be made to develop the correct standard time.

The advantage of predetermined motion times, such as inherent in methods time measurement (MTM), is that the time for any conceivable method can be predetermined to develop the best line balance without a series of trial-and-error attempts. The savings in time and the enhancement of the professional image is considerable, and the effect of changes can be easily predicted. The following illustrates the use of predetermined time standards and its application to line balancing.

The two most common types are conveyor assembly lines either rigidly paced and spaced as with automobile assembly lines or the more flexible flat belts. The process of balancing these lines is basically one of determining the work content of each station on the line and organizing the work crew in the most effective manner. To accomplish this the following steps are suggested:

1. Determine output required per day or per shift as the case may be. There are various possibilities here where the process may not be continuous and the line may actually be run only spasmodically. However, we shall discount this possibility here and consider full-time continuous operation.

2. Determine the total man-hours of true work per unit of output at standard operating efficiency.

3. Multiply the output required per day or shift by the true work standard to determine the total hours of work per day or shift.

4. Divide total hours by the number of hours in the normal work period at standard operating efficiency to find the number of crew members who will be required to produce the necessary output.

5. Divide the total work per unit by the optimum crew size to arrive at the theoretical work cycle for each crew member per unit of output.

Example Assume a production requirement of 5,000 pairs of heels per eight-hour shift. Assume 0.385 minute per heel total true work.

Therefore, 5,000 pairs $\times$ 2 $\times$ 0.385 = 3,850 minutes of work per shift.

3,850 $\div$ 480 minutes per shift = 9.6 or approximately 10 crew members.

0.385 $\div$ 10 = 0.0385 minute, the approximate ideal work cycle per heel.

We can now divide the total work so that each operator on the line will have approximately a 0.0385-minute work cycle.

There are several alternatives for developing this particular line balance. We may put all 10 members of the crew on the same side of the belt performing work sequentially and having an approximate cycle of 0.0385 minute each.

On the other hand, we may want to have five members on each side of the belt performing the same operation, having a cycle of 0.077 minute each. A third alternative would be to have one member of the crew feed the belt, another take off, and four members on each side of the belt, each having approximately a 0.077-minute work cycle.

The above illustrates the seemingly endless variations possible when developing balanced lines. Some of the considerations which would determine which of these combinations to use might be as follows:

1. *Differences in Job Rate.* Line feeders and line emptiers often have a lower job rate than assemblers. Therefore, two crew members could have lower-rated jobs, reducing the total cost, other things being equal.

2. *Long-cycle Elements.* There may be an indivisible element longer than the desired work cycle. This requires two identical work cycles performed on the same or possibly opposite sides of the belt.

3. *Floor Space and Layout Limitations.* Possibly the belt is not long enough to have 10 members working on the same side. In this case one would be forced to distribute crew members on both sides of the belt.

4. *Right- versus Left-handedness.* In many cases an element of work performed on one side of the belt with the work coming toward the operator's left side may be completely different when the situation is reversed and the work approaches the right side. Sometimes the operators can be trained to work either way, but in other cases extra movements and hence extra time may be involved.

Testing the Balance. With short, rigidly defined cycles it is never possible to balance the line exactly. By this we mean that not every operator can be assigned exactly the same amount of work. Therefore, since the pace is that of the slowest or longest cycle, we obtain a certain degree of imbalance which cannot be eliminated. To test the amount of imbalance and establish acceptable criteria for acceptance or rejection of the balance, the following procedure can be used. A rule of thumb is that the line is acceptably balanced when the peak cycle times the number of operators is less than the total true work plus 25 percent.

Station	Option 1	Option 2
1	0.050	0.042
2	0.035	0.040
3	0.039	0.036
4	0.030	0.038
5	0.045	0.040
6	0.030	0.035
7	0.037	0.037
8	0.040	0.039
9	0.029	0.040
10	0.050	0.038
Total work	0.385	0.385
True work + 25%	0.481	0.481
Peak	0.050	0.042
Peak × 10 =	0.500	0.420
	(Breakdown not acceptable)	(Breakdown acceptable)

Incentive Payment for Balanced Lines. The decision to accept or reject a given line-balancing solution should be made on the same basis regardless of whether the operation is paid day work or on an incentive basis.

For lines of the type indicated above, the incentive payment, if any, must be paid on the basis of the peak cycle just as if everyone had the same amount of work. This is a group situation where all members of the crew must produce the same number of units. One operator's pace cannot be different from another except as caused by differences in assigned work, over which the individual operator has no control whatever. Therefore, a true group standard should be used with the total standard minutes equal to the peak cycle times the number of operators.

Machine-oriented Line Balance. The considerations so far pertain to balancing lines primarily geared to labor distribution with a fairly uniform work cycle and tasks. Other considerations are encountered when lines are machine oriented, and labor may not be the most important criteria. Such a case is encountered with blooming mills at steel plants where there is a line to balance extending from the soaking pits to the slab yard. The jobs on the line typically would be.

Heater operator—soaking pits
Pit crane operators
Ingot buggy operator
Laborers
Head roller
Manipulator
Shear operator
Stamper
Slab-yard crane operator

In this instance each position on the line will have a different work load depending upon the shape rolled. The question of balance now becomes simply one of how many men are needed in each position to keep the mill running at top efficiency and what their work load is when doing so. There is little that can be done about balance. It is merely a question of whether or not to add another man.

INDUSTRIAL RELATIONS AND EFFECT ON MANPOWER

Industrial relations includes both the individual employer-employee relationships as well as the employer-union relationship. While industrial relations is a highly specialized staff function, the primary responsibility for the effective use of the assigned work force is that of the line supervisor. An understanding of the industrial relations concepts is essential for the effective management of manpower.

A survey of industrial relations in a company can reveal whether the effect upon manpower production has been positive or negative.

Employee Relations. The degree to which "employee relations" contributes to the successful operation of a company may be measured by the respect that labor and management have for one another. This respect is built up through the years by an intelligent and realistic approach to personnel administration and labor relations.

Wage levels, company policies, and working conditions in total not only can, but will, affect a workman's performance. Wage levels may be determined by the collective-bargaining process, but company policies and working conditions are largely in management's control. If this control is used wisely, the company will have better employee relations and can have lower costs than its competitors.

Selection and Training of Employees. The word "selection" when applied to new employees would indicate that an excess of applicants is available and a selection can truly be made. If this is not the case in your company, examine carefully your wage levels, company policies, and working conditions. If all three are not only competitive, but a little better than the competition, the recruiting of new employees is simplified.

Supervisory training is more important than employee training. The ratio of supervisors to employees may average 1:10. Nevertheless, supervisory skills will provide a climate where 10 well-supervised employees will outperform 10 others.

The well-trained supervisor will analyze his employee-training requirements and lay out long-range plans to meet them. He will have written job descriptions and checklists for new employees. He will have a step-by-step procedure for introducing new employees to the job. This procedure should be coordinated with the personnel department.

Employee training does not stop with the new employee's understanding of his first job. He must be measured against known standards for each job. There is also the continuous task of training employees for transfer or promotion. In spite of interviews, written tests, and follow-up of references, the selection of new employees is far from foolproof. This is not so true when selecting a present employee for promotion. It is very important for management to select only the most capable employees for promotion and to have a tested training program for their next assignment.

Collective Bargaining. The sessions where labor and management sit together to negotiate new labor agreements is known as the "collective-bargaining" process. Formerly, these were local negotiations and agreements. In recent years the tendency has been to expand the agreements to cover an entire multiplant company, or even an entire industry. As this trend toward expansion has developed it has been accompanied by two opposing trends toward localization. In one case a local union resolves to continue to work after a national strike has been called. Often, this occurs after the labor contract has expired. It takes place with the understanding that the settlement reached will apply to the local union just as though it had been on strike.

The other trend is toward continuation of a strike by the local union after higher-level negotiations for a new contract are complete. The statement is made by the local union that the strike will continue until local grievances are settled. These situations were not created at the bargaining table. They are the result of day-to-day confrontations on local issues and the gradual buildup of disrespect between management and labor.

Our definition of "collective bargaining," then, must be revised. It is not just the session where new labor agreements are negotiated. It is any discussion throughout the year between management and labor of their common problems. Any discussion between a foreman and a man who works for him in reality constitutes collective bargaining.

Wage and Salary Administration. Sound management practice dictates that the administration of wages and salaries should be standardized. A clock is a very poor tool to measure the amount of work peformed. Two employees on the same job will seldom turn out identical rates of production unless the production rate has been standardized in some way. Management realized this fact many years ago and as a result established a variety of piecework, incentive-rate, or bonus plans. These could be group or individual plans. They have one thing in common. Any change in material or equipment or method makes the old standard invalid. How much change? If you say "any change at all," it will take an army of industrial engineers to keep up with them all. If you say "any change that the foreman determines is sufficient cause," you have a variety of incentive plans in effect at the same time.

Modern management practice trends are toward measured-daywork systems. This puts the burden on the foreman and on other management personnel to meet the standard. Management has set the standard without any negotiation with labor. The standard provides predetermined costs for budgeting and for pricing. No change of methods or materials will affect an employee's pay. Therefore, management can make changes which affect production rates at its own discretion. In addition, sound standards provide the data necessary for equipment and crew scheduling, and lead to lower costs.

Records, Reports, and Research. The personnel-record keeping starts, of course, when a prospective employee applies for work. All application blanks should be retained. The applicant's files should be cross-indexed by name and job applied for. Successful applicants will have added to their file copies of numerous government forms, health and insurance forms, union checkoff authorization, etc.

Research into personnel problem areas should be tied in directly with reports. A few regular, routine reports to management may be necessary. More than the few significant reports are not essential and should be eliminated.

However, suppose personnel turnover has become a problem. Research is required and some special reports should be issued for a stated period of time. Determine your plant's percentage of labor turnover by dividing the number of separations by the number of employees on the payroll and multiplying the answer by 100. Compute this percentage for a number of past periods. Plot the results on a graph. Analyze separately the reasons for employees laid off and for voluntary separations. Make allowances for, but do not disregard, unavoidable separations. Set a goal for the labor turnover rate which will be acceptable. Change policies to correct the reasons for a high rate of separation. Measure progress toward the goal, and make special reports to management on this progress. Discontinue the reports when the goal is reached, or when turnover is no longer considered a problem.

The same approach should be applied to any other personnel problem.

Coordination with Industrial Relations. The impact of personnel problems on production outputs cannot be overemphasized. No attempt has been made in this section to provide specific guidance to the production and inventory control manager in the solution of such problems. We have, however, provided him a yardstick so that he is better equipped to measure the effectiveness of industrial relations in his company and thus be in a position to act as a constructive force in the coordination of personnel actions affecting manpower.

ORGANIZATION FOR MANPOWER MANAGEMENT

Due to the quick response required in today's competitive business environment, the effective management of manpower resources has become both increasingly complex and critically important. The most effective organization to manage manpower planning and control is one that:

1. Specifically assigns responsibility for achieving results
2. Inspires active participation and cooperation between line manufacturing, production control, sales, and finance functions

TABLE 1   Manpower Planning and Control Responsibilities

Task area	Responsibility	Department or function* (line or staff responsibility)
Planning:		
A. Long range.........	Establishing company performance objectives	Gmnfs
	Reconciling long-range sales forecasts	Gfs
	Inventory-level planning	CF
	Production planning	CMnf
	Broad manpower-level planning:	
	Direct	CMnf
	Indirect	CGmfs
B. Resource planning (shorter range)......	Sales forecasting	Sf
	Inventory-level and production plan balancing	Cmnf
	Determination of manpower and machinery requirements:	Mnf
	Simulation techniques (with or without computer)	CF
	Resource balancing:	
	"Normal man per work center" definition	Nf
	"Normal" machine utilization	Nf
	Work-center resource targets:	
	Manpower targets	Nf
	Machine utilization targets	Nf
	Establishment of work-center manpower plan	Mnfc
Acquiring and training....	Determination of lead time required for skills needed (availability in area, extent of training required, etc.)	Pm
	Attention to company's local competitive position in acquiring workers	Pm
	Review and analysis of interviewing testing, and other hiring procedures to maintain their relevance in meeting the company's manpower needs	PM
	Training programs (on the job, special, technical, etc.)	Mpn
Control:		
A. Measurement.......	Work-measurement programs (timed standards, standard data, estimated standards, ratio, delay studies, etc.)	NMpf
B. Information processing, analysis, and reporting..........	Coordinating objectives of program	Cf
	Development of meaningful control reports for line managers and supervisors that will show performance against these targets and objectives	MFC
	Establishing definitive feedback information for revisions to resource and long-range plans	CFmn
C. Supervision and control of manpower....	Direct and indirect	M
	Coordination with planning and other control functions	Mfc

*Lower-case letters denote staff responsibilities; upper-case letters denote line responsibilities: Cc—production control; Ff—finance; Gg—general management; Mm—manufacturing; Nn—manufacturing support (industrial engineering, manufacturing engineering, etc.); Pp—personnel; Ss—sales.

Whether its prime focus is a production planning committee or an individual manufacturing manager, the organization should recognize the importance of coordination between the numerous interrelated responsibilities and functions outlined in the next section.

Line and Staff Responsibilities for Manpower Planning and Control. Responsibilities for manpower planning and control can be divided into three important task areas:

1. Planning
2. Acquiring and training
3. Control

The importance of the responsibilities within each of these areas will vary considerably depending upon the company size, growth pattern, product-design stability, cyclical pattern of business, types of manufacture, and the labor skills required.

Table 1 enumerates many of these responsibilities, defines the line or staff nature of each, and suggests the department or function in the company to which the responsibility would probably be assigned.

Using Consultants. A consultant may be called upon to define any of the planning and control responsibilities previously outlined, recommend policy and organization structure, or even write operating procedures. In using a consultant, however, it is important to realize that, in most cases, he will not expound new truths but will more likely bring into the open the thinking within the organization, catalyzing it into meaningful policies or plans.

The choice of an appropriate consultant for a particular project is not an easy task. No professional standards exist which will enable the client to differentiate between well-qualified firms or individuals and inexperienced or incompetent ones. A bitter experience can occur even with a reputable firm, depending on the individual assigned to the project and if less than extreme care is used by the consultant in evaluating the problem. Therefore, choice is critical and the client must undertake a comprehensive review of the qualifications of potential consulting firms. The following minimum considerations should guide the investigation:

1. Evaluate the background and experience of the principals.
2. Relate the firm's experience to the project at hand.
3. Question former clients regarding:
   a. Work assigned
   b. Performance
   c. Personnel
   d. Action taken on recommendations
   e. Repeat work performed

Upon completion of the preliminary investigation and prior to making a final selection, the client should request of one or more firms a written proposal clearly defining:

1. The objectives of the assignment
2. The work to be accomplished and the approach to be followed
3. The involvement and coordination required of the client
4. Possible difficulties that might hinder success in achieving the objectives
5. The experience of personnel to be assigned to the project and the role each will play
6. Statement of fees and the basis on which they are to be paid

It is important to realize in reviewing a formal proposal that the use of a consultant does not permit management to abrogate its responsibility for making decisions, adopting a course of action, and obtaining results.

Finally, the use of a consultant is not inexpensive. However, the expense will be lessened through clear definition of the problem and by close coordination and cooperation between client and consultants.

MANPOWER DATA COLLECTION AND ANALYSIS

Management decisions must be based on accurate, up-to-date, factual information. The methods which should be used to obtain such information are dependent upon the type, amount, and timeliness of information required, and the return on investment for data acquisition and analysis. Data collections methods can be manual, semiautomatic, or automatic.

Manual Data Collection. Manual procedures are usually employed by small factories with limited resources for data collection. Typically, a timekeeper may perform the dual functions of recording factory labor and dispatching. The data which can be collected manually are limited to:

1. Recording "In" and "Out" times for each employee
2. Reporting the elapsed time spent on each specific job or operation
3. Establishing a queue of factory orders for assignment
4. Updating departmental schedules
5. Reporting departmental loads (in terms of available man-hours and/or machine time)

Manual systems can become unduly complicated and expensive. Consequently, system costs must be evaluated with respect to the value of information which they produce.

Semiautomatic Data Collection. When data collection requirements are too complex for a manual system, use of a semiautomatic system must be considered. One common technique is the use of automatic data processing in conjunction with centralized timekeeping and dispatching.

Located at a central communications console similar to a telephone switchboard, the timekeeper can exchange information with individual call stations located throughout the work area. The departmental call stations are usually located at several points in a department to reduce walking time. Suitable equipment may be rented or purchased from intercommunications equipment manufacturers.

The timekeeper records pertinent information on preprinted forms for key punching. The key-punched cards can then be used to generate a variety of reports, as required for specific analyses and/or decisions. This method is practical for either long or short production runs, and two timekeepers can service plants with several hundred employees.

A second method of semiautomatic data collection is the prepunched-card system. Generally used for production of a repetitive nature, this system can be applied to a piecework, incentive-rate, or day-rate manufacture. The prepunched cards are arranged into either a labor deck or an operation deck. As each operation is completed on a given part or assembly, the corresponding operation card is removed from the deck.

The piecework system lends itself readily to prepunched cards, since no clocking in or out is required. Each card is the equivalent of a pay ticket and if the operator loses his card, he simply does not get paid. A major disadvantage of this system can be the accumulation of completed cards by an operator to enhance a future pay period. But through strong management, operators can be trained to turn in completed cards at the end of each shift.

The prepunched cards must be punched for a specific part number, quantity, operation, machine center, labor rate, and whatever other information is required. Additional information can be obtained by strategically locating information cards throughout the labor deck.

The incentive or day-rate systems follow almost the same procedure as the piecework system; however, the machine operator must be provided a means of clocking in or out, since the individual prepunched cards are not assigned a fixed time value with respect to dollars paid. This can be accomplished by locating time clocks conveniently near the work centers, by providing a timekeeper, or by writing in the times.

Automatic Data Collection. Modern electronic data processing (EDP) installations are capable of converting vast quantities of information into meaningful management reports at an extremely high rate of speed. If EDP equipment is to be utilized for maximum return on investment, manpower data collection must be accomplished either by "off-line" or "on-line" techniques.

Off-line Data Collection. This technique is usually employed in conjunction with a dispatching control center. Some data collection systems employ a central control center, while others can be used in conjunction with departmental dispatchers. In either case, the control center directs and monitors all production activities, and the information is collected on cards or tapes. At the end of each shift, the collected data are converted to machine language and the records are updated.

A network of transmitters is located throughout a plant area linked together through a common transmission cable. These transmitters are input units which collect information for transmission to the receivers used in conjunction with the control console. The transmitters collect constant data from coded tape, cards, and/or employee badges. Some transmitters are capable of accepting variable data either by means of dials or written information by the employee.

On-line Data Collection. This method provides high-speed transmissions from remote locations directly into a computer. A configuration of transmitters identical to that described for the off-line network can be used. However, should the computer be off-line, these on-line data collectors provide a means of accumulating information. In this manner, the information is collected and stored for subsequent processing.

Because of the rapid advancement in electronic data processing, the reader should contact the manufacturers of automatic data collection systems when considering an installation.

Reporting Manpower Status to Management. Successful management must be able to produce customer orders at a profit while building a quality product. In order to accomplish these tasks, management must have accurate, current, and concise information. The amounts of information required will vary for each company. Production control must supply management with master plant and/or department schedules and schedule status so that total factory manpower requirements and capacities can be planned. The factory labor force required to meet delivery requirements can be ascertained from estimated times, historical time standards, or engineered time standards. It is particularly important that the loading method be adjusted to include efficiencies. The efficiencies should be reported to management as another means of control.

MANPOWER COST TECHNIQUES

It should be highlighted that any techniques, whether for manpower cost control or for any other aspect of business, do not in themselves offer a "control" or "determine implications" of a situation or ultimately "make decisions." Properly designed, they provide timely and accurate information which intelligent management uses as a basis for decision making. That is to say, solutions to problems are derived from proper analysis and evaluation of facts provided by the "technique" and executed by "man," the manager.

A natural follow-on to manpower planning techniques which support the planning approach, these cost techniques provide management with the tools it requires to properly determine costs and evaluate the return on investment and profit.

Estimating Manpower Costs. From time immemorial estimators have collected little black books, secret formulas, rules of thumb, and innumerable other gimmicks and devices for estimating labor costs. Management demanded estimates upon which to base price quotations, plan personnel buildup, and schedule deliveries. Any standard is still better than no standard, so that almost any figure could be used that seemed halfway reasonable. The standard technique of the estimator was to explain why the estimate was wide of the mark. Changed methods or specifications were a convenient alibi and were equally hard to prove or disprove. Thus, the "guesstimator" made his way.

In the aircraft industry, during and after World War II, estimates were commonly made by the pound. The relative size, complexity, or type of aircraft was not a part of the formula; just a calculation of the weight, and the hours and cost were derived automatically.

Fortunately or unfortunately, depending on the point of view, things are not so simple today and considerable sophistication has been introduced into cost estimating, with the result that accuracy is considerably improved and the results much more dependable. Accurate cost estimating is possible today through the use of scientifically developed standard data which actually have developed to the point where the term "estimating" is no longer apropos. Rather, standard data applicators have superseded estimating per se and have a completely different implication.

The accuracy with which standard data can be applied is entirely a function of how precisely the method of production can be defined. If the exact method is known, the exact time is also known. When the number of unknowns increases, accuracy decreases since successive assumptions, the validity of which is always subject to question, must be made.

To illustrate the method of cost calculation and the problems typically encountered, the following process may be useful. The development of costs for a single part is included with the understanding that the procedure would be the same for all parts and eventually for complete assemblies or whatever.

The first step is to list the processes by which the part will be made. This involves decisions as to whether a casting or raw stock will be used and a list of the operations and inspections necessary to produce the finished part.

Example A typical list of operations may be as follows:

1. Cut raw stock to length   Do-all saw
2. Turn to shape   Engine lathe
3. Grind to final dimension   Centerless grinder
4. Drill and ream   Sensitive drill press
5. Plate   Chrome plate
6. Inspect

Having detailed the process by which the part will be produced, the next step is to develop the detail for each operation to the depth necessary to apply data. A word of explanation is necessary here concerning the different degrees to which data synthesis can be carried and their effect upon the accuracy of results and the time necessary to apply the data. It is axiomatic that the number of variables considered determines the accuracy of measurement and the time necessary to apply data. The degree to which details are taken into account is normally a function of the volume of the item to be produced. High volumes require more accuracy and as a result data which permit consideration of a great many variables. On the other hand, making one part may allow the consideration of very few variables.

Example To illustrate how this works we can consider operation 4, drill and ream, for the hypothetical part.

Variable 1—Fixture. If a tool drawing is available, exact data may be obtained of how the piece is placed and removed from the fixture and of the type and number of clamps. This information together with the dimensions and weight of the piece make possible an exact time value. If a fixture is to be used, but no drawing is available, assumptions must be made about the fixture and the data applied on the basis of these assumptions, with a corresponding degree of uncertainty and loss of accuracy for the final result.

Variable 2—Material Specifications. If the precise material from which the part is made is known, the exact drilling feed, speed, and time are known. However, if this has not been determined, again an educated assumption must be made and the data applied accordingly.

Variable 3—Hole Diameter and Depth. Usually this information is readily available and thus if material is known, an accurate time and cost can be determined. However, for very rough standards, such as might be used for maintenance parts, any hole up to $\frac{1}{2}$ by $\frac{1}{2}$ inch might be considered as one, and up to 1 by 1 inch as a multiple thereof, in order to reduce the calculations and hence the time to arrive at the cost.

Variable 4—Materials Handling. To arrive at a completely accurate standard, the type and size of container in which the parts are delivered for the operator should be known. If not certain, assumptions based on the usual shop practices must be made.

Variable 5—Lot Size. This factor has an obvious effect upon setup times, which are constant per lot rather than per piece. It also has an influence upon the degree of proficiency operators can attain in making a particular piece. If there are few pieces, the operator may not develop his full potential production, especially if tooling and fixtures are complex.

The use of standard data to calculate, rather than estimate, manpower costs is preferred to all other methods. Even if few variables are defined, all costs will have a known degree of accuracy depending upon the refinements built into each standard.

This method of determining manpower costs has led to *standard data developers* and *standard data applicators,* who have replaced cost estimators. The standard data developer must be familiar with work measurement and the techniques of standard data development. The applicator, on the other hand, must know the processes, such as drilling and milling. The data applicator must be able to predict each move the operator will make to produce the piece. Knowing each move, he can apply the data accurately.

Overhead Rates. The method of determining overhead rates is one of the most controversial areas of cost accounting. Every cost accountant seems to have fixed ideas about the subject which he is prepared to support at length.

HOW MANY COST CENTERS? The best answer to this question is: As few as possible consistent with accurate and realistic accounting. Keep in mind that the only reason for having more than one cost center is to distinguish between costs of items passing through one center as opposed to another. If the costs are not different in each center, there is no justification for differentiation in the first place.

Expressed another way, the reason for isolating a cost center is to ensure that a product will not be unjustly burdened or too lightly burdened with over-head costs.

Cost centers are often referred to as "responsibility" centers, and this may be a valuable key to how the plant should be divided for calculation of overhead rates. If one supervisor or manager can be identified with a center, you are well on the way.

Another key to watch for is processes which utilize special equipment that is very costly, or which take an inordinate amount of space, or which, like plating, utilize unique and costly materials. Any item not passing through these areas of cost characteristics should not be burdened with their costs. The costs should be absorbed only by those items which use them.

If, however, there is a uniformity of flow so that all products go through two areas having widely different cost characteristics, there is no real reason to separate them. Only when some products do and some do not pass through such areas should different cost centers be maintained.

EXPENSE DISTRIBUTION: Having defined cost or responsibility centers, the next step is to distribute all plant overhead expense to each cost center. The basis of distribution can be simple or varied depending upon the nature and magnitude of the expense. When selecting the basis of distribution, you should keep in mind that splitting hairs and expense have much in common. You must con-stantly be aware of the importance of the changes in the final result that can be caused by each decision. Some common expense items and suggested bases for distribution are as follows:

Item	*Basis of Distribution*
1. Heat and light	Floor space occupied
2. Power	Installed horsepower*
3. Depreciation	Actual machines installed
4. Supervision	Actual supervisors assigned or part thereof
5. Indirect labor	Direct-labor hours
6. Supplies	Direct-labor hours
7. Indirect materials	Actual utilization
8. Real estate taxes	Space occupied
9. Social Security taxes	Payroll dollars
10. Vacation and holiday pay	Payroll dollars

* If metered separately; otherwise estimate percent of total expense for light and power separately.

INDIRECT CENTERS AND REDISTRIBUTION: Some responsibility centers such as maintenance, shipping-receiving, stock rooms, tool rooms, personnel department, etc., occupy space, have supervision and indirect labor, and use heat, light, and power—but do not, however, produce anything. Good practice usually indicates that original expense distribution be made to these centers just as with the direct production centers. The expenses of these indirect centers are then redistributed to the direct centers on some logical basis. For example, personnel department expenses might be distributed on head count or direct-labor hours, shipping and receiving expenses by pounds processed, tool room expenses to applicable departments on an actual record basis. The exact basis of distribu-tion is usually not of paramount importance if it is fairly realistic and logical. For example, whether expense is distributed by head count, labor hours, or payroll dollars, overall final results will not differ significantly.

The order in which indirect departments are distributed and redistributed can be the subject for endless, unresolved debate and is usually not too significant in the final results. To illustrate, the maintenance department definitely does some work for the tool room, occasionally for shipping-receiving, and very infrequently for the personnel department and stock rooms. Therefore, if the maintenance expenses are distributed first, each of the other indirect departments can get a small share which in turn is redistributed. But the personnel department also works for maintenance as well as all other indirect centers, so maybe *it* should distribute first—and so on ad infinitum. The answer is to distribute all simultaneously so each can get its share of the other. The complexities are endless. To resolve this a good rule is: Distribute only to direct centers and ignore as insignificant to the final result all redistribution of redistributions.

EXCESS DIRECT-LABOR COSTS: Excess labor costs *do* exist. You can just ignore them but eventually they must be absorbed in standard costs or the plant will go out of business. Therefore, make it a rule to include in overhead rates a reasonable amount of excess direct-labor cost. The standard cost, or overhead rate, should be a cost reasonably attainable. It should not be a will-o'-the-wisp. Standard costs and overhead rate should be reasonably attainable for the period to which they apply. Therefore, excess direct-labor costs should be included.

CALCULATION OF OVERHEAD RATE: Having distributed all shop expenses plus planned excess indirect labor to cost or responsibility centers, the overhead rate for each cost center can be established. The rate can be established per machine-hour, direct-labor-hour, or some unit of production such as pounds, tons, yard, etc.

Of all the possible bases expressing the rate, the direct-labor-hour method is probably the most widely used and the most accurate.

Machine-hours are used where the process is primarily machine controlled, such as with spinning in textiles, where the direct-labor-hour is somewhat nebulous. Machine-hours are also used in certain process industries. The unit of production is closely related to machine-hours for most products, and for any given item one can be free to convert from one to another. The selection of one or the other is largely one of convenience.

Whichever basis of expression is used, the projected activity of the cost center, expressed in direct-labor-hours, machine-hours, or pounds, yards, etc., is divided into the allocated expense to obtain the rate.

BUDGETS FOR DIRECT MANPOWER: The development of budgets for direct manpower can be as accurate as the ability to forecast the volume of production and product mix that will evolve as sales for the period are realized. Budgets can be established in a number of ways, but the preferred way is through the application of standards to accurately forecast production. Of course, this is not always possible or practical, and many firms develop budgets by taking the trend of actual expenses for the past several years and extrapolating on them for the next year on the basis of an educated guess. This unscientific but nevertheless sometimes accurate approach to budgeting needs no further analysis here, since the techniques are fairly obvious and self-explanatory.

Budgets for direct manpower have several aspects and connotations for different persons. The several aspects of budgeting might be classified as:

Profit planning and forecasting

Forecasting manpower requirements

Control of manpower costs

A budget is a plan and cost control tool and every company should have one if they are to maximize profits. Budgeting as related to profit planning starts with a sales forecast, which combined with selling prices results in the income plan or budget. When all items of expense, including manpower costs, are compared with income, a profit for the year is obtained. The more detailed and accurate the sales forecast becomes as to volumes of items and product mix, the more accurate the budget becomes. Operating with this type of budget implies management action to keep all aspects in line with the plan. If sales fall off they must be stimulated. If costs do not develop as planned, they must be brought into line if the profit objectives are to be met. Control mechanisms, to keep management advised at each step of the period, in each aspect of the plan, are necessary if at the end of the period the planned profit is to be realized.

The forecasting of manpower requirements is an outgrowth of the budget. If increased sales are forecast and manpower needs are planned accordingly, management is given the lead time necessary to recruit and train personnel to meet forecast needs. Knowing the time necessary to develop people for each phase of the productive process, a schedule for hiring and training can be developed to meet future needs.

The concept of budgeting as a control mechanism is considerably more complex and introduces the idea of a flexible budget. In this context, the flexible budget tells management how much manpower and associated cost are required not only for forecast levels, but for the quantities actually produced. Whereas the budget, based on a forecast, works well when sales are what was actually contemplated, it lacks flexibility and hence usefulness when volume becomes either more or less than was forecast.

For example, if the volume of production is less than was forecast, the budgeted expenditures for manpower should be less. On the other hand, if production and sales increase, comparison to the budget may look unsatisfactory because more manpower is being used than anticipated while in reality the exact opposite may be true.

The flexible budget is not related to forecasts and only indirectly related to profit planning, but more accurately reflects the current performance and thus is most valuable as a control mechanism. Flexible budgets that contract as output contracts, and increase when production increases, compare performance against actual units produced and are in reality more realistic and valuable.

To be wholly effective and accurate, flexible budgets should be based not only on units shipped or transferred to finished stock, but also on the actual production achieved at each operation during the productive process. Unless this is so, changes in "in-process" inventories will distort the flexible budget and produce a false reading.

For example, if in-process inventory is reduced, the finished units produced will give a reading that is too high. Conversely, if in-process inventories are being increased, much useful work can be accomplished without actually producing finished units.

To illustrate the development of a manpower budget using standards and forecast production, the following simplified examples are suggested.

Example Let us assume that sales are forecast for the five products manufactured for a company as follows:

Product A	100/month
Product B	500/month
Product C	50/month
Product D	800/month
Product E	950/month

The standard cost sheet shows among other things the following labor and material requirements for product A. Similar cost sheets exist for products B, C, D, and E.

Standard Cost Calculation—Product A

I. *Materials*

Steel sheet 1040 A	100 pounds/unit
Wire, copper no. 10 regular	50 feet/unit
Paint, industrial enamel	0.50 gallons/unit

II. *Direct Labor*

	Hours/unit	*Rate/hour*	*Cost/unit*
A. *Cutting Dept.*			
1. Do-all saw	0.2650	$3.25	$0.8613
2. Shear	0.4078	3.35	1.3661
3. Brake	0.2160	3.30	0.7128
B. *Assembly*			
1. Subassem. 1	0.5065	3.20	1.6208
2. Subassem. 2	0.7862	3.20	2.5158
3. Final assem.	1.6035	3.40	5.4519
C. *Finish and pack*			
1. Spray paint	0.1345	3.28	0.4412
2. Touch up	0.0756	3.15	0.2381
3. Pack	0.6300	3.10	1.9530

The application of the standards to the production forecast, simplified to illustrate the process, would be as shown in Table 2. The resulting calculations show the authorized manning for each department, based upon the forecasted production requirements. Control reports which show the relationship of the forecast to the actual mix will indicate the validity of the original budget.

TABLE 2   Development of Manpower Budget: Direct Labor

Product	Cutting dept.			Assembly			Finish and pack			Total
	Saw	Shear	Brake	Sub 1	Sub 2	Final	Paint	Touch up	Pack	
A 100	26.50	40.78	21.60	50.65	78.62	160.35	13.45	7.56	63.00	462.51
B 500	...	...	...	...	...	...	...	...	...	...
C 50	...	...	...	...	...	...	...	...	...	...
D 800	...	...	...	...	...	...	...	...	...	...
E 950	...	...	...	...	...	...	...	...	...	...
Total man-hours/month	753.25	835.56	685.60	940.36	1260.50	2580.36	436.12	350.48	1080.31	8922.54
Employees required	4.38	4.86	3.99	5.47	7.33	15.0	2.54	2.04	6.28	51.88
Manpower budget	13.23			27.80			10.86			

The illustrated budget is valid, provided that the departments operate at standard, which, of course, is not always the case. If the actual productivity levels are substantially different from standard, the manpower figures can be factored for planning purposes, although for cost control the variance from standard may be highlighted.

INDIRECT MANPOWER BUDGETS: "Indirect labor or manpower" is a term which is widely used in a number of different senses. In the narrowest sense it is defined as labor which doesn't contribute anything to the value of the product, and would include such activities as materials handling, service personnel, inspection, and actual operations such as mold cleaning and shake-out in foundries. This strict definition serves no useful purpose and seems to confuse the issue and budget concepts involved here.

At the other extreme is the concept often associated with the aircraft and aerospace industries, where manpower is indirect if it cannot be identified with a given contract. Under this very loose definition almost any activity such as stockkeeping, maintenance, personnel, purchasing, design, etc., can be classified as direct if the persons perform their function for only one contract. This definition is too broad and is useful only for invoicing against a cost-reimbursement type of contract.

For budgeting and control purposes better definitions of indirect and direct labor would be:

Direct Labor: Any labor activity which varies directly with the volume of output

Indirect Labor: Any labor activity which does not vary directly with the volume of output

These definitions result in some activities, such as inspection and materials handling between processes, becoming classified as direct labor. This constitutes no problem. There is no reason not to establish standards per unit of output for these operations and control them as for conventional direct labor, which by definition varies directly with output. For budgeting purposes these may therefore be treated exactly as direct labor.

With indirect labor, which now by definition includes those labor activities which do not vary directly with volume, our budgeting problems are more clearly defined. Examples of such indirect labor are:

Maintenance workers

Oilers and cleaners

Stock-room attendants

Inventory control clerks

Tool-crib attendants

Shop clerical employees

Janitors

Some may argue that some manpower is more indirect than other, and this is true. Even indirect labor bears some relationship to volume of output, but in these instances the relationship is not direct and hence it is correctly classified as indirect.

Budgets for indirect manpower, and incidentally, indirect costs, must be related to a given volume of output. Therefore, when sales and output have been forecast and the direct manpower established, the indirect labor may be predicted.

When comparing actual indirect to budget, as opposed to direct, the variances must be expressed in two ways. It is obvious that if the number of units produced are reduced, the earned budget for indirect expenses will also be reduced if the flexible approach is maintained. This will produce a variance which should be termed "volume variance," which is actually the result of the change in output.

A second type of variance would come about when volume was actually as forecast, but the expenditures were more or less than contemplated in the budget. This variance is rightly termed "performance variance" and must be expressed independently of volume variances. In actual practice it is common to have one variance offset the other, one being negative and the other positive. The following examples illustrate the interaction of volume and performance variances and the significance of each:

Example A

Plant activity (volume of output)	80 percent
Budgeted indirect manpower at 100 percent	$8,500/month
Flexible budget at 80 percent activity	$6,800/month
Actual expenditure	$8,500/month
Volume variance (negative)	$1,700/month

Example B

Plant activity (volume of output)	120 percent
Budgeted indirect manpower at 100 percent	$8,500/month
Flexible budget at 120 percent activity	$10,200/month
Actual expenditure	$9,000/month
Performance variance (negative)	$500/month
Volume variance (positive)	$1,700/month
Net variance (positive)	$1,200/month

The above approach to indirect manpower budgets is an interesting exercise in algebraic addition and serves to illustrate actual performance against a budget and against a planned profit. It shows why you may or may not realize profit objectives and in this sense is a control mechanism. However, it is not the complete answer to control since there is no indication whatever as to what mangement is actually getting for the amounts expended. Supervisory appraisal is the only assurance that control is maintained. You may be well within budget, but way out of line in relation to actual work accomplished.

The answer, of course, is a budget within a budget in which indirect activity is measured and evaluated on the same basis as direct labor. By definition, an activity is indirect when it is not related to units produced or sold. For example, the floor must be swept once per day regardless of the volume of units produced. Measuring and controlling indirect activity can ensure that the hours of work paid for are correct for the work actually accomplished even if it is completely unrelated to the profit plan.

Order Costs versus Standard Costs. "Job-order costs versus standard costs" is synonymous with saying "standard versus actual costs." From a modern control technique viewpoint, job-order costs per se serve a historical purpose only. As history is evolved, comparisons with the past provide a continuous stream of information, but for control purposes this is of little value.

In this context, job-order costing means identification of various costs with a job order and the collection of these costs to obtain the total cost of the job. The process starts with the requisitioning of materials from stock. Material requisitions contain job-order numbers, and costs are posted to the job-order cost card.

For factory labor, each operator records the hours worked against each job, and when extended and posted to each job-order these records form the basis for collection of costs. When a job is finally completed and shipped, the costs entered on the *cost-accumulation sheet* may be summarized and compared to an estimate or budget. Subsequently, this record is useful in estimating future jobs and a complete history is thereby obtained.

The difference between this approach and the standard costing approach is that the job-order cost system provides no frame of reference, no anchor point to tell management where the performance was good or bad. Relative performance records, of course, are available, and comparison with past records and estimates is possible and useful. However, it does not offer a qualitative determination, i.e., whether the performance was what it should be or could be, and whether it was good or bad in an absolute sense.

The prerequisite of a standard cost system is good labor standards. To attempt to install one without them is to perpetuate the job-cost system. Standards should be established on an engineered basis, with setup standards separately identified.

With standards in existence, these will naturally be used for control as well as cost purposes. This implies that operators will report the time and units of production. The performance of each individual against standards is determined on a daily or weekly basis. The way standards are used for control purposes, however, differs to a great extent from the way they are used for standard costs even though they may be the same standards.

For control of individual performance it is usually advisable to segregate setup standards, and to differentiate between elements of operations which vary with the number of units processed as opposed to those elements which vary per batch, per shift, or on some basis other than units produced. The reason for this is that you must prevent variances over which the individual operator has no control.

At times standards for control purposes are applied on an "as incurred" basis, such as "cobbles" on a cold reduction mill. This is the best way to determine and control the performance of individuals. For cost purposes, however, these "as incurred" standards, such as setup, batch, and lot constants, must be included in unit standard costs at a standard or average frequency basis.

Another significant difference between job-order and standard costs lies in the way in which excess costs, for delays, breakdowns, etc., are customarily handled. Under the job-cost system excess costs usually get charged to the job the individual was working on at the time. As such, they may produce significant variations in individual job costs. Under the standard cost system, however, there is usually provision for charging delays, breakdowns, interruptions, etc., as "off standard time." These charges find their way into overhead and are applied to all jobs rather than falling at random on a particular job.

Another similar feature involves differences in skill and effort of various individuals in the shop. Under the job-shop, or actual-cost system, a neophyte who happens to be assigned to a job is unduly penalized. Under the standard cost system, on the other hand, a job has only one standard regardless of to whom it is assigned. Variances from standard or losses through failure to make standard are not all loaded onto a particular job but absorbed evenly by all jobs.

To summarize, standard costing is more refined than job costing because it establishes a "should be" cost on an absolute level. It is also more equitable in that it results in excess costs for delays and substandard performance to be absorbed by all jobs rather than by one or two selected on a random basis.

SUMMARY

Efficient manpower planning may be the deciding factor in the success or failure of a manufacturing operation. Responsibility for efficient manufacturing makes it imperative that production control be fully acquainted with:

Master scheduling
Manpower capacity
Manpower loading
Work simplification
Work measurement
Production-progress functions
Make-or-buy analyses
Industrial relations
Manpower data collection
Manpower costs

Only by an intelligent application of these techniques can efficient manufacturing be possible.

REFERENCES

1. Arthur Hugh Jenkins, *Adam Smith Today: An Inquiry into the Nature and Causes of the Wealth of Nations,* Kennikate Press Inc., Port Washington, New York, 1969.
2. Thomas Robert Malthus (1766–1834), *An Essay on Population,* E. P. Dutton & Co., Inc., New York, 1914.
3. David Ricardo, *Principles of Political Economy and Taxation,* G. Bell & Sons, Ltd., London, 1903.
4. Alfred Marshall (1842–1924), *Principles of Economics,* Macmillan & Co., Ltd., London, 1898.
5. Alfred Marshall and Mrs. Marshall (1842–1924), *The Economics of Industry,* Macmillan & Co., Ltd., London, 1879.
6. Joseph Alois Schumpeter (1883–1950), *Business Cycles* (two volumes), McGraw-Hill Book Company, New York, 1939.
7. Joseph Alois Schumpeter, *Capitalism, Socialism, and Democracy,* Harper & Row, Publishers, Incorporated, New York, 1942.
8. Thorstein Veblen (1857–1929), *The Theory of the Leisure Class: An Economic Study of the Evolution of Institutions,* The Macmillan Company, New York, 1899.
9. John Maynard Keynes (1883–1946), *The General Theory of Employment, Interest, and Money,* Harcourt, Brace & World, Inc., New York, 1936.
10. Chris. Argyris, *Understanding Organizational Behavior,* Richard D. Irwin, Inc., Homewood, Ill., 1960.

BIBLIOGRAPHY

Andress, F. J.: "The Learning Curve as a Production Tool," *Harvard Business Review,* January-February, 1954.

Biegel, J. E.: *Production Control,* Prentice-Hall, Inc., Englewood Cliffs, N.J., 1963.

Black, J. M., and V. T. Black: *The Front-line Manager's Problem Solver,* McGraw-Hill Book Company, New York, 1967.

Broom, H. N.: *Production Management,* Richard D. Irwin, Inc., Homewood, Ill., 1964.

Buffa, E. S.: *Modern Production Management,* 2d ed., John Wiley & Sons, Inc., New York, 1965.

Carroll, Phil: *Better Wage Incentives,* McGraw-Hill Book Company, New York, 1957.

Chamberlain, N. W., and J. W. Kuhn: *Collective Bargaining,* 2d ed., McGraw-Hill Book Company, New York, 1965.

Clark, W.: *The Gantt Chart,* Sir Isaac Pitman & Sons, Ltd., London, 1938.

Dickie, H. F.: "Six Steps to Better Inventory Management," *Factory Management and Maintenance,* August, 1963.

Gibson, R. E.: *Wages and Salaries,* American Management Association, New York, 1967.

Greene, J. H.: *Production Control Systems and Decisions,* Richard D. Irwin, Inc., Homewood, Ill., 1965.

Hannon, J. W.: "New Approaches to Employee Training," *Business Management,* June, 1967.

Holt, C. C., et al.: *Planning Production, Inventories, and Work Force,* Prentice-Hall, Inc., Englewood Cliffs, N.J., 1960.

Ireson, W. G., and E. L. Grant: *Handbook of Industrial Engineering and Management,* Prentice-Hall, Inc., Englewood Cliffs, N.J., 1956.

Krick, E. V.: *Methods Engineering,* John Wiley & Sons, Inc., New York, 1962.

Lynton, R. P., and W. Pareek: *Training and Development,* Richard D. Irwin, Inc., Homewood, Ill., 1967.

MacNiece, E. H.: *Production Forecasting Planning and Control,* 3d ed., John Wiley & Sons, Inc., New York, 1961.

Maynard, H. B.: *Industrial Engineering Handbook,* 2d ed., McGraw-Hill Book Company, New York, 1963.

Muth, J. F., and G. E. Thompson: *Industrial Scheduling*, Prentice-Hall, Inc., Englewood Cliffs, N.J., 1963.

Personnel Audits and Reports to Top Management, National Industrial Conference Board, Studies in Personnel Policy, no. 194, New York, 1964.

Personnel Practices in Factory and Office, National Industrial Conference Board, Manufacturing Studies in Personnel Policy, no. 194, New York, 1964.

Personnel Procedures Manuals, National Industrial Conference Board, Studies in Personnel Policy, no. 180, New York, 1961.

Rice, W. B.: *Control Charts*, John Wiley & Sons, Inc., New York, 1955.

Starr, Martin K.: "Modular Production: A New Concept," *Harvard Business Review*, vol. 43, no. 6, November-December, 1965.

——— *Production Management, Systems, and Synthesis*, Prentice-Hall, Inc., Englewood Cliffs, N.J., 1964.

——— and D. W. Miller: *Inventory Control: Theory and Practice*, Prentice-Hall, Inc., Englewood Cliffs, N.J., 1962.

Stokes, P. M.: *Total Job Training*, American Management Association, New York, 1966.

Taylor, J. W.: *How to Select and Develop Leaders*, McGraw-Hill Book Company, New York, 1962.

Timms, H. L.: *Production Function in Business*, Richard D. Irwin, Inc., Homewood, Ill., 1966.

Voris, W.: *Production Control*, 3d ed., Richard D. Irwin, Inc., Homewood, Ill., 1966.

Wright, T. P.: "Factors Affecting the Cost of Airplanes," *Journal of Aeronautical Sciences*, February, 1936.

Wright, W.: *Forecasting for Profit*, John Wiley & Sons, Inc., New York, 1947.

Chapter **11**

Long-range Planning

EDITOR:

Robert L. Janson *Senior Consultant, Ernst & Ernst, Cleveland, Ohio*

CONTENTS

Long-range planning as a business technique goes back in history less than 100 years. During the late nineteenth century, and as a direct result of the growth of the scientific management movement, the use of this tool in American business became popular. The early pioneers of this technique sought to replace rule-of-thumb methods of operating by a more scientific approach. They coined and introduced numerous techniques of "planning" factory performance and business activities.

Around the year 1900, long-range planning was an informal organizational arrangement which is in strong contrast to today's formalized organizations. The long-range planning at that time relied in great measure on intuitive judgment in contrast to today's, which relies more on a systematic approach to the problem. This early planning was strategic, rather than being implemented. It was undertaken by some companies, but few organizations reached a stage of planning that detailed activities over a long-range period of time.

Strategic planning at the turn of the century was of two major types. The first was personalized planning for growth which was undertaken by the aggressive business tycoons and the early empire builders. The second was a type of intuitive look ahead where a president would attempt to assess the long-range future to ascertain what opportunities could be exploited by his company. Oftentimes this early long-range planning, in addition to being aggressive, was led by extensive personal drive. Its hope was to obtain consolidations, a type of vertical integration, and a very rapid expansion of the existing sources and facilities.[1]

Planning in Early 1900s. In 1916, a French industrialist, Henri Fayol, referred to *five key functions* of management. These were *planning, organizing, command, coordination,* and *control.* Fayol commented about planning, "the plan of action is, and one in the same time, the result envisioned, the line of action to be followed, stages to go through, and the methods to be used." In his view, planning meant both "to access the future and make provisions for."[2]

The early 1920s foresaw the initial work of optimum-size lots. A decade later was the introduction of safety-stock inventory. Both of these analyses had a number of industrial applications but did not stimulate further scientific or professional work.

In 1926, in an early American Management Association's Production Executive Series Bulletin, one of the authors wrote, "the simplest way is to get from the sales department an estimate of what deliveries may be expected to be on each line of product. But what if the sales department cannot give a reliable estimate of what sales will be over the period?" The author, Leonard Tyler, was stating one of the frustrations of management. How do you forecast and make plans for longer than just a few months in advance? This was one of the early formal references to the problems of sales forecasting and the attendant long-range planning requirements. Tyler continued, discussing the benefits that could be obtained from any valid attempt to forecast a production program. He thought we should consider the purposes for which a budget or forecast is adopted. Two of these he noted were:[3]

1. Plan ahead for the volume of work anticipated so that it may be begun and carried through smoothly and as rapidly as possible.

2. Set up standards, both of performance and cost analysis, by which what is actually done can be checked.

Subsequent authors[4] noted that the customer was the only person for whom a company exists and the only true customer a plant has is the sales department. This was a rather revolutionary view at that time. Managers stated that orders should be placed by the sales department, and if the sales people could not dispose of these orders after they were produced, it was the fault of the sales department.   Many people felt general management could not hold manufacturing responsible for the creation of inventories if such sales orders were incorrect.

Planning in 1930–1945.   In the early 1930s, Professor Paul Holden and two associates of the Stanford Business School surveyed 31 large organizations, concentrating their efforts and attention upon the interest of the top managers on planning.   This survey disclosed that only two of the companies had formal plans for five years ahead, but half or more of the companies had laid plans for some or all of their operations up to one year in advance.   This study left its authors to conclude, "one of the greatest needs observed during the course of this study is for more adequate planning and clarification of future objectives, both near term and long-range."[5]

In 1931, Dean W. B. Donham of the Harvard Business School produced an important contribution to corporate long-range planning.   In his book[6] he anticipated some of the business development planning that was to take place in the late 1950s.   One of his comments was that the time seemed right to review the whole subject of forecasting, including its limitations.   He said any planning theory should approach the subject from a scientific point of view.   Each situation and its potential success would depend upon the ability to reduce the number of variables involved to a manageable number.   Any theory of forecasting (he referred to it as "foresight") has well-defined characteristics which one must recognize and provide as major elements for the solution of each problem.

In the later 1930s, the Tennessee Valley Authority project of the United States government utilized some of the approaches to long-range planning.   While public power systems were not new, this extensive concentration in one area caused the chairman at the time, David E. Lilienthal, to describe its approach as "unified development"[7] and to say that this was synonomous with long-range planning as performed by corporations.

Planning in Post-World War II.   With the completion of World War II, a revolution came about in the business community in regard to planning.   The extensive conversion necessary from government-oriented production to consumer applications necessitated dramatic changes in many companies.   In addition, the problems of late 1940s and 1950s on leveling manpower because of union demands, and on lower inventories because of the high cost of carrying them, led to a reevaluation of the current business theories in use.   The thought of using a statistical approach, the possibility of extending the wartime success of operations research, the availability of new tools such as linear programming, and a general awareness of scientific knowledge in business operations, all invited new attention and interest in scientific quantitative analysis and long-range planning

Planning in Decade of 1970s.   A study in a leading magazine, *Business Management,* attempts to answer the questions, "What does corporate planning mean to company managers, and how are the various functions delegated?"   The answers to these questions are most interesting and are indicative of the level of long-range planning in American industry today.   Some 101 companies were queried.   The survey answers are shown in Fig. 1.   All but one company indicated that they were engaged in some kind of planning.   The overall majority (84 percent) establish some type of goal for sales, share of the market, and/or return on investment.   A great majority used planning for only one-time projects, yet 50 percent of the companies surveyed admitted they were involved in long-range planning to some degree.

One of the conclusions drawn from this was that as a company grows, so does its long-range planning and its inclination to look to the future. This raises an interesting question: Is long-range planning a cause or effect of company growth? One of the other major conclusions of this study concerned the participation of operating managers in long-range planning. Ninety-two percent of the companies reviewed said their operating managers do participate in the

1. Does your company have a formal program for either short- or long-term corporate planning?
      Yes—99 %   No—1 %
2. What is the nature of this planning?*
      Budgeting—54 %
      Project planning—54 %
      Long-range planning (three or more years)—50 %
      Project scheduling—37 %
      Day-to-day scheduling—29 %
3. How far in advance do you plan your company's activities?
      Less than one year—14 %
      One to three years—36 %
      Four to five years—23 %
      Five to ten years—24 %
      Over ten years—3 %
4. Who is in charge of your planning program?
      President—69 %
      Planning specialist—11 %
      Line vice president—10 %
      Budget director—3 %
      Other—7 %
5. Has your company set goals for sales, share of market, and/or return on investment?
      Yes—84 %   No—16 %
6. Do you make use of PERT or other network techniques in project planning?
      Yes—16 %   No—79 %
      No answer—5 %
7. Do you use a computer in planning?
      Yes—30 %   No—66 %
      No answer—4 %
8. If so, how do you use the computer?*
      To gather information—83 %
      To simulate market conditions—33 %
      Other (e.g., to do production scheduling)—16 %
9. Do your operating managers participate in planning?
      Yes—92 %   No—8 %
10. Do operating managers submit departmental plans tied to long-range goals?
      Yes—69 %   No—25 %
      No answer—6 %
11. Do operating managers make estimates of the manpower they need to reach company goals?
      Yes—67 %   No—25 %
      No answer—8 %

* The figures total more than 100 percent because some respondents checked more than one answer.

Fig. 1 Survey of corporate planning practices. (*From "How 101 Companies Handle Corporate Planning," Business Management, September, 1967.*)

planning process. Some only paid minor lip service to the concept, but a majority of them submitted some type of departmental plan. An almost equal number based their estimates of manpower needs in the future on some type of long-range plan.

Thus, as the decade of the 1970s begins, detailed, broad-scale, long-range corporate planning is not widespread. However, many companies do agree they must do some sort of advance looking and managing.

ROLE OF PRODUCTION AND INVENTORY CONTROL IN LONG-RANGE PLANNING

In the early development of the production and inventory control function, it was often referred to as being similar to the nervous system or the heart of the human body. Of late, this concept has changed somewhat. More and more, the practitioners of production and inventory control in American industry have stressed its coordinating functions. By this, the members of the profession feel they have an opportunity to participate at various levels and can coordinate many diverse functions of a corporation. In effect, a production and/or inventory control manager has a strong functional *dotted-line* relationship with other departments, and this function might be called "production control and coordinating department."[8] In his day-to-day activities, he works closely with sales,

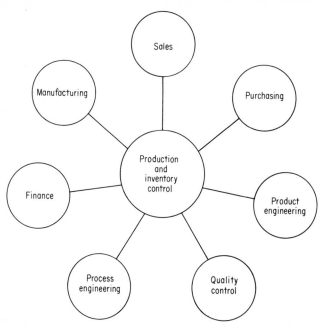

Fig. 2 Coordinating position of production and inventory control.

engineering, purchasing, manufacturing, etc., (Fig. 2), and has a unique opportunity to assist in maintaining the operation of his company by this coordinating type of position. If it is true that long-range planning will grow, then by the very nature and position of production and inventory control, this profession can assist, coordinate, and contribute extensively to their companies' success and profits.

History and experience have proved that the companies which plan ahead are the most successful. The decade ahead will be the one where a stabilized labor force will be a definite asset to a company. While this is an intangible asset to measure, there is no question that long-range planning is one excellent method to help a corporation.

It has been commented that long-range planning is an essential and inseparable part of every management job. The proper use of this management tool may allow managers to spend their time on the offense, instead of being on the defense—making the better things happen rather than always reacting to what is happening.

Long-range planning is not a fallacy, but it is a difficult concept to tie down in concrete terms. A logical question is often raised: How does production planning and control fit into long-range planning? Can this profession really assist corporations in such a complex technique? Agreeing that we are relatively new, how can we aid the company and help direct its progress in the ensuing years?

Production Control's Contribution to Planning. The production and inventory control manager, supervisor, planner, scheduler, and other members of this profes-

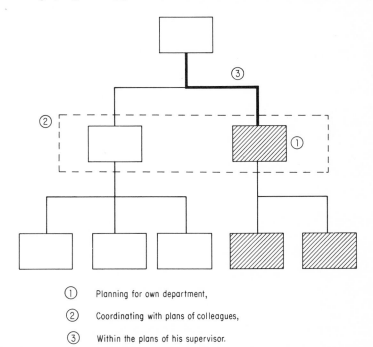

    ①   Planning for own department,

    ②   Coordinating with plans of colleagues,

    ③   Within the plans of his supervisor.

Fig. 3 Three methods to contribute. [*From E. J. Green, "How to Make Plans that Will Really Work for You," Factory, August, 1966. By special permission of Modern Maufacturing (formerly Factory). Copyright by McGraw-Hill, Inc.*]

sion can contribute toward the various types of planning in one of three methods (see Fig. 3):

1. In their own area of responsibility where they can utilize techniques for short-, intermediate-, and long-range planning in the daily performance of their various jobs.

2. In their work with other individuals at their own level within the company, assisting in coordinating and contributing toward the corporate long-range planning.

3. In utilizing plans of their superiors as a framework to plan for a long period.

The first method is applicable to every employee in a company, irrespective of his level of authority and responsibility. Each position has two types of content—acting and planning. At the production scheduler's level the content of his job is much more acting than planning. Any planning efforts are limited and are short or intermediate in range. Conversely, at the top of the ladder, the great majority of the individual's time, whether he be the general manager, vice president, or president, is engaged in long-range planning. But in every instance, regardless of the level of authority, the planning has to be a continuous dynamic process which keeps the individual constantly reviewing what he is doing and its relationship with the future.

In addition to the reporting level of the individual, there are factors of secondary consideration, such as the size of the company, policy of the company, and whether the employee has a line or staff relationship. But each person will have a direct influence on planning to some extent. Figure 4 graphically illustrates the level of influence possible in long-range planning within a company, as directly related to the employee. Each person can locate his current position on the chart and get a concept of his involvement in the various types of planning.

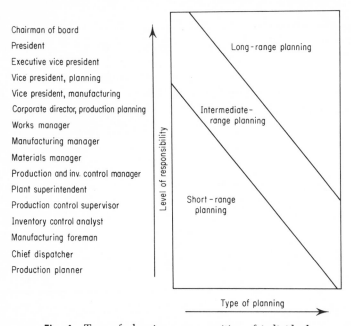

Fig. 4 Type of planning versus position of individual.

The second method permits those in production and inventory control to enter this function at any one of a number of stages. Members of these departments can assist not only in their own job but with their associates as well in establishing objectives, making assumptions, analyzing, developing alternatives, and even in assisting in making the final choice of long-range planning (see Fig. 5).

The third method concerns the coordinating aspect of production and inventory control functions. Here they can work under a corporate framework to achieve plans for up to 10 to 20 years ahead.

There is a final reason for including production and inventory control in the overall view of corporate long-range planning. Many feel that most of the decisions which contribute to the profit or loss of a company are made at the middle-management level. This is the day-to-day conduct of the business as opposed to the higher general policy and master planning done by the top executives. The middle-management team has more integrated involvement in a corporation than the lower levels and has a better understanding than the higher level of the cause-and-effect relationships. Middle management has an excellent communication system, less turnover, and provides not only the strength of today but the growth of the future for many companies.

LONG-RANGE PLANNING CONSIDERATIONS

Experience in long-range planning is very limited in business today. It has been used extensively in the past for financial and profit planning, but seldom by production and inventory control which can make distinct contributions.

Since details in specifics are limited, this chapter will serve as a base upon which to prepare a plan of action for the long range. Explanation of functions in addition to those of production and inventory control will be covered because of the opportunity available.

This chapter, therefore, intends to:
1. Give highlights of long-range planning
2. Illustrate various types, techniques, and examples
3. Explain how they can be utilized
4. Caution what problems and difficulties can be encountered
5. End with a comprehensive list on this subject for subsequent detailed references

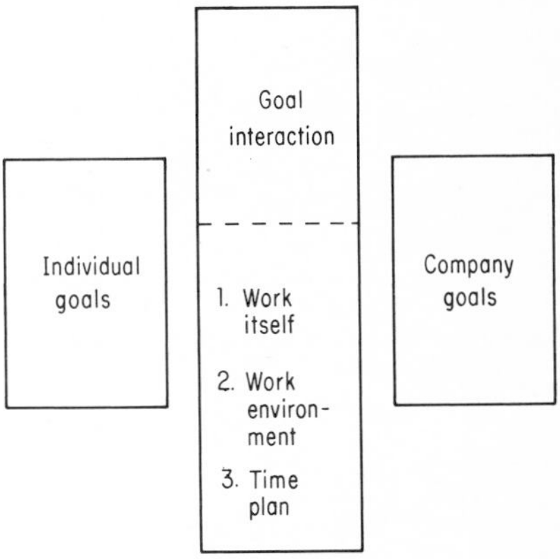

Theory of Long-range Planning. Long-range planning is difficult, full of educated guesses, replete with uncertainties, and time consuming. Yet it is highly necessary for successful company growth and realistic development if managers truly wish to make optimum use of expenditures of corporate time and materials. Agreeing that the day of the specialist has arrived and companies must start thinking not just of today

Fig. 5 Relationship between individual and company planning. (*From C. L. Hughes, Goal Setting: Key to Individual and Organizational Effectiveness, American Management Association, New York, 1965. Reprinted by permission of the publisher. ©1965 by the American Management Association, Inc.*)

but of 10 years from today, one would probably agree that production and inventory control as a profession cannot ignore long-range planning. It will be seen that the principles and perspective of this function are the same for everyone[9]—that all one has to do is modify them as necessary for individual and corporate use.

DEFINITION: "Long-range planning" has been defined as "a systematic means by which a company can become what it wants to be."[10] It is an organized method whereby we can give identity and direction to the hope, aspirations, and thinking of the company. At the same time, it is a philosophy and a tool a businessman can use to exert greater control over his own department's or division's destiny. It is also a discipline that can force each function within a corporation to coordinate its objectives with those of every other departments' function in context of predetermined objectives.

Going back some years in the development of scientific innovations, it used to be every 50 to 100 years between major inventions. Today we see the dynamic innovations such as television, laser, etc., arrive at intervals of from 5 to 10 years.[11] In the future, it probably will be an even shorter period of time, as indicated in Fig. 6. The businessman of today is realizing that he cannot do business any longer by rule of thumb. He is unable to limit his thinking to just a matter of months ahead. He must think in terms of products, markets, production schedules, organization demands, manpower, financial needs, etc., to a minimum of a 10-year period of time.

Long-range planning, then, is a tool to be used for this type of forward thinking. One expert remarks that it is "setting forth goals of a company in all fundamental phases of its operations on a yearly basis of not less than 5 years and preferably 10 years"[12] in the future. The goals would be the result of a realistic appraisal of the company's strengths, weaknesses, and especially its position within the marketplace. Thus today, managers, supervisors, etc., must be wholly committed to some form of long-range planning. Assuming planning is a coordinating area of a company, then production and inventory control can use its position to help a company decide what it is going to do

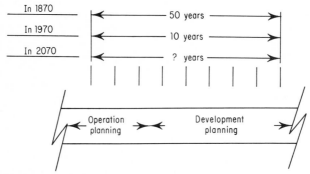

Fig. 6 Comparison of planning in time dimensions. (*From R. F. Stewart, A Framework for Business Planning, Long-range Planning Service Report 162, Stanford Research Institute, Menlo Park, Calif., February, 1963.*)

with its sales, what it intends to do about the future, and how it will take into account the peaks and valleys and project them into a trend line for a smoother future.

OBJECTIVE: One of the primary missions of production and inventory control is to achieve delivery economically. A way to aid in doing this is long-range planning. This means preparing for the anticipated but uncertain future, to have facilities, machinery, people, materials, etc., available for whatever time they will be particularly needed.[13] Long-range planning, therefore, has as its objective the development of a well-organized system to draw together in parallel relationships as much as possible, and to develop different degrees of details as necessary, the various requirements of the future. It is, in lay terms, to plan the production and operation requirements for anticipated future sales. To some exent, long-range planning is an extension of production scheduling, but incorporating a greater number of variables and, of course, uncertainties. A corporation must have the ability to meet expected production levels and be flexible to move toward alternative courses of action. Instead of having producduction scheduling on a short-term view of a matter of weeks or months, thinking must be in terms of years into this uncertain future. It will be necessary sometimes to sacrifice short-term gains and even short-term profits at the expense of long-range planning costs.[14]

JUSTIFICATION: Long-range planning from both the production control manager's departmental view and the overall company aspect does not require full-time effort in most circumstances. It does necessitate considerable expenditure of time and money for successful use of this management tool. The justification of long-range planning includes:

1. Potential of improved delivery preformance
2. Lower overtime expenditures
3. Shorter lead times
4. Greater utilization of men and materials
5. Less outside subcontracting

On the wider viewpoint, long-range planning techniques will assist top management to:

1. Make decisions regarding stabilizing profits and improving return on investments
2. Plan long-term facilities development
3. Train supervisory personnel replacements
4. Organize long-range sales programs
5. Develop procurement plans for purchase parts and materials
6. Level the increases and decreases in the numbers of hourly employees
7. Smooth production peaks and valleys

The Lockheed Aircraft Corporation was one of the early pioneers of this technique and has had a long-range planning department and a long-range plan for some period of time. Their philosophy for using a long-range master plan is that it:[15]

1. Becomes the basis for management decision
2. Establishes a method of getting at major deterrents in the future
3. Establishes the framework for organizing value judgments
4. Stimulates thought about the company's policy, strategy, and future development
5. Helps prevent short-term piecemeal solutions to long-range problems
6. Becomes a major integrating force for the corporation
7. Brings a comprehensive and unified picture of present and future business for the corporation to those who must operate the corporation

Disadvantages of Delaying the Long-range Plan. It has been found that a lack of or a delay in long-range planning can cause many elements of production to become marginal and inadequate. Poor delivery can result from long-range plans that are incomplete. A possible plan toward the future in this respect can prevent and minimize such trouble. Some companies feel that the money spent in long-range planning is more than justified by the savings in short-range delivery. Conversely they note that the lack of long-range planning, or even delay in doing it, can cause their competitive situation to deteriorate and be a potential loss of sales. Sometimes long-range planning enables a company to take advantage of consolidating its actions. Other times long-range planning can enable the production supervisor to better utilize his personnel and machines for the upcoming years. Finally, long-range planning, if properly implemented and coordinated by a production and inventory control manager, can bring to the corporate top management the information proving that it is more profitable to construct a plant today than it would be to modernize and use an older facility in the ensuing years.

It should be noted that long-range planning results can be negative as well as positive in terms of the future of a company. It is possible, and in fact often desirable, to learn through a long-range plan that a company should not be in a particular business, or that the market will phase out in the future. It also may be important to learn that a particular piece of equipment will not be adequate in the coming years.

TIME CONSIDERATIONS

One of the first questions to be answered concerns the length of time covered by long-range planning compared with intermediate- and short-range planning (see Fig. 7). The actual answer to this query depends directly upon the product of the company involved. For example, a corporation building heavy truck assemblies will use 5 to 10 years in long-range planning. Aircraft manufacturers will consider 10 to 20 years as a long-range period of time. An original-equipment supplier to the automobile industry might consider 3 to 5 years a long term, while a retail store would use 2 years. It is possible to even consider a six-month period of time as long-range planning, as would be the case in a food store.

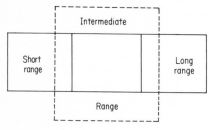

Fig. 7 Relationship among three types of planning.

Long-range Planning. Assume for discussion that the long-range plan will cover a period of from 5 to 10 years ahead of the current date. It is recognized that many companies consider it difficult and nearly impossible to project their growth 10 years out. However, once they get into the planning, they learn that with the assistance of market-research economists and just good management "guesstimates," a "map" of the future can be made.[16] When the plan is being developed, normally one-year intervals are suggested for review and for reconsideration of the long-range plan.

Intermediate-range Planning. As a general rule, intermediate-range planning is from one to five years. Again companies break this period into one-year intervals, though it is often further divided into half-year or quarter-year increments. The intermediate period of time can be used as a transition from the short-range scheduling view to the long-range prognostications of the future. More finite determinations and estimates can be made in contrast to the more general long-range and more accurate short-range considerations. It is also a period within which production planning and control can make extensive contributions by extending their knowledge of short-range scheduling.

Short-range Planning. Short-range planning generally ranges from a one-month to a one-year period of time. Occasionally it extends to a two-year consideration. It is closely allied to scheduling—that is, producing to anticipated requirements in the short term. More accurate statistics are available concerning production levels, overtime needs, delivery trends, lead times, manpower requirements, and even the specifics of sales requirements by particular part or assembly number. The short-range plans are usually revised quarterly and often monthly. Occasionally they are "moving" plans which are adjusted as necessary for specific needs. These reviews are related closely to the trend of orders, the general economic picture, the company market situation, and the short-range industry trends. Monthly periods of time are of overriding importance in consideration, and based on company desires for performance for a particular month, can negate one month as compared with the next. A short-range plan uses the sales forecast as a strong base and then relates as necessary to inventory, production, and manpower needs.

Comparison between Long- and Short-range Planning. A plan is considered to be long range when it requires the hiring of people, the training of employees, and the use of capital to purchase machinery, lease buildings, or construct facilities. In contrast, it is considered short range if it is a specific reaction to a sales requirement and is done in a time interval between the receipt and the general shipment of an order, considering normal lead times. If the preparation of planning must be done outside of the normal production cycle, it is considered long-range planning. If it is a specific demand, for instance, by a part number, then it is viewed as a short-range outlook.

TYPES OF LONG-RANGE PLANNING

There are three general categories of long-range planning: theoretical, corporate, and production. The use made of these depends upon one's position within the corporation and the overall goal desired. These groups are:

Group A—Theoretical Planning
1. Comprehensive
2. Functional
3. Socioeconomic
4. Government

Group B—Corporate Planning
1. Financial
2. Profit centers
3. Physical
4. Facilities and equipment
5. New products
6. Product standardization
7. Product simplification
8. Computer conversion
9. Systems planning

Group C—Production Planning
1. Equipment
2. Manpower
3. Personnel training
4. Vendor analysis and other purchasing functions
5. Inventory reduction
6. Programs or contracts

Theoretical Planning. Included in the various types of long-range planning are a number of approaches that are theoretical in content. These apply much more to the educator than the top corporation executive. They are used more by the staff employee than by the line. They are more suited for the 10-year plan than the closer 2 to 5 years. For an excellent discussion of these types of planning see M. C. Branch, *The Corporate Planning Process.*[17]

1. *Comprehensive* (Fig. 8). In one sense or another, all planning is comprehensive, because the scope of the considerations must be complete for what is being planned. No significant aspect can be ignored. Comprehensive planning includes both the overall planning for the organization as an entity and functional planning related to one part of the organization. Comprehensive planning is the continued formulation of objectives and guidance toward the attainment of this goal.

2. *Functional.* The purpose of functional planning is to focus on a particular element of the total problem. It might pertain to manufacturing, finance, or public relations, and could be associated with some other type of planning. It could focus on several closely related activities, or it may be very narrow in scope, but in any case it is intensive in its review.

3. *Socioeconomic.* This type of planning is not commonly used in business, but is extensively practiced by the government. Socioeconomic planning includes such forms as health insurance, retirement programs, diversification of products, educational institutions, and even political support for a particular idea.

4. *Government.* This type of planning refers to the applications of the process of planning within the areas of government activity. It may be comprehensive in scope, may be functional in nature, and may include physical planning. This is a general designation to indicate who is doing the planning and for what broad sector of the economy the planning is intended. It does not necessarily describe what is being planned.

Fig. 8 Comprehensive planning. (*From R. F. Stewart, A Framework for Business Planning Long-range Planning Service Report 162, Stanford Research Institute, Menlo Park, Calif., February, 1963.*)

Corporate Planning. The following types of planning are those in which production and inventory control can participate in coordinating. Generally, these control departments have neither the responsibility nor authority to actually make decisions in these areas. They can assist and furnish valuable information for use by higher executives. Figure 9 summarizes the types of corporate planning.

1. *Financial.* This type of planning has been fairly common and is the best known today of all types of long-range planning. It includes budgets, inventories, profit and loss, and all the attendant parts of financial planning. However, this handbook will not delve into this subject. While it is very important and complex, it is more than adequately covered in other books available on the market today.

2. *Profit Centers.* A trend in recent years has been the consideration of each individual plant and even parts of a plant as a specific operational profit center. This type of long-range planning is somewhat unique in the functional organization of the business. It enables a very direct control over the profitability of a specific product or specific production facility. Long-range planning is important here because it extends the consideration of the competitiveness of not only the product but also the method of producing it. It provides an opportunity for evaluating the true capabilities of a specific department or plant.

3. *Physical.* Physical planning is characterized as considering the use of cities and regions of the country by the business for the location of a physical plant. It is important to consider the location of a city as related to suppliers, channels of distribution, and the type of labor force. In looking at plant location, it is germain to consider the value of expanding an existing facility or the construction of a completely new building for the future.

4. *Facilities and Equipment.* Long-range planning for facilities and equipment includes a review of what machines may be obsolete, or approaching
obsolescence, and what the attendant dollar replacement value would be. This
implies the evaluation of competitive equipment and the projection of operating
costs over a period of time. Long-range plans in this aspect need to consider
what equipment will be necessary for expansion and possibly for contraction.

Considered are trends in equipment development and what new techniques
in manufacturing might obsolete a potential investment. The relationship be-

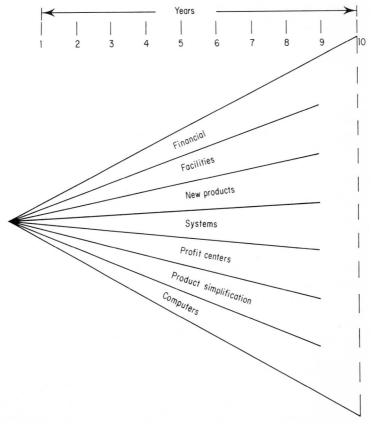

Fig. 9 Corporate planning illustrating several types. (*From M. C. Branch, The Corporate Planning Process, American Management Association, New York, 1962. Reprinted
by permission of the publisher. ©1962 by the American Management Association, Inc.*)

tween facilities planning and equipment planning is very close, because one
constitutes a consideration of the other. Too often equipment decisions are
made without the attendant review of the facility. Figure 10 gives an example
of a typical planning sheet for facilities and equipment.

Any review of facilities and equipment must consider:[18]

  a. Do we need a new plant?
  b. Where should it be built?
  c. Would we be wiser to expand our existing facility?
  d. When should we make the move?
  e. Will we be prepared for the long-term future?

5. *New Products.* A considerable amount of new-products planning is being done today by projecting outward from 5 to 20 years in terms of time. New-products planning is true long-range planning because it considers all the requirements necessary to develop, test, market, and produce a particular product. See Fig. 11 for an example of this plan.

6. *Product Standardization.* The increasing desire by customers for numerous equipment modifications places an emphasis on standardizing a configuration on which optional accessories can be added. If such a long-range plan is not made, the company will find their inventories will increase substantially. Any gains in marketing a greater variety of products can often be lost because of the cost of carrying excess inventory.

Standardizing the product requires an extensive use of the engineering capabilities of the company. Included should be the consideration of semifinished con-

EDP No.	Item	19_	19_	19_	19_	19_	19_	19_	19_	19_	19_
087	Land										
093	Land improvements										
104	Building A										
108	Building B										
109	Building C										
131	Building installation A										
148	Building installation B										
156	Machinery and equipment A										
181	Machinery and equipment B										
193	Total										

Fig. 10 Typical physical, facilities, and equipment planning sheet. (*From Eugene Root and George A. Stiner, "The Lockheed Aircraft Corporation Master Plan" in D. W. Ewing (ed.), Long-range Planning for Management, Harper & Row, Publishers Incorporated, New York, 1964. Reprinted by permission of the authors.*)

figurations of the product to which "add-ons" can easily be made as required by the customer.

7. *Product Simplification.* This type of planning for the long term is closely allied to product standardization. The difference is that simplification is the elimination of a component such as a bracket, fastener, etc. This should be done for an easier produced product necessitating fewer different types of parts. Inventory control practitioners realize that the *amount* of inventory often increases with the square of the number of different types of parts and not in a direct relationship. They thus should be aware of needs to simplify the product.

8. *Computer Conversion.* A relatively unknown type of long-range planning is the conversion to computers. With today's trend toward computer assistance in American business, this type of long-range look is critically needed. It includes:

a. Feasibility study of what type of equipment is to be purchased

Fig. 11 New-product schedule. [From Bruce Payne, "Steps in Long-range Planning" in D. W. Ewing (ed.), *Long-range Planning for Management*, Harper & Row, Publishers Incorporated, New York, 1964; originally appeared as an article in *Harvard Business Review, Mar.–Apr.*, 1957, pp. 95–106. Reprinted by permission of the *Harvard Business Review*.]

Year	Marketing organization	Sales effort	Advertising	New products	Production control
1,2			Research and development		
3			New-product selection		
4			Prototype production		
5			Transition period to full production		
6 Nov.	Formulate sales organization policies, pricing plan, forecasting program		Plan catalogs, national advertising		Construct factory fixed budget; make historical cost system
Dec.	Complete new sales plans		Consult with advertising agency	Select industrial designers	Determine EDP requirements; manually schedule production of product
7 Jan.		Outline new policies and programs to personnel	Analyze media		Begin work on overall production control plan; construct variable budgets for each department
Feb.	Select sales manager		Select media; complete cooperative program	Consult with designers on product line	Complete production control plan; begin experimental run of plan
Mar.	Begin recruiting new salesmen	Introduce new selling procedures Continue sales training		Mock-up construction	Hire production control and scheduling supervisor
Apr.			Begin planning outdoor advertising campaign		
May.		Start new salesmen	Begin national advertising program		
June.			Begin regional advertising product line	Market tests for new-product-line styles	Review all production schedules; prepare progress reports
July.	Recruit new salesmen for South and Southwest	Assess new sales plan; hold meetings with dealers			Hire industrial engineering assistant
Aug.					Meetings on quality control and inspection standards
Sept.			Outdoor advertising campaign: Chicago, Detroit, and other cities	Show selected new-product-line styles at fall trade shows	Inventory modernization program to reduce in-process inventories
Oct.	Appoint new Midwest district managers	Special meetings with managers of product line			Fixed and variable budgets with tighter operating budgets

b. Educating personnel in capabilities and limitations of this management device

c. Implementing the transition from the existing manual or mechanized system to the new computer

The few companies that have performed such studies[19] are pleased with the results and find that their returns on investment, while intangible, appear to be sizable. Because of the lack of understanding and acceptance of computers, especially in manufacturing today, this type of forward look is critically needed.

9. *Systems Planning.* This long-range planning includes the engineering and integration of components and subassemblies into the overall design. It also brings into the review an analysis of the flow of papers and reports necessary for the successful operation of the corporation.

Production Planning. The downtime of machines, the accuracy and effectiveness of schedules, the type of production delays, the effectiveness of inventory controls, and turnover rates are all key considerations for this group of planning activities. Production and inventory control personnel share with manufacturing a direct responsibility in this area.

1. *Equipment.* Equipment age, depreciation, necessary maintenance, replacement schedules, and improvement of equipment design are some of the considerations in equipment long-range planning.

2. *Manpower.* Important to long-range planning is the determination of the manpower necessary to perform a particular type of job. With the trends in education today, and the move toward more white-collar and fewer blue-collar employees, this type of planning is of utmost importance. Managers should review the changes from direct to indirect labor and the possibility of automated equipment requiring employees of higher skill. They also have to consider what the effect of any product changes would make on the type of employee needed in the time period being considered.

3. *Personnel Training.* An appraisal of labor and supervisor training programs should be made as part of the long-range analysis. This would include a look at wage scales, supervisory programs, quality of supervisors, and what particular emphasis on employee relations are needed in the future.

4. *Vendor Analysis and Other Purchasing Functions.* This necessitates the inclusion of vendor analysis in any consideration of planning. The materials management concept places one manager in charge of inventory control, purchasing, production control, and often traffic.

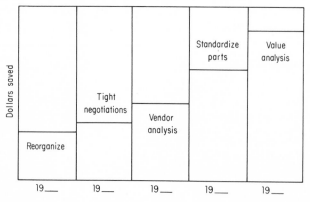

Fig. 12 Long-range plan for purchasing department.

By careful analysis of the characteristics of suppliers, both substantial savings and better vendor relationship can be obtained for the future. This vendor review should include the current ability to give fair prices, good quality, and delivery when requested. Then the plans for the coming years should include the association with these qualified suppliers. Such a projection can be made, correlating it with a five-year savings program, as detailed in Fig. 12.

5. *Inventory Reduction.* One of the most successful methods for controlling inventories is through a planned approach reducing the existing inventory to the minimum level needed to meet management policies and goals. Long-range planning techniques can be used to lower the inventory and then maintain it at the desired level. An example of such a program is shown in Fig. 13.

Category	Task	Responsibility	Timetable
Phase I......	Program announcement	President	June 19—
Phase II.....	Policy and procedure determination	General manager	July 19—
Phase III....	Short-range efforts:		August 19—
	A. Service inventory	Service manager	
	B. EDP reports	DP manager	
	C. Steel inventory	Inv. control mgr.	
	D. Open-purchase orders	Purchasing agent	
	E. Program reschedules	Prod. control mgr.	
	F. Return rejected material	Receiving supr.	
Phase IV....	Intermediate-range efforts:		February 19—
	A. Employee training	Inv. cont. mgr.	
	B. Parts classification	Service manager	
	C. Machine loading	Prod. cont. mgr.	
	D. Warehouse locations	Sales manager	
	E. Combine production and service inventories	Works manager	
Phase V.....	Long-range efforts:		March 19—
	A. Production standardization	Engineering mgr.	
	B. EDP control	Inv. cont. mgr.	

Fig. 13   Long-range planning for inventory-reduction program.

6. *Programs or Contracts.* Included in this form of long-range planning is the review of specific programs for the future. This includes building models with extensive long-lead time, obtaining materials for this production, and using proper techniques to accomplish deliveries required.

STEPS IN LONG-RANGE PLANNING

True and effective long-range planning is a complicated effort (see Fig. 14) requiring considerable expenditure of time and energy, close corporate coordination and communication, and patience to complete the effort. Much of the work that is done today under the guise of "long-range planning" is really intermediate- or inaccurate long-range planning. True long-range planning is still a rarity and involves a complicated sequence of activities.

The general steps are the same for almost all industries, but they must be tailored to the individual company needs. A definite program must be established using a considerable amount of thought, and it must be adhered to with some degree of rigidity. The steps necessary for successful long-range planning are:

1. Determine the objectives of the company.
2. Select the method of approach.
3. Establish the corporate policies to guide the long-range plan.
4. Select the procedures for the course of action.
5. Recheck the initial decisions for validity.
6. Establish a budget including methods of auditing the program.
7. Select the type of personnel to undertake this program.
8. Select the techniques to assist in the long-range plan.
9. Publicize the objectives of the company and the reasons to all concerned within the company.
10. Implement the program including a schedule of activities.
11. Evaluate the progress including changing and replanning as necessary.
12. Use the results and act on the decisions from the long-range plan.

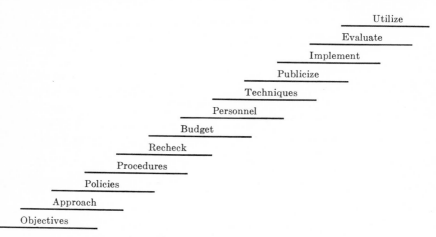

Fig. 14 Twelve steps in long-range planning.

Determining the Objectives.   The first step in long-range planning is determining the company goals, often called the "objectives" of the business.   This involves a review using clear, sharp considerations of the past and future trends, thinking ahead to what the desires of the corporation are and anticipating what situations might evolve in the coming years.   Sometimes it requires selecting from a series of alternatives.   Sometimes it necessitates an optimistic approach.   But in any event, confusion must be avoided, along with rigidity and stagnation.   Change, flexibility, and progress must be accepted, and the future must be approached in a creative and constructive manner.

For example, the objectives of one company might be:
1. Planned investment
2. Turnover desired
3. Return on investment expected
The objectives of one division within this company might be:
1. Volume of sales desired
2. Growth anticipated
3. Profit percentage by product line
Another division might list their objectives as:
1. Markets to be approached

2. Net sales
3. Facilities planned
4. Division investment
5. Community and employee relations
Another example is shown in Fig. 15.

Con-trol No.	Item	19_	19_	19_	19_	19_	19_	19_	19_	19_	19_
	Sales value of 40-hour capacity										
101	Target										
102	Previous target										
	Market										
103	Present estimate										
104	Previous estimate										
	Net Sales										
105	Target										
106	Percent of 40-hour capacity										
107	Percent of market										
108	Previous target										
109	Percent of 40-hour capacity										
110	Percent of market										
	Earnings before taxes										
111	Target										
112	Percent of net sales										
113	Previous target										
114	Percent of net sales										
	Facilities program										
115	Capital										
116	Authority expense										
117	Total										
	Investment — average										
118	Target										
119	Turnover										
120	Percent return before taxes										

Fig. 15 Summary of company objectives. (*From "Determining and Rpeorting Division Objectives at American Brake Shoe Co., Guide to Profit Improvement Program," American Brake Shoe Co., August 1, 1959.*)

Selecting the Method of Approach. In practice, there are two general methods of approaching the long-range plan. The first is to establish the desired corporate goals and then use a long-range plan to understand and reach these goals. The other approach is for each department or division to calculate its own future as accurately as it can without regard to other divisions of the company or any particular emphasis on a *most desirable* corporate goal. Both approaches have been successfully tried and there is neither a right nor a wrong approach. It is up to the company involved to evaluate both of them, weigh one against the other to see which has the most desirable pattern, and then fit it into the overall long-range plan.

Should the approach be by division or department, the method must be consistent with any previously established company-wide objectives. By disseminating this data to the individuals involved, a manager can transform the broad long-term company objective into specific plans for his department.

Establishing the Corporate Policies. The next step in long-range planning is to establish the policies under which the company is to operate. Such policies are normally general statements or understandings which will channel the thinking and actions of the entire company in the long-range plan. For members of production and inventory control departments, it often will include a consideration of the production characteristics, the complexity of the manufacturing, the degree of product specialization, the capacity and flexibility of production facilities and warehousing, and the quality requirements.

An example of a typical policy statement of one corporation included:[20]

1. A general statement regarding the operations
2. The minimum acceptable profits to be expected
3. The markets to be undertaken
4. The general rules establishing product lines
5. A statement with respect to sources of supply and policies such as reciprocity
6. A statement with respect to company organization, principles, and practices
7. A statement regarding any planned research programs
8. A statement regarding finance, including the use of working capital, company debt, and dividend plans
9. A statement with respect to personnel policies for all levels and types of employment
10. A general statement with respect to public relations

Selecting the Procedures. This step in the long-range plan includes defining all the productive elements. These production elements (see Fig. 16) may vary considerably from one business to another but generally speaking should include the following considerations:

1. Accurate promises
2. Rapidity of change
3. Internal departmental flexibility
4. General company flexibility
5. Procedural and policy plans
6. Capital limitations

Outside of the company's control are a number of other elements, such as the political climate, the economic conditions, the speed of technological change, and the status of labor. These generalized elements are to be considered in this step.

The long-range plan should enumerate tangible and intangible items for specific considerations. These items include:

1. Sales
2. Cost of sales
3. Existing capacity
4. Administration expenses
5. Capital expenses
6. Research and product development
7. Personnel development
8. Machine capacity
9. Material requirements or limitations

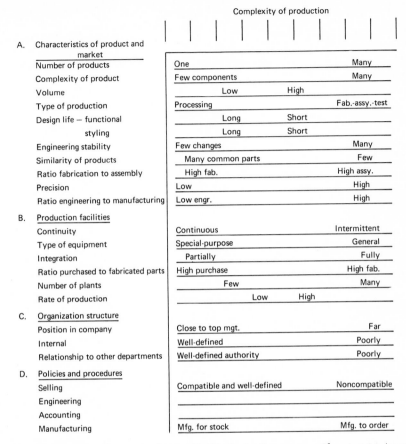

	Complexity of production
A. Characteristics of product and market	
Number of products	One ... Many
Complexity of product	Few components ... Many
Volume	Low ... High
Type of production	Processing ... Fab.-assy.-test
Design life — functional	Long ... Short
styling	Long ... Short
Engineering stability	Few changes ... Many
Similarity of products	Many common parts ... Few
Ratio fabrication to assembly	High fab. ... High assy.
Precision	Low ... High
Ratio engineering to manufacturing	Low engr. ... High
B. Production facilities	
Continuity	Continuous ... Intermittent
Type of equipment	Special-purpose ... General
Integration	Partially ... Fully
Ratio purchased to fabricated parts	High purchase ... High fab.
Number of plants	Few ... Many
Rate of production	Low ... High
C. Organization structure	
Position in company	Close to top mgt. ... Far
Internal	Well-defined ... Poorly
Relationship to other departments	Well-defined authority ... Poorly
D. Policies and procedures	
Selling	Compatible and well-defined ... Noncompatible
Engineering	
Accounting	
Manufacturing	Mfg. for stock ... Mfg. to order

Fig. 16 *Production elements. (From B. W. Scott, Long-range Planning in American Industry, American Management Association, New York, 1965. Reprinted by permission of the publisher. © 1965 by the American Management Association, Inc.)*

Rechecking the Initial Decision. The fifth step in the long-range plan is to review the efforts and decisions to date and examine the possibility of alternative courses of action. There is seldom a long-range plan which does not have reasonable alternatives available. These should be evaluated and a decision made to stay on the established course or change directions. It is possible, for instance, to recheck the validity of the sales projection and take whatever corrective action is called for in this projection.

Establishing the Budget. A budget (Fig. 17) is an integral part of a long-range plan. It can be a statement of expected results in numerical and financial terms, or it can be just a complex set of expected results of policies and procedures which would come from the long-range consideration. It may include methods of correlating and relating short-range with long-range programs. It often includes a flexible timetable which gives the planners an opportunity to make whatever moves might be necessary.

One part of the budget is a provision for periodic review. Normally the long-range plan is analyzed once every six months, but it can be as frequently as every three months.

Step	Estimated cost		Documents required?	Target date
	Salaries	Expenses		
1. Objectives.......				
2. Approach........				
3. Policies..........				
4. Procedures.......				
5. Recheck.........				
6. Budget..........				
7. Personnel........				
8. Techniques......				
9. Publicity........				
10. Implement.......				
11. Evaluate........				
12. Utilize..........				
Total cost.........				

Fig. 17 Long-range planning budget (outline).

It is often possible to set up controls on an exception basis. When there is a deviation from a norm, it can be spotted and its correction becomes a type of review.

Whatever the approach, the important thing is to establish the budget, measure the results against this budget, either in numerical or intangible measures, and exercise whatever type of action is necessary for the future.

Selecting Personnel. Of understandable importance is the type of individual to be used in making the long-range plan. It is possible to take one of several approaches: use individuals either full or part time, use staff specialists, obtain assistance from outside or internal consultants, or use a long-range planning committee. There is no particular best method in selecting the mode of operation for the long-range plan. Judgment is important, and often parallel approaches can be used. All have apparently worked well and will be discussed later in this chapter.

Selecting Techniques. A number of step-by-step and mathematical techniques can be used in the long-range planning efforts. These include such basic techniques as historical statistics, forecasting, and Gantt charts. Intermediate tools are the use of trends, machine loading, various indicators, and extrapolations. Advanced techniques would include operations research, PERT, linear programming, and the technique of simulation. (For details, refer to other chapters of this handbook as appropriate.)

The actual decisions on the type of technique used depend on the accuracy required, the complexity of the problem, and the validity and accuracy of the input data, as well as the results desired.

Publicizing Objectives. It should now be obvious that considerable efforts are required in successful long-range planning. In reality, it involves establishing the corporation's objectives and using techniques which will permit it to control its future. Companies engaged in long-range planning learn that there is a side benefit when plans including the company goals, objectives, and so forth are publicized. A new spirit emerges and individuals take the goals as their own or departmental goals and strive to contribute to the objectives. There should be no concern that the wrong person might learn of these objectives, since generally speaking these are internally oriented. Even if a corporation's sales or profit objective should become known on the outside, it might do no harm, since it gives a progressive impression of the corporation. Once long-range plans are started, they should be disseminated to all interested parties. This *must* include the hourly employees within the corporation.

Implementing the Plan. Implementation of the long-range plan might seem obvious, but in truth it necessitates a great deal of effort. Part of the implementation is establishing a schedule, as will be indicated later in this chapter. This schedule is somewhat of a "budget" of the planned effort noting various checkpoints to ascertain the progress to date.

Evaluating Progress. Experience indicates that more often the long-range plan is changed than used without any revisions. Usually, any reevaluation takes place with regard to timing and not in the steps of the action to be taken. Sometimes the loss of a key individual or a large surge of business demands that efforts be put in other directions. Should this happen, the plan should not be destroyed, but merely temporarily suspended for a period of time until the efforts can begin again.

During the long-range plan period, a number of problems will arise as well as a considerable amount of important information which should be analyzed at the end of the six-month period of time previously suggested. Whatever changes are necessary should be made in the long-range plan. If trouble appears inevitable, corrective action should be taken. If problems emerge, they should be tackled. Ample opportunity must be set forth to examine the plan to redirect it as necessary.

Using Results. The information gained from long-range planning *must* be used. Too much work will have been done to waste. It might be used in terms of required expansion. Perhaps it would be in context of exploring new product lines. It may be in relation to manpower development and employee training. Irrespective of the information which comes from long-range planning, the data must be taken, disseminated, and integrated into the corporation. Increases in the effort of people and monetary investment may be necessary, but they will go for nought if the results are not used. This comment may seem unnecessary, but so few companies have realized the results of their efforts that it is stressed at this point.

TECHNIQUES USED IN LONG-RANGE PLANNING

Once the type of long-range planning desired has been determined, the steps to be taken decided, and the personnel to perform the long-range planning selected, the time comes to consider which of the various techniques can assist in the long-range plan. These can range from the basic analysis of historical statistics and current bookings to the complicated techniques of linear programming and computer simulation.

These techniques are examined in detail in other chapters of this handbook. They are noted here to advise what aids are available in long-range planning.

Basic Statistics. Any company that plans for the long range immediately discovers an ardent desire for good historical statistics about the company's activities. Often this information concerning bookings, production, shipments, etc., is not available, and the company has to recreate data for the last year or two. Special emphasis should be placed on the most recent year's activities. A projection should be made of this information into the forthcoming year. The importance of historical and continuing statistics cannot be overstressed, as it becomes the basis of history upon which to forecast the future. The company must know what has happened in the immediate past, and they must compile the information if it is not readily available.

Forecasts. The subject of forecasting is covered in detail in Chapter 8, but since it is an integral part of long-range planning, a few necessary comments and important observations should be made.

In the early days of long-range planning, a monthly, quarterly, and/or annual analysis of sales was often made. From this was developed a manufacturing plan to use in the future. The more sophisticated companies in these early days would prepare elaborate charts (see Fig. 18) and attempt to determine definite schedules for future periods. In a later period the sales department would tell the production department what to produce and/or what to keep in stock. Few economic forecasts were available and often field opinion, salesmen, and executives in the various sales districts had a lot to do with the forecast of the coming year.

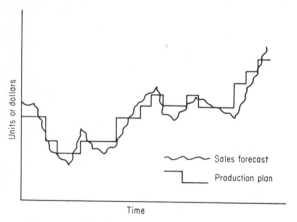

Fig. 18   Sales forecast versus production plan.

More recently, the errors in forecasts have been decreased,[21] but companies are still misled by dramatic economic changes, modifications, customer desires, deviations in production capacity, etc. A point of diminishing returns in forecasting improvement can be reached so that caution is advised before putting extensive efforts on these techniques.

Gantt Charts. Listing information makes it difficult to quickly note highs and lows in any certain pattern. One effective basic technique to show information graphically is the Gantt chart. This graphical presentation is a very effective method for displaying information. It can be used to indicate shipments, backlogs, production capacity, manpower available, and similar factors. The Gantt chart can be used to project in advance an estimated work load, to see where problems are arising and where extra efforts such as overtime, transfer of personnel, etc., will be necessary. A typical Gantt chart is illustrated in Fig. 19.

Trend Lines. One type of forecast of demand is to use a trend line (Fig. 20). In such a technique, past demands are considered and trend lines established. Control limits (Fig. 21) can be developed which are based on past fluctuations of actual sales from the trend. A certain percentage (often 95 percent or more) of the demand can usually be expected to fall within these various limits.[22]

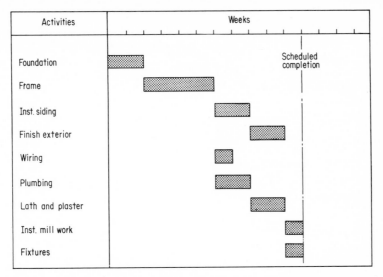

Fig. 19 Gantt chart for building project. (*From "Training Manual: Production Planning and Inventory Control," private paper, Peat, Marwick, Mitchell & Co., New York, October, 1966.*)

Extrapolations. Extrapolations of trends are well suited to production control and its related forecasts, since this approach is adaptable to routine clerical procedures. As Fig. 22 indicates, an extrapolation has been made and an average forecast determined over a period of time. This technique has a built-in danger, as it assumes the conditions of the past will hold true in the future.

In certain instances, the extrapolation of a trend line can be compared with a new forecast and control limits used. If the forecast falls outside of control

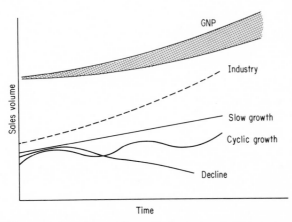

Fig. 20 Trend-forecast examples. (*From H. Igor Ansoff, "Strategies for Diversification" in D. W. Ewing (ed.), Long-range Planning for Management, Harper & Row, Publishers Incorporated, New York, 1964; originally appeared as an article in Harvard Business Review, Sept.–Oct. 1957, pp. 113–124. Reprinted by permission of the Harvard Business Review.*)

lines, then data should be questioned. If it plots within the limits, then it can be assumed to be acceptable.

Machine Loading. Good historical production information and current orders from customers can be combined in machine loading to indicate short and intermediate production levels.

In making this analysis, a careful review of the past and an awareness that the future may not always contain the same product mix are necessary. However, effective machine loading can give more than adequate insight into

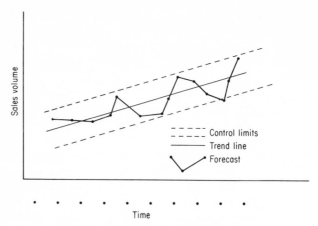

Fig. 21 Trend line using control limits.

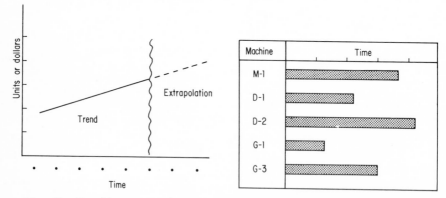

Fig. 22 Trend-line extrapolation.   **Fig. 23** Machine-loading Gantt chart.

the future and can aid the overall long-range plan. See Fig. 23 for a machine-loading Gantt chart.

Wright's Indicators. In 1953, a Standard Oil of New Jersey economist, Ashley Wright, developed a device for determining turns in the business cycle. Wright made use of the normal distribution curve, often called a "bell-shaped" curve, and noted that the upturns and downturns in a large number of business indicators would show such a distribution pattern. By using Wright's theory, a general business cycle can be forecast and used as part of long-range planning. This concept also has applications in utilizing internal corporate statistics.

PERT and CPM. °   PERT and CPM use a chart (Fig. 24) on which all the individual tasks to complete a particular program are graphically illustrated.[23] This chart is called a "network" and is comprised of events and activities representing a specific program.   The "events" are individual accomplishments, while an "activity" represents the time and resources which are necessary to progress from one event to the next.   These events and activities use a set of rules which allows the determination of critical and secondary paths.

The critical path is the longest continuous time path.   This critical path is frequently calculated by a computer, though in more simple projects it can be done manually.

In CPM, only the average time estimate is used for each activity.   Three time estimates are made for each activity in PERT: the most optimistic, the most likely, and the most pessimistic time.   The most optimistic time is an

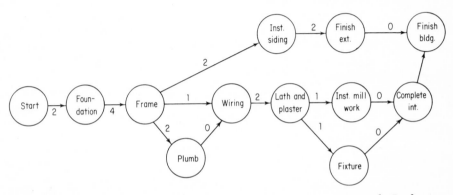

Fig. 24   PERT network for building project. (*From "Training Manual: Production Planning and Inventory Control," private paper, Peat, Marwick, Mitchell & Co., New York, October, 1966.*)

estimate of the minimum amount of time an activity will require to take place, while the pessimistic is the maximum amount of time considering unusually poor experience.   The most likely is the average or normal time required to perform a particular activity.

The original PERT technique was developed as a method of planning and controlling the Polaris ballistic missile program of the United States Navy.   Its purpose was to place emphasis on management's planning of complex research and development programs.   Since then, a number of variations of PERT, such as PEP, which is used by the United States Air Force, PRESS, and others have been developed, but all use similar concepts.

As control devices, PERT and CPM focus attention on the most important areas of management action.   They do not point out the small delays but do denote the critical areas upon which immediate attention should be given.

Linear Programming.   This technique is a mathematical method to determine the optimum combinations of a limited set of resources to maximize some objective.   It uses a set of algebraic equations which represent the extent to which a goal can be achieved.

°PERT is the acronym for program evaluation review technique.   CPM is the critical path method.

One example of a linear program is showing the best balance between production stability, inventory level, and customer service. Factors such as demand characteristics, cost of holding inventory, cost of modifying production levels, etc., can be put together in a whole range of alternatives from which a model can be developed. Linear programming is often based on rather rigid assumptions but has applications in production planning.

Simulation. One outgrowth of operations research has been simulation, normally using computers, but sometimes hand methods. By simulation, a whole production complex can be evaluated by inserting a number of variables into a program. Changes in product mix, delivery, quality, and seasonal effects are examples of variables that can be incorporated. Computer simulation is highly mathematical, and although an exact duplicate of the actual operation is seldom obtained, an answer of plus or minus 10 percent can be achieved. The results possible are more than adequate to simulate the factory operations and therefore give an idea of the behavior in advance.

The development of a model for simulation is difficult, requiring a complex and extensive series of developmental tests before it can be used. Once a model is developed, it is then put into a specific application.

PERSONNEL REQUIRED

To establish the number and type of persons to perform long-range planning, two approaches are possible. The first is assigning one individual, either a division manager, a line man in one of the divisions, a specialist from staff, or an inside or outside consultant. The second is to use a committee approach such as a growth committee, steering committee, long-range planning committee, etc.

The Individual Approach. Assuming a full-time effort on the long-range plan, a single-individual approach generally works well. The individual can establish a working relation with the corporation chief executive officer and extend his efforts into an effective long-range plan. He is often considered a manager (if not already at this level) and is given the privilege of exercising some independent judgment. He must coordinate information from various sources, adhering to the previously established corporate goals and policies.

The purpose of the long-range plan is to force someone to think carefully through the plans of the company for future years and recognize the implications of the various objectives and goals. By assigning one man to this task, it is possible to minimize any superficial approach. One person can focus attention on the mechanics as well as make a careful analysis of the factors which produce the information. The most important value of this coordinating activity is the uniformity of understanding by the various units of the corporation, including the board of directors. A single individual can often tackle the problems and take steps to meet them as necessary.

One excellent by-product of long-range planning is the crystallization of top-management thinking. Another is that the investigations and deliberations are an excellent means of keeping the top executives informed about the different aspects of the business. Experience indicates that the individual can most effectively serve his corporation when all involved understand from the beginning the extent of his participation. The individual, therefore, is able to stimulate communications and understanding among various company officials. He cannot, however, make broad general estimates and assumptions on his own.

Functioning in the proper manner, long-range planning involves a series of meetings and substantial exchanges of informal information among key officers. An individual in charge of long-range planning, whether he be a staff specialist, a line man, or a consultant, must take as part of his function the assignment of indicating the implications of the various assumptions that have been made and pointing out where they are inconsistent or unrealistic. He must then reconcile differences, arrange follow-up meetings, and revise the factors involved numerous times.

A consultant's greatest contribution to long-range planning lies in two areas. (These following comments are applicable to internal corporate consultants as well as outside management consultants.) First, a consultant serves to promote communication. This involves raising questions, requesting information, holding informal conversations, and maintaining a continual definition of the problem and plans. Second, he can serve more objectively than any other person in compiling and accumulating the various facts and information, preparing progress reports, and contemplating policy decisions. One example of an individual's approach in a medium-sized company is illustrated in Fig. 25.

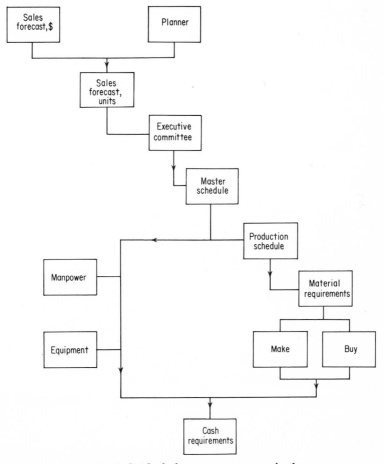

Fig. 25 Individual-planner-sequence work chart.

The Committee Approach. A planning committee (see Fig. 26) is normally a staff function and often includes in addition to the long-range planner two or three line or staff advisors from the various departments or organizations involved. The approach of a committee is to use specialists so that a more effective long-range plan can be obtained. In large companies where no single employee can possibly know enough to do the entire planning, a committee approach will be quite successful. It is possible to obtain a group of individuals from several operations of the business, such as an administrative vice president, materials manager, supervisor of production control, etc. One man serves as chairman of the committee, frequently referred to as the "planner," which may be a full-time position. The men selected for the committee must have proven ability and flexibility, and bring to their assignment objective thinking. They have to give a fair review of the problems which arise, irrespective of the company level from which they come. As previously mentioned, the middle-level managers are good sources of information. Members of production and inventory therefore have an excellent opportunity to participate on such a committee. As with production and inventory control, the long-range planning committee has a coordinating function (review Fig. 2). The prime reason for including middle-management personnel is that their day-to-day functions give them a considerable amount of experience which is very valuable in successful long-range planning

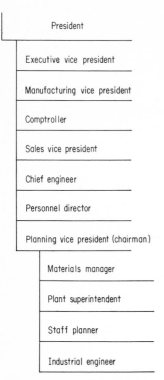

Fig. 26 Scalar organization chart of long-range planning committee.

OPERATION OF LONG-RANGE PLANS

In his early writings on long-range planning, Henri Fayol noted that a good plan demands the art of handling men, requires considerable energy with a measure of moral courage, a degree of competence, and a certain amount of general business experience. Since bad planning is quite common, there are a number of challenges built into long-range planning that require a considerable amount of advance thought.

Experience indicates that even with careful planning for a long-range plan, the organization seldom understands the magnitude of the problems to be attacked and the effort necessary. Managers apparently tend to focus their attention on compiling and analyzing figures but give very little attention to the development of the basic plan. This particular problem must be overcome at the beginning or the company will prove inadequate for the task.

At the early stages, there must be a strong understanding of the problems involved if long-range planning is to serve as a basis for future efforts. If assumptions are needed, they should be made initially and with complete agreement.

Sometimes groups will exist within the organization who may wish to promote a particular long-range plan to strengthen their own position. One must be careful with such groups, since objectivity can be lost easily and with it the best interests of the corporation.

Full participation must be given by all officers, managers, and employees involved. All must approach their assignments with enthusiasm, and let us stress again, as much objectivity as is humanly possible.

Executive Support. We have discussed already how the long-range planning is difficult at best and replete with problems. One way to attack these problems is to meet them through a planning implementation schedule as illustrated in Fig. 27. This schedule shows specific steps to be taken and actions to be made to vary the plan as necessary as time progresses and more information is known. It is also useful in overcoming one of the major problems in long-range planning, that is, in selling it to the corporation executives and other individuals. Quite often the chief executive is not sold on long-range planning, and he may feel that these uncertain efforts are not worth the expenditure by the corporation. Should the objectives not clearly reflect the interests of the company, then the long-range plan will tend to negate itself and true gains will not be achieved.

			Target dates		Actual progress dates				
Control No.	Program step	Techniques to use	Start	Finish	Survey	Evaluate	Design	Approval	Implement

Long-range planning implementation schedule

Division _____ Type of LRP _____

General manager _____ Date _____

LRP chairman _____

LRP committee members _____

Fig. 27   Implementation schedule.

The chief executive, as well as others, must be cognizant that adequate factual background is necessary so that when goals are set, they will not be too far above or below the ability of the company. On other occasions, there is an impatience if immediate results are not achieved. It must be stressed at the very start that long-range planning will not give immediate return on the time invested, but is a long, slow road.

Paper Work. As with every other task, long-range planning requires forms and paper procedures. It is more successful when the long-range planning blends into the existing information network and does not make paper work a separate chore. The forms which are to be used to collect the information should be standardized, and the number kept to a minimum. The record keeping and analysis should be centralized, and when data are obtained, they should be summarized and disseminated to those individuals who can use them. Because a myriad of information will be obtained in long-range planning, a record such as a loose-leaf notebook is most desirable. One of the important gains from long-range planning is to make people think and evaluate the future of the corporation. Informal conferences and telephone contacts are most important and part of the key to success. Such contacts should be used to the greatest extent possible and informal notes recorded.

Implementation Schedule. Regardless of the accuracy and effectiveness of the long-range plan, success cannot be had without implementation. This includes not only a list detailing the various tasks, responsibility, and time schedule, but also plans which will preclude a one-shot-and-then-forget-it type of planning. Planning, as previously noted, must be a continuous dynamic process. Things must be made to happen which might not otherwise occur.

As an adjunct to the implementation schedule, a functional organization chart is very important. These two documents will place in proper perspective the role of the various individuals. The documents together will give the proper approach to long-range planning and implementing the various tasks.

Whether we have a one-man approach or a committee approach to long-range planning, the implementation schedule should be used to give continuing data collection and feedback to the individual or individuals involved. It is a device that will enable the contributions of a number of different departments to go into the central planning area and be reviewed. It can be used to make a continuous revision of the long-range plan to achieve details that might otherwise be overlooked. A proper schedule standardizes the approach and yet allows for changes in the long-range policy as time progresses. (See Fig. 27.)

Replanning. The long-range plan must include provisions for increases and decreases, both for the company as a whole and for specific elements. The plan must be flexible because of changes in company concepts, ideas, and people involved, all of which may have an effect on the initial long-range plan.[23] Someone once remarked that what is needed is "a system for changing your system. You need a super system."[24] To a certain extent, this is true of long-range planning.

Replanning, then, is looking back at the initial plan, determining where there have been slippages or delays and whether it is achieving the results anticipated, whether economic or other conditions necessitate a revision of the original.

Indicators of Progress. Because long-range plans normally do not manifest an immediate return on the efforts invested, managers have a tendency to become disenchanted. Therefore some indicators of progress will help not only in selling the long-range plan and the continuing efforts, but in giving the individuals involved an idea as to the progress. These indicators are:

1. General recognition among key individuals regarding the impact of the long-range plan upon the company and its management. If agreement is achieved among the management team, there is a much greater opportunity for success.

2. Continuing top-management support by use of the long-range plan. If this should be lacking, then it can be taken as a negative.

3. Intelligent and enthusiastic participation of the personnel involved in the long-range plan. Included is the integration of the planning system and existing management system. Reliable information obtained must be passed on and used for the day-to-day operations as well as for the long-range planning.

4. Decided improvement in the information-gathering, reporting, and decision-making processes. Since the long-range plan itself is slow in developing, more effective management does result from the imposed input of information.

5. Success of the one person responsible for the long-range plan. This is true whether he is an individual or the chairman of the long-range planning committee. If he is well received for performing certain services such as feeding back information, it is an indication effective planning is being achieved.

6. One last indicator is a continuous program of training, indoctrination, and motivation regarding the long-range plan.

Reasons for Failure. Reasons exist why long-range planning fails. A number of these are listed below to alert you to some of the pitfalls:

1. Failure to adequately explain and sell the importance of the long-range plan to the executives and managers involved. If an environment of acceptance is not created at the outset, the long-range plan does not have a good chance for success.

2. Failure to plan in advance for a disciplined step-by-step approach using the most modern techniques applicable in the long-range plan.

3. Failure to work out in advance the path to follow and a disciplined adherence to this plan as time progresses.

4. Failure of management to recognize the time required on the part of the individuals involved in the long-range plan.

5. Failure to put one single individual in charge, either as a committee chairman or as a coordinator, or as the sole person to oversee the long-range planning. Along with this, there often is a failure in the delegation of the work. One man can be in charge in small- and medium-sized companies, but he must be given the privilege of obtaining assistance as necessary.

6. Failure to establish an implementation schedule and to regularly evaluate the progress of the long-range plan; replanning as necessary.

7. Failure to define each problem as it arises and to study what in truth are "symptoms" and not actually the causes.

8. Failure of the executive in charge to replace the long-range planning coordinator or committee if he or they should fail. Since long-range planning is difficult, many men who assume they have the ability to be the coordinator or chairman of the committee discover they are not capable of carrying out this challenging assignment. Should this point be reached, then the individual must be removed and replaced by a more competent individual.

Criteria for Evaluation. A number of questions can be asked which will serve as a guide to whether the long-range plan is succeeding and enable evaluations to be made:

1. Have we achieved an open-minded, enthusiastic attack in the long-range planning?

2. Does the long-range plan evaluate those things influencing the corporate growth?

3. Are the strengths and weaknesses of the corporation adequately analyzed and studied?

4. Does the company have capabilities in the various functions to support the long-range plan?

5. Is there a good practical timetable, but also one that is flexible?

6. Have provisions been made for alternative courses of action?

7. Is one individual or committee specifically charged with the responsibility of developing the long-range plan?

8. Are the key operating personnel included in the long-range plan? Do they agree with it?

9. Are reviews being made on a continuing basis and roadblocks being removed?

10. Does the corporation have sufficient courage to stick to the long-range plan in spite of temporary problems?

11. Do we have adequate yardsticks to evaluate the performance? Do we know whether the objectives are being reached?

SUMMARY

It may appear to the reader that some parts of this chapter have been included in an effort to "sell" long-range planning. If this is the reaction, then the inclusion of these selling points on purpose was meaningful, for many have been privileged to observe long-range planning in action and succeeding. Long-range planning has also failed, but in almost every instance, the executives of the company were not sold on the excellent benefits obtainable from using this management tool.

Detailed examples of long-range planning are limited since the technique is in its first generation of development. This form of future looking has a long way to go. However, use the contents of this chapter as a base on which to begin your own plan. Then move out, don't be discouraged by the slow pace. Sell your program and eventually you and your company will reap the benefits.

REFERENCES

1. B. W. Scott, *Long-range Planning in American Industry,* American Management Association, New York, 1965.
2. Henri Fayol, *General and Industrial Management,* Pitman Publishing Corporation, New York, 1949.
3. Leonard Tyler, *Forecasting the Manufacturing Program,* American Management Association, Production Executive Series, no. 27, New York, 1926.
4. A. S. Rodgers and Huge Diomer (eds.), *How to Set Up Production Control for Greater Profits,* McGraw-Hill Book Company, New York, 1930.
5. P. E. Holden, L. S. Fish, and H. L. Smith, *Top Management Organization and Control,* Stanford University Press, Stanford, Calif., 1941.
6. W. B. Donham, *Business Adrift,* McGraw-Hill Book Company, New York, 1931.
7. D. E. Lilienthal, *TVA: Democracy on the March,* Harper & Row, Publishers, Incorporated, New York, 1944.
8. A. R. Krames, "The Cost of Poor Production Control," *Optimizer Newsletter,* American Production and Inventory Control Society, Cleveland Chapter, October, 1967.
9. Nyles Reinfeld, unpublished speech, American Production and Inventory Control Society Seminar, Youngstown Chapter, Mar. 4, 1967.
10. J. K. Allen, *The Corporate Planner and His Job,* Long-range Planning Service Report 125, Stanford Research Institute, Menlo Park, Calif., January, 1962.
11. R. F. Stewart, *A Framework for Business Planning,* Long-range Planning Service Report 162, Stanford Research Institute, Menlo Park, Calif., February, 1963.
12. Bruce Payne, *Planning for Company Growth,* McGraw-Hill Book Company, New York, 1963.
13. *Training Program,* American Production and Inventory Control Society, Chicago, 1966.
14. D. W. Ewing (ed.), *Long-range Planning for Management,* Harper & Row, Publishers, Incorporated, New York, 1964.
15. *Ibid.*
16. H. B. Maynard (ed.), *Industrial Engineering Handbook,* 2d ed., Sec. 7, McGraw-Hill Book Company, New York, 1963.
17. M. C. Branch, *The Corporate Planning Process,* American Management Association, New York, 1962.
18. J. C. Hetrick, "Mathematical Model in Capital Budgeting," *Harvard Business Review,* vol. 39, no. 1, pp. 49–64, 1961.
19. J. D. MacLean, "Crash Computer Conversion," *Management Controls,* Peat, Marwick, Mitchell & Co., New York, June, 1967.
20. R. A. Pritzker and R. A. Gring (eds.), *Modern Approaches to Production Planning and Control,* American Management Association, New York, 1960.
21. O. W. Wight, "Principles of Production Planning," *Proceedings of Ninth Annual National Conference,* American Production and Inventory Control Society, Philadelphia, Sept. 29, 1966.
22. J. F. Magee and D. M. Boodman, *Production Planning and Inventory Control,* 2d ed., McGraw-Hill Book Company, 1967.

23. F. R. Denham, "Network Planning Techniques in Manufacturing," *Proceedings of Fifth Annual Seminar,* Canadian Association for Production and Inventory Control, Toronto, May 12, 1966.
24. Ken Leavery, "Managing Systems Change," *Proceedings of Fifth Annual Seminar,* Canadian Association for Production and Inventory Control, Toronto, May 12, 1966.

BIBLIOGRAPHY

Ewing, D. W. (ed.): *Long-range Planning for Management,* Harper & Row, Publishers, Incorporated, New York, 1964.

Green, E. J.: "How to Make Plans that Will Really Work for You," *Factory,* August, 1966.

Hughes, C. L.: *Goal Setting: Key to Individual and Organizational Effectiveness,* American Management Association, New York, 1965.

Payne, Bruce: *Planning for Company Growth,* McGraw-Hill Book Company, New York, 1963.

Scott, B. W.: *Long-range Planning in American Industry,* American Management Association, New York, 1965.

Stewart, R. F.: *A Framework for Business Planning,* Long-range Planning Service Report 162, Stanford Research Institute, Menlo Park, Calif., February, 1963.

Production Control Operations

Chapter 12

Work Authorization, Dispatching, and Expediting

EDITORS:

Philip A. Link *Production Control Manager, Automatic Electric Co., Northlake, Illinois*

Robert E. Collins *Manager, Switchgear Production Control, Automatic Electric Co., Northlake, Illinois*

CONTENTS

The man who directs production control must have some tools to do the job. He must have knowledge, information, and an emotional temperament to act effectively. This man, in operating the *central nervous system* of the production unit, deals constantly with time.

This chapter discusses the techniques, methods, and principles which can be applied to get work started on time and kept moving until the end product is shipped. It tells how to measure performance at all stages of manufacture and how to spot delays or bottlenecks in production which will delay shipment.

Control starts with the issuance of a *work authorization* to an operator. This is the first shop contact with management direction through the dispatcher. As work progresses, the process of feedback, reporting, and corrective action takes place. Controls are operated by various elements of management in a great variety of ways, but all are intended for the one purpose of turning out a product on a timely basis at a reasonable cost.

Human error, unforeseen problems, and special service for a customer create situations which require extra attention. Expediting is the recognized means of searching out and correcting such problems. Planned and organized expediting will be more effective, more efficient, and less disrupting than spontaneous, uncontrolled reactions.

The following pages are intended to help guide the practitioner and management in adapting proved practices to their particular situations to meet the objectives of customer service, minimum inventory investment, and maximum manufacturing efficiency.

WORK AUTHORIZATION

Purpose. Some recognized form of work authorization is an essential element in management control over production. This provides an organized medium for conveying information to the foreman. He must be told *what* to make, *how much* to make, and *when* to make it. In conveying this information, management exercises control over labor expenditures. Since labor and equipment represent capacity, authorization to proceed with work constitutes a release against that capacity, to start the entire production cycle. The work authorization becomes the basic document for control.

Various Forms. The work authorization can take on many forms. In smaller shops, it may simply be verbal instructions from the owner or manager. However, an informal note is preferred since it will provide a basic written record to fix the date, amount, and item. It is not uncommon in some shops to use the drawing, sketch, or print upon which is written the quantity to be made, and possibly, the customer's name, address, and the order number. When signed by a person in authority, this form of work authorization becomes a valid document.

There are many advantages in using a *manufacturing order*, regardless of the size of operation. It is defined as "a document or group of punched cards conveying authority for the manufacture of specified parts or products in specified quantities. The manufacturing order sometimes also shows the date when the job must be completed and sometimes shows due dates for each individual operation that has been assigned by the scheduler."[1] "Shop order," "job order," "production order," and "work order" are synonymous terms.

Manufacturing orders take on many different forms and sizes, usually being designed to fit the particular needs for each company. Some typical forms are illustrated in Figs. 1, 2, and 3. You will observe on the form that certain basic information or its equivalent is common to all, such as:

1. Part or assembly number
2. Part name
3. Quantity
4. Manufacturing-order number

5. Date written or issued
6. Start date
7. Required completion date
8. Routing or operations sequence, showing operation number and numbers for department in which work is to be done

Other information may also be included, depending upon particular preference or need, such as:

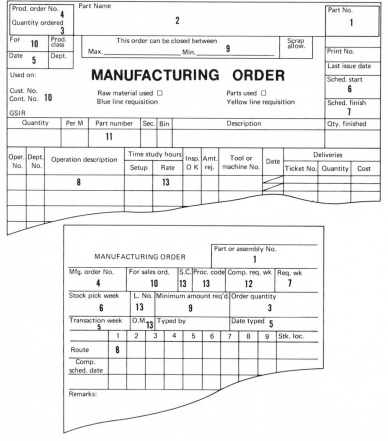

Fig. 1 Typical forms of manufacturing orders for manual preparation on a typewriter or by hand.

9. Minimum amount required
10. Sales-order number or customer reference
11. Raw-material quantity or parts required
12. Raw material or component required date
13. Various significant code numbers or abbreviations for accounting or control purposes

Schedules are also used as the primary authorization and control document in some systems (see Fig. 10).   In such cases, the schedule contains the essential information for the foreman and other personnel in management. Usually, where the schedule is used as the work authorization, secondary forms such as work tickets, control cards, identification tags, move tags, or similar paper identify the work in process.

It should be recognized that once work is put into process with proper authorization, the presence of material or the product at secondary operations carries inherent authority to produce. Schedules or secondary paper are sufficient to proceed without the need for a manufacturing order.

Authority. The release of work into production should be in accordance with

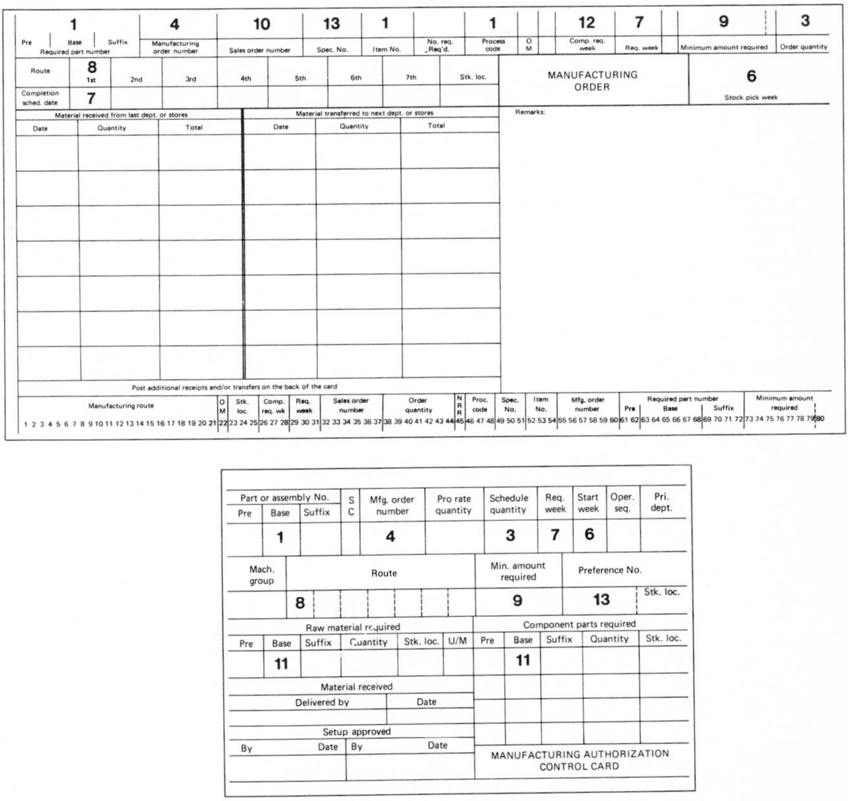

Fig. 2 Two types of manufacturing orders prepared by a computer or data processing equipment.

the overall production plan approved by top management. This may originate from a *release committee* consisting of key executives representing marketing, finance, and manufacturing, or the production levels may be approved by the vice president of manufacturing.

The production control department is the usual medium for translating production plans into action by preparing the orders and schedules. Orders may be prepared manually by an analyst or mechanically by a computer. In either case, they go to the scheduler for scheduling and shop loading. Computer systems create manufacturing orders and schedules from the requirements input according to a production plan controlled by the scheduler. Orders and schedules are then released to departmental dispatchers who become the final extension of authority.

The flow of authority for labor expenditures has other paths than through the production control department. Plant supervision carries responsibilities for effective use of labor which may supersede the plans of production control. The plant superintendent or factory manager must adjust for overloads and underloads, repairs, maintenance, and labor problems. These responsibilities carry

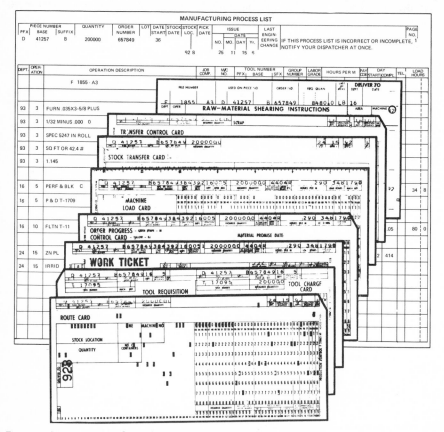

Fig. 3 A computerized work-authorization system comprised of a combination shop order and route sheet, called a "manufacturing-process list," and a deck of cards for various activities.

the authority to order work done. So too, the foreman must order repairs or rework. Generally, plant supervision is not permitted to create inventory without production control's consent.

The process engineer who prepares the route sheet has an important responsibility in specifying the operations on a part and the sequence of these operations. He must have the authority to order extra or alternate operations when the occasion demands. He may also find it necessary to experiment with methods and techniques to solve manufacturing difficulties. In small shops this responsibility and authority may quite likely revert to the machine operator.

The product engineer or designer requires the latitude to order materials, parts, and assemblies to develop prototypes or experimental models under blanket or specific management approval. Engineering changes will generate additional work for the shop under the same authority.

Usually such ordering can be accomplished through production control for better coordination, especially where the work must be done by the regular production force. If separate model-shop or prototype facilities are provided, work authorization may be made by the person in charge, by other designated individuals, or through a control group.

DISPATCHING

Definition. "Dispatching" is the selecting and sequencing of jobs to be run at individual work stations and the assignment of these jobs to workers[2] in accordance with departmental schedules and expediting priorities. This production control activity is an instrument of control. It implements the planning, ordering, and scheduling that have gone on beforehand. Releasing work according to schedule assures the management that labor is being used as planned.

REPORTING PROGRESS OF WORK: Progress reporting is a by-product of work assignment and is an important dispatching responsibility. Reporting should be timely and consistent, i.e., daily, weekly. Reports should consider:

1. Orders behind schedule
2. Orders ahead of schedule
3. Orders which are short stock

Figure 4 illustrates how this can be done, including progress through operations described as assembly, wiring, and inspection. Figure 5 is another method of progress reporting which graphically illustrates the behind-schedule position in three control areas: stock room, assembly, and inspection. This chart compares the situation week by week over an entire year. As with any chart, it reveals trends and fluctuations at a glance, and at the same time identifies trouble areas.

Figure 6 is a weekly output report for several assembly departments. The report has the following columns of information:

1. The number of units scheduled for the week
2. The number of units produced during the week
3. The number of units produced ahead of schedule
4. The number of units behind schedule not yet finished
5. The change in the behind-schedule position

Another technique, shown in Fig. 7, carries the inventory or work banks in front of various operations rather than reporting production as in Figs. 4 and 6. By reporting inventories at various work stations, the dispatcher can alert shop supervision of any buildup of work that is or will become a production bottleneck.

ASSIGNING WORK ACCORDING TO SKILL: With advance planning and agreement between production control and shop, it is sometimes desirable to have the dispatcher assign work according to skill or job complexity. However, when this is done, it is most important that the rules to be followed are clearly defined. For example, operators could be classified as A, B, or C grade, depending upon their skill or length of service. The work must then be classified prior to assignment into A, B, and C categories according to its complexity. If the rules the dispatcher is to follow in this type of work assignment are not well defined, there is a possibility that he will be accused of favoritism. This is a particularly critical problem when the operators are on some form of incentive pay.

Dept. A   FINAL ASSEMBLY STATUS REPORT   Date _____

Operation		Units		Remarks
Input	Scheduled	5	5	*Will meet this if promise of delivery on circuit card
	Delivered	* 13	5	SK-174965 from dept. C is met by noon Friday.
Assembly	Scheduled	5	5	
	Completed	16	0	
Wiring	Scheduled	6	0	
	Completed	18	0	
Inspection	Scheduled	8	0	
	Completed	5	0	

SCHEDULE CONDITION

Operation	Units		Remarks
	Ahead	Behind	
Input	0	0	*5.0 scramblers and 1.0 consoles require circuit changes.
Assembly	3	0	Engineering promises by next Friday.
Wiring	0	0	
Inspection	1	*6	

R. L. Moore
Dispatcher

Fig. 4 A type of progress report, prepared by the departmental dispatcher, reporting progress of work through key operations.

BALANCING LOADS AT DEPARTMENTAL LEVEL: Many times the dispatcher can help level the work load in a department or work center. When secondary operations are running short on work, he can start jobs that have secondary work content. Combining similar parts and assemblies into one job assignment can reduce the number of setups that have to be made. Mixing easy job assignments with difficult ones can avoid bottlenecks and will keep the work moving through the department. As with assigning work according to skill, this type of dispatching requires a close working relationship, direction, and cooperation with the foreman.

Dispatching Methods. There is a wide variety of dispatching methods which may be employed, using job tickets, control cards, or tags, in numerous sizes, shapes, and colors. A common dispatch technique for a job that has to be

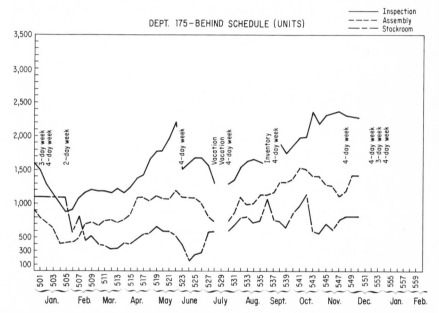

Fig. 5 Graphical form of progress reporting in terms of units scheduled but not completed. Each week the chart is extended to show status at the end of that week. Numbers at bottom of chart are computer-week numbers in lieu of dates.

assigned everytime it moves to another operation is illustrated in Fig. 8. The manufacturing order with a control card for each movement of the job is given to the dispatcher. The first control card, A, is a record of the shortages that must be resolved before the job can be started. The second control card, B, is used by the dispatcher to assign the first operation when he is informed that all stock is available. Upon completion of the first operation, control card B is returned to the dispatcher, who is then ready to assign control card C for the second operation. This routine can go on for as many operations as are required. The control cards can also be color-coded and placed in a display rack. This rack can then be used to make periodic reports on the progress of work in the department.

Figure 9, called a "board tag," is a multiple-part perforated tag which is attached to a job or a container. As the job progresses from one operation to another, the perforated sections of the tag are removed and sent to the dispatcher. Here again, color-coding can be helpful. For example, if the tag is printed on a variety of colored stock, each week the color of the board tag can be changed. This will allow the operators to start on jobs based upon their color priority, e.g., green jobs are three weeks old, yellow jobs are two weeks old, white jobs are in the current week's schedule.

VERBAL INSTRUCTIONS: Dispatching should be as simple as possible. Many times verbal instructions are sufficient to maintain the necessary communication and control. The dispatcher can tell the operator what job to run next from

Mr. C. E. Rollins

Subject: Weekly Production Report — Week Ending 7/16

	Schedule	Output	Ahead of schedule	Behind schedule	Change in behind schedule
Department 860 Frames	393,772	366,145	124,987	43,626	+2,835
Department 861 Blocks	9,834	9,449	1,215	5,772	+189
Departments 218 and 238 Terminals	326,759	317,979	111,208	121,058	+24
Reeds	15,342	19,180	15,831	9,775	+2,556
Department 288 Cords	4,342	4,203	693	1,003	+98
Department 298 Connectors	807	652	507	0	0
Resistors	81	107	36	12	+1
Department 336 Armatures	65,305	58,397	24,600	607	−1,318
Coils	45,000	68,055	4,581	24,804	−17,535
Department 560 Springs	70,812	78,834	49,042	3,112	+2,098
Lever assemblies	3,088	3,100	105	1,134	−563
Latch assemblies	8,911	9,000	6,199	20	+5

T. M. Smith

T. M. Smith

Fig. 6 A weekly output report for several assembly departments showing performance in relation to schedule.

the open-order file or a printed schedule (see Fig. 10). Dispatching through verbal instructions usually requires a more experienced person and more personal follow-up.

ISSUANCE OF WORK AUTHORIZATION: Some form of ticket is necessary if work assignments are frequent and the work is varied. Figure 11 is an example of a dispatch package consisting of three elements:

1. The manufacturing authorization, which is returned to the production control office when the job is completed.

2. The department schedule, which is a listing of all the manufacturing authorizations scheduled in one week. The dispatcher checks off each line as the item is completed.

3. The labor control ticket, which is the assignment ticket authorizing labor to be applied to the job.

COMPUTER INQUIRY: The computer can remove many clerical chores from the dispatcher. With remote stations that have access to a central computer, the open-order record and job progress can be maintained without keeping departmental records. Computer-generated prepunched job tickets can travel with work or be assigned to the operator by the dispatcher. The progress of work will be recorded as operators report their time. The system can also furnish

Date _____

Mr. R. G. Service

Subject: _____ Inventory Counts on Equipment in Inspection Areas

Dept. 30.0

Assembly inspection	Mon.	Tues.	Wed.	Thurs.	Fri.	Sat.
Reed strips, unit mountings, files and misc. combined	58	105	46	38	42	
Wiring inspection	Mon.	Tues	Wed.	Thurs.	Fri.	Sat.
Unit mountings and reed strips	75	54	92	68	75	
Card files	21	18	19	33	35	
Miscellaneous	13	35	15	42	46	
Total units	109	107	126	143	156	
Circuit and computer test	Mon.	Tues.	Wed.	Thurs.	Fri.	Sat.
Unit mountings	410	418	407	423	451	
Card files	173	191	186	197	205	
Total units	583	609	593	620	656	
Quality control	Mon.	Tues.	Wed.	Thurs.	Fri.	Sat.
Unit mountings	89	50	45	41	64	
Card files and miscellaneous	37	1	18	28	68	
Total units	126	51	63	69	132	
Department 176 relay adjustment	Mon.	Tues.	Wed.	Thurs.	Fri.	Sat.
Unit mountings	97	89	75	78	76	
Miscellaneous	20	25	8	6	8	
Total units	117	114	83	84	84	

A. Carnelli
Dispatcher

Fig. 7 Report of units of equipment at various work stations awaiting inspection. Daily count will reveal buildup or reduction of work banks.

prepunched move tags which in turn may be used to report quantity of parts moved and time of movement from one operation to another.

Computers with random-access memory allow production control to maintain one central record in the computer. Any portion of the record, such as quantity on order, location of the order, or number of operations remaining, can be obtained through departmental inquiry stations.

Organization. Dispatching organizations are as varied as products and companies. Dispatching functions may report to a central, local, or departmentalized production control organization, or directly to shop supervision. There are advantages and disadvantages in each arrangement.

1. *Centralized Production Control.* Dispatching in a centralized production control organization tends to be more schedule-conscious and less sympathetic to the reasons the shop cannot meet the schedule. A central organization also makes it easier to communicate and carry out company policy as it applies

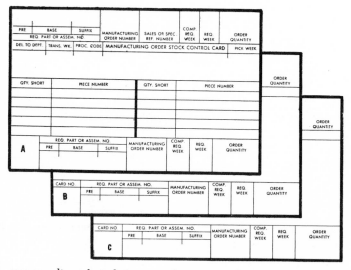

Fig. 8 A common dispatch technique employs a manufacturing order with a control card for each movement of the job.

to labor, inventory, and customer service. Greater uniformity of procedures and dispatch techniques can be expected from central control.

2. *Localized Production Control.* Localized production control is organized around a product, a plant, or an area within a plant. Thus dispatching under localized control is more specialized and dedicated to local problems and products.

3. *Under Shop Supervision.* Dispatchers are frequently thought of as "assis-

tants to the foreman." This is because good dispatching is one of the most helpful services a foreman can get. The foreman or shop supervisor should always actively provide guidance and direction to dispatching. Dispatching that reports directly to shop supervision removes the "front office" implication from the dispatcher. However, the risk is increased that the front office will get less candid reports on the work progress.

4. *Work Centers.* Dispatching can be organized around combinations of centralized and decentralized responsibilities. Dispatch functions can be oriented around a specific machine center or employee center and still report directly to a centralized production control department. This gives the dispatching function a specialized knowledge of the work center and yet the advantages of the centralized organization.

5. *Operations.* If the size warrants, dispatching can be dedicated to specific operations. For example, a punch press department could have a dispatcher for all punch presses of 60 tons and over, and another dispatcher for all punch presses under 60-ton capacity. An assembly department could have its dispatching organized so that one dispatcher would be responsible for checking stock and starting the assembly; another dispatcher for assigning all the wiring operations in the assembly; and still another dispatcher to assign the first test and inspection. Dispatch organizations such as this, with the use of operation control cards (see Fig. 8), can inform one another of work completed at one operation and ready for assignment to another operation.

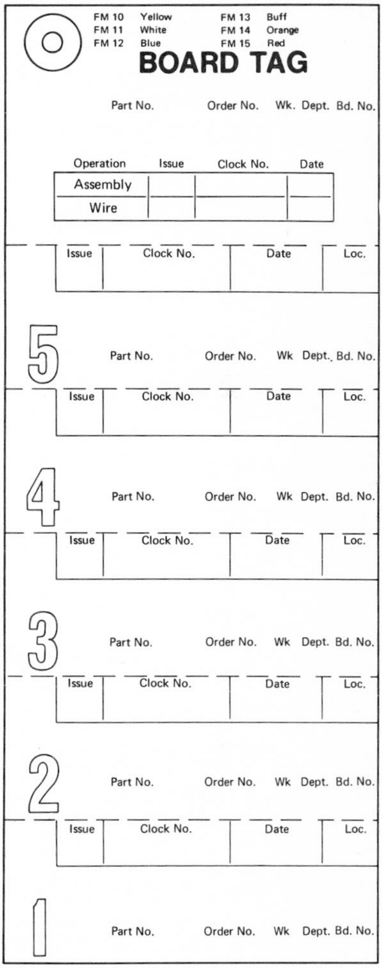

FEEDBACK

Purpose. Feedback is the flow of information back into the control system so that actual performance can be compared with planned performance. Control can be exercised only when there is knowledge of what is being done.

Fig. 9 A multiple-part tag which is attached to a job or container. Perforated sections are removed as job progresses.

To be useful, feedback to production control should report progress or lack of progress on current production objectives. A departmental production report such as Fig. 12 illustrates a basic form of feedback in performance to a production schedule. Other areas of interest would include:

1. Parts or material shortages
2. Shipments to promise
3. Inventory change

4. Labor turnover
5. Production delays
6. Backlog
7. Stock-room performance in picking stock and delivering parts or material to using departments, as in Fig. 13

FLOW CONTROL PRIMARY SCHEDULE FOR START WEEK 465

Preference number		Part number	Mach. ctr.	Mach. grp.	Operation	hours	L C	LG	Oper. seq.	Order quantity	Order number	Start week	S C	Qty. prorate
464 3 0 920	D	83043	A	16C	1602	28.7	R	04	10	4400	623516	465	3	
465 2 0 960	D	30018	B	16D	1781	5.5	R	04	5	2800	322425	465	2	
465 2 0 960	D	30111	A	16D	1801	3.4	R	04	5	2000	322427	465	2	
465 2 4 921	P	11657		16D	1792	6.5	D		5	5400	980926	465	2	
465 2 5 960	D	41482	A	16D	1783	90.9	R	04	5	24000	322388	465	3	
465 2 7 960	D	30179	A	16G	4460	16.8	R	04	5	1000	322332	465	3	
465 2 8 921	D	56530	B	16B	1700	133.6	R	04	5	51000	983976	465	3	20000
465 3 6 920	D	78932	A	16D	1783	9.3	R	04	5	4400	624503	465	2	
465 3 7 921	D	731765	A	16D	1792	.9	D		5	2200	944635	465	2	
465 3 8 920	D	47962	D	16D	1801	.2	D		5	110	620625	465	2	
465 3 8 929	H	881492	A	16D	1783	5.5	R	04	6	3300	621162	465	2	
465 3 9 928	D	542260	A	16C	1602	53.0	R	04	5	22000	624017	465	3	
465 4 6 960	D	730493	A	16C	1670	5.6	D		5	3500	704538	465	2	
465 4 8 960	D	109621	A	16C	1602	12.8	R	04	5	10000	310833	465	3	
466 2 1 960	H	78790	9	16D	1783	9.0	R	04	5	8000	322463	465	2	
466 2 5 921				16D	1781	4.0	D	0	5	4000	980780	465	2	
466 2				16D	1840	29.1	R	04			719075	465	3	
				D	1840	1.2						465		

FLOW CONTROL SECONDARY SCHEDULE START WEEK 465

Preference number		Part number	Mach. ctr.	Mach. grp.	Operation	hours	L C	LG	Oper. seq.	Order quantity	Order number	Primary dept.	S C	Qty. prorate
460 0 0 926	D	470248	B	16D	1840			D	20	1	627842	16H	2	
461 0 0 926	D	470266	B	16D	1840			D	35	1	627844	16H	2	
462 3 0 926	D	470299	B	16D	1840	.1		D	40	13	627848	16H	2	
463 2 0 960	D	30208	A	16D	1802	34.7	R	04	10	10000	322851	16E	2	
463 2 0 960	D	30208	A	16D	1840	36.1	R	04	12	10000	322851	16E	2	
464 3 0 926	D	470268	A	16D	1840	.1		D	30	26	624571	16H	2	
465 2 0 960	D	30018	B	16D	1802	3.4		D	15	2800	322425	16D	2	
465 2 0 960	D	30111	A	16D	1781	2.5	R	04	15	2000	322427	16D	2	
465 3 6 920	D	78932	A	16D	1783	16.9	R	04	20	4400	624503	16D	2	
465 4 0 960	D	63145	A	16D	1781	9.2	D		22	3300	310889	16A	2	
465 4 4 920	D	78431	A	16D	1801	39.6	R	04	10	18000	704473	16A	2	
466 2 0 92D	D	63157	A	16D	1840	17.0	R	04	28	12000	715791	16A	3	
466 2 5 921	P	11887		16D	1840	11.5	R	04	10	4000	980780	16D	3	
466 2 5 921	P	11887		16D	1792	12.8	D		15	4000	980780	16D	3	
466 2 7 920	D	490024	B	16D	1781	18.8	R	04	10	8300	719075	16D	2	
466 2 7 920	D	490024	B	16D	1781	31.9	R	04	15	8300	719075	16D	2	
466 3 7 929	D	490028	G	16D	1840	1.1	D		10	420	624573	16D	2	
466 4 7 920	D	490028	P	16D	1840	20.4	R	04	10	5500	704595	16D	3	
466 4 7			E	16D	1840	5.1	R	04	10					
					16D	1802	63.3	R	04					

Fig. 10 Printed schedules may be used to determine which job to run next.

Various Forms. *Verbal communications* are continuous in the relationship of people working together in an organization. Often the most significant piece of information is picked up in casual conversation. It may be a comment on the illness of an essential operator or setup man, damage to a tool or machine, rejection of material or workmanship, or other happenings which affect performance to schedule. Verbal information may be casual, or directed and face

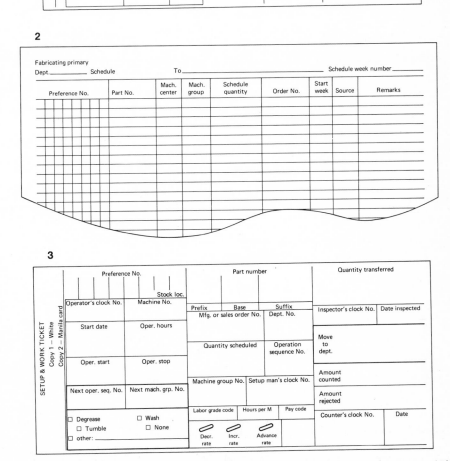

Fig. 11 A dispatch "package" consisting of (1) manufacturing authorization, (2) department schedule, and (3) labor control ticket.

to face, or over the telephone. Regardless of circumstances, the spoken word is the most revealing form of feedback.

Written reports are a more reliable and dependable source of information on what is happening. A daily delay report as in Fig. 14 is specifically designed to report deviation from planned performance. A summary of departmental reports such as Fig. 15 provides higher levels of management with an overall

OUTPUT REPORT
DEPARTMENT 23D   Week ending_____

Week number_____

Coils	Mon.	Tues.	Wed.	Thurs.	Fri.	Sat.	Total
Resistance							
Relay							
Vertical and rotary							
Reed assem.							
Receiver							
Spark							
Miscellaneous							
Total							

Foreman_____
(signature)

Fig. 12 Departmental production report is one form of feedback.

view of the flow of work through the shop. Such information in factual form provides data for evaluation.

Teleprocessing has built-in feedback in computer-oriented systems (see Chapter 25). A system such as diagramed in Fig. 16 transmits information from the shop and production control to the computer where it can be analyzed. Reports can then be issued by the computer according to the wishes or needs of management. This form of feedback has the advantage of pre-prepared programs which will continually monitor designated activities and report only what is desired.

Frequency. Every system should have regular feedback to ensure a steady flow of information on current conditions. This may be daily, weekly, monthly,

Subject: Weekly input for week no. 545

Relay department:
   Relays scheduled for picking   883
   Relays picked and delivered complete   857
   Percentage of schedule picked complete   97.1%
   Total relays staged in stock room (all schedules)   213
Switch department:
   Units scheduled for picking   791
   Units picked and delivered complete   778
   Percentage of schedule picked complete   98.4%
   Total units staged in stock room (all schedules)   45
Class C performance for week no. 545—99.87%
Class A performance for week no. 545—92.80%

                        T. H. Howler
                        Subassembly dispatching

Fig. 13 Stock-room report of performance against schedule in picking stock for two departments. Percentage figures show level of service.

SECONDARY OPERATION
DAILY DELAY REPORT

To_____ Dept. foreman   Department_____

_____ Dept. scheduler   Date_____

From_____ Dept. expediter

Part No.			Opr. No.	Preference number	Order number	Quantity delayed	Days delayed	Remarks
Pfx.	Base	Sfx.						

Fig. 14 Daily delay report of items at a particular machine center but not in work is specifically designed to report deviation from planned performance.

or any suitable period of time as seems appropriate. Dependence upon spasmodic reporting is satisfactory for emergencies where it is clear to everyone that immediate action is necessary, but it could be disastrous if this is the only means of feedback. Creeping change can be detected before it becomes a crisis through analysis of routine reports. The most valuable feedback is usually that which is given in response to a direct request (see Fig. 17). It is then that timeliness and need are at a maximum so that information supplied will be the most useful.

Timeliness. As in any form of communication, some identification of the degree of urgency is necessary. It is difficult to make rules in this area, as it is largely a matter of judgment on the part of the person initiating the message. The

SUMMARY OF SECONDARY DELAY REPORTS

P = Parts
C = Containers

Date_____

Machine center	03		04		07		08		16		24		31		35	
	P	C	P	C	P	C	P	C	P	C	P	C	P	C	P	C
A					5	10	2	3	1	2	1	1	1	1	3	4
B			10	20	20	430	2	3	1	2					2	6
C	5	5	4	12												
D	10	15					4	5	(3)	5						
E																
F			3	3					2 Tool ups		5	15				
G									T-2 151							
H			(1)	1					D-6 3080-A							
J			5	5					T-2 059							
K	Tech.								D-11 340-B							
L	assistance BB-11037-A															
M																
N																
P																
R																
T																
Inspection																
Stock area																
Hold area																5	11
Total	15	20	23	41	25*	440	8	11	5	9	6	16	1	1	10	21

Total No. of parts = 68

* Dept. 07 total not included in total no. of parts

Fig. 15 Summary of delays reported in Fig. 14, for all departments and machine centers, provides management view of work flow through the shop.

degree of urgency to a large extent dictates the form or method of communication. It would be ridiculous, for instance, to write a letter to the fire department about a fire in progress. In the same vein, if routine matters are continually brought up in an urgent manner, the real emergencies will be overlooked. It is necessary for management to evaluate feedback in this regard and develop discrimination within the organization as to the appropriate form and timing.

Timeliness is also a factor when decisions are involved. Any information received after a decision is made has lost a considerable part of its value. It must be left to the judgment of the individual in making routine or spasmodic reports. Where timing is important when information is requested, a time limit should be established for the reply.

Accuracy and Reliability. Needless to say, wrong information is worse than none. Reports which express opinion, hearsay, or rumor can be dangerous unless

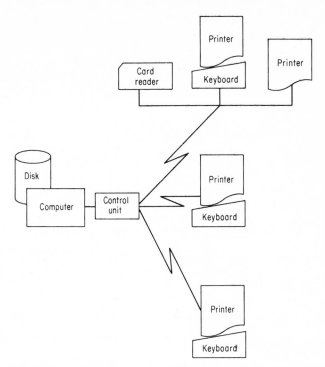

Fig. 16 Diagram of teleprocessing system which transmits information between computer and printer-keyboard stations in shop or production control.

properly evaluated. Either a means for quick verification or a convenient audit trail should exist if a communication is to be accepted and used for control. Hearsay or opinion on some subjects can be valuable if properly identified at the time it is received. Prudent management requires that feedback for control must be based upon fact.

Subject: Status of unit mountings behind schedule

As requested, a numerical inventory was taken to position the unit mountings scheduled for production prior to this week and not yet completed. Units were found in various stages of work as follows:

In staging area, short parts	11
Being checked in by assembly department	18
In assembly and/or ahead of assembly	76
In assembly inspection	48
In wiring and/or ahead of wiring	103
In wiring inspection	53
In wiring repair	6
In and/or ahead of testing	192
In visual inspection	57
In quality control	47
Total	611

A. J. Germane
Electronic assembly dispatching

Fig. 17 Feedback upon request: an inventory of units in process, at each location in the shop. Report points out bottleneck operations and motivates corrective action.

PROGRESS REPORTING

Purpose. Progress reporting provides the means for measuring and recording production. Historical records of basic production figures can become invaluable for subsequent analysis and comparison. A daily output report (see Fig. 12) gives a detailed record of production generally of most advantage to first levels of supervision. A weekly production report such as Fig. 18 contains the advantage of comparing output to schedule. It may also furnish current status in terms of units produced ahead of schedule and units not yet produced which are behind schedule. This enables various levels of supervision to obtain a quick summary of conditions. Reports may become quite detailed as in the factory output report (Fig. 19), depending upon desires or needs of management.

ELECTRONIC DEPARTMENT
WEEKLY PRODUCTION REPORT

Week number 545   Week ending November 20

Equipment	Dept.	Schedule	Output	Ahead of schedule	Behind schedule
Matrix cabinets	Prod.	24	24	2	2
	Insp.	24	20	0	4
Electro-mechanical cabinets	Prod.	11	10	5	1
	Insp.	11	10	0	1
Electronic cabinets	Prod.	20	21	1	0
	Insp.	20	20	0	0
Translator units	Prod.	13	10	0	6
	Insp.	14	12	0	8

K. A. Jannsen
Dispatcher

Fig. 18 Weekly production report compares output to schedule and gives number of units both ahead of and behind schedule.

Various Forms. *Verbal reports* are probably the most effective if limited in number and scope. "We made our schedule this week," has an impact that is lacking in the numerical listing on a prepared form. While effective, verbal reports lack permanency and are subject to errors of interpretation and memory. They should be confined to situations where a quick, personal communication is appropriate.

Written reports are the accepted means of recording production information. While it is customary to think in terms of printed forms, filled in with appropriate figures, handwritten notes may suffice. With widespread use of computers, a detailed or summary printout on a periodic basis is becoming familiar. The computer output may be from a high-speed printer with multiple copies or via teleprocessing to remote stations. Teleprocessing has the obvious advantage of swift transmittal if distances are involved.

Charts are an extremely effective means of reporting where trends, fluctuations, and comparative levels are of interest. Regular reporting in chart form, of units behind schedule, tells at a glance whether production is going out on schedule. It will also show the volume coming out late and whether the situation is improving or worsening (see Fig. 5). A plan or commitment to improve a condition may be projected as a dotted line. This can serve as a constant reminder of the goal.

Frequency. It is customary to issue production reports at regular intervals. Daily, weekly, monthly, and annual reports serve overlapping but different purposes. Generally the larger the time span, the less detail is included. Monthly reports tend to summarize broad areas of activity. Since most accounting is reported in monthly increments, production reports for the same periods give

FACTORY OUTPUT REPORT Week ending Week No.			Report No. Issued weekly Sheet 1 of 3	
EQUIPMENT	Output of productive department		Output of final inspection	
	Units	Labor units	Units	Labor units
AUTOMATIC SWITCHBOARDS				
Keith uprights				
Keith shelves				
Rotary shelves				
Line finder boards				
Automatic relay racks				
P-A-X, P-A-B-X & P-B-X boards				
Power boards				
Miscellaneous				
Schedule				
Total units				
Behind schedule				
MANUAL				
Toll boards				
Attendant's cabinets				
P-B-X's				
Test desks				
Information desks				
Repair clerk's desks				
P.P.C.S. desks				
Toll test equipment				
Rotary interrupter				
Test sets				
Test turrets				
Misc. turrets				
Miscellaneous				
Schedule				

Fig. 19 A weekly factory output report may be quite detailed, depending upon desires or needs of management.

comparative information of value to management. Output in units and value may then be related to inventory, shipments, payroll, indirect expense, purchases, and sales. Annual reports tend to serve as a broad overall view of production activity and are retained for historical records.

PERIODIC REPORTS: Reports issued at time of completion of a task or job have special value in contract work. In a job shop, it is important not only to know the volume of work going through the plant as reported in daily or weekly units of production, but to know when each job is finished as well. A case in point is where payment is made by the customer as work progresses on a contract.

ON REQUEST: Not all reporting is on a regular periodic basis. It is better to wait until an interest or need is shown for rarely used information than to regularly report unnecessary volumes of detail. An occasional inquiry about unreported information can be handled through investigation or study at less cost than issuing regular voluminous reports. Judgment must be applied in making decisions about what to report on a regular basis, or new reports will spring up like mushrooms with each inquiry and be with you long after anyone can remember why they were initiated.

By Whom? *The dispatcher* originates most production reporting. Where dispatching is recognized and organized as a separate task, production reporting is an important part of the dispatcher's duties. This reporting is not confined to periodic production figures but includes special reports on key items or jobs, bottlenecks, delays, work stoppage for any reason, exceptional loads, and possible current or future problem areas.

The foreman may also report to higher levels of line supervision in addition to reports made by the dispatcher. If his reporting supplements that of the dispatcher, it tends to be verbal and to include concurrent comments upon conditions or problems. The practice of holding daily or weekly production meetings between foreman and general foremen or factory superintendent illustrates this principle. Such meetings, when properly conducted, serve a multiple purpose:

1. The foreman is called upon to account for his stewardship.
2. Problem areas are quickly and easily brought to attention.
3. A spirit of teamwork can be developed within the production organization.
4. Sometimes, a competitive attitude may be generated to provide incentive.

Worker-initiated reports are generally a by-product of work reporting in the form of time tickets, incentive tickets, setup tickets, or similar shop paper which become input into a system. Shop-located data collection devices which input data into a computer commonly use information provided by the worker under system controls.

CORRECTIVE ACTION

By Whom? *The person with knowledge of the need* for improvement is the one who should initiate correction. Initiating action should start at the lowest level of authority, which is usually the dispatcher in the production control department. He is the source of reports on performance and progress of work. He should also call to the attention of his supervisor and the foreman any situations which prevent timely and efficient performance to schedule. The supervisor, in turn, should report any situations he is unable to correct to the production control manager.

It is customary to channel corrective action according to the type of problem encountered. Various levels of factory supervision take care of labor problems such as absenteeism, overtime, training, workmanship, increases or reduction in force, and efficiency. Shop supervision also normally maintains machinery, tools, fixtures, and other plant facilities.

Industrial engineering, process engineering, or the methods department is responsible for technical problems associated with manufacturing. When processes or methods set up by them are not producing a satisfactory product, they act upon notification to investigate and correct the cause of the problem.

Production control takes responsibility for having material, parts, or components available on time. Shortages then are the primary concern of production control. Beyond expediting missing items, continuous analysis of causes or reasons for shortages should be made to prevent recurrence, if possible. Shop paper work such as manufacturing orders, schedules, stock-room requisitions, and production reports must be accurate and issued on a timely basis. If repeated problems are encountered with paper work, production control must take action to bring about improvement.

The general manager, vice president, president, or owner takes steps to correct situations which cover several areas of responsibility of lower management, or where disagreement, misunderstanding, or undefined responsibility results in inaction. Top management, which must continuously monitor the operation of the business, also acts to control costs, service, quality, investment, and profits, when it appears lower echelons are not performing satisfactorily.

What Triggers Corrective Action? *Control points* at which reporting is initiated usually reveal deviation from the production plan and set off discussion and investigation. Such control points are not limited to reporting output from key operations, but include inspection and quality control.

Bogeys which establish production goals will more likely trigger action to corrrect difficulties than routine reports, since the purpose of setting target levels is to direct everyone's attention to the need for meeting the goal.

Direct inquiry about progress of an order may also result in follow-up to improve performance, overcome delays, or break bottlenecks in the manufacturing cycle, depending upon the person who makes the inquiry and the degree of his interest in results. Inquiries about production can originate from anywhere in the company or from the customer.

Aging reports such as the behind-schedule report illustrated in Fig. 20 are excellent devices to uncover problems which need correcting. It is not unusual for some portion of production to fall behind schedule because of the many variables in manufacturing, but when the delay stretches out in time or is concentrated in one department, there is trouble.

Periodic review of the most significant or useful reports and charts will keep the manager continuously informed of conditions in key areas. This will show up trends or changes in output, shortages, behind-schedule conditions, or rejections, as they occur.

Form of Action. Corrective action normally begins with an investigation, questioning, or analysis of pertinent data to make certain the cause of the trouble can be identified. A meeting of knowledgeable persons may be called to discuss the problem, or the topic may come up for discussion in a regular production meeting.

A recommendation for change should be made by the individual or committee to the person in authority who can effect the change. Such a recommendation would likely point out the need for improvement in the labor situation, such as more people, better training, or better supervision. It may involve some aspect of facilities such as space, benches, fixtures, tools, gauges, or working conditions. Likewise, routing, processing, methods, handling, paper work, control methods, attitudes, and any of a myriad of other contributing causes may be included in the recommendation.

Accomplishment of corrective measures may take the form of additional instruction of employees, disciplinary measures, improved motivation, better attention, and similar human relations in addition to physical changes outlined above. The dissemination of information about a problem may in itself provide sufficient corrective measures.

Switchgear Behind-schedule Aging Report, Week Ending 325

Department	Prior to week 320	Week 320	Week 321	Week 322	Week 323	Week 324	Week 325	Week 326	Week 327	Week 328	Total behind schedule
Dept. A (automatic equip.), units	0	0	2.1	0	0	1.3	4.7				8.1
Dept. B (automatic equip.), units	0	0	0	0	0	14.2	8.6				22.8
Dept. C (power), units	0	0	0	0	1.0	0	0				1.0
Dept. D (contacts), units	0	0	0	0	1,155	31,080	79,840				112,075
Dept. E (manual equip.), units	0	0	0	0	0	1.2	.3				1.5
Dept. F (manual equip.), units	0	0	4.5	0	1.2	0	3.3				9.0
Dept. G (manual equip.), units	0	0	0	0	0	3.1	10.8				13.8
(Misc. subassem.), orders	2	0	3	7	2	8	23				45
Dept. H (fuse panels), units	0	0	0	8	1	4	78				91

Fig. 20 A report of units behind schedule, segregated by weeks and departments, uncovers problems by showing quantities and number of weeks overdue.

Don't overlook the value of verbal requests for help in problem solving—they often accomplish better results in enlisting cooperation than a written report or communication. Too often, the written word becomes "a point of honor" which must be defended. Once a defensive attitude hardens, minor problems can become major obstacles requiring high-level solutions. Corrective action can be a challenging and rewarding experience if the human relations aspect is skillfully handled.

EXPEDITING

Necessary Evil? Expediting should be a planned production control activity. No system or administration can avoid all possible causes of stock outs. Perfect service requires infinite inventory. You never achieve either one.

While the need for expediting is always present, the amount or degree varies according to the service levels desired. A common objective is 95 percent service. This means that 95 out of 100 requisitions submitted to the stock room will be filled and 5 will be short of stock. Expediting, in taking care of the 5 percent, is necessary for production efficiency and not a "necessary evil." It can be, however, if used to bolster areas of poor performance or unreasonable customer demands.

Many variables upset plans. Human error is probably the biggest reason for expediting. People must handle orders, post to record cards, keypunch computer input, count and move material, and put away stock. Errors in any of these activities can result in stock shortages.

Manufacturing orders behind schedule in the shop can result in parts and assemblies not being available when they are needed. Machine failure, material failure, poor workmanship, and labor absenteeism are some of the many reasons for manufacturing orders to fall behind schedule. When these delays occur, expediting must frequently provide the push to make up for the delay and lost time.

Like behind-schedule shop orders, vendor falldown causes back orders and shortages. If orders from vendors are not expedited, the shortages will delay starting subassemblies or shipping customer orders.

Many items are stocked in anticipation of future sales demand. Sales volume that exceeds the forecast will not be supported with sufficient material in stock. This requires the issuance of special rush orders on the shop or with suppliers.

Initiating Action. While it is difficult to predict what will have to be expedited, it is not difficult to predict what will initiate expediting.

1. *Customer's Inquiries.* Customers frequently inquire about orders past due or request orders to be delivered ahead of schedule. Because the company image is affected, it is important to give prompt, dependable follow-up. In this area, more than any other, expediting must assure compliance to the promised dates.

2. *Material and Part Shortages.* Shortages usually are discovered when the stock room cannot fill requisitions. This will cause delays in shipping orders or starting assemblies on time in the shop. When a stock-room shortage is acknowledged, the requisition becomes a back order and should be placed in a shortage file. If the shortage is a component of an assembly, the stock room should also set aside in a staging area the available component parts until the shortage is satisfied. This staging area and shortage file usually becomes the hub of expediting activity.

Figure 21 is an example of a *performance chart* issued weekly by the expediting group. This chart illustrates the quantity of subassemblies behind schedule and the quantity of subassemblies held in the stock-room staging area. It is not surprising to see a close correlation between orders behind schedule and orders having stock shortages.

Material damaged or lost in the shop is another major cause of part shortages. If replacement material is not available in the stock room, a shortage is created and should be added to the stock-room shortage file.

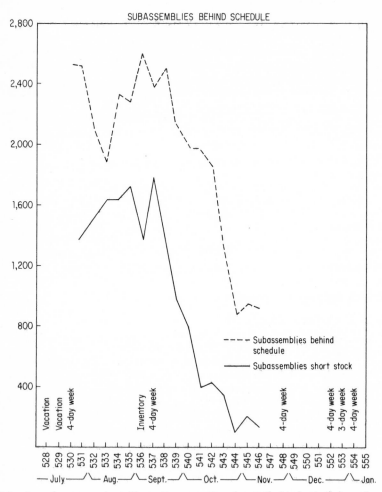

Fig. 21 A performance chart illustrating quantity of units behind schedule and number held because of shortage of parts. Chart is extended each week.

3. *Falldown Reports.* Falldown reports similar to that in Fig. 22 are another source of expediting. This type of report can be initiated from:
  a. Shipping department—customers' orders behind schedule
  b. Stock room—items in the shortage file or broken safety banks
  c. Shop—orders behind schedule in a particular department or work center
  d. Office—purchase orders behind schedule
4. *Engineering Changes.* Engineering changes frequently make parts obso-

lete, change parts, or create the need for new parts. When this happens, work in process is delayed until the correct parts are made available. Expediting effort is needed to implement the changes and minimize the delays. Expediting, in this situation, might have to hasten the release of new orders as well as chase stock.

5. *Anticipated Stock Out.* If stock outs can be anticipated, expediting can take action before the stock out occurs. The practice of expediting parts that fall below a minimum stocking level is one example of this. Also, stock status records may reflect future requirements. If so, stock on hand and on order can be compared with the requirements. Expediting should be initiated prior to a stock out where future deliveries will not be adequate.

Aging reports, similar to that in Fig. 20, point out not only the total number of items behind schedule in a department, but also the age of these orders. Every order behind schedule does not necessarily create a shortage in the stock

Falldown Report

Sales order	Ship date	Spec.	Item	Amt.	Part number	Lot number	Shop sch.	Route	Remarks
7841	2/11	674	27.34		E.O. power wire	9396		PUR	Lost in Shpmt. Reissue
	4/1		46.53		E.O. cable	5955		PUR	51-2&3 Shpd.
	8/5		54		E.O. power wire	6637		PUR	Submitted 8/15
	8/13	695	4	1	H-885931-8	66022	482	653	
	8/12		5	2	H-885931-10	66023	482	653	
	8/12		6	1	H-885134-1	65480	488	623	
	10/28	698	15	8	KH-840941-A30A			IN-651	
	10/28		16	3	H-886863-4	33737	499	653	
	10/28		17	3	H-887006-4	19142	499	653	
	10/28		19	4	H-886155-1	08826	500	300	
	10/28		20	2	H-885851-1	08825	500	300	
	10/28		21	8	H-885740-1	08824	500	300	
	10/28		22	1	H-886590-4	33222	499	653	
	10/28		24	11	H-886676-5	33733	498	653	
	10/28		25	6	H-885907-2	18469	498	654	
	10/28		26	6	H-886036-2	18472	497	180	
	10/28		27	2	KH-1001-A	26347	499	790	

Fig. 22 Falldown report details items on customer's order which are overdue in the shipping room and require expediting.

room, but the longer the order is behind schedule, the greater the chance of a stock out. For example, in the illustration, the miscellaneous subassembly department only has 45 orders behind schedule, but 2 of these orders are over seven weeks old and 3 orders are five weeks old.

Methods. Methods of expediting can be as varied as the reasons.

PERSONAL CONTACT: Personal expediting is the most costly method of expediting but the most effective. The expediter out in the shop carrying a clipboard with listings of shortages and promise dates is still the most positive way of getting something done in a hurry.

Expediters in the shop have the advantage of dealing directly with dispatchers and foremen. They can observe that action is being taken and can assist the department in obtaining materials, tools, and prints that might otherwise delay the job. These same advantages are true for outside expediters who visit vendors' plants. Here again, they can observe the effort a vendor is giving the expedited order. The fact that a company is willing to spend time and money to send an expediter to the supplier's plant can be impressive.

TELEPHONE: The telephone is an excellent expediting instrument. It has many of the advantages of personal contact and is less time consuming. However, it limits the number of items which can be effectively discussed. Dispatchers use the telephone to communicate with each other to report the movement of critical items. The phone can also be used on a conference hookup to communicate an expediting plan at the same time to everyone involved.

LISTINGS: The use of shortlists is the most common form of expediting. A list similar to the list in Fig. 23 can be issued daily, weekly, or monthly. These

Shortlist, Department 020				
Department 020s assembly number	Parts short	Making dept.	Department 020s completion week	Labor units
H-887694-1	1-H-982405-1	280	546	0.5
H-88479-8	2-D-825138-A	320	547-548-H	10.0
	2-D-813538-A	222		
	1-H-88526-13	090		
	1-H-88526-14	090		
	1-H-88501-5	140		
	1-H-88526-3	090		
	1-H-88641-2	090		
H-884954-1	1-DH-85502-77A	320	547	4.0
	2-DH-85502-78A	320		
	1-D-825124-A	320		
H-883757-1 Expediting shows job complete	H-88530-24	090	547	3.0
H-460107-3	1-H-886985-1		547	1.0
	8-H-886987-1	320		
	1-H-982504-1	280		
	1-H-982504-1	280		
H-887616-1	1-D-251604-A	290	534	2.0
Special addition—no print available				
H-886914-1	1-H-880238-13	320	547	0.3
H-883380-1	2-D-825017-B	320	547	2.0
H-880009-16	1-H-56356-5	140	548-H	4.0
	1-H-880238-13	320		
H-884290-1	1-DH-850259-A70A	320	548-H	2.0
H-885262-1	1-H-884449-5	090	548-H	2.0
	1-H-884449-6	090		
H-884627-1	1-H-884635-1	320	548-H	0.5
H-883379-1	2-DH-85650-73A	320	548-H	3.0
	10-DH-85651-71B	320		
	1-DH-85654-71B	320		
	1-DH-85655-71A	320		
	1-DH-85656-71A			
H-460107-3	6-DH-85005-70A	320	548-H	0.5
	1-H-881581-1	090		
H-460107-3	9-DH-850014-72A	320	548-H	5.5

Fig. 23   A shortlist or "hot list" is commonly used for expediting.

shortlists can be initiated by the:
1. Stock room
2. Shipping department
3. Production department
4. Receiving department
5. Computer
6. Expediters

For shortlists to be effective, promise dates should be obtained on all items listed. Then it is necessary to follow up and review performance on each item until the list is completed. If the list of shortages becomes too voluminous and has little follow-up, it will lose its value.

TELEPROCESSING: Computers, with their random-access features, are fast becoming a major expediting tool. One company that has open orders in computer memory processes all the shortages against the open-order file. The computer

PART NUMBER	ORDER #	M.A.R.	BEHIND SCHEDULE PURCHASE PARTS BALANCE DUE	REQWK	WK,548 ROUTE	NET BEHIND	PAGE 2 REMARKS
	799 75	6,CCO	6,000	548		6,400	EXPEDITE
PD 1703	2 898 94	100,000	100,000	547	85.0 24	100,000	EXPEDITE
PD 6804	1 899 44	250,0C0	250,000	537	85.0	250,000	
PD 7613	1 899 70	300,0C0	7,000	542	85.0 24	7,000	
PC 109131	A 898 91	50,0C0	50,000	545	85.0	50,000	
PH 880586	2 899 76	4,997	4,855	540	85.0		
	898 98	10,0C0	10,000	548		14,855	EXPEDITE
PH 880586	4 899 77	4,335	4,335	540	85.0	4,335	SFTY-BROKEN
PP 1474	1 898 53	25,000	25,000	541	85.0 24	25,000	
PP 1945	1 899 77	10,0C0	10,000	544	85.0 24	10,CC0	SFTY-BROKEN
	830 80	500,CC0	300...			...CC0	

Fig. 24 Expediting notice printed by computer after processing stock-room shortages against the open-order file.

then prints out the following information (see Fig. 24):
1. Open orders by number
2. Minimum amount required
3. Balance due
4. Required week
5. Route
6. Net quantity behind schedule

Teletype is another method of reporting shortages from outlying warehouses. This has the advantage of having typewritten shortlists at both the sending and receiving stations.

Inquiry stations located in the shop and connected to a central computer can be used to keep expediters informed of stock movement. Knowledge that a critical part is on the receiving dock or delivered to the stock room can save many hours of delay in getting a job started or shipped.

MEETINGS: Meetings are effective as an expediting tool if they are well organized and attended by people who can do something about the shortages. To be most effective, these meetings should have limited objectives and not attempt to solve all shortage problems. For example, meetings should be channeled to specific subjects, such as a weekly meeting to review purchase-part shortages, a weekly meeting to review fabricated-part shortages, or a monthly meeting to review shipping performance. Each of these meetings should have a report to measure progress or performance. Figure 25 is an analysis of purchase orders which reports late orders, percent of late orders to total orders, number of purchase orders pulled up, and other pertinent information.

PURCHASE-ORDER ANALYSIS

Week No.____327____

Ordering groups	No. of orders issued	Percent of orders issued	* Late orders issued	Percent of orders issued late	** No. of exp. requests issued for late orders	Percent of exp. requests issued for late orders	No. of pull-ups causing late orders	Exp. requests issued for behind sch. orders	Late orders issued No. of wks. late			
									1	2	3	4 & over
Class B switchgear E.J. Crandle	203	43	30	15	30	100	33	12	0	0	1	29
Class B Product shop R.J. Block	34	7	1	3	1	100	3	0	0	0	0	1
Class C L.E. Allen	48	10	0	0	0	0	0	3	0	0	0	0
Class D D.A. Kott	36	8	3	8	3	100	0	7	0	0	1	2
Raw material T.J. Frank	135	32	14	9	14	100	16	3	2	1	0	10
Total	474	100	48	10	48	100	52	25	2	1	2	42

*A purchase order is defined as "late" if the order is received in the purchasing department with less than 95 percent of the procurement interval.

**Expediting requests will be prepared if less than 75 percent of the procurement interval remains upon issuing a purchase order.

Fig. 25 Analysis of purchase orders issued during a week to reveal extent of expediting required for current and past-due requirements.

To: J. D. Manning

Subject: Shipping performance report through week No. 243

 I. Behind-schedule position
  A. Items behind schedule at beginning of week   6
  B. Items behind schedule at end of week   1
  C. Items not completed on schedule during week 1
  D. Total items behind schedule at beginning of new week 2
 II. Performance to schedule
  A. Number of units scheduled   31,072
  B. Number of units shipped   31,040
  C. Shipped as scheduled   99.99 %
 III. Performance to repromise
  No. of repromise Status   Percentage
    4   Met   100 %

             T. M. McIntosh

Fig. 26 Weekly report of units shipped to original promise (schedule) and to repromise. Behind-schedule tells number of items which were not completed.

Figure 26 reports on the shipping performance and compares the behind-schedule position at the beginning of the week with the behind-schedule position at the end of the week. It also reports on the performance to schedule and to repromise.

Organization. The expediting activity can report to a central authority or to many local authorities. Figure 27 is one form of central organization, and Fig. 28 is one form of local organization.

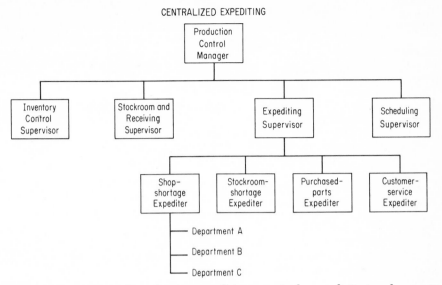

Fig. 27 Organization chart showing expediting organized as a distinct and separate function under centralized control.

CENTRALIZED OR LOCAL? Centralized expediting has the advantage of having full-time expediters who can become specialists. The organization becomes more expert at resolving shortage problems and can be more analytical of the conditions that cause the shortages. This is a valuable source of feedback to management on areas that need correcting. Centralized expediting also has the ability to

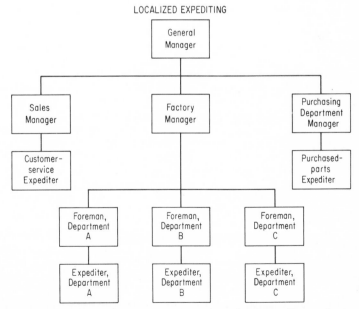

Fig. 28 Organization chart illustrates one form of localized expediting where expediters work directly for the department foreman or manager.

consolidate similar shortages and reduce duplication of expediting efforts. Priorities can be established more easily for critical capacities, and there is more assurance that stock will not be diverted to lower priority requirements.

Localized expediting has the advantage of being right on the firing line. This produces a better awareness of the changing urgency in a department or on an assembly line.

ORGANIZED OR INFORMAL? The way expediting is organized depends to a great extent on the size of the company, the type of product, and management attitude on service. Some expediting activities are highly organized with 50 or more people. This is appropriate if the plant is large and the products complex. Some expediting activities amount to no more than a telephone call from one foreman to another. This is appropriate if the plant is small or the products simple.

A combination of organized or formal expediting which permits informal personal contact between key supervision is most successful. Another effective expediting technique is to have *project expediters*. This technique assigns a person to a condition that requires expediting. For example, an order from an important customer is received and the company wants to be sure the order is shipped on time. To accomplish this, a person is assigned to stay with the order until it is shipped.

CONTROLLED OR UNCONTROLLED? Expediting, by its very nature, is a disrupting activity. It causes added setups to be made, jobs stopped, and in general reduces the efficiency of a department. To allow just anyone to expedite and determine priorities can be a costly practice. Some foremen enjoy expediting and take it on as a special challenge, leaving their departments suffering for lack of direction. Low efficiency and low productive output can be directly attributed to uncontrolled expediting. Controls which follow some basic ground rules are necessary to limit disruption caused by expediting.

Some effective "ground rules" are:

1. Only district sales managers can pull up orders.
2. A setup will not be taken out if the job will finish within two hours.
3. All expediting requests will clear through the department dispatcher.

Effectiveness. Expediting in any form, or in any degree, costs time, money, and loss of efficiency. However, not to expedite can be even more costly in lost business and shop delays. Because of this, it is necessary to evaluate the effectiveness of the expediting effort. Figure 29 charts the number of stock-room shortages every week. In this illustration, the expediting is not too effective because stock-room shortages have increased since the early part of the year.

Expediting will only be as effective as the authority it is given. The desire to have dependable schedule dates must start at the top of the management ladder. Department heads should understand that orders behind schedule represent potential stock outs or shortages.

MOTIVATION: Expediting can be a very unrewarding activity for the expediter. When one stock out is resolved, it is replaced by another. Both the expediter and those being expedited must be continuously motivated to overcome this handicap.

Motivation comes easiest when people can identify themselves with the problem and the solution. A weekly report on stock delivery, such as in Fig. 13, measures the percent of stock delivered on time for a given schedule period. This provides motivation for those responsible for stock deliveries because it measures their performance against an established goal.

Figure 17 is an example of what can be done if a particular product is not moving through the shop fast enough. This is an inventory status report

showing where 611 unit assemblies are located in the shop. The report points
out the bottleneck operations and helps motivate everyone along the route to
keep the assemblies moving. Expediting must provide the initiative and imagination to convince people that their special efforts contribute to accomplishing
company objectives.

RECOGNITION: It is as important to measure good performance as it is to
measure poor performance. One company has a traveling trophy that goes
to the department with the least number of orders behind schedule. Letters
from satisfied customers, circulated to the departments and expediters that contributed to the accomplishment, extend appreciative recognition where it counts.

PERSEVERANCE AND INITIATIVE: As pointed out earlier, even a successful operation will always have stock outs. Expediting is a never-ending task that can

Fig. 29 Plotting the number of stock-room shortages each week helps evaluate effectiveness of expediting effort.

become routine, boring, and neglected by the expediter and those being expedited. To avoid this, new approaches to communicating shortages and performance must be used. For example, a routine weekly report can become an
attention getter if the cost of the orders being delayed is periodically written
into the margin of the report.

Expediting is an art. Understanding the process and the product enables
the expediter to anticipate the problems he will encounter, but knowing how
to deal with people is as important as the short list itself. While he must be
given authority, the success of an expediter depends upon his ability to convince
those who must get the job done that it is important, desirable, and necessary.
Exercise of authority to force unwilling compliance is a poor substitute for willing
cooperation. In the final analysis, an expediter is an in-plant salesman who
is always selling inconvenience, disruption, and *customer service*.

SUMMARY

Systems, methods, and techniques are the tools used to control production to conform as closely as possible to the management plan. It is people, however, who must employ those tools, and their success will depend upon how well they are trained and motivated. A production control organization under good leadership can be successful with almost any system since it is people who make the system work. Good tools, properly selected and adapted, will make the job easier and produce better results. On the other hand, the best devised system employing the most advanced techniques and equipment will not compensate for a poorly led, ill-trained organization.

REFERENCES

1. *APICS Dictionary of Production and Inventory Control Terms,* 2d ed., American Production and Inventory Control Society, Washington, D.C., 1966, p. 22.
2. *Ibid,* p. 12.

BIBLIOGRAPHY

Magee, J. F., and D. M. Boodman: *Production Planning and Inventory Control,* 2d ed., McGraw-Hill Book Company, New York, 1967.
Moore, F. G.: *Manufacturing Management,* Richard D. Irwin, Inc., Homewood, Ill., 1961.
Plossl, G. W., and O. W. Wight: *Production and Inventory Control,* Prentice-Hall, Inc., Englewood Cliffs, N.J., 1967.
Reinfeld, Nyles V.: *Production Control,* Prentice-Hall, Inc., Englewood Cliffs, N.J., 1959.
Scheele, E. D., W. L. Westerman, and R. J. Wimmert: *Principles and Design of Production Control Systems,* Prentice-Hall, Inc., Englewood Cliffs, N.J., 1960.
Voris, W.: *Production Control: Text and Cases,* rev. ed., Richard D. Irwin, Inc., Homewood, Ill., 1961.

Chapter 13

Scheduling and Loading Techniques

EDITOR:

Richard E. Edgerton *Director of Information and Systems, Lansing General Hospital, Lansing, Michigan*

CONTRIBUTORS:

Norman E. Finck *President, GENOR Associates, Long Beach, California*

Dr. Colin L. Moodie *Associate Professor of Industrial Engineering, Purdue University, Lafayette, Indiana*

Arnold O. Putnam *President, Rath and Strong, Inc., Management Consultants, Boston, Massachusetts*

Dr. Donald E. Scheck *Associate Professor, Department of Industrial and Systems Engineering, Ohio University, Athens, Ohio*

Dr. Warren H. Thomas *Associate Professor, Department of Industrial Engineering, State University of New York at Buffalo, Buffalo, New York*

CONTENTS

Scheduling and loading are two of the most important manufacturing tools used in America today. Most manufacturers have to meet some type of competition. These manufacturers are vitally interested in anything that can make their production more efficient. They want something that will give them control over production. No matter what they are making, aircraft carriers or toy trains, they have common problems and they would like to know how to solve these problems in advance. They want to look into the future and they want production control. This is exactly what scheduling and loading attempt to do.

Manufacturers are not the only ones interested in these tools. The service industries, government agencies, nonprofit agencies, and others are using them. Hospitals do not have departments entitled "production control," but they are scheduling operating rooms, laboratories, and other facilities. Radio and TV broadcasters are scheduling commercials. Colleges and other schools are scheduling classes. Scheduling and loading are so important to some manufacturers that they have developed and implemented sophisticated computerized systems for production control. The process industries were the first to do this.

Broadly speaking, there are three types of production:
1. Continuous or process type
2. Intermittent or batch type (sometimes called "job-shop")
3. Project type

The petroleum refinery is a good example of continuous production. Crude oil is continuously fed into one end of the equipment and petroleum products continuously emerge from the other end. An automobile repair shop is a good example of intermittent production. Cars enter one at a time, are worked on, and leave. Building a skyscraper is a good example of project production. There is a major piece of work (building the building) which is broken down into smaller pieces (the plumbing, the electrical work, etc.).

This chapter will include scheduling and loading of all three production types. It is meant to be a practical source of information about scheduling and loading, covering both the traditional and modern methods. It attempts to provide answers to specific problems that production control people encounter. It also attempts to give them guidance in applying scheduling and loading techniques to their production problems.

The chapter begins with a discussion of the scheduling and loading environment for both process- and intermittent-type production. It then presents a number of methods for scheduling:

In the "Line of Balance" section, a method of project scheduling that is popular with the U.S. Navy

In "Critical-ratio Scheduling," another method of scheduling intermittent production

In "Network Planning Methods," a method of project scheduling that was developed for the Polaris missile system.

In "Linear Programming," a method which is particularly useful for process industries

Miscellaneous solutions to job sequencing problems in intermittent-type productions

Simulation models as they apply to production scheduling and loading

The Bibliography at the end of the chapter is divided by subject matter for further reference.

THE SCHEDULING AND LOADING ENVIRONMENT

Process-type Production. The distinguishing feature of process-type production is that work flows through a fixed and continuous manufacturing process. This differs from a job shop where work is processed intermittently by job order or lot. Examples of continuous-process-type manufacturing are to be found in the chemical industry, food industry, paper industry, and the portland cement industry.

Since work *flows* through a continuous manufacturing process, production control in this type of industry is often called "flow control." The rate of flow can usually be varied, although there are processes where the rate can be varied little if at all. Paper mills, for example, can usually shut down on weekends, but the production of sulfuric acid can have but a small variance in the rate of flow and probably will not be shut down more often than once a year.

Another important factor is the ease with which the flow may be varied. An automobile assembly line may be built to vary between 60 to 120 cars per hour. However, a line set up to produce 60 cars per hour cannot produce 120 cars per hour without some major changes in setup and personnel. A line set up to produce 120 cars per hour would be very uneconomical if operated at a much slower rate.

The importance of production control and scheduling in a continuous manufacturing process is directly proportional to the ease and the amount by which the flow may be varied. If the rate of flow can be varied easily and significantly, management is more apt to vary it. The more it is varied, the more effort is required to keep the system under control and the greater the need for the production control function.

There are several other factors which are important in process manufacturing. The production equipment is usually *single purpose* and used for one product or type of product. Because of this, it is difficult, if not impossible, to make a nonstandard product. Since standard products are made in large quantities, they are usually made for inventory rather than for a customer's order. Because process manufacturing is continuous, and because shutdowns are usually costly, it is very important to keep adequate supplies of raw materials flowing to the process and to keep the finished product flowing away from the end of the process.

SCHEDULING: To do production scheduling, the production control department must know:

1. What to make
2. When to make it
3. Where to make it
4. How to make it
5. What to make it of
6. How much time is necessary to make it

A sales forecast, bill of material, and a process sheet usually supply this required data.

Since production is usually for inventory, sales forecasting is usually very important and will provide input data to a production control scheduling system. Although the sales forecast may extend for planning purposes into the distant future, scheduling is usually done for only the near future of perhaps one or two months. Established company policy will usually require that production control schedule production to meet the requirements of the forecast. In some companies, however, production control is allowed to second-guess the forecast. Actually, there is some second-guessing in either case in that production control may revise the schedule to use overtime or increase the rate of production, if necessary, to meet the forecast or to meet actual sales.

Once production control knows what to make, they must know of what the product is made. That information should be available from a bill of material. A bill of material shows the structure of the product. For an illustrative example let us consider a packaged drug product such as vitamins. Assume that this is a multiple vitamin sold in bottles of 36 tables and that the product identification code is MU2836. A bill of material for this product might show that it is an assembly consisting of 36 MU8000 multiple-vitamin pills placed in one GB5844 glass bottle with one LB2836 label and placed in one CB2836 box.

Now that production control knows what to make and what it is made of, they must next know how to make it. This data should be available from a process sheet. Other names, such as "routing," "traveler," "formula sheet," are used for this document. In intermittent manufacturing, to be discussed later, the process sheet probably will contain considerable detail, but this is not usually the case in continuous-process manufacturing.

The manufacturing equipment used in intermittent manufacturing is generally of a multipurpose nature, and it is set up between jobs to handle many different types of products. Single- or special-purpose machines designed to handle only one product or type of product are not justified, since the runs are small and the equipment would be idle much of the time. This is not so with continuous manufacturing, since large quantities are involved and the equipment will be in use most of the time. This justifies, then, special- or single-purpose equipment. In the example used above, the vitamin product would have a packaging line of its own. This line might also be used to package other vitamins or drugs that go into the same size bottle, providing the pills are about the same size as the vitamin pill. Therefore, since the equipment setup is simpler, the process sheet will be simpler. It will identify the equipment or lines on which the product is to be manufactured, the production rates applicable, the raw materials involved, and the quantities of raw materials required.

Scheduling a product in continuous-process manufacturing can be quite simple. For our vitamin-packing example, if nothing else is processed on the packaging line, then the question is: "Are we going to operate this packaging line, and if so, at what rates are we going to operate it?" For a case this simple, probably the most difficult scheduling job will be scheduling deliveries of raw materials from the vendor to the manufacturing plant. There would probably be more people concerned with scheduling deliveries of raw materials than people concerned with scheduling production. Also there would be more people, and not necessarily in production control, scheduling the shipments of the finished product away from the line or warehouse.

If more than one product is packaged on the packaging line, then the move is away from continuous processing back toward intermittent processing and its problems of sequencing, run lengths, and setups.

If continuous processing exists and the vitamin-packaging line is going to operate, the scheduling problem has been resolved to determining the production rate to be used in operating the line.

There are different ways to vary the production rate in continuous-process production:

1. The line equipment may be operated for more or fewer hours.
2. The line may be operated with more or fewer personnel.
3. The line may be operated intermittently with the personnel doing other work.
4. The line may be operated in two or more stages by pulling the partially completed product from the line and accumulating an in-process inventory. After this inventory is built up to a certain point, the first phase of the process may be shut down and the second phase operated by feeding in the in-process inventory. The same personnel would be used in both phases.

Continuous-process manufacturing has an advantage over intermittent production in that feedback, the comparison of what was scheduled versus what was actually produced, is easier. Since there is a "flow" of material, it is usually possible to utilize some means of automatically and continuously measuring this flow in terms of pieces, gallons, feet, pounds, etc. Feedback, of course, is required to maintain the scheduling process.

Generally, scheduling a continuous manufacturing process is easier than scheduling an intermittent manufacturing process. However, there is often enough difficulty so that computers and modern scheduling techniques have been successfully applied.

Intermittent-type Production. Intermittent production is defined in the *APICS Dictionary* as "a production system in which jobs pass through functional departments in lots." A plant with production of this type is usually called a "job shop." A home kitchen can be thought of as a job shop with the refrigerator representing one department, work counters a second, and the stove a third. Contrast this with a cannery where tomatoes are fed into one end of a processing line and continuously processed until they emerge from the other end in cans.

Anyone scheduling and controlling this type of production is faced with several types of problems. One of these is the requirement for data on the status of the system. Such questions as these are common: "When will order 4763 be done?" "Is it behind schedule?" "Where is it?" "How long will it take to fill this rush order?" "Where can we make this new product?" "How long will it take to make it?" "A machine is down, a product was scrapped, a key employee is absent; what does this do to our schedule?" "Why do you change the schedule so much?" "Why didn't you tell us yesterday that we must work overtime today?"

An associated problem is that much of the data pertaining to the production system is not available, not readily available, unreliable, or reliable for only a short period of time. Thus, many decisions must be based on insufficient data, and consequently performance is often not what it could or should be. The cost of obtaining better data may be prohibitive, however.

Another basic problem is deciding what to schedule and how to schedule it. Should *products* be scheduled or should *machines* be scheduled? What about a combination of these? Should all products or machines be scheduled or just some of them? Should departments or work centers be scheduled? What are the scheduling rules? How should they be applied?

There is little or no problem involved in determining the objectives for a production scheduling system. The problem is to achieve them. A good production scheduling system should give a smooth, efficient, profitable, low-overall-cost operation with minimum inventories of production materials, in-process materials, and finished goods. It should be reliable, deliver orders on time with minimal lead times, and have fast reaction times to sudden status changes due to breakdowns, rush orders, late arrival of materials, and employee absences. Finally, it should give an objective clear-cut feedback of results.

There are no easy answers to the questions raised here, but the next few pages should be of some help.

Scheduling and Loading Techniques. There are two techniques for controlling a production system. One of these is scheduling; the other is loading. Of the two, loading is easier to do, but scheduling can give more control. Loading, however, can be very useful.

LOADING DEFINED: A "load" is the *amount of work assigned to a facility* and "loading" is the *assignment of work to a facility.* Loading does not specify the sequence in which the facility is to do the work or when it is to do it. The facility may be a machine, a group of machines, a department, and so forth.

Why use loading? The biggest reason is that it can predict some future events. A chart, instead of the late orders, tells of an overload, and it tells us this in advance. This same chart can warn of excess capacity before the machines and workers are idle. Therefore, loading is most useful to dispatchers, foremen, and production schedulers scheduling shop work. Loading can be used to smooth the work load from month to month or between machines. It is an aid in identifying the critical departments or machines and in judging the effect of breakdowns, rush orders, and new products. It is also useful for documenting the requirements for more or less capacity.

LOADING TECHNIQUES: To begin with, three things must be available:
1. The work assignments
2. The work content of the assignments
3. Notice of assignment completion

The work may be assigned by the nature of the job. If the work can be done by more than one facility, then it must be assigned to one facility. If it can be done by only one facility, there is no alternative but that one facility. If the work is drilling a hole and there are three drill presses, assignment must be made to one of them or the three of them can be considered as one facility. The work may be assigned on an individual-job basis, but if the jobs are repetitive, they may be assigned on a standard basis by use of routings. *Standard routings* show, for each part or assembly, all the operations that must be done to make that part or assembly. In addition to the operations required, the routings also usually show the facility that performs the operation and the standard time required to perform it.

If standard routings are not available, someone must assign the individual jobs to the facilities and must estimate the work content of the assignments. This work content must be in terms that are comparable between jobs. Measures that may be used are hours, pieces, pounds, batches, gallons, etc., per hour, per shift, per day, etc.

Work assignments must be accumulated by facility in order to calculate the load on each facility. One method is to use a ledger where for each facility the job numbers and the job loads are entered. When a job is completed, it is marked off. The jobs are then added periodically to obtain the load on the facility.

Another method is to accumulate the assignments in "buckets"—one bucket for each facility. The bucket may be a box, a file, a peg, etc. A ticket is prepared for each job assigned to the facility and placed in the box, in the file, or on the peg. A perpetual total of the facility load may be kept for each bucket. Job tickets, as they are added to the bucket, are added to this total. When completed and removed from the bucket, they are deducted from the total.

Another method is to keypunch the assignments into cards and process the cards on data processing equipment to obtain the loads. If a computer is available, the buckets may be a computer file. If standard routings are available, these can be kept in cards or computer files. Then only the part number and the quantity need be entered for each job, and the computer or electronic accounting machine can extend the quantities, make the assignments, and calculate the load.

Example Assume that one of the items made by Acme Manufacturing is a slip plate. They usually combine customer order quantities, add an allowance for scrap, and prepare a production order for the shop. Someone in production control prepares a production-order routing sheet, as in Fig. 1, which shows the shop what is to be done. The copy actually issued to the shop need not show the hours of work involved. Since these slip plates are a common production item, the routing is standard and is made up ahead of time for use with all orders. To prepare it for issue someone enters the order number, order quantity, and order date, extends the standard pieces per hour times the order quantity, adds the setup time, and writes in the extended time. Someone will also prepare a job ticket (see Fig. 2) for each work

PRODUCTION ORDER—ROUTING SHEET					
Acme Manufacturing					
1403 SLIP PLATE					
Part No. Description					
B1838 25					1/14/
Order No. Quantity			Order date		
Oper. No.	Operation description	Work center	Setup time, hours	Std. pcs./hour	Extend time, hours
10	CUTOUT PLATE	28	0	0.2	5.0
20	GRIND EDGES	70	0	0.4	10.0
30	DRILL HOLES	45	0.3	0.1	2.8
40	POLISH	72	0.2	0.2	5.2
50	INSPECT	110	0.3	0.2	5.3
	END				
Authorized by J.K. Gramming 1/14/					

Fig. 1   Production-order routing sheet.

JOB TICKET
Work center ____ *45*
Load (hours) ____ *28*
Part No. ____ *1403*
Operation No. ____ *30*
Order No. ____ *131838*
Qty. (pcs) ____ *25*
Date ____ *1/15/*
Remarks _____
_____

Fig. 2   Job ticket.

center and operation on the routing. The job tickets are used to prepare the load monitor (Fig. 3). Once each day the job tickets added yesterday and the job tickets removed yesterday are totaled separately and entered on the load monitor to obtain the amount of work load for each work center. When a new production order is issued, hours are added only to the work centers involved. Only when a job is finished is its load removed from the work center. Note that this is an example of how a company might do loading. It can be done other ways as long as the end result (the amount of load on a work center, machine, department, etc.) is obtained in a usable form.

There are some other considerations in loading. How detailed should the loading be? Should every job and every facility be loaded? Most facilities do not have unlimited capacity; therefore, should a limit be set on the allowable load for a facility?

The answers to these questions depend upon the needs of each production system. If a facility is not being operated near capacity and the load is fairly stable, there may be no need to monitor its load. If the converse situation prevails, there are important reasons for monitoring its load. In fact, loading alone may not be enough. Scheduling may be indicated.

LOAD MONITOR				
AND WORKSHEET				
				1/17/
Work center	Current load	Added yesterday	Removed yesterday	New load
10	60.4	15.5	7.8	
15	115.1	. . . .	. . .	
17	79.8	5.3	18.4	
20	72.2	27.1	. . .	
28	87.3	13.9	6.2	
30	94.0	. . .	9.3	
35	90.8	22.4	. . .	
40	83.7	8.0	7.1	

Fig. 3   Load monitor and worksheet.

SCHEDULING WITH A LOADING CHART: Why schedule? Scheduling, like loading, can predict some future events, and it is done for the same reasons that loading is done. Scheduling is more difficult to do than loading, but it pays off more. Betting on the horses would be even more popular than it is if the bets could be placed after the race was run. Scheduling offers that promise for a production system: The bets are placed after the race has been run (the schedule made). Of course, a horse may stumble (a breakdown) in the real race. Scheduling can aid in solving the problems outlined in the introduction to this section. It can smooth production, minimize inventories, shorten lead times, increase profits, eliminate bottlenecks, aid in analysis of the production systems, and so forth.

Loading, as explained, is the assignment of work to a facility without specifying the sequence in which the facility is to do the work or when it is to do it.

"Scheduling" is the *assignment of work to a facility and the specification of when the work is to be performed and the sequence in which it is to be performed.* Scheduling then is the time phasing of loading (see Chapters 9 and 11 for further discussion on scheduling).

Since scheduling is time phasing, a point in time where scheduling is to begin is required. This may be either the required delivery date or the day the order was received.

1. If the *delivery date* is used, the time phasing is done *backwards.* The

last operation is scheduled first, the next-to-last operation is scheduled next, etc., until the first operation is scheduled and the beginning date of the schedule is then known.

2. If the *order date* is used, the time phasing is done *forwards*. The first operation is scheduled first, the second operation is scheduled second, etc., until the last operation is scheduled and the finish date is then known.

Most scheduling systems are based on either forward or backward scheduling, and although they may be as simple as the methods just outlined, they may also be more sophisticated and more useful. They may consider such things as move and wait time between operations, capacity of facilities, customer priorities, profitability, costs, probabilities of schedule reliability, availability of tooling or special equipment, inventory levels, setup and teardown times and costs, rush orders, breakdowns, and others. Naturally more sophistication implies more complexity and more cost to develop and operate. At some point of sophistication, the complexity makes the system unworkable without a computer.

No matter what method is chosen, a basic set of scheduling rules must be spelled out before scheduling begins, and they must be applied consistently. For backward scheduling with loading, they could be as illustrated in this example.

Example   We will have two work documents:

1. An operations-scheduling sheet (Fig. 4), which gives the sequence of the operations, the facilities required, the time required, and space for entering scheduled-operation start dates

2. A facilities-loading chart (Fig. 5), which records the facility work load per time period

ROUTING

Northern Custom Keg Co.

1127D	DELUXE KEG	3		AJ12
Item No.	Description	Qty.		Order number
12/10/				10/28/
Shipping date				Order date

Operation number	Operation description	Work center	Process time	Scheduled start date
10	MAKE STAVES	6	18	
20	MAKE KEG ENDS	6	9	
25	MAKE HOOPS	5	6	
30	ASSEMBLE	2	3	
40	ROUGH FINISH	4	2	
50	SEAL AND PAINT	3	2	
60	LABEL	1	2	
	END			

Fig. 4   Routing sheet with standard operations.

Each operation is scheduled by following these steps:

Step 1. Each operation must end before the subsequent operation begins. The last operation must end prior to the shipping date.

Step 2. Consult the routing scheduling sheet to determine the facility and process time required for the operation.

Step 3. Add this time to the facility's work load for the applicable time period.

Step 4. Subtract the process time from the start date of the subsequent operation to obtain the start of this operation.

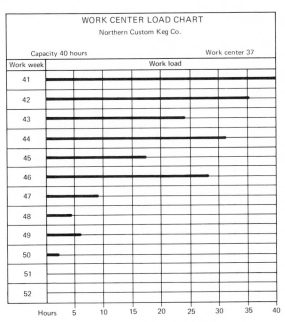

Fig. 5 Work-center load chart.

Step 5. If step 3 exceeds the facility's capacity, determine when capacity is available.

    a. If capacity is not available until a future date, remove from the work load for each facility all the operations scheduled so far for this order. Begin scheduling anew by advancing the shipping date as required from step 5.

    b. If capacity is available for some earlier time period, schedule the operation in that time period and continue scheduling.

Step 6. If, after all operations have been scheduled, the start date of the first operation is prior to the current scheduling date, the shipping date must be advanced and scheduling must be completely redone.

Figure 5 represents a form printed in advance. The work-center number and the week numbers are written in the form. As hours are loaded to this facility, a bar is extended from left to right representing the hours loaded. If it is necessary to remove hours from the load because of rescheduling, an equivalent part of the bar is erased.

After analyzing these steps, it is easy to see that forward scheduling from the order date would eliminate the rescheduling that arises in backward scheduling, since when a facility is already loaded to capacity, the operation start date is advanced in time until capacity is available and prior operations need not be rescheduled.

If the last operation is scheduled to be finished before the desired shipping date, the finished item may have to be stored, which may cause finished-inventory levels to rise significantly. In-process inventories may also rise if the operations cannot be performed immediately, each after the other. For instance, if an operation begins a week after the previous operation was finished, the item must have been stored for a week. To eliminate these problems, rescheduling should be done if any significant delays are encountered or if the finish date is significantly sooner than the shipping date.

GANTT-CHART SCHEDULING

Without a doubt the Gantt-chart principles are the most extensively used scheduling techniques. They may be used with a simple chart drawn on graph paper or with one dressed up in some of the commercial display panels discussed in Chapter 21. The purpose here is to discuss only the principles and not the applications.

There are advantages to be found in the Gantt chart which can be found in none of the other techniques. These can be briefly stated as follows:

1. A plan has to be made. Often this is the most important advantage of any scheduling technique.

2. It shows the work that is planned and when it is to start and end. At the same time it also shows the work that has been accomplished.

3. Gantt charts are easy to understand and work.

4. The Gantt chart is dynamic and shows a *moving picture* of what is being planned and accomplished.

5. Gantt charts require very little space considering the amount of information displayed.

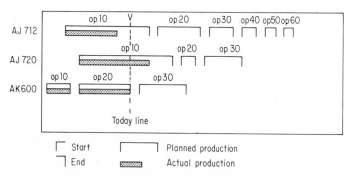

Fig. 6 Schedule chart by order number.

Like most of the other scheduling techniques, the Gantt chart requires an understanding of a certain language or set of symbols. These are illustrated at the bottom of Fig. 6.

The two inverted L's indicate when a task is to begin and end. The light line connecting these two L's shows what is to be accomplished. This line may be scaled in units of either time or production. Progress of the work is indicated by a heavy line. A "today" line must be placed on the chart to show when it was last brought up to date. In the example a caret is used. Other symbols may be added to the chart as desired. For example, a crossed-out entry as shown might indicate that a machine is down for repair.

As discussed previously, there are two ways of entering information. We may start with the present time and work *forward*, or we may start with some future date and work *backward*. The choice will depend upon the cost of the product, as well as availability of transportation, storage, capital, and other considerations.

For scheduling manufacturing, there are two choices in the way the chart is set up. If getting production out is the important problem, the chart will be set up by manufacturing orders as shown in Fig. 6. However, if keeping the machines loaded is of paramount importance, the chart should be set up as shown in Fig. 7. Notice that in the first figure the manufacturing orders are listed in the left-hand column, while in the second illustration the machines or work centers are listed.

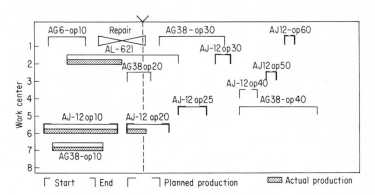

Fig. 7 Schedule chart by work center.

In operating the chart it is essential that information such as move orders or time cards be available to serve as *feedback* for updating the chart. Operating the chart successfully requires a person with a certain type of personality, a person willing to accept changing conditions and work with details.

Reading the chart is relatively simple. For example, in Fig. 6:

1. AJ720 is ahead of schedule.
2. AK600 is on schedule.
3. AJ712 is behind schedule.

On Fig. 7 you will notice that there are a number of jobs shown for each work center. If each work center is manned, the scheduler will probably want to keep all the vacant spaces filled, which will mean a more efficient plant.

The scheduler will have to be flexible and willing to adjust the schedule from hour to hour. For example, it appears that order AG38, operation 20 is not going to be started before the time it is to be completed. This will require a reshuffling of the operations for AG38.

These are the basic principles of the Gantt chart. From here one can make modifications which will fit his particular situation.

CRITICAL-RATIO SCHEDULING*

Critical-ratio scheduling is a technique for use in production scheduling to establish and maintain relative priorities among jobs. The priority is based

* Based on APICS National Training Kit #2, by Arnold O. Putnam, President, Rath & Strong, Inc., and Robert Cronan, Principal, Rath & Strong, Inc.

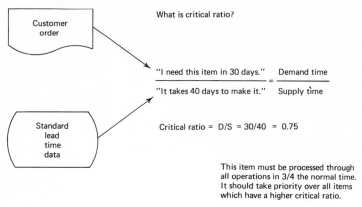

Fig. 8   What is critical ratio?

on a combination of when the completed job is required and how much time is required to complete it (see Fig. 8).

A. At any given work center, some jobs will be ahead of schedule, some behind, and some on time. Some earlier rules used to determine priorities for job sequence have been:

1. The job which arrived first.
2. The oldest job, based on date started.
3. The job with the earliest scheduled completion date, sometimes with these dates derived from complex backdating and explosion procedures.

On the other hand, frequently none of these methods produce the best sequence.

B. The job farthest behind schedule is that which proportionately (1) has the earliest requirement date, based on up-to-date knowledge of requirements, and also (2) has the longest time left for its completion, based on knowledge of lead times and routing.

C. Critical ratio converts the *time* relationship between supply and demand into an index number:

$$\text{Critical ratio} = \frac{\text{demand time}}{\text{supply time}}$$

This makes all jobs, at any point in the process, directly comparable, regardless of the date they are needed or the date they will be completed.

D. Critical ratio can be used in applications which require economic grouping or sequencing of jobs in order to minimize setup or changeover costs. This requires a two-step procedure. The first step groups or sequences like sets of jobs, as required, within specified delivery restraints. Then critical ratios establish the relative priorities of the respective sets.

E. Critical ratio is a dynamic system, utilizing frequent feedback of both supply and demand information. In a stock-replenishment application, for example, regular reporting of updated on-hand balances enables the critical ratio to expedite those items for which demand is higher than normal. Equally important, the remaining items (for which demand is less than normal) are *automatically* "set aside" to permit critical jobs to move faster.

Critical-ratio Applications.   The critical-ratio technique can be incorporated into most production scheduling systems to:

A. Determine the status of a specific job.

B. Establish relative priorities among jobs on a common basis.

C. Provide the ability to relate both stock and make-to-order jobs on a common basis.

D. Provide the capability of adjusting priorities (and revising schedules) automatically for changes in both demand and job progress.

E. Permit dynamic tracking of job progress and location.

F. Eliminate the expediting functions of job-progress look up, redating of all associated documents, special hand-carrying, etc., by providing foremen and dispatchers with proper job sequence based on most current information.

G. Provide basic data for overall queue control and manning decisions.

Critical-ratio Formulas for Production Scheduling.   The general supply–demand–time relationship is developed as follows:

$$\text{Critical ratio (CR)} = \frac{(\text{date required}) - (\text{today})}{\text{days required to complete job}}$$

If CR > 1.0, the job is ahead of schedule.   The date on which it will be available is earlier than the date on which it is required.

If CR = 1.0, the job is on time.

If CR < 1.0, the job is behind schedule (critical).   Based on its standard lead time and normal rate of progress through the manufacturing process, it will take longer than the required date to obtain it.   The *lower* the critical ratio, the *more* critical (further behind schedule) the job is.

A. *Stock-replenishment Formulas* (see Fig. 9)

If the job is for replenishment of a stock item, the requirement date (measured from today) is equal to the days of supply of stock remaining in inventory assuming average daily usage.   Normally, actual usage varies from the average. Critical ratio takes this into account.   Whenever usage is below average, CR increases in value and delivery of the job can be delayed by producing more

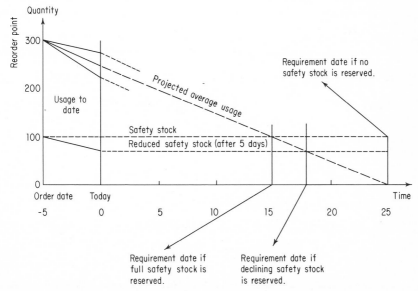

Fig. 9   Critical-ratio demand-time stock replenishment.

critical jobs in the queue first. Conversely, whenever usage is greater than average, CR decreases in value, and the job moves faster through the process by taking a higher position in the queue.

Prior to implementing the formulas presented below, a decision must be made regarding the use of safety stock. Should the replenishment order be continuously monitored to time its arrival when:

On hand = safety stock?

On hand < safety stock, but > 0?

On hand = 0?

The alternative selected would depend on the nature of demand (large, sporadic demands versus small, frequent demands) and the nature of the manufacturing process (flexible and responsive versus costly and time consuming to make changes).

	Know:		Usage to date:
	ADU	10 units	(A) 50 units (average)
	LT	20 days	
	LTR	15 days	(B) 75 units
	SS	100 units	
	RP	300 units	

	$\dfrac{(\text{OH} - \text{SS})/\text{ADU}}{\text{LTR}}$	$\dfrac{[\text{OH} - (\text{SS})(\text{LTR}/\text{LT})]\text{ADU}}{\text{LTR}}$	$\dfrac{\text{OH}/\text{ADU}}{\text{LTR}}$
(A)	$\dfrac{(250 - 100)/10}{15} = 1.00$	$\dfrac{[250 - (100)(15/20)]/10}{15} = 1.17$	$\dfrac{(250/10)}{15} = 1.67$
(B)	$\dfrac{(225 - 100)/10}{15} = 0.83$	$\dfrac{[225 - (100)(15/20)]/10}{15} = 1.00$	$\dfrac{(225/10)}{15} = 1.50$
	Rescheduled to arrive when OH = SS	Rescheduled to use part of SS and arrive when OH = SSR as a result of LTR on last operation	Rescheduled to arrive when OH = O

Fig. 10 Critical ratio formulas: stock replenishment. Formula 3 is equivalent to either formula 1 or 2 with safety stock set to zero.

1. *Full safety stock reserved* (see Fig. 10)

$$\text{CR} = \frac{(\text{OH} - \text{SS})/\text{ADU}}{\text{LTR}} \tag{1}$$

where OH = inventory on hand
    SS = safety stock
  ADU = average daily usage
  LTR = standard lead time remaining

The first column in Fig. 10 illustrates this formula in action. In Example B, actual usage to date has been equal to average usage. The inventory on hand, *after* reserving 100 units of safety stock, equals 15 days of supply with 15 days of work remaining to be done. As a result, CR = 1.00, and the job should proceed at a normal rate through the process in order to arrive in stock when OH = SS = 100 units. Examples A and B would be delayed and accelerated, respectively, in order to arrive at the time when inventory is at this level.

2. *Reserving declining safety-stock balance*

$$CR = \frac{[OH - (SS)(LTR/LT)]/ADU}{LTR} \qquad (2)$$

where LT = total standard lead time (all operations).

This formula schedules the stock-replenishment order to arrive after some of the safety stock has been used but before the stock on hand falls to zero. The amount of safety stock reserved is directly proportional to the time remaining to complete the job (LTR/LT). It should be noted that LTR never reaches zero, so some safety stock is always reserved. Use of a proportional reduction is based on the ability of critical ratio to accelerate delivery into stock if an unusually high variation in usage occurs.

Note that in Figure 10 this formula yields a higher CR than the first one, and that a job becomes critical only when actual usage is greater than the sum of average usage plus the allowed safety-stock depletion.

3. *No safety stock reserved:* Whenever zero is substituted for safety stock in either of the above formulas, the result is to schedule receipt of the order when OH = 0.

This alternative would be satisfactory *only* if management is willing to accept a high level of stock outs (although the duration of stock outs would be relatively short).

B. *Make-to-order Formula* (see Fig. 11)

For make-to-order items, the requirement date equals a predetermined delivery date rather than a calculated stock-depletion date. The delivery date may be customer shipment date, or by explosion, the date a component must be delivered to a stock point for use in a higher-level assembly. Frequently, this date must be changed between the original release of the order and its completion. All such changes must be kept current in order to calculate accurate critical ratios.

The formula is

Demand time = days remaining to required date, or
(due date) − (today)

←— Days remaining —→

Original   Today   Date
order   required
date

Required date, though subject to change, represents a
"firm" commitment:
for assembly schedules
for customer shipments

Time is measured in working days.

Fig. 11 Critical-ratio demand: make-to-order items.

$$CR = \frac{\text{due date} - \text{today}}{LTR} \qquad (3)$$

where all days are working days.

C. *Standard Lead Time Remaining (LTR)* (see Fig. 12)

Standard lead time remaining is the common denominator in all variations of the CR formula. It is defined as the expected *elapsed* time required for the job to pass through predetermined work centers from its present location to job completion. Since our concern is *time* remaining, not *work* remaining, the LTR is more than just the sum of setup and run times for all remaining operations.

$$LTR = \text{total lead time} - \text{lead time for operations completed} \qquad (4)$$

1. *Lead time calculations:* The elapsed time, or standard lead time, for any

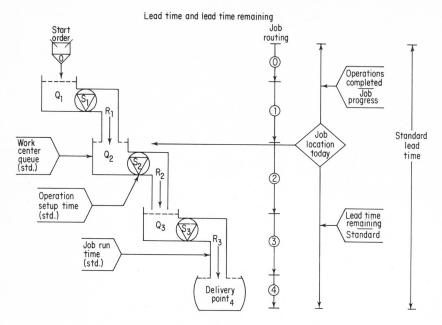

Lead time = time required for operations 0, 1, 2, 3, 4.
Lead time remaining = time required for operations 2, 3, 4.

Fig. 12 Critical-ratio supply time.

specific work center is described by the following formula:

$$LT = SQ + \frac{SU + QR}{HE} \qquad (5)$$

where SQ = standard queue allowance in days
  SU = setup time in hours
  Q = lot size
  R = run time in hours
  H = hours worked per day
  E = percent effectiveness in meeting standards

Note that queue allowance is included, and that the daily production rate is adjusted to represent a realistic estimate of what can be produced. When expanded this formula is used to calculate the total lead time for any item:

$$LT = O + \Sigma \left(\frac{SQ + SU + QR}{HE} \right) + \Sigma\, T \qquad (6)$$

where O = order preparation time
  T = added allowance for transit time between operations, where applicable

2. *Simplified formulas:* It is possible to simplify the above formulas in cases where setup and run times are short (hours rather than days) and queues relatively long (several days per operation). That portion of the formula dealing with work remaining can be set equal to zero, leaving:

$$LT = O + \Sigma\, (SQ + T) \qquad (7)$$

3. *Basic data requirements:* In addition to knowledge of total lead times, which is required for every production and inventory control system, critical-ratio scheduling requires:

    a. Knowledge of operation lead times

    b. Elemental breakdown into queue, setup, and run times

    c. Definition of "standard" queue allowances

Use of Queue Allowances. Traditionally queues have been maintained at each work center to:

1. Provide a pool of work within which an economic sequence can be developed

2. Provide a backlog to reduce the probability of a production shutdown whenever significant variations between supply and production occur

The optimum queue is the minimum amount of work which will satisfy the above objectives. For our purposes, it is sufficient that a standard (not necessarily optimum) queue be defined. The critical ratio can be used to:

1. Sequence jobs (or economic groups of jobs) according to criticality

2. Summarize the work in queue to determine whether delivery dates can be met

3. Summarize the total shop load to determine whether changes in the overall production rate are necessary

Critical ratio operates by changing the relative positions of jobs in queue. It is effective to the extent that job sequence is variable and individual jobs can be accelerated or delayed in the process.

Lead-time Contol. The manufacturing department must be capable of producing most jobs within the standard lead time, and some jobs in less time. Its ability to do so depends upon the total supply-demand relationship.

1. Whenever requirements exceed capacity for any length of time, queues increase, job completions lag, and all jobs become increasingly critical (possibly to the point that CRs become meaningless).

2. When capacity exceeds requirements for some time, queues shrink, jobs become less critical, and some work centers may run out of work.

In both cases, management action to adjust capacity is necessary to maintain standard lead times, queue flexibility, and the effectiveness of critical ratios. Critical-ratio queue and load analysis provides the basic information for controlling overall lead times:

A. *Information Required for Capacity Decisions*

The general information required falls into three categories:

1. What has been happening recently, i.e., have average order receipts been significantly greater or less than the production rate?

2. What is the current status? Are the present work-center queues more or less critical than they should be?

3. What is the expected impact on various work centers in the near future? Is the total work load of all orders on hand for all work centers significantly greater than that which can be done within standard lead times?

B. *Summary Critical-ratio Load Report*

One method of consolidating and integrating this information is illustrated in the report format shown in Table 1. Each column is numbered to correspond with the following numbered paragraphs, which describe the content and relationships:

1. Identification of work center.

2. New orders written during the current period (week, month, etc.).

3. Long-term average of new orders during past periods. Large random variations in demand will be revealed in comparing columns 2 and 3.

TABLE 1   Summary Critical-ratio Load Report

Work ctr.	Curr. rcts.	Ave. rcts.	Curr. prod.	Ave. prod.	Std. queue	Actual queue			Total load	Ave. load	Comts.
						<0.8	<1.2	>1.2			
1	2	3	4	5	6	7	8	9	10	11	12
A											
B											
C											
Total											

4. Current-period production. Comparison with column 2 will reveal likely changes in critical queue at present or in the near future.
5. Long-term average production rate is a measure of capacity. Comparison with column 4 may signal significant production problems. Comparison with column 3 will reveal the need for adjusting production rates to maintain lead times.
6. Standard queue allowance.
7., 8., and 9. Hours actually in queue and the degree of criticality. The queue is out of control when more than the standard queue is less than 0.8 or greater than 1.2. The nature and extent of corrective action can be determined from the earlier comparison of receipts and production.
10. Total load is the sum of the work required for all orders in the "house regardless of their present location.
11. Average total load is another measure of "normal conditions" and comparison of columns 10 and 11 frequently provides advance information for decision making.
12. This column should be used to indicate conditions which require action.

Using Critical Ratio: an Example

A. *General Background* (see Fig. 13)

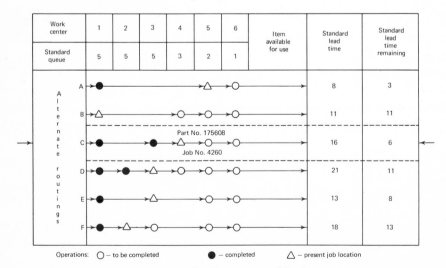

Fig. 13 Example of routings and lead times.

A small machine shop will form the basis for our example. The shop has three production work centers, plus the supporting and time-consuming activities of order preparation (work center 1), final inspection (WC 5), and transfer to stock (WC 6).

1. *Routings:* Six common routings are shown (A through F), ranging in complexity from simple reinspection of a purchased part to processing in all work centers.
2. *Queues and transit times:* Each work center has a standard queue allowance as shown. All jobs are expected to flow through a given center within this standard time. The total amount of work at a center at one time should not exceed this level.
3. *Standard lead times:* The standard lead time for a job depends on its routing and the queue allowances for the work centers through which it passes [using the simplified lead-time formula given earlier, Eq. (5)]. Standard lead times for all six routings are shown.
4. *Job progress and lead time remaining:* An active job for each routing is shown and its present location indicated. Compare routings D and E. Two jobs are presently located at work center 3. Because of the different routings, however, D had three days longer lead time remaining. All other things being equal, it should be produced ahead of E.
5. From this point on we shall be concerned with part 175608, being produced on job 4260, presently located at work center 4. We wish to know:
   a. Is the job on time?
   b. If behind schedule, how does it compare with other jobs at the work center? Can it be expedited to completion on time without putting other jobs behind schedule?
   c. Can all jobs in queue be produced on time?
   d. Is total shop load such that some adjustment in the production rate should be made in order to maintain standard lead times?

B. *Critical-ratio Calculation*

1. Part 175608 is a stock item. The following is known about the item:

$$\text{Stock on hand} = 18 \text{ units}$$
$$\text{Safety stock} = 12 \text{ units}$$
$$\text{Average daily usage} = 2 \text{ units}$$
$$\text{Lead time remaining} = 6 \text{ days}$$

Using critical-ratio formula (1),

$$CR = \frac{(OH - SS)/ADU}{LTR}$$
$$= \frac{(18 - 12)/2}{6}$$
$$= 0.50$$

2. *Conclusion:* Either usage to date has been above average since the job was started or the job has been delayed in process. In either case, progress must now be accelerated to avoid a potential stock out. How is this done?
3. *Status of other jobs:* Prior to taking specification, the critical ratio of all other items at this work center must be calculated. Some of them may be even more critical than this one, requiring a higher priority.

C. *The Production Schedule* (see Fig. 14)

1. After calculating all critical ratios and sorting them in low-to-high sequence, the schedule shown in Fig. 14 is produced.

Work center 4 grinding   11/20/7x
                                          Daily capacity 15.0 hours

| Job no. | Part no. | Hours of production, critical jobs | | Critical ratio |
		This job	Cumulative	
4592	115604	2.54	. . . . .	0.25
3654	223982	3.60	6.14	0.30
4260	175608	4.21	10.35	0.50
4109	598325	2.10	12.45	0.55
3785	600507	9.86	22.31	0.77
Total critical 5		. . . .	22.31	1.5 days

Fig. 14   Production schedule—jobs in queue.

2. Two jobs should be produced before job 4260. Nevertheless, our critical job can be produced today. It will not sit for the normal three days in this work center. Moreover, it will automatically be produced in the proper priority sequence *without detailed personal follow-up* because the critical ratio has slotted it in its proper place near the top of the queue.

3. It is not necessary to

   a. Locate the job physically and move it to a preferred place in queue.

   b. Locate all related documents and change dates or attach a "rush" signal.

D. *Summary Queue and Load Status* (see Fig. 15)

The overall status of the shop load does not look as promising. The present queues are beginning to become increasingly critical.

1. In work center 4, the critical and slack hours are nearly equal. Critical queue is equal to half the standard queue, providing ample capacity for expediting *at present.*

2. However, as we move backward through earlier work centers, we note

| Work Center | Daily receipts | | Daily production | | Standard queue | | Actual queue | | | Total load | |
	This week	Average	This week	Average	Days	Hours	Critical	On time	Slack	Actual	Average
1	12.0	10.0	10.0	9.5	5	47.5	45.0	20.0	6.0	71.0	47.5
2	22.3	21.0	15.5	20.0	5	100.0	75.6	40.2	20.6	285.7	225.0
3	26.5	24.0	19.6	21.0	5	105.0	65.7	32.7	27.3	405.2	335.0
4	19.2	16.1	16.5	15.0	3	45.0	22.3	14.0	23.3	322.6	270.0
5	. . . .	. . . .	11.0	9.2	2	18.4	9.0	5.0	6.0	207.0	180.0
6	. . . .	. . . .	9.0	9.2	1	9.2	5.0	4.0	3.0	219.0	189.0
Grand total	68.0	61.1	51.6	56.0	. . .	250.0	163.6	86.9	71.2	1013.5	830.0

Fig. 15   Summary queue and load status. Entries for work centers 1, 5, and 6 are by number of jobs rather than hours. They are not included in the grand totals. Total load may be broken down by time period or degree of criticality if desired.

that queues become increasingly critical and the total queues also are significantly above standards.

3. Analysis of average order receipts versus production and current total load versus average load reveals that

   a. Orders exceed production by 9 percent and have done so for some time.

   b. An additional 5.1 hours of production per day are needed to keep up with incoming orders; more if the total shop overload of 183.5 hours is to be reduced to normal.

   c. The rate and duration of the increase in receipts is sufficient to justify corrective action. The absolute increase is too small to justify hiring additional people.

   d. Selective overtime should be worked—on critical jobs—to keep the critical queue in any work center to less than 75 percent of the standard queue, slightly below the level at which we have defined a job as critical (0.8). This will maintain queue flexibility and avoid paying a premium for work on noncritical jobs.

Critical Ratio for Purchase-order Follow-up. While standard lead times for purchased items are generally known, there frequently is no elemental breakdown into checkpoints, comparable to production work centers, for reporting progress and determining lead time remaining. Once such a breakdown is made, the same critical-ratio formulas used in production scheduling can be applied to purchase-order follow-up.

Some or all of the following checkpoints should have standard times associated with them and should have automatic feedback for status reporting:

1. Requisition forwarded to purchasing

2. Purchase order forwarded to vendor

3. Vendor acknowledgment received; promised shipping data compared with lead time and LTR adjusted accordingly.

4. Vendor shipment made

5. Order received

6. Material inspected and approved

7. In stock, available for use

Although critical ratio is a very powerful scheduling technique, we have seen that it is relatively simple and straightforward to use. Its biggest advantage is that it converts the time relationship between supply and demand into an index number which makes all jobs comparable. It can be readily used with a computer to handle a large number of orders.

Critical ratio is one of the newest techniques available, but it has already seen widespread use.

LINE OF BALANCE*

In this day and age of ever more complicated and sophisticated systems and procedures, coupled with expensive computerized capabilities, a simple, twenty-five-year-old, economical, garden-variety charting technique has been dressed up in "new clothes" to give meaningful answers to top management. The top management referred to are those executives at the level of department head, plant manager, program manager, contract manager, division manager, and higher.

---

* This section contains excerpts from N. E. Finck, "Line Of Balance Gives the Answer," *Systems and Procedures Journal*, July–August, 1965, and N. E. Finck, *What's New with Line of Balance*, ASTME Technical Paper MM66-703, 1966.

The "new clothes" referred to is the ability to chart:

1. *Customized* and *repetitive* efforts simultaneously
2. Prototypes or first-article effort showing not only when each milestone is to be completed but also when it is to be started

These two general problem areas are usually thought to be unsuited to the line-of-balance charting technique; yet a simple, meaningful presentation is a real challenge as manufacturing programs become more complex and more programs are involved simultaneously.

The charting technique presented is *line of balance*, frequently referred to as "LOB." "Line of balance" is defined as *a management-oriented charting technique designed to broaden management's visibility of program progress and aid in implementing corrective action wherever necessary.*

Those familiar with manufacturing have all seen status charts at the shop level which are kept by lead men, assistant foremen, and foremen. But how can this detailed, floor-level status be transmitted into a meaningful, easily understood chart for upper management?

For a moment, let's examine the need for line-of-balance charts. First, there are many kinds of planning and control techniques undertaken at the outset of a program, such as parametric estimates, historic S curves, projected shop loads, and estimates of the number of drawings, tools, shop orders, and parts. After the program is moving along, there is usually a requirement for a device which will show the cross-sectional view of the whole program. LOB is a method of measuring how program progress compares with program requirements to meet contractual obligations.

Second, many management meetings can turn into a numbers game. For example, it is very possible to hear an engineering department report that, out of an estimated 4,750 drawings for the program, the schedule calls for 10 percent to be completed at this time. Since the department has actually completed 450 or $9\frac{1}{2}$ percent of the drawings, it feels that it is only slightly behind schedule and, hopefully, will catch up in two weeks at the latest. Sounds reasonable, doesn't it? And it is probably very accurate, too.

But, the timeliness of this effort, or more precisely, the lack of timeliness, may be such that the follow-on departments are almost shut down because the first things needed are not coming out first. A finished product cannot be made from subassemblies, which were made from parts, which were fabricated from tools, which were the result of planning effort, which originated from blueprints, which never came out of the engineering department!

Finally, many management reports are necessarily nondescriptive. For example, for a particular airplane construction program there is an engineering manufacturing status report which gives in numerical form the detailed status of the program in four major departments. This report for the initial 20-airplane release has 4,368 meaningful part numbers. There is the same kind of report for each customer, showing the same information for customized (different from the basic airplane) effort. Currently there are seven different reports for the program, which means a maximum possibility of 7 times 4,368 or 30,576 different numbers to evaluate on this program alone. Is there a device which can reduce these numbers to a simple "picture" for management?

In management's search for the answer to the foregoing questions, line of balance came up with the answers. More managements are finding that LOB provides the answer to their problems.

History. LOB was originally devised by the members of a Goodyear Tire and Rubber Company group headed by George E. Fouch, just prior to World War II as a means of monitoring production effort. It was the first of the latter-day control techniques, which include PERT and CPM.

Upon mobilization, George Fouch, an officer in the Naval Reserve, was ordered to the U.S. Navy Bureau of Aeronautics, where he introduced the line-of-balance technique. The Navy widened the scope of its LOB applications and used it for the production planning and scheduling of their huge material requirements during World War II and the Korean War. Other military services and agencies of the government, as well as industry, now use this technique.

Aside from the basic method of line-of-balance charting (Fig. 16), two interesting and most helpful variations have been generated.

The first variation is to display customized or nonrepetitive items along with a basic repetitive release on the same line-of-balance chart (Fig. 17). This is most helpful when all customers get a similar finished product which contains certain items that are customized to suit each customer.

The second variation applies to a first-article or prototype effort and shows in line-of-balance fashion when each milestone or event should be completed along with the time when each milestone should have started (Fig. 18). This version readily discloses if an organization is working on the right things at the right time and if they started on time. It prevents the surprise sometimes associated with the discovery that an event was not completed on time, since clues indicating this possibility were being posted all along.

Basic Line-of-balance Chart (Fig. 16). Before we discuss the two variations referred to above, it is imperative that the reader understand the basic line-of-balance technique used so frequently in communicating subcontractor status to prime contractors and to the government. Figure 16 illustrates the basic LOB chart used in monitoring subcontractor performance.

There are four ingredients required for a basic line-of-balance chart:

1. *Production Plan.* The flow chart illustrated in the lower half of Fig. 16 shows the key critical events (milestones) which were taken from the master production plan. These are plotted on the chart from right to left starting with the end of any production plan (shipment). They are numbered, however, from left to right to indicate the priority of things which must occur before shipment can be accomplished. The abscissa (horizontal scale) of the chart is in units of time. The timing (days or weeks) ahead of shipping date for each milestone is taken from the master production plan.

2. *Cumulative Schedule.* This is illustrated in the upper left-hand corner of Fig. 16. The cumulative schedule must be known so that the cumulative requirement for each milestone, x weeks or days ahead of the shipping date, can always be determined. Quantity is shown as the ordinate (vertical scale) of the chart. The dates selected for the abscissa are generally chosen as Friday of every week; however, any other day of the week will do if it is desired by local management or required by the contract, but in no case should it be less frequent than the management reporting cycle. "Schedule" and "Cumulative Schedule" are taken from the contract with the cumulative-schedule curve plotted as shown. "Delivered" and "Cumulative Delivered" are generated during the life of the contract with the actual curve plotted to the "Time Now" line (report date) as shown.

3. *Production Progress* (upper right-hand chart). In a vertical Gantt-chart fashion the least number of units cleared through each milestone is plotted. For example, if a milestone represents more than one assembly, activity, or part, and varying quantities of each have been completed, the smallest number is posted.

4. *Line of balance* (upper right-hand chart). This is the stairstep type of line (high on the left and low on the right) which is derived by determining for each milestone the cumulative quantity of units which must be completed to meet the shipping schedule in accordance with the production plan.

The line of balance is usually generated weekly or monthly, depending upon management reporting requirements. Any milestone having actual status posted below the line of balance is in trouble and therefore requires remedial action if the schedule is to be met. Those milestones *at* or *above* the line of balance are either *on* or *ahead* of schedule and therefore present no particular problem for the current reporting period.

The method of generating the line of balance warrants further explanation since this point is the usual "stumbling block," but when once mastered, makes LOB charting easy.

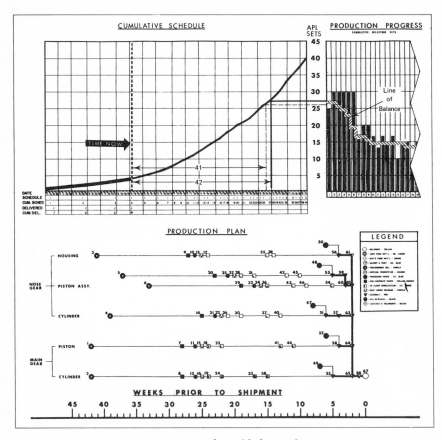

Fig. 16   Basic line-of-balance chart.

Referring to the production plan flow chart, note that milestones 1 and 2 should be completed 42 weeks prior to shipment according to the production plan. Moving 42 weeks to the right of the "Time Now" line on the "Cumulative Schedule" and extending a line vertically, we find that 27 airplane (APL) sets must be shipped by that date, November 24, to meet the scheduled requirement. Since the production plan has a 42-week span for milestones 1 and 2 through 67, it should be obvious that 27 sets of "Main Gear Piston Assembly" material (milestone 1) and 27 sets of "Main Gear Cylinder Assembly" material (milestone 2) must have been ordered to date by purchasing to meet the production plan.

Draw a horizontal line across milestones 1 and 2 at 27 on the production-progress chart.

In similar fashion, note that milestone 3 should be completed 41 weeks prior to shipment; and 41 weeks to the right of the "Time Now" line discloses that 26 APL sets must be shipped by that date, November 17, to be on schedule. Again draw a horizontal line across milestone 3 at 26. Repeat this step for the remaining milestones, continuing to work from left to right on the production-progress chart, and the horizontal lines will take on a stairstep pattern. Connect each higher line on the left to the next lower line on the right with a vertical line, and the line of balance is completed.

As time goes on, it may become evident that the production plan must or can be shortened considerably. In this case, leave all scales the same and superimpose a new, shortened production plan on the old one and proceed as before.

In an *accelerating* program, the production plan is frequently shortened for each successive unit. In this case, leave the "Weeks Prior to Shipment" off the production plan of the LOB chart since this is easier to handle on numerical tables which give due dates for each milestone for each successive unit.

When a production plan involves a relatively small number of milestones (Fig. 16 has 67), it is easy to identify the various functions within a production plan, such as engineering, planning, and so forth, by using a different color for posting status for each function.

When several hundred milestones are involved in each of several different functions, a separate line-of-balance chart is drawn for each function or department showing the production-progress portion only. The milestone identification then is issued as a published list. For example, "1. Raw Material Order— Main Gear Piston" and "2. Raw Material Ordered—Main Gear Cylinder" would be the first two milestones on the list if the 67 milestones were published in list form.

The production plan is issued as another list showing in the proper order which APL set is due to be completed in each department and the date it is due to be completed. The shipping requirements, daily, weekly, and cumulative, are also issued in list fashion. These LOB charts, one for each department, are then displayed or presented in the same order as their occurrence. For example, engineering, planning, tooling, fabrication, and assembly would be a typical left-to-right arrangement for display or first-to-last order for presentation to management.

Customized and Repetitive-effort Line-of-balance Chart (Fig. 17). Having covered the foregoing basic technique as usually applied to a repetitive effort, the technique used to display basic (repetitive) and customized (nonrepetitive) effort on the same line-of-balance chart will be discussed. Stated otherwise, suppose a shop order for 20 basic units (airplanes, missiles, etc.) was released in which several different customers were involved, each wanting a few modifications of the basic unit. A shop order would be written for all the parts common to all 20 units. Other shop orders would be written for those items which are peculiar to each customer's requirement.

To see how this can be handled on a single line-of-balance chart, refer to Fig. 17. Here we see plotted an initial basic release for 20 airplanes and a second basic release for 25 more airplanes along with the different configuration effort for each customer's first airplane.

The milestones on this chart are called "MI (master index) numbers," which are three-digit numbers used as scheduling designators which have assigned to them all the parts and units of work due to be completed during a particular

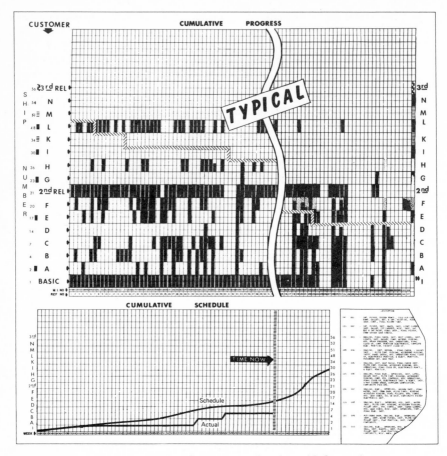

Fig. 17 Customized and repetitive-effort line-of-balance chart.

week in a given functional area of the airplane. Each of the three digits can be closely allied to area, zone, and subzone type of work-breakdown structure analysis.

All effort in each major department (engineering, planning, tooling, fabrication, etc.) is tracked by the MI. There are 147 different MIs with each MI having possible involvement in each department. It was decided, therefore, to make a master chart which would be applicable to all departments. A departmental chart is put into use by entering the appropriate department's name in the proper place on as many master charts as are required.

The parts common to each of the first 20 airplanes are released in production-order quantities of not less than 20 airplane sets per part and are all reported against airplane 1 since each lot is due to be finished in time for airplane 1's requirements. It is possible then to report customized effort for each customer's first-airplane configuration within the first block of 20 airplanes released.

Airplane 2 is for a customer A, and only those MIs having configuration effort different from airplane 1 are reported, since the customized effort for each customer is reported against that customer's first airplane. Airplane 4 goes to customer B, and once again, only those MIs having configuration effort different from airplane 1 are reported.

Projecting this idea further, airplanes 2, 3, 5, 8, and 11 are alike. So airplane 2, the first one to be built for this customer, is the only one reported. Again, airplanes, 4, 6, and 9 are for the same customer, so airplane 4 is the only one reported. Airplanes 7, 10, and 13 are for customer C, so airplane 7 is the only one reported. Airplanes 14, 15, 21, and 24 are for customer D, so airplane 14 is the only one reported. And so it goes for every first airplane for each customer. Note that airplane 21, which is for an earlier customer D, would normally not be reported. It is reported, however, because it is the first airplane in the second release for 25 airplanes, and in this case the parts common to the next 25 airplanes, airplanes 21 through 55, are reported against airplane 21.

Just a few words on posting the chart: The vertical space allotted each airplane represents 0 to 100 percent. A light line is drawn through each space at the 50 percent level for ease in posting. All status is posted in black, and all MIs are posted on a basic release. On customized airplanes, all known customized MIs are indicated in a light color to indicate a known requirement, a different color for each customer. As progress by MI is reported, the colored tape is gradually covered with black as status moves from 0 to 100 percent complete. Note that all MIs not customized are not reported against a customer's airplane, since the basic release takes care of these and this space is left blank with no colored tape. Obviously then, any exposed colored tape below the line of balance indicates past-due customized effort.

It must be realized that the idea of reporting only the customer's first unit will not work in an assembly department. The same master chart is still applicable, but for an assembly department each successive unit is indicated and progress is posted accordingly.

Prototype or First-article Line-of-balance Chart (Fig. 18). At the outset it would seem likely that the only difference between a repetitive-effort line-of-balance chart (Fig. 16) and a prototype LOB chart (Fig. 18) for first-article effort would be in the ordinate of the prototype chart. Basically, this is a safe assumption. Recall that the repetitive-effort chart started at 0 and stopped at 20, 50, or any other number of units established on the vertical scale. The chart for a prototype unit also starts at 0 and stops at 100 percent on the vertical scale. Progress is then posted in terms of percentage completed. The line of balance is generated from a predetermined schedule for the completion of each milestone. There is, of course, no need for the "Cumulative Schedule" portion of Fig. 16 to be shown on Fig. 18, since Fig. 18 pertains to one unit only whose shipping date is shown as the last milestone of the production plan.

Obviously the production-progress portion of these two different charts, Figs. 16 and 18, will appear quite similar. This is fine, except for one thing: Suppose that in addition to indicating when a milestone should be completed, an indication of when it should be started is desired. If we can get a clue as to when an event or milestone should start, there is a better chance of having it completed on time.

It is evident that portions of this chart are similar to the previous ones. However, those portions which are different enable this chart to tell a most interesting story.

The ordinate, 0 to 100 percent, should present no problem at all, since we are presenting a single unit. However, the abscissa now has five elements:

1. The milestones (events) are defined in the reference table at the side of the chart.

2. "Week Due" follows a manufacturing calendar; for example, week 826 is the last week in June, 1968; week 935 is the last week in August, 1968, etc.

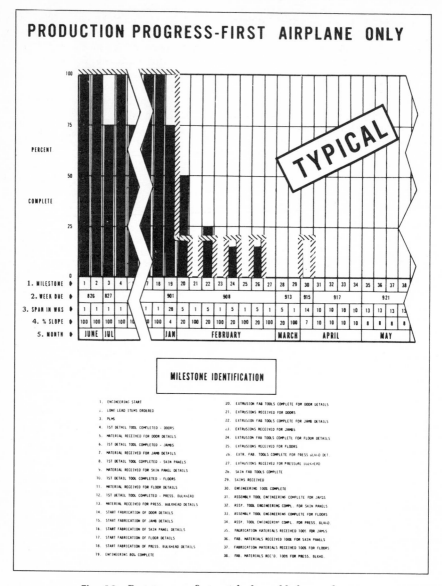

Fig. 18 Prototype or first-article line-of-balance chart.

3. "Span" is in terms of weeks and is taken from the various flow charts already in existence which depict the production plan.

4. "Percentage Slope" is obtained by dividing 100 by the number of weeks in the span omitting decimals.

5. So that the observer can quickly get some idea of the volume of work involved in a given month, the appropriate month is indicated at the bottom along the horizontal scale.

The 0 to 100 percent posting of each milestone is no problem. Different-

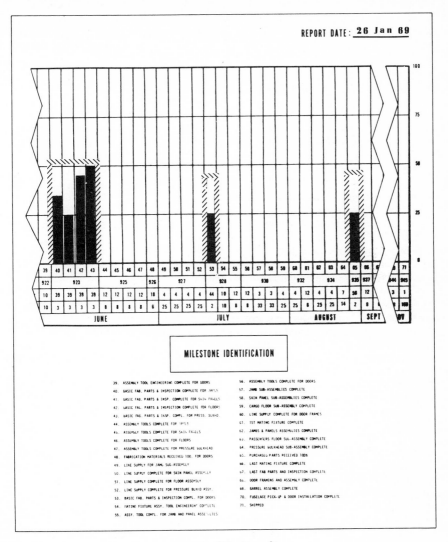

Fig. 18 (*Continued*)

colored tape assigned to each function shown in the legend makes the chart easily read and therefore more useful to the manager who needs this chart.

The line of balance is located in such a way as to indicate the percent of the "Span in Weeks" which has elapsed for each milestone. Note that the report date is Jan. 26, 1969. This date is the end of week 904 on the manufacturing calendar used in this case. Therefore, all milestones should be complete and the line of balance is placed at 100 percent through milestone 19. Milestones 20, 22, 24, and 26 are five-week jobs due to be completed in week 908, four weeks from now. Simple arithmetic discloses that $\frac{1}{5}$ or 20 percent of the time span has elapsed; so we place the line of balance at 20 percent.

Milestone 30 finishes in week 915; it is a 14-week job with $\frac{3}{14}$ or 21 percent of the time span elapsed, so the line of balance is placed at 21 percent. Milestones 40, 41, 42, and 43 finish in week 923. These are 39-week jobs with $\frac{20}{39}$ or 51 percent of the time span elapsed, so the line of balance is placed at 51 percent. Similar logic is applied to any other milestone which should have started as of "Report Date," such as milestones 53 and 65. Milestones 22, 24, 26, 30, 40, 41, 42, 43, 53, and 65 have broken the usual stairstep pattern. This condition is only temporary, since the line of balance for these milestones is approaching 100 percent at a slower rate than the other milestones due to be completed in the same week. Note that the line of balance currently stands at 20 percent for milestones 20, 22, 24, and 26. In four weeks, week 908, the line of balance will be at 100 percent for milestones 1 through 27; at 50 percent for milestone 30; at 10 percent for milestones 31, 32, 33, and 34; at 62 percent for milestones 40, 41, 42, and 43; at 55 percent for milestone 53; and at 46 percent for milestone 65.

The prototype line-of-balance chart tells us if everything is completed as planned, and at the same time it tells if we are starting our work according to plan. Note that milestones 20 and 22 show progress above the line of balance. Yet milestone 30 has no progress posted. This is a clear indication that work is being done which is not in phase with the plan.

Now we have a really unique chart! It shows us everything past due while at the same time serving as an automatic work-assignment chart. After all, any chart that shows what we are supposed to be working on and when we should start or have started is a simple work-assignment chart. It should be noted that on the prototype chart only it is not fair to conclude we are in trouble when any posted milestones are below the line of balance. We are actually in trouble only when those milestones fall short of 100 percent when the line of balance stands at 100 percent. For example, milestones 3, 5, and 19 are the only ones past due. All other milestones below the line of balance are no particular cause for alarm because they may reach 100 percent at the same time or before the line of balance gets there. However, if any of these milestones do develop into "behind-schedule" items, it should not be a surprise to anyone since the clues to this possible condition were being posted all along.

Incidentally, the prototype chart can also be functionalized, that is, one chart per function or department. In fact, one of the most successful applications to date was used in an engineering department displaying 358 different milestones which were involved with several dozen different systems in the prototype article, and there were 3,265 different drawings involved.

Conclusion. If you feel your management needs a clear, cross-sectional view of program progress presented in such a way as to disclose the timeliness of events and at the same time show areas in trouble, you should try line of balance. It will certainly do that and more.

If you suspect that using line of balance is expensive, nothing could be farther from the truth. It requires a minimum of personnel, since the data required to support it is already in existence somewhere in your organization. You need only to master the technique and, as required, produce a line-of-balance "picture" of overall program progress from these numbers. This is usually a part-time assignment for one person. It is only when programs become more complex, more customized, and more numerous that full-time line-of-balance personnel are required.

If you subscribe to the idea that line of balance has been outmoded, you had better take another look. The simplest presentation which gets the "point" across is usually the most effective. The two variations to basic line of balance discussed in this section *carefully* applied are most effective, especially when used in conjunction with the basic technique.

Interested? Try it. We think your management will like it.

NETWORK PLANNING METHODS

Although essentially unknown a few years ago, the use of network techniques for scheduling complex projects is commonplace among industry today, thus attesting to their usefulness. It is the purpose of this section to describe the characteristics of these methods and the types of problems for which they are generally applicable.

While network methods for project planning carry a variety of titles, there are only two which shall concern us here. Most other terms encountered in practice are merely variations or renaming of these two.

The first technique to be considered is the critical-path method (CPM), which has both construction and industry origins. Two basic variations are presented.

The second technique to be described has origins in the area of military R&D planning. PERT (program evaluation and review technique) was first utilized by the Navy in the management of the Polaris missile-system development and has frequently been credited with shortening the project completion time by several years.

Although stemming from different origins, these methods have become quite similar. In fact, today the names are occasionally used interchangeably.

Network methods are applicable to projects where tasks are combined in various ways to achieve a single objective. Examples of such projects would be the construction of a building or other structure, a major repair activity, the design and construction of a complex weapon system, and the production of a large piece of equipment.

These projects have several common characteristics:

1. They are comprised of a well-defined collection of tasks which, when completed, mark the end of the project.

2. The tasks are *ordered* in that they must be performed in a given sequence (e.g., a board must be sanded before it can be painted).

3. The time to complete each task is known in advance (or can be estimated closely). In PERT, greater uncertainty is incorporated by permitting the planner to submit several estimates which bound the completion time. The method of specifying task-completion time represents the principal difference between CPM and PERT.

4. A task once started is allowed to continue without interruption until it is completed.

5. A succeeding task does not need to start immediately upon completion of an immediate predecessor task, although it, of course, cannot commence until the prior one has been completed. This characteristic causes some difficulty in the application of CPM or PERT to continuous-processing industries in which interruption between process steps is not permitted.

The first variation of the critical-path method to be discussed in this section is the event-on-node method, the one in most widespread use today. A significant variation, activity-on-node, which promises to become increasingly important, is discussed below.

Event-on-node Method. A network is a pictorial description of a plan showing is composed of *arrows* connecting *nodes,* as shown in the diagram on the next page.

The time-consuming elements of a network are known as "activities." An activity is represented by an arrow connecting two nodes.

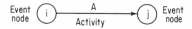

The nodes (circles on network) represent "events." Events are well-defined points in time. For example, an event might represent the time at which all parts are on hand to permit the assembly of an item. The assembly itself, being a time-consuming element, is an activity.

The direction of the activity arrow represents a precedence relationship. Event i must occur before activity A can commence. Similarly, event j cannot occur until activity A has been completed.

Consider as an example the development of a network to describe the relationships of the activities involved in the manufacture of a large machine in which subassemblies 1 and 2 are combined into subassembly 4, which is then joined with subassembly 3 to make the final product. Because of the need to match certain items in subassembly 3 with corresponding items in subassembly 2, 3 cannot be built until the parts for 2 are on hand.

The principal activities required to build the machine are those identified in Table 2. The network describing these activities is as shown in Fig. 19a. Note that there is a single *origin* event and a single *terminal* event. With the exception of these, every event has at least one activity leading into it and at least one leading from it. Every activity provides an unique connection between two nodes, thus making it possible to identify an activity by the events that it connects (e.g., activity D is equivalent to activity 2-5). The event nodes have been numbered to provide for their identification. By convention they are numbered so that all activities lead from lower numbered nodes to higher numbered nodes.

Occasionally, a precedence relationship between activities exists which cannot be represented correctly with merely the above activities and even nodes. Consider Fig. 19b as a possible network segment for showing the relationships among activities B, C, E, and G. However this would be in error for it implies that E follows C, which would be incorrect since the assembly of subassembly 2 need not follow the procurement of parts for subassembly 3. The reverse is the only restriction. To permit correct representation, a *dummy activity* is used which requires zero time units for the completion. The dummy activity identified by a dashed arrow and the letter X has been added to the network to correctly portray the relationship. Dummy activities can be

TABLE 2   Example Problem—Building a Large Machine

Activities ID	Description	Duration, days	Immediate predecessors
A	Procure parts for subassembly 1	5	None
B	Procure parts for subassembly 2	3	None
C	Procure parts for subassembly 3	10	None
D	Build subassembly 1	7	A
E	Build subassembly 2	10	B
F	Build subassembly 4	5	D and E
G	Build subassembly 3	9	B and C
H	Final assembly	4	F and G
I	Final inspection and test	2	H

used whenever necessary to show a relationship that cannot otherwise be depicted. They are merely a device for forcing a desired relationship without affecting the actual project.

COMPUTATION OF EVENT TIMES: The ultimate purpose of the network is to provide guidance for the scheduling of the individual activities. To do this one needs first to know the *earliest possible* and *latest permissible times* each event can occur.

Let $t_i(E)$ equal the *earliest time* event i can occur.

$$i = 1, 2, \ldots, n$$

where n is the number of events in the network.

Let y_{ij} represent the duration time of the activity connecting events i and j.

Since an event cannot occur until all activities leading into it have been completed and since an activity cannot commence until its prior event has occurred, we calculate as the earliest time for each event the length of the longest path from the origin to the event.

Starting with event 1 in Fig. 20, proceed in order through each event to the terminal event n. Place in a square beside each event the earliest possible time for the occurrence of the event.

We usually start with zero for the first event, $t_1(E) = 0$. For subsequent events, consider *all* activities leading into the event. Calculate for each activity the earliest time of the prior event plus the duration of this activity. Since the succeeding event cannot occur until all prior activities are completed, the earliest possible time for the event in question is the maximum of these various times. In other words, the earliest time for event j is

$$t_j(E) = \begin{cases} 0 & \text{if } j = 1 \text{ (origin)} \\ \max\{t_i(E) + y_{ij}\} & 2 \le j \le n \end{cases}$$

with the maximization over all i's connected to j by an activity i-j. Computation proceeds until the earliest time for terminal event n has been computed.

In the example,

$$t_2(E) = t_1(E) + y_{12} = 0 + 5 = 5$$
$$t_3(E) = t_1(E) + y_{13} = 0 + 3 = 3$$
$$t_4(E) = \max \begin{Bmatrix} t_3(E) + y_{34} = 3 + 0 = 3 \\ t_1(E) + y_{14} = 0 + 10 = 10 \end{Bmatrix} = 10$$

These and the other earliest-event times are shown in Fig. 20.

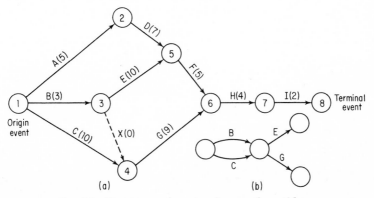

Fig. 19 Event-on-node network example problem.

The earliest time for the terminal event, $t_8(E) = 25$, represents the earliest possible time that the entire project can be completed.

Let $t_i(L)$ equal the *latest time* event i can occur without affecting the completion of the total project.

Starting with the last event n, proceed backward through the events. On the network place the computed latest time in a *circle* beside the event. We usually set for the terminal event the latest time equal to the earliest time.

$$t_n(L) = t_n(E)$$

It could, however, be set equal to any specified time.

To compute the latest time for any event i ($i < n$), consider all activities leading from it. Compute for each such activity the latest time of its following event minus the activity duration. The smallest of these becomes the latest time for event i.

$$t_i(L) = \begin{cases} t_n(E) & i = n \\ \min\{t_j(L) - y_{ij}\} & 1 \leq i \leq n - 1 \end{cases}$$

with the minimization over all j's connected by an activity i-j. The computation proceeds until the latest time for the origin (event 1) has been computed.

The latest event times are shown in Fig. 20. In the example,

$$t_5(L) = t_6(L) - y_{56} = 19 - 5 = 14$$
$$t_4(L) = t_6(L) - y_{46} = 19 - 9 = 10$$
$$t_3(L) = \min \begin{cases} t_5(L) - y_{35} = 14 - 10 = 4 \\ t_4(L) - y_{34} = 10 - 0 = 10 \end{cases} = 4$$

The maximum time an event can be delayed without causing a delay in the total project completion time is known as the "slack time" for the event.

Let S_i equal the slack time for event i. Then

$$S_i = t_i(L) - t_i(E)$$

CRITICAL-PATH CALCULATIONS: If the latest and earliest time for an event are the same ($S_i = 0$), no slippage in the event is permissible. Those events which have zero slack time are on the *critical path*. In the example, events 1, 4, 6, 7, and 8 are therefore on the critical path.

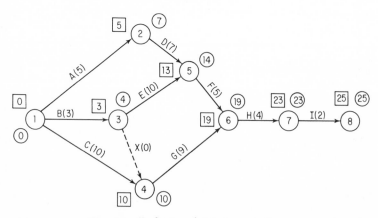

Fig. 20 Earliest and latest event times.

The critical path is a connected sequence of activities and events extending from the origin to the terminal such that a delay in one would cause a delay of the final project completion. Conversely, those activities and events not on the critical path may be delayed by a nonzero amount of time without affecting total completion time. From the network it can be seen, for example, that event 2 can be delayed $7 - 5 = 2$ units of time without affecting the project completion.

Therefore, control of a project should devote primary attention to those activities on the critical path. If reduction in total project completion time is desired, effort should be applied to the reduction of only those activities on the critical path. Across-the-board "crashing" of all activities is obviously wasteful, and should be avoided.

It should be noted that it is possible for the critical path to change as the duration of an activity is reduced. For example if either activities C or G are reduced more than 1 unit of time, the critical path will change to events 1-3-5-6-7-8. Hence, care should be taken to ensure that excessive reduction is not made.

COMPUTATION OF ACTIVITY TIMES: Control of any project is affected by regulating the starting and stopping of activities, not the occurrence of events, since it is the set of activities which comprise the tasks necessary for project accomplishment. It is therefore desirable to provide specific activity scheduling information in terms of the earliest and latest times that each activity can be started and finished. As can be seen, the critical path passes through those activities for which the earliest and latest start (or finish) times are identical, thus permitting no delays.

The *earliest start* time for an activity is the earliest time an activity can be started assuming all previous activities are completed as early as possible. Let ES_{ij} equal the earliest start for activity i-j. Since an activity cannot commence until its predecessor event has occurred, $ES_{ij} = t_i(E)$ where the subscript i represents the predecessor event for activity i-j. It follows that if EF_{ij} equals the *earliest finish* for activity i-j,

$$EF_{ij} = ES_{ij} + y_{ij}$$

The *latest start* and *latest finish times* are computed in a reverse manner.

The latest finish time for an activity is the latest time it can be completed without delaying the final project completion time. Let LF_{ij} equal the latest finish for activity i-j. Since an activity can be completed no later than the latest permissible time for successor event j to occur,

$$LF_{ij} = t_j(L)$$

The latest start, LS_{ij}, can be then computed by

$$LS_{ij} = LF_{ij} - y_{ij}$$

Table 3 contains the results of these computations applied to the activities of the example.

FLOAT TIMES: For the purpose of scheduling the various activities, it is useful to have certain other results indicating the degree of scheduling freedom under a variety of conditions. These, which are analogous to the slack time for events, are the float times. There are four types which will be considered.

1. *Total Float.* The total float for activity i-j, TF_{ij}, is the maximum time that an activity i-j may be delayed without causing delay in the final project completion. It implies that all predecessor activities must be accom-

TABLE 3   Event-on-node Method: Activity Earliest and Latest Start and Finish Times

Activity	Predecessor event i	Successor event j	Duration y_{ij}	Earliest Start ES_{ij}	Earliest Finish EF_{ij}	Latest Start LS_{ij}	Latest Finish LF_{ij}
A	1	2	5	0	5	2	7
B	1	3	3	0	3	1	4
C	1	4	10	0	10	0	10
D	2	5	7	5	12	7	14
E	3	5	10	3	13	4	14
F	5	6	5	13	18	14	19
G	4	6	9	10	19	10	19
H	6	7	4	19	23	19	23
I	7	8	2	23	25	23	25

plished as early as possible and that all successor activities are forced to be accomplished as late as possible.

$$TF_{ij} = LS_{ij} - ES_{ij}$$
or
$$LF_{ij} - EF_{ij}$$

An activity is on the critical path if it has zero total float.

Table 4 shows the total float for the example. Activities C, G, H, and I are on the critical path since they have zero total float. Activities A and D can be delayed a maximum of two days, whereas B, E, and F can be delayed only one day.

2. *Free Float.* The maximum time an activity may be delayed without affecting the start of the next task if all prior activities are finished as early as possible is measured by the free float, FF_{ij}. As with total float all predecessor activities are assumed to be accomplished as early as possible. However, since free float measures the time available without affecting succeeding jobs, successor activities are permitted to start as early as possible.

$$FF_{ij} = t_j(E) - EF_{ij}$$

The free float for an activity may never be larger than the corresponding total float time.

TABLE 4   Activity Float Times

Activity	Predecessor event i	Successor event j	Total float TF_{ij} (1)	Free float FF_{ij} (2)	Independent float IF_{ij} (3)	Safety float SF_{ij} (4)
A	1	2	2	0	0	2
B	1	3	1	0	0	1
C	1	4	0	0	0	0
D	2	5	2	1	0	0
E	3	5	1	0	0	0
F	5	6	1	1	0	0
G	4	6	0	0	0	0
H	6	7	0	0	0	0
I	7	8	0	0	0	0

As shown in Table 4 only activities D and F have nonzero free float. Although D could be delayed a total of two days (total float), it can be delayed only one day without affecting other following activities. Any delay in activity A, which has a total float of 2, forces a delay in other activities as is indicated by its zero free float. Activities on the critical path obviously have zero free float.

3. *Independent Float.* If one is responsible for the accomplishment of a particular activity, planning could be severely disrupted if prior activities were *not* completed as early as possible (as assumed in the total- and free-float computations). Independent float, IF_{ij}, is the maximum time an activity may be delayed without delaying successor activities if all prior activities are finished as late as possible. It gives a measure of time available if following tasks are not to be affected and the worst possible conditions prevail in the predecessors. Hence, the name "independent" is appropriate.

$$IF_{ij} = t_j(E) - [t_i(L) + y_{ij}]$$

or zero if above is negative

In the example problem, let us calculate the independent float for activity D which is identified in terms of its events as activity 2-5.

$$IF_{25} = t_5(E) - [t_2(L) + y_{25}]$$
$$= 13 - [7 + 7] = -1$$

Hence, since it is negative, we set $IF_{25} = 0$. As is shown in column 3 of Table 4, all activities in our elementary examples have zero independent float. The departments responsible for accomplishing activities D and F which have one unit of free float will find that they have no float time if their predecessor activities are completed at their latest limits.

4. *Safety Float.* To the individual responsible for the accomplishment of an activity, a useful measure is the maximum time that an activity may be delayed without affecting the final project completion if predecessor activities are completed as late as possible. This is the safety float, SF_{ij}. Although the project completion is not affected, successor activities may be delayed.

$$SF_{ij} = LS_{ij} - t_i(L)$$

For example, the safety float for activity A is as found by

$$SF_{12} = LS_{12} - t_1(L)$$
$$= 2 - 0 = 2$$

The safety-float results for the example problem are shown in column 4 of Table 4. Activities A and B only are assured of having float time available (because they have no predecessor activities in this case). All other activities would be denied float time if A and B utilized their safety float.

One might ask: Of what value are the various float times? The first obvious answer is that zero total float identifies an activity on the critical path as one to be closely monitored and controlled. All the floats are useful when determining exactly when an activity is to be accomplished. In many cases, the labor or equipment needed to accomplish an activity must compete with other activities for available supplies of these resources. The various float times provide assistance when actually assigning these resources to each activity. Float time permits some freedom in attempting to balance resource demands.

Activity-on-node Method. An alternative formulation of the problem, activity-on-node, has recently been developed. It possesses sufficient advantages over the older event-on-node method that it may become the more common method used for project planning.

The primary difference in this method is that activities are represented by nodes with arrows merely representing precedence relationships.

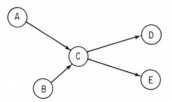

The concept of event is not needed, and is not included. All computations concern activity start and finish times directly. Because there is no need to include events, the network construction task is greatly facilitated.

Further, as will be seen, there is no need at any time to create dummy activities. Any precedence relationship can be expressed correctly without them.

The construction of the network is facilitated by adding two fictitious activities. The first, which we label as "start," precedes all other activities, and the other, "finish," follows all activities. Each has zero duration.

The example previously considered, when represented by the activity-on-node method, appears as shown in Fig. 21. Note that not only is the network very

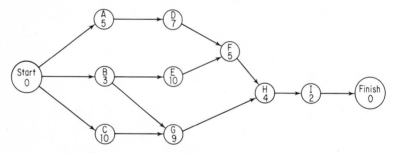

Fig. 21   Activity-on-node network example problem.

different in appearance but also the correct precedence relationships are represented without dummy activities.

COMPUTATION OF ACTIVITY TIMES:
Definitions:

y_i = duration time of activity i.
P_i = immediate predecessor set of activities for i. This is the set of activities which immediately precede activity i.
S_i = immediate successor set of activities for i. This is the set of activities which directly follow activity i.

For the example these definitions yield Table 5.

$ES(i)$ = earliest start for activity i
$EF(i)$ = earliest finish for activity i
$LS(i)$ = latest start for activity i
$LF(i)$ = latest finish for activity i

TABLE 5   Immediate Predecessor and Successor Sets

Activity i	Duration y_i	Immediate predecessor P_i	Immediate successor S_i
Start	0	None	A, B, C
A	5	Start *Step* 1	D
B	3	Start	E, G
C	10	Start	G
D	7	A	F
E	10	B	F
F	5	D, E	H
G	9	B, C	H
H	4	F, G	I
I	2	H	Finish
Finish	0	I	None

COMPUTATION OF EARLIEST TIMES: Let $ES(\text{start}) = 0$. Next, calculate the earliest start and finish times for the other activities. Since the early start time of an activity can be no smaller than the early finish of any of its immediate predecessors, it is necessary to consider activities in such a sequence that the EF times of all activities in P_i are computed before activity i is considered.

$$ES(i) = \max \ EF(x)$$

where the maximization is done over all activities in the immediate predecessor set of i.

$$EF(i) = ES(i) + y_i.$$

Computation continues until the earliest times have been computed for all activities.

For the example problem let us illustrate the procedure for computing the ES and EF times of Table 6. The predecessor sets are obtained from Table 5.

TABLE 6   Activity-on-node Method: Activity Earliest and Latest Start and Finish Times

Activity i	Earliest Start $ES(i)$		Finish $EF(i)$		Latest Start $LS(i)$	Finish $LF(i)$	
Start	0		0		0	0	
A	0	*Step* 2	5	*Step* 3	2	7	
B	0	*Step* 4	3	*Step* 5	1 *Step* G	4	*Step* F
C	0		10		0	10	
D	5	*Step* 6	12	*Step* 7	7	14	
E	3	*Step* 8	13	*Step* 9	4	14	
F	13	*Step* 10	18	*Step* 11	14	19	
G	10		19		10	19	
H	19		23		19 *Step* E	23	*Step* D
I	23		25		23 *Step* C	25	*Step* B
Finish	25		25		25 *Step* A	25	

Step 1. For activity A, $P(A)$ contains start only (Table 5)
Step 2. Therefore, $ES(A) = EF(\text{start}) = 0$ (Table 6)
Step 3. $EF(A) = ES(A) + y_A = 0 + 5 = 5$
Continuing with these steps for several other activities:
Step 4. $ES(B) = EF(\text{start}) = 0$
Step 5. $EF(B) = ES(B) + y_B = 0 + 3 = 3$
Step 6. $ES(D) = EF(A) = 5$
Step 7. $EF(D) = ES(D) + y_D = 5 + 7 = 12$
Step 8. $ES(E) = EF(B) = 3$
Step 9. $EF(E) = ES(E) + y_E = 3 + 10 = 13$
Step 10. $ES(F) = \max \begin{Bmatrix} EF(D) = 12 \\ EF(E) = 13 \end{Bmatrix} = 13$
Step 11. $EF(F) = 13 + 5 = 18$

Table 6 contains the complete list of earliest start and finish times. Comparison with Table 3 shows that these results are identical to those obtained with the event-on-node method as would be expected. They have been obtained, however, directly without intermediate event-time computations.

COMPUTATION OF LATEST TIMES: Let $LF(\text{finish}) = LS(\text{finish}) = EF(\text{finish})$. The calculation of the *latest finish* and *start times* of the other activities proceeds in a reverse manner to those just calculated. Since the latest finish time of an activity can be no larger than the latest start time of any of its immediate successors, activities must be selected in a sequence whereby the activity is not considered until the LS times of all activities in its S_i have been computed.

$$LF(i) = \min LS(x)$$

(minimization over all x's in S_i) and

$$LS(i) = LF(i) - y_i$$

Computation proceeds for all activities until eventually the latest times for the activity start have been computed.

In the example shown in Table 6:
Step A. $LS(\text{finish}) = LF(\text{finish}) = EF(\text{finish}) = 25$
Step B. $LF(I) = LS(\text{finish}) = 25$
Step C. $LS(I) = LF(I) - y_I = 25 - 2 = 23$
Step D. $LF(H) = LS(I) = 23$
Step E. $LS(H) = 23 - 4 = 19$
Step F. $LF(B) = \min \begin{Bmatrix} LS(E) = 4 \\ LS(G) = 10 \end{Bmatrix} = 4$
Step G. $LS(B) = 4 - 3 = 1$

FLOAT TIMES: The definitions developed previously for total, free, independent, and safety float naturally still apply. The computations take a slightly different form inasmuch as the notion of events is not present.

1. *Total Float:* $TF(i)$. The total float for activity i is found by

$$TF(i) = LS(i) - ES(i)$$
or
$$= LF(i) - EF(i)$$

Those activities with zero total float are a part of the critical path.
Total float for activity D:

$$TF(D) = LS(D) - ES(D)$$
$$= 7 - 5 = 2$$

2. *Free Float:* FF(i)

$$FF(i) = \min ES(x) - EF(i)$$

(minimization over all x's in S_i)
Free float for activity B:

$$FF(B) = \min ES(x) - EF(B)$$

where $x = $ those jobs in the immediate successor set of B. From Table 5 this set is activities E and G.
Hence,

$$FF(B) = \min \left\{ \begin{matrix} ES(E) \\ ES(G) \end{matrix} \right\} - EF(B)$$

$$= \min \left\{ \begin{matrix} 3 \\ 10 \end{matrix} \right\} - 3 = 3 - 3 = 0$$

3. *Independent Float:* IF(i)

$$IF(i) = \min ES(x) - [\max LF(z) + y_i]$$

(minimization over all x's in S_i; maximization over all z's in P_i) or zero if this is negative.
Independent float for activity F:

$$IF(F) = \min ES(x) - [\max LF(z) + y_F]$$

where $x = F$'s immediate successor set (H)
$z = F$'s immediate predecessor set $(D$ and $E)$

$$IF(F) = ES(H) - \left[\max \left\{ \begin{matrix} LF(D) \\ LF(E) \end{matrix} \right\} + y_F \right]$$

$$= 19 - \left[\max \left\{ \begin{matrix} 14 \\ 14 \end{matrix} \right\} + 5 \right]$$

$$= 19 - 19 = 0$$

4. *Safety Float:* SF(i)

$$SF(i) = LS(i) - \max LF(z)$$

(maximization over all z's in P_i)
Safety float for activity B:

$$SF(B) = LS(B) - \max LF(z)$$

where $z = B$'s immediate predecessor set (start).

$$SF(B) = LS(B) - LF(\text{start})$$
$$= 1 - 0 = 1$$

When applied to the example problem, these will yield the float times identical with those previously listed in Table 4.

PERT. PERT (program evaluation and review technique) differs from the critical-path method only in the manner in which activity durations are entered. The networks developed under both methods would be identical. Instead of a single time estimate for each activity, three time estimates are given. These permit the planner to indicate quantitatively the degree of uncertainty associated with his prediction of the completion time. Because research and development projects are characterized by difficulty in the prediction of the duration of various tasks which by their very nature cannot be completely known in advance, PERT has found its principal usefulness in this environment.

For each activity, estimates are required as to the *most likely time, minimum time,* and *maximum time.*

The most likely time, m, is the time which the planner thinks has the highest probability of being the actual time required. However, if things go unusually well a shorter time might result. Therefore, a minimum time, a, is given, which reflects the shortest duration time that could possibly result. On the other hand, an activity may experience unusually bad luck. The maximum time, b, represents the longest activity time that might be anticipated short of catastrophic failure.

For each activity the planner provides an estimate for each of these three times.

These are then combined for each activity into a single expected duration, and an estimate of the variance of the duration. These computations are based on an assumption that the actual duration times for each activity follow a *beta* distribution. The expected duration y_e of activity is given by

$$y_e = \frac{a + 4m + b}{6}$$

while the estimate of the variance $\sigma_y{}^2$, is

$$\sigma_y{}^2 = \left(\frac{b - a}{6}\right)^2$$

Once a single expected duration has been obtained for each activity, the problem is identical to the critical-path method described previously with the expected time y_e used as the single time estimate. All CPM computations are therefore applicable.

Once $t_n(E)$ has been obtained for the project, we introduce the notion that the actual activity times are random variables. Since the duration of each activity may be a random variable, it follows that the time of occurrence of any event, and in particular the event n, is also a random variable. If we let t_n represent the actual completion time of the project, we concern ourselves with the determination of its distribution; in particular the mean and variance of the final completion time.

The application of some elementary concepts of probability theory yield the following results:

The mean value of t_n is $t_n(E)$ computed from the CPM phase of the computations (using y_e for each activity).

The variance of t_n (denoted as $\sigma_{t_n}{}^2$) is equal to the sum of the variances of the activities on the critical path when activity times are assumed independent.

The central-limit theorem permits us to assume that t_n is normally distributed with mean $t_n(E)$ and variance $\sigma_{t_n}{}^2$.

We use this information to determine the probability that t_n is less than or equal to some arbitrary scheduled completion date, $t_n(S)$. Figure 22 shows graphically the problem for which we seek an answer. This probability can be obtained from

$$Pr\{t_n \leq t_n(S)\} = Pr\left\{z \leq \frac{t_n(S) - t_n(E)}{\sigma_{t_n}}\right\}$$

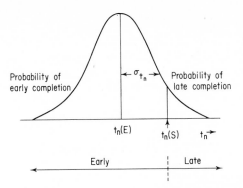

Fig. 22 Distribution of actual project completion times.

where z is the corresponding point in the standardized normal (mean $= 0$, variance $= 1$),

$$F(z) = \int_{-\infty}^{z} \frac{1}{\sqrt{2\pi}} e^{-y^2/2} \, dy$$

A variety of interpretations of the probability measure is possible. Generally, probability values between 0.35 and 0.65 represent an acceptable range to proceed with the project. A value below 0.35 indicates that the scheduled time $t_n(S)$ cannot be reasonably met, whereas values above 0.65 may indicate that excess resources are built into the network.

Summary. All too often, the earliest time a project's completion can be anticipated is later than some desired or required completion date.

In other cases, and earlier completion may hold some financial advantage if, for example, personnel can be released to other jobs, leased equipment can be returned, or accounts receivable can be realized sooner. Often the duration of an activity is subject to management control to some degree. By the assignment of additional personnel or more or better equipment, an activity's duration can often be decreased. This decrease comes, however, at a higher cost. The problem is to find the level of effort, or equivalently, the appropriate duration, for each activity to optimize the costs associated with the project. For solutions to this cost optimization problem, see references 1, 2, or 3 at the end of the chapter.

A second problem concerns the fact that the basic CPM or PERT model assumes the unlimited availability of manpower and facility resources. Often, however, such an assumption creates a situation wherein during a particular portion of time the demand for a resource exceeds its supply.

To alleviate this problem, some activities are shifted in time so that the overlap of demand by several activities is minimized. The float times provide some assistance by indicating which activities can be delayed and by what amount of time. Often, however, the float times do not provide sufficient flexibility. References 1, 4, and 5 provide some guidance in the solution of this problem.

LINEAR PROGRAMMING

Linear programming (LP) is a practical mathematical tool for production managers. It is especially suited for problems in which many simple trade-off relationships exist among a large number of variables. As the name implies, the objective of the decision-making function must be stated mathematically as a linear relationship such as:

$$\text{maximize } Z = C_1 X_1 + C_2 X_2$$

where C_1 and C_2 are constants and X_1 and X_2 are variables representing production quantities. In any realistic situation, the value of the variables, that is, the decisions, will be constrained within limits. These limitations must also be linear relationships in order to apply LP. Example of linear constraints might be

$$a_1 X_1 + a_2 X_2 \leq b_1$$
$$a_3 X_1 + a_1 X_2 \geq b_2$$
$$a_5 X_1 + a_6 X_2 \cong b_3$$

where a_1 through a_6, and b_1, b_5, and b_3 are constants and
    $\leq$ means "less than or equal to"
    $\geq$ means "greater than or equal to"
    $\cong$ means "approximately equal to"

The first two relationships imply that under no circumstances can the inequality be violated. The third constraint implies that there is a penalty associated with deviating very far from the preferred value (b_3). In addition, the use of LP requires that all variables must have a zero or positive value. The variables in most production control problems meet this nonnegativity requirement.

LP techniques include several methods for solving problems as described above. Only large, difficult decision-making problems with many variables and numerous constraints require a powerful tool like LP. However, the concepts involved in LP can be demonstrated with a simple problem as follows.

Assume that a production manager has two products which must pass through three machines. Profit for product 1 is $4 per unit and profit for product 2 is $2 per unit. He wants the optimum profit, or

$$\text{maximum profit} = \$4X_1 + \$2X_2$$

where X_1 and X_2 represent units of products 1 and 2. The production time required on each machine by each product is given in Table 7. The last

TABLE 7 Production Data

Machine	Time to produce a unit		Maximum time available
	Product 1	Product 2	
A	1	2	6
B	3	1	10
C	1	1	4

column of the table shows the total hours available for each machine during the planning period. The information in the table is equivalent to the following inequalities:

$$1X_1 + 2X_2 \leq 6$$
$$3X_1 + 1X_2 \leq 10$$
$$1X_1 + 1X_2 \leq 4$$

and X_1 and $X_2 \geq 0$ from the nonnegativity requirement.

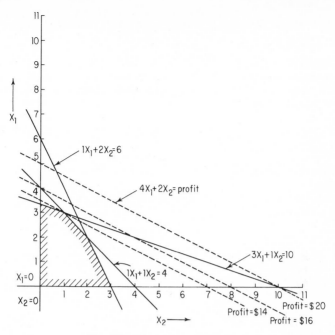

Fig. 23 Linear programming.

These relationships are represented graphically on Fig. 23. The values of X_1 lie along the vertical axis and X_2 values along the horizontal axis. Since each restriction is of the less-than or equal-to type, only those values of X_1 and X_2 which lie in the shaded area would be feasible, i.e., compatible with all three constraints. The objective is to maximize profit, that is, find the value or values of X_1 and X_2 in the shaded area that yield greatest profit. The objective function

$$\text{profit} = \$4X_1 + \$2X_2$$

really is a whole family of lines, all parallel to each other. Several of them are shown in the figure as dotted lines. Note that every point on each line has equal profit and that the profit increases as the line is positioned farther from the origin. The objective is to find the profit line farthest from the origin yet containing at least one point in the shaded area. The heavy dashed line meets the requirement. Since the shaded area is *convex*, that is, it only has outside corners, in general the maximum-profit point will be one of these outside corners. A special case would exist if the maximum-profit line coincides with one of the restriction equations. But even in that situation, an outside corner would still have maximum profit.

Since the shaded area contains an infinite number of points, a trial-and-error approach, examining the profitability of every one of these points, is out of the question. The analytical techniques of LP have means for investigating only that set of points which is certain to contain the maximum-profit values. These points are the outside corners. In our two-dimensional example the values of X_1 and X_2 at outside corners can be found by considering each constraint as an equality and solving any two of these equations simultaneously. Certain tests are used to eliminate from consideration the pair of equations

$$1X_1 + 2X_2 = 6$$

and
$$3X_1 + 1X_2 = 10$$

which intersect outside the shaded area.

Once the solution for any one corner is obtained, the profit can be computed. More important, a criterion exists for determining if the profit is the true maximum, and if not maximum, the technique indicates which corners are more profitable. Consequently, a unique solution can be obtained within a limited number of trys.

A mathematical solution of the example problem may improve the understanding of the theory behind LP. A general method called the "simplex algorithm" will be used.

Since the simplex works with equations, all inequality constraints must be changed to equations. The relationship

$$1X_1 + 2X_2 \leq 6$$

could be an equation if the left-hand side were increased enough to always equal 6. The exact amount required is not known, but can be represented by a variable which will be designated S_1. The restriction now has the form

$$1X_1 + 2X_2 + S_1 = 6 \tag{1}$$

Similarly, the other two constraints are converted to equalities:

$$3X_1 + 1X_2 + S_2 = 10 \tag{2}$$
$$1X_1 + 1X_2 + S_3 = 4 \tag{3}$$

The new variables, S_1, S_2, and S_3, are called "slack" variables since they represent unused or slack time on machines A, B, and C, respectively.

The slack variables and their cost or value are also included in the objective function. In some applications, slack variables may have value. For example, they might represent machine time that could be rented to another firm. In this application, the idle time will be assigned the value of zero. The objective function becomes

$$\$4X_1 + \$2X_2 + 0S_1 + 0S_2 + 0S_3 = \text{profit} = Z \tag{O}$$

Z is the symbol commonly used to represent the objective.

The simplex method consists of determining the values of the variables at each corner of the convex set shown in the figure and testing optimality of the solution. If the solution is not optimum, the method indicates which adjacent corner would have a better solution. This process is called "iterating" and is repeated at the indicated corner. Iterations are continued until an optimum solution has been found. High school algebra is a sufficient basis for solving the restriction equations. Understanding the test for optimality depends upon two economic concepts: marginal profit and opportunity cost.

Most managers think of marginal profit as the difference between the selling price of a unit of product and the cost of labor and material required to produce just one more unit. Marginal profit has the same connotation in the simplex method. However, in an LP problem, the costs are not simply a matter of extra material and labor. An LP problem exists because several different products are competing for the same limited resources. If they are allocated to one group of products, the firm must forgo the opportunity to produce a different set of products. The opportunity cost is the marginal profit from one or more products that the firm forgoes in order to produce another group of products. Marginal profit in the LP sense is the selling price of the product less all the costs including opportunity costs. Therefore, if a solution results in all variables having zero or negative marginal profit, the optimum solution has been found.

To start the LP solution, an initial solution is required. Since Eqs. (1), (2), and (3) contain more than three variables, they do not have a unique solution. If the value of all but three of the variables is established, a unique solution for the other three can be obtained algebraically. Inspection of the restriction equations shows that if the X_1 and X_2 were arbitrarily assigned the value zero, the unique solution would be $S_1 = 6$, $S_2 = 10$, $S_3 = 4$. This solution is hardly the optimum, but it will get the simplex process started.

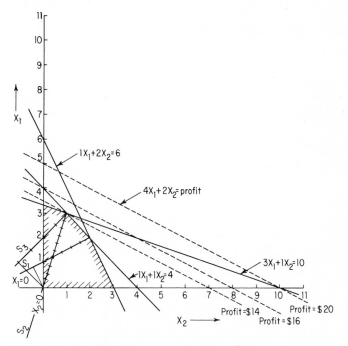

Fig. 24 Linear-programming solution.

A brief digression from the simplex may clarify why the arbitrary value was zero. Figure 24 is Fig. 23 with the addition of axes for variables S_1, S_2, and S_3. The orientation of the axes was obtained from the restriction equations. Equation (1) yields the following result:

$$S_1 = 6 - 1X_1 - 2X_2 \tag{4}$$

From principles of geometry, Eq. (4) is a straight line at right angles to Eq. (1). The S_1 scale is such that $S_1 = 6$ when $X_1 = X_2 = 0$. The S_1 axis could have been drawn anywhere along the line $1X_1 + 2X_2 = 6$, just as the X_1 axis can be drawn at any convenient location along the X_2 axis. By a similar argument,

$$S_2 = 10 - 3X_1 - 1X_2 \tag{5}$$
$$S_3 = 4 - 1X_1 - 1X_2 \tag{6}$$

Examination of each corner of the solution space reveals that two of the variables must have the value zero.

After obtaining the initial solution, its optimality must be tested. X_1 and X_2 are not in the solution in the sense that they are not part of the scheduled production. The solution cannot be the optimum if either has a positive marginal profit.

The coefficients of the objective function, Eq. (O), represent the profit margin of products X_1 and X_2 above their direct-labor and material costs. These figures do not take into consideration the opportunity cost associated with a different allocation of the resources. The coefficients of X_1 in Eqs. (1), (2), and (3) represent the cost of a unit of X_1 in terms of units of S_1, S_2, and S_3, respectively. That is, if X_2 is unchanged, and X_1 is increased by one unit, S_1, S_2, and S_3 would be reduced by 1, 3, and 1 units, respectively. The cost of forgoing these units is zero in this instance because S_1, S_2, and S_3 were previously defined as having zero value.

Similarly, two units of S_1 and one each of S_2 and S_3 would be forgone to schedule a unit of X_2, but the opportunity cost is zero. Therefore, the marginal costs of X_1 and X_2 remain at \$4 and \$2, respectively. The marginal costs of S_1, S_2, and S_3 are zero, since an extra unit of any one of these items could be obtained only by sacrificing another unit of the same product.

The above solution cannot be optimal because X_1 and X_2 have positive marginal profit. Allocating resources to either X_1 or X_2 or both would increase profit. The simplex method introduces only one new product into the new production schedule in each iteration. The choice between X_1 and X_2 is based on the magnitude of their marginal profits. The next iteration will contain X_1.

The value of X_1 in the next solution is controlled by the nonnegativity constraint on all variables. Assuming that all the resources were devoted to X_1 production, Eqs. (1), (2), and (3) would allow the values $X_1 = 6, \frac{10}{3}$, and 4, respectively. Equation (2) sets the upper limit on X_1. A higher value for X_1 would require some other variable to be negative in order to balance Eq. (2).

If X_1 is $\frac{10}{3}$, then all the machine B time is devoted to X_1 and the slack variable S_2 must be zero. Solving Eq. (2) for X_1 yields.

$$1X_1 + \tfrac{1}{3}X_2 + \tfrac{1}{3}S_2 = \tfrac{10}{3} \tag{2'}$$

The new allocation of resource to S_1 and S_3 can be obtained by eliminating X_1 from Eqs. (1) and (3), respectively. The usual algebraic method of elimination is applied.

	$1X_1 + 2X_2 + 1S_1$		$= 6$	(1)
minus	$1X_1 + \tfrac{1}{3}X_2$	$+ \tfrac{1}{3}S_2$	$= \tfrac{10}{3}$	(2')

$$\text{yields} \qquad \tfrac{5}{3}X_2 + 1S_1 - \tfrac{1}{3}S_2 = \tfrac{8}{3} \tag{1'}$$

and $\qquad 1X_1 + 1X_2 \qquad\qquad\qquad + 1S_3 = 4$ (3)

minus $\qquad 1X_1 + \tfrac{1}{3}X_2 \qquad\qquad + \tfrac{1}{3}S_2 \qquad\qquad = \tfrac{10}{3}$ (2')

$$\text{yields} \qquad \tfrac{2}{3}X_2 \qquad\quad - \tfrac{1}{3}S_2 + 1S_3 = \tfrac{2}{3} \tag{3'}$$

The new solution is $X_1 = \frac{10}{3}$, $S_1 = \frac{8}{3}$, and $S_3 = \frac{2}{3}$, while X_2 remains at zero and S_2 becomes zero. Is the solution optimum?

The marginal profits of X_2 and S_2 were \$2 and \$0. A diversion of resources to X_2 or S_2 may involve an opportunity cost. Each unit of X_2 would eliminate $\frac{5}{3}$ units of S_1, $\frac{1}{3}$ unit of X_1, and $\frac{2}{3}$ unit of S_3. Each of S_2 would require $-\frac{1}{3}$ unit of S_1, $\frac{1}{3}$ unit of X_1, and $-\frac{1}{3}$ unit of S_3. Only the loss of marginal profit from X_1 would affect the marginal profit of X_2 or S_2. Their marginal profit can be obtained as follows:

$$MP_{X_2} = \$2 - \tfrac{1}{3} \text{ unit of } X_1 \text{ at } \$4 \text{ per unit} = \$\tfrac{2}{3}$$
$$MP_{S_2} = \$0 - \tfrac{1}{3} \text{ unit of } X_1 \text{ at } \$4 \text{ per unit} = -\$\tfrac{4}{3}$$

The marginal profits for all the variables can be obtained more easily. The current unique solution contains X_1, S_1, and S_3. Among these variables, only X_1, the new member of the solution, has a nonzero marginal profit. Equation (2) is solved for X_1; therefore, the coefficients in this equation represent the units of X_1 that must be forgone to produce a unit of another variable. These are the opportunity costs which are expressed in dollars by multiplying Eq. (2′) by \$4, the marginal profit of X_1.

$$\$4 \times \text{Eq. (2')} = 4X_1 + \tfrac{4}{3}X_2 + \tfrac{4}{3}S_2 = \tfrac{40}{3} \tag{7}$$

subtracting Eq. (7) from Eq. (O) yields Eq. (O′)

$$4X_1 + 2X_2 + 0S_1 + 0S_2 + 0S_3 = Z \tag{O}$$
$$4X_1 + \tfrac{4}{3}X_2 \qquad\quad + \tfrac{4}{3}S_2 \qquad\qquad = \tfrac{40}{3} \tag{7}$$

$$0X_1 + \tfrac{2}{3}X_2 + 0S_1 - \tfrac{4}{3}S_2 + 0S_3 = Z - \tfrac{40}{3} \tag{O'}$$

The coefficient of Eq. (O′) is the marginal profit of the variables relative to the current solution. Since S_1 and S_3 had zero marginal profit no opportunity cost would be forgone by diverting resources away from S_1 and S_3. Equation (O′) is the new form of the objective function. Its right-hand side may be regarded as the difference between Z, the potential profit, and the profit from the current solution.

Since X_2 has a positive marginal profit, the optimum solution has not been found. Another schedule with an allocation of resource to product 2 must be obtained. The value of X_2 in the next iteration must be compatible with the nonnegativity constraint. Solving the constraint equations for X_2 yields the following results:

$$X_2 = \tfrac{8}{5} \tag{8}$$
$$X_2 = 10 \tag{9}$$
$$X_2 = 1 \tag{10}$$

Equation (10) is the most severe restriction on X_2, which means that all resources previously allocated to S_3 are now diverted to X_2, and Eq. (3′) becomes

$$1X_2 - \tfrac{1}{2}S_2 + \tfrac{3}{2}S_3 = 1 \tag{3''}$$

Equations (1′) and (2′) are again solved for S_1 and X_1.

X_2 can be eliminated from Eq. (1′) by mutliplying Eq. (3″) by the coefficient of X_2 in Eq. (1′) and subtracting the result from Eq. (1′).

$$\tfrac{5}{3}X_2 + 1S_1 - \tfrac{1}{3}S_2 \qquad\qquad = \tfrac{8}{3} \tag{1'}$$

minus $\quad \tfrac{5}{3} \times \text{Eq. (3'')} = \tfrac{5}{3}X_2 \qquad\quad - \tfrac{5}{6}S_2 + \tfrac{5}{2}S_3 = \tfrac{5}{3}$

yields $\qquad\qquad\qquad\qquad 1S_1 + \tfrac{1}{2}S_2 - \tfrac{5}{2}S_3 = 1 \tag{1''}$

Similarly, X_2 is removed from Eq. (2′).

$$1X_1 + \tfrac{1}{3}X_2 + \tfrac{1}{3}S_2 \qquad\qquad = \tfrac{10}{3} \tag{2'}$$

minus $\quad \tfrac{1}{3} \times \text{Eq. (3'')} = \qquad\quad \tfrac{1}{3}X_2 - \tfrac{1}{6}S_2 + \tfrac{1}{2}S_3 = \tfrac{1}{3}$

yields $\qquad\qquad\quad 1X_1 \qquad\qquad + \tfrac{1}{2}S_2 - \tfrac{1}{2}S_3 = 3 \tag{2''}$

The solution is now $X_1 = 3$, $X_2 = 1$, and $S_1 = 1$. These values coincide with the optimum solution shown in Fig. 23. An analytical check can be made by computing the marginal profits of the variables.

Inspection of Eq. (O') reveals that X_1 and S_1 have zero marginal profit, but X_2, the new variable in the solution, has a positive marginal profit of $\$\frac{2}{3}$. The marginal profits relative to the new solution are obtained as above. Equation (3″) was solved for X_2; therefore, the coefficients of Eq. (3″) represent the opportunity costs in units of X_2. Multiplying Eq. (3″) by the marginal profit of X_2 and subtracting from Eq. (O') yields the new form of the objective function.

$$0X_1 + \tfrac{2}{3}X_2 + 0S_1 - \tfrac{4}{3}S_2 + 0S_3 = Z - \tfrac{40}{3} \qquad (O')$$

minus $\qquad \tfrac{2}{3} \times$ Eq. (3″) $= \qquad \tfrac{2}{3}X_2 \qquad\qquad - \tfrac{1}{3}S_2 + 1S_3 = \tfrac{2}{3}$

$$0X_1 + 0X_2 + 0S_1 - 1S_2 - 1S_3 = Z - 14 \qquad (O'')$$

The solution given by Eqs. (1″), (2″), and (3″)

$$X_1 = 3, \ X_2 = 1, \ S_1 = 1, \ S_2 = 0, \ S_3 = 0$$

must be the optimum since all the marginal profits are zero or negative. The profit is $14.

The objective function plus the constraints are called the "model." Mathematical manipulation of the model yields an optimum solution, but at times, for many reasons, the optimum solution may not or perhaps cannot be implemented. However, LP techniques include a sensitivity analysis of the model. The decision maker not only gets a solution, but he can determine the cost of deviating from the solution. In addition, LP can tell him how much his estimate, the constants, could be in error before the solution is not optimum. Armed with this information he has a good basis for implementing the solution and also knows which constants need more accurate estimates.

LP has had many short- and long-range applications in production planning. In general, the technique becomes more practical as the problems grow in size. Problems involving only two or three variables can be solved graphically but are of no practical importance. If 10 to 20 variables and a similar number of constraints are involved, the decision maker's judgment may not give sufficient weight to all factors and suboptimum decisions may be made. Business judgments need to be supplemented particularly if quick, short-term answers are required. For example, a commercial livestock-feed manufacturer may be required to quote on a special mix. LP can enable him to quote a profitable price and a reasonable delivery date within minutes of the inquiry. Such a rapid response may mean the difference between sale or no sale or profit and loss.

As the problem grows larger—hundreds of variables and/or constraints—judgment alone cannot cope with all the ramifications of the problem. The solution time may be hours rather than minutes, but if the problem is linear, LP can yield optimum answers economically.

LP can be used in many different types of production situations. These applications can be categorized into the following six classes:

1. The diet problem
2. The product-mix problem
3. The transportation or distribution problem
4. The machine-loading (assignment) problem
5. The stock-cutting problem
6. The production scheduling problem

The classes of problems may have some overlap, and several different linear-programming methods may be used within one class. Each class has a characteristic formulation which may be adapted to many applications that fall within the class. Applications of each class of problem are described in the following sections.

The Diet Problem.[2,3,4,5] The diet problem gets its name from an early application which was to determine the most economical human diet. The feed and fertilizer industries use this technique routinely. The problem occurs in the form of chemical requirements for a product which is made largely from naturally occurring raw materials. The supply and analysis of raw materials is quite variable, and the market price may change with the seasons, weather, and other uncontrollable factors. Consequently the most economical blend must be repeatedly determined. The chemical requirements in the feed may also vary according to the availability of other feeds and the marketing practices of the feeder.

The linear-programming model yields the most economic blend. In addition, a sensitivity analysis of the cost or availability may be even more useful for predicting a "safe" price to bid on a job and to ensure that delivery will be possible. Such problems take the form of

$$\text{minimize } Z = C_j X_j$$

subject to

$$\sum_{j=1}^{n} a_{ij} X_j \geq b_i$$

where $i = 1, 2,$ or m

and

$$X_j \leq b_j$$

where $j = 1, 2,$ or n
C_j = cost of raw material X_j
a_{ij} = yield of substance i from raw material j
b_i = requirement of substance i
b_j = availability of resource j
n = number of raw materials
m = number of requirements

The Product-mix Problem.[6,7,8] The product-mix problems usually involve situations in which short-term limitations on materials, machines, and manpower restrict total production. Such problems are usually formulated as profit maximizing in which the available resources are applied toward meeting the most profitable sales potentials.

In general a product-mix problem is strictly short range. Bottleneck resources will be disclosed by the linear-programming solution. Corrective action such as buying additional machines, hiring more personnel, or finding new sources of material can eliminate almost any bottleneck. Consequently, the model must be updated periodically and new solutions obtained. However, if management accepts the solution as a guide rather than a hard-and-fast schedule, linear programming can make a significant contribution to overall planning.

If the model is updated frequently, and the planning horizon is very short range, specific schedules can be generated. An example is in the meat-processing industry. Except for processed meats such as sausages, very little inventory is kept on hand. The raw materials, that is, livestock, are never stored. Therefore, the buying and cutting must be adapted to the current supply and demand. The product mix, the various cuts of meat, is limited by livestock shipments to market which can only be estimated and the sales potential which also must be forecast. The week's buying and cutting schedule may be followed quite closely, but the same schedule may be unsuitable for the following week.

A more typical example of product-mix planning is taken from a heavy-capital-goods manufacturer. The firm assembles finished machines and also produces many of the component parts. Vendors supply several key components which require rather specialized manufacturing facilities. The variety within the product line is very great, i.e., the number of models could be in the hundreds of thousands if every minor variation was considered a separate product. For convenience, the models are classified into about one hundred groups. The basic problem is to ensure reasonable delivery promises that can be kept and to avoid production interruptions for lack of critical components. Historically, the firm has experienced material-procurement problems although any one bottleneck item can always be obtained.

In this situation, the vendors are limited in their capacity and require some rather long lead times. Three weeks to three months would not be unusual. During normal times, the average order can be filled in about one month; consequently, the demand for some individual components must be forecast. An order usually is not in the plant long enough to generate its own material requirements. The material controller must place purchase orders on the shop or the vendors based on a forecast. Within reasonable limits the order quantity can be reduced before the goods are delivered. Sometimes a quantity can be increased if the supplier has second-guessed the material controller and started excess pieces through the production cycle. The entire plant would operate much smoother without any of these last-minute changes.

For practical purposes, the material availability is limited to previously placed purchase orders and historical material and delivery performance. Therefore, the short-term production should be compatible with the material availability and also should tend to keep a reasonable backlog of orders. The objective is usually to maximize profit. For this firm marketing and manufacturing are separate functions. Manufacturing's concern is to meet schedules. Consequently, the optimum manufacturing plan is to maximize the units produced on schedule. These mathematical relationships can be stated as follows:

$$\text{maximize } Z = \sum_{j=1}^{n} X_j$$

where X_j represents the units of model class j produced during the planning period, e.g., a month, and n is the total number of model classes; subject to the following restrictions:

$$X_j \leq S_j$$

$$\sum_{j=a}^{b} X_j \leq L_k \qquad \text{for } k = 1, 2, \ldots, K$$

$$\sum_{j=1}^{n} P_{ij} X_j \leq M_i \qquad \text{for } i = 1, 2, \ldots, m$$

where S_j = sales potential for model j
L_k = production capacity for the kth assembly line on which models $a, \ldots,$
$\qquad b$ are produced
K = total number of such facilities
M_i = availability of the ith component
P_{ij} = fraction of model j that takes the ith component
m = total number of products in critical supply

The solution to this problem is only a guide to the actual production output. Each coefficient P_{ij} is the average of historical part usage which varies from month to month. Since the coefficients are random variables, the linear-programmed schedules are not expected to coincide with actual production. In addition, the product of $P_{ij}X_j$ usually will not be an integer. Obviously, a model uses an integer number of parts. Nevertheless, the computed product mix is sufficiently accurate for the purpose of making man assignments and for predicting needs of minor components.

The Transportation or Distribution Problem.[2,9,10] This class of problem often occurs as part of a larger problem, but it may be independent. Whenever a quantity of goods must be delivered from two or more locations to two or more destinations, the delivery route must be chosen. If several alternative routings are possible but have different costs, a linear-programming formulation may be desirable.

Perhaps no other linear-programming model has been as widely used. Examples can be found in the food, mining, petroleum, and many other industries where several sources of supply such as canneries are located fairly close to the origin of the raw material and finished goods are shipped nationwide. Each source-customer combination has a shipping cost associated with it. The supply at each source and the needs of each customer must be established. The quantity is often stated in terms of movable units such as truckload, since a formulation that allows shipments of excessively small quantities may be ridiculous.

The Machine-loading (Assignment) Problem.[4,11,12,13,14,15,16] This problem occurs whenever a set of discrete tasks must be assigned to specific men or machines and each has the capacity to perform the task but at different levels of efficiency. The ideal is to assign the task to the man or machine that can perform it most efficiently. In practice, this arrangement may not be practical because all tasks may have to be done simultaneously. The problem is to make the least-cost assignment.

Simple assignment problems may be found in many service-type industries and in some job shops. Many delivery tasks fall into this category: for example, the assignment of crews to switching trains, planes and crews to nonscheduled flights, or stations or customers to petroleum delivery trucks. These applications usually require some simplifying assumptions which may eliminate the possibility of true optimum solutions. For example, the model must usually be based on a discrete time period such that several tasks must be accumulated into assignments of comparable duration.

The Stock-cutting Problem.[18,19,20,21,22,23] This class of problem is commonly found whenever a group of items of various shapes and sizes can be cut from or loaded into a limited number of larger pieces of containers, respectively. An example is the planning of stamping-pattern layouts on sheet stock or cutting various sizes of paper stock from large rolls of various widths. Another example is the sizing of containers to make maximum use of space within standard freight cars or trailers or the problem of selecting an array of standard package sizes to ship products which have a variety of shapes.

An optimum solution to these problems can be obtained using the simplex method. However, if every possible configuration is considered, the model usually grows beyond reasonable size. Consequently, the problem is solvable in theory but not in practice. Modifications to the general simplex method must be used in order to bring the problem down to reasonable size. Simplification is obtained at the expense of possibly missing the optimum solution. By judicious modeling, the result will be optimum or very close to it.

The Production Scheduling Problem.[17,24] The term "production scheduling" is not very definitive since almost all of the five problem categories discussed above are associated with scheduling or planning some phase of production. Within this category are problems of the following type:

1. Balancing inventory and production costs for batched production subject to limitations on productive equipment and storage capability

2. Planning the operation of an underground mine subject to the limitations of the mining and ore-dressing equipment, the geometry of the ore body, and the quality of the ore

3. Scheduling the production of commodities where the available equipment and the method of its operation can affect the output quality and quantity

An example of the first type can be found in the problem of producing, warehousing, and distributing a seasonal product. Production capacity was well below the peak seasonal demand. Consequently preseason production had to be stored. In addition, an end-of-season carryover was not desired. This problem can be formulated to fit the transportation method.

The production of transistors is an excellent example of a problem of the third type. Transistors are made in a three-stage manufacturing process. First the transistor is built up as a sandwich-type assembly of thick wafers of silicon with a thin wafer (about 0.001 inch) of germanium in between. Next the sandwiches are fused together at a high temperature in an operation called "firing." Both the firing temperature and the length of the firing period affect the operating characteristics of the finished component. After firing, the subassembly is tested. Most can be assembled into salable components. Some may be refired to bring their operating characteristics within specifications. A significant portion are worthless and must be discarded. The final operation is called "mounting." Leads are attached to the satisfactory assemblies and the entire unit is sealed in a protective cap. The finished units are tested before they are accepted for shipment. Unsatisfactory but reworkable units are reprocessed.

A production schedule is needed to start the correct wafer assemblies through the process to ensure that sufficient good units will be available. During any one planning period a number of different types of transistors may be required. Each type has a different proportion of rejects. In addition, rejects from one type may be reworked into other types.

Firing and mounting capacities limit production. Sales by finished transistor type are the demand restriction. The objective is to minimize production cost. The initial sandwich assembly is an expense in every unit. Therefore, the problem can be formulated as follows:

$$\text{minimize } F = C_f \sum_{n=1}^{N} F_n + C_r \sum_{i=1}^{I} R_i + C_m \sum_{i=1}^{I} M_i \tag{11}$$

where C_f, C_r, and C_m = cost of firing, refiring, and mounting a subassembly, respectively

F_n = number of subassemblies fired using firing pattern n

R_i = number of subassemblies refired from transistor category i

M_i = number of subassemblies mounted from category i

subject to

$$\sum_{n=1}^{N} U_{in} F_r + \sum_{i=1}^{I} V_{ij} R_j \geq M_i + R_i \tag{12}$$

where U_{in} = yield of category i subassemblies from firing pattern n

V_{ij} = yield of the jth subassembly from refiring the ith subassembly and capacity for firing subassemblies is

$$\sum_{n=1}^{N} F_n + \sum_{i=1}^{I} R_i \leq K_f \tag{13}$$

capacity for mounting subassemblies is

$$\sum_{i=1}^{I} M_i \leq K_m \tag{14}$$

restriction to ensure that completed assemblies do not exceed mounted subassemblies is

$$\sum_{i=1}^{I} W_{ik} M_i \geq \sum_{l=1}^{L} Y_{kl} \tag{15}$$

and demand restriction for product l (overshipment not allowed) is

$$\sum_{k=1}^{I} Y_{kl} \leq D_l \tag{16}$$

where W_{ik} = yield of the kth product from mounting the ith subassembly
Y_{kl} = allocation of the kth transistor category to satisfy demand for product l
D_l = demand per period for product l

Both Eqs. (15) and (16) may not appear necessary. However, not all of one period's production need be shipped. The use of two equations permits greater flexibility.

It must also be pointed out that the mounting cost C_m is actually a variable. The mounting process consists of several steps. After each step some assemblies are scrapped. The cost of mounting prorated over the number of subassemblies actually mounted will vary with the quality of work being done.

This model requires the accumulation of a great deal of information on the yields of various firing patterns. Since the transistor industry was in its infancy, the model was an excellent tool for evaluating and modifying the process as well as for choosing which subassemblies should be started through the system and which ones should be reworked. The dollar value of the savings that resulted from this linear-programming application was not divulged, but a phenomenal improvement was implied.

Before trying to apply LP, the production manager should appreciate its capabilities and limitations. The LP model uses many estimated constants. If their values are only good in the short term, the optimum solution may not be valid over a long period of time. For example, an optimum blend of raw materials for a heat of steel may vary with the content and price of the raw materials. Yesterday's solution or blend may not be best for today's operations.

LP can be used for rather long-range planning of production. The solution or plan may be optimum, but factors beyond considerations of the model may prevent its implementation. For example, orders for goods may be canceled, increased, or reduced. Vendors may not deliver as anticipated in the model. Consequently, production must be changed and unplanned work used to fill the schedule. If the LP solution is to be used as an operating tool, frequent updating of the model and solutions is required.

If the manager appreciates the limitations of LP, it can help him handle his day-to-day problems. As he works with the model, he will see opportunities for changing the real situation by eliminating troublesome constraints. In this sense, LP becomes a simulation tool for testing ideas before applying them to the actual plant.

Solving a linear-programming problem and building a linear-programming model are two separate tasks. Solving LP problems has been reduced to a rote set of rules or algorithms which can be followed by any person skilled in arithmetic or by a properly programmed digital computer. Since large problems cannot be solved economically by hand, a digital computer is a prerequisite to any applications. However, since every commercial computer manufacturer's software package contains an LP routine, any in-house data process center or commercial computer service center can obtain the necessary programs. All these programs use essentially the same input format so that a problem too large for one machine may be shifted to more capable machines without changing the format.

The model is the objective function and constraints that fit the particular application. The format may be similar to other applications, but the input—the constants—is unique for each application. Canned LP models are not available. Building the model requires an LP specialist. Obviously he should be thoroughly familiar with linear programming and understand its capabilities. Such a person may be available in-house if the firm employs a capable operations research or system analysis staff. Competent, professional linear-programming assistance also can be purchased from a consulting firm or the staff of nearby universities. The model builder must become reasonably familiar with the operation before a successful model can be constructed. For a trial run, manual accumulation of input data (the constants) is usually most practical. If the LP model proves useful, a system can be devised for automatically updating the model. Any application is doomed to failure in a dynamic world if the update link is not provided.

Interpretation of an LP solution requires some knowledge of the mathematical aspects of LP. Part of the model builder's responsibility would be to put the LP output in a form suitable for management use. If the model builder does his job, LP will be a powerful tool for the production manager.

QUANTITATIVE METHODS IN DISCRETE-PART PRODUCTION CONTROL

The Tactical Problem of Sequencing Jobs to Machines. The scheduling material presented so far in this chapter has been concerned for the most part with due-date determination for orders and shop loading. In discrete-part manufacturing there exists even shorter-range planning which will aid in the control of production. The aspect of production control which has not been previously discussed is the sequencing of different jobs to the required machines as they progress through the shop. Discrete-part manufacture in situations which behave like job shops allows for control by priority-dispatching rules, which in turn are easily adapted to computer control.

Sisson[25] defines "sequencing" as *determining the order in which units requiring service are serviced.* He also notes that "scheduling" should be reserved for procedures which give the time of arrival of units requiring service. In most cases the time required to perform an operation on a particular job is known in advance with a reasonable degree of accuracy. When this is the case, the problem of improving the performance of the production shop becomes one of sequencing the jobs to the machines.

If there are n different jobs scheduled to a shop with m machines, there is a good chance that at certain times there will be more than one job waiting to be processed on a single machine. How should the conflict be resolved? The shop performance in terms of job completion time or machine utilization will probably be different if different job sequences are used. Sequencing is a combinatorial problem. In order to evaluate all sequences, a brute-force manual approach would be necessary.

Given n jobs to be processed on m machines, Sisson[25] notes that there are as many as n^m different possible sequences. The alternative to a manual-solution method is to develop efficient mathematical algorithms which will search through the possible permutations of the job-machine combinations. Much work has been directed toward this end during the last 20 years. The availability of digital computers has facilitated this research.

There are several criteria which are relevant to optimization in the job-shop environment: minimize the maximum make span for a given set of jobs, minimize the maximum lateness, maximize machine utilization, minimize in-process inventory, just to name a few.

The optimum mathematical approaches which will be discussed in this section search out the job-machine sequence which minimizes the make span of the last job to be processed. This is equivalent to minimizing the length of the bar of the Gantt chart for a group of jobs. The priority-dispatching rules which will be discussed later also determine the sequence of jobs to machines. They will be shown to be more practical than mathematical algorithms even though an optimal solution is not guaranteed.

Some Mathematical Solutions to the Job-shop-sequencing Problem. It would be very desirable to be able to solve the job-shop-sequencing problem by simply substituting values in an equation or following some simple rule. Very small problems can be solved in this way, quite simply, for an optimum solution.

An early contribution (1954) toward optimal solutions was given by Johnson.[26] His procedure, which can be proved to be the optimal solution, can be applied to a two-machine flow-shop situation. All jobs must go first on machine I and then onto machine II. The sequence of jobs to machine II will be identical to that of machine I because all jobs go immediately from I to II. Johnson's sequence-determining rules are the following:

Job no.	Processing time on I	Processing time on II
1	I_1	II_1
2	I_2	II_2
3	I_3	II_3
4	I_4	II_4
.	.	.
.	.	.
.	.	.
n	I_n	II_n

1. List the jobs and their processing times on machines I and II.
2. Scan all the processing times for the smallest one.
3. If it is for machine I, order the corresponding job first.
4. If it is for machine II, order the corresponding job last.
5. Cross off both times for that job.
6. Repeat the steps until all jobs have been crossed off the list.
7. In the case of ties, for the sake of definiteness, order the item with the smallest subscript first.

Consider the following example:

Job no.	Processing time on I	Processing time on II
1	4	5
2	4	1
3	30	4
4	6	30
5	2	3

The optimal sequence is 5, 1, 4, 3, 2. A Gantt-chart representation of this sequence is shown in Fig. 25.

The total processing time for this sequence is 47 time units and the total idle time is only 4 time units. We cannot get a better sequence for minimizing the make span for the group of five jobs.

Fig. 25 Gantt-chart representation.

This result may seem rather trivial but it has encouraged research on less limiting cases. Mitten[27] developed a procedure which will give an optimal solution for two-machine flow shops in which the start time for a specific job on the second machine can occur prior to the shop time for that job on the first machine. This could occur where the job consisted of a batch of parts. Mitten also shows how this approach can be applied to bottleneck problems. The

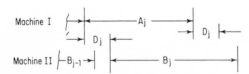

Fig. 26 Gantt-chart representation.

start and stop relationships for the two machines defined by this solution procedure are shown in the Gantt chart in Fig. 26.

A_j = time for job j on machine I
B_j = time for job j on machine II
D_j = time after start of j on machine I that it can start on machine II

Jackson[28] extended Johnson's flow-shop results to a two-machine job shop. Jobs can have routings which require one machine or the other or both. Consider the four different types of jobs: A represents the set of jobs which have only one operation, and that are to be performed on machine I. B represents the set of jobs which have only one operation, and that are to be performed on machine II. AB represents the set of jobs which have two operations, the first to be performed on machine I, the second on machine II. BA represents the set of jobs which have two operations, the first to be performed on machine II, the second on machine I. (See Table 8.)

TABLE 8

Job no.	Operation no.	Time on A	Operation no.	Time on B
1	1	5	2	4
2			1	7
3	1	4	2	6
4	1	3		
5	2	5	1	3
6	2	2	1	7
7	1	7		
8	1	5		
9	2	10	1	12
10	1	7	2	4

AB Sequenced by Johnson's Rule   *BA Sequenced by Johnson's Rule*

3	5
10	9
1	6

Order of jobs on machine I:

$$3, 10, 1, 4, 7, 8, 5, 9, 6$$

Order of jobs on machine II:

$$5, 9, 6, 2, 3, 10, 1$$

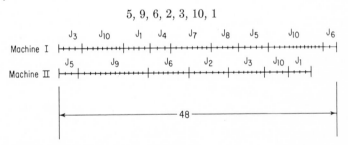

A procedure which will develop a sequence of jobs to machines and minimize the maximum completion time is the following:

1. Sequence the AB jobs by Johnson's rule.

2. Sequence the BA jobs by Johnson's rule.

3. The ordering of A jobs and B jobs will not affect the maximum completion time, so have arbitrary ordering within these sets.

General rule: On machine I—jobs in AB before jobs in A before jobs in BA; on machine II—jobs in BA before jobs in B, before jobs in AB.

Thus we have the sequence of the given 10 jobs to the two machines which minimizes the make span of the last job completed, or alternately the sum of the make spans of all jobs has been minimized.

At present it is not possible to get optimal solutions via mathematical algorithms for problems which are much larger than the two- or three-machine case. Except in special cases other means must be resorted to for sequencing jobs to machines in larger shops. Priority-dispatching rules are a means for accomplishing this end which are finding use in existing job shops.

Priority-dispatching-rule Solutions to Job-shop Sequencing. Dispatching, as defined by Conway and Maxwell,[29] is the final step of the production scheduling process: "The final decision—what should be done next? that is asked each time a man or machine completes a task." The manufacturing shop can be visualized as a set of decision centers, each of which consists of one or a group of machines. The technological sequence associated with each job (route card) will direct jobs to the various machine centers as it progresses through the shop. As jobs queue up at different machines the foreman or machinist can either randomly choose a job from among those waiting or choose according to some logical rule, when the machine becomes available for another job. If the latter procedure is followed, a concept of priority will have been instituted.

A commonly seen example of the use of priority-dispatching rules is at supermarket checkout counters. Usually there is at least one channel for customers with six items or less. This is a fast-moving line, but it is limited to small orders. In a sense small orders are given priority. The obvious result of this strategy is that checkout-counter lines are shorter than they would have been and more people are served in a given amount of time.

In recent years reports of many experimental investigations of the performance of priority-dispatching rules in job shops have appeared in the technical literature. Some early work was done by Rowe.[30] Conway[31,32] has also contributed much in this area. A good recent review of job-shop dispatching-rule research is given by Moore and Wilson.[33] The results of much of this research are beginning to be used in operational systems which schedule and control job-shop production by computer. These will be discussed in a later section of this chapter.

The performance of priority-dispatching rules in an industrial situation can be appreciated if we look briefly at some of the optimal properties of a few rules in the n job—one-machine situations where all jobs are simultaneously available. If the n jobs are sequenced to the machine in the order of increasing processing time, the following are a few of the optimal properties which accrue to the set of jobs: the sum of the make spans (includes waiting) of all jobs is minimized, average make span is minimized, the average number of jobs in process is minimized, and if the lateness is defined as the difference between job completion time and job due date, then the average lateness is minimized.

For example, consider the following five jobs which are simultaneously available and are to be processed on a single machine.

Job number	Processing time on machine, in hours
1	4
2	7
3	3
4	6
5	5

If these jobs are processed in chronological order, the completion time of each job is as follows:

Job	Completion time, in hours
1	4
2	11
3	14
4	20
5	25

The sum of the completion times is 74 hours. If, instead of processing in the above order, we process in order of increasing processing time, the job sequence and completion times will be as follows:

Job	Completion time, in hours
3	3
1	7
5	12
4	18
2	25

The sum of the completion times for this sequence is 65 hours. There are no other sequences which will give less summed completion times.

Conway, Maxwell, and Miller[34] describe the n job, one-machine case in detail and develop mathematical proofs for the optimal properties of several rules (including shortest processing time). It should be obvious, however, that this case does not happen often in practice. Most often there are many machines and the jobs do not all arrive at the same time. When this is the case, each machine will consider only the jobs which are waiting to be processed by it. The next job will be chosen from the queue of those waiting by a local priority rule (such as shortest process time, for example). The goodness of the various types of rules is evaluated against measures of shop performance such as machine utilization, job lateness, etc.

It can be said, in general, that using any consistent rule is better than random selection of jobs from among those awaiting processing—for at least some measures of performance. Rules can be divided into two types: those which are based on attributes of the job, such as processing time; and those which are based on attributes of the environment, such as due date or shop congestion.

Conway[31] reports on an investigation of such local priority rules as first come, first served; shortest processing time (SPT); longest processing time; slack; and due date, all in terms of their effect on work-in-process inventory and job lateness in a multimachine job shop. SPT and slack rules were found to be particularly good in these studies. Rowe,[30] in another study, investigated such rules as first come, first served; first come, first served within priority class; shortest processing time; longest processing time; earliest start date; and a sequential rule based on the concept of slack and due dates.

Examples of priority rules of a more dynamic nature follow. Elmaghraby and Cole[35] developed a rule which considers the due date of the part as well as the number of remaining operations. Priority for part i given as follows:

$$P_i = \left\{ D_i - D_o - \left[\frac{H_{ij}(k) + A(k)}{8} \right] \right\}$$

where D_i = due date (days)

D_o = current date (days)

$H_{ij}(k)$ = operation time in the remaining operations through which the part must pass

$A(k)$ = allowance for interference and unavoidable delays, a function of the remaining stations in the route

K = number of future operations

D_i and D_o refer to working days rather than calendar days.

In this formulation a small (if negative, most negative) P_i would indicate the highest priority.

Another local priority rule of this type was presented by Bulkin, Colley, and Steinhoff.[36] Their priority is determined by slack time. Jobs with the least slack time are given highest priority.

$$\text{Slack time per operation} = \frac{RT - RPT}{NOR}$$

where RT = remaining calendar time to the due date
RPT = remaining processing time to order completion
NOR = number of operations remaining

Computer-based Sequencing and Scheduling Systems for Job-shop Production Control. In general it is not practical to use the sequencing procedures discussed in the preceding pages unless they are part of a computer-based production scheduling and control system. Such systems are becoming more common in American industry as the availability and data processing capabilities of digital computers increase. Hughes Aircraft, Texas Instruments, Burroughs Corp., and Fairfield Mfg. Co., just to name a few firms, have successful operating systems.

The ultimate goal of these systems is to approach the automation concept realized by automatic control systems in the continuous-process industries. This ideal will not be reached because the various work centers or machines in the shop are relatively independent and humans are operating them. However, sequencing rules used in conjunction with periodic shop-status update aid the

TABLE 9   System Comparisons

Basis for comparison	Hughes	Fairfield	Texas Instruments	Western Electric
Shop-size statistics	2,500 orders in process 120 work centers 1,000 machines	2,500 orders in process (60,000 operations) 220 work centers 1,750 machines	5,000 orders in process	500 orders in process
Periodic simulation used as a basis for scheduling?	Each day	Twice weekly	No	No
Output reports	Shop load forecast location report; coordination report; order schedule; hot-order visibility report	Load report; shop schedule; job-status report	. . . .	Load report; shop schedule; shop station report; job-status report; station priority listing; shipping report
Priority-dispatching rule used	Slack time per operation: $$P = \frac{RT - RPT}{NOR}$$	Slack type		Slack time: $$P_i = \left\{ D_i - D_o - \left[\frac{H_{ij}(k) + A(k)}{8} \right] \right\}$$
Type of computer used	IBM-1410 IBM-1301	IBM-360/30	IBM-1440 IBM-1301-1311	Monrobot XI
Interval between job-status update	Once daily	Semiweekly	Every three hours	Once daily
Direct interrogation of computer possible?	No	No	Yes	Yes
Benefits claimed for system	Reduce cycle time; increase productivity; meet more due dates; reduce expediting	Increase productivity	Reduce cycle time; reduce expediting; increase productivity; meet more due dates; reduce late-penalty costs	Reduce cycle time; increase productivity; reduce in-waiting inventories

human decision maker to close the control loop. Before we look at some of these systems in detail, a comparison of some properties of four existing systems will quickly show what can be expected from this approach to production control (see Table 9).

There is nothing magic, new, or mathematically rigorous about these computerized production control systems. They combine known concepts of data processing, simulation, priority-rule sequencing, and computer programming. All

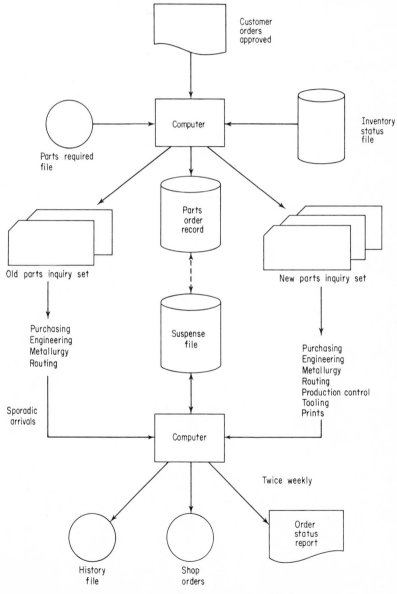

Fig. 27 Data flow system (simplified).

the work systems have much in common, but the individual shops are different enough to make each system a uniquely designed entity. It is the combination of the above concepts, in a specific design, to meet the particular needs of the shop, which determines the potential of the system.

Figure 27 shows a typical data-flow configuration for a simulation scheduler.

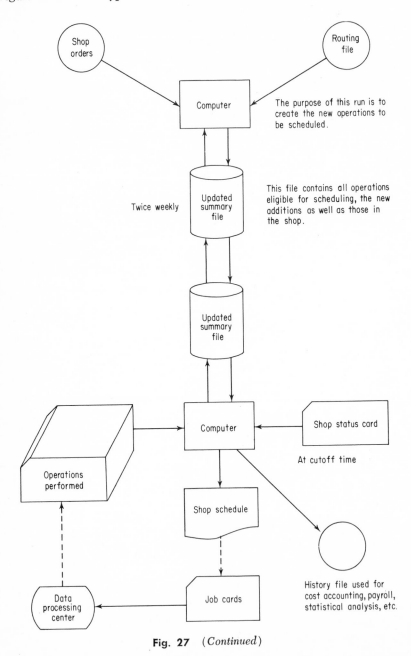

Fig. 27 *(Continued)*

From this the reader can get an idea of how information flows and is processed to aid in the production control decision-making procedure. The computer is central to the entire system, and given that the workers follow the rules utilized by the computer, it can be said to be controlling the shop.

In some of the computerized systems a symbolic mathematical model is made of the shop, and this is programmed for computer simulation. (The details of developing simulation models are discussed later in this chapter.) Also, contained within computer memory are data on all jobs now in process in the shop. This includes job routings, operation times, transportation times, etc. Information on new jobs to come to the shop is placed in computer memory as it becomes available. The standard operational procedures of the shop, i.e., dispatching-decision rules, are contained within the simulation program so that a "good" estimate of how the shop should react during the first shift is available before the actual shift starts.

The simulation feature which some of these computerized systems have can increase control significantly. If it can be assumed that the simulation will portray the future events of the shop with reasonable accuracy, then a powerful tool is at hand. Each machine center will get a computer printout of the simulation's results as they affect that work center. This information dispersal increases the control potential of manufacturing management. Elmaghraby and Cole[35] sum it up quite well: "The system realizes the principle of placing the tool of control (information) in the hands of the person (or persons) responsible for achieving that control."

The results of research on priority-dispatching rules are usually imbedded in these systems. The Hughes Aircraft Simulation Scheduler uses the *slack per operation* rule; the Western Electric Marginal Analysis system (not simulation) uses the *slack due date* rule. The Fairfield system uses a *first come, first served within priority class* rule.

The Western Electric System has been in operation since 1962 and combines what could be termed "scheduling" and "sequencing" within the same computer control. The system attempts to pool future deliveries of orders which are going to be produced this period in order to utilize excess available manufacturing capacity. A pooling preference factor which evaluates the economic advantage of producing next period's deliveries with this period's deliveries is calculated for each future order. This calculation essentially determines the trade-off between a reduced number of setups and increased inventory cost. After the shop has been "loaded" in this manner, the progress of the individual orders through the shop is controlled by the dispatching rule. Daily status is sent to the computer via 15 remote input devices.

The Texas Instruments production control system approaches more what could be considered a real-time controller. "On-floor" data transactors feed back order-status information to the computer every three hours. Orders are scheduled to the shop in the following manner: Order information such as due date, technological sequence, operation-time estimates, etc. is fed to the computer, which in turn searches the load already assigned to machine groups to determine if the order can be scheduled in time to meet the desired due date. The computer can then print out a day-by-day, hour-by-hour routing for the job. If a job cannot be scheduled in a way that will have a high-priority due-date completion, the computer evaluates alternative strategies such as lot splitting, overtime, changing schedule priorities, etc. The schedule containing the new order (orders) is released to the plant.

A feature of this system is that the information on job status, location, and machine status is available only by request. An interested person can query the computer from an off-line station and receive his information within minutes. A single report is published weekly, and this contains information on jobs that are behind schedule.

Future Systems for Controlling Production.   It has been shown that an evolution toward real-time computer control of discrete-part production has been under way for the past several years.   What of the future?   What improvements can be expected in the present systems in the near future?   Colley[37], who has done development work in this area, anticipates the development of real-time scheduling systems with simulation capability.   He notes that the realization of this requires more powerful computer software and hardware than that which was available in 1967, but he outlines how such a system might operate at the detailed level.

1. Foreman would begin a shift with the work plan derived from a short-run simulation, such as the Hughes-El Segundo scheduling system.

2. As work progresses, shop status would be updated with current shop status always available in the computer's memory.

3. The system would respond instantly to inquiry from the foreman through a look-ahead capability.   This look-ahead feature would involve a partitioned simulation of the subset of total shop operations which might affect the inquiring machine group during the remainder of the shift.

SIMULATION AND MODELING FOR SCHEDULING

Probably everyone has some familiarity with children's toys.   Most toys are models.   A toy truck is modeled after real trucks.   A toy airplane is a small replica of real airplanes.   When a child plays with a toy, he usually tries to simulate the performance of the real item.   With a toy airplane he will imitate the performance of a real airplane.   These toys are physical models of reality, of the real item.   If a child does not have a toy, a physical model, he may use his imagination; he may pretend that he has a toy airplane.   Again he will imitate the performance of a real airplane, but now he has a logical model (an abstract) which he has created in his mind and with which he simulates the performance of the real plane.   Actually, we are all old hands when it comes to modeling and simulation, we just don't realize it.

The simulation and models that we shall discuss here are more complex, of course, than a child's toy; but if we could make a physical model of a production scheduling system it would be of no use to us.   Logical models are the kind that we need.

A logical model may consist of rules, equations, formulas, instructions, etc.   It probably will initially be set down on paper but may eventually end up in other form as in a computer's memory.   A logical model represents the performance of the real item with little or no regard to the shape, while the physical model represents the shape of the real item with little or no ability to represent the performance.

Why simulate?   Man has been a long time gathering the knowledge that he now has.   He has answers to a lot of questions and can solve a lot of problems.   There are, however, a lot of problems which he cannot yet solve.   Simulation is one way of attacking these problems.   In other words, simulation is used to solve a problem when we do not know a better way or when we are unsure of the better way.   Simulation is used to gather data or to obtain understanding of the problem.   Probably the most important reason for using simulation is that it allows us to tinker with the system under study without affecting the real system at all.   We can try things that would create utter chaos with the real system and we find out what happens, but meanwhile the real functions as usual. With such tinkering we may be able to prove or disprove a hypothesis. Simulation can also shorten time. Years of operation can often be simulated in minutes.

How Simulation is Done. There are three methods of simulation open to the production control manager.

The first method is to construct a mathematical model of the scheduling or loading system. Such a model will consist of mathematical formulas, equations, and functions. It will be largely unintelligible to anyone not trained in mathematics, and experienced personnel will be required to construct and interpret such a model. This is the more difficult route to take and often cannot be taken at all.

The second method is to do a Monte Carlo (or random walk) type of simulation. This is a much easier method to utilize and a skilled mathematician is not required. An illustrative example will be presented below.

The third method is to utilize a general-purpose computer-scheduling program that is already available. The major computer manufacturers, some of the computer service bureaus, and some universities have developed such programs. If you already have a computer or are doing business with a service bureau, ask what they have available. If your company is new to the computer world, contact one of the computer manufacturers or service bureaus for further information. You will find that they are interested in helping you, that the cost is generally reasonable, and that your company can do most of the work itself. Gathering appropriate data to use in the simulation usually will comprise more than half of the task.

There also are a number of computer programming languages available that are designed for programming simulations with computers. Anyone who passed college algebra should be able to learn one of them in a few days from an appropriate manual. Again, these are available from the major computer manufacturers and service bureaus.

The production control manager should explore the possibility of having someone on his staff learn one of these languages and then write the simulation program. The advantage of this method is that the production control department will be much closer to the simulation, will therefore understand it better, will be in a better position to modify the program, and will gain more from the simulation. The following example could be easily done in one of these languages.

Monte Carlo Simulation. We first must construct an accurate logical model of the system that we are going to duplicate. We must know the relationships between the factors and construct a flow chart of the system, and tables of

TABLE 10   Order Analysis

Order quantities	No. of occurrences	Frequency, percent
0	6	10
1	12	20
2	18	30
3	24	40
4	0	0
Total......	60	

TABLE 11 Portion of a Random-numbers Table*

46	16	28	35	54
70	29	73	41	35
32	97	92	65	75
12	86	07	46	97

* Such tables are used by picking a starting point and going consistently in one direction. Example: For numbers from 0 to 9 start with the upper left-hand corner. Going to the right we get: 4, 1, 2, 3, 5, or 6, 6, 8, 5, 4; going down: 4, 7, 3, 1, or 6, 0, 2, 2, 1.

TABLE 12 Random-number Assignment

Order quantity	Frequency of order quantity*	Random-number digits
0	10	0
1	20	1, 2
2	30	3, 4, 5
3	40	6, 7, 8, 9

* From Table 10.

TABLE 13 Simulation Results*

Day number	Order qty.	Process time, days	Machine load, days	Start time†	Finish time†	Wait time, days	Idle time, days
(1)	(2)	(3)	(4)	(5)	(6)	(7)	(8)
1	2	1.0	1.0	1M	1E	—	—
2	3	1.5	1.5	2M	3N	0.5	—
3	2	1.0	1.5	3N	4N	0.5	—
4	1	0.5	1.0	4N	4E	—	—
5	2	1.0	1.0	5M	5E	—	—
6	2	1.0	1.0	6M	6E	—	—
7	2	1.0	1.0	7M	7E	—	—
8	2	1.0	1.0	8M	8E	—	—
9	1	0.5	0.5	9M	9E	—	0.5
10	3	1.5	1.5	10M	11N	0.5	—
11	2	1.0	1.5	11N	12N	0.5	—
12	3	1.5	2.0	12N	13E	1.0	—
13	2	1.0	2.0	14M	14N	1.0	—
14	3	1.5	2.5	15M	16N	1.5	—
15	3	1.5	3.0	16N	17E	2.0	—
16	0	0.0	2.0	—	—	—	—
17	1	0.5	1.5	18M	18N	1.5	—
18	2	1.0	1.5	18N	19N	1.5	—
19	2	1.0	1.5	19N	20N	1.5	—
20	2	1.0	1.5	20N	21N	1.5	—
21	2	1.5	1.5	21N	22N	1.5	—
22	3	—	2.0	22N	24E	2.0	—

* After the order quantities were simulated, this table was calculated as follows: (1) Order quantity is known at the beginning of the day. (2) Order processing time (col. 3) is added to the machine load (col. 4) at the beginning of the day. Machine load equals yesterday's machine load plus the processing time required for today's orders minus yesterday's production (all times are in days). (3) The start date is equal to the day number plus the wait time.
† M = morning, N = noon, E = evening.

values for the variables.   The values will be obtained from historical data.   We have an example to illustrate the method.

Consider a production facility that must be analyzed.   The production capacity is 2 units per day.   The only other data that is readily available is the past history of the daily order quantities.   This data was analyzed for 60 working days.   The number of days that the order quantity totaled zero was counted and entered in Table 10 and the same was done for the other quantities.   The frequency with which each order quantity occurs was then calculated as shown in the right-hand column of the table.

Order quantities for the simulation will be obtained by a technique using a *random-numbers table*, Table 11. Each digit in a random-numbers table has as much chance of appearing as any other.   For example, the digit 1 appears 10 percent of the time, 2 appears 10 percent of the time, etc.

In Table 10 an order quantity of zero occurs 10 percent of the time.   Therefore in preparing Table 12 one digit is assigned for this order quantity.   Order quantities that occurs 20 percent of the time will have two digits assigned to them since each digit occurs 10 percent of the time.   Order quantites occuring 30 percent of the time require three digits, etc.   The random-number digits need not be assigned in any special order as long as the correct number of digits is assigned.

Table 13 is prepared next by following the steps given in the flow chart in Fig. 28.   Using the random-number table (Table 11), the first number is 4∮.   According to Table 12 a random number of 4 is equivalent to an order quantity of 2.   Thus for the first day of the simulation, the day's orders total 2 and 2 is entered under "Order Quantity."   The next random number is 7∮, so 3 from Table 11 is entered as the order quantity for the second day.   Table 13 is completed in this manner. If this were an actual simulation instead of a textbook example, it would be best to run it for more than 22 days.

The steps for doing a Monte Carlo simulation are:

1. List the factors that bear on the system to be simulated.

2. Determine the controlling factors (what powers the system).

3. Determine the values that these controlling factors can assume and determine the frequency of occurrence in percent.

4. Assign an equivalent percent of the random numbers to each value.

5. Prepare a flow chart of the simulation system.

6. Following the flow chart, "drive" the system and calculate the results.

A simulation is as good as the data and analysis that go into it.   If the flow chart accurately represents the actual system and the data are accurate, the results will be accurate.   The longer the simulation is run, the better the

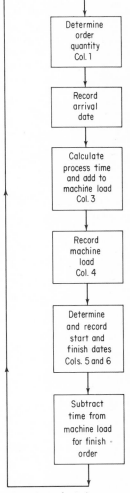

Repeat once for each day of simulation

Fig.   28 Simulation flow chart (used to prepare Table 4).

results will be. The simulation shown in Table 13 does not represent exactly what will happen in the first 22 days of operation. What it does represent is a fairly accurate indication of the wait and idle times. If the simulation were rerun for another 22 days, the results would be very close to the first results. Also, both results would be close to what really would happen in the actual system.

SUMMARY

This chapter has attempted to do four things:

1. Establish the need and importance of scheduling and loading. It mentioned that because of competition most manufacturers are attempting to make their production as efficient as practicable.

2. Introduce the scheduling and loading environment for intermittent and continuous production and list the pertinent factors applying to them.

3. Introduce a number of scheduling and loading techniques. It began with some of the relatively simple, old standbys and progressed to the newer and often more sophisticated and complex techniques.

4. Provide a link between these techniques and the production control environment. This is perhaps the most important part. Examples were used where feasible, and the coverage of each technique was in terms applying to production control.

The chapter did not cover all the techniques available nor go into complete detail on them. There are complete books available on most of these techniques, listed in the Bibliography below.

REFERENCES

Linear Programming

1. J. S. Aronofsky, "Growing Applications of Linear Programming," *Communications of the ACM,* vol. 7, no. 6, pp. 325–332, June, 1964.
2. E. H. Bowman, "Production Scheduling by the Transportation Method of Linear Programming," *Operations Research,* vol. 4, no. 1, pp. 100–103, January, 1955.
3. Tibor Fabian, "Application of Linear Programming to Steel Production Planning," *Operations Research,* vol. 3, p. 565, November, 1955 (abstract).
4. Louis J. Rago, *Production Analysis and Control,* International Textbook Company, Scranton, Pa., 1963.
5. L. W. Swanson and J. G. Woodruff, "Sequential Approach to Feed-mix Problem," *Operations Research,* vol. 12, no. 1, pp. 89–109, January, 1964.
6. J. H. Greene, K. Chatto, C. R. Hicks, and C. B. Cox, "Linear Programming in the Meat Packing Industry," *Journal of Industrial Engineering,* vol. 10, no. 5, pp. 364–372, September-October, 1959.
7. W. G. Jones and C. M. Lope, "Linear Programming Applied to Production Planning: A Case Study," *Operational Research Quarterly,* vol. 15, no. 4.
8. Frederick D. Wright, "Maximizing the Profit of a Coal Preparation Plant by Linear Programming," TP61F16, *AIME Transactions (Mining),* vol. 220, pp. 82–92, 1961.
9. R. Vaswani, "Intra-city Trailer Movements," *Operational Research Quarterly,* vol. 7, no. 3, pp. 91–96, September, 1956.
10. K. B. Williams and K. B. Maley, "A Practical Application of Linear Programming in the Mining Industry," *Operational Research Quarterly,* vol. 10, no. 3, pp. 131–137, September, 1959.
11. C. W. Churchman, R. L. Ackoff, and L. E. Arnoff, *Introduction to Operations Research,* John Wiley & Sons, Inc., New York, 1957, pp. 343–367.

12. J. J. Clowes and E. S. Page, "Assignment Problems," *Computer Journal*, vol. 6, no. 4, pp. 304–307, January, 1964.
13. G. B. Dantzig, "Solution of a Large Scale Traveling-Salesman Problem," *Operations Research*, vol. 2, no. 4, p. 393–411, November, 1954.
14. K. Eisemann, "The General Stepping Stone Method for the Machine Loading Model," *Management Science*, vol. 11, no. 1, pp. 254–176, September, 1964.
15. R. O. Ferguson, "Linear Programming," Special Report 389, *American Machinist*, p. 122, Apr. 11, 1955.
16. J. F. Muth and G. L. Thompson, *Industrial Scheduling*, Prentice-Hall, Inc., Englewood Cliffs, N.J., 1963, pp. 185–220.
17. Aharon G. Baded-Dov, "Solving a Paper Procurement Program by Linear Programming," *The Western Electric Engineer*, vol. 9, no. 4, pp. 2–10, October, 1965.
18. G. B. Dantzig "Discret-variable Extremum Problems," *Operations Research*, vol. 5, no. 2, pp. 266–277, April, 1957.
19. N. D. Jackson and G. W. Smith, "Linear Programming in Lumber Production," *Forest Products Journal*, vol. 11, no. 6, pp. 272–274, June, 1961.
20. P. C. Gilmore and R. E. Gomory, "Linear Programming Approach to Cutting-stock Problem," *Operations Research*, vol. 9, no. 6, pp. 849–859, November-December, 1961.
21. "Multi-stage Cutting-stock Problem of 2 or More Dimensions," *Operations Research*, vol. 13, no. 1, pp. 94–120, January-February, 1965.
22. M. H. Gotterer and D. Zanniker, "Models for Scheduling a Paper-making Machine," *TAPPI*, vol. 47, no. 7, pp. 435–439, July, 1964.
23. S. B. Smith, "Planning Transistor Production by Linear Programming" *Operations Research*, vol. 13, no. 1, pp. 132–139, February, 1965.
24. C. G. White and E. W. Peiker, Jr., "Analysis of Shaft and Level Development, Slope Production and Planning, and Ore Transportation for a Simulated Copper Mining Operation Using Optimization Programming," *Quarterly of the Colorado School of Mines*, vol. 59, no. 4, part B, pp. 969–996, October, 1964.

Quantitative Methods in Discrete-part Production Control

25. R. L. Sisson, "Sequencing Theory," *Progress in Operations Research*, John Wiley & Sons, Inc., New York, 1961, vol. 1, chap. 7.
26. S. M. Johnson, "Optimal Two- and Three-stage Production Schedules with Setup Times Included," *Naval Research Logistics Quarterly*, vol. 1, no. 1, 1954.
27. L. G. Mitten, "Sequencing Jobs on Two Machines with Arbitrary Time Lags," *Management Science*, vol. 5, no. 3, 1959.
28. James R. Jackson, "An Extension of Johnson's Results on Job-lot Scheduling," *Naval Research Logistics Quarterly*, vol. 3, no. 3, 1956.
29. R. W. Conway and W. L. Maxwell, "Network Scheduling by the Shortest-operation Discipline," in J. F. Muth and G. L. Thompson, *Industrial Scheduling*, Prentice-Hall, Inc., Englewood Cliffs, N.J., 1963, chap. 17.
30. A. J. Rowe, "Toward a Theory of Scheduling," *Industrial Engineering*, vol. 2, no. 2, 1960.
31. R. W. Conway, "Priority Dispatching 2nd Work-in-process Inventory in a Job Shop," *Industrial Engineering*, March-April, 1965.
32. R. W. Conway, "Priority Dispatching and Job Lateness in a Job Shop," *Industrial Engineering*, July-August, 1965.
33. J. M. Moore and R. C. Wilson, "A Review of Simulation Research in Job Shop Scheduling," *Production and Inventory Management*, vol. 8, no. 1, 1967.
34. R. W. Conway, W. L. Maxwell and Miller, *Theory of Scheduling*, Addison-Wesley Publishing Company, Inc., Reading, Mass., 1967.
35. S. E. Elmaghraby and R. T. Cole, "On the Control of Production in Small Job Shops," *Industrial Engineering*, July-August, 1963.
36. M. H. Bulkin, J. L. Colley, and H. W. Steinhoff, "Load Forecasting, Priority Sequencing, and Simulation in a Job Control System," *Management Science*, vol. 13, no. 2, 1966.
37. J. L. Colley and J. B. Turner, "A Comparative Analysis of the Use of Simulation

for Real Time Scheduling of Job Shops," Thirty-first National Meeting, Operations Research Society of America, New York, June 1, 1967.

BIBLIOGRAPHY

Line of Balance

Finck, N. E.: "Line of Balance Gives the Answer," *Systems and Procedures Journal,* July-August, 1965.

————: *What's New with Line of Balance,* Technical Paper MM66-703, ASTME Engineering Conference at Los Angeles, 1966.

Line of Balance Guide for System and Subsystem Acquisition, a Management Procedure for Production Planning and Control, Aeronautical System Division, Air Force Systems Command, Wright-Patterson AFB, Ohio, AFSCM 174-1, Apr. 6, 1964.

Line of Balance Technology, Office of Naval Material, Department of the Navy, NAVEXOS P1851 (rev. 4-62).

Mundorff, George T., and William Bloom: *Managing a Development Program,* Technical Publication PB171841, U.S. Department of Commerce.

Quantitative Methods in Discrete-part Production Control

The editors of *Business Week:* "Computer Programming Unsnarls the Job Shop," Apr. 2, 1966.

Joshi, Anand: Burroughs Corp., private communication, July 27, 1967.

LeGrande, E.: "The Development of a Factory Simulation System Using Actual Operating Data," *Management Technology,* vol. 3, no. 1, May, 1963.

Moodie, C. L., and D. J. Novotny: "Computer Scheduling and Control Systems for Discrete Part Production," *Journal of Industrial Engineering,* vol. 19, no. 7, 1968.

Parkinson, G.: "Simplified Computer Control: The Mechanics of the New Production Control System," *Factory,* October, 1966.

Simulation and Modeling for Scheduling

Giffler, B.: "Simulation Models in Production Scheduling and Inventory Control," *Production and Inventory Management,* vol. 7, no. 3, p. 1, July, 1966.

LeGrande, E.: "The Development of a Factory Simulation System Using Actual Operating Data," *Management Technology,* vol. 3, no. 1, p. 1, May, 1963.

Moore, J. M., and R. C. Wilson: "A Review of Simulation in Job Shop Scheduling," *Production and Inventory Management,* vol. 8, no. 1, p. 1, January, 1967.

Naylor, T. H.: *Computer Simulation Techniques,* John Wiley & Sons, Inc., New York, 1966.

Trilling, D. R.: "The Use of a Job Shop Simulator in the Generation of Production Schedules," *Production and Inventory Management,* vol. 7, no. 3, p. 57, July, 1966.

Section Five

Inventory Control

Chapter 14

Elements of Inventory Control

EDITOR:

Jack N. Durben *Manager, Materials Control, Miles Laboratories, Inc., Elkhart, Indiana*

CONTRIBUTORS:

Emil Albert *Manager, Production Planning and Procurement Department, The Adams and Westlake Co., Elkhart, Indiana*

John E. Anderson *Supervisor, Production and Inventory Control, Miles Laboratories, Inc., Elkhart, Indiana*

Calvin Wayne Churchman *Production Planning Manager, Automatic Electric Company, Northlake, Illinois*

James L. Somers *Coordinator, Manufacturing Production Control, Collins Radio Co., Cedar Rapids, Iowa*

C. J. Myers *Supervisor, Materials Control, Dodge Manufacturing Corporation, Mishawaka, Indiana*

CONTENTS

The purpose of this chapter is to introduce basic inventory control policies, functions, and techniques and to provide the production and inventory control practitioner with basic tools for establishing a workable system for his manufacturing operations. Also, mastering the concepts and techniques included here will provide a basis for understanding and applying the more advanced material included in the later chapters on inventory.

Why Inventories? The economies of the United States and other countries are closely related. This means that materials might be transported great distances between successive stages of production. Because of this, a means to support the isolated suppliers, producers, and consumers is required.   Inventories serve this purpose.

A second reason for inventories is caused by the type of production—continuous versus intermittant or job shop.   Inventories mean that material can be produced in the economical quantity—considering setup costs and carrying costs.

Inventories compensate for different production rates of succeeding operation in the production cycle.   If inventories were not provided between successive operations, fast operations would sit idle waiting for slow operations, thereby increasing production costs.   The increased in-process inventory costs are generally more than compensated for by savings that are realized in keeping the operations going.

Inventories serve as *anticipation stocks*.   Because our affluent society demands delivery of items off the shelf, manufacturers must be continually building inventories in anticipation of consumers' desires.   The volatility of anticipation stocks is related to the necessity of the product to the consumer.   The size of the anticipation inventory will have to be adjusted commensurate with customer service policy.

Another function of inventories, closely related to the need for anticipation stocks, is the need for a cushion between actual and forecasted demand.   The extent to which inventories will be needed is a function of the accuracy of forecasting and the variations in actual demands.

Inventories and Business Cycles.   Studies of historical data covering the last 40 years or more indicate that each recessionary period in the United States economy has had a substantial change in actual physical inventories.   This indicates a connection between inventories, business cycles, and production and inventory control practices.

That changes in inventories do affect business is a basic fact understood by individuals, firms, and governments.   If too much inventory exists, production is slowed down until consumption catches up.   Likewise if shortages exist, production has to be speeded up to replenish supplies.

The reasons why production becomes out of balance with consumption, resulting in inventory fluctuations, are not completely understood or agreed upon by students of business cycles.   It is suggested that changes come about because of the following reasons:

1. The variations that develop between forecasted and actual sales are minor. Because of modern forecasting and reporting techniques, adjustments can be made quickly and in small increments.   Therefore, this is no longer a major factor.

2. Unexpected supply interruption is a second factor which will affect the relationship between inventory levels and consumption.   As an example, when war or other disaster destroys or damages the source of supply, it will have to operate at a high level when back in service to replenish the supplies.   Hence business activities will be at a higher than normal level.

3. It is proposed that the major factor causing changes in business activity is the change in inventories which comes about because of anticipated interruptions to the supply of a durable commodity.   The two important points are *anticipated interruptions* and *durable commodity*.   If a commodity is durable, it can be stored for future needs; and if there is an anticipated supply interruption, there is a reason for users to stockpile the commodity ahead of normal requirements.

These periods of stockpiling have two characteristics.   The period preceding the threatened interruption is one of increased business activity while the stockpiling is accomplished. The period following the threatened interruption, whether or not it occurs, is a period of reduced activity. The below-normal activity is a function of the stockpile's size and duration of interruption.

Examples of the above theory are to be found in a number of situations. A classic example has been the steel stockpiling caused by the threatened interruptions of supplies because of strikes. Excluding cases such as when wars or threats of wars affected the pattern, a review of history will indicate periods of increased activity prior to labor contract deadlines followed by a period of reduced business activity in the months immediately following contract settlement.

Inventories and the Financial Statement. Inventories represent stocks of raw materials, work in process, and finished goods which are held for a short term to be converted into sales dollars. They are one of the most active elements of a business operation. Inventories appear not only on the balance sheet and the manufacturing statement of the business but also on the profit-and-loss statement. Inventories are of vital concern not only to the management but also to the stockholders, who are concerned about any drastic changes that might occur from time to time.

Since inventories are used in determining the profit, which is subject to taxation, they are of vital concern to both the state and federal government. Consequently the government has established strict regulations concerning methods of pricing inventories. The method of costing includes *cost or market, whichever is lower.* An individual involved in this activity would do well to read the government manuals pertaining to this subject.

The accounting department is usually involved with the pricing of inventories and is familiar with the various regulations. It is interested not only in complying with the law, but also in developing financial statements which are honest and enhance the company's image. It is important to note that the inventories are not taxed at the state and federal level. The value of the inventories is, however, used to determine the profit—and it is the profit which is taxed.

However, the inventories are taxed at the local government level. At this level the value of the inventory is assessed and the tax is leveled against this value. This is one of the reasons why it might be desirable to keep inventories at the lowest possible value—at least during certain times of the year.

INVENTORY IDENTIFICATION

More than one company has become bogged down with a poorly conceived product identification system. Too often the system is developed by an individual who does not understand all the ramifications of data processing, engineering changes, product service requirements, inventory storage considerations, and others. The inventory classification and identification system is of concern to all the functions of the business and should be modified only after the most careful deliberations.

For some products the industry has established the method of classifying and coding the product. For example, the electrical industry has established a standard color code for resistors. Where this arrangement exists in an industry there is no alternative but to follow suit. In many other industries it is necessary for a company to develop its own inventory identification system. If you are involved in this, approach it with extreme caution and be sure to discuss the proposed changes with all the departments involved. In certain cases you might do well to discuss proposed changes with your customers and vendors—and even with your competitor.

The following material discusses some of the methods for classifying and coding materials in inventory.

Classes of Inventory. There are three basic classes of inventory:

1. Raw materials
2. Work in process
3. Finished goods

Raw materials are those items purchased to be further processed. They may be chemicals, fabrications, metals, packaging, etc., to be stored for future use and manufactured into finished goods. The items may be purchased from outside or may be supplied from another division.

Components or *assemblies* purchased outside may be classified separately but are often considered as raw materials.

Work-in-process inventories are raw materials that have had labor and burden added to them and are awaiting further processing into finished goods.

Finished goods are those finished products available for delivery. They may be carried in inventory or may be shipped upon completion.

Simplification and Standardization. As a firm grows it continues to develop new products and revise the old ones. These product changes to meet the marketing demands are healthy and provide new lifeblood for the firm. Progress denotes growth, but it leaves in its wake potential inventory problems. New products obsolete old, and revised designs replace old components and materials. These obsolete materials increase total inventories and the related costs of increased storage space and reduced material turnover. Eventually this tends to increase the cost of goods sold.

Standardization of materials is the determining of fixed sizes, shapes, quality, and dimensions of material. Standardization follows a more scientific plan than simplification of inventory. Again, inventory control cannot directly accomplish standardization of materials, but it must encourage the use of standards. When specifications are issued every effort should be made to specify the accepted industry standards.

Value-analysis techniques can be a purchasing tool. They are a combination of simplification and standardization in a practical, before-the-fact approach. This approach determines the function and attempts to find the one best way to solve the need. Savings by reducing inventory space, obsolescence, handling costs, and inventory as well as improved product quality are available to the inventory manager who can implement simplification and standardization in his business.

Classification. * Before a useful coding method is selected and applied, it is necessary to establish the data classification plan and identify the data items within it. The classification plan concerns the grouping of like data items in some manner which best suits the needs of the user. Magazine publishers, for example, would logically classify their name and address master file according to Zip code, state, city, and post office to conform to postal requirement. They would further subdivide according to last name, initials, street address, etc., for inividual-subscriber file maintenance. All uses to which the data are to be put must be considered in the development of the classification plan, so that as many major classifications and subdivisions may be devised as are neces-

* Material in this and the succeeding section, "Coding Methods and Their Uses," is abstracted from *Coding Methods,* IBM Manual, F20-8093, International Business Machines Corp., White Plains, N.Y.

sary to satisfy all requirements.   To do this, several questions must be answered:

1. Who is responsible for maintenance of the data and who are its users?

2. What are the data used for, and in what order or degree of detail are they best presented for each user?

3. How much of the data does each user require?

4. With what frequency are the data used, and what are user priorities?

5. Are the data complete in enough detail to meet all user requirements?

6. Will the data satisfy anticipated future requirements for each user?

7. What methods will be used to process the data?

With answers to these questions the classification plan needed to identify each item for all users can be defined.   During the identification procedure it is advisable to record a *dictionary of standard nomenclature* for items within each classification subdivision so that uniformity may be maintained for all future usage.   This dictionary will serve as a reference guide for identification and classification of new items and should be maintained on a current basis as long as the data file is in use.

After the classification plan has been completed and the data items have been identified within that plan, the coding method is selected.   The particular method selected should be:

Expandable.   The code must provide space for additional entries within each classification for new items.   There must also be capacity to expand existing classifications and add new ones to take care of future changes.

Precise.   The code structure must be such that only one code may be correctly applied to a given item.

Concise.   The code should require the least possible number of digits to adequately describe each item.

Convenient.   The code must be easily understood by each user and simple to apply, whether encoding or decoding.

Meaningful.   If possible, the code itself should indicate some of the characteristics of the items.

Operable.   The code should be adequate for present and anticipated data processing machine methods, as well as for manual reference.

The coding method having these qualities will be an efficient implement with which to accomplish the data-handling objectives.

Coding Methods and Their Uses.   Sequence Codes: The sequence method of coding is the simplest to use and apply.   It is the assignment of consecutive numbers, beginning with 1, to a list of items as they occur, just as man-numbers might be assigned to employees as they are hired.

This method makes no provision for classifying groups of like items according to specific characteristics and cannot be used where such requirements exist.   It is practical only for coding short lists or for numbering longer lists where the code serves only as a convenient substitute title, as in account numbering or invoice numbering.

A sequence code always requires the use of a directory for decoding, since it has no relation to the item characteristics.   It is therefore normally applied to lists of items which have been arranged in some order to aid this decoding process.   The items in the following example have been arranged in alphabetic order of last name:

Code Number	Employee Name
1	George Adams
2	John Beldon
3	Arthur Brown
4	John Callahan

The advantage of the sequence code is its ability to code an unlimited number of items by using the fewest possible code digits. As new items occur they are simply assigned the next-higher unused number in sequence. It should be noted, however, that this assignment of the next-higher available code number to new items invalidates the original item order. If maintenance of some arrangement is necessary or desirable, some other coding method should be employed, depending upon the purpose of the arrangement.

BLOCK CODES: Block coding is a minor refinement of the simple sequence code. A series of consecutive code numbers is divided into blocks, each block of numbers being reserved for the identification of groups of items having some common characteristics. The quantity of code numbers set aside in any given block is based on the quantity of items requiring identification, plus some unassigned numbers for new items. Arrangement of the blocks by specific 10- or 1,000-series numbers is not necessarily attempted unless usage requires it.

Code Number	Data Item	
1	Razor blades—packed 10	
2	Razor blades—packed 25	Codes 1 through
3	Razor blades—packed 50	5 reserved for
4		blades
5		
6	Safety razor—gold	
7	Safety razor—silver	
8	Safety razor—chrome	Codes 6 through
9	Safety razor—aluminum	12 reserved for
10		safety razors
11		
12		

Block coding provides a data classification system which uses a few code digits to identify each item. Expansion of the code to include additional items within each block is confined to those numbers left unassigned when the plan is originally established. New blocks of any quantity of code numbers for new classifications may be added as required, beginning with the next-higher unreserved code number in sequence.

As in the sequence code method, decoding is usually accomplished through some form of cross-reference directory. With this method, decoding is more easily accomplished, since reference is directed to the range of code numbers within the blocks, thus narrowing the scope of search.

GROUP-CLASSIFICATION CODES: Group-classification codes are those which designate major and minor data classifications by successively lower-order groups of code digits.

Example

	Major group	Intermediate group	Minor group
Code digits	XX	XXX	XX

The quantity of digit groups required in the code is determined by the number of different classifications necessary for data identification. For example, if raw-material items are classified according to four factors (say, type of material, shape, chemical composition, and size), then four groups of code digits are required. The quantity of digits required in each group is determined by the number of items in each classification. If the shape classification, for instance, includes five items (say, strips, sheets, bars, castings, and tubing), then only one group digit is required for this classification.

Raw Material Code

	Type of Material	Shape	Chemical Composition	Size	
Code digits	1 2	3	4 5 6	7 8 9	
	0 6				Carbon steel
		4			Sheets
			0 6 1		Cold rolled
				0 9 2	4' × 8'

The nine-digit code construction above provides for identification of 100 material types, 10 shapes, 1,000 different chemical compositions, and 1,000 sizes. Additional items in any of these classifications will mean additional digits. Similarly, the need for further classification identification will result in the use of an additional group or groups of code digits.

Group-classification codes are widely used for a variety of code applications. The group code is readily constructed and easy to understand and apply. Capacity for expansion is provided by simple addition of classification groups or group digits. Machine processing is facilitated since a sort on specific digit groups causes separation of the desired class of data for processing. For example, the carbon-steel items in the raw-material code shown above may be separated by selection of records coded 06 under "Type of Material" (code digits 1 and 2).

SIGNIFICANT-DIGIT CODES: Significant-digit codes are those in which all or some of the code digits describe weight, dimension, distance, capacity, or other characteristics of the items themselves. The code for a specific item, therefore, is determined by, and signifies, the physical makeup of the item itself.

The most important accomplishment of a significant-digit code is reduction or elimination of the decoding usually required to associate a code with an item. A familiar use of this type of code is found wherever automobile or truck tires are stocked:

Code	*Description*
TT 670 15 B 1	Tube type, size 670 × 15, blackwall, 1st line
TT 670 15 W 1	Tube type, size 670 × 15, whitewall, 1st line
TT 710 15 B 1	Tube type, size 710 × 15, blackwall, 1st line

The user who is familiar with the item's characteristics recognizes individual items from the code itself without further reference to a descriptive list keyed by code number.

FINAL-DIGIT CODES: Final-digit coding is a technique which uses the last digit of a code to indicate simple separation of items in a classification. It is used to modify some other coding method and is not a complete code itself.

The most familiar application of the final-digit code is the assignment of telephone numbers ending in 0 or 00 to indicate large private switchboards, thus signaling operators to try more than one line. The special importance of these particular numbers is indicated without changing or adding to the basic telephone number system. Most important, no additional code digit is required to impart this special meaning.

DECIMAL CODES: The decimal method of coding is used primarily for indexing libraries or classifying written correspondence. It is a subjective classification and coding system. A representative example is, in part:

Decimal Code	Subject
520.	Astronomy
530.	Physics
531.	Mechanics
531.1	Machines
531.11	Lever and balance
531.12	Wheel and axle

That portion of the decimal code which is placed to the left of the decimal point is constructed in the same fashion as a group-classification code. Code digits placed to the right of the decimal point (decimal places) are used to distinguish specific topics within the subject classification. As new topic subdivisions occur, new decimal places are added to the code. In the example, 531.11, "Lever and balance," has been added as a subdivision of 531.1, "Machines."

Pure decimal code construction does not lend itself to machine data processing methods, because fixed-code field definition, normally required for machine processing, is inconsistent with the decimal-expandability code feature. Where machine processing is required, the decimal code construction must necessarily be altered to take on some of the characteristics of a group-classification code.

MNEMONIC CODES: Mnemonic code construction is characterized by the use of letter and number combinations which describe the items coded, the combinations having been derived from descriptions of the items themselves. The combinations are designed to be an aid to memorizing the codes and associating them with the items they represent.

There are no definite rules to follow in constructing a mnemonic code except that an effort be made to select the combinations which best suggest the item they represent. The letters I, O, and Q should be avoided because of their similarity to the numbers 1 and 0. The sequence and position of the letters and figures constituting a mnemonic code may be given significance if their arrangement is made to conform to a system of classification:

Code number				Item description
Item	Size	Color and style	Mfr.	
BY	010	RB	01	Bicycle, 10″, red, boy's, Comet
BY	010	RB	02	Bicycle, 10″, red, boy's, Red Star
BY	020	RB	01	Bicycle, 20″, red, boy's, Comet

In this arrangement the letters of the alphabet are interspersed between the numbers so that the code is more easily remembered and the classifications more readily recognized.

Although the use of mnemonic codes is widespread, there are some difficulties connected with their use for identification of long, growing lists of items. Wherever item names beginning with the same letters are encountered, there is a conflict of mnemonic use. To overcome this, the number of code characters is necessarily increased, with the likelihood that the combinations will be less memory-aiding. Also, since descriptions may vary widely, it is difficult to maintain a code organization which conforms with a plan of classification. For these reasons mnemonic codes are not well adapted to machine data processing methods.

Mnemonic codes are used to best advantage for identifying relatively short lists of items coded for manual processing where it is necessary that the items be recognized by their code from memory.

NUMERICAL-ALPHABETIC CODES: Numerical-alphabetic codes are those designed to maintain the data they identify in some form of alphabetic sequence without use of alphabetic characters in the codes themselves. This type of coding is usually found where lists of individuals or company names, usually account names, must be maintained in alphabetic order. The numerical construction of these codes is particularly advantageous for machine processing, rather than an unwieldy alphabetic code. The simplest form of numerical-alphabetic code is constructed in such a way that the two high-order code digits are 01 through 26, corresponding to the letters of the alphabet.

CONSONANT CODES: Consonant codes are made up of abbreviations of the alphabetic data items themselves. The initial letter is always retained, but all subsequent vowels are dropped (including W and Y under special circumstances). Codes derived in this fashion from the different item characteristics will be unique to the items and may be used for sorting procedures:

Consonant Code	Item Name
JNS	Jones
PMPHNDLS	Pump Handles
SMTH	Smith
SNDL	Snodel
SNWLY	Snowley
TRCK MTRL	Track Material

The principle of consonant coding may be used to identify any type of data item but is commonly used to develop codes for large-volume name and address files where coding and decoding of numerical codes is not practical.

The primary advantage of this method is the ease with which the code may be established for new items. In most cases typists or card-punch operators can, with little practice, automatically encode each item as it is recorded. Similarly, decoding is readily accomplished after comparatively little experience. Consonant codes are practical in connection with some data processing procedures.

EXAMPLE OF A WORKABLE CODE SYSTEM: The raw-material and supply code described here meets the criteria of flexibility, expansion, machine compatibility, and convenience. It is a code currently in use by a large manufacturer. Processing is performed on both unit-record and large-scale data processing equipment.

This coding system consists of a nine-digit code which has most amply satisfied the user's need. While the nine digits may seem excessive, the degree of identification given to the individual item outweighs the processing disadvantage.

The coding structure is divided into two basic parts—raw materials and supplies.

RAW-MATERIAL CODING: For raw materials the code is known as follows:

```
1 2 3 4 5 6 7 8 9        Number
X X                      Class
    X                    Form or shape
      X X X              Chemical composition
            X X X        Size
```

Example

0 6 4 0 6 1 0 9 2	Nine-digit code
0 6	Carbon steel
4	Strip
0 6 1	AISI C-1010 analysis—cold rolled
0 9 2	Assigned arbitrarily

When engineering drawings are prepared, the material specifications are shown in the form of a five-digit code which corresponds to the "class" and "chemical composition" parts of the material code. This facilitates the translation of engineering specifications into finished products by reducing the possibility of misunderstanding.

Example

06–060	Material code on engineering drawing
06	Carbon steel
060	AISI C-1010 analysis

The two-digit raw-material code is as follows:

01	Aluminum	15	Unclassified metallic materials
02		16	
03	Copper, brass, and bronze	17	Card stock
04		18	
05	Iron	19	Laminated insulating material
06	Steel—carbon	20	Insulated wire
07	Steel—alloy (except tool and emergency metals)	21	
		22	Paper, except card stock
08	Steel—tool	23	Plastics—thermoplastic
09	Emergency metals	24	Plastics—thermosetting
10		25	Rubber
11		26	
12	Magnesium	27	Wood
13		28	
14	Zinc	29	Unclassified nonmetallic materials

Note that the 01–29 block leaves a number of blanks for additional materials. The "form or shape" category is as follows:

0	Special forms	Castings, forgings, special extruded shapes, and commercial shapes such as angles, channels, etc., or any form not otherwise classified
1	Round	A solid round section having a continuous periphery and furnished in straight lengths, excluding mechanical wire (see item 7)
2	Square	A solid square section with four equal sides and four equal angles, furnished in straight lengths
3	Hexagonal	A solid hexagonal section with six equal sides and six equal angles, furnished in straight lengths
4	Strip, sheet	A solid rectangular section up to and including 0.249 inch in thickness. Widths up to 24 inches will be designated as "strip." Widths 24 inches and over will be designated as "sheet."
5	Flat	A solid rectangular section 0.250 inch and over in thickness in any width
6	Tubing	A hollow section having a continuous periphery, either seamless or welded, including piping
7	Wire	Round—mechanical
8	Bulk	Materials in bulk form—e.g., molding compounds, pellets, etc.
9	Rectangular coil stock	Rectangular shapes in coil form

The "chemical composition" refers to such things as the temper, the type of alloy, or chemical properties of the item. The fourth, fifth, and sixth digits taken from a special listing called the "raw-material code outline" is kept current by the manufacturing standards department.

The seventh, eight, and ninth digits are assigned arbitrarily.

SUPPLIES CODING: In the supplies category fall the following: small hand tools, small machine tools, and supplies. The coding structure is as follows:

```
1  2  3  4  5  6  7  8  9      Number of digits in code
X  X                          Class
      X  X                    Kind
            X  X              Type
                  X  X  X     Size
```

The first two digits are based upon the following table:

30	Abrasives	57	Livestock supplies
31	Acids and chemicals	58	Lubricants—coolants, etc.
33	Belting—hose	60	Packing material
34	Brushes—brooms	61	Paints and varnish
35	Building material	62	Patterns
37	Candy, soft drinks, tobacco	64	Recreational accessories
38	Conduit—pipe and fittings	65	Repair parts—general equipment
39	Containers	66	Repair parts—printing equipment
41	Decorative articles	67	Repair parts—tool equipment
42	Drawing—reproducing material	68	Restaurant and kitchen supplies
43	Dyes—inks (except stationery)	72	Sanitation and cleaning supplies
45	Electrical supplies and parts	73	School and library supplies
47	Fastening material	74	Seeds—fertilizers
48	Firearms and ammunition	75	Small tools—hand
49	Foodstuffs	76	Small tools—machine
50	Fuel	77	Small tools—carbides
52	Glass (except container and electrical supplies)	80	Technical and medical supplies
		81	Textiles and fiber
54	Hardware—wire goods, etc.	83	Waste material
56	Literature and supplies—promotional	84	Wearing apparel
		85	Wooden articles

The "kind" and "type" digits (3 through 6) are assigned on the basis of the supply code outline, a portion of which is shown below. The last three digits are assigned arbitrarily.

	Class	Kind	Type
Abrasives...........................	30	00	00
Buffing and polishing wheels..............	30	01	00
Buffing wheel........................	30	01	01
Polishing wheel rubber................	30	01	02
Buffing and polishing compounds.........	30	02	00
Alphabetical list of compounds..........	30	02	01

THE INVENTORY CONTROL ORGANIZATION

Seldom will you see inventory control departments in the simplified organization chart, yet no other single department affects the destiny of the rest of the firm so much.

"Eliminate overtime," "reduce inventory investment 7 percent," "incorporate these product revisions in next week's production," "sustain a 27 percent sales increase with no back orders," "balance the work load in the finishing department." These are the demands that inventory control hears from other departments. It is the hub of the firm's activities as well as the sponge that soaks up the problems of all departments. No other department is involved in the extensive coordination of the firm's operations. The flow of material, from determining the need of incoming parts to the shipment of the final product, requires interaction with purchasing, receiving, inspection, production, sales, accounting, and shipping.

Because of the extensive volume of communication and interdependence with other departments, inventory control must keep the problems in proper perspective with an efficient system.

Basic Inventory Control Systems. The inventory control system will follow a basic cycle regardless of the size of the firm. The cycle of operations begins with determining the production need and is completed with filling the customer order. Records and information will flow from similar sources, although the timing, accuracy, frequency, and completeness will be a function of the firm's size and reliance on data processing systems.

The most basic record is a *material list* of the products to be manufactured. The parts from the materials list times the scheduled quantity—plus any loss for scrap—are deducted from existing inventories. A negative figure of inventory indicates the need to requisition parts for delivery prior to production. A *traveling requisition* is well suited for repetitive requisitioning. This contains the part number, specifications, drawings, historical purchase data, and sections for quantity and delivery instructions.

Inventory Records. The *perpetual inventory record* is a *continuous account of the incoming materials, outgoing materials, and the balance on hand.* It takes many forms. It may be a card record system, a page in a ledger book, a visual control board, or a tag tacked to the bin where the material is stored. A simple card record will be discussed here as the same ideas apply to the other forms of recording inventory information.

At practically any instant the perpetual inventory record should give the balance on hand and the activity for any particular inventory item. The record has two sections: a *heading* where the permanent information is to be found and the *body* of the card where the changing information occurs.

The heading should contain the *part number* and *part description*. It is also the place to record the reordering information such as the *reorder point*, *reorder quantity*, and sometimes the list of vendors and their *vendor rating*. Part location is also placed on the inventory records at times, as are part numbers which might be used as substitutes. Any other useful information may be added, but the card should not contain useless information.

In the basic inventory record (see Fig. 1), there will be three columns in the body, which contains information about receiving the material, issuing the material, and the remaining balance. These columns should be further divided so that each transaction can be traced. For example, the "received" column should have the document number—perhaps the receiving-report number—the date, and the quantity. Raw-materials records will have transaction information which is entirely different from finished-goods records. This is illustrated in Fig. 1.

This basic inventory record with just three columns often does not present sufficient information for adequate control. When the ordering cycle is long and there are apt to be several orders out at one time, it may be desirable to add another column showing what is "on order." This will help prevent duplicating orders. It also adds to the confusion of keeping the records and should not be included in the system unless absolutely essential.

An "allocated" column might also be added to the record. This is used in circumstances when it is desirable to allocate material to customers and to orders awaiting production.

BIN TAGS: Some inventory control systems are operated with a perpetual inventory card attached to the bins. At times such a card system has been operated in conjunction with a perpetual inventory record system.

Bin tag systems are not always satisfactory. The cards are apt to get dirty, and the stores clerks are often careless in how they fill out the record—frequently neglecting to do so at all.

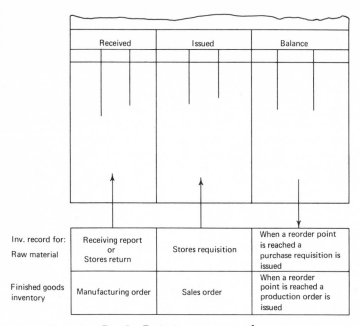

Fig. 1 Basic inventory records.

Basic Stores Layout and Operation (See Chapter 15). There are four basic storeroom operations: receiving, storing, issuing, and returning. The complexity of each operation will vary according to the size and type of business, but all must be performed. The inspection function is not included as it is a function of quality control.

The layout of the stores area is a function of space available, size of materials, part-number system, material similarities, and special consideration.

Centralized stores provide advantages of fewer personnel, less space requirement, less dated inventory, better record control, and less record duplication. The case against centralized stores is that the time for material movement to using areas is lengthy, involving added labor and handling equipment.

Certain low-value materials are better controlled by no control. The change of inventory item to an expendable supply item without a requisition reduces the overhead associated with that item, and inventory control effort may be placed where control is needed.

Protection or security of inventory is especially important when items stored may have value or use elsewhere. "Midnight raiders" can cause unexplained shortages that can shut down production when material is available "on paper" but not physically available.   Material delivery upon requisition, use, and return must accurately reflect proper quantities if a control inventory or data processing stock status are to be used.

Regardless of location, number of items stored, or layout, the goals of maximum service at the lowest cost are to be achieved for effective support to the firm.

Principles of Taking the Annual Physical Inventory.   A listing of all the techniques that are possible for taking the annual physical inventory can't be presented here.   But, as in almost every other area of manufacturing control, the principles are most important and the fact that we seem to miss some of these is evidenced by the cliché, "the inventory records are never more suspect than immediately after the annual physical."

This is hard to believe, when we think of the large amounts of money spent on taking the annual physical inventory, the fact that these results are usually approved by outside auditors, and the fact that most managements are extremely concerned—at least once a year—with the accuracy of inventory records.

Why is inventory taking done so poorly?   Admittedly, it's a big, complex job involving a lot of people, many departments, and many activities, and it's usually rushed since an annual physical inventory involves a costly plant shutdown period.   The problems typically are poor preparation, improper counting procedures, failure to account for paper work, and ineffective checking of significant discrepancies.   Let's take a look at each of these problems separately:

1. *Preparation.*   Getting ready to take a physical inventory involves four phases:

   a. Housekeeping: Getting materials located and arranged properly so that they can be inventoried easily.

   b. Identification: Ensuring that each part to be inventoried is correctly identified.   Errors in counting affect only one record, but errors in identification make two records wrong.   In many companies, the shop-floor and stockroom control systems are weak, and identification is a critical function in inventory preparation.   Unfortunately, only a limited number of people are capable of checking on identification.   It's important to use their talent effectively prior to inventory.   Equally important is to identify those items which are not to be inventoried to avoid useless confusion at inventory time.

   c. Instruction: Reviewing detailed inventory-taking procedures with all key personnel immediately prior to taking inventory.   Unfortunately, changing conditions and turnover of personnel seem to be the rule rather than the exception and even those people who have taken inventory before usually don't remember the details a year later.   The answer to this problem isn't always detailed written instructions.   The best approach is meetings with department heads and supervisors responsible so that the important elements of inventory taking can be identified and responsibility assigned.

   d. Training: Here actual practice is recommended in taking physical inventory, especially where counting scales and mechanical hand counters are likely to be used and familiarity with their proper operation is essential. You might as well bring people "down the learning curve" in a practice session both to improve the accuracy of the inventory and to reduce the time required.

2. *Counting Procedures.*   Accurate counting is difficult under the best of circumstances.   An *inventory team* is recommended consisting of one or two counters, a checker, and a writer.   The counters are usually factory workers who do the actual work of handling, identifying, and counting the material.   A foreman, inspector, or production control man checks the count and item identi-

fication. The writer can be an office employee, frequently from accounting, who posts the physical count to the inventory card. One checker can work with two or more inventory teams. The team should move through each area in an orderly fashion to avoid the possibility of skipping any items. *A few competent people should be on call throughout the inventory taking to resolve questions quickly.*

It's worthwhile to have personnel from the accounting or cost department act as *internal auditors* to sample-check inventory counts after the teams have completed their work. Outside auditors will also sample these counts.

Equipment is available to speed up counting and improve accuracy since hand-counting quantities that exceed 50 pieces often yields questionable results. Both floor- and bench-type counting scales are available, and they are normally accurate to plus or minus 1 percent. The biggest problem in using such scales is the tare weights for the containers. An oil-soaked shop box can weigh considerably more than a brand-new shop box. The best results will be achieved by weighing the empty containers separately and then transferring parts into them immediately prior to counting. One type of counting scale (100:1 ratio) includes the quantity of items in the small counting pan in the total count indicated. Another type (99:1 ratio) requires that the number of pieces in the pan be added to the scale reading to get the total count. Try to stick to one or the other type of scale in your plant. Mixing them can cause a great deal of confusion and potential error.

Hand counters with felt marker tips can be used to record the count. Each time the felt tip is pressed against the material the item is counted. These devices are particularly useful for counting bar stock and piled items which don't have to be moved to be counted. They also leave a mark on the counted items which assists in avoiding duplicating counts.

Adequate space and sufficient containers help to make an inventory easier and more accurate. It's a good idea, too, to have extra containers available to allow separation of mixed loads and permit counting while transferring parts from full to empty containers. A good housekeeping program prior to physical inventory can pay off.

Many auditing firms permit the omission of low-value items from the count if adequate substitutes for valuing such items have been agreed upon. Some companies established a percentage of the total inventory value for these inexpensive items. Others accept a fixed dollar total for low-value inventory, and this helps a great deal since such items usually represent a large percentage of the total number of parts. Eliminating their counting can greatly reduce the cost of the physical inventory, and more attention can be paid to the more important high-value items.

There is always a temptation to allow the continued movement of materials at least on an "emergency only" basis. This is an invitation to errors, and few companies have been able to do this and maintain inventory accuracy. The best approach is to *seal off an area while it is being inventoried* until it has been checked by both groups of auditors and also by those following up major discrepancies between records and physical counts.

3. *Inventory Paper Work.* Serially numbered inventory cards may be used to ensure that all items counted will be accounted for. Many companies use a prepunched deck of tabulating cards primarily to assist in speeding up the processing of inventory data after the actual counting has been done. This also makes it possible to reduce the number of inventory errors by minimizing handwritten information. When using this approach, however, it's important to decide how many cards are necessary for each item at each location, to

avoid physical damage to the data processing cards, and to devise suitable means for locating the proper inventory card quickly.

One of the biggest problems is clearing the normal paper-work channels prior to taking the inventory of all issues, receipts, uncashed requisitions, scrap reports, etc. Here's where systems people, people who really understand the paper-work flow, can assist. Don't forget to count materials in the shipping dock, export holding areas, returned-goods departments, marketing displays, and the like. Of course, the computer room itself shouldn't be overlooked for records, and once operations have been resumed, editing stations should be set up with individuals cautioned to look for paper work that might have gotten through with dates prior to the physical inventory so that corrections can be handled speedily,

4. *Recognition of Significant Variances.* Get the inventory information posted to the production control records *quickly.* Even if this has to be done manually, it is essential if the physical inventory is going to be accurate. The *essence of record verification is timeliness.* The audit team should check any discrepancies before material starts to move again.

Since available manpower can usually cope only with a relatively small number of checks, the definition of a "significant variance" is important. Obviously, attention should be concentrated on the high dollar discrepancies and checking should begin even while the inventory is being taken.

Taking the annual physical inventory is like painting a house. The time spent in preparation will pay off handsomely in the final results. Responsibilities need to be pinned down ahead of time and the whole operation organized so that it will go like clockwork. The modest extra expense involved in doing the job properly and having the proper audit teams available is well worthwhile when you consider the total cost in terms of lost production and the importance of accurate inventory records, especially if a modern computer system is being used.

When inventory taking is over, everyone would like to forget it, but this is just the time when one shouldn't. A *post-inventory review* with the people who were deeply involved with inventory to recount the mistakes so that they can be documented and avoided the next time is one of the most important steps in improving inventory-taking quality. Make sure this is done while the problems are fresh in everyone's mind.

Two other points are important. The first is *cycle counting.* Is it really a good idea to take annual physical inventories or should you cycle-count items in inventory during the year? This allows you to concentrate more effort on the high-value items and to use professional counters who do it all the time. The problem here is in picking up the paper work in the system for record reconciliation. Second, the best physical inventory is no substitute for *maintaining system integrity* and the necessary disciplines in year-round operation. Inventory-record accuracy is the basis of any system, be it manual or computer. We are often dismayed to see companies doing very sophisticated things with their inventory calculations all of which are based upon an "on-hand" figure which is highly suspect. It seems to be easier to do third-order exponential smoothing than to maintain stock-room paper-work flow accurately.

Schedules and Instructions for Physical Inventory. It is difficult for one person to keep the physical inventory procedure in mind from year to year. Changes in personnel can cause a severe break in continuity so that the procedure might become lost. To overcome all these difficulties it is imperative that a written standard procedure be prepared which can be referred to year after year. This does not mean that the system is rigid and cannot be adjusted from year to year. An example of a schedule and instructions for physical inventory is given in Fig. 2.

Feb. 26
  I. Order blank inventory and *precount cards.*
  II. Remind all people who are doing the ordering not to schedule anything for delivery between June 14 and July 15 unless urgently needed.

Apr. 25
  I. Get master inventory cards ready to be reproduced.
    A. Delete cards where necessary.
    B. Add cards where necessary.
    C. Add new items.
      1. Data processing run on new items:
        a. Items with inventory—add to inventory deck.
        b. Items with no inventory—reproduce deck.
          (1) Original deck—add to inventory deck.
          (2) Duplicate deck—hold until items are checked out.
    D. Add blank cards.
    E. Load header cards.

May 6
  I. Instruct multilith department to produce inventory cards to be used for storage areas and precount cards for both storage areas and work in process.

May 8
  I. Load header items for inventory cards on computer.

May 13
  I. Instruct data processing to reproduce onto the new inventory cards the following information:
    A. Reproduce part number in card column 1–6 from master inventory card deck and keep in its sequence. (Do not punch old sequence number.)
    B. Punch description in card column 7–38 from computer.
    C. Sequence new inventory cards in card column 74–79.
      1. Start sequence number with X00000.   (X refers to year.)
    D. Interpret part number, column 1–6, description, 7–38, and sequence, 55–60.
  II. Reproduce inventory card information on bin identification card.
  III. Interpret identification cards.
  IV. Inventory cards are in card sequence. Print out a list showing sequence number, part number, and description on four-part narrow paper.
  V. Sort inventory cards into part-number sequence after step IV is completed. Print a list showing part-number description and sequence number on four-part narrow paper.
  VI. Collate the new inventory cards with the bin cards. The inventory card is placed first in the sequence.

May 23
  I. Instruct data processing to return one collated set of inventory cards and two printed lists.
  II. The fourth copy of the printed sequence-number list should have the sequence numbers deleted. Add the following heading and duplicate.

For dept.———				
Seq. No.	Part No.	Description	Location	Assigned to

    1. Distribute list and blank inventory cards.
      a. One to storage area.
        (1) It is best to give out one sheet at a time with its blank cards.
      b. One copy stays in production control as a master list for blank numbers.
        (1) As lists come back from the shop, the master list should be checked.
  III. Distribute printed inventory card listings (one by part number and one by sequence number).
    A. One to cost department.
    B. One to department.
    C. One to department.

Fig. 2   Schedule and instructions for physical inventory.

D. One (copy with blank numbers missing) to storage area.
IV. Cancel header items that were loaded on computer inventory records.
May 25
    I. Production control starts placing bin cards into stock bins.
       A. "Pull" all old bin cards and extra checkouts.
       B. So cards won't get lost, slip inventory cards into boxes.
       C. Use status sheets as a guide.
       D. Put part number on blank bin cards.
May 30
    I. Order rubber date stamps that are needed for inventory.
June 3
    I. Inventory crew to start count.
       A. Put inventory quantity in "count" column on cards.
       B. As parts are received for use, quantities should be posted to inventory cards.
       C. If there is no inventory card in bin, use precount card.
       D. Be sure to record the number of containers or bins involved if more than one is inventoried and recorded on one inventory card.
    II. Separate voided inventory cards that are returned.
June 14
    I. Discontinue the issuing of purchase orders.
June 18
    I. Run the work orders for assemblies that may be required shortly after the inventory period. These will include:
       A. Assemblies that have the fewest items backlogged.
       B. Assemblies for which parts will be available shortly after inventory.
       C. Assemblies for which parts will be made in June.
          1. Write red X on bills of material so multilith department will know which bills of material and routing cards are to be returned to expeditors.
    II. Data processing to sequence old input cards for bills of material for regular orders and subassemblies.
    III. Stop all warehouse orders unless items are urgently needed. Box and label cards until notice to scrap them comes from production control.
    IV. Continue to allocate and ship as long as orders are received.
June 19
    I. Stop all component-part orders unless they are urgently needed. Box and label cards until notice to scrap them comes from production control.
    II. Enough work is sent by expeditors to assembly departments so the lines will be supplied until one week after shutdown.
       A. Remind the assembly department to start supplying the lines ahead so all parts will be *pulled* before the storage areas are closed.
June 20
    I. Stop generating bills of material unless urgently needed (the urgent items will be specified by production control).
    II. Stop processing 30-day checkout cards (discard cards).
    III. Make sure all stationery supplies have been ordered for inventory before stationery stores are closed.

Fig. 2   (*Continued*)

ABC INVENTORY ANALYSIS

The ABC technique is an analytical management tool for focusing attention and applying effort in the area which will give greatest results. While this technique has universal application in many areas of human endeavor, this discussion will concern only its use in inventory control.

The creation of inventory results from ordering material, material which is ordered for both known and forecasted requirements. When orders are issued for known requirements, the tightest degree of ordering control can be achieved. This may be designated as "required" or "unique" inventory. The ABC technique of ordering control does not apply to this low-risk inventory.

When material is ordered for stock based on forecasted requirements, inventory is created in anticipation of needs. This can create high inventory values, so there must be a technique available which is capable of applying the greatest effort to the high-annual-usage-value items.

From a control viewpoint the value of an item can be defined by its *annual usage value*. This is calculated by multiplying the quantity—usage past or forecasted—used in a year by the unit cost of the item. The *dollar value of annual usage* is the common factor for categorizing the inventory items.

Annual usage, without applying the dollar value, gives no meaningful common factor for making comparisons. For example, the same attention may unwisely be given to ordering 500 screws as is given to ordering 500 electric motors. Yet, the order value for the screws may be only $20 as opposed to $10,000 for the order value of the electric motors.

TABLE 1   Selected List of Inventory Items Ranked by Annual Usage Value

Item number*	Part number	Cost per unit, dollars	Annual usage	Annual usage value, dollars	Accum. annual usage value, dollars
(1)	(2)	(3)	(4)	(5)	(6)
1	FD-101	0.175	10,601,733	1,855,303	1,855,303
2	D-5102	1.184	1,318,779	1,561,434	3,416,737
3	D-28462	0.968	1,186,456	1,148,489	4,565,226
4	D-3837	0.644	1,349,578	869,128	5,434,354
5	FD-102	0.180	4,023,976	724,316	6,158,670
10	D-5216	0.237	2,166,712	513,511	8,982,966
15	D-4665	1.160	341,307	395,916	11,081,861
20	D-4619	0.261	1,343,610	350,682	12,877,146
25	D-437	0.225	1,406,582	316,481	14,520,424
250	WA-101	10.062	5,262	52,946	40,216,073
500	D-28306	0.132	200,441	26,458	49,557,607
750	D-15006	0.277	62,339	17,268	54,897,995
1000	D-5805	0.105	116,294	12,211	58,527,225
1231	FD-100	1.190	8,034	9,560	61,004,981
1250	D-6882	0.356	26,394	9,396	61,184,819
1500	FD-400	278.330	27	7,515	63,302,335
1750	MC-4225	0.830	7,534	6,253	65,014,705
2000	D-4241	0.488	10,535	5,141	66,433,279
2250	D-28188	0.471	9,131	4,301	67,607,577
2500	D-6765	0.084	43,424	3,648	68,593,110
2750	GB-1013	0.007	448,772	3,141	69,437,792
2842	MP-600	0.097	30,930	3,000	69,719,585
3000	D-15017	0.002	1,377,559	2,755	70,174,851
3250	D-28550	0.610	3,929	2,397	70,819,676
3500	H-88085	2.421	863	2,089	71,378,523
3750	GB-1014	0.007	265,461	1,858	71,872,492
4000	D-9406	0.210	7,812	1,641	72,307,554
4250	H-88473	0.141	10,462	1,475	72,696,462
4500	D-2707	3.370	384	1,294	73,042,385
4750	D-7157	0.113	10,323	1,166	73,349,007
5000	D-28131	0.838	1,244	1,042	73,623,828
5250	D-6770	0.060	15,769	946	73,871,584
5500	FD-106	0.200	4,253	851	74,096,117
5750	H-88660	0.910	843	767	74,298,016
6000	FD-10	0.650	1,049	682	74,478,735
6500	H-88033	0.202	2,796	565	74,788,851
7000	D-28408	0.024	19,523	469	75,046,820
8000	D-49002	0.699	475	332	75,442,845
9000	D-78077	0.365	636	232	75,722,325
10000	H-88549	0.513	329	169	75,920,932
19840	H-8896	0.006	57	1	76,366,187

* Note: These are only representative items.

The importance of the decision should not rest only on inventory investment considerations. Since the order is being issued for material in anticipation of needs, the accuracy of the forecast becomes a very important consideration to minimize inventory risk for high-value items.

Steps for an ABC Analysis. What are the steps in making an ABC analysis? First, consider all the items in Table 1 which are ordered for stock and determine their annual usage value (column 3 times column 4 equals column 5). Next, arrange the items in descending order in accordance with their annual usage value (column 6), which is developed by adding the value of each successive item.

The data include 19,840 items ordered for stock, and their total annual usage value is $76,366,187. A review of the data quickly reveals that there is a wide range of values for the items ordered for stock. However, approximately 3,000 of the items constitute about 90 percent of the total value. These data can be more clearly represented in chart form.

Figure 3 shows the accumulated annual usage value in chart form. The purpose of the chart is to give visual impact of where logical breaks occur in the curve. Generally, one can expect to find that approximately 10 percent of the items will constitute 75 percent of the total value and 75 percent of the items will constitute only 10 percent of the value. This is a typical distribution; however each inventory analyzed will deviate around this proportion.

In practice one must apply judgment to determine the two points on the curve which divide the inventory into the three ABC categories. Usually the points are selected by observation where the curve seems to change shape.

In this particular analysis the first 1,231 items, which are 6 percent of the total, account for slightly over $61 million or about 80 percent of the total accumulated annual usage. Judgment dictates the exact control point at which the high-value A inventory limit is set. The fewer the number of A items there are, the greater the amount of individual attention which can be applied. Considerable latitude can be exercised to conveniently round out the control point. For instance, a point was selected on the curve to limit the A items to the first 1,231 high-value items. It would have been just as logical to set the limit at 1,000 items.

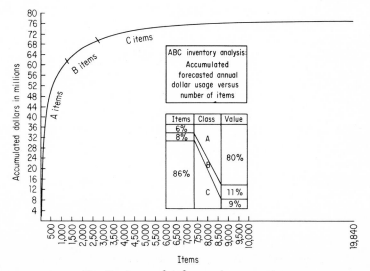

Fig. 3   Accumulated annual usage value.

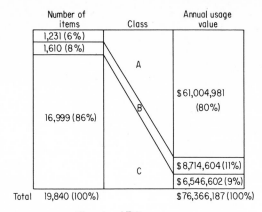

Fig. 4   ABC summary.

The next logical break in the curve appears to fall between the first 2,500 to 3,500 items in the sequence.   The point chosen in this analysis is after the 2,841st item.   The balance of 16,999 items, which are 86 percent of the total items, accounts for nearly $7 million or about 9 percent of the total value.   These items, with the lowest annual usage value, are classified as the C inventory.   For controlling an individual item, these are given the least attention.

The middle-value items, resulting from setting the lower limit for A and higher limit for C items, are identified as the B class inventory.   The B inventory group in this analysis would consist of 1,610 items and represent 8 percent of the total items.   The annual usage value would be $8,714,604 or 11 percent of the total value.

The data discussed in the last three paragraphs can now be summarized by Fig. 4 showing the ABC distribution.

In addition to charting the accumulated annual usage as shown, it is also convenient to chart the annual usage value for each item illustrated in Fig. 5.

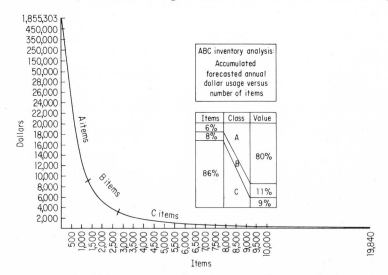

Fig. 5   ABC inventory analysis (item annual usage value).

The purpose of this chart is to allow the proper ABC identification of the annual usage limits on a per-item basis. Item 1,231 has an annual usage value of $9,560, and this becomes the lower-limit value for a class A inventory item. Item 2,842 has an annual usage value of $3,000, and this becomes the upper-limit value for a class C inventory item. A class B inventory item would have an annual usage value ranging between $3,001 and $9,559. These inventory limits are summarized as follows:

| | Usage range | | |
Category	Lower limit	Upper limit	Number of parts
Class A........	$9,561	None	1,231
Class B........	3,001	$9,560	1,611
Class C........	0	3,000	16,998

Separate inventory control policies should be established for each of the classifications. These policies should govern the following areas:
1. Forecasting techniques
2. Order-quantity determination
3. Reserve- or safety-stock calculation
4. Lead-time determination
5. Issuance of stock to using departments
6. Perpetual inventory record versus physical control

In summary, most inventory analyses are based on a classical accounting distribution of raw material, purchased parts, work in process, and finished goods. A more meaningful analysis would further segregate this distribution into *as-required* inventory and *stock* ABC inventory. An example of structuring an inventory analysis in this manner is shown in Table 2. It can be ascertained quickly from this analysis where the inventory dollars are tied up and whether they are proportionate to their activity.

PLANNING THE REPLENISHMENT OF INVENTORIES

Inventories must be maintained to carry out the objectives of a company, and the company's success depends on how well their inventories are planned. In fact, inventories are of such primacy that they appear on the most important financial statements. They are listed as a current asset on the balance sheet, and both beginning and ending inventories are included in the calculation for the cost of products on the profit-and-loss statement.

The Need for a Formal Analysis. The importance and necessity of inventories are well established throughout the management structure. However, the function that they should serve is not so well established. Typically, the sales people feel that inventories provide a means for giving good customer service. Therefore, they would like plenty of everything to be available at all times.

On the other hand, the part of the organization that is concerned with the financial aspects of the business regards inventories in an entirely different light. They view them as tying up the working portion of the current assets (circulating

TABLE 2 Structuring an Inventory Analysis

Inventory	Class A				Class B				Class C			
	Items	Percent	Value, $	Percent	Items	Percent	Value, $	Percent	Items	Percent	Value, $	Percent
Raw-material:												
In stock room.........	300	33	785,000	71	180	20	110,000	10	420	47	210,000	19
Weekly usage..........			79,000				9,000				7	
Weeks of usage........			9.9				12.2				30.0	
Purchased-parts:												
In stock room.........	230	16	731,000	73	360	25	155,000	16	850	59	112,000	11
Weekly usage..........			90,000				14,000				4,000	
Weeks of usage........			8.2				11.1				28.1	
Work-in-process:												
In production, total....			1,084,000				236,000				91,000	
In stock room, total...			2,275,000				494,000				312,000	
Total.............	600	16	3,359,000	75	750	20	730,000	16	2,350	64	403,000	9
Weekly usage..........			350,000				63,000				14,000	
Weeks of usage........			9.7				11.6				28.8	
Finished-goods:												
In warehouse.........	95	11	5,168,000	80	130	15	980,000	15	625	74	320,000	5
Weekly usage..........			385,000				75,000				15,000	
Weeks of usage........			13.5				13.0				21.4	
Total.............	1,225	18	10,043,000	77	1,420	21	1,975,000	15	4,245	61	1,045,000	8

TABLE 2 (Continued)

Inventory	Inventory ordered for stock, total		As required inventory				Total inventory			Annual cost of sales or usage, $	Turn-over
	Items	Value, $	Items	Percent	Value, $	Percent	Items	Value, $	Percent of total		
Raw-material:											
In stock room........	900	1,105,000	100	10	95,000	8	1,000	1,200,000	8.6	5,050,000	4.2
Weekly usage........		95,000			10,000			105,000			
Weeks of usage......		11.7			9.5			11.5			
Purchased-parts:											
In stock room........	1,440	998,000	650	31	85,000	8	2,090	1,083,000	7.8	5,750,000	5.3
Weekly usage........		108,000			12,000			120,000			
Weeks of usage......		9.3			7.1			9.1			
Work-in-process:											
In production, total.....		1,411,000			630,000			2,041,000			
In stock room, total.....		3,081,000			47,000			3,128,000			
Total.............	3,700	4,492,000	5,250	59	677,000	13	8,950	5,169,000	37.1	26,000,000	5.0
Weekly usage.......		427,000			113,000			540,000			
Weeks of usage.....		10.5			6.0			9.6			
Finished-goods:											
In warehouse.........	850	6,468,000	0	0	0		850	6,468,000	46.5	22,750,000	3.5
Weekly usage........		475,000						475,000			
Weeks of usage......		13.6						13.6			
Total..........	6,890	13,063,000	6,000	47	857,000	6	12,890	13,920,000	100.0	26,000,000	1.9

capital). Thus, they feel that inventories should be maintained at a minimum in order to increase capital turnover.

Those connected with production have still another point of view. They would like long production runs with a minimum number of setups. Therefore, production people consider inventories as a means for obtaining an efficient plant operation.

From this discussion, it appears that inventories should be planned so that good customer service is achieved, the inventory investment is kept at a minimum, and the most efficient plant operation results. It is apparent, however, that these are opposing objectives. This means that inventories must be planned according to what is best for the company, rather than what is best for a particular department.

The inherent dangers in planning inventories by an intuitive approach should also be emphasized. As the word "intuitive" implies, the company using this method tries to gain a quick and ready insight into the problem based on the knowledge of the individual who is planning the inventories. However, this individual will be biased by the traditional thinking of that part of the organization to which he has belonged. Although his intentions will be good, it is doubtful that he will be looking at the problem from the proper perspective.

Inventories have a profound effect on the movement of money within an organization. A company cannot afford to plan its inventories in a haphazard manner if it expects to prosper. Neither can it afford to plan its inventories from a partisan point of view. Effective planning demands analyzing the problem as a whole.

There are basically two questions that must be answered: (1) *When* should the inventory be replenished? (2) *By how much* should the inventory be replenished? Earlier it was pointed out that there are opposing objectives that must be considered to answer these questions. Therefore, it is not surprising that there are opposing costs that correspond to these objectives. That is, as some costs are reduced, the costs associated with other objectives will increase. The answers to the two questions above should be such that the total cost of the inventory is a minimum. Needless to say, such an analysis must be carried out formally. It entails too many considerations to arrive at good results by an intuitive approach.

The Basic EOQ Model. The formal analysis of inventories is referred to as "scientific inventory control." The idea is to construct a mathematical model that represents the interaction of the opposing costs that are related to the inventory. The model that has received by far the most attention is the basic EOQ (economic order quantity) model, and with good reason.

The basic EOQ model has been used more than any other model. With slight modifications, it is used by nearly all companies that calculate economic order quantities. The model is an extremely simplified representation of actual inventory situations. However, in many cases the model gives good approximations to more complex models. Its simplicity also makes it relatively easy to calculate EOQs.

The basic EOQ model is used almost exclusively by authors as a foundation upon which the more complex inventory theory is built. The simplicity of the model makes it ideal for illustrating the philosophy behind inventory models. It is also important because several of the more complex models are nothing more than refinements or extensions of the basic model.

The basic EOQ model assumes that the inventory situation can be represented as in Fig. 6. It is apparent that this is quite a simplified representation of the inventory for an actual stockkeeping item. It is assumed that the demand is known and that stock is withdrawn continuously at a constant rate. It is also assumed that the inventory can be replenished instantaneously. That is, it takes zero time to replenish the stock. A third assumption is that the inventory is replenished when the stock on hand drops to zero. No stock outs or back orders are allowed to occur. The inventory is replenished by the same amount, q, each time. Since the saw-tooth inventory pattern has been assumed, the average inventory on hand will be $q/2$. Therefore, the average inventory depends directly on the order quantity.

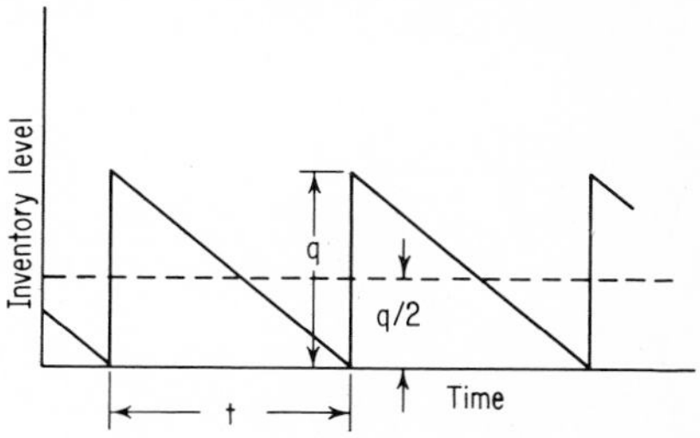

Notice in the figure that there is a relationship between the order quantity and the time between replenishments. The order quantity q is equal to the demand rate D times the replenishment

Fig. 6   The inventory pattern.

cycle t. That is, $q = tD$. Hence, the size of the order affects the number of times that the inventory must be replenished.

The effect of varying the size of the order quantity can be seen by considering Fig. 7. If the order quantity is cut to one-third of the original quantity, the average inventory is only one-third as large. At the same time the replenishment cycle is only one third as long, and hence, the inventory must be replenished three times as often. The same idea can be extended for reducing the quantity by any fraction.

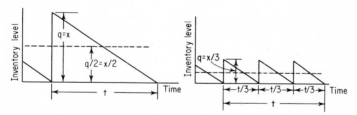

Fig. 7   Effect of order-quantity size.

To determine the best order quantity, the costs that are associated with the stockkeeping item must be considered. These costs may be placed in three broad categories according to their effect on the size of the order quantity:

1. Costs that tend to increase the order quantity
2. Costs that tend to decrease the order quantity
3. Costs that have no effect on the order quantity

The first group of costs are those connected with the replenishment of the inventory. Suppose that it costs R dollars to replenish the inventory one time. The number of times it must be replenished is equal to the demand D divided by the order quantity q. Therefore, in general, the cost of replenishing the inventory every year is $R \times D/q$. An increase in the order quantity decreases the number of times the inventory must be replenished. Therefore, the cost of replenishing the inventory is also reduced by using larger order quantities. This can be seen from Fig. 8.

Those costs that tend to decrease the order quantity are associated with holding the inventory in stock. Included in this group are:

1. Cost of obsolescence
2. Cost of depreciation
3. Taxes
4. Insurance
5. Interest on capital invested
6. Cost of storage facilities
7. Handling costs

These cost elements are referred to compositely as the "inventory carrying charge." Typical values in application tend to fall somewhere between 15 and 35 percent. However, this need not be true in every case. Each company

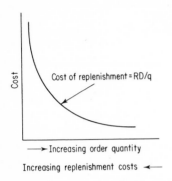

Fig. 8   The cost of replenishment.

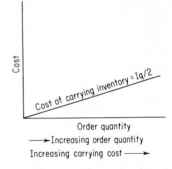

Fig. 9   The cost of carrying inventory.

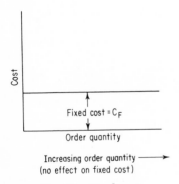

Fig. 10   Fixed cost.

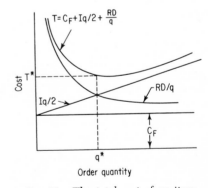

Fig. 11   The total cost of an item.

should establish its own estimate for the inventory carrying charge and should not use handbook values.

Suppose that the cost of holding one unit of an item per time period is I. The cost of carrying the item in inventory will be I times the average inventory, which was seen to be $q/2$. The fact that the cost of carrying inventory tends to decrease the order quantity can be seen from Fig. 9.

The third group of cost elements has no direct bearing on the size of the order quantity and is referred to as "fixed costs." These costs are shown graphically in Fig. 10.

All the costs can now be added together to obtain the total cost for the stockkeeping item. The result is shown in Fig. 11. The graph of the costs for a stockkeeping item will always have this same general appearance regardless of the value of the parameters.

The original object of developing the model was to obtain that order quantity which minimizes the total cost for a stockkeeping item. Therefore, from Fig. 11, the optimum order quantity q^*, is chosen that corresponds to the minimum total cost T^*.

Several conclusions can be drawn from this figure:

1. The optimum order quantity q^* will be the same regardless of the value for the fixed cost. The only effect the fixed cost has is that it raises or lowers the base upon which the variable costs are added.

2. The optimum order quantity q^* occurs when the cost of carrying inventory is equal to the replenishment cost; that is, when $Iq^*/2 = RD/q^*$.

3. The curve for the total cost is relatively flat near the optimum order quantity. Thus, there can be some error in the order quantity without significantly affecting the total cost.

From the first conclusion, it is evident that only the replenishment cost and the cost of carrying inventory need be considered to determine the optimum order quantity.

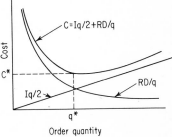

Fig. 12 The total variable cost.

Therefore, the problem can be reduced to that shown in Fig. 12. From the second conclusion, the optimum order quantity can be found analytically. Since q^* occurs when $Iq^*/2 = RD/q^*$,

$$q^* = \sqrt{\frac{2RD}{I}}$$

It can be seen from the figure that q^* does in fact give a minimum cost.

The relationship between the minimum variable cost C^* and the optimum order quantity q^* can also be determined from the second conclusion. From Fig. 11, the variable cost is

$$C = \frac{Iq}{2} + \frac{RD}{q}$$

The minimum cost can be found by substituting q^* into the cost equation:

$$C^* = \frac{Iq^*}{2} + \frac{RD}{q^*}$$

However, the second conclusion says that $Iq^*/2 = RD/q^*$. Therefore

$$C^* = \frac{Iq^*}{2} + \frac{Iq^*}{2}$$

or

$$C^* = Iq^*$$

This says that the minimum variable cost is directly proportional to the optimum order quantity, and further, the constant of proportionality is simply the inventory carrying charge.

This result can be extended to solve for C^* directly.

$$C^* = Iq^*$$

but

$$q^* = \sqrt{\frac{2RD}{I}}$$

Hence

$$C^* = I\sqrt{\frac{2RD}{I}} = \sqrt{2RDI}$$

For those who are more comfortable with more rigorous mathematical approaches, the following development is extended. The total variable cost for a stockkeeping item has been shown to be

$$C = \frac{Iq}{2} + \frac{SD}{q}$$

The calculus can be used to determine the order quantity as follows. Take the first derivative of C with respect to q and set it equal to zero.

$$\frac{dC}{dq} = \frac{I}{2} - \frac{RD}{q^2} = 0$$

Then

$$\frac{I}{2} = \frac{RD}{q^2}$$

$$q^2 = \frac{2RD}{I}$$

and

$$q^* = \sqrt{\frac{2RD}{I}}$$

which is the same result obtained before.

This can then be substituted into the cost equation to obtain the minimum variable cost:

$$C^* = \frac{I}{2}\sqrt{\frac{2RD}{I}} + \frac{RD}{\sqrt{2RD/I}}$$

$$= \sqrt{\frac{RDI}{2}} + \sqrt{\frac{RDI}{2}}$$

$$= 2\sqrt{\frac{RDI}{2}} = \sqrt{2RDI}$$

Again the result is the same as obtained before. The proportionality of C^* and q^* can also be shown by

$$\frac{C^*}{q^*} = \frac{\sqrt{2RDI}}{\sqrt{2RD/I}} = I$$

or

$$C^* = Iq^*$$

To be mathematically complete, the second derivative should be taken to be sure that C^* is in fact a minimum and not a maximum. Doing this,

$$\frac{d^2C}{dq^2} = \frac{2RD}{q^3}$$

This is positive, and hence, C^* is a minimum.

Equations have been developed here to calculate both the optimum order quantity and the total variable cost for a stockkeeping item. Thus, the question of *how much* has been answered. It remains to determine *when* an order should be placed.

To do this, consider again the assumed inventory pattern in Fig. 13. According to the assumptions of the model, the inventory is to be replenished at exactly the time when the stock is depleted. Since it takes time to replenish the inventory, the order must be placed ahead of this time.

The time from when it is realized that the inventory must be replenished until the stock is added to the inventory is called the "lead time." The lead time is made up of such activities as processing the order, setting up for the production run, and manufacturing the item. The lead time is shown as T.

The lead time must now be expressed in terms of the inventory level, since this is the information that appears in the inventory records. The inventory level at which an order should be placed is referred to as the "reorder point." The reorder point is determined by multiplying the lead time T by the demand rate D. The reorder point is shown as L. An order is placed when the inventory level drops to L.

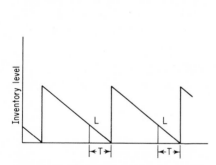

Fig. 13 Lead time and reorder point.   **Fig. 14** Effect of error on the variable cost.

So far, it has been assumed that the demand, the inventory carrying charge, and the replenishment cost can be estimated exactly. This is not true in practice. Therefore, it is important to understand the sensitivity of the model. It was noted that the cost curve in Fig. 12 is relatively flat at the bottom. This indicates that some error can be made in determining the optimum order quantity without significantly affecting the cost.

This conclusion can be extended. Suppose that the order quantity found is in error by 100 p percent. That is, suppose the optimum order quantity is determined to be $(1 + p)q^*$. The effect that this error has on the variable cost can be determined from Fig. 14.

1. Find p on the bottom scale.
2. Move vertically up the curve.
3. Move horizontally from the curve to the vertical axis.
4. Read the effect on the variable cost from the vertical axis.

It also happens that the variable cost is equally sensitive to the demand, the inventory carrying charge, or the replenishment cost. The effect of an error in one of these parameters can also be found from the figure. Suppose that a parameter is in error by 100 $\bar{p}$ percent. Find $\bar{p}$ on the top scale and the effect can be read from the vertical axis.

Manufacturing versus Buying. Although purchased inventories and manufactured inventories present entirely different problems from an operating point of view, both can be represented by the basic EOQ model. The only difference comes when the cost elements are determined for the replenishment cost.

In the first case, the replenishment cost is composed of the variable costs connected with placing and receiving an order, and it is generally referred to as the "procurement cost." For the case of manufactured inventories, the replenishment cost is made up of the variable cost elements associated with setting up for a production run, and it is usually referred to as the "setup cost."

Methods for Determining the Order Quantity. In computer applications of the basic EOQ model, the square-root equation, $q^* = \sqrt{2RD/I}$, is usually solved directly. There are situations, however, when limited computer memory can be a problem. In this case, one possibility of reducing the storage requirements is to group the items according to their replenishment costs. Then an average replenishment cost $\bar{R}$ can be used to calculate the order quantity for all items in a group. This eliminates the need for storing the replenishment cost for each item.

This method should be used only when it is absolutely necessary, because accuracy is lost. When using this method, extreme care should be taken when establishing the range of replenishment costs that should be included in a given group. Appropriate ranges and the effect on the variable cost can be determined by Fig. 14.

In manual applications, the square-root equation can be solved directly; but if the number of stockkeeping items carried in inventory is large, the task becomes quite burdensome. For this reason many companies use tables, graphs, nomographs, or special slide rules.

TABLE 3   Typical Order-quantity Table
R = \$6.40, I = 0.20.

Annual usage, dollars, D	Order, dollars, q^*	Annual usage, dollars, D	Order, dollars, q^*
10	26	2,500	400
25	40	5,000	566
50	57	7,500	689
75	70	10,000	800
100	80	25,000	1,260
250	126	50,000	1,790
500	179	75,000	2,190
750	219	100,000	2,530
1,000	253		

SOURCE: W. Evert Welch, *Tested Scientific Inventory Control*, Management Publishing Corp., Greenwich, Conn., 1959.

TABLES FOR INVENTORY DECISIONS: Tables work best for families of stockkeeping items that have only one parameter that varies. For example, suppose a group of items has the same inventory carrying charge I and the same replenishment cost R. That is, only the demand rate D varies. An example is shown in Table 3. Tables can also be used when more than one parameter varies, by making separate columns for different values of the second parameter. Suppose that only I is the same for all items and R and D both vary. This situation requires a table such as Table 4.

TABLE 4   Typical Order-quantity Table
I = 0.20

Annual usage, dollars, D	Order quantity, dollars		
	R = \$6.40	R = \$10.00	R = \$16.70
10	26	32	41
25	40	50	65
50	57	71	92
75	70	87	112
100	80	100	129
250	126	158	204
500	179	224	289
750	219	274	354
1,000	253	316	408
2,500	400	500	646
5,000	566	707	914
7,500	689	866	1,120
10,000	800	1,000	1,290
25,000	1,260	1,580	2,040
50,000	1,790	2,240	2,890
75,000	2,190	2,740	3,540
100,000	2,530	3,160	4,080

SOURCE: W. Evert Welch, *Tested Scientific Inventory Control*, Management Publishing Corp., Greenwich, Conn., 1959.

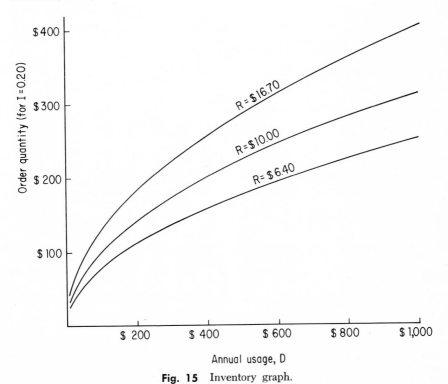

Fig. 15 Inventory graph.

GRAPHS FOR INVENTORY DECISIONS: The same information can be represented more compactly on a graph than in a table. Graphs have another advantage over tables in that the need to interpolate between values in the table is eliminated. As shown in Fig. 15, the lines on the graph are not straight. If the information is plotted on log-log paper, the lines will be straight. Choosing between the use of graphs plotted on coordinate paper and graphs plotted on log-log paper is simply a matter of preference.

NOMOGRAPHS FOR INVENTORY DECISIONS: Another popular method of solving the equation is by the use of nomographs. They are particularly useful where the ranges of the parameters make tables or graphs impractical and cumbersome. It is also possible to have the nomographs printed on the backs of the production order or other documents so that the calculation of the order quantity becomes a part of the permanent records.

A typical nomograph used to solve for economic order quantities is shown in Fig. 16. To illustrate its use, the nomograph has been used to solve for

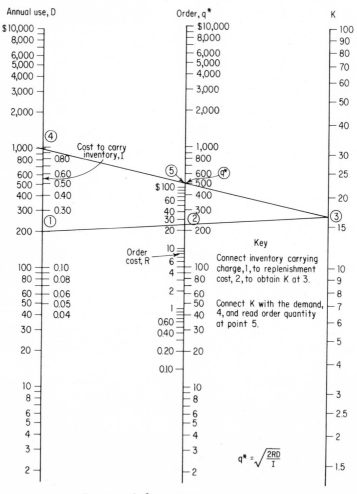

Fig. 16 Order-quantity nomograph.

the EOQ of an item having the following parameters: $R = \$25$, $D = \$100$, and $I = 0.20$. The order quantity for the item is $500.

SLIDE RULES FOR INVENTORY DECISIONS: Special slide rules for solving the square-root equations are also available commercially. Such a device is shown in Fig. 17. With perhaps some slight variations, the above procedures indicate what is available in order to reduce the mechanical difficulties of obtaining order quantities.

Practical Considerations. The basic EOQ model is a fairly simplified representation of real-world inventories. Therefore, difficulties may be encountered in applying the model. Methods of correcting such problems are discussed in other chapters of the handbook. The purpose here is to become aware of possible difficulties and to realize their significance.

THE EFFECT OF VARIABILITY: The basic EOQ model has been discussed thus far as if the demand and lead time were known exactly. In practice, one

Fig. 17 Slide rule. (*Courtesy of Van De Mark, Inc.*)

or even both of these may vary significantly. When this is the case corrections must be made or customer service can suffer drastically.

First consider the case where demand is not known with certainty. Such an inventory pattern is illustrated in Fig. 18. When the demand rate is known, an order can be placed when the inventory level is at L, and the inventory will be replenished by the time it is depleted. Now suppose the demand cannot be predicted exactly and L is found by using an average demand. This means that half of the time the demand will be greater than has been planned and a *stock out* will occur, as shown.

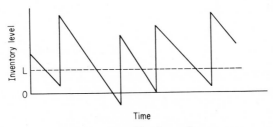

Fig. 18 Variable demand rate.

In order to correct for this, management must establish a service factor. That is, it must specify the number of times it is willing to be out of stock. Then statistical methods can be used to adjust the reorder point L so that the service level is maintained.

The same problem, stock outs, can occur if the lead time is subject to variation. Even when the demand is known, if the lead time is longer than expected, the inventory will not be replenished in time to avoid a stock out.

Another way of looking at the problem is to consider the equation for the reorder point. Recall that

$$L = DT$$

where L = reorder point
D = demand rate
T = lead time

The reorder point is determined so that the inventory is replenished just as it is depleted. However, suppose L has been calculated for a demand of D when in fact the demand turns out to be D', which is greater than D. The reorder point should have been $L = D'T$, and hence, will not be large enough to prevent a stock out. The same reasoning can be extended to explain the effect of variability in the lead time. Therefore, if good customer service is to be maintained, corrections will have to be made where this variability is appreciable.

FINITE PRODUCTION RATES: The basic EOQ model assumes an instantaneous replenishment rate. However, this is not actually the case in practice. It takes time to produce parts, move them into storage, etc. A better approximation of the actual case is shown in Fig. 19. In the figure, the replenishment rate is shown to be P, and the demand rate is D. Since stock is being added to and taken from the inventory at the same time, the net effect is that the inventory level increases at a rate of $(P - D)$ while it is being replenished.

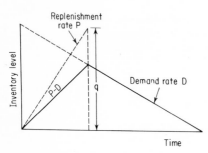

Fig. 19   Finite production rate.

If the replenishment rate is relatively large, the situation approaches that of the basic EOQ model. However, as the replenishment rate becomes smaller, the variable cost can be affected significantly and the order quantity should be adjusted accordingly. As a rule of thumb, if the ratio $D/P \leq \frac{1}{3}$, the effect can be neglected. If, however, $D/P > \frac{1}{3}$, the optimum order quantity should be adjusted. In this case the order quantity becomes

$$\text{Optimum order quantity} = \frac{1}{\sqrt{1 - D/P}} q^* = \frac{1}{\sqrt{1 - D/P}} \sqrt{\frac{2RD}{I}}$$

PRICE DISCOUNTS: The basic EOQ model assumes that the cost per unit for a stockkeeping item remains constant. It does not account for the possibility of price discounts. If it were known in advance what price range the order quantity would fall into, that cost could be used in the equation and all would be well. However, there is no easy way to obtain the appropriate price range a priori. Since the price per unit will have an effect on the order quantity, additional calculations must be made to arrive at the best answer.

UNWANTED INCREASES IN INVENTORY INVESTMENTS Another problem that may be encountered is an unwanted increase in the inventory investment. There are two reasons why such an increase can occur when the basic EOQ model is used.

1. There may be too much error in the estimates of the demand, the inventory carrying charge, and/or the replenishment cost. Naturally, such errors will affect the order quantities, and if the errors are large enough, the order quantities may be unreasonable.

2. Another possibility is that the estimates are correct, but the company is not in a financial position to carry out the "optimum" policy indicated by the equations. The model does not consider the financial condition of the com-

pany. Also, when the model is used, the order quantity is determined for each stockkeeping item as if it were completely independent of the other items in the inventory. The model gives no consideration to the aggregate results.

If there is an indication that the model will cause large, undesirable increases in the inventory, it may be necessary to incorporate techniques that give consideration to the aggregate results.

CHOOSING, TESTING, AND USING A MODEL: The basic EOQ model is the most explored model, but it is not the only one available by any means. The literature abounds with models that have been proposed to solve inventory problems; and, of course, it is entirely possible to construct an original model. In choosing, developing, or refining a model, there is a prime requisite that should not be lost sight of: *The model must be justified economically.*

Remember that the more elaborate a model is, the more time and money will be required to calculate the order quantities and the reorder points. It does not make sense economically to spend additional money refining the model and calculating order quantities if that money cannot be returned in cost savings.

The model that is proposed for use should also be tested. Regardless of how much care has been expended in formulating or choosing the model, there is still a chance that it will not yield "workable" order quantities. The time to find out that a model will not work is *before* large amounts of time and money have been spent installing it.

There is another important point regarding the use of inventory models: *The model is not the decision maker; it is an aid to the decision maker.* A practical model cannot be constructed that will handle all the peculiar situations that may occur. There will be times when the model does not come up with the right answers. The inventory system should have *management by exception* built into it.

Inventory models can be a great asset to management and can result in substantial savings. However, models must not be used blindly. Management should understand the model and its weaknesses thoroughly before putting it into practice.

SUMMARY

The primary objective of this chapter has been to outline certain basic inventory concepts which are necessary for a successful inventory program.

The reasons for the existence of inventories and their importance to the company and the national economy are discussed. Examples are used to explain how to calculate an EOQ along with the logic behind the EOQ models. The ABC inventory system is also included in this chapter.

Some elementary inventory record-keeping ideas are included in this chapter. Classifying inventories for better control through the use of simplication, standardization, and coding is a subject which is also extensively covered.

Also considered in this chapter are the principles and procedures which should be followed to satisfactorily conduct an annual physical inventory.

A secondary objective of this chapter has been to serve as a prelude to more sophisticated inventory techniques to be found in the following chapters.

BIBLIOGRAPHY

Biegel, John E.: *Production Control: A Quantitative Approach,* Prentice-Hall, Inc., Englewood Cliffs, 1963.

Brown, Robert G.: *Decision Rules for Inventory Management,* Holt, Rinehart and Winston, Inc., New York, 1967.

Buffa, Elwood Spencer: *Production Inventory Systems,* Richard D. Irwin, Inc., Homewood, Ill., 1968.

Carroll, Phil: *Practical Production and Inventory Control,* McGraw-Hill Book Company, New York, 1966.

D'Anna, John P.: *Inventory and Profit,* American Management Association, New York, 1966.

Eilon, Samuel: *Elements of Production Planning and Control,* The Macmillan Company, New York, 1962.

Greene, James H.: *Production Control: Systems and Decisions,* Richard D. Irwin, Inc., Homewood, Ill., 1965.

Imperial Chemical Industries, *Techniques of Production Control,* D. Van Nostrand Company, Inc., Princeton, N.J., 1966.

Naddor, Eliezer: *Inventory Systems,* John Wiley & Sons, Inc., New York, 1966.

Parton, James Allan: *Production Control Manual,* Conover-Mast Publications, Chris P. Steres, New York, 1955.

Plossl, G., and W. O. Wight: *Production and Inventory Control,* Prentice-Hall, Inc., Englewood Cliffs, N.J., 1967.

Prichard, James W.: *Modern Inventory Management,* John Wiley & Sons, Inc., New York, 1965.

Rago, Louis J.: *Production Analysis and Control,* International Textbook Company, Scranton, Pa., 1963.

Scheele, Evan D., William L. Westerman, and Robert J. Wimmert: *Principles and Design of Production Control Systems,* Prentice-Hall, Inc., Engelwood Cliffs, N.J., 1960.

Stockton, Robert S.: *Basic Inventory Systems,* Allyn and Bacon, Inc., Boston, 1965.

Van de Mark, Robert L.: *Inventory Control Techniques,* Jensen-Townsend Printing Company, Port Huron, Mich., 1964.

———: *Production Control Techniques,* Gilson Press, Grand Rapids, Mich., 1964.

Voris, William: *Production Control: Text and Cases,* Richard D. Irwin, Inc., Homewood, Ill., 1956.

Welch, W. Evert: *Tested Scientific Inventory Control,* Management Publishing Corporation, Greenwich, Conn., 1959.

Chapter 15

Physical Control of Inventories

COEDITORS:

John R. Mason   *Lybrand, Ross Bros. & Montgomery, New York, New York*

Walter H. Warrick   *Associate Professor, Operations Management, Northwestern University, Evanston, Illinois*

Management Research & Planning, Inc. Staff   *Evanston, Illinois*

CONTRIBUTORS:

W. J. Jones   *Dodge Manufacturing Company, Mishawaka, Indiana*

C. Raymond Kenyon   *Assistant Vice President, Lion Knitting Mills Company, Cleveland, Ohio*

Stanley Larson   *Inventory Control and Systems, Cessna Aircraft Co., Wichita, Kansas*

CONTENTS

Investment in physical inventories often represents a substantial portion of the total current assets of a company. Therefore, it is a primary responsibility of management to establish a means for safeguarding the physical inventories of the company. Physical control over inventories is normally vested in the storekeeping function, frequently a part of the production control organization. Responsibilities assigned to storekeeping normally include:

1. Receiving and holding all materials and supplies for safekeeping and protection until needed

2. Furnishing, as authorized, materials and supplies to other departments and to agencies outside the company

3. Maintaining accurate storeroom records

4. Controlling in-process material to be used in subsequent production operations

5. Planning the layout of stores areas and the efficient utilization of stores equipment

6. Maintaining the stores areas in a neat and orderly manner

7. Taking physical inventories of materials and supplies within the stores areas

Regardless of the location of the storekeeping activity within the company plan of organization, certain basic principles of operation must be adhered to if acceptable controls over physical inventories are to be achieved. This chapter, therefore, describes the activities that are necessary for maintaining physical controls over inventories and for their accomplishment in an efficient and effective manner.

The physical controls over inventories outlined in this chapter are primarily directed at storerooms operated in conjunction with manufacturing operations and normally under the control of the manufacturing function. It is recognized that in some industries field warehouses are operated by the company as part of their total distribution system. Field warehouses are frequently operated apart from the manufacturing function and may report directly to the sales or service department. Regardless of the physical location of the field warehouse and organizational relationship, the same basic principles of operation and control outlined in this chapter apply as for any other storeroom.

SECURITY

The security requirements vary widely within companies and are dependent upon the nature of the material, its value, weight, size, application, and resaleability. As a rule of thumb, the more valuable a commodity, the greater the need for security, although there are exceptions to this. Items of low value that can be used for home or personal use require additional controls, while relatively expensive items such as raw gray iron castings require little or no protection because of their size, weight, and limited utility.

A company can take preventive measures to safeguard inventories by establishing and enforcing storeroom regulations and by periodically auditing the storeroom operation. The following measures apply to storeroom operations.

1. Prohibit general access to stores areas.
2. Keep storerooms locked except during normal working hours.
3. Count, weigh, or measure all receipts of incoming material, and check carefully against purchase orders or other documents (at point of receipt).
4. Independently check material *entering storerooms* for quantity, condition, and identification.
5. Require requisitions for all material requested from stores.
6. Keep valuable articles in locked cabinets, or in a safe if necessary.

The following measures provide additional protection for inventories of the company.

1. Periodically spot-check inventories on hand against inventory records.
2. Review inventory procedures to ascertain that the system complies with policy and method of operation.
3. Investigate unusual consumption for improper usage, unauthorized usage, or possibly theft.
4. Periodically check requisitions for authenticity of signatures and for alterations.
5. Provide security bonds for storeroom personnel to protect the company against losses through negligence and theft.

Many companies have an internal audit function which provides for the periodic auditing of inventories. Inventory items to be audited are selected independently and at random. A count of the inventory on hand is made for each item selected, and the count is compared against the balance of the inventory records. Another informal method is to check the balance on hand of the inventory records for each stores item when a very low or stock-out condition exists. Discrepancies between physical balances and inventory records can be investigated and the records reconciled. Constant adjustment to the inventory records is a cause for further investigation of systems and procedures and for improvement of security regulations and practices.

Most companies, as a matter of company policy, carry some form of indemnity insurance which protects the company against loss through improper or careless acts on the part of its employees. It is not unusual to have the chief storekeeper included among the "bonded" employees of a company.

ORGANIZATION AND
ADMINISTRATIVE CONTROLS

Industry has been moving toward a total-materials management concept in which one person is responsible for the level and flow of material into and through the productive process. The objective is to reduce the total investment in inventory. This section is concerned with the management of and control over physical inventories within the plant, not with the basic production planning and control system itself.

Figure 1 is representative of a typical manufacturing organization with production control having direct control over in-plant inventories. The double-lined boxes indicate the three areas that have direct responsibility for physical control over the inventories. These functions are:

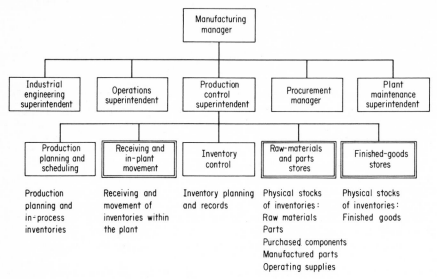

Fig. 1   Organization for control of inventories.

1. *Receiving and in-plant movement,* to receive and record all incoming materials and to transport incoming materials to the proper stores area. To transport authorized materials and parts releases from stores, to move work-in-process materials between operations as designated, and to deliver finished goods to finished-goods stores.

2. *Raw materials and parts stores,* to store and protect parts, supplies, and materials in an efficient manner until they are needed, and then to release only those items and in quantities that are authorized and approved.

3. *Finished-goods stores,* to receive and store finished goods efficiently, to safeguard the material while in stores, and to release goods on hand against approved sales orders and authorized material transfers.

A few companies divide the responsibility for inventories. Occasionally materials control may be placed under the purchasing agent or even the controller. Likewise, finished goods may be found under the control of the sales division. Normally, there are peculiar circumstances that lead to these conditions, such as the need to coordinate purchasing of bulk materials with storage facilities, the policy of buying materials based upon market conditions rather than current requirements, or the need to exercise closer controls over the allocation and location of finished goods to meet customer demands. Each company must adopt the organizational alignment that will produce the most efficient operation. Thus, many companies have found that it is far more logical to have the responsibility and control of inventories centered in one place, *manufacturing,* under the head of production control. While some authorities feel that this plan of organization vests too much authority in the manufacturing function, a balance between inventory requirements and inventory levels can be established through administrative control procedures and timely evaluations of operations by the controller's office.

Administrative control over actual inventories is primarily a question of recognizing the stores function as the guardian of company materials and establishing formal systems and procedures to control the flow of materials to and from stores and through the productive process. *A cardinal principle for controlling physical inventories is that no material is accepted, issued, or moved without an accompanying authorization.* Thus material can be controlled throughout the production cycle from its entry into the plant as raw material until its shipment as an end product.

Administratively, materials are frequently grouped according to their type, use, or condition. The same groupings are used for accounting purposes as well as physical storing and handling. The following are commonly designated inventory groups or categories:

1. *Raw materials* include items that are purchased and converted by processing into finished or component parts. Common items included in this category are forgings, castings, sheet stock, bar stock, tubing, ingot, bulk materials, and chemicals.

2. *Component parts* include items that are either purchased or manufactured from raw material and stored for use in assemblies or for sale to customers as repair or replacement parts. (Note: Parts may be held in component-parts stores and still require further processing or finishing at final assembly.)

3. *Supplies* are expense items or nonproductive materials. They are used to support productive operations but do not normally enter or become part of the end product. They include coolants, lubricants, cleaning materials, repair parts for equipment, maintenance materials, and processing supplies.

4. *Work in process* includes all materials that are in the process of being fabricated from raw material or assembled into finished products. Items in process but temporarily held between operations are included. Parts that have been processed and sent to storerooms for further processing or assembly are considered component parts.

5. *Finished goods* are complete units and assemblies carried in stock ready for delivery to customers or for transfer to other plants. Generally, they are items that have been produced by the company, although they may include complete items purchased for resale.

Some companies do not segregate raw materials. This is particularly true of process industries and automobile-assembly plants. In these cases the time interval between the receipt of raw material and shipment of the finished product is limited, and all direct material is considered to be "in process."

Industrial operations must be planned and controlled to be efficient. Likewise control over materials requires an adequate and systematic procedure if efficient and reliable service is to be rendered to production. Therefore, a knowledge of the basic concept of materials flow and the principles and practices for materials control is essential for a successful operation. The development and definition of the complete materials control system assures administrative control over the movement, level, and consumption of inventories.

A TYPICAL SYSTEM

Sound inventory management dictates that controls be maintained over all categories of inventories from the time they enter the plant until they are shipped. A total inventory control system provides for:

Analyzing and planning inventory requirements

Procuring needed raw materials and component parts to schedule in the amounts required

Receiving and recording the receipt of purchased materials

Providing adequate facilities to store purchased materials and manufactured components

Maintaining accurate records of inventories on hand and on order

Installing realistic controls over materials in stores and over the issuance of materials, parts, and supplies

Simply stated, good inventory management provides the proper quantity and quality of material at the right time and place, and maintains accurate records and physical control over the materials used in the production process. The flow diagram in Fig. 2 shows the flow of material and the control documents

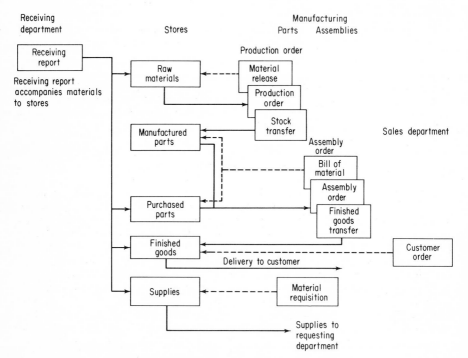

Fig. 2 Typical control system for inventories.

in a typical production and inventory control system. It should be noted that every demand for material and material movement is accompanied by a corresponding control document which authorizes the release of a specified quantity of material, describes the operations to be performed, and indicates the destination of processed material and assemblies. Thus, inventories are controlled from the time they are received in the plant, throughout the production process, and until they are shipped to a customer or transferred to another plant or division of a company.

A typical inventory control system starts to .function when sales forecasts and/or customers orders are released by the sales department. Inventory control systems must be tailored to conform to the sales policies of the particular company for which they are designed.   These policies are frequently based upon the characteristics of the products produced.   In some companies, inventory planning is based either upon sales forecasts or upon incoming customer orders. However, in most companies, inventory planning is based upon a combination of the two.   As shown in Fig. 3, there is a sequential flow of events following the release of sales forecasts and customer orders by the sales department.

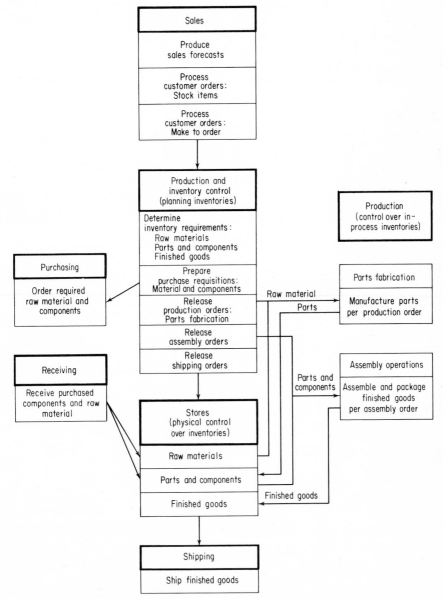

Fig. 3   A typical production and inventory control system.

While the actual inventory control methods and practices applied and the organization of functional activities may vary somewhat within individual companies, the basic inventory control concept is universal. In other words, inventories must be planned and controlled if a plant is to produce efficiently. The activities outlined are basic to sound inventory management and are integral components of a typical inventory control system. Table 1 clearly shows that the inventory

TABLE 1   Inventory Planning and Controls

Inventory control activity	Control documents	Control exercised
1. Planning. Based upon sales forecasts and/or customer orders, determine inventory requirements and initiate actions to obtain proper quantities of: Purchased material	Purchase requisitions	Authorizes the amount of material to be purchased and establishes the delivery date.
Manufactured parts and components	Production orders	Establishes the quantity and production schedules for parts and components to be manufactured.
Finished goods and assemblies	Assembly orders	Establishes the quantity and schedules for assemblies and packaged units.
2. Record keeping. Maintain accurate inventory records of physical and/or available quantities of: Raw materials and purchased components	Receiving reports	Confirms the amount of material received and delivered to stores.
	Material requisitions	Confirms the amount of material issued by stores to each production order.
Manufactured parts and components	Completed production orders	Confirms the quantity of manufactured parts and components delivered to stores.
Finished goods and assemblies	Parts lists	Confirms the amount of material issued by stores to each assembly order.
	Completed assembly orders	Confirms the number of units assembled.
	Customer orders and/or shipping orders	Confirms the number of units of finished goods shipped on each customer order:

control system can be designed to maintain complete control over all categories of inventories through a series of control documents that authorize and report the movement and location of each production inventory item, from the receipt of raw material through the shipment of finished goods. The effectiveness of a system, however, is directly related to the administration of sound operating practices and techniques.

The system described in this chapter is primarily conceptual and not oriented to a particular system, company, or industry. In selected types of operations, the system can be completely manual. In other instances, the system can be computerized as part of a total management-information system. In either case, the system can be equally effective in providing complete control over inventories.

STORAGE AND MOVEMENT OF MATERIALS

Modern-day inventory management includes the provision for storing and handling all categories of materials used in the production process. Unfortunately there is no single formula that can be applied in planning stores and materials-handling operations. Each stores operation must be carefully planned and designed to provide services and controls that are considered most desirable for the plant or company as a whole. The following factors must be considered in planning for the storage and handling of materials:

Complete information on the materials to be stored

The availability and location of space

In-plant transportation facilities

Storage procedures and controls

Storeroom equipment

Storeroom layout

All these factors should be considered, and a combination should be determined that will provide for a maximum of service with a minimum of cost. The following pages define in greater detail the considerations included in each of these factors.

Materials to Be Stored. Detailed information should be gathered about each inventory item that will be stored and moved. This information should include:

The size and weight of each item to be handled

If packaged, the quantity per standard container

The minimum and maximum quantities to be stored

The frequency of issuance and the normal quantity issued

The receiving point and the areas to which the material is delivered

Special handling requirements for storing and transporting items such as combustibles, explosives, and other dangerous or toxic materials

Unusual facilities requirements such as humidity and temperature controls, heat, light, ventilation, and security

The Availability and Location of Space. There are many considerations that must be investigated regarding the selection of space to be used for storage. Included are:

1. The size and shape of available areas related to the items to be stored

2. The location and adequacy of areas available for stores

3. The physical characteristics including allowable floor loads, ceiling heights, accessways, etc.

4. The location in relation to receiving docks, manufacturing areas serviced, and, in multiple-story buildings, elevators

5. The type of storeroom equipment that can be most effectively used

6. The compliance with building codes, fire laws, health and safety regulations, and insurance regulations

In-plant Transportation Facilities. The storage and movement of materials and parts present many problems that influence the effectiveness and costs of storeroom operations and the service that can be provided to operating departments. The following should be given consideration in planning the stores operations:

1. Facilities for loading and unloading

2. The types of materials-handling equipment suitable for moving and storing items included in the stores operation

3. The use of fork trucks and pallets in storing and moving materials

4. The need for overhead cranes and elevators

5. The use or application of mechanized or conveyorized materials-handling systems

6. The work load in terms of total materials handling and movements, and the extent of delivery services performed by stores

Storage Procedures and Controls. Methods of storing and moving materials depend upon the nature of the material. Nevertheless, the procedures used for storing materials frequently influence the actual layout of stores areas. Therefore, well-planned storage procedures are essential for an efficiently organized stores operation and will provide the following benefits:

1. Allow for efficient utilization of space
2. Permit ready accessibility to materials
3. Allow some flexibility in arrangement of inventory
4. Assist in identifying and moving older stocks
5. Provide for rapid identification of inventory items
6. Reduce the need for material-handling and storeroom equipment
7. Facilitate counting during physical inventories
8. Permit ready inspection of inventory levels and condition of stocks

Storage procedures and controls also include the use of standard or unit containers, and control methods for the issuance of materials.

UNIT CONTAINERS: A primary objective of stores operations is to minimize the handling of stores items. The most economical arrangement would be for material to pass directly from the receiving point to the place of use. However, this is not feasible in most operations, and stores act as a middleman by holding materials from the time they are received until they are required by production. To minimize these handling costs, which also include shrinkages due to handling, the use of unit packaging is widely practiced. Unit packaging consists of receiving, storing, and issuing items in standard-sized containers containing a multiple number of small parts or articles, or a standard amount of bulk materials such as drums of paint or bags of cement. Thus, materials can be delivered to the using departments in containers in which they were received. This minimizes shrinkage and eliminates the need for unpacking and measuring bulk inventories and issues. Whenever possible, stores issues should be made in standard quantities based upon the quantity per unit package and multiples thereof. Frequently material can be stored more efficiently in unit containers rather than in bulk.

CONTROL METHODS FOR ISSUING MATERIALS: Material held in stores over a period of time may deteriorate, become obsolete, or be damaged by repeated handling. Sound inventory practices dictate that as a general rule old stocks should be used first. Several practical methods that can be used are outlined below.

1. *Double-bin System.* The area or bin space allocated to an item is approximately twice the amount required for a standard lot or shipment. As each new lot is received, it is placed in the empty space and not used until the older items have been used. This system has a drawback in that the additional space required is frequently unavailable.

2. *Coupon System.* This system requires that an identifying coupon be attached to each container for each lot or shipment. The identifying coupons should indicate the time when the goods were received. This can be done by recording the date received on each item, by using a color date code, or the coupons may simply be sequentially numbered. Thus each container can be identified by lot, and the oldest lot should be used first. This system is difficult to use when large quantities are involved and all containers are not

readily visible or accessible. Some systems use serially numbered coupons for each item to control and count inventories.

3. *Gravity-feed or Sequence System.* This system is probably the easiest to administer, although it does require either special equipment such as gravity-feed storage bins or double-access bins. In either case, incoming material is sequenced behind the old stock. Thus, the old stock is removed first either from the front of the bin or from the lower end of the rack or incline. The pitch of the sloping rack depends upon the units being stored and the type of rack used. Roller racks require but a small pitch and are probably the most efficient.

Storeroom Equipment. The ability of the storeroom to render efficient and dependable services is greatly increased through the use of proper equipment and a well-planned layout. The final stores layout cannot be accomplished until the equipment requirements have been established. The equipment used in stores operations depends, to a large degree, upon the quantity and types of material carried in stores. The following list describes the types of standardized equipment that are currently used in typical storeroom operations.

1. *Steel Shelving.* Standard steel shelving has widespread use and may be purchased in a variety of forms and sizes. It is available in open and closed types, and may be reinforced for heavy loads. Examples of each type are shown in Figs. 4 and 5. The use of shelving greatly increases the capacity of available floor area.

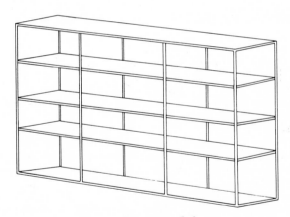

Fig. 4 Open-type shelving.

Steel shelving has many advantages, including the following:

a. It is readily available. Standard units are mass produced, carried in stock, and economical.

b. It is flexible. It can be assembled on site, disassembled, and moved as required.

c. It has multiple uses. Packaged goods, assemblies, and piece parts can be stored interchangeably. Shelving is normally movable and can be adjusted to accommodate individual items.

d. It is strong and durable as well as fire-resistant.

e. It is expandable. As need arises, additional sections can be obtained and added to the original installation.

f. It can be modified for special applications with the addition of doors, shelf dividers, etc.

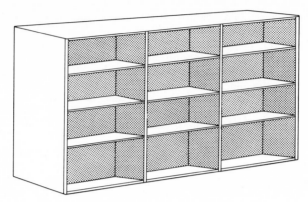

Fig. 5 Closed-type shelving—double-faced.

2. *Wood Shelving.* Wood shelving is not nearly as popular as it once was. Although it is cheap to install and can be fitted for special layouts, for most permanent installations it has been replaced by steel shelving, which is easier to maintain and has a longer service life. Unlike steel shelving, it is difficult to disassemble and move. If not treated, wood shelving may present a fire hazard.

3. *Bin Fronts and Shelf Dividers.* Bin fronts may be added to closed-type shelving (closed ends and backs) to make a series of storage boxes which will accommodate small, irregularly shaped items. These items are normally stored unpackaged and cannot be stacked.

4. *Doors.* Doors may be added to closed-bin sections. They offer additional protection against theft, dust, etc.

5. *Slide Drawers.* Slide drawers offer additional protection for small and intricate parts. For small parts, a section of slide drawers provides for greater utilization of standard shelf space.

6. *Roller Shelves.* Roller shelves were formerly used to store highly finished parts such as gears, shafts, and pinions which are subject to nicks and scratches. More recently, the practice of using protective plastic coatings on such parts has permitted the use of peg-and-hole boards in place of roller shelving. Peg-and-hole boards have further advantages as they can be used to transport items to and from stores and can be used with standard shelving.

7. *Open-type Removable Bins.* These are normally steel although there are some plastic types. They are used for small items such as nails, washers, and bolts. They are used to store unpackaged items and are readily accessible for the issue of small quantities at frequent intervals. The bins can be removed individually.

8. *Stack Boxes.* These are somewhat similar in construction to the open-type removable bins except that they are interlocking and do not need a frame or shelf for support. The stack boxes are useful in transporting and storing small parts as they can be easily carried or transported and quickly form a self-supporting stack for temporary storage. They are frequently used to carry parts between operations and to parts stores, and to deliver parts to assembly stations where they can be stacked until needed.

9. *Storage Racks—Bar Stock.* These racks are made in many varieties. Normally they are solidly built to store long lengths of materials such as bar stock, pipe, structural shapes, and lumber. There are two principal types: a Christ-

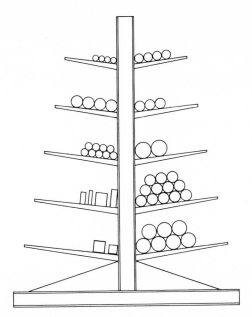

Fig. 6 Christmas-tree rack for bar stock and pipe.

mas-tree type with horizontal arms and a conventional, open-end, multiple-opening rack. The latter is generally stronger and has more capacity, while the former offers greater accessibility. Figures 6 and 7 are sketches of storage racks commonly used for bar stock, pipe, and tubing. These are generally permanent installations and are constructed to meet the specific needs of the plant. The use of bar-stock racks allows for the segregation of material by

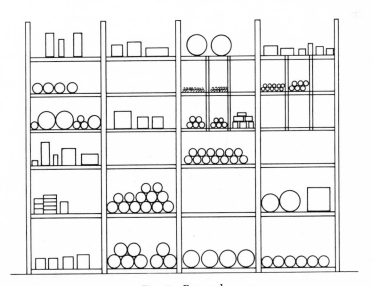

Fig. 7 Bar rack.

size and type and permits easy access for removal of stock. Similar types of storage racks can be used for coil stock.

10. *Storage Racks—Pallets.* These are heavy-duty racks and are used to store palletized loads. The pallets are positioned and removed by fork truck. The racks are of standard design and accommodate standard pallets. The horizontal members are adjustable for various pallet loads and vertical dimensions. Pallet racks are now widely used and may be obtained in standard and heavy-duty units depending upon the pallet-load specifications. The use of pallet racks allows pallets to be stored vertically to the ceiling, and any pallet can be removed at will regardless of its position. A typical pallet-rack construction and pallet arrangement is shown in Fig. 8.

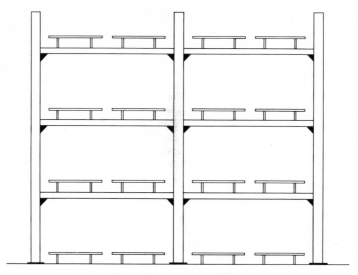

Fig. 8   Pallet racks showing pallets in position.

Pallets may be stacked vertically without pallet racks provided that there are numerous pallet loads of identical material. The use of pallet racks permits higher stacking of heavy material, is safer, and permits far more flexibility in moving pallets in and out of position.

11. *Pallets and Skids.* Pallets and skids are used almost universally to store and transport materials. They are fabricated from steel or wood although other materials are used. In addition, they come with fixed and collapsible sides, as well as many other special parts-locating, stacking, and protective features. Pallets are one of the most economical means of reducing handling and storage costs, and permit the economical utilization of space. The design and use of pallets should be coordinated with the storage facilities, internal material handing, and receiving and shipping procedures if maximum benefits are to be realized. The economics of steel versus wood or plastic pallets should be thoroughly investigated for long-term, reusable applications.

12. *Conveyors.* The movement of large quantities of materials on a regular or continuous basis may make it more efficient to use conveyors to dispatch materials to and from stores. There are many types of conveyors in use, many of which are designed for specific purposes. The types in service include overhead chain conveyors, cable conveyors, belt conveyors, roller conveyors, slat conveyors, tramrails, overhead cranes, and similar devices.

The selection of the material-handling equipment for the storeroom frequently is made in consultation with materials-handling engineers and equipment manufacturers. They can recommend the best type of material-handling and storeroom equipment to meet the needs of a particular operation.

Storeroom Layout. After all information relating to the types and quantities of stores inventories has been established, the space requirements and types of storeroom and material-handling equipment can be determined. Both these steps should be completed before the layout of the storeroom is planned. The following data are basic to the layout and should be considered in developing it:

1. The nature of the items and quantities to be stocked at any one time
2. The method of packaging or containers to be used for stored materials
3. The kind and amount of bins, shelving, and racks that are required
4. The method of storing or piling stores items
5. The method of handling materials in and out of storeroom
6. The need for special dispensing equipment and the system used to control counts
7. The frequency of demand and number of movements for individual items, and their destination
8. The location of the stores area in relation to the receiving dock, elevators, and the departments to which material is delivered
9. The need for and location of secondary or specialized stores areas such as bulk stores for chemicals, oils, castings, lumber, building materials, etc.
10. The location and method of keeping inventory records
11. Stores items requiring special handling, security, temperature and humidity controls, etc.
12. Constraints imposed on storage or handling due to industry codes, federal or state legislation, local fire or safety codes, or special insurance company requirements

As indicated earlier, it is impossible to make detailed storeroom layouts until all the particulars are known. However, there are certain basic elements that should be considered in planning the majority of stores areas. A typical layout, shown by Fig. 9, has the following features:

1. Material flow is from receiving at one end to the distributing point at the other.
2. A main center aisle controls the flow of material within the storeroom.
3. Provisions are made for outside storage of raw castings and lumber.
4. A separate, fireproof area is provided on the receiving dock for oils, paints, etc.
5. Bar stock is stored close to the receiving point where it can be cut to size upon demand.
6. Provisions have been made for various types of storage including bins, shelving, pallet racks, and palletized bulk stores.
7. Outgoing issues (small lots) are segregated for easy pickup to minimize internal traffic.
8. Each stores area has been identified for permanently assigning space to individual stores items.
9. Aisles are sufficiently wide to accommodate mechanical material-handling equipment such as lift trucks.
10. There are sufficient cross aisles to provide ready access to bins and shelf areas.
11. Unpacking is done in the receiving area, which avoids storeroom confusion and allows for disposal of unwanted packaging material.
12. Provisions are made to keep valuables or items subject to pilferage under lock and key.

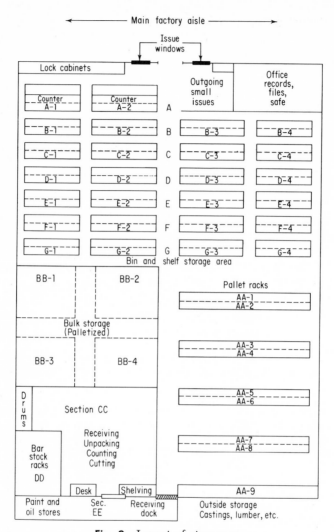

Fig. 9 Layout of storeroom.

In a layout example of this type, it is impossible to give exact dimensions. There are, however, certain guidelines that can be followed in storeroom planning.

1. Main aisles should be wide enough to permit two-way traffic. They may be as wide as 10 to 12 feet.

2. Secondary aisles leading to pallet racks must be wide enough to allow fork trucks to position loaded pallets on the racks. Aisles up to 11 feet in width are required, depending upon the mechanized equipment used.

3. Aisles between bins and shelves can be limited to one-way traffic and range in width from 3 to 5 feet.

4. The material being warehoused frequently dictates the practical height of the storage facility required depending upon its weight, bulk, and size, and the capacity of material-handling equipment.

5. Slow-moving items should be located away from main aisles to facilitate materials handling and improve the traffic pattern.

6. All items regularly stocked should be assigned regular bin or rack locations. A location file should be maintained to aid in inventory planning and to assist personnel to locate stored materials.

A well-organized stores operation includes the identification of stores areas, the assignment of suitable space to individual stores items, and the recording of the location of each stores item. In Fig. 9 the following system is used:

1. The shelf area is coded A through G starting at the front of the storeroom. It has four sections which are numbered 1 through 4 starting from the left. Thus an item located in the third row and second section would be in C-2. If desired, a further subdivision can be made for each shelf within a rack. Thus an item could be located in C-2-21, meaning the item would be found on shelf 21 in row C, section 2.

2. Palletized storage areas are assigned the designation BB, and each area within the bulk storage area is consecutively numbered as shown.

3. Pallet racks are assigned the designation AA, and each rack is consecutively numbered starting at the front.

4. Other areas have identifying codes as shown, including:

Drum storage, CC
Bar-stack racks, DD
Paint and oil stores, EE

Within each of these areas, additional coding can be used depending upon the arrangement and size of the installation. As an example, if there were 48 sections in the bar-stock racks, they could be numbered DD-1 through DD-48.

A master stock-location index should be maintained and all items stored in their regularly assigned location. A sample of a stock-location index card is shown by Fig. 10.

No attempt has been made to describe a mechanical or automated stores operation. These are special installations and must be designed to meet the needs of an individual company. Where conditions warrant it, substantial cost savings in material handling can be realized. Systems of this type must be designed and installed by materials-handling engineers and equipment manufacturers. The degree of automation or mechanization should be based upon the planned volume of material to be handled and the resultant cost savings.

STOCK LOCATION INDEX CARD			
		Location	
Part or code No.	Nomenclature	Area	Shelf or bin
A124368-1	Support bracket — LH	D-3	20
A124368-2	Support bracket — RH	D-3	22
XC124369	Casting	AA-9	
C124369	Motor support	E-1	7
C124369-1	Motor support	E-1	9
PC125370	3/4 hp motor — 220 V 60 cy.	G-3	2 & 3
PC125372	3/4 hp motor — 440 V 50 cy.	G-3	8 & 9
PC125375	3/4 hp motor — 220/440 V 50/60 cy.	G-3	10-14
A125392	Pin —	A-2	16-1
A125395	Bearing —	B-2	14

Fig. 10 Stock-location index card.

RECEIVING

The plant receiving section, frequently associated with stores, is the only means by which incoming material should enter the plant. The receiving section should have a complete file of "open" purchase orders. The purchase orders are, in turn, the authorization to accept shipments. Immediately upon receipt of material at the receiving dock, the shipping papers included with the shipment should be checked against the proper purchase order. The shipment should then be checked for type, model, condition, and quantity, and a receiving report prepared. A typical receiving report (Fig. 11) contains all the pertinent data relating to the material received. It is a multiple-copy form with the following distribution:

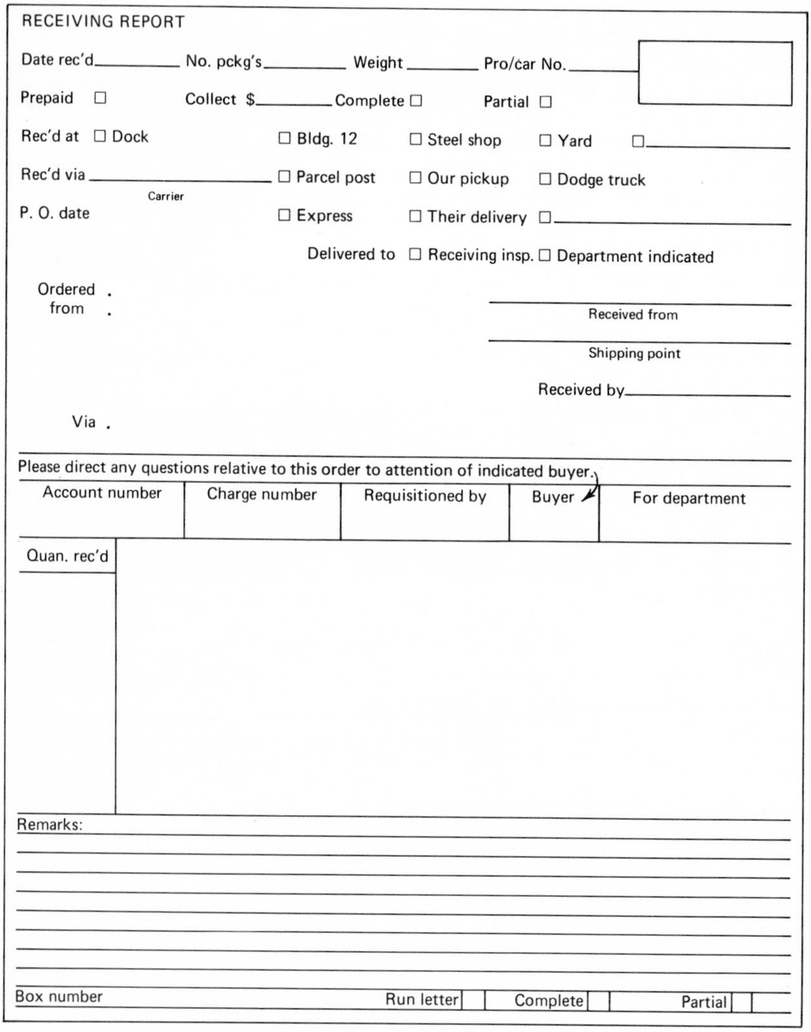
RECEIVING REPORT

Date rec'd______ No. pckg's______ Weight______ Pro/car No.______

Prepaid ☐ Collect $______ Complete ☐ Partial ☐

Rec'd at ☐ Dock ☐ Bldg. 12 ☐ Steel shop ☐ Yard ☐______

Rec'd via ______ (Carrier) ☐ Parcel post ☐ Our pickup ☐ Dodge truck

P. O. date ☐ Express ☐ Their delivery ☐______

Delivered to ☐ Receiving insp. ☐ Department indicated

Ordered from .

______ Received from

______ Shipping point

Received by______

Via .

Please direct any questions relative to this order to attention of indicated buyer.

Account number	Charge number	Requisitioned by	Buyer	For department

Quan. rec'd

Remarks:

Box number Run letter Complete Partial

Fig. 11 Receiving report.

Copy 1. *Accounting.* Used to verify the invoice for material received and to authorize payment for same. Extended value is also used to increase the inventory ledger accounts.

Copy 2. *Production Control.* Used to record receipt of material and calculate the new balance on hand on inventory records. Forwarded to purchasing department after posting to inventory records.

Copy 3. *Stores.* Accompanies material to stores area (or receiving inspection) to identify material and authorize acceptance.

Copy 4. *Receiving.* Attached to purchase order and held in open-purchase-order file until shipments are completed.

More modern systems, involving the use of punched cards with computers, are reducing the amount of manual work performed by the receiving section. Prepunched cards are filed in the receiving department, a card for each item of each purchase order. All pertinent data except the date and quantity received are prepunched. Upon receipt of a shipment, the date and quantity received are recorded on the card and whether the order is completed. The receiving information is then fed into the data processing system and disseminated as required. For partial shipments, a new card is issued showing the original

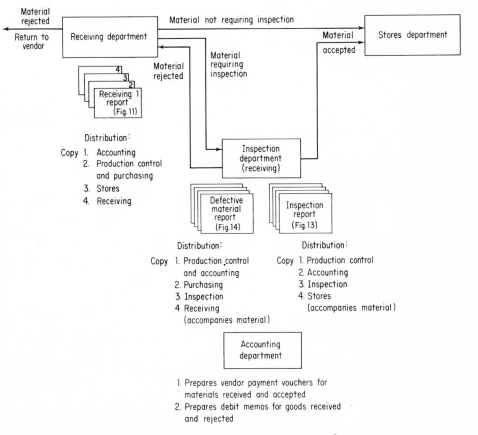

Fig. 12 Flow diagram—incoming materials.

INSPECTOR'S REPORT OF FINISHED PRODUCTS		
	Production control and accounting copy	No. M 009317
Date		
Order number	Deliver TO dept.	Commodity code
Item No.	Deliver FROM dept.	
Description		

Quantity	Cost	Unit	Extension	Received by	Inspected by

All forms must be accounted for — if spoiled, mark void and turn in to the production control department

Fig. 13 Inspector's report of finished products.

quantity ordered and the remaining balance together with all other pertinent data relating to the purchase order.

If the material received requires inspection prior to acceptance, the material is directed to the receiving or incoming inspection section.   A copy of the receiving report accompanies the material.   Figure 12 is a schematic diagram showing the route of incoming material and the preparation and distribution of control documents relating to each incoming shipment.   Receiving inspection plays a very important role to ensure that incoming material meets company specifications.   This function is frequently located in or adjacent to the receiving department.   Receiving inspection generates two documents for incoming material, either an inspector's report (Fig. 13) or a defective-material report (Fig. 14).

The inspection report indicates that the incoming material has been checked

Date		Shift	DEFECTIVE MATERIAL Production control copy X COPY		Drawing No.	95273	
Vendor				Part name			
Responsibility Operator	Defect appeared opr. No.	Qty. rec'd	Qty. insp.	Qty. rej.	Pur. order No.	Work order No.	Item
Equipment	Dept.	Rework	Mach.	Charge dept.	Charge acct.	Last operation	Cost thru opr. No. $
Defect							

Instructions for rework or packing for return to vendor

Inspector

Disposition				Reason			Charge				
Use	Return	Rework	Scrap	Def. mat'l	Def. work	Obsol.	Vendor	Purch.	Engr.	Facty.	Sales

Fig. 14 Defective material report.

and found free of defects and is released for production use. It is a multiple-copy form with the following distribution:

Copy 1. Production Control. Notifies production control of the quantity of material that has been accepted and is available for release to production.

Copy 2. Accounting. Verifies the quantity of acceptable material received for which the vendor should be paid.

Copy 3. Inspection. Remains in the inspection department as a record of the acceptance of material.

Copy 4. Stores. Accompanies material to stores area certifying that the material has been inspected and accepted.

The defective-materials report indicates the quantity of material that has been received but which does not meet specifications, and describes the cause for the rejection. This is a multiple-copy form with the following distribution.

Copy 1. Production Control and Accounting. Notifies production control department of the amount of material that that has been rejected. It is passed on to the accounting department to withhold payment of the vendor's invoice and to prepare a debit memo and prepare paper work for the return of the defective material to the vendor.

Copy 2. Purchasing. Advises the purchasing department of the rejection of material and the reason for the rejection.

Copy 3. Inspection. Remains in the inspection department as a record of the rejection of material.

Copy 4. Receiving. Accompanies the material to the receiving department. It identifies the material, quantity, and cause for rejection. The material should remain in a holding area in the receiving department until proper instructions are received for the disposition of the material, such as scrap or for return to the vendor.

DISPATCHING

The responsibility for safeguarding all materials, parts, supplies, and all other items carried in stock normally rests with the storekeeping function. All stores items, whether purchased or manufactured, should be delivered to the proper storeroom for safekeeping until they are needed. Material held in stores as part of the physical inventory should not be dispatched until its release is duly authorized by requisition or production release. In many companies, company policy and stores practice require that storerooms be locked, that unauthorized persons not be permitted in stores areas, and that no material move into or out of stores without properly prepared and authorized paper work. The same basic ground rules apply to all categories of inventory. However, the size, bulk, or frequency of handling may permit exceptions to the basic principle that all stores items be physically handled and dispatched by stores.

There are numerous ways in which material may be requisitioned from stores and dispatched to the area or work center requiring the material. The following are among the production methods which influence the manner in which material is released and dispatched to production.

1. *Continuous production,* such as performed by refineries, chemical plants, etc. Material is dispatched to the using department based upon a production schedule. Material requirements can be delivered daily, by shift, or as required or indicated by the production schedule. Production schedules are authorizations to produce and may be issued daily, weekly, or monthly depending upon individual plant demands. Revisions to production schedules may be authorized

which will automatically change the amounts or types of material dispatched from stores.

2. *Repetitive mass production,* such as automotive and major electrical appliances produced in assembly plants separated from parts manufacturing. Parts and components are received from vendors and parts-manufacturing plants in preplanned quantities equal to the scheduled production for each day. These parts are delivered directly to assembly-line stations. Small and inexpensive parts such as hardware may be stocked in bulk at the assembly plant. Bulk items are withdrawn from stores to supply the assembly lines as needed.

3. *Planned production orders,* in which materials and parts requirements are predetermined by a production planning activity. A production order including a material requisition for needed material and parts is released to stores prior to the starting date for the first operation. On or before the starting date, the necessary materials are dispatched to the department in which the first production operation will be performed.

An alternative method releases the production order to the manufacturing department. The department foreman or shop dispatcher forwards the material requisition to stores in sufficient time so that the material can be delivered prior to the setup date.

4. *Unplanned production orders,* including orders for small quantities and unplanned operations in which material requirements are not preplanned or when no production control system exists. In these cases, the foreman determines the requirements and prepares requisitions for materials as required. Material is dispatched as requested.

5. *Bulk transfers,* including materials which may be more easily or economically stored in the area of its use. Rather than receive and hold large quantities of material in stores and parcel it out as needed, selected materials may be delivered directly to the production area. Materials in this category may include large and bulky components that are difficult to move and store, such as cast bases for machine tools and major subassemblies, high-precision parts that may be damaged by additional handling, and other items that may be used in selective-type assemblies. Control over the usage and requisitioning of replacement supplies must be built into the production control system.

Other items in this category may include scrap and pig iron used in foundry operations, lubricants used in assembly operations, and small, low-cost items used in high-volume assembly operations. Small, low-cost components may be produced and stored adjacent to the assembly line and used as needed. In other cases, low-cost parts may be withdrawn from stores in bulk and charged to the department. This is sometimes called "bin stock," as it is used as required and not charged directly to a specific work order.

6. *Special or nonscheduled use,* in which material may be issued and dispatched to persons authorized to approve the requisitioning of material. This would include foremen, department heads, and executives. Material dispatched from stores in this manner includes material for the replacement of scrap, shortages, nonstandard parts, incorrectly issued material, tool tryouts, and so forth.

Operating supplies and nonproductive material for use in the plant, office, and maintenance are frequently withdrawn on material requisitions authorized by department or division heads who require the material. Frequently, maintenance and tool manufacturing departments operate their own storerooms and install separate ordering and control procedures. Certain materials may be transferred from central stores on material-transfer forms. Dispatching of materials that are transferred from central stores to substores or divisions would follow one of the normal dispatching procedures outlined below.

Dispatching Methods. There are many methods of dispatching materials from stores to the requisitioner or user. The exact dispatching method varies with the type of material, the material-handling equipment, the quantity of material, and the need for the material. Perhaps the most commonly used methods of dispatching material from stores are:

1. *Direct pick-up,* in which the person or department requisitioning the material either waits for the requested material or arranges to pick up the material as soon as it is ready.

2. *Direct delivery,* in which the size or quantity of material to be dispatched from stores requires special handling equipment, i.e., bundles of steel, drums of material, bulk materials, etc. In these cases, the material is dispatched directly to the using area as soon as suitable material-handling equipment is available.

3. *Scheduled delivery,* in which case the storeroom provides regularly scheduled deliveries throughout the plant. Material requisitions are handled by stores on a routine basis. As material is selected and released for delivery, it is picked up on a scheduled basis and delivered over a predetermined route. When applicable, this is the most economic method of dispatching material from stores. The actual delivery service may be provided by stores personnel or by the plant transportation department.

4. *Special delivery,* including unscheduled delivery of materials direct to the requisitioner to meet emergency demands for materials and supplies, or to deliver material to areas not normally serviced by a scheduled delivery plan.

The method of dispatching materials from stores must be tailored to meet the individual requirements and operations of each plant. Among the factors that influence the stores-dispatch function are:

1. The type of material being dispatched
2. The material-handling equipment available for material delivery
3. The frequency of dispatching materials to each location
4. The size and weight of the material dispatched
5. The types of containers required to hold the material being dispatched

Forms Used to Dispatch Material. Many different types of forms are used to draw materials from stores. Most frequently a copy of the requisition is used to dispatch the material to its destination. It also serves as a means for the recipient to check the quantity and type of material being delivered. The following are typical of the forms and their use in industry today.

1. *Material Requisition or Material Release.* These are commonly used forms

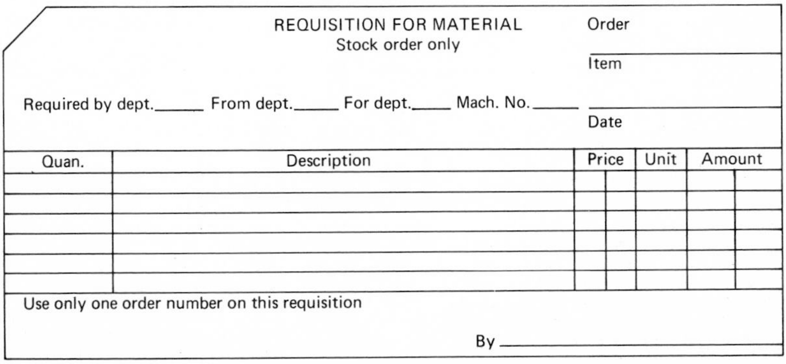

REQUISITION FOR MATERIAL
Stock order only

Order

Item

Required by dept._____ From dept._____ For dept._____ Mach. No._____

Date

Quan.	Description	Price	Unit	Amount

Use only one order number on this requisition

By __________

Fig. 15 Requisition for material (tabulating card).

Req. No. 014673

MATERIAL REQUISITION

Deliver to __________ Charge to Order No. Acct. No. __________

Quan.	Part No. Code No.	Description	Price	
			Unit	Total

Stores: Issue exact quantity requested. If out of stock, draw line through item.	Approved by __________ Date __________ Issued by __________ Date __________

Fig. 16 Material requisition.

Quantity	Date released / /	BILL OF MATERIAL	Sheet ______ of ______
Assembly No.	Nomenclature		Order No.

Part or stock code No.	Description	Stock location	Quantity			Cost	
			Unit	Rec'd	Issued	Unit	Total
Total cost this sheet							
Total cost this order							

Stores must issue exact quantities specified

Notes: 1. In-stock location column indicates item is carried as bench stock in department. 2. If total quantity requested is not available, notify inventory planning of shortage but do not hold order for such parts.	Approved by Date Order filled by Date

Fig. 17 Bill of material.

to requisition material for production or manufacturing orders. Use of this form limits the requisitioning of material to production or direct materials for one specific order. The requisition may be prepared by machine in the planning section of production control, or it can be prepared manually by any department foreman. Normally, this form is not used for assembly orders except to obtain supplementary items to replace scrap, shortages, etc. The material requisition shown in Fig. 15 is a standard-size tabulating card and may be machine-printed

ASSEMBLY ORDER		C. J. Myers				Item No.			
Quantity	Part No.	Description of assembly	Run	Wk supply	Date	St.	R.O.	Required in warehouse
5	060385	3 DBLE INT PIL BLK 2B	B		02/26		X	/

Total required	Part No.	Description of component parts	B/L	Inventory balance	Open production			Material made good
					Run	Quantity	Schedule	
5	060536	2 15/16 DI OUTER HSG ASSY 2B NE		79				
5	060450	2 15/16 DBL INT D UNIT HSG		684				
10	060466	2 15/16 DBL INT INNER GR SEAL		684	E	9000		*
10	060481	2 15/16 DBL INT OUTER GR SEAL		5074				
10	060106	2 15/16 DYNAFACE SEAL		733	X	5000	3 18	*
20	400146	1/2-13 X 3/4 SOC SET SCR CP		1418				
10	060050	2 15/16 DBL INT COLLAR		723	H	1196		*
10	401024	2 15/16 DBL INT SNAP RING		8121				
5	402030	34300DE TIMKEN CONE		100				
10	403012	34478 TIMKEN CUP		5020				
5	404732	3 DI COVER NAMEPLATE NE		26				
5	405041	1 5/8 X 843 HINGED LUBE COVER		9870				
5	405012	5/8 X 23/32 DI LUBE STUD		3368				
5	405015	1/8 HYDRAULIC GREASE FITTING						
5	427076	2 15/16 X .004 TYPE E ADJ SHIM						
5	427086	2 15/16 X .006 TYPE E ADJ SHIM						
5	427096	2 15/16 X .015 TYPE E ADJ SHIM						
10	427125	2 15/16 X .005 DI HSG SHIM 2BNE						
5	440209	# 209 BOX		445				

ASSEMBLY ORDER					Page 2			
Quantity	Part No.	Description of assembly	Run	Wk supply	Date	St.	R.O.	Required in warehouse
	060385				02/26			

Total required	Part No.	Description of component parts	B/L	Inventory balance	Open production			Material made good
					Run	Quantity	Schedule	
5	499560	INSTRUCTION MANUAL						
5	498978	NO RECORD						

Fig. 18 Assembly order.

and keypunched. An example of a manually prepared material-requisition form used for production material or supplies is shown by Fig. 16. The size and shape of manually prepared material-requisition forms are peculiar to individual companies.

2. *Assembly Bill of Material* (Fig. 17). Frequently copies of a bill of material or parts list are used as requisitions for issuing balanced groups of materials

Description or part number	Work order or release No.	Unit meas.	Qty. shp'd	Qty. rec'd	Unit price	Amount

INTERDIVISION TRANSFER ORDER

IDTO No. 28528

Requested by or IDRO No._____ Approved by_____ Date_____19___

Transferred from_____ Division to _____ Division

From dept. or stockroom No._____ To dept. or stockroom No._____ For_____

Shipped by_____ Date_____19___Received by_____ Date_____19___

Distribution of copies

1—Accompany material to rec. div. interdivision shipping and receiving—forward to rec. div. accounting dept.
2—Accompany material to rec. div. interdivision shipping and receiving—retain and file there.
3—Accompany material to rec. div. interdivision shipping and receiving—forward with material to person requesting transfer.
4—To be forwarded to transferring division accounting dept.
5—To be forwarded to transferring division accounting dept.
6—To be retained and filed by interdivision shipping and receiving of transferring division.

Account coding (for use of accounting depts. only)

Account number	Amount	Account number	Amount	Account number	Amount

Fig. 19   Interdivision transfer order.

and parts for assembly orders. A typical form is shown which is a reproduction of an engineering bill of material. Many companies are now preparing and issuing assembly orders and parts requirements by computer. An example of an assembly order prepared by computer is shown as Fig. 18.

3. *Material Transfer* (Fig. 19). Material transfers are used in larger operations to effect the transfer of material between stock rooms and/or divisions of the company. The material transfer not only identifies the material being transferred and its destination, but also permits the accounting department to properly transfer the value of the material to the proper account.

4. *Shipping Authorization* (Fig. 20). Shipping authorizations are used to

release stores materials for shipping to outside vendors for processing and fabrication. The same form can be used to return materials for rework if they have been found defective or substandard after they have been accepted and placed in stores. The shipping authorization is a form of material requisition with limited application.

SHIPPING AUTHORIZATION

Date________

No. 34777

Ship to________

Via________

Transportation charges________

Declared value________

Company expense________
Vendor expense________
Vendor code No.________
Sent from dept. No.________
Return to company Yes__No__
Return to stockroom or dept.

Route Copies:
1. With material to shipping________
2. Sender's file________
3. Writer's file________
Pur. order No.________

Item No.	Qty.	Code	Part No. and description

Reason for shipment________

Approved by________ Dept.________
Full name

Fig. 20 Shipping authorization.

5. *Service-parts Transfer Order* (Fig. 21). This form is used to transfer parts from parts stores for resale to individual customers. It is a specialized form of a material transfer limited to the transfer of parts from stores accounts to customer accounts. In some companies, it may be called a "parts order—sales." This form is not a customer invoice but is used only to issue material from stores.

6. *Stores Requisition* (Fig. 22). The stores requisition is most frequently used to requisition indirect materials such as operating supplies, repair parts, and office supplies from stores. It has the same general format as the material requisition (Fig. 16) and differs only in title and possibly the color of the paper. Parts and materials are charged to department overhead accounts or specific nonproductive orders (repair orders, maintenance orders, installation orders, etc.). In many companies, separate forms are used to requisition mate-

rials for production orders and expense accounts. This is done to aid accounting in keeping more accurate records; however, with the advent of machine accounting, the need for separate forms has lessened and a single material-requisition form can suffice for all purposes.

The six forms above are all used to requisition material and to ensure that the material is dispatched to the proper department or area requiring it. Concur-

---

SERVICE PARTS TRANSFER ORDER

Service parts center   No. 26048

Requested by _____ Approved by _____ Date _____ 19_____

Transferred to: Dept. or stockroom No. _____ For _____

    Commercial div. (RGB) 40_____ Commercial div. 41_____ Special code_____

    Military div. (RGB) 42_____ Military Div. 43_____ Marketing Div. 47_____

Part number	Description	Bin location	Unit measure	Quantity shipped	Quantity received

1. Accompany material to rec. dept. — forward to rec. div. accounting dept.
2. Accompany material to rec. dept. — retain and file there
3. To be forwarded to service parts scheduling — forwarded to comm. div. accounting
4. To be retained and filed by service parts center.

Fig. 21   Service-parts transfer order.

---

rently, copies of these forms are used to relieve an inventory account and allocate the charges to the proper expense or production account.

The following forms are used in stores operations and have an effect upon the dispatching function.

1. *Move Order* (Fig. 23). In some companies, a separate move-order ticket is prepared to authorize each material movement. This form does not replace the material-requisition or transfer form, nor can it be used to withdraw material from stores. It is normally used in conjunction with material requisitons and

Quantity	Description	Price	Unit	Amount

REQUISITION FOR MATERIAL
Plant order and expense

Order _____
Item _____
Date _____

Required by dept. _____ From dept. _____ For dept. _____ Mach. No. _____

Use only one order number on this requisition

By _____

REQUISITION FOR MATERIAL
Regular, petty and PA orders

Order _____
Item _____
Date _____

Required by dept. _____ From dept. _____ For dept. _____ Mach. No. _____

Quantity	Description	Price	Unit	Amount

Use only one order number on this requisition

By _____

Fig. 22 Stores requisition.

MOVE ORDER   A 78579

Move from _____

Move to _____

	Date	
Mo.	Day	Yr.

Part No.	Part name

Quantity	U. of M.	No. Made on order	Ship on ➤	No. Parts order	No. Shipping auth.	Check mark only Contract

Remarks: _____

Return to _____

Prepared by _____   _____   _____
          Badge No.   Dept. No.   Full last name

Fig. 23 Move order.

HOLD

DO NOT RUN UNTIL RELEASED

(a)

MATERIAL HOLD TAG

NOTE: This material is held for:

Order No. _____

Part No. _____

Amount required _____

This material shall not be used for any other purpose without the approval of the Manager-Materials Dept.

(b)

Fig. 24   Material hold tag: (a) front, (b) back.

production orders to authorize a transportation unit to move the material from stores to the proper work or service area or between production operations.

2. *Material Hold Tag* (Fig. 24).   This form is used to identify and hold certain material in stores for specific orders.   Material thus identified should not be dispatched except in accordance with the order specified by the material hold tag.   Examples of material hold orders include materials that are purchased to exacting specifications or tolerance for specific parts, or material set aside and reserved for a specific customer order to assure delivery of the finished

product. This ticket is frequently printed on colored stock to attract attention and is attached directly to the material.

3. *Material Credit* (Fig. 25). Occasionally surplus material accumulates in production departments or even in other departments where parts may have been used for display or marketing purposes. Surplus materials should be returned to the appropriate storeroom with a properly executed material-credit form so that inventory records can be adjusted and the proper accounts credited.

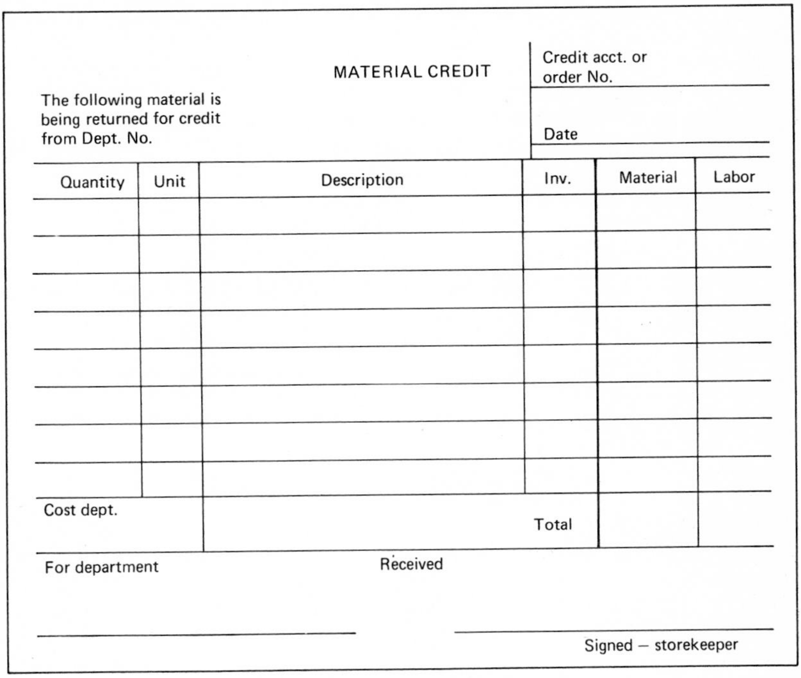

Quantity	Unit	Description	Inv.	Material	Labor

MATERIAL CREDIT

Credit acct. or order No.

The following material is being returned for credit from Dept. No.

Date

Cost dept.

Total

For department   Received

Signed — storekeeper

Fig. 25   Material credit.

PHYSICAL INVENTORIES AND AUDITS

The term "physical inventory" refers to the periodic auditing of the inventory balances on hand as a means of verifying and maintaining accurate inventory records. Inventory records must be correct in both quantities and values. If need be, inventory records could be checked to the last penny. However, for production planning and financial records, a reasonable degree of accuracy generally suffices. The inventory records may be manually posted, machine posted, or maintained by computer. Under any system, certain clerical errors may occur either in feeding data into the inventory records system or in manually computing balances after each transaction.

At times, discrepancies between inventory records and actual stock quantities may occur because of errors in the storerooms. These errors may be caused by inaccurate descriptions of material, mistakes in counts or weights, or issuing improper materials. Mistakes like these can be avoided if standard symbols and descriptions are used for all materials and if the stock bins and stock materials are accurately and clearly marked. With the advent of mechanized inventory control systems, clerical errors are minimized. However, discrepancies still occur, perhaps due to the human element. Thus, the need for taking physical inventories periodically still exists.

Inventory Methods. An inventory or count of all materials on hand should be made at least once each year. The physical inventory should include the following categories of material: raw materials, component parts, finished goods, and operating supplies. The physical inventory count should be evaluated so that actual discrepancies in the inventory records and general ledgers can be adjusted. There are two principal methods of taking inventories that are commonly practiced:

1. The *physical inventory method* requires a complete count or measurement of all categories of inventory taken over a short period of time. For most industries, an annual inventory is sufficient, although some operations such as supermarkets may use monthly physical inventories and eliminate detailed inventory records.

2. The *cycle inventory method* requires a continuous counting of actual inventories throughout the year. The stock items to be checked may be selected at random or against a predetermined plan. The actual count is checked against the inventory record. Records can thus be adjusted as discrepancies in counts are identified.

Both methods have advantages and disadvantages depending upon the characteristics of the operation. If only one physical inventory is taken per year, it should be timed to coincide with the fiscal year end. Frequently, fiscal years are established to coincide with the yearly low point in production and inventory levels. This is particularly true in businesses that are highly seasonal.

The following are advantages of annual physical inventories.

1. Operations can be closed down for the inventory period, and work in process can be checked more accurately.

2. Frequently employee vacations can be arranged to coincide with the inventory closedown.

3. More knowledgeable persons may be available for taking inventories.

4. The factory can be cleaned and maintenance repairs accomplished during the inventory closedown.

In addition to the annual physical inventory, selected items such as precious metals, jewelry, and watches may be inventoried more frequently. It is not unusual for some items to be inventoried weekly or even daily in order to limit the chances of loss through theft or mysterious disappearance. The frequency of taking physical inventories is often determined by the value of the inventory item and the ease of disposing of such items on the open market.

The cycle inventory method for stores items is becoming more widely accepted in modern industry. It permits regularly assigned stores personnel to carry out the counting of inventories during lulls in their assigned duties. Requests for an inventory verification count may be generated by the inventory records section on a random basis, or on a planned basis so that each item will be checked at least once a year. Important items may be scheduled for checking more frequently. With a computer, the cycle checking of inventories can be planned and programmed so that the work load is spread evenly throughout the year, and periodic checks made dependent upon the importance of the inventory item. In any event, discrepancies should be noted on verification slips or cards and sent to the inventory records section for correction of records. Typical forms to verify records are shown in Figs. 26 and 27. After reconciliation of the inventory records, the adjustments should be sent to the accounting department for adjustment of the materials accounts.

```
┌─────────────────────────────────────────────────────────────────────────┐
│                        INVENTORY VERIFICATION                             │
│                                                                           │
│  Storekeeper:_____          Date_____                     │
│                                                                           │
│               Please inventory the item noted and return                  │
│               this card to central stores immediately.                    │
├──────────────────┬──────────────────────────┬────────────────────────────┤
│ Part No./Stock   │ Part name or description │           Count            │
│ code             │                          ├──────────┬─────────┬───────┤
│                  │                          │  Stores  │ Records │ Adj.  │
│                  │                          │          │         │       │
│  Account No.     │                          │          │         │       │
├──────────────────┴──────────────────────────┼──────────┴─────────┼───────┤
│  Inventory             Date_____        │                    │       │
│  by_____                        │   Unit value       │       │
├──────────────────────────────────────────────┼────────────────────┼───────┤
│  Inventory adjustment  Date_____        │                    │       │
│  approved by _____                      │  Total adjustment  │  $    │
├───────────────────────────────────────────────────────────────────┴───────┤
│        Accounting:  The inventory records have been adjusted as indicated.  │
└────────────────────────────────────────────────────────────────────────────┘
```

Fig. 26   Inventory verification form: manual notification card.

```
┌──────────────────┬──────────────────┬────────────┬───────────┬──────────┬──────────┐
│ Part No./Stock   │ Part name/       │ Unit meas. │ Unit cost │ Location │ Acct. No.│
│ code No.         │ Description      │            │           │          │          │
├──────────────────┴──────────────────┴────────────┴───────────┴──────────┴──────────┤
│                        INVENTORY VERIFICATION                                       │
├──────────────────┬──────────────────┬────────────┬────────────────────────────────┤
│  Stores count    │  Record count    │ Quantity   │ Dollar                          │
│                  │                  │ adjusted   │ adjustment                      │
├──────────────────┴──────────────────┴────────────┴────────────────────────────────┤
│  Inventory adjustment approved by_____        Date_____           │
│                                                                                     │
│                                                                                     │
│                                                                                     │
└─────────────────────────────────────────────────────────────────────────────────────┘
```

Fig. 27   Inventory verification form: data processing notification card.

The cycle inventory method has these advantages:

1. The plant does not have to be shut down with the related loss of production delays in delivery.

2. Errors are discovered more quickly with inventory records adjusted throughout the year.

3. Random verification may uncover irregularities and indicate need for further investigation.

4. The inventory counts are not done under pressure and probably result in more accurate measurements.

Inventory Preparations.   Taking the annual physical inventory is a major task in most plants and requires extremely careful planning.   The larger the inventory, the greater the need for careful preparation.   Inventory procedures should be formalized and detailed instructions issued to each person participating in the inventory.   The following points should be covered in preparing to take a physical inventory:

1. The starting date and target completion date

2. The selection of personnel and the assignment of their duties and responsibilities

3. The scope of the inventory and categories of inventory included with special instructions for each category

4. Forms to be used and specific instructions governing their use

5. Methods for measuring and counting inventories including those that may be estimated because of the physical characteristics

6. Procedure for checking and reconciling the inventory records

7. Method of tabulating the inventory, auditing the results, and releasing inventoried materials

Many firms have prepared inventory manuals containing explicit instructions and detailed procedures. Thus, procedures are standardized and consistent from

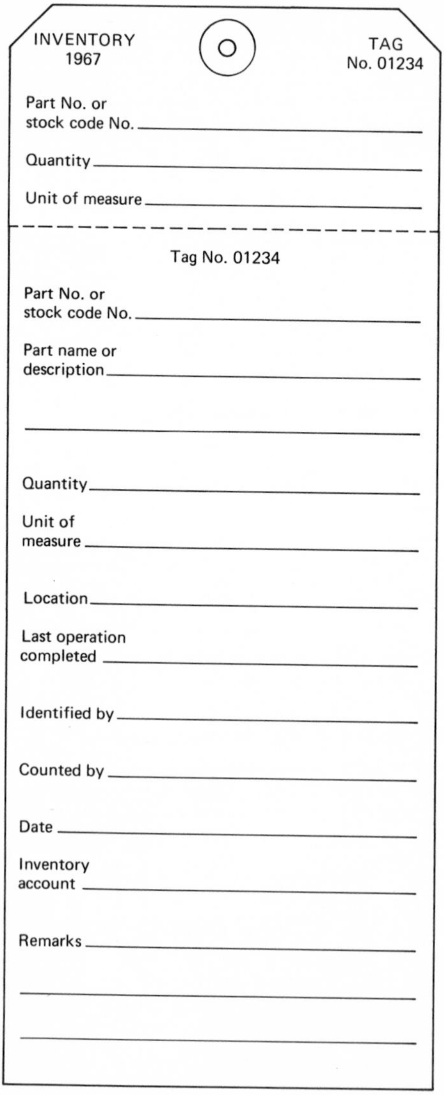

```
 _____
|                                                 |
|  INVENTORY        (  O  )        TAG            |
|    1967                       No. 01234         |
|                                                 |
|  Part No. or                                    |
|  stock code No. _____ |
|                                                 |
|  Quantity _____ |
|                                                 |
|  Unit of measure _____ |
|  - - - - - - - - - - - - - - - - - - - - - - - - |
|                                                 |
|              Tag No. 01234                      |
|                                                 |
|  Part No. or                                    |
|  stock code No. _____ |
|                                                 |
|  Part name or                                   |
|  description _____ |
|                                                 |
|                _____  |
|                                                 |
|  Quantity _____ |
|                                                 |
|  Unit of                                        |
|  measure _____ |
|                                                 |
|  Location _____  |
|                                                 |
|  Last operation                                 |
|  completed _____  |
|                                                 |
|  Identified by _____  |
|                                                 |
|  Counted by _____  |
|                                                 |
|  Date _____  |
|                                                 |
|  Inventory                                      |
|  account _____  |
|                                                 |
|  Remarks _____  |
|                                                 |
|                _____  |
|                                                 |
|                _____  |
|_____|
```

Fig. 28   Inventory tag.

year to year, and modified only when necessary to meet new conditions. Personnel assigned to inventory tasks become more skilled when procedures are standardized.

In preparation for the physical inventory, each department foreman and storekeeper should arrange his area so that like materials are grouped together and properly identified. The purchasing department should advise vendors of the scheduled inventory dates and request that deliveries be withheld during this period. Likewise, a holding area should be set up in the receiving department, and any materials received during the inventory period should be held and excluded from the inventory count. Similarly, internal movements and shipments of material should be suspended for the duration of the inventory period except for emergencies. If the inventory taking requires several days, customers should be advised of the shutdown dates.

Normally, the date for taking an inventory coincides with the end of an accounting period. The extent of the closedown for physical inventories depends upon the amount and type of inventory. Careful planning for the physical inventory can minimize the extent of the plant shutdown.

In planning the physical inventory, procedures must be prepared to handle the following categories of material:

1. Materials specifically excluded from the inventory
2. Materials shipped or transferred during the course of the inventory
3. Materials invoiced but not received (from vendors)
4. Materials invoiced but not shipped (to customers)
5. Materials supplied to vendors and subcontractors
6. Rejected, salvaged, and scrap materials
7. Supplies and perishable tools

Recording the Physical Inventory. There are two basic forms which are generally used in taking physical inventories: the *inventory tag* and the *inventory summary sheet.* Previously, both these forms were prepared manually; however, the advent of the computer permits preprinting primary data on the inventory tags and preparing inventory summary sheets by machine.

The tag method for identifying and recording inventories is universally used and is considered to be the most convenient. One inventory tag can be used for all categories of inventory. Sample forms are shown in Figs. 28 and 29. The same basic data is recorded on both forms; however, one is a punched card with preprinted data such as the part or stock code number, part name or description, unit of measure, unit cost, inventory account, and location. The

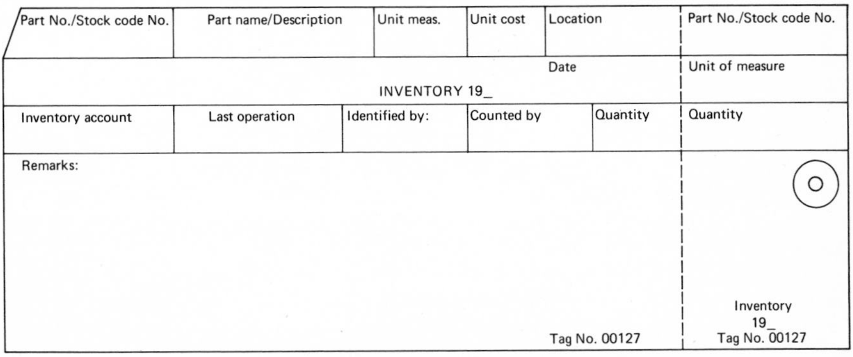
Part No./Stock code No.
Part name/Description
Unit meas.
Unit cost
Location
Part No./Stock code No.
Date
Unit of measure
INVENTORY 19_
Inventory account
Last operation
Identified by:
Counted by
Quantity
Quantity
Remarks:
Tag No. 00127
Inventory
19_
Tag No. 00127

Fig. 29 Inventory tag—data processing.

			INVENTORY VERIFICATION SHEET				

Inventory category_____ Date_____

Item No.	Stock count	Record count	Part number stock code	Part name, description	Qty. adj.	Unit value	Adjustment $
1							
2							
3							
4							
5							
6							
7							
8							
9							
10							
11							
12							
13							
14							
15							
16							
17							
18							
19							
20							
21							
22							
23							
24							
25							

Total value of inventory adjustment	$

Stores count_____	Inventory records corrected by_____ Approved_____ Date_____	Inventory account No._____ Approved_____ Date_____

Fig. 30 Inventory verification sheet.

tags are divided (perforated) so that the smaller portion can be detached and remain with the material after the count is completed. In some instances a two-part form is used with the "flimsy" copy going to the inventory records section and the card copy directed to the accounting department.

All tags are serially numbered and controlled by a central source, normally the controller's office since the inventory is primarily a financial check. Tags should be issued in blocks of numbers and assigned to the person in charge of the inventory in each specific area. Each department head should normally supervise the inventory in his area of responsibility. All inventory tags that are issued should be accounted for at the end of the inventory. Incorrectly marked tags should be voided and turned in with all unused inventory tags. Slow-moving items in stores may be inventoried a few days in advance of the regular inventory and any movement explained on the inventory tag.

Inventory teams normally consist of groups of two or more people. One person writes tags and places them on the materials, while the rest of the team checks the materials identification and counts the material. When the team completes its work, the department head should check the area to ensure that each lot of material is covered by an inventory tag. Before the tags are removed, a person assigned to the area by the controller's office should spot-check the inventory for coverage, completeness, and accuracy. After he is satisfied with the inventory, the serial numbers should be checked to see that no tags are missing. If two part tags are used, the top section of the tag remains with the material as a guide to locating "lost tags" and to facilitate recounts when necessary. All tags should be accounted for before a department is authorized to resume production.

The inventory records and physical inventory should be reconciled from the inventory tags—the date, inventory tag number, and quantity should be posted to the inventory record. Then the inventory data from the tags should be transferred to the inventory summary sheets, grouping items by inventory category and materials accounts. The inventory summary sheets shown in Fig. 30 should include the quantity, the part number or stock code number, inventory tag number, unit cost, and total value of inventory items. Thus, the total value can be calculated for each material control account and the accounting records adjusted accordingly.

For the computer, the data that has been manually added to the tab card is keypunched. The cards can be sorted and fed into the computer for calculation and reconciliation of materials control accounts. Likewise the inventory summary sheets, containing the same information as if prepared manually, can be printed by machine.

Work-in-process tags are used to check the open-production orders and are then tabulated and used to reconcile the work-in-process inventory accounts.

SUMMARY

Physical control over inventories is normally vested in the storekeeping function. The storekeeping operation is a service to manufacturing and has a direct bearing upon the accuracy of inventory records and the accounting of materials for cost purposes. If the storeroom does not do its job efficiently and control inventories effectively, the manufacturing effort may be hampered and become more costly. The purpose of this chapter has been to furnish guidelines for establishing a sound approach to the organization of the physical control function over inventories.

A well-located and carefully planned storeroom coupled with sound inventory management has a direct bearing on profits and is therefore worthy of careful attention. The systems and controls outlined in this chapter form the basis for developing effective physical controls over inventories.

Chapter 16

Inventory Control Systems

EDITOR:

Oliver W. Wight *Partner, Plossl and Wight Associates, Wilton, Connecticut*

CONTRIBUTORS:

H. W. Powell *Vice President, Management Consulting, Executive Computer Leasing, Inc., Oakbrook, Illinois*

T. G. Weeks *Manager of Production Planning, Training and Research, Armstrong Cork Company, Lancaster, Pennsylvania*

CONTENTS

The objectives of inventory management are to provide maximum customer service with maximum plant efficiency and minimum inventory investment.

In a company that has a competitive product and an aggressive marketing organization, a high level of *customer service* will usually result in increased market penetration, increased business, and added profits. It is difficult to assess the value of customer service quantitatively, but many companies have had great increases in their growth rate as a result of improved customer service.

The objective of *plant efficiency* is easiest to see in the calculation of economic order quantities. Obviously, a plant runs more efficiently with longer production runs which reduce setup costs. It is also important for most companies to maintain fairly stable production rates in order to keep a skilled labor force and minimize overtime, hiring, and layoffs.

The third objective, *minimum inventory investment,* is important since funds are usually limited and the same funds that are used in inventory are the ones that are needed for research and development, investment in capital equipment, advertising, marketing programs, and the like. It is important, therefore, to balance these objectives, which are obviously in conflict for any company, so that a minimum inventory is maintained consistent with efficient plant operations and a satisfactory customer service level. This is the purpose of inventory systems, and today some fairly standard techniques are available for use in these systems.

THREE BASIC QUESTIONS OF
INVENTORY SYSTEMS

Resources for control are almost always limited, whether the system is controlled manually or with a computer—where main computer memory, file storage, computing time, and maintenance cost money. It is therefore important to determine the items or groups of items that deserve the maximum control effort. This stratification of inventory into its most important elements is usually called "ABC analysis." This is the determination of *what* the system should concentrate its control efforts on.

The second question is *how much* to order when an order is placed. In most systems, it is important to order in lot sizes that minimize inventory carrying costs and ordering costs. The best-known technique for handling the lot-size calculation is the economic-order-quantity (EOQ) calculation. Use of EOQ and related techniques is described in folowing sections.

Probably the most critical question that must be answered for each item in any inventory system is *when* it must be reordered. The determination of order-placement time, either by order-point or requirements planning techniques, establishes the safety stock that will be carried, and this has a direct bearing on the level of customer service that will be realized.

WHAT SHOULD BE CONTROLLED:
THE ABC PRINCIPLE

Vilfredo Pareto, an Italian economist and sociologist (1842–1923), generated some highly debatable concepts of economics and sociology. One that is most interesting to a student of inventory management is the concept known as "Pareto's law." Pareto arrived at the general conclusion that income distribution patterns were basically the same in different countries and in different historical periods. Pareto's studies showed that a very small percentage of the total population always seemed to receive the bulk of the income. He concluded that there was a natural economic law in existence which would always establish the shape of the income distribution and could not be overridden by any political or sociological reforms. Current economic theory tends to discount Pareto's *conclusion* that economic reforms cannot materially affect the distribution of income among the population. His conclusion may not have been valid, but his observation that this type of distribution will occur naturally *was* valid for income and almost any other statistical "population." J. M. Juran, in an article in *Management Review*, noted Pareto's law, stating:[1]

In any series of elements to be controlled, a selected small fraction in terms of numbers of elements always accounts for a large fraction in terms of effect. A few percent of the quality characteristics account for the bulk of the customers complaints and the bulk of the scrap and rework. A few percent of the various piece parts entering the final product account for the bulk of the scheduling and delivery date failures. A few percent of the purchase orders account for the bulk of the dollar purchases. A few percent of all customers account for the bulk of the credit losses and the bulk of unjustified returns. A few percent of the decisions made account for the bulk of the total effect of all decisions.

This is not a relationship, therefore, that is unique to economics, any more than it is a relationship that is unique to inventory. As Juran goes on to say, "It is important to any control system or any management planning that the 'vital few' be separated from the 'trivial many.'" This concept is as applicable to inventory as it is to any area of management. This general relationship was brought to the attention of people concerned with inventory management by H. Ford Dickie,[2] who applied Pareto's law to inventory and developed the general concept of *ABC analysis*. Like so many ideas, however, it has not been completely understood. Many people refer to the "ABC System" or the "ABC technique." The idea of distribution of value for inventory stratification is neither a system nor a technique; it's a fundamental management principle with universal application potential.

ABC Analysis Example. The steps in computing an ABC analysis are:

1. Calculate the annual usage in units for each item. Since this type of analysis usually is done for the following year, it is better to base usage estimates on forecasts rather than history.

2. Extend the annual usage in units times the unit cost to get the annual usage in dollars for each item.

3. Rank the items from highest annual dollar usage to lowest annual dollar usage and assign categories.

In a typical ABC analysis, 20 percent of the items will represent 80 percent of the annual requirements. There is nothing sacred about the assignment of these categories. This could as easily be 20 to 70 percent or 10 to 90 percent or another relationship. Where the A, B, and C lines are drawn is not of critical importance. A common approach is to consider the first 20 percent of the items to be A items, then the next 30 percent to be B items, and the next 50 percent to be C items.

Table 1 shows a representative ABC analysis where 10 items have been studied and annual usage extended by unit cost to get annual usage in dollars.

TABLE 1   ABC Analysis: Annual Usage, in Dollars

Item	Annual usage, units	Unit cost	Annual usage, dollars	Ranking
10501	30,000	0.10	3,000	6
10502	280,000	0.15	42,000	1
10503	3,000	0.10	300	9
10504	110,000	0.05	5,500	4
10505	4,000	0.05	200	10
10506	220,000	0.10	22,000	2
10507	15,000	0.05	750	8
10508	80,000	0.05	4,000	5
10509	60,000	0.15	9,000	3
10510	8,000	0.10	800	7

Table 2 shows the ranking and assignment of A, B, and C categories for items.

Table 3 is a summary of this ABC analysis showing that 20 percent of the items represent 73.1 percent of the annual usage; 30 percent of the items represent 21.1 percent of the annual usage; and 50 percent of the items represent only 5.8 percent of the annual usage.

In most situations, resources are limited. The resources may be management attention, record maintenance for inventory updating, and the like. The ABC concept tries to isolate the vital few so that the bulk of the resources can be devoted to controlling them. From the example above, it can be seen that doubling of the C item inventory would have a negligible effect on the inventory level. If the effort saved in controlling C items could be applied to reduce

TABLE 2   ABC Ranking

Item	Annual usage, dollars	Cum. annual usage, dollars	Cum. percent	Category
10502	42,000	42,000	48.0	A
10506	22,000	64,000	73.1	A
10509	9,000	73,000	83.4	B
10504	5,500	78,500	89.6	B
10508	4,000	82,500	94.1	B
10501	3,000	85,500	97.6	C
10510	800	86,300	98.6	C
10507	750	87,050	99.4	C
10503	300	87,350	99.6	C
10505	200	87,550	100.0	C

TABLE 3   Summary of ABC Analysis

Class	Items	Percent of items	Dollars per group	Percent of dollars
A	10502, 10506	20	64,000	73.1
B	10509, 10504, 10508	30	18,500	21.1
C	All others	50	5,050	5.8

the A-item inventory by 25 percent, the overall inventory would go down quite substantially. Items in the A category should have a very tight control including regular surveillance by supervisory personnel, while B items should have a normal amount of effort exerted for their control, and C items should be given a minimum control effort in the system. Historically, the techniques that are usually closely associated in the minds of many people with ABC analysis are the low-value techniques that are intended to reduce control effort so that it can be concentrated on high-value items.

Control of Low-value Items. One of the techniques that is most commonly associated with the control of C items in an ABC "system" is the two-bin technique. Using this approach, an amount of stock that is equal to demand during the order lead time plus some reserve stock is segregated and placed in a sealed bin or container with instructions that it is not to be opened until all other stock has been used. At that time, notification is sent to inventory control to replenish the stock. This makes it possible to replenish the inventory without keeping perpetual records. An approximate history of usage can be obtained from the purchasing department based upon either their purchase orders or requisitions that have been sent to them.

Many people have tried the two-bin system and some have been disillusioned with it. Unfortunately, the term "loose control" as applied to C items seems to create many misunderstandings. We are indulging in a form of "loose control" by segregating a predetermined amount of stock and maintaining minimum records and prices. Nevertheless, *discipline* is required to make this type of system work well, just as it is required to make an inventory record-keeping system work well. Someone must be responsible for ensuring that people do not break into the segregated stock before all the other stock is used up, notifying purchasing or inventory control that new stock must be ordered, segregating a predetermined amount of stock when a new order quantity is received, etc. Lack of discipline in handling C items can result in a stock out at the assembly line that will be just as serious as an error in the records for A items.

In some circumstances where it is not possible to assign responsibility for maintaining the "bin reserve" or two-bin system, another approach called "periodic visual review" has been used with considerable success. Supermarkets as well as manufacturing concerns have found that they can use a very economical type of control system by simply having a clerk review all the low-value items periodically and see how much is on hand and on order. Since the orders for these low-value items tend to be very large and infrequent, with short lead times, it is not usually a major problem to determine the amount on order when stock is being reviewed. This type of system can be used in a manufacturing company which does not have enclosed stock rooms and where responsibility for maintaining a two-bin control cannot be easily assigned. It requires that stocks of low-value items normally be kept in a very few known locations so that they can be checked readily with a preprinted list of the items.

Another form of low-value control is often encountered where the stock room uses the "bulk withdrawal" method. This is related to the two-bin system since it involves sending out a bulk quantity of screws, washers, nuts, bolts, etc. to the assembly floor as required and then reordering when the quantity left in the stock room gets down to a particular level.

A modification of this system has the stock room itself responsible for replenishing the inventories of low-value items on the floor. There is some advantage in doing this, for occasionally even low-value items will tend to be in short supply. Stockkeepers handling replenishment of inventory on the factory floor may be in a better position to know where overstocks may exist on the factory floor even when the stock room itself is actually out of stock for a particular component.

Using the ABC Principle in Inventory Systems. It is often assumed that the ABC concept involves some form of two-bin system on C items and an order-point system of some kind on B items, and that A items will be ordered only as needed using a requirements planning technique. This might very well be done in some circumstances, but there are many other considerations involved.

An inventory can be classified from many points of view other than the annual dollar usage. In practice, it is more important to determine whether an item has a *dependent* or *independent* demand when determining whether to use requirements planning or an order-point system on request than it is to make some blanket assumptions that all A items will be ordered using requirements planning while all B items will be ordered using the order-point system.

Finished-goods items are usually *independent*-demand items because demand for each item has no relation to demand for other inventory items. Components used on a higher-level assembly are *dependent*-demand items since their demand is dependent upon demand for the higher-level assemblies. In general, independent-demand items must be forecast, and some form of reorder point for inventory control should be used, while dependent-demand items should be calculated using requirements planning. These concepts are discussed in more detail in a later section of this chapter.

The idea of using order points on all B items is a case of *technique* being confused with *principle*. The ABC principle still applies, but the best ordering technique can be determined by classifying items as dependent and independent first. It might well be, however, that C items *should* be reordered using some kind of order-point system such as perhaps a two-bin technique. This is because the time and computer files required to explode requirements would not be justified for the low-value items even though the demand is definitely dependent. In this case, it might be worthwhile to carry the extra inventory of the low-value items to keep the control effort to a minimum.

A good inventory system should recognize many other characteristics of items in addition to their annual dollar usage. Some items may be highly susceptible to obsolescence. It's not unusual to find that 80 percent of the inventory write-offs take place in 20 percent of the general categories of components. It would be well to identify these items so that very low inventories can be maintained through application of special ordering rules. These items subject to obsolescence should be very carefully reviewed before ordering a large quantity to take advantage of a quantity discount.

There are other items that are kept in stock primarily for one customer. It would be absurd to make an ABC analysis and apply a rigid set of ordering rules to these items based solely upon their annual dollar usage. Nevertheless, the ABC principle applies *within* other categories that may exist in inventory, and the principle is very simple: *Maximum control effort should be devoted to the vital few.*

The ABC concept can be applied by product groups as well as individual products. It may not be very meaningful to do an ABC analysis for all the components that go into all assemblies, particularly if they are made in different parts of the factory. It might be more meaningful to start by doing an ABC analysis for the final products and categorize all items. By isolating the vital few *major product lines,* the production control manager can devote his major efforts to these product lines. This could be more practical than trying to exercise tight management control over a series of high-value items that are not related in any other way.

In many respects—such as shop priority—a low-value component going into a high-value assembly deserves more attention than a high-value component going into a low-annual-dollar-usage assembly. The production control manager might find that he wanted to have some regular summary reports of activity for the small number of product lines that are responsible for the total number of dollars in inventory. He might also find that he could use the ABC principle in isolating the major-component manufacturing departments that require the bulk of his management attention. If he used the ABC principle in categorizing products from a capacity point of view, he would undoubtedly find that about 20 percent of the items going through a particular department generated 80 percent of the capacity requirements and that his production planning efforts could best be exerted on these items. Applying this principle further, he might even segregate out of the A-category products a very small number of individual products requiring his personal attention.

It is commonly said that 20 percent of the items represent 80 percent of the annual dollar requirements, but at the same time, 20 percent of *this* 20 percent of the items should represent 80 percent of *this* 80 percent. In other words, 4 percent of the total items ought to represent about 64 percent of the total annual usage, and this concept could help the production control manager to direct his limited resource—management effort—more effectively. If he used the ABC principle as a proper management tool, he would find it of value in analyzing his major problems every week and categorizing them so that he could help direct management's attention to those few problems that are creating most of the delays and missed schedules.

Common Misunderstandings about ABC. The ABC principle is a universal one; since this principle is often misunderstood, there are a number of classic objections or excuses for not using ABC in a particular company. Some of these follow:

1. "We tried using the ABC system but we found that we could shut down the assembly line for lack of a lock washer as easily as we could shut it down for lack of a high-priced subassembly."

The problem here is that the concept of "loose control" has been misunderstood. The general idea behind the ABC principle is to *have plenty* of the low-value items. It is not to have a lackadaisical control that will result in running out of stock. By having plenty, it would be practical to direct more control efforts to the higher-value items without running out of stock on the low-value items.

2. "We tried using the ABC system but it didn't result in any decrease in the A inventory although the C inventory did increase."

Here again, a basic principle of ABC has been ignored: Devote management attention saved on trivial items to the vital few in the system.

3. "We made an ABC analysis and we put all the C items on a monthly periodic-visual-review system. In retrospect, it seems a little foolish to be visually reviewing some components monthly that are only used once a year at the time when we assemble the product they go into."

Here again, the ABC principle has been forgotten. The principle says we should have loose control on low-value items, but loose control does not necessarily mean visual control and no records. These infrequently used components might be maintained better on a manual record rather than on a periodic-visual-review system. But the items should have a very roughly calculated economic order quantity, plenty of safety stock, etc., in order to reduce control effort. A periodic-visual-review system should be applied to low-value items only when it will result in a reduction of control effort.

4. "Our highest-value items are chemicals. We buy these in 55-gallon drums and we don't see that the ABC system with daily posting of all usage would necessarily result in a better control."

Undoubtedly this is true, but here again, the ABC principle does not say that all high-value items should have inventory records posted. It might be better to do a little "barrel peeping" *daily* for the high-value chemicals to see how much is left in each of the storage drums and reorder them on a *daily* basis rather than try to maintain manual records. The real point is that high-value items should have a very tight control, and this doesn't necessarily mean maintaining manual records.

5. "We categorized our items by units of value and, oddly enough, in our business most items have roughly the same unit value, so we can't do a real ABC analysis."

One of the most basic misunderstandings about ABC analysis is that it implies a ranking by unit values. An ABC analysis is made by extending unit value *times* annual usage. A company making standard-size plastic paneling might well find that each unit has roughly the same value, but the extension of unit cost times annual usage provides the basis for an ABC analysis.

The ABC principle as it is known in inventory management is a universal principle. It's a basic principle that should be applied in any management control system. The professional manager in production and inventory control who understands the ABC concept will be using the principle in many areas of production and inventory management, while the amateur may be citing many reasons why this "technique" doesn't apply to his particular company. No company should apply the ABC "system" to its inventory items, but all companies should have the ABC *principle* deeply imbedded as one of the basic elements of their overall inventory management system.

INDEPENDENT-DEMAND INVENTORY SYSTEMS

Finished inventory maintained on the shelf or parts carried in inventory only for service requirements can be classed as "independent-demand" items for purposes of designing an effective inventory system. The term "independent" indicates that each item stands alone in the inventory as contrasted with component parts or semifinished products whose demand is *dependent* upon demand for the subassemblies, assemblies, or finished products they are used in. This distinction is significant when designing the "how much" and "when" parts of the system, since the classical economic-order-quantity and order-point-related techniques apply best to independent-demand items while dependent-demand inventory items, which must all be brought together at one point in time, are usually more efficiently controlled with techniques discussed later. The independent–dependent-demand concept is also discussed in more detail in a later section.

These independent-demand techniques are well known in industry today. Widely used techniques like the "min-max" approach are derived from the order-point–order-quantity techniques. A "minimum" ordering level is simply an order point with a different name. A "maximum" is the minimum plus the order quantity. Most systems, however, do not recognize in practice the need to determine ordering points and quantities rationally, but instead use empirical estimates that can almost always be demonstrated to require far too much inventory for the plant efficiency and customer service that results. The following pages describe current practical quantitative approaches for determining reordering parameters.

"How Much" to Re-order: The EOQ Concept. Assume an item for which the annual dollar usage is known to be exactly $12,000 and a demand that occurs continuously and evenly throughout the year. Further, assume that the replenishment time (lead time) is known to be exactly one month. When the inventory position drops to the lead-time usage ($1,000), an order must be placed. The question then is: How much should be re-ordered?

To answer this question, the economics of several alternative ordering strategies could be examined.

Assume that all the cost elements of ordering add up to $12 per order and the annual cost of carrying inventory is 20 percent of the average inventory investment. If a year's supply were ordered at one time, the inventory flow would be as represented in Fig. 1. The inventory would build up to $12,000 on order receipt and would be zero one year later. The average inventory for the year would be $6,000. This average working stock is most frequently referred to as "cycle stock" to distinguish it from safety stock. The cost of carrying a $6,000 average inventory for a year at a carrying cost of 20 percent is $1,200. Since only one order would be placed a year, the annual ordering cost is $12. Assuming that there are no other costs that vary with the number of orders placed or the amount ordered, the total cost of ordering once a year is $1,212.

One way to reduce the high inventory maintenance cost of $1,200 is to order very frequently, for example, once a week. If weekly orders were placed, the ordering cost for the year would be $624 (52 × 12). The order quantity would be approximately $230 ($12,000/52). The cycle stock would be approxi-

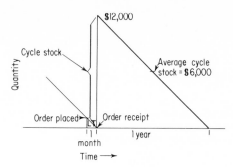

Fig. 1 Inventory flow.

mately $115, and the annual cost of carrying inventory would be $23. (0.20 × $115). The total annual cost of ordering and maintaining cycle stock would be about $647. In this case, the ordering costs are unreasonably high.

Table 4 shows the total variable cost for other order frequencies and the resulting order quantities. As the number of annual orders increases, there is a direct increase in ordering cost and a reduction in inventory carrying cost. Starting with one order a year, the total variable cost drops sharply at first as additional orders are placed. In this example, a point is reached between 8 and 12 orders where there is little change in the total cost. Thereafter, the cost rises sharply again.

For the ordering frequency and order quantities calculated, the lowest total cost exists when 10 orders for $1200 each are placed. A chart of the costs in the table is shown in Fig. 2. The economic order quantity is that which produces the *lowest total cost*.

EOQ FORMULA DERIVATION CONSIDERATIONS: Formulas giving the order quantity which results in the lowest total cost can be derived so that the economic order quantity can be calculated directly. The assumptions made are as follows:

1. Only one product is involved. It may be manufactured or purchased for delivery into inventory in batches.

2. During the delivery period the batch is put into stock at a uniform daily rate (called "noninstantaneous receipt") or all at once ("instantaneous receipt").

3. Usage from inventory is at a uniform rate over the full period covered by the demand forecast.

4. Reserve or safety stock is constant over the forecast period.

TABLE 4   Total Order-quantity Costs

Annual number of orders	Ordering cost, dollars	Order quantity	Cycle stock	Inventory carrying cost, dollars	Total variable cost, dollars
(1)	(2)	(3)	(4)	(5)	(6)
1	12	12,000	6,000	1,200	1,212
2	24	6,000	3,000	600	624
4	48	3,000	1,500	300	348
8	96	1,500	750	150	246
12	144	1,000	500	100	244
24	288	500	250	50	338
52	624	230	115	23	647
100	1,200	120	60	12	1,212

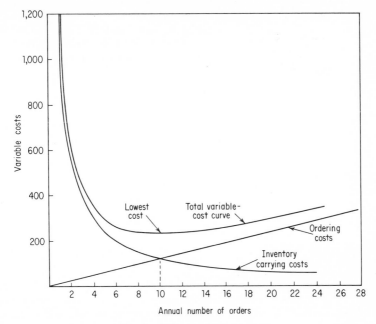

Fig. 2 Order quantity costs.

5. The unit cost of the item includes direct labor, material, and only that portion of the overhead which varies with the size of the lot ordered; it does *not* include charges such as machine setup associated with each order placed.

6. Ordering costs include all preparation or make-ready charges such as writing orders, machine setup, inspection of first piece or lot sample, invoicing, cost accounting, etc.

7. The *calculated* order quantity will be used every time the lot is ordered during the forecast period.

8. The costs of carrying the item in inventory includes charges for the capital employed, taxes, insurance, obsolescence, deterioration, handling, etc. which vary with the size of the average lot-size inventory.

SYMBOLS FOR ECONOMIC ORDER QUANTITIES

Q	Economic order quantity (EOQ)
q	Order quantity
P	Daily rate of receipt, in pieces, gallons, pounds, etc. per day
U	Forecasted daily rate of usage, same units as receipt rate
N	Number of working days in forecast period
A_u	Forecasted annual usage, in *units* per forecast period, NU
A	Forecasted annual usage, in *dollars* per forecast period, NUC
C	Unit cost of items, in dollars per piece, per gallon, per pound, etc.
I	Inventory carrying cost, in dollars per dollar
S	Ordering cost per lot, in dollars per lot
R	Reserve, safety stock
T	Total of all costs over a forecast period
OP	Anticipated usage during anticipated lead time

INSTANTANEOUS-NONINSTANTANEOUS RECEIPTS: Considering the second assumption, economic-order-quantity equations will be presented for the *instantaneous-receipt* and *noninstantaneous-receipt situation* in this order. The difference be-

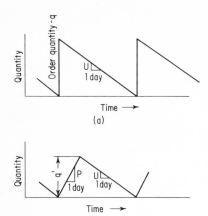

Fig. 3 (a) Instantaneous and (b) noninstantaneous receipts.

tween the two situations is readily seen in Fig. 3. Illustrated in Fig. 3a is the instantaneous receipt of material as shown by the abrupt increase of the quantity. Figure 3b illustrates a noninstantaneous situation with the material being received as it is used.

In both situations the material is being withdrawn at the rate of U units per day. For the noninstantaneous situation the inventory is being replenished at the rate of P units per day. It is obvious that P must be greater than U or the inventory will be depleted. It is apparent from the diagram that the instantaneous situation is just a special case of the noninstantaneous situation. Because most companies assume that material is received instantaneously, the economic-lot-size model will be developed for it. It is also easier to understand.

EOQ: INSTANTANEOUS RECEIPTS: As was seen in Table 1, the cost of ordering increases as the inventory carrying costs decrease. The economic order quantity, Q, is that quantity which minimizes the sum of these two costs—called the "variable costs." Although the results are the same, most economic-order-quantity equations minimize *the total annual cost, T,* as illustrated in Fig. 4.

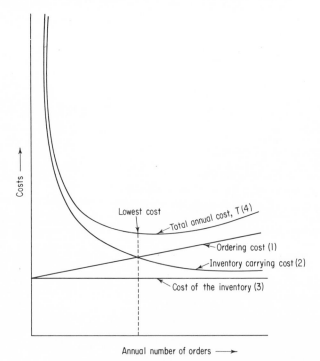

Fig. 4 Economical ordering quantities.

The total annual cost T is composed of three costs: the ordering costs and the carrying costs presented in the previous example and in addition the cost of the material purchased for the inventory during the year. Each of these costs will be presented as an equation which is also illustrated in the figure.

$$\text{Ordering costs} = \frac{\text{quantity used during period}}{\text{ordering quantity}} \times \text{cost to order}$$

$$= \frac{NU}{q} \times S \tag{1}$$

$$\text{Carrying cost} = \text{average inventory} \times \text{unit cost} \times \text{carrying charge}$$

$$= \frac{qC}{2} \times I \tag{2}$$

Cost of the inventory = inventory used during the forecast period $\times$ unit cost

$$= NUC \tag{3}$$

Combining these into the total annual cost:

$$T = \frac{NUS}{q^2} + \frac{qCI}{2} + NUC \tag{4}$$

The minimum value of T will occur when the order quantity q is equal to the economic order quantity Q. This optimum value Q can be determined by differentiating Eq. (4) with respect to q, setting the resulting equation equal to zero, and solving it for $q(Q)$.

$$\frac{dT}{dq} = -\frac{NUS}{q^2} + \frac{CI}{2} + 0$$

$$\frac{dT}{dq} = 0$$

$$Q = \sqrt{\frac{2NUS}{CI}} \tag{5}$$

It is apparent that the cost of the inventory during the year, NUC, dropped out of the solution and had no effect upon the answer. Therefore, as one might expect, solving for the *total annual cost* gives the same results as solving for *total variable cost*. This explains why reserve stocks, R, have no influence upon the economic lot size and need not be included in the equation.

In practice, the number of days in the forecasting period and the daily rate of usage are combined to give the forecasted annual usage, A_u. This results in a simplified equation:

$$Q = \sqrt{\frac{2A_uS}{CI}} \tag{6}$$

EOQ: NONINSTANTANEOUS RECEIPTS: Disregarding the reserve quantity R in the inventory, the maximum quantity is q. For the noninstantaneous situation, however, the inventory is something less than q, which will be designated as q' as shown in Fig. 3b.

The economic-order-quantity equation can be developed for noninstantaneous receipts as in the previous example, except that q' will be used for determining the carrying costs.   To do this it is necessary to state q' in terms of q.

To deliver q pieces (one lot) into inventory at a rate of P pieces per day requires q/P days during which the inventory is increasing at a rate of $(P - U)$ pieces per day. The maximum inventory will be

$$q' = \frac{q}{P}(P - U)$$

$$q' = q\left(1 - \frac{U}{P}\right) \tag{7}$$

The total annual cost for the noninstantaneous-receipt situation is

$$T = \frac{NUS}{q} + \frac{q'CI}{2} + NUC$$

Substituting for the value of q',

$$T = \frac{NUS}{q} + \frac{q(1 - U/P)CI}{2} + NUC$$

$$\frac{dT}{dq} = -\frac{NUS}{q^2} + \frac{CI(1 - U/P)}{2} + 0$$

$$\frac{dT}{dq} = 0$$

$$Q = \sqrt{\frac{2NUS}{CI(1 - U/P)}} \tag{8}$$

As before, the equation may be simplified by substituting A_u for NU.   Also, the reserve stock may be ignored since it would have no effect upon the answer.

$$Q = \sqrt{\frac{2A_uS}{CI(1 - U/P)}} \tag{9}$$

If monthly, weekly, or other forecast periods are used, the forecast usage A_u should be multiplied by 12, 52, or another constant to convert it to an annual basis before substituting it in equations.

EOQ EXPRESSED IN DOLLARS: Frequently it is desirable to express the order quantity in terms of dollars per order rather than pieces, pounds, etc.   The economic order quantity for this situation is

$$Q = \sqrt{\frac{2NUCS}{I}} \tag{10}$$

As before, NU can be replaced by A_u. To further simplify the equation, the total demand during the forecast period in terms of dollars, NUC, can be replaced by A.   The economic order quantity expressed in *dollars* now becomes

$$Q = \sqrt{\frac{2AS}{I}} \tag{11}$$

Example: Returning to the example used previously where A = $12,000, S = $12 per order, and I = 0.20:

$$Q = \sqrt{\frac{2 \times 12,000 \times 12}{0.20}} = \sqrt{\frac{288,000}{0.20}} = \$1,200 \text{ per order}$$

For this order quantity:

Number of orders = $12,000/$1,200 = 10 per year
Total ordering cost = 10 × $12 = $120 per year
Average lot-size inventory = $1,200/2 = $600
Total carrying cost = 0.20 × $600 = $120 per year
Total annual cost = total unit cost = $12,000
                    + total ordering cost =   120
                    + total carrying cost =   120
                                                 ─────────
                                                 $12,240

Any other order quantity will result in a larger annual cost, *if the assumptions used in deriving Eq. (11) are valid.*

When applying such equations in practice, it is important to determine the aggregate effects on any limitations such as capital investment, storage space, setup capacity, machine capacity, manpower, and others. Comparing these new lot sizes with those in current use it is essential to point out areas where savings can be achieved from the use of EOQ.

USING COSTS IN THE EOQ CALCULATION: The problem of variable versus fixed costs is well demonstrated in the companies that use a *standard cost* system. This standard cost is made up of labor, material, and overhead. Thus it is often said that a product has a "cost" of, say, $6, and this should be the cost used in calculating EOQ. In fact, only the labor, material, and *variable* portion of the overhead should be used.

It will be necessary to explain to managers just what costs are being used in the calculations. It would not be wise to predict a small inventory increase based on larger EOQs using variable costs and later have the manager see a large increase because the inventory was priced at full standard cost. It is important to understand the conventions of the accounting system and to be able to work with the proper cost figures that actually relate to the decision at hand.

The mathematical theory used in deriving the equation demands, for the sake of complete accuracy, that only marginal—or *incremental*—cost should appear in the ordering cost and the inventory carrying cost. The marginal costs of ordering are those which increase with the number of orders. For example, assume that a computer is being used to write orders and the total computer time used is less than the minimum rental figure. The computer cost of order preparation is not a marginal cost that could be realized as a saving if order-writing volume were reduced, and it should not appear in the formulation of the cost of ordering. However, the cost of the paper work generated for each order *is* definitely a variable that changes with the number of orders generated.

The basic theory behind the derivation of the EOQ formula states that I, the inventory carrying cost, should contain only those costs which do increase as the amount of inventory increases. The elements normally included in the inventory carrying cost include:
1. Obsolescence costs
2. Storage-space costs
3. Taxes
4. Insurance
5. Cost of capital (such as interest on money borrowed)

There is little debate on the method of deriving the first four costs, but there is open debate on item 5. One . school of thought states that the cost of capital should be included merely as the current rate of interest which the company must pay for borrowing money. A second school states that inventory is just one of many capital investments competing for available cash, and that the cost of money should be the desired rate of return on a capital investment.

One of the best-developed approaches to the use of an inventory carrying cost based on desired rate of return on capital is the ROCE concept.[3] ROCE (return on capital employed) is basically a different philosophy for determining the I value to be used in the EOQ calculations. The ROCE philosophy maintains that longer runs reduce the frequency of out-of-pocket expenditures for setups but in turn increase inventory investment. Consequently, there must be a measure of the amount of investment entailed to achieve reductions in setup costs per year. ROCE is a "tool of management" in directing the use of all of the company assets. Whether or not the ROCE philosophy is used, there is no question that in practice, the cost or the use of money ends up being a management decision, and therefore, could be classed as a management policy variable.

In an article in the *APICS Quarterly Bulletin,* R. G. Brown stated: "Some managers take the point of view that the carrying charge is merely one of the policy variables in the control system. It makes it possible to vary the balance between investment on the one hand and the out of pocket cost of the other." Brown is one of the many authorities who imply that there is no fixed, definite cost of carrying inventory but that the inventory carrying cost which is to be used in the EOQ formula should be manipulated in order to get the results that management wants. One computer manufacturer's inventory analysis program, for example, has one I that is used to evaluate the monetary savings due to reducing inventory and another I which is a management policy variable used to calculate the EOQ. This concept will be explored in a later section.

THE RESULTS OF APPLYING EOQS: As a general rule, the application of the EOQ formula to high-dollar items results in an increased number of setups or orders and a subsequent reduction in cycle stock. Therefore, for the few (say, 10 percent) fast-moving items, the number of orders will be increased, but there will be a reduction in the cycle stock for the items which account for a large percent of the total inventory investment.

The application of EOQ to the large number of low-dollar items results in a significant reduction in the number of orders and an increase in cycle stock. Across the complete line of items, the normal combined results are a reduction in the number of orders and a reduction in cycle stock.

According to the ABC theory, maximum control effort should be applied to A items. Some practitioners have interpreted this to mean that, in implementing a system, they should calculate EOQs first for the higher-dollar items and later proceed to the low-dollar items. The application of EOQs to the A items only could lead to disastrous results in a manufacturing plant that is already producing to capacity. The computed EOQs for the A items will almost certainly increase setups and reduce production capacity as they reduce the cycle stocks. EOQs should be implemented over the fast-, medium-, and slow-moving items at the same time, perhaps product line by product line.

The result of applying EOQs in a manufacturing plant can lead to practical problems such as:

1. The EOQ results, if applied, demand another setup man but none is available. How can some actual savings be realized without increasing the number of setups?

2. The EOQ results suggest fewer setups, but an increased inventory for

which there is no space. How can actual savings be realized without increasing inventory?

Two approaches to answering these dilemmas are discussed below.

The EOQ Application for a Group of Items: LIMIT. In W. E. Welch's book,[5] a technique is presented for using the EOQ theory to meet each of the two practical but opposite restrictions:

1. Keep the number of orders (setups) the same, but reduce inventory as much as possible.

2. Reduce the number of setups as much as possible while keeping the inventory the same size. Using the square root equation [Eq. (11)]

$$Q = \sqrt{\frac{2AS}{I}}$$

Welch breaks it down into the following formula:

$$EOQ = \sqrt{K} \sqrt{A} \tag{12}$$

This formula simply assumes that the constant 2, the ordering cost S, and the inventory carrying cost I are combined and considered to be a constant for many different items in inventory and can, therefore, be calculated once and expressed as K.

He then shows a method for determining the K factor to use in calculating EOQs to give the same number of orders as is used currently or to give the same level of inventory. The K factor is then used to calculate the practical economic order quantities for all items which as a group must obey the restrictions.

Welch's technique has created a considerable amount of interest and fostered much development activity. There are, however, two problems that make this excellent instruction technique somewhat awkward to apply practically:

1. When all the orders do not have an equivalent ordering cost, the Welch technique requires the use of an "equivalent K value" which makes the mathematics quite cumbersome.

2. The K value has little practical meaning to plant operating people.

The interest in Welch's technique culminated in an APICS special report[6] in which the authors developed a technique for managing the lot-size inventory in such a way that they could calculate the lowest possible lot-size inventory for any given number of orders or setups, or setup hours, and then show the alternatives open to management for balancing the results against the theoretical lot-size inventory results. This technique is called "lot-size inventory management interpolation technique" (LIMIT).

Assuming that the inventory carrying cost is more of a policy variable than an exact value, the authors of LIMIT use it as a management policy variable in calculating alternatives for the optimum EOQ. These alternatives are calculated for groups of items in order to show the choices to management in terms of *total* inventory costs compared with total ordering costs. The advantage of this approach is that it changes the focus of EOQ calculations from individual calculations to evaluating the economic impact of EOQs on a firm. Looking at groups of items and evaluating what would happen if EOQ were used can help in determining whether an inventory carrying cost is reasonable, where savings should come from, and whether lot sizes that can be obtained by manipulating the value of I used in the formula might be more profitable in practice than the theoretical EOQs.

Table 5

	.20	Inventory carrying charge
		Fixed-order cost
	$2.80	Setup cost per hour

Lot-size inventory management interpolation technique

Item No.	Annual usage	Setup hours per ord.	Unit cost	Pres. ord. quantity	Yearly setup pres.	Trial ord. quantity	Yearly setup trial	LIMIT ord. qty.	Yearly setup LIMIT
1 A	3,000	5.5	6.12	600					
2 B	2,000	6.0	2.85	350					
3 C	8,000	7.0	0.56	1,500					
4 D	1,100	4.0	2.26	400					
5 E	600	4.0	4.08	300					
6 F	1,200	2.0	0.91	950					
7 G	300	4.0	3.09	150					
8 H	2,000	2.0	0.42	1,000					
9 I	275	8.0	2.05	275					
10 J	615	6.0	0.79	310					
Total	19,090	- - -	- - -	5,835					

Table 6

	.20	Inventory carrying charge
		Fixed-order cost
	$2.80	Setup cost per hour

Lot-size inventory management interpolation technique

Item No.	Annual usage	Setup hours per ord.	Unit cost	Pres. ord. quantity	Yearly setup pres.	Trial ord. quantity	Yearly setup trial	LIMIT ord. qty.	Yearly setup LIMIT
1 A	3,000	5.5	6.12	600	27.5				
2 B	2,000	6.0	2.85	350	34.3				
3 C	8,000	7.0	0.56	1,500	37.4				
4 D	1,100	4.0	2.26	400	11.0				
5 E	600	4.0	4.08	300	8.0				
6 F	1,200	2.0	0.91	950	2.5				
7 G	300	4.0	3.09	150	8.0				
8 H	2,000	2.0	0.42	1,000	4.0				
9 I	275	8.0	2.05	275	8.0				
10 J	615	6.0	0.79	310	11.8				
Total	19,090	- - -	- - -	5,835	152.5				

Example The following is a brief excerpt adapted from the APICS special report explaining the LIMIT calculation (see Table 5):

The first step in the LIMIT calculation is to determine the present annual setup requirement for each part and for all parts based on the order quantities now in use no matter how they were determined (Table 6). The following formula is used:

$$\text{Yearly setup} = \frac{\text{annual use}}{\text{present order quantity}} \times \text{setup hours/order}$$

For Item 1-A in the table the calculation is

$$\frac{3,000}{600} \times 5.5 = 27.5 \text{ setup hours/year}$$

This is calculated for each item and entered in the column "Yearly Setup, Present." The column total of 152.5 is shown in the table.

The next step in the LIMIT analysis is to calculate *trial order quantities* using the standard EOQ formula:

$$\text{TOQ} = \sqrt{\frac{2A_uS}{CI}} \tag{6}$$

where TOQ = trial order quantity
A_u = annual use, pieces/year
S = setup cost (or fixed-order cost for purchased items), dollars/order
I = inventory carrying cost, decimal or fraction, dollars/dollar
C = unit cost, dollars/piece

The trial order quantity is calculated for each item entered in the "Trial Order Quantity" column as shown in Table 7.

Table 7

		.20	Inventory carrying charge					
			Fixed-order cost					
		$2.80	Setup cost per hour					

Lot-size inventory management interpolation technique

Item No.	Annual usage	Setup hours per ord.	Unit cost	Pres. ord. quantity	Yearly setup pres.	Trial ord. quantity	Yearly setup trial	LIMIT ord. qty.	Yearly setup LIMIT
1 A	3,000	5.5	6.12	600	27.5	274	60.0		
2 B	2,000	6.0	2.85	350	34.3	343	35.0		
3 C	8,000	7.0	0.56	1,500	37.4	1,673	33.5		
4 D	1,100	4.0	2.26	400	11.0	233	18.9		
5 E	600	4.0	4.08	300	8.0	128	18.8		
6 F	1,200	2.0	0.91	950	2.5	271	8.9		
7 G	300	4.0	3.09	150	8.0	104	11.6		
8 H	2,000	2.0	0.42	1,000	4.0	516	7.7		
9 I	275	8.0	2.05	275	8.0	173	12.7		
10 J	615	6.0	0.79	310	11.8	361	10.2		
Total	19,090	...	...	5,835	152.5	4,076	217.4		

For item 1A the following answer would be obtained for the trial order quantity, using a carrying cost I assumed to be equal to 0.20:

$$\text{TOQ} = \sqrt{\frac{2(3,000)(5.5 \times 2.80)}{(0.20)(6.12)}} = 274$$

The yearly setup hours, resulting from the use of the trial order quantities, is then established using the same approach as above.
Item 1A is calculated as follows:

$$\frac{3,000}{274} \times 5.5 = 60.0$$

This value is calculated for each item and entered in the column "Yearly Setup, Trial." The column is then totaled as shown in the table. Note that the order quantities calculated using an I of 0.20 would give a 31 percent increase in setup hours.

Having calculated the total yearly setup hours that result from the present order quantities (152.5 hours) and the total yearly setup hours that result from the trial order quantities (217.4 hours), the analyst is now in a position to apply the LIMIT formula:

$$R_L = R_T \left(\frac{H_L}{H_T}\right)^2 \tag{13}$$

and

$$M = \left(\frac{H_T}{H_L}\right) \tag{14}$$

where H_L = total setup hours per year resulting from *present* order quantities, which will be equal to the total for the LIMIT order quantities, since this is the limiting factor

H_T = total setup hours resulting from trial order quantities

R_T = inventory carrying cost used to calculate trial order quantities

R_L = the implied inventory carrying cost used in calculating the LIMIT order quantities

M = a multiplier used to adjust TOQs to LIMIT OQs

Equation (13) is used to calculate the implied inventory carrying cost of the LIMIT order quantities.

Equation (14) is used to arrive at a multiplier factor. The trial order quantities, when multiplied by this factor, give the value of the LIMIT order quantities for each item and for the group. These are the most economical order quantities that can be used and yet stay with the present setup limitations as shown below:

$$R_L = 0.20 \left(\frac{152.5}{217.4}\right)^2 = 0.098$$

$$M = \frac{217.4}{152.5} = 1.428$$

Using the multiplier factor, the LIMIT order quantity (LOQ) for item 1A is calculated as follows:

$$\text{Trial order quantity} \times \text{multiplier factor} = \text{LOQ}$$
$$274 \times 1.428 = 391$$

Table 8

	.20	Inventory carrying charge
		Fixed-order cost
	$2.80	Setup cost per hour

Lot-size inventory management interpolation technique

Item No.	Annual usage	Setup hours per ord.	Unit cost	Pres. ord. quantity	Yearly setup pres.	Trial ord. quantity	Yearly setup trial	LIMIT ord. qty.	Yearly setup LIMIT
1 A	3,000	5.5	6.12	600	27.5	274	60.0	391	42.3
2 B	2,000	6.0	2.85	350	34.3	343	35.0	490	24.4
3 C	8,000	7.0	0.56	1,500	37.4	1,673	33.5	2,389	23.4
4 D	1,100	4.0	2.26	400	11.0	233	18.9	333	13.2
5 E	600	4.0	4.08	300	8.0	128	18.8	183	13.1
6 F	1,200	2.0	0.91	950	2.5	271	8.9	387	6.2
7 G	300	4.0	3.09	150	8.0	104	11.6	149	8.1
8 H	2,000	2.0	0.42	1,000	4.0	516	7.7	737	5.4
9 I	275	8.0	2.05	275	8.0	173	12.7	247	8.9
10 J	615	6.0	0.79	310	11.8	361	10.2	·516	7.2
Total	19,090	...	...	5,835	152.5	4,076	217.4	5,822	152.2

The LOQ is calculated for each item and entered in the table as shown in Table 8.

The yearly setup hours resulting from the use of the LIMIT order quantities are then calculated. For item 1A:

$$\frac{3,000}{391} \times 5.5 = 42.3$$

This figure should be calculated in a similar way for each item and entered in the column "Yearly Setup, LIMIT." This column is then totaled as shown in the table.

Note that the total "Yearly Setup, Present" is equal to the total "Yearly Setup, LIMIT." If we determine the dollar value of the present and the LIMIT lot sizes (Table 9) and divide by 2 to get the *average* lot-size inventory, we see that there

Table 9

No.	Pieces			Unit cost	Dollars		
	Present	Trial	LIMIT		Present	Trial	LIMIT
1A	600	274	391	$6.12	$ 3,672	$1,677	$2,393
2B	350	343	490	2.85	998	977	1,396
3C	1,500	1,673	2,389	0.56	840	937	1,338
4D	400	233	333	2.26	904	527	753
5E	300	128	183	4.08	1,224	522	747
6F	950	271	387	0.91	864	246	352
7G	150	104	149	3.09	464	321	460
8H	1,000	516	737	0.42	420	217	309
9I	275	173	247	2.05	564	354	506
10J	310	361	516	0.79	245	285	407
Total	5,835	4,076	5,822		$10,195	$6,063	$8,661

has been a $767 reduction with no change in setup. This is a reduction of 15 percent in inventory investment with no increase in operating expense.

In the preceeding steps the LIMIT order quantities were calculated to obtain the most economical quantities possible within the present setup limitation. A series of total order quantities that will result from various setup or inventory limitations can be calculated by using Eq. (14). For example, if management wanted to know what the minimum average lot-size inventory would be (for this family of items) using only 250 hours of setup time, it could be determined as follows:

$$M = \frac{217.4}{250} = 0.87$$

The value of the total trial order quantity, in dollars, is $6,063. The total lot-size inventory for a 250-hour setup limitation would therefore be

$$\$6,063 \times 0.87 = \$5,275$$

and the average inventory

$$\frac{\$5,275}{2} = \$2,637$$

Figure 5 shows the average lot-size inventory for various setup levels for this family of items. It also shows the present average inventory level and total setup requirement (point A). It is possible to reduce the present inventory level to point B without increasing the setup, or to reduce the total setup requirement to point C without increasing the average inventory level. Both of these result in savings with *no* offsetting increases in cost.

By calculating the data required and developing the curve shown in Fig. 5, management can be shown the alternatives that are available in managing the order-quantity portion of the inventory for "all" items in the inventory. This is what management is interested in—the total inventory, not the individual bits and pieces.

The implied inventory carrying cost for any point on the curve can be determined by using Eq. (13). For the 250-hour setup versus the $2,638 average inventory point, the implied cost of carrying inventory is calculated as follows:

$$I = 0.20 \left(\frac{250}{217.4} \right)^2 = 0.264$$

While the example above emphasizes the application of LIMIT where there is a constraint on setup, a constraint on inventory could be evaluated based on the curve. The significance of LIMIT in inventory management is that it focuses attention on the fact that the primary value of the EOQ calculation, from a management point of view, comes from looking at the impact of EOQ on *groups* of items that go through common facilities and making sure that EOQ generates savings or reductions in inventory than can actually be realized.

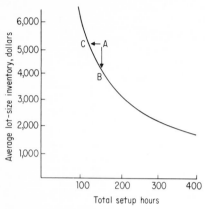

Fig. 5 Setup hours vs. inventory.

Common Setups. In practice, there are often sets of items that share the ordering or setup costs. Screw machines, for example, frequently involve a major setup for the family and minor setups for each item in the family. Another example is the ordering of many items on one purchase order. There are certain ordering costs that are related to the entire order, such as the cost of the form, mailing, and preparation of vendor names and addresses. This group is called "header costs" and is comparable to the major setup costs, and does not vary with the number of items. The cost of adding individual items to the order is called the "line cost" and is comparable to the minor setup.

One of the fundamental assumptions of the EOQ formula—that the order quantity for one item has no effect on the ordering or maintenance of other items—is violated here. The EOQ formula can be used to calculate the family order quantity in dollars:

$$\text{Family EOQ} = \sqrt{\frac{2\Sigma A\Sigma S}{I}} \tag{15}$$

where ΣS = sum of the major and minor setup costs/order
  ΣA = projected annual dollar family usage
  I = carrying costs

If every item is to be ordered every time there is a major setup, Eq. (15) gives the most economic *group* order quantity in dollars.

When the order frequency for each of a family of items is made to coincide with the order quantity, this technique is called "joint replenishment." If the group is to be jointly replenished, the group order quantity is calculated, but the amount to be ordered for each item varies with each order cycle.

The technique for determining the quantity of each item to be ordered is called "allocation." The principle of allocation is that each item in the family will be ordered in an equal-time supply based on the item's current stock position, current forecast, *and* forecast error. This means that each item should be ready for reorder at approximately the same time. Some items might be ordered most economically every second or third time the family was reordered.

The precise evaluation of the economics of joint replenishment versus item EOQs is an extensive one, and it is not always economical to force a joint setup. The practitioner should experiment with individual EOQs *and* joint replenishment before choosing the most appropriate one for his application.

Seasonal Production.* The application of the EOQ to a seasonal item violates the assumption that demand is uniform and continuous throughout the year. In practice, such an application will produce an excessive number of orders during the off season and excessive stock during the peak season.

One approach is to calculate a predetermined time supply to order each time, using the EOQ formula to generate the time supply as follows:

$$Q = \sqrt{\frac{2AS}{I}}$$

$\dfrac{A}{Q} = N$, the number of annual orders

$\dfrac{12}{N}$ = time supply in months for each order quantity

If the normal application of the EOQ formula suggested 12 orders per year, the common supply for seasonal ordering is one month's supply. In this case, the order quantity for the item would be the *seasonally adjusted* month's supply.

When there are extreme seasonal peaks as in gardening supplies, it is usually worth analyzing the inventory to determine which items should be produced furthest ahead of the peak season. The objective of off-season production is to *store man-hours.* This can be done most effectively by making those items which store the most labor, with the least inventory carrying cost, further in advance of their requirement. The analysis is usually done by comparing the ratio of labor to material costs for the items under consideration. The problem of using inventory to smooth production where the sales pattern is seasonal is discussed in Chapter 10.

Quantity Discounts. Many purchased items can be obtained at substantial savings based on quantity discounts quoted by the vendor. If an item does have a discount schedule, the regular EOQ calculation should be extended to see if the larger quantity should be ordered.

Assume the following data for an item:

$$\text{Annual usage, } A = 2,000 \text{ units}$$
$$\text{Unit cost, } C = \$1 \text{ each}$$
$$\text{Ordering cost, } S = \$15.00$$
$$\text{Inventory carrying cost, } I = 20\%$$

The standard EOQ calculation using Eq. (6) is

$$Q = \sqrt{\frac{2AS}{CI}}$$
$$= \sqrt{\frac{2 \times 2000 \times \$15}{.20 \times \$1}}$$
$$= 548 \text{ units}$$

This EOQ would be correct if unit cost did not vary with the size of the order quantity. If a discount of 1 percent for quantities of $1,000 were offered by the vendor, it would be necessary to calculate:

1. The extra inventory costs
2. The reduced ordering costs
3. The savings from taking the discount

These would then be compared with the costs associated with the economic

* See also Chapter 17.

TABLE 10   Discount Calculation

Present			With discount	
548		Lot-size (1,000 − 1%)	990	
274		Average lot-size inventory	495	
	$54.80	Inventory carrying cost (20%)		$99.00
3.7		Reorders per year	2.0	
	55.50	Cost of orders ($15 each)		30.00
		Savings from discount		−20.00
	$110.30	Total yearly cost		$109.00

order quantity.   This type of calculation is shown in Table 10, and by a slim margin the discount seems worth taking.

This calculation is fine, but once again the practitioner should relate his mathematical calculations to the real world.   This requires looking at current lot size and proposed lot sizes to be sure that they are practical from the point of view of available storage space, available cash to invest in inventory, etc.

The solution described applies where the unit price depends upon the amount ordered and that supplied in *one* shipment.   This is not the solution where the unit cost is based on the annual blanket purchase order with periodic releases.   In this case, the *release* EOQ should be calculated using the contracted unit costs in the standard EOQ calculation and using only the costs for generating a release as the "ordering costs."

Pitfalls to Avoid.   There have been many instances where EOQs have been calculated, examined, and discontinued because the results did not seem practical.   In most cases a slight change in the EOQs would have given a practical solution and maintained much of the economics.

It can be seen in Fig. 4 that the *total annual cost curve* is very flat near the lowest-cost point.   In fact, if the theoretical EOQ is raised 20 percent, the total cost is raised only 2 percent.   Because of this, EOQs can be rounded off without a significant loss in economics.   EOQs should be rounded:

1. To the nearest pack size
2. To at least cover the demand between the opportunities to order, such as the review time or periodic shop schedules
3. Down to the maximum time supply set by a policy, such as the common policy "no EOQ can exceed a one-year supply"
4. To reasonable production lots such as 100, 900, 1,000, instead of 92, 921, or 1063.

Unless most present-order quantities are high and setups low, the increase in setups for fast-moving items will be offset by the fewer setups for slow-moving items.   However, it is imperative that the total setups produced by the EOQs be compared with present setups before actually implementing the EOQ.   If the EOQ setups are excessive by some measurement, the LIMIT calculation could be used to bring the setups back in line until more setup capacity is available.

WHEN TO REORDER: THE ORDER-POINT CONCEPT

When should a replenishment order be placed for an independent-demand inventory item whose usage is uncertain?   That is, how low can the available quantity (quantity on hand plus quantity on order) drop before a replenishment order is placed and still maintain the desired inventory service level? The inventory level at which a replenishment order must be placed is called the "order point."

The concept of the order point can be explained best by starting with a rather ideal item as illustrated in Fig. 6. In this example, the future usage for the item is assumed to be exactly 100 per week and the lead time is assumed to be exactly three weeks. If an order is placed when the available inventory reaches 300, the item will arrive in exactly three weeks (lead time) and the usage during the three-week order cycle will be exactly 300. Therefore, just as the last unit is consumed the replenishment order will arrive. This would

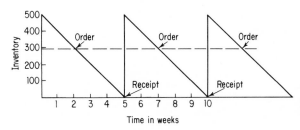

Fig. 6 The reorder point.

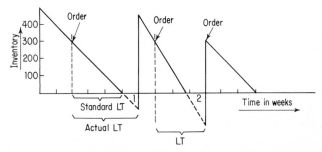

Fig. 7 Varying lead time and demand. (1) Actual lead time = 4 weeks, resulting in lost sales or backorders of 100 units. The chart assumes backorders. (2) Demand during lead time (3 weeks) was 500 (200 above average), resulting in lost sales or backorders of 200 units. The chart assumes backorders.

be a perfectly managed inventory which has only working or cycle stock. An equation for this relationship is

$$\text{Order point (OP)} = \text{anticipated usage during lead time} \qquad (16)$$

However, since neither demand nor lead time is usually known precisely (see Fig. 7), the formula could be altered to:

$$\text{OP} = \text{anticipated usage during anticipated lead time} \qquad (17)$$

Since actual demand should exceed the average demand 50 percent of the time, the order point in Eq. (17) would result in a stock out during 50 percent of the reorder cycles. Therefore, to maintain a high service level when there is an uncertain demand, the reorder system cannot permit the inventory level to drop as low as the average usage during the lead time before an order is placed. In Fig. 8 a more realistic system is charted. The equation for the order point is

Order point = anticipated average usage during lead time + safety stock (18)

This safety stock is referred to by various names, such as "reserve stock," "buffer stock," or "protective stock." Whatever the terminology, its purpose is to provide a high level of service where expected demand and/or lead times are uncertain.

It is the intent of the order point to provide a reorder signal in time to replenish the inventory and still meet the expected demand during the next replenishment lead time. The order point allows safety stock to provide a contingency for uncertainty in demand and lead time. It is most important to note that the demand in the order point is the expected demand during the *next* lead time. Therefore, an order-point system must have the provision for *forecasting* the expected demand during the lead time.

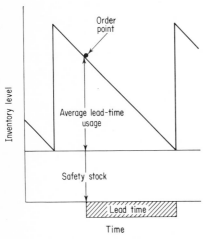

Fig. 8 Order point with safety stock.

THE CONCEPT OF FORECAST ERROR

The key reason for safety stock is the presence of *forecast errors*. Many inventory system have fallen far short of the potential savings because safety stocks were based on a fixed rule and not on the forecast error for each item. No forecast is likely to be perfect, and it is important, in any inventory system where there is uncertainty in demand, to measure forecast error and provide protection against it. Error is inherent in forecasts, but lead-time variations *should* be controllable through better production control or better vendor follow-up (or perhaps better choice of vendors). For this reason most well-designed systems try to *control* lead times and *protect* against forecast error.

An examination of the demand for two items for five months will illustrate the importance of providing for the forecast error in setting safety stock:

Month	Demand for Item A	Demand for Item B
1	100	100
2	102	152
3	96	72
4	98	48
5	104	128
Average =	100/month	100/month

Assuming that the lead time is one month, the typical forecast for the demand of each item for the lead time would be approximately 100. A system with an across-the-board safety-stock rule based on forecast only might set the safety stock at a one-week supply or approximately one-fourth of the monthly forecast for all items. Consider this rule for items A and B. Under the fixed rule, both items are reordered when the available inventory reaches 125. For item A, the monthly demand never exceeds 104, and there would be an excess of safety stock of at least 21 at all times. Item B would be reordered when the available inventory reaches 125 and would have stock outs if a reorder was required during months 2 and 5. A rule of four units in safety stock for items A would cover the service for that item. A safety stock of 28 for item B would have eliminated the stock out in month 5 and greatly reduced the stock-out amount in month 2. The service level could be raised for item B by setting safety stock at 52, thus eliminating one more stock out in month 2.

Of course, these conclusions about items A and B assume that the five months shown are a representative sample from which conclusions can be drawn about months 6, 7, 8, etc. Five periods is a very small sample, yet going back further to get more history might include data that are no longer valid (the average demand for item A or B might have been well above or below the current average of 100 units, for example). A dynamic inventory management system, therefore, starts with four basic elements:

1. Selection of an appropriate forecast model
2. A means of updating the forecasts of average usage on a routine basis
3. A means of measuring forecast errors so that reserve stocks can be calculated for each item rationally
4. A means for updating the estimate of forecast error so that reserve stocks will reflect current forecasting ability

If the order point is not revised upward as demand increases, orders will not be placed on time and excessive stock outs will result. If the order point is not revised downward as demand drops off, an order will be placed before required and an excessive inventory will be built up while demands are actually dropping off. A good rule of thumb is that the forecast and the forecast error used in setting the order point should be revised at least twice during the replenishment cycle.

Developing the Forecasting Technique. In forecasting the demand for most items for the coming lead time, the use of the "intrinsic" approach is recommended. Intrinsic forecasting is the projection of information contained within the products' past history into the near future. "Extrinsic" forecasting would be the use of such external indicators as the Federal Reserve Board index, new housing starts, and gross national product to forecast the use of an item.

It is seldom practical to use extrinsic forecasts for item forecasts; they are usually used to forecast product groups and then current-item forecasts are pro-rated against the new group forecast to reconcile the two. The terms "intrinsic" and "extrinsic" generally refer to "statistical" as opposed to "judgment" forecasts. Obviously, individual items such as new products, products being promoted heavily, etc. must have some judgment used (until more dependable mathematical techniques are available) for forecasting their future demand.

The first step in intrinsic forecasting is to find the past pattern of demand. Pattern identification is most often referred to as "forecast-model selection." A discussion of the demand for the items shown in Table 11 will illustrate the process of forecast-model selection. The demands for items A, B, and C were made artificially stable to make the model, or pattern, selection easier.

Intrinsic forecasting is the extension of the past pattern into the future. An extension of the exact horizontal pattern for item A would produce a forecast of 17 units for month 6. Note that all five demands fit exactly on a "horizontal" line which has a "height" of 17, and this item would thus require a "horizontal" model.

An extrapolation of the pattern for item B produces a forecast of 6 units for B in month 6. The demand pattern or "model" for item B is "trend." An extrapolation of the demand for item C produces a forecast of 3 units for month

TABLE 11—Demand Models

Months	Item A	Item B	Item C	Item D
1	17	1	1	120
2	17	2	3	83
3	17	3	1	107
4	17	4	3	90
5	17	5	1	95
6	?	?	?	?

6. The demand pattern for item C is "seasonal." The pattern and forecast for item D is more difficult to recognize. The selection of the forecast model is difficult because, in this more realistic example, the demand varies erratically about the pattern and more data are required in order to determine whether a horizontal trend or seasonal model best applies. An analysis of the demand for a similar item shown in Fig. 9 will illustrate the problem. This is the plot of two years of demand recorded in four-week periods.

A close examination of this demand indicates that there is little or no significant trend. The peaks and valleys of demand cannot be reliably attributed to seasonal effects since the peak in one year occurs three periods earlier in the following year. Figure 10 indicates that the pattern (or model) is simply a horizontal one with the horizontal line representing the average demand of 100. The demand does *vary* significantly about the horizontal line, but its variation would be wider about a trend line or a seasonal pattern. This brief exercise in forecast-model selection with realistic data indicates the complexity of the job, particularly when it must be done for thousands of individual inventory items. To assist in this analysis, some computer manufacturers supply programs

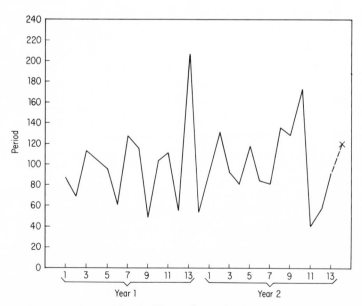

Fig. 9 Demand pattern 1.

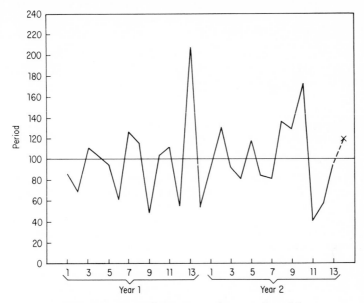

Fig. 10 Demand pattern 1—horizontal model.

that will analyze past data, screen out unusual demands, and select the most appropriate forecast model. The best forecasting model will produce the least-average forecast error and will require the least safety stock.

The next element required is a forecast updating technique. This updating technique must be a compromise, since as we have seen in Fig. 10, the best forecast for this erratic demand pattern is 100. Nevertheless, a good forecasting technique should be sensitive enough to react to a real increase or decrease in demand that persists. At the end of year 2, the best forecast is still 100 units. Assume that demand in the following period is 120. A logical series of steps in updating or "correcting" the old forecast of 100 might be

$$\text{New forecast} = \text{old forecast} + \text{correction}$$

or

$$\text{New forecast} = \text{old forecast} + \text{forecast error}$$

or

$$\text{New forecast} = \text{old forecast} + (\text{demand} - \text{old forecast})$$

For example,

$$\text{New forecast} = 100 + (120 - 100)$$
$$\text{New forecast} = 120$$

This means that we have corrected the forecast by the full amount of the forecast error, thus reacting dramatically (obviously too dramatically) to the forecast error. A better approach that would meet our requirement for a "compromise" between reacting and overreacting would be to correct the old forecast by a fraction of the forecast error. The formula would then be

$$\text{New forecast} = \text{old forecast} + \alpha \, (\text{demand} - \text{old forecast})$$
$$\text{New forecast} = 100 + \alpha \, (20) \tag{19}$$

The value of α would be 0.10 if it is decided to correct the forecast by 10 percent of the difference between current demand and the old forecast. In this example the new forecast would be 102 units.

This technique of forecasting is known as "exponential smoothing." This particular technique employed for the horizontal item is known as "first order" or "single exponential smoothing." The term "single" is used because the technique is revising the single point (average) which designates a horizontal line. The percentage adjustment of the forecast error is called "alpha" (α). We used 0.1, which will react roughly equivalent to a 19-period moving average. A higher alpha would react more quickly to changes in demand (0.2, for example, reacts like a 9-period moving average), but results in a more erratic forecast. There have been articles and textbook chapters dedicated to the selection of alpha. There is a theoretically correct technique for the selection of alpha based on the forecasting model, the number of periods of past data, and the reliability. Today, most authorities recommend against elaborate research to determine an optimum alpha. One company dedicated six man-months and 100 computer-hours to this process with questionable results. Generally for an item that has a horizontal pattern and at least 12 periods of data, an alpha of 0.1 will be a satisfactory starting value until experience shows that a more stable (lower alpha) or reactive (higher alpha) forecast is really required.

Let us now examine the implications of raising the forecast when demand exceeds the old forecast. For example, in the previous example, the forecast (100) was low (demand was 120), resulting in at least a dangerous reduction in safety stock. To correct this error, this forecasting system would:

1. Raise the forecast, which would
2. Raise the order point, which would
3. Cause an earlier order to be placed, which would
4. Cause an earlier replenishment, which would
5. Restore inventory to the proper level

To be accurate and keep inventory property adjusted, the forecast, and therefore, the order point, must be revised frequently. Using the alpha of 0.1 and some assumed demands, the forecasting results for several periods of assumed data are shown in Table 12.

TABLE 12   Exponential Smoothing

Period	Old forecast	Demand	Forecast error	New forecast
1	100	120	+20	102
2	102	92	−10	101
3	101	81	−20	99
4	99	119	+20	101
5	101	111	+10	102
6	102	82	−20	100

Using the single-order exponential-smoothing formula to forecast all items, however, could be disastrous. Figure 11 shows a different type of demand pattern. A horizontal line will not accurately represent the demand for this item. This is a trend item and a trend forecast model would work here. A trend line can be represented with two points or as a point and a slope. The technique for forecasting the item in Fig. 11 with a two-point model is known as "double smoothing," which is really single smoothing with a trend correction.

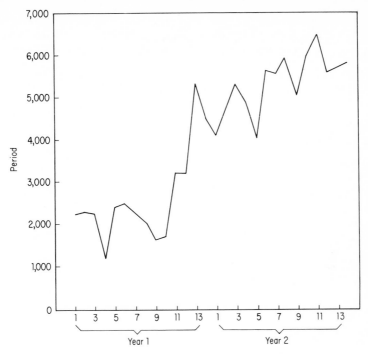

Fig. 11   Demand pattern 2—trend model.

Using double smoothing, the forecast is made up of two parts usually designated as A and B.

$$A = \text{old forecast} + \alpha\,(\text{demand} - \text{old forecast}) \tag{20}$$
$$B = \text{old } B + \alpha\,(\text{new } A - \text{old } B) \tag{21}$$

The first part, A, is simply single exponential smoothing as given before. B provides a point against which trend can be measured. This correction is made by adjusting the first point A by the difference between A and B.

$$\text{New forecast} = A + (A - B)$$
$$\text{New forecast} = 2A - B \tag{22}$$

This is the proper forecasting formula when exponential smoothing is to be used to update the forecast for a trend item. The key element here is that the trend item can be forecast just as accurately as the horizontal item if the right technique is elected. This means that the trend item could have the same service level with the same approximate safety-stock to sales ratio. High forecast errors mean high safety stocks; low forecast errors mean low safety stocks.

Figure 12 is a classical example of a seasonal item. A horizontal or a trend model would not work well in forecasting an item of this type.

Companies sometimes say that they have tried exponential smoothing and it has failed. In many cases, the failure was due to using single smoothing on either a trend or seasonal item or using trend forecasting on a seasonal item.

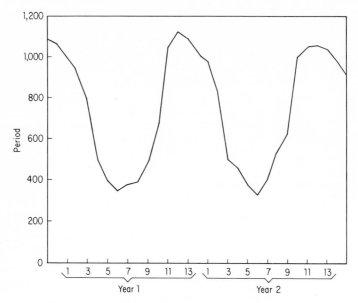

Fig. 12 Demand pattern 3—seasonal model.

There are forecasting techniques that fit the seasonal item. The simplest of these is to use some sort of seasonal index or percentage. If the year were divided into 13 four-week periods, for example, an *average* period would be one-thirteenth of the year's sales, or 7.7 percent. If demand in period 13 is normally 12.0 percent of the year's sales, then in forecasting sales for that period they would be adjusted upward to reflect this. For example, if the exponential-smoothing forecast was 700 units per period and the forecast was being made for period 13, the following calculation would be involved:

1. Forecast for an "average" period (7.7 percent) = 700
2. Adjustment for period 13 = 12.0/7.7 × 700
3. Forecast for period 13 = 1,091

Incoming demand data are *deseasonalized* in the same manner, making the data equivalent to an average month's sales before they are entered into the exponential-smoothing formula.

Exponential smoothing is a simple and well-accepted method for updating item forecasts. The four basic forecast models that could be applied using the forecasting-updating techniques discussed above are:

1. Horizontal model: single exponential smoothing
2. Trend model: double exponential smoothing
3. Horizontal-seasonal: single smoothing with seasonal adjustment
4. Trend-seasonal: double smoothing with seasonal adjustment

Measuring and Updating Forecast Error. No forecast will ever be perfect. Forecast error is inherent in every forecast. To set the minimum safety stock for a desired level of customer service, safety stocks should be established based on forecast error. Techniques for measuring forecast error and updating these measures of error are discussed below.

In Table 12 the sum of the algebraic forecast errors is zero, as it should be if the *correct* forecasting technique is being used. There are two common statistical techniques which are used to calculate the average dispersion (forecast error here) in such a way that the positive values will not cancel the negatives:

1. Square the forecast errors, sum the squares, and divide by the number of errors to give the average squared error. Then take the square root. This calculation is called the "standard deviation," and the formula is

$$\text{Standard deviation} = \sqrt{\frac{(\text{forecast error})^2}{\text{number of errors}}} \qquad (23)$$

The precise calculation of the standard deviation to give an *unbiased* sample would require that the denominator in Eq. (23) read "number of errors minus one." For simplicity this has been ignored in this chapter.

2. Take the absolute value (treat all values as positive) of each error, sum the absolute (i.e., ignoring plus and minus signs) value, and divide by the number of errors. The result is known as the "mean (average) absolute deviation" (MAD). The formula is

$$\text{MAD} = \frac{\text{sum of absolute errors}}{\text{number of errors}} \qquad (24)$$

TABLE 13   Standard Deviation

Forecast error	Squared error	Absolute error
+20	400	20
−10	100	10
−20	400	20
+20	400	20
+10	100	10
−20	400	20
Sum 0	6 | 1800	6 | 100
Average	300	16.67

1. Standard deviation = $\sqrt{300}$ = 17.32
2. MAD = 16.67

Table 13 illustrates this calculation and is taken from the example in Table 12.

Most companies now use MAD rather than the standard deviation in inventory calculations for the following reasons:

1. MAD is simpler to calculate.
2. MAD can be updated conveniently using exponential smoothing.
3. MAD is the average amount of the underforecasts and the average amount of the overforecasts when the proper forecasting technique is used.
4. MAD is also the *average* amount of each stock out if no safety stock is used.
5. MAD is the expected forecast error for the next forecast period.

In summary, MAD is recommended because it is easier to calculate and has more practical meaning. It is theoretically less precise than the standard deviation but close enough for most inventory applications. MAD and standard deviation have a numerical relationship for the normal distribution:

$$\text{Standard deviation} = 1.25\ \text{MAD (approximately)} \qquad (25)$$

The above relationship makes it easy to convert statistical tables established for the standard deviation so that they can be used with MAD.

Single-order exponential smoothing is recommended for updating MAD for horizontal trend items. MAD should be revised each time the forecast is recalculated. Exponential smoothing is also recommended for calculating the deseasonalized MAD for a seasonal item. The smoothing formula for recalculating MAD is

$$\text{New MAD} = \text{old MAD} + \alpha \, (\text{error} - \text{old MAD}) \tag{26}$$

The quantity (error) is the absolute forecast error. To illustrate this calculation, some data from Fig. 12 are used in Table 14. An alpha of 0.1 is used here. A starting value of 15 for MAD is assumed.

TABLE 14   Updating MAD

Old MAD	Forecast error	Absolute error	(Error − old MAD)	0.1(Error − old MAD)	New MAD
15	+20	20	+5	+0.50	15.5
15.5	−10	10	−5.5	−0.55	14.9
14.9	−20	20	5.1	+0.51	15.4

Note that MAD is increased in the first and third periods because the actual error was larger than expected (old MAD).

Using Forecast Error in Calculating Order Points. Earlier, it was stated that an order point is equal to the forecast of demand over lead time plus safety stock. Using MAD as the measurement for forecast error, the order point, OP, becomes:

OP = anticipated average usage during lead time plus safety stock.
Safety stock = anticipated error [Eq. (18)] for the forecast of usage during lead time (MAD) multiplied by a service factor.

This service factor is obtained from standard statistical tables like that shown in Table 15 and is usually designated k. Larger values of k will result in

TABLE 15   Safety Factors for "Order-cycle" Service

Safety Factor, k	Percent of Order Cycles with No Back Order or Stock Out
0.00	50.00
1.00	78.81
1.25	84.13
2.00	94.52
2.50	97.72
3.00	99.18
3.75	99.87

more safety stock and a higher level of service as discussed in the following section. The safety stock can then be expressed:

$$\text{Safety stock (SS)} = k \times \text{MAD}_{\text{LT}} \tag{27}$$

and order point becomes

$$\text{OP} = \text{forecast}_{\text{LT}} + k \times \text{MAD}_{\text{LT}} \tag{28}$$

Note that the forecast and MAD are for the *lead time*. The order point can be described as the *maximum reasonable demand for the lead time*. That is, the order point is the expected lead-time usage plus enough safety stock to cover the additional demand up to a maximum economical level. The forecast and MAD for each item are normally calculated for an even time interval such as one week, four weeks, or one month. The calculated forecast and MAD must then be projected to cover the lead time.

For a horizontal item, the lead-time forecast is

$$\text{Forecast }_{LT} = (\text{forecast}) \left(\frac{\text{lead time}}{\text{forecast interval}} \right) \tag{29}$$

Example

$$LT = 6 \text{ weeks}$$
$$\text{Forecast interval} = 4 \text{ weeks}$$
$$4\text{-week forecast} = 100 \text{ units/week}$$
$$\text{Forecast}_{LT} = (100)(\tfrac{6}{4}) = 150$$

The extrapolation of the trend item is more complicated because the trend for the forecast interval must be added. The formula is

$$\text{Forecast}_{LT} = (\text{forecast})(T) + (T) \frac{(T + 1)}{2} \text{ trend} \tag{30}$$

where T = lead time/forecast interval. Equation (30) is exact where T is an integer and is a close approximation where T is not an exact integer.

In extrapolating the forecast for a seasonal item, the seasonal effect must be added for each period contained in the lead time.

It is logical that the average percent of forecast error for a one-week forecast will be higher than the percent of error in an annual or a monthly forecast. Therefore, MAD for four weeks will be less than four times MAD for one week. Brown[7] suggests a useful general relationship based on the results of extensive simulation. This relationship is

$$\text{MAD}_{LT} = \text{MAD}(0.65 + 0.34T) \tag{31}$$

Example

$$\text{MAD} = 20$$
$$LT = 4 \text{ weeks}$$
$$\text{Forecast interval} = 1 \text{ week}$$
$$T = 4$$
$$\text{MAD 4 weeks} = 20(0.56 + 0.34 \times 4)$$
$$= 20 \times 1.92 = 38.4$$

SELECTING SAFETY FACTORS: The elements of the order point in Eq. (19) are forecast, k, and MAD. The selections above have described the theory and techniques for calculating the forecast and MAD. The discussion below explains some useful techniques for selecting the safety factor (k) once the desired definition and the service level have been specified.

Two of the most frequently used definitions of the item service level are:
1. Percent of order cycles with no stock outs
2. Percent of dollar demand filled off the shelf (without back orders)

For an item, the dollar service level and unit service level are identical. The above two measurements are the two that can be set easily using statistical tables directly. (The *IMPACT Implementation Manual* has an excellent discussion of other service levels such as percent of line items filled and percent of shelf items in stock.[8])

In using either of the two definitions of service mentioned above, both a stock out and a back order are a "disservice." That is, if the quantity desired is not on the shelf at the time the order is entered, there is a disservice by the definition of statistical service. It will also be assumed that *forecast errors* (not demand) are normally distributed. If the correct forecasting technique is used, this assumption can be used safely (even though it is not always theoretically correct) for all items except those with demand characterized by extreme variations and frequent zero demand, often called "lumpy" demand.

The measure of service based on order cycles is the simplest service measure. If k were zero, safety stock would be zero and an order would be placed when the available inventory reached the forecast usage for the lead time. Normally, in 50 percent of the order cycles, the demand will exceed the forecast and result in a stock out. It is most important to remember that the stock out occurs in 50 percent of the *order cycles*, not specifically weeks, months, or years. If the order quantity is a one-week supply, 26 stock outs are expected in a year with zero safety stock. If the order quantity is a two-year supply, only one stock out every four years will result, since a stock out will be likely to occur only every other order cycle.

For the selection of k, refer to Table 15, which is an excerpt from the normal-distribution tables with the k's adjusted to act as the MAD multiplier instead of the usual standard-deviation multiplier.

Problem 1 Select k, set safety stock and order point where

$$\text{Forecast}_{LT} = 200$$
$$\text{MAD}_{LT} = 50$$
$$\text{Desired service} = 97.72$$

Solution From Table 15 a k of 2.50 is selected to meet the specified service level of 97.72 percent and

$$k = 2.50$$
$$\text{SS} = k(\text{MAD})_{LT} = (2.5)(50) = 125$$
$$\text{OP} = \text{FCST}_{LT} + \text{SS} = 200 + 125 = 325$$

In Problem 1, an item with an order quantity of *one week's* supply will fill all demand during 97.72 percent of the weekly order cycles or result in approximately one stock out per year. An item with an order quantity of one year's supply would theoretically be out of stock only 2.28 $(100 - 97.72)$ times in 100 years. Note that if the same percentage service level were specified for all items in inventory, the result would be a high service to the low-dollar-volume items (large time supply OQs) and a low level of service to the high-dollar-volume items (small time supply OQs). To use this service measure properly, service should first be established in terms of the number of stock outs per year that can be tolerated; this should be expressed as a service percentage, and *then* the value of k should be obtained from the table.

Assume service level set at one stock out per year in the examples below.

Example A
1. OQ = one week's supply
2. 52 reorder cycles or chances for a stock out
3. 51 out of 52 cycles per year with no stock out: $\frac{51}{52} = 98$ percent
4. $k = 2.5$ (from Table 15)

Example B
1. OQ = six months' supply
2. Two reorder cycles per year
3. One out of two cycles with no stock out $= \frac{1}{2} = 50$ percent
4. $k = 0$ (from Table 15)

To use the service measure based on percent of *unit or dollar demand* filled instead of reorder cycles, a calculation must be made before the statistical tables are used. This calculation is called the "service-function" calculation, and the equation is

$$g(k) = \frac{\text{usage during order cycle } (1 - p)}{\text{MAD}_{\text{LT}}} \tag{32}$$

where p = desired service level expressed as a decimal.

If the item has a standard order quantity, this quantity is the usage during the order cycle and the equation becomes

$$g(k) = \frac{\text{OQ}}{\text{MAD}_{\text{LT}}} \times (1 - p)$$

Use Table 16, which is a condensed service-function table.

TABLE 16   Safety Factors for "Unit" Service

Safety Factor, k	Service Function, $g(k)$
2.0	0.0294
1.6	0.0600
1.4	0.0829
1.2	0.1131
1.0	0.1510

Problem 1   Select k and calculate safety stock and order point:

$$\text{FCST}_{\text{LT}} = 800$$
$$\text{OQ} = 600$$
$$\text{MAD}_{\text{LT}} = 200$$

Desired service = 95%

$$g(k) = \frac{\text{OQ}}{\text{MAD}_{\text{LT}}} (1 - p) = \frac{600}{200} (1 - 0.95)$$
$$= (3)(0.05) = 0.15$$

The safety factor for a $g(k) = 0.15$ in the table is 1.0 and

$$\text{Safety stock} = (1.0)(\text{MAD}_{\text{LT}}) = 200$$
$$\text{Order point} = \text{FCST}_{\text{LT}} + \text{SS}$$
$$= 800 + 200 = 1,000$$

Problem 2   Repeat Problem 1 for a service level of 98 percent.

$$g(k) = 3(1 - p) = (3)(0.02) = 0.06$$

In the service-function table, the k corresponding to a $g(k)$ of 0.06 is 1.6 and

$$\text{Safety stock} = K \times \text{MAD}_{\text{LT}}$$
$$= (1.6)(200) = 320$$
$$\text{Order point} = \text{FCST}_{\text{LT}} + \text{SS}$$
$$= 800 + 320 = 1,120$$

The selection of the service level usually ends up being a management decision. It is strongly advised that a study covering six to eight weeks be made to establish the present service level to be used to select a k to start. It is important that the statistical measure of service be equated to management's concept of service before installing a statistical inventory control system.

The findings of studies to determine the optimum service level based on a "stock-out cost" have usually been overruled because it is almost impossible to determine the future costs of present lost sales and customer dissatisfaction.

The best technique for selecting a service level is to show management the present service level and the inventory levels that will be required for various service levels, and have them select the level. The inventory management programs available from various computer manufacturers can be used to develop the type of curve, as shown in Fig. 13.

The curve clearly shows that the marginal cost of service rises sharply

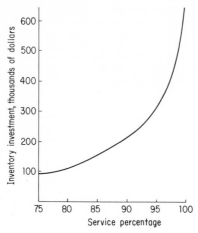

Fig. 13   Inventory investment vs. service.

as the service is raised above 95 percent. Management cannot be told what the service level should be, but they can be shown the amount of inventory required to give the service level they select.

Manufacturers often specify a service level to be the percent of the demand filled within a specified time.

Example   95 percent of the demand is to be filled within five days of order entry. To set this level, the length of allowable delay should be subtracted from the actual lead time before the forecast and MAD are extrapolated. The order-point formula then becomes

$$OP = FCST_{LT\text{-delay}} + (k)MAD_{LT\text{-delay}} \tag{33}$$

THE POISSON DISTRIBUTION: In all the discussion above, the statistical concepts of a normal distribution were used and the general form of the order-point formula was

$$\text{Order point} = \text{forecast}_{LT} + k(MAD)_{LT} \tag{28}$$

Frequently, articles and books on inventory management suggest a general order-point formula that is some variation of

$$\text{Order point} = \text{forecast}_{LT} + k\sqrt{\text{forecast}_{LT}} \tag{34}$$

Comparing Eq. (34) with Eq. (28), it becomes apparent that Eq. (34) *assumes that the standard deviation or its approximation (MAD) is always equal to the square root of the demand during lead time.* This is true if demand follows a *Poisson* distribution, but it is extremely dangerous to assume that it is true for most inventory items. This approach was popular in literature before the concept of MAD was developed because it avoided the tedious standard-deviation calculation. It should not be used unless analysis has shown that it can safely be assumed that the standard deviation is indeed equal to the square root of demand. The MAD calculation is far more generally applicable and will work whether or not the square root of demand is equal to the standard deviation.

DEMAND FILTERS AND TRACKING SIGNALS: If demands which are extreme are used to update the forecast and MAD, the forecasts will lose their stability. The safety stock might be greatly increased because of one nonrandom demand event such as a sales promotion. All forecasting systems should pass the current demand through a *filter* before using it to revise a forecast.

A *high filter* and a *low filter* can be designed. The equations for the filters are:

$$\text{High filter} = \text{FCST} + (N)(\text{MAD}) \tag{35}$$
$$\text{Low filter} = \text{FCST} - (N)(\text{MAD}) \tag{36}$$

N is selected from the normal tables based on the degree of certainty desired in saying that the demand is nonrandom and can be rejected. For example, if $N = 3$ is chosen from Table 15, there is only a 0.82 percent $(100 - 99.18)$ chance that a demand outside of either of the two filter limits is actually random. That is, it would generally be wise to toss out such a demand on the basis that it was created by some nonrepetitive cause.

Example

$$\text{FCST} = 300$$
$$\text{MAD} = 90$$
$$N = 3$$
$$\text{High filter} = 300 + (3)(90) = 570$$
$$\text{Low filter} = 300 - (3)(90) = 30$$

The demand would be used to revise the forecast if its value were between 30 and 570. The forecast, MAD, and order point would *not* be revised for a demand greater than 570 or less than 30. Obviously, the filters must consider the seasonal effects for a seasonal item.

The demand filter is used to screen out unusual demand, and an additional "quality control" technique is required to determine if the forecast errors have a directional bias. This second technique is called a "tracking signal."

If the correct forecasting technique is being employed for an item, the algebraic sum of the forecast errors should tend to zero. An extreme buildup of forecast errors for an item in either the positive or negative direction is a statistical indication that the system is no longer properly forecasting the item demand. The reason might be a change in forecast model, a sharp but permanent change in demand level, or poor initial values for the forecast or MAD. It *does not* indicate that the current value of alpha is wrong. The tracking signal is normally calculated as

$$\text{Tracking signal} = \frac{\text{algebraic sum of forecast errors}}{\text{MAD}} \tag{37}$$

When the tracking signal for an item exceeds a predetermined level, it is said to "trip." Exception reports can then indicate only those items that have "tripped" the signal and require attention.

In specifying the value of the tracking signal that requires action, it must be remembered that there will sometimes be some random buildup of errors sufficient to cause a trip. The idea then is to set the limit at a level that will hold the random trips to a workable level and still indicate the items in trouble.

Statistically, there is a calculation problem: The standard deviation required for calculating reasonable limits around the tracking signal must consider the distributions of error *sums*, and this value is not the same as the regular normal-distribution table used above. The relationships for error sums in terms of alpha and MAD are shown in Table 17, which shows the number of MADs required for specified percentages of random trips for single smoothing.

An example of the meaning of Table 17 is:

TABLE 17   Tracking Signal Limits

Percent trips	Number of MADs for = 0.1	Number of MADs for = 0.2
10	4.72	3.27
8	5.01	3.47
6	5.38	3.72
5	5.61	3.88
4	5.86	4.06
3.6	6.00	4.16
2	6.66	4.61

SOURCE: Based on R. W. Sittler, "Lectures on Sampled Data Systems Analysis," MIT Lincoln Laboratory, Aug. 22, 1957.

1. An inventory manager is willing to look at 6 percent *chance* (random) trips. For items using an alpha of 0.1 for single smoothing, limits of plus or minus 5.38 MADs will produce 6 percent random trips.

2. If an alpha of 0.2 is used, the limits would be 3.72 MADs.

3. If, for an alpha of 0.1, the load of random trips should be lightened to 2 percent because the inventory manager finds too many items tripping the signal, the limits should be raised to 6.66 MADs.

Table 17 can be used for double smoothing by first doubling the alpha before referring to the table. If an alpha = 0.05 is used, and 4 percent random trips is allowable, the limits would be plus or minus 5.86 MADs. The alpha = 0.05 was doubled, giving 0.1, so that the alpha = 0.1 column was used in the table.

The tracking signal is a management tool and should be used accordingly. The number of random trips allowed should be a balance between work load and sufficient reaction to out-of-balance conditions. Accordingly, the limits should be *managed* to meet these requirements. It is recommended that low limits be set for the A items by dollar volume. A somewhat higher level should be set for the B medium items, and a still higher limit for the C items.

An example of this strategy for an alpha of 0.1 is:

1. Limits of plus or minus 5 MADs for the high-dollar items would produce 8 percent random trips in the high 10 percent.

2. Limits of plus or minus 5.9 would give approximately 4 percent random trips for the medium items.

3. Limits of plus or minus 6.7 MADs would give approximately 2 percent random trips for the slow movers.

The same tracking-signal limit for all items would mean that the inventory manager would spend much more time examining low-dollar items than high ones. This is a clear violation of the principles of ABC.

A tracking-signal trip indicates that the item must be examined to determine the cause, and corrective action must be taken. It does not mean that the alpha should be changed. The *IMPACT Implementation Manual has* a good discussion of the common conditions causing trips and the action to be taken as well as a more technical discussion of tracking-signal theory.

A forecasting system without demand filters and tracking signals will eventually lose its accuracy and reliability. No forecasting system is complete without both.

PERIODIC-REVIEW SYSTEMS: In the order-point-quantity system, as usage varies, the *timing* of order placement varies. Another approach can be used where it is more practical to vary the *quantity* and keep the timing constant. Where it is desirable to reorder material every two weeks, for example, a system could be designed to review inventory every two weeks and order each item up to a predetermined level usually called an inventory "target" or "order-up-to" level. Using this approach, as usage fluctuates, the *quantity* rather than the *timing* of order placement is the variable. The target inventory level is the sum of

1. Anticipated demand during lead time
2. Anticipated demand during review time
3. Safety stock based on forecast error over lead time plus review time

Lot sizes can be rounded off to approximate multiples of demand during review period and minimum order quantities set. This means that some items will be reordered every second or third review period.

The principles explained above for use with an order-point system apply to the periodic-review system equally well. It can embody techniques like exponential smoothing and the use of MAD in calculating safety stocks to make the system more efficient than one that uses inventory targets established on a "judgment" basis.

SUMMARY

Three questions of inventory management have been discussed in this chapter:
On *what* items should the inventory control system efforts be exerted?
How much material should be reordered?
When should a reorder be placed?

The ABC concept, answering *what,* and the economic lot size, answering *how much,* have been available to practitioners for many years. They are based on sound principles and can be applied very successfully as long as the practitioner understands the principles involved and does not follow the techniques blindly.

The concept of statistical inventory control has been discussed in the literature for a good many years. With the advent of computers it has become a practical reality and is applied in many companies. Statistical inventory control provides a rational method for updating forecasts and allocating reserve stock based on forecast error. If used properly in a system, significant reductions in inventory or improvements in customer service should result. This is because the system sets reserve-stock levels rationally and has the capability of updating the forecasts and reserve stocks on a regular basis. Two important points should be kept in mind if real success is to be achieved with these techniques:

1. The practitioner must understand the principles behind the techniques.
2. He must use the proper technique in the proper application.

The following chapter describes other techniques for inventory systems that will work significantly better in particular applications than those described in this chapter.

REFERENCES

1. J. M. Juran, "Universals in Management Planning and Controlling," *Management Review,* November, 1954.

2. H. Ford Dickie, "ABC Inventory Analysis Shoots for Dollars," *Factory Management and Maintenance,* July, 1951.
3. For further information, see "ROCE Determination of Economic Production Lot Sizes," by T. G. Weeks, *APICS Quarterly Bulletin,* October, 1964.
4. R. G. Brown, "Use of the Carrying Charge to Control Cycle Stock," *APICS Quarterly Bulletin,* July, 1961.
5. W. E. Welch, *Tested Scientific Inventory Control,* Management Publishing Company, Greenwich, Conn., 1956.
6. J. D. Harty, G. W. Plossl, and O. W. Wight, *Management of Lot-size Inventories,* a Special Education and Research Report of the American Production and Inventory Control Society, Washington, D.C., 1963.
7. R. G. Brown, *Smoothing, Forecasting, and Prediction,* Prentice-Hall, Inc., Englewood Cliffs, N.J., 1963.
8. *IMPACT Advanced Principles and Implementation Manual,* no. E20-0174, International Business Machines Corp., White Plains, N.Y., pp. 25–28.
9. *Ibid.,* pp. 10–15.

BIBLIOGRAPHY

Brown, R. G.: *Decision Rules for Inventory Management,* Holt, Rinehart and Winston, Inc., New York, 1967.
————: *Statistical Forecasting for Inventory Control,* McGraw-Hill Book Company, New York, 1959.
Buchan, Joseph, and Ernest Koenigsberg: *Scientific Inventory Management,* Prentice-Hall, Inc., Englewood Cliffs, N.J., 1963.
Greene, James H.: *Production Control: Systems and Decisions,* Richard D. Irwin, Inc., Homewood, Ill., 1965.
IMPACT General Information Manual, no. E20-8105, International Business Machines Corp., White Plains, N.Y.
Lander, Jack R.: *A Basic Training Program in Production and Inventory Control,* American Production and Inventory Control Society, Washington, D.C., 1964.
Magee, John F., and David M. Boodman: *Production Planning and Inventory Control,* 2d ed., McGraw-Hill Book Company, New York, 1967.
Moroney, M. J.: *Facts from Figures,* Penguin Books, London, 1957.
Plossl, G. W., and Oliver W. Wight: *Production and Inventory Control: Principles and Techniques,* Prentice-Hall, Inc., Englewood Cliffs, N.J., 1967.

Chapter 17

Requirements Planning Systems

EDITOR:

Oliver W. Wight *President, Oliver Wight, Inc., Wilton, Connecticut*

CONTRIBUTORS:

J. A. Chobanian *Corporate Control & Systems Engineer, J. I. Case Company, Racine, Wisconsin*

J. C. Zimmermann *Marketing Manager, Data Processing Division, International Business Machines Corp., Riverside, California*

CONTENTS

DEPENDENT-DEMAND INVENTORY SYSTEMS

Many companies make assembled products which are, in turn, made up of subassemblies and parts. The term "components" is usually used to cover both of these categories. The demand for these components is *dependent* upon demand for the assemblies. If, for example, 100 of a particular product are to be made, then 100 sets of components must be ordered far enough in advance so that the assembly can be put together by the desired date. Requirements planning (or *materials planning*) is a technique for determining the quantities of components that will be required to build a product. The techniques of requirements planning translate the demand or forecast of demand for the end product (usually called the "master schedule"), into calculated requirements for the components.

Some companies use order points to reorder components as they are used. Order points treat each item independently and do not try to pull all required components together at the same time when there are many levels of inventory (raw material, semifinished components, etc.). They tend to reorder an item as soon as it is used whether or not it is needed.

Other companies use an order point and "reservation" system to order components. They establish the order point based on average usage and then deduct actual known requirements from the inventory in order to generate replenishment orders sooner. Using this approach, it is difficult to establish just *when* a replenishment order is required. Will *all* future requirements be prededucted from the inventory, or just those for the next month, or two months, etc.? The system usually is not as effective for determining the precise timing of replenishment orders as a multiperiod or time-series materials plan.

The objective of a good reordering system should be to provide information to determine the relative priority of each item. Far too many reordering systems order *too much too soon*, and they rely on expediters to "chase" the most needed items through production (or from vendors). A good requirements planning system should generate requirements in fairly precise time periods so that the system will provide the right information to get components through as required rather than depending on expediters with "hot lists" based on assembly shortages. A later section in this chapter discusses the pros and cons of requirements planning versus order-point techniques for various applications. In general, it can be said that requirements planning techniques are more suitable for ordering dependent-demand items, i.e., the components that go into an assembled product. The following sections discuss various approaches to planning requirements for components whose demand is dependent upon demand for the assembly on which they are used.

Number 9 Pinup Lamp

Date 8/12/7_

Mfg. code 1020314   Approved AES

Component		Qty. required	Source	Remarks
Number	Description			
X18	Switch	1	Purch.	
Y2L	Socket	1	Purch.	
9P	Shade	1	Mfg.	
414	Hanger	2	Mfg.	
4107	Cord set	1	Purch.	

Fig. 1 Bill of materials.

Single-level—Single-period Requirements Planning. Figure 1 shows a simple bill of materials for a lamp. If 100 of these lamps were to be assembled, 100 switches, sockets, shades, and cord sets would be required, while 200 hangers would be required since each lamp requires two hangers. Extending this quantity for the assembly required through the bill of materials in order to plan the number of each component required is called "explosion."

If this quantity of 100 lamps was to be assembled in the thirty-fifth week, then all the components would need to be on hand at that time. It would be a simple thing to order these components from vendors and from the company's own manufacturing facilities well in advance of week 35. Some very basic systems do place all the orders for all the components at the same time. If the lead time for sockets is six weeks and the lead time for switches is three weeks, a better control over work-in-process inventory would exist if lead time for each was taken into account for each component. In this case, sockets should be ordered in week 29 while switches should be ordered in week 32 based on lead times. Placing all orders at the same time would obviously bring switches in well before they are required, unless a late delivery date was specified. This calculation of the lead time for the components is called "lead-time offsetting."

Number 9P Shade

Date	Rec'd.	With-drawn	Available on hand	On order	Required	Available to plan
3/12	400	. . .	1,844	. . . . .	600	1,244
3/14	. . .	600	1,244	. . . . .	. . . . .	1,244
3/23	. . .	. . .	1,244	. . . . .	2,500	1,256
3/23	. . .	. . .	1,244	1,300	2,500	44

Fig. 2 Inventory record card.

Figure 2 shows an inventory record card reflecting requirements. In this case, there is a requirement of 600 for March 12 and a requirement of 2,500 for March 23, and whenever the amount on hand and on order, called "available to plan," drops below the amount required, a new replenishment order must be placed. Note from this record that 2,500 lamp shades will be required on March 23. This is the *gross* requirement, but since there are 1,244 units available to plan, the *net requirement* is 1,256 units, which was rounded up to 1,300 units when the manufacturing order was created.

Single-level–single-period planning assumes a fairly simple product where a single period's requirements are planned separately. In the example above, a separate explosion would have to be made for each lot of lamps that was planned to be assembled. This approach to requirements planning is often used by companies which firm up their assembly schedule (usually called the "master schedule") periodically, perhaps monthly, six to nine months in advance of the desired assembly date. Then an explosion of requirements is made and orders placed for each component based on that component's lead time. This is requirements planning in its simplest form.

Single-level–Single-period Multiple-product Requirements Planning. Figure 3 shows another bill of materials for another lamp which is identical to the lamp shown in Fig. 1 except for its shade. The switch, socket, hanger, and cord set are said to be "common" components, and obviously, it would be economical to combine the requirements of these components and run them through production or order them from vendors together. Figure 4 shows an "explosion chart" or "matrix bill of materials" which can be used for combining requirements. In

Number 9 Wall Lamp

Date 8/10/7_

Mfg. code 1010218

Approved AES

Component		Qty. required	Source	Remarks
Number	Description			
X18	Switch	1	Purch.	
Y2L	Socket	1	Purch.	
9W	Shade	1	Mfg.	
414	Hanger	2	Mfg.	
4107	Cord set	1	Purch.	

Fig. 3 Bill of materials.

Assembly	Required Qty.	X18 Switch	X27 Switch	Y2L Socket	Shade No. 7W	Shade No. 7D	Shade No. 9W	Shade No. 9D	Shade No. 9P	Shade No. 11D	Shade No. 11P	414 Hanger	418 Hanger	VT Base	UP Base	No. 4107 Cord set
No. 7 Wall	2,000											2				
No. 7 Desk																
No. 9 Wall	2,000	2,000		2,000			2,000					2 4,000				2,000
No. 9 Desk																
No. 9 Pinup	2,500	2,500		2,500					2,500			2 5,000				2,500
No. 11 Desk																
No. 11 Pinup	2,000		2,000	2,000							2,000		2 4,000			2,000
Total Required	6,500	4,500	2,000	6,500			2,000		2,500		2,000	9,000	4,000			6,500
Total Available		7,105	15,423	7,002			4,595		1,244		4,715	29,531	11,648			6,400
To Obtain		✓	✓	✓			✓		(1,256)		✓	✓	✓			(100)

Fig. 4 Explosion chart (product line—lamps).

this particular explosion chart, *all* models of lamps are shown, and reading horizontally, the number 7 wall lamp takes an X18 switch (but *not* an X27 switch), a Y2L socket, a 7W shade, two 414 hangers, and a 4107 cord set.   Each horizontal row in the chart actually represents the bill of materials for the corresponding assembly in the left-hand column.   In this example, 2,000 number 9 wall lamps are required, and the requirements for each of its components are posted in the blank spaces of the charts.   The requirements for these components are then summarized in the row labeled "total required" and these requirements are then compared with the "total available."   In this particular example, 1,256 9P lamp shades and 100 number 4107 cord sets are required but not available.

The explosion chart provides a simple way of summarizing requirements for a simple product family.   Note that if it were desired to plan requirements for one time period, this could easily be done with the explosion chart.   Planning requirements for a second time period would require filling in a second explosion chart.   Lead-time offsetting would have to be done separately.   The explosion chart simply shows the amount required to assemble a given product for a single planning period.

Number 9 Pinup Lamp

Date 8/18/7_

Mfg. code 1020314

Approved AES

Level 1 component number	Level 2 component number	Description	Quantity required	Source	Remarks
X18		Switch	1	Purch.	
Y2L		Socket	1	Mfg.	
	Y2L-S	Shell	1	Mfg.	
	Y2L-B	Base	1	Mfg.	
	Y2L-SI	Shell Insulator	1	Purch.	
	Y2L-BI	Base Insulator	1	Purch.	
	Y2L-XI	Screw stem	1	Mfg.	
9P		Shade	1	Mfg.	
414		Hanger	2	Mfg.	
4107		Cord set	1	Purch.	

Fig. 5 Indented bill of material.

Multiple-level–Single-period Requirements Planning.   Figure 5 shows a new bill of materials.   In this case, it has been assumed that the Y2L socket which was previously purchased will now be manufactured, and it will be made up of some manufactured and some purchased components.   These components are shown on the bill of materials in *levels*.   For clarity, level 2 components are shown indented to the right of level 1 components in the figure.   It is customary to speak of the final assembly itself as the zero level and the components going into this zero-level assembly as the "level 1 components."   Components going into the level 1 components are called the "level 2 components," etc., based on the way the product is actually made.

These multiple-level components could be ordered by simply exploding the assembly requirements through the bill of materials.   In the earlier example with the 9P shade, the gross requirement was compared with the inventory level to determine net requirements.

With a multilevel product, it is sometimes practical to do a *quick-deck* explosion where quantities of components at all levels are simply ordered to meet assembly quantity requirements. This would mean that a requirement of 100 lamps, for example, would simply require 100 sockets and thus 100 shells, bases, etc. This approach is called a "quick-deck" since it is usually associated with simple punched-card approaches where explosions are done through each level assuming that no inventory exists at these levels.

The gross-to-net approach, on the other hand, assumes that some inventory will exist at each level. Even when subassemblies are not stocked, this inventory does tend to exist in the real world because of scrap, rework, corrections to inventory records, and the like. In most manufacturing companies, the gross-to-net approach is preferable since it tries to bring component inventories into balance each time requirements are calculated.

Using the gross-to-net calculation with this new bill of materials and assuming that 100 number 9 pinup lamps are to be made, the *gross* requirement for Y2L sockets would be 100. If 20 sockets are available, the *net* requirement would be 80. The gross requirement for Y2L-S shells would thus be 80; if 10 are available ("available" for planning, i.e., on hand plus on order) the net requirement is 70. Obviously, this approach takes longer since inventory records must be referenced at each explosion level, but it avoids the assumption that all previous usages left a balanced inventory.

In planning requirements for multiple-level products, gross requirements for level 1 components are determined from a *master schedule*. Then the respective inventory records are referenced to determine the net requirement, which is the additional quantity of level 1 components which must actually be obtained after the amount in inventory has been taken into account. The net requirement for level 1 components is a gross requirement on level 2 components. Net requirements for level 2 components are then calculated by deducting the available inventory for each level 2 component from the gross requirement.

In a product like the pinup lamp, it obviously would save time to accumulate all gross requirements for Y2L sockets going into all lamps before calculating the net requirements for Y2L sockets so they will not have to be recalculated again and again.

Frequently, an item like a switch would be a level 1 component in one product and a level 2 or 3 component in another product. It would then be necessary to know that this switch is in level 3 of one product so that its net requirement would not be calculated before accumulating the requirements from level 3 of the other product. Various techniques are used in practice to avoid this type of recalculation.

One technique is called "low-level coding." The switch in question would bear in its record a low-level code of 3 to indicate that until gross requirements for level 3 components have been calculated, net requirements for the switch should not be computed.

Another technique is called a "where-used check-off," which is simply a listing of all the uses of a component so that net requirements for an item like the switch would only be calculated after all net requirements for items using it had been determined.

Multiple-period Requirements Planning. For single-period requirements planning, the requirements for each period in the future are calculated and added to requirements made for previous periods. This is fine until it is desired to change the product mix for previously planned periods. Then the calculations become extremely awkward and it would really be desirable to replan all the periods. For most companies today, these changes and schedules are a way of life rather than an exception, and as a consequence, *multiple-period requirements planning* is being used by many companies.

Using this approach, requirements are entered into the system periodically, or even continuously in some computer systems. Based on current on-hand inventory and scheduled receipts of replenishment orders, a new materials plan is projected. This plan is usually shown on a horizontal time grid as in Fig. 6.

This technique is usually called "time-series" or "time-phased materials planning." The end-item master schedule shows the requirements for the pinup lamp which are then posted as requirements for *projected usage* for the 9P shade. Note that there are 1,244 shades on hand, that the planned requirement of 500 in week 16 will reduce the on-hand inventory to 744, and in period 22, 256 pieces will be required; assuming no lot sizing is done, 256 will have to be ordered four weeks earlier in period 18 (since the lead time is four weeks) to satisfy this requirement.

Assembly Requirements
Number 9 Pinup Lamp Master Schedule

	Past due	Week 14	15	16	17	18	19	20	21	22	23	24	25	26
	....	....	....	500	...	...	500	...	...	500	....	....	400	.....

Number 9P Shade Materials Plan

Lead time: 4 weeks

	Past due	Week 14	15	16	17	18	19	20	21	22	23	24	25	26
Projected usage		....	....	500	...	...	500	...	...	500	....	....	400	.....
On hand	1244	1244	1244	744	744	744	244	244	244	−256	−256	−256	−656	−656
Scheduled receipts		....	....											
Planned order release		....	....			256	...	...	400	....				.....

Fig. 6 Time series material plan.

For all practical purposes, it can be said that time-series materials planning became a usable technique when the computer began to be applied to manufacturing companies. It requires having the inventory records and the bills of material stored and available for cross-referencing. After the master schedule had been posted to the pinup lamp record (Fig. 6), the bill of materials for that lamp would be referenced and the projected usage would then be posted against each of the components used. Then the projected on-hand balances would be calculated, and whenever scheduled receipts plus the on-hand balance did not cover the projected usage for the period, a planned-order release would result.

Note that these planned orders will not be released until the current period. In Fig. 6, the current period is 14, and each week the plan is extended one week and the current period is advanced one week. This is called the "time shift." When a planned-order release shows up in the current period, it will be the signal to inventory control personnel to release a production or purchase order.

The format for time-series materials planning shown here is a fairly common one. In this plan, the projected on-hand quantity continues to show negative even though replenishment orders have been planned. There would be nothing wrong with increasing the projected on-hand quantity by the amount of the planned order in the time period when that planned order should be received.

It would also be possible to show another category usually called "allocation." This category is used to differentiate projected usage from "uncashed requisitions." These uncashed requisitions exist in most companies because a picking order has been sent to the component storeroom but components have not yet been withdrawn from the storeroom. The practitioner should keep in mind that a variety of formats is possible and that there is no "right" format. The best one is the one that meets his requirements as a user most satisfactorily.

In this example, it was assumed that the inventory on hand and on order should always be equal to projected usage. In some circumstances, it might be desirable to carry some safety stock, and then instead of planning an order release when the inventory balance equals zero, the order release would be planned when the inventory balance equaled or fell below the safety stock. In Fig. 6, if a safety stock of 300 units was desired, a scheduled receipt would be required in week 19 instead of week 22.

Time-series materials planning provides a method for reflecting changes in requirements right down to the lowest component. It does not assume that previously planned requirements are still valid and thus provides for rapid reaction to forecast error or changing customer demand. Contrast the multiple-period approach in Fig. 6 with the explosion chart shown in Fig. 4. The explosion chart, or matrix bill of materials, shows requirements for only one time period and does not incorporate lead times to show when components must be ordered. Multiple-period, or *time-series*, materials planning is a more precise and responsive techniques for planning, ordering, and rescheduling requirements.

Materials planning can be done manually for a small number of components, but in practice it is really a computer-oriented technique due to the large number of calculations which must be made. Computer approaches to materials planning are discussed further in a later section.

Multiple-period-multiple-product Requirements Planning. The example shown in Fig. 6 assumed that there was only one end use for the number 9P lamp shade. The Y2L socket, on the other hand, is used in many lamps. Figure 7 shows master schedules for three of these lamps that are carried down into a materials plan for the socket. Note that there are also service requirements (replacement parts) shown in this plan and that a lot size of 1,500 units is assumed but no safety stock is assumed in the example.

If replenishment orders were widely spaced, it might be advantageous to calculate a lot size for service requirements that would cover the forecast (50 units per week) and the forecast error between replenishment periods. This would tend to ensure that service-parts requirements would always be run with assembly requirements.

To make the calculation shown in Fig. 7, each lamp master schedule would have to be referenced to the bill of materials for that lamp. Requirements would then be posted to all the component records indicated in the bills of material. The Y2L socket inventory record is the only component record shown for this example, but obviously, requirements would have to be posted to other

Lamp Master Schedules

	Past due	Week 14	15	16	17	18	19	20	21	22	23	24	25	26
No. 9 Pinup	..	..	..	500	..	..	500	..	..	500	..	400	..	..
No. 9 Wall	100	..	300	..	..	200	..	..	300	..	..	400	..	..
No. 11 Pinup	..	..	..	..	1000	..	..	..	..	1000	..	..	..	..

Y2L Socket Materials Plan

Lot-size: 1,500
Lead time: 2 weeks

	Past due	Week 14	15	16	17	18	19	20	21	22	23	24	25	26
Projected assembly usage	100	..	300	500	1000	200	500	..	300	1500	..	800	..	..
Service parts	..	50	50	50	50	50	50	50	50	50	50	50	50	50
On hand	400	350	..	-550	-1600	-1850	-2400	-2450	-2800	-4350	-4400	-5250	-5300	-5350
Scheduled receipts	500	..	..	..	..	..	..	..	..	..	..	..	..	..
Planned order release	..	..	1500	1500	..	..	..	1500	..	1500	..	..	..	..

Fig. 7 Multiproduct materials plan.

component records also. The Y2L socket has 500 units on hand and 1,500 on order scheduled to arrive in week 15 (from an order that has already been released). As higher-level requirements are summarized, they and the service-part requirements are deducted from the inventory and the new balance is projected time period by time period. Whenever the calculated inventory balance equals zero, a planned order results. This order is scheduled for release two weeks earlier based on the lead-time offset. Note that planned orders are not real orders and do not show as "scheduled receipts" until they are released to manufacturing or a vendor. They simply exist for planning requirements at lower levels.

If the Y2L socket were made up of components, these records would now be posted with requirements of 1,500 in weeks 15, 20, and 22. These are *net* requirements for Y2L sockets, but at the next lower level they would be gross requirements. If there was an inventory balance of 100 for a component used in the Y2L socket, the net requirement for the component would be 1,400 units. Note that net requirements at one inventory level are analyzed for lot sizing and these lot sizes provide gross requirements for the next lower level of inventory.

Lot Sizing for Discrete Requirements. The example shown in Fig. 7 assumed a predetermined lot size. The standard approach to economic-order-quantity calculation assumes that demand will be level, and where a forecast of end-item usage based on a technique like exponential smoothing is being used, this is a fair assumption. Where requirements tend to be discrete as in a materials plan, the square-root EOQ approach is not as applicable as the time-series order-quantity approach. This technique is shown in Fig. 8. The general idea is the same as economic-order-quantity calculation: to balance the cost of carrying inventory with the cost of ordering. The logic is extremely simple in that requirements for each time period could be made in earlier time periods at a cost of carrying inventory but at a savings in ordering costs. The technique simply asks the question: "If requirements for two time periods are combined, one setup will be saved, but must inventory be carried as a result?" If the inventory carrying cost is less than the setup saving, this should be done. This is the basic logic of the "least total cost" approach to lot sizing.[1] The example shows that combining the requirements in weeks 15 and 21 would generate setup savings to offset the additional inventory carrying costs, while trying to make week 32's requirements at the same time would generate inventory costs that outweighed the setup savings.

The technique described above is very simple and easy for users to understand. Specific formulas for making this calculation are given in References 1 and 4. More complex techniques have been developed and probably the best known is the Wagner-Whitin algorithm. Under certain circumstances the Wagner-Whitin algorithm could provide results that are slightly more precise than the technique described[2] but it is not yet widely accepted in practice because of the considerable amount of calculation required.

Use of a time-series order-quantity approach for materials planning makes good sense in practice. It avoids the assumption that demand is uniform and is, therefore, useful where demand tends to be in discrete quantities. It is more applicable to seasonal items than the standard square-root EOQ. It avoids the problem of mismatching component EOQs (assembly A uses components B and C and the EOQ for B could be 500 while the EOQ for C might be 1,800). It is useful for make-to-order plants that wish to calculate the most economic way to combine future orders for an item with present requirements to reduce setups.

Part No. 17321
Inventory cost = 20% or 0.4% per week
Unit cost = $0.80
Setup cost = $18.00

Quantity		Week required	Cum. lot size, dollars	Excess inventory, dollars	Weeks in stock	Setups saved
Pieces	Dollars					
500	400	15	400	...	...	...
700	560	21	960	560	6	1
1,000	800	32	1,760	800	17	2
400	320	40	2,080	320	25	3

A. Combine weeks 15 and 21:
   1. Order $960 to be delivered week 15
   2. $560 excess will be carried in stock 6 weeks
   3. One setup will be saved
Thus:
Additional inventory costs = $560 × 6 × 0.004 = $13.44
Setup savings = 1 × $18.00   = $18.00
B. Combine weeks 15, 21, and 32:
   1. Order $1,760 to be delivered week 15
   2. $560 excess will be carried in stock 6 weeks
   3. $800 excess will be carried in stock 17 weeks
   4. Two setups will be saved
Thus:
Additional inventory costs = $560 × 6 × 0.004 = $13.44
                         $800 × 17 × 0.004 = $54.40
                                   Total $67.84
Setup savings = 2 × $18.00   = $36.00

Fig. 8 Time series order quantity (least total cost).

In short, this little-known approach to lot sizing is better than the square-root EOQ when demands tend to be discrete. It does not replace the less cumbersome square-root EOQ but instead provides the practitioner with another useful method for calculating lot sizes that is particularly useful where an item's demand is *dependent* and independently calculated lot sizes could generate excess inventory through mismatched component lot sizes.

EDP Approaches to Requirements Planning. The use of electronic data processing equipment in business has been a real help to the practitioner needing to explode requirements. This job is tedious and repetitive, but essentially simple in its logic, and it is an excellent application of the equipment.

PUNCHED-CARD MATERIALS PLANNING: One of the simplest approaches is the "quick-deck" approach mentioned earlier. A summarized bill of materials showing all the parts, regardless of level, going into the product is prepared. This deck of punched cards also contains the quantity of each component needed to make one assembly (two hangers are required to make one lamp, for example). The master-schedule quantities are then exploded to get total gross requirements for each component. This is one of the quickest types of explosion to run because it does not calculate lead times or reference intermediate inventory levels. It simply orders sets of parts to meet each planned requirement.

Quick-deck explosion can be applied where no subassemblies are maintained in inventory, but even under these circumstances, supplies of components tend to get mismatched very quickly and it is generally preferable to calculate gross requirements, reference the available inventory, and then calculate net requirements. The gross-to-net technique tries to force all components into balanced quantities while the quick-deck ignores any inventories that may exist.

With simple punched-card equipment, it is easy to explode requirements. In many companies, this is done for each level of the product structure to calculate gross requirements, which are then posted on manual ledger cards and compared with inventory and order quantities calculated to generate net requirements. These are then punched into a new deck of cards and gross requirements are calculated for the next level down. Generally, this type of requirements planning has been superseded by approaches where the inventory records are also available in punched cards or on computer files so that the gross-to-net calculation can be done quickly. Techniques that utilize punched cards and manual records inevitably require long time periods to complete an explosion. With rapidly changing schedules, this delay in replanning component requirements can be very costly in terms of excess inventory and poor customer service—particularly since it is just those low-level items which must be ordered first for which the explosion techniques will generate requirements last.

Punched-card approaches can be used effectively where the inventory is also punched into cards so that gross-to-net calculations can be made during the same run. Lead-time offsetting and discrete lot sizing would add complexity for simple punched-card equipment. For that reason, most companies with any sizable number of products find that a computer approach to materials planning is more practical.

MATERIALS PLANNING ON A COMPUTER: Two basic files are required to do materials planning on a computer: an *item master record* containing among other things the current inventory status, and a *product-structure* or bill-of-material file. This product-structure file should show the bill of materials in levels representing the way it is actually manufactured. It will probably also indicate a low-level code for each component to indicate the lowest level in the product structure where this component is used. The low-level code tells the program not to calculate the gross-to-net requirement calculation until all requirements from the lowest level have been posted. This precludes exploding the same item many times.

Typical steps in materials planning would be:

1. Post requirements to the respective level 1 master records from the master schedule.

2. After all requirements have been posted to level 1 items, the gross-to-net calculation and *order action* will take place. Order action includes lead-time offsetting, lot sizing, and any other calculations (like scrap allowances) required to calculate planned-order releases.

3. Reference the product-structure file to identify components required and explode these requirements, posting them to the level 2 item master record.

4. This routine is repeated for all levels until all requirements have been exploded. A material plan for each part number could then be printed out.

Obviously, this procedure has been shown in a generalized form. If the computer utilized tape files, sorting would need to be done to accumulate all requirements in part-number sequence before posting to the item master records. A direct-access (usually disk) system would probably post each requirement as it was generated.

The most common approach to requirements planning today is called "regeneration." Using this approach, the entire materials plan is recalculated periodically, usually once a week based on latest requirements. This obviously requires a considerable amount of computer time since every product must be reexploded and every inventory record for which there is a requirement must be referenced.

Another modern approach to requirements calculation is called "net change," where requirements are not recalculated periodically for every component but instead additions or subtractions from the master schedule are entered. The requirements change is then calculated down through the bill of materials *only* for the components affected. The net-change technique obviously requires direct-access files and is applicable where there is activity on only a small percentage of the total number of items for which bills of material are maintained or where periodic regeneration of requirements does not give rapid enough response.

In some companies, for example, it is desirable to be able to access the effects of schedule changes immediately without waiting for the next scheduled requirements calculation. Under these circumstances, the net-change approach, while usually more expensive in terms of computer time and file requirements, is the better approach.

Net change can be handled either continuously or in batch processing. Some companies use the net-change approach with continuous processing. They are able to process any transactions in inventory or changes in the master schedule as they occur, generating exception reports where schedule changes must be made as a result of the change in the master schedule. This obviously requires either a *dedicated* computer or *multiprogramming.* Other companies process master-schedule changes on a net-change basis but only once a day, usually on the night shift, when the computer can be dedicated to this type of calculation.

Which approach is better, regeneration or net change? Neither. They each have good applications. Some of the criteria to consider are:

1. Regeneration is basically simpler and tends to be less difficult to maintain. A false requirement entered one week will probably not be repeated the following. With net change, this requirement will always stand until it is removed. Regeneration tends to be self-purging while net change requires strict maintenance.

2. Net change works by exception and responds more quickly to schedule changes.

3. Regeneration can be handled with less file-storage requirements than net change where all files of requirements must be on line all the time.

4. In general, regeneration is simpler but less responsive because it is run periodically. Net change requires more discipline (and better-educated users) and is highly responsive to changes in requirements.

Some other considerations for the systems designer are:

1. *How big should time "buckets" be?* Four weeks? Two weeks? One week? Generally the smaller the time period for planning, the more precise the planning will be. Our examples used a one-week "bucket," and that is most popular today. Smaller planning buckets facilitate planning in smaller lead-time increments at each level. Larger buckets require less file space.

Some companies currently plan in *daily* buckets. This obviously makes it impractical to reserve a bucket for each possible time period out into the future, so each requirement is "chained" to the next and any new requirement that falls between existing requirements will require restructuring the chain. This is obviously a more precise materials planning technique that requires a more sophisticated data processing approach.

2. *How far out should the materials plan extend?* Far enough to cover the sum of the lead times through all component levels used for materials planning purposes. Since the materials plan provides input for capacity planning, it will probably be necessary to extend the plan out further periodically (perhaps monthly) when capacity planning is being done.

3. *How often should requirements be regenerated?* The net-change system avoids this question by providing for recalculation of changed items *only*, continuously or daily. But the net-change system can be maintained best by periodically (monthly or quarterly) regenerating requirements to purge the files.

Most companies using a regeneration system run their program weekly. This provides fairly quick response to changes in requirements. Less often than weekly could only be practical in a company with fairly stable requirements.

4. *Should low-value C items be materials planned?* Most practitioners don't want their planners reviewing low-value items regularly, and it seems a waste of computer time and file storage to maintain time buckets and explode items down to the level of cotter pins and washers. On the other hand, some practitioners feel that the precise control of materials planning is inexpensive and should include all items. Here are some of the criteria to consider:

a. If demand for the low-value items is fairly continuous, an order-point or two-bin system can be used *if* safety stock is set high and the system is run with proper discipline. Order points based on a quick-deck explosion of future requirements will be more effective than order points based on past usage. Remember that these may be low-value parts, but without them production can stop.

b. If demand for these hardware items is erratic or if they really have an impact on capacity requirements (a screw-machine part using considerable capacity might be a low-value item), the more precise priorities available from materials planning could justify including these items.

c. It might be reasonable to materials plan all but the lowest-level hardware items but not print out regular reports on them. The planners might see the materials plans for A and B items regularly while seeing C items only on request or when action is indicated.

OUTPUT FORMATS: In using a materials plan, the planner will probably be trying most frequently to answer four questions:

1. Are the components going to be available to make a given assembly?
2. How will a parts shortage affect my assembly schedule?
3. How can I best release the items going into a particular manufacturing area?
4. What is the current inventory status for a given item?

If only the last question were to be answered, a listing of the materials plans for each item in part-number sequence would be most useful. The first question can be answered by a listing in "family tree" sequence (number 9 pinup lamp followed by the materials plans for the X18 switch, Y2L socket, followed by the plans for all Y2L socket components, etc.). This obviously requires duplicating the printouts of the materials plans for the Y2L socket and its components each time an assembly using it is listed. On the other hand, it provides the answer to question 1 far quicker than a straight part-number listing.

Questions 2 and 3 could best be answered if the printout were in *where-used* sequence with each component shown followed by the materials plans for the subassemblies and their assemblies. Once again, there would be obvious duplication.

Here a dilemma faces the system designer: how to provide the user information in the format he requires without flooding him with paper. One solution is to generate reports only on those items that have had schedule changes or require a planned order to be released, and let the user inquire into the system for other information. In a continuous net-change system, this would be straightforward. In a daily-batch net-change system this information could be available once a day. A regeneration system could be designed to generate a report in the most frequently required sequence weekly and store other possible information formats in files to be printed out periodically as requested.

More and more systems are being designed that have the computer itself actually doing the analysis that used to be the function of the planner. The computer can be instructed to signal when material should be rescheduled because it is coming in too early or too late, when planned orders are being generated, when an order already exists in a later period and should probably be rescheduled, etc. This type of analysis can also be the basis for exception reports and can aid materially in reducing the manual effort required to use a materials planning system.

PEGGED REQUIREMENTS: Often a planner will wish to know where a given requirement came from. He may know that a component is in short supply and wonder what it affects and how he should reschedule assemblies accordingly.

Figure 7 shows a simple family-tree format, and it is fairly easy to determine, for example, that the 1,500 requirement in week 22 is composed of 500 units for the number 9 pinup lamp and 1,000 units for the number 11 pinup lamp.

With a more complex product, it might be desirable to retain a record of each of the higher-level orders that created demands on components, and this is called "pegging" requirements. Since it is difficult to predetermine how many different requirements any item might have, a variable number of records must be available, and this poses certain file-organization problems.

A compromise approach is to show, as was done in Figure 7, the assembly requirements and service requirements separately and to show a where-used listing for live requirements only. This would enable the planner to reference those inventory records he wishes to see without referring to a separate cross-reference list or looking at any assemblies without live requirements.

ANALYSIS VERSUS SYNTHESIS: Two terms which are often used when discussing requirements planning techniques are "analysis" and "synthesis." The requirements planning techniques discussed above are generally techniques that would be classified as *analysis* techniques, since each level in the product structure is exploded and analyzed, working *down* through the levels of bills of material. *Synthesis* techniques work from a bill of material in where-used sequence. Consider the difference in the approaches assuming that tape rather than the direct-access files are being used:

A. *Analysis*
1. Post level 1 gross requirements and calculate net requirements and order action.
2. Sort all level 1 planned orders by part number prior to posting as gross requirements for level 2.
B. *Synthesis*
1. Post level 1 gross requirements as above.
2. Select first level 2 component, find all level 1 requirements for assemblies using this component, post these requirements against this component, etc., then do the same for the second component.

The synthesis approach works from the other end of the bill of materials—the where-used list. Its primary advantage is where sequential-processing techniques are in use and it is necessary to sort the gross requirements derived at one level prior to posting inventory records and calculating net requirements at the next level. The synthesis approach overcomes this sorting requirement, since the bills of material are kept in where-used form and in part-number sequence. In general, synthesis methods are not as popular today as they once were because direct-access files have made it more practical to handle transactions without sorting.

Pointers to Consider when Designing a Materials Planning System. Like any other good system, a materials planning system must be custom-designed for the particular application. Some points to keep in mind that bear upon the overall design concept are listed below.

1. *Priorities.* One of the prime objectives of a good requirements planning system is to respond quickly to changes in demand—right down to the lowest component level. If a schedule change requires moving a planned order up to an earlier date or back to a later date, this will have little effect upon the action the planner will take unless the order has moved into the current time period. At this point he will, of course, try to release it to manufacturing or to a vendor.

A change in the due date for an order that is already released, however, should be reflected in that order's priority. This priority change will be reflected in the dispatching function. Thus a job can be moved ahead or pushed behind others that are competing with it for manufacturing capacity either in the manufacturing facility or at the vendor's location.

Many companies find it helpful to maintain time buckets in their materials plan which go back beyond the current week. For example, if this is week 14, time buckets may be maintained back through week 4. This enables them to recalculate priorities to show the relative priority of items that are past due. The thinking here is that it is very important to distinguish between an item that is one week late and one that is five or six weeks late. Establishing relative priorities by previous time periods permits relative priorities to be distinguished rather than lumping all items that are late into one "past-due" category.

2. *Family Groupings.* There is a growing recognition for the need to tie inventory control and production control together more effectively. An inventory control system normally generates an erratic random demand upon manufacturing facilities, and under most circumstances, the plant cannot respond to this erratic demand. Many companies today give the planner the responsibility for leveling out this demand before it goes to the manufacturing facilities. This makes it important to show in the inventory record (or chain it to the routing file) at least the critical manufacturing facilities that an item goes through. With this kind of coding, a planner can readily determine the items that go through a machine group such as a group of punch presses and determine, based on the materials plan, which items he will feed into production to meet a particular planned production rate.

It can also be helpful to indicate in these family groupings those items that go through common setups. Chapter 16 discusses the lot-size calculation for this circumstance.

3. *Allocating Components to the Assembly Schedule.* Many companies that have common components used in many assemblies find that the best approach for optimizing inventories and meeting assembly schedules is to have a separate review of the components and assembly requirements on a daily basis. This is usually done by reviewing, usually with a computer program, each assembly order's priority sequence. If all components are available, the order is released so components may be pulled from the storeroom and sent to the assembly department. If any components are short, none of the components are released. Instead they are made available for any other assembly, unless, on an exception basis, it is necessary to hold these components awaiting a part that is in short supply.

This approach if used properly can avoid generating artificial component shortages by allocating components against an assembly which will not be made for lack of another component. It also provides for utilizing common components to meet the latest assembly priorities. It can also be used to generate a list of all the assemblies that could not be made, as well as component shortages.

4. *Scrap Factors.* If there has been a significant experience of scrappage on a particular part, it may be necessary to include a scrap factor in the materials plan. This scrap factor should show up in the planned orders, and if the scrap factor were 10 percent, a net requirement for 1,000 pieces would generate a planned order for approximately 1,100 pieces. To avoid including the scrap allowance in the inventory netting calculation the scrap factor should not be reflected in the scheduled receipts.

5. *Lot Sizing Level by Level.* A product with subassembly levels can easily have its demand amplified down through the materials plan, particularly if the square-root EOQ approach is used. A change in the master schedule of 10 units in a time period, for example, might generate a requirement at the first component level of 1,000 units because of lot sizing. This, in turn, might generate a demand at the next lower level of 10,000 units because of lot sizing. The discrete lot-size calculation discussed previously is recommended for materials planning in most situations to reduce this amplification effect.

6. *"Backing-out" Requirements.* A net-change system where the requirements are maintained perpetually must be designed with the possibility of reducing as well as increasing requirements. Often this is not as easy as it sounds. Consider, for example, the assembly that has a component with a lead time of six weeks. As manufacturing performance improves, this lead time drops to four weeks, and this improved lead time is reflected in the materials planning system. Now it is desired to reduce a requirement for this assembly from 1,000 to 500. The computer program expects to find this requirement reflected in the component requirement four periods ahead, but since lead time has been changed in the interim, the requirement obviously will not be in the correct time period.

There are solutions to this type of problem, such as only changing lead times when requirements are being periodically regenerated. This is normally done once a month or once a quarter even with a net-change system. The important point to remember is that the system designer must anticipate this problem ahead of time and design his system to cope with it.

7. *Safety Stocks.* These can be used with requirements planning as well as order-point systems. Proper determination of these safety stocks has not received the amount of attention as have safety stocks for reorder points. In its simplest form, safety stock can be expressed in time. In Fig. 6 the master schedule for the number 9 pinup lamp was shown. If there is a good possibility that the lot of 500 originally planned for week 19 might be required in week 18, then all components might well be ordered in advance to have them available. Safety stock is thus expressed in time by moving requirements up one week. When a component goes into many end products, it is more difficult to express safety stock in time periods on a rational basis.

Safety stock can also be expressed in quantity. Figure 9 shows an example for an electric-motor manufacturer. In this case, there are five different electric motors in a family which has many common components. The forecast for motor A1 is 1,000 units, but since these are made to customer order, the company recognizes that they might very well make 500 or 1,500 in any given week. Components that are peculiar to motor A1 will have to be ordered so that there are 500 units of safety stock available. Other components are used on

Component	Forecast	Forecast error
Motor A1........	1,000	±500
Motor A2........	1,000	±500
Motor A3........	1,000	±500
Motor A4........	1,000	±500
Motor A5........	1,000	±500
Total	5,000 units	2,500 units

Forecast error *all* type A motors = 1,100 units.

Fig. 9 Reserve stocks for common components.

all type-A motors, and since the possibility of motor A1 having its maximum requirement in the same period as motor A2 is extremely low, the forecast error for all type-A motors is considerably less than the sum of the forecast errors for each motor. Thus, the component safety stock for common components is equal to 1,100 units (the square root of the sum of the squares of the individual safety stocks) rather than the 2,500 units that might seem to be the appropriate safety stock.

8. *Inventory Transactions.* Like any other inventory control technique, materials planning requires an inventory balance record. This inventory balance record could represent the inventory balance left in the components storeroom. In that case, deductions from inventory would occur when material is withdrawn from the components storeroom. One problem that sometimes occurs with this type of inventory balance record is that the bill of materials shows a subassembly level which actually does not exist for any period of time in the process because the subassemblies are consumed and go into a higher-level subassembly in a fairly continuous flow.

At this point, the systems designer faces a dilemma. He can remove that level from the bill of materials. This will make it awkward for him to provide an inventory record identification in case there are subassemblies left over that have to be stored. On the other hand, he can insist that these subassemblies be routed through the stock room (an expensive approach) so that the inventory records would correctly show the subassembly going into inventory and then being withdrawn. An alternative to this is just to have the paper-work transaction occur without the actual material flowing through the stock room, but this is awkward also.

One solution to this problem is to use a so-called phantom bill of materials. This approach is not really a revision of the bill of materials as such but simply an indication in the system that a particular subassembly should not be treated as an inventory item and that the explosion should proceed right down through to its components. This approach avoids a good many of the problems of "self-consumed" subassemblies and makes it unnecessary to have paper work that is not really required.

In some companies the bulk of the manufacturing tends to be continuous. Companies making appliances, tractors, etc., seldom have stock rooms for the components and subassemblies. This means that the inventory balance that is used for requirements planning is really the amount of inventory out on the shop floor. When a subassembly is made, its components are deducted from the shop-floor inventory and the balance is thus reduced. Obviously, this type of inventory balance requires good shop-floor discipline so that counts are reported accurately.

A third approach is a combination of the two above. In this case, anything in the stock room is maintained on one inventory balance. When it goes out of the stock room it goes into the shop-floor inventory balance. When it is used because a subassembly is manufactured, the shop-floor inventory balance is reduced. Obviously, this approach makes the most sense where production tends to be continuous but there are frequent overruns to be stored in the stock room.

Summary of Dependent-demand Methods. Most of the literature of inventory control, particularly that of an academic nature, has dealt solely with the continuous or independent-demand inventory systems. Whenever demand for a component is dependent upon demand from a higher level, the *dependent-demand inventory systems* involving requirements planning and discrete-requirement lot-size calculations should be seriously considered. Even where the end demand is fairly continuous, lot sizing down through levels of inventory tends to make component demands quite discrete. A requirements planning approach is typically much more effective in handling this type of inventory item, since it will tend to drive inventory down to zero in periods of no demand. Perhaps more important, it seeks to match assembly requirements to parts in inventory rather than ordering each independently to replenish intermediate levels of inventory.

An order point is equal to the forecast of demand during lead time plus reserve stock. Requirements planning also forecasts demand during lead time plus reserve stock. The important difference is that in a requirements planning system the forecast of demand during lead time is not assumed to be level based on past history but instead is calculated based on the best estimate of demand for the assemblies.

Any inventory system should have as its basic goal ordering the right items in the right quantity at the right time. Too many inventory systems simply generate orders for everything that might possibly be needed far in advance of any real requirement date. Expediters must then expedite the items that are actually needed prior to the many items that have been ordered which aren't needed in the immediate future.

The design of a dependent-demand inventory system is extremely important. Any company making an assembled product can easily have high inventories and poor service at the same time if they don't have control over their product components. This situation exists because one component can keep an assembly from being delivered. If all other components are being held waiting for this missing component, inventories *will* be high while service is poor.

Preallocation of items in inventory has long been a subject of discussion for practitioners. Preallocation, when time periods are not specifically pinpointed, has often generated excess inventories and confused the entire inventory record-keeping procedure. Materials planning is a methodical, orderly method of pre-allocation, and it basically tries to drive the inventory level to zero when there are no requirements (unless a safety-stock level has been predesignated). It also tends to match up components and bring them together to meet a scheduled assembly date. The proper application of materials planning versus order-point-type techniques is discussed in some detail later in this chapter.

Obviously, any explosion technique requires bills of material. A bill of material in its simplest form is a parts list, but there is much more to it than that, and the proper format and structure of bills of material are extremely important if a usable materials planning system is to be developed. The following discussion covers this important problem.

Inventory Control System's Use of Bills of Material. A bill of material in its simplest form is nothing more than a parts list—a listing of each component required to make a product or a unit of a product. Part number, description, and quantity are indicated on most parts lists as a minimum. Lists of parts together with engineering drawings constitute the definition of the product specifications.

Information contained in a bill of material basically defines the relationship between a group of components and the product. This information is used by virtually every department in a company that manufactures an assembled product. Costing, estimating, purchasing, scheduling, materials planning, and engineering all have valid needs for information contained in the bills of material. However, the needs of each function are different. They depend upon that function's responsibilities, the nature of the product, and manufacturing facilities and methods.

Because of these different needs and the pronounced trend toward increased product complexity in terms of the numbers of products, options, and special features, there is no one universally acceptable definition of a bill of material. In the *APICS Dictionary* several of the more common types of bills of material have been identified and defined in terms of the most accepted practice and usage.

It is not our purpose here to expand these definitions and provide illustrations. Our objectives are threefold:

1. Identify the significant problems associated with the use of bills of material in inventory control systems.

2. Review certain common bill-of-material formats.

3. Describe methods for structuring bill-of-material data to answer some of the needs of inventory control systems.

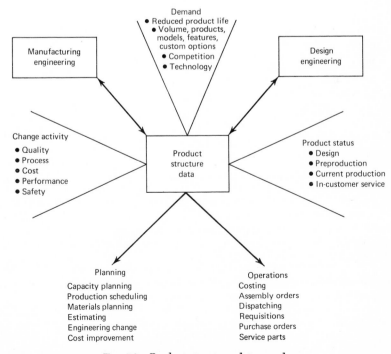

Fig. 10 Product-structure-data needs.

Problems with Bills of Material. Figure 10 points out the scope and complexity of bill-of-material data. In this illustration, bill-of-material data are referred to as "product-structure" data, the two terms being synonomous. The functions generating product-structure data are:

DESIGN ENGINEERING: A function normally associated with the creation of a new product in design engineering is the preparation of drawings and bills of material. It follows then that the maintenance of these documents is also the responsibility of this group. In recent years, this has become a task of considerable proportions due to customer requirements for product variations and the volume of engineering-change activity.

MANUFACTURING-INDUSTRIAL ENGINEERING: The function of determining how the product is to be manufactured may further complicate an already severe problem. Many times while determining the stages of production, the manufac-

A1054

Part no.	Description	Quantity
10544		1
24555		1
34508		4
44601		3
56000		1

Fig. 11   Simple parts list.

*Quantites used at each level greater than one are indicated by the number within parentheses.

Fig. 12   Product makeup.

turing-engineering department must modify the original product structure of the design engineer.

For example, Fig. 11 shows a complete definition of the components that are required to assemble one of product A1054. This bill of material, together with a purchase specification (buy) and/or a detail drawing (make) for each part number, and an assembly drawing for the assembly itself, provides complete product-structure specifications.

However, if manufacturing engineering, taking into account commonality of components between products, available manufacturing facilities, and inventory policy, decides that the best way to manufacture this assembly is as shown in Fig. 12, two versions of the same product-structure data have already been created. In this example, two levels of subassembly and three new part numbers, B3055, C2841, and D1458, have been added.

The original parts list is of little value in determining the impact of a proposed engineering change or when a purchased component should be scheduled for delivery. It is of little value to those functions concerned with the way production is planned, product scheduling, manufacturing, and when the components should be ordered and received.

Conflicting versions of product-structure data may exist, then, from the outset: the manufacturing version versus the design engineering specifications. This problem is compounded by the only factor which can be considered a "constant" when discussing bills of material, that of *change*.

Demand in terms of the customer, technology, and competition has increased the number of different products, options, and special features. In itself this has brought about a great deal more product-structure data for an increasing number of product variations. These factors have also brought about multiple variations of the *same product* in terms of prototype, preproduction, current production, and out-of-current production but required for service parts.

From the time of initial design through the product's life cycle, it seems that an almost continuous flow of engineering changes modify the product-structure data. It is not uncommon to find that at least three versions of the bills of material exist upon completion of the design engineering and prototype phase:

1. Preproduction: Used for preparing cost estimates, for make-or-buy decisions on new materials and components, for establishing manufacturing procedures, and for placing orders for components needed at some future time.

2. Current production: Product costing, inventory control, requirements planning, assembly orders and storeroom "picking lists," scheduling, etc.

3. Out of production: Service parts—manufacture and purchase—and the physical distribution of stockkeeping units.

The magnitude of this problem increases with the numbers of different products and product complexity. That the problem exists in most companies, there can be little doubt. The more products and the more complex the product, the more difficult and the more profitable a solution becomes. Yet many companies have failed to achieve a reasonable solution.

It is not uncommon to find product-structure data files maintained in different formats to suit their different needs in accounting, material control, service parts, and the engineering functions previously mentioned. This results in added cost to maintain the multiple files of common information which when compared are seldom consistent or complete. When considering the pivotal role this information plays in planning and controlling inventories and production, it appears contrary to good business judgment to permit the existence of anything but one official version of the bill of material.

The problems in using bills of material may be summarized by saying that duplicate departmental files of product-structure data are costly to maintain, generally inconsistent, but do provide information in formats that are generally most useful to the needs of a department. One only has to look at the distribution list on an approved engineering-change notice to understand the magnitude of the unofficial-files problem. On the other hand, it is difficult to envision how one file of product-structure data may be organized and maintained economically to provide accurate, current information when needed, in the most useful format.

Bill-of-material Formats. In the following discussion of individual formats, it is important to keep in mind that each example will be limited to the basic data that generally appear in any format: assembly part number or product designation, component part numbers, and quantities. Additional information is usually present and tailored to the specific uses a particular format is intended to satisfy. These variations are unlimited.

As individual formats are reviewed here, it is worthwhile to remember that in most companies no one format can be universally suitable for all the uses of bill-of-material data. The underlying consideration in selecting the proper format for a given company is whether it is possible to maintain correct bill-of-material files and provide from these files information about components and their relationship to products in the most usable form.

Most variations of the basic parts-list definition of a bill of material are derived from the data content and organization. The hypothetical products shown in Fig. 13 will be the basis for illustrating certain common formats.

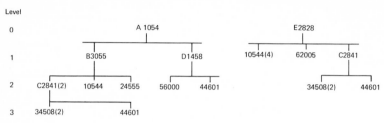

Fig. 13 Product makeup—two products.

Assembly	Components	Qty. required
A1054		
	10544	1
	24555	1
	34508	4
	44601	3
	56000	1
	(B3055)*	(1)
	(C2841)	(2)
	(D1458)	(1)
E2828		
	10544	4
	34508	2
	44601	1
	62005	1
	(C2841)	(1)

* Subassemblies indicated by parentheses.

Fig. 14 Product Summary formats.

GRAPHIC FORMAT: This is the graphic representation of the way the products are assembled sometimes referred to as "product-makeup" or "Christmas-tree" structure. Each successive level of assembly is numbered starting from the end item or product which is level zero and proceeding to the lowest point. In our example, products A1054 and E2828 are level-zero items. A1054 has three levels of assembly while E2828 has only two.

Note that part numbers C2841, 10544, and 44601 are common to both products but appear at different levels. In addition, part number 44601 is also used on different levels for product A1054.

PRODUCT-SUMMARY FORMAT: This bill-of-material format lists the components required to make a product without indicating levels of assembly. Figure 14, although it does not indicate the specific levels of assembly or product structure, does identify their existence. A *quick-deck* is an example of a product-summary format. It is defined as a summarized parts list showing the total quantities of all components required to put together a product.

The main characteristics of the product-summary formats are:

1. The entire product is defined in terms of all components.

2. The component quantities represent the total usage summarized in one line entry of information; i.e., each component is listed once regardless of multiple usage within a product.

3. Subassemblies may or may not be included, but the individual levels of assembly are not defined.

4. Components common to more than one product appear in the bill of material for each product.

The utility of this format is governed by the nature of the product and how it is assembled. It is most useful for planning and requisitioning products with no subassembly levels and is typical of products assembled on a continuous assembly-line basis. It is not suitable for a product with subassembly orders and parts requisitions, materials planning, assembly scheduling, and other functions dependent upon the precise definition of the contents and levels of assemblies. Although of limited value in the production control–material control areas, it has valid uses in other areas of many companies where summarized component usage in terms of a given products is meaningful. Examples of these uses are:

1. Product cost: Estimates, budgets, and actual costs

2. Cost analysis: Cost reduction, impact of component's cost change on total product cost

3. Sales: Parts lists, price lists

The product-summary formats are product oriented. That is to say, product-summary bills of material exist individually for each product.

Another summary format is called a "matrix," "explosion chart," or "tabular bill of material." It is a rearrangement and consolidation of the same type of data. It is rearranged from product orientation to component orientation, and consolidated for product families having considerable common components.

Figure 15 shows all the components listed on the left of the matrix with a group of products (models) across the top. Where a number appears under a product, this is the number of that component required to build one unit of the product. A dash indicates that the component is not used in that product.

	Models				
Component part no.	A1054	A1055	E2828	E2829	E3000
10544	1	2	4	4	4
24555	1	1	—	—	2
34508	2	6	2	2	2
44601	2	3	1	1	1
56000	1	1	—	—	—
62005	—	2	1	2	2
(B3055)	(1)	—	—	—	(1)
(C2841)	(2)	(2)	(1)	(1)	(1)
(D1458)	(1)	(1)	—	—	—

Fig. 15   Matrix format.

An advantage of this format is the consolidation into one format of the components and quantities that apply to two or more distinct but related products. It is particularly useful where no levels of subassembly exist and where there is a large number of common components within a product group. The less the component commonality, the less useful this format becomes because of wasted space which can result in a list of unwieldy size in terms of effecting and publishing changes. Furthermore, the size of the matrix in terms of quantities of components and products within a group may also result in a file that is difficult to maintain. An earlier section of this chapter gave an example of the use of this bill format.

The significant characteristics of the matrix format are the same as those for the product summary if the phrase "product line" is substituted wherever "product" appears. Where no levels of subassembly exist, this format offers an extremely fast and simple means of calculating gross requirements (extending component quantities by product-order quantities) and summarizing them for a group of related products. Similarly, other uses already mentioned for the product-summary format apply to the matrix format.

A1054

Part no.	Description	Quantity
B3055		1
C2841		2
34508		2
44601		1
10544		1
24555		1
D1458		1
44601		1
56000		1

Fig. 16   Product-structure format—indented.

PRODUCT-STRUCTURE FORMAT: The summary formats are useful whenever summarized information is meaningful to a particular function or department. They are especially useful where no levels of subassembly exist for purposes of production and material control. However, where these levels do exist, product-structure formats reflecting the way the product is actually assembled are more useful. Levels of subassembly are accounted for, and each component usage is related to the assembly level it is used on starting with a product or final assembly and proceeding downward through each level of subassembly. It is, in effect, a bill-of-material format which precisely mirrors the Christmas-tree structure of a complex or multilevel product.

The "indented parts list" or "indented bill of materials" is a common type of product-structure bill since the levels of assembly are often identified by offsetting or indenting either the part numbers or description. Figure 16 illustrates this format.

Levels in a product-structure format may be identified by a number indicating the level rather than by indenting, as shown in Fig. 17. Here, it is essentially the sequence in which the components are listed that characterizes the product-structure format. Starting at the top with the product, components are listed until the first subassembly is encountered. The listing continues showing that subassembly's components until another subassembly is encountered, etc. Re-

E2828

Level	Part no.	Description	Quantity
1	10544		4
1	62005		1
1	C2841		1
2	34508		2
2	44601		1

Fig. 17 Product-structure format—level numbered.

maining components at level 1 are not indicated again until all successively lower level subassembly contents have been identified as belonging to the subassembly first encountered. The advantages of this format are that both assembly level and contents are defined and it provides for easy tracing of component usage upward or downward in a given product.

The principal disadvantage is that it requires large files and is therefore most costly in terms of file maintenance. In Figs. 16 and 17, note that subassembly C2841 is a component of both A1054 and E2828. C2841 and its contents are duplicated. If C2841 were a component of 30 different products, it and all its components would be repeated 30 times. If a change were to be made to a component of C2841, then 30 bills of material would have to be updated with each change.

This format is convenient for calculating gross and net requirements, subassembly scheduling, scheduling deliveries of purchased components, and establishing due dates for fabricated components. In these areas, it is most useful where there are relatively few common subassemblies, a limited number of products, and where changes to the structure of the product are infrequent. However, just as in the case of the summary formats, there are other product-oriented uses of this format in most companies:

1. Service parts catalogs: product variations within the serial number
2. Manufacturing methods or process analysis
3. Cost buildup and cost analysis
4. Reference documents supplied to customer

Another product-structure format is the inverted product structure, "indented where-used," or "where-used trace." Figure 18 shows how this format traces

Component part no.	Assembly used on	Description	Quantity
44601	C2841		1
	B3055		2
	A1054		1
	E2828		1
	D1458		1
	A1054		1
10544	B3055		1
	A1054		1
	E2828		4

Fig. 18 Inverted product structure.

the direct and indirect usage of a component upward through all levels of assembly in all products.   This is a hybrid format that is useful in analyzing the effect of cost or engineering changes and has additional application in the areas of model configuration control and parts-provisioning documentation for certain government contracts.   Its application is limited at present since this format by definition specifies that each component, whether a piece part or a subassembly, has its own specific inverted structure incorporating all its uses at each level in every product.   This fact makes continuous file-maintenance cost prohibitive in most instances.   In practice, such a format therefore is prepared typically for one-time, special purposes.

SINGLE-LEVEL FORMAT: Product summary and structure formats present information about all components and their relationship to the end item or product itself.   The single-level bill of material specifies only those components required at a particular level of assembly.   Figure 19 shows the single-level bills of material that specify the product makeup of A1054 and E2828.   Note that subassembly C2841 is shown as a component of subassembly B3055 and product

Assembly	Component part no.	Description	Quantity
A1054	B3055		1
	D1458		1
B3055	C2841		2
	10544		1
	24555		1
C2841	34508		2
	44601		1
D1458	44601		1
	56000		1
E2828	10544		4
	62005		1
	C2841		1

Fig. 19   Single-level bills of material.

E2828.   However, since the components required to assemble C2841 are the same regardless of where C2841 is used in higher-level assemblies, its single-level bill of material is shown just once.   This is the most significant characteristic of this format.

This format is the most compact in terms of file size, and therefore the easiest to maintain.   With the same example used in the product-structure-format description, the contract in terms of file maintenance is easy to see.   If C2841 were used on 30 products and it became necessary to change a component listed on C2841's bill of material, only one change to the file would be required.

The main disadvantage of this approach lies in the fact that there is no capability inherent to the format itself to link together various single-level bills to create a complete bill of material for a given product.   An index must be established and maintained which indicates which single-level bills are components of which products and at which level.   The alternative to this approach is to trace manually from top level or product downward.   Starting with the single-level bill for A1054, single-level bills for B3055 and D1458 can be retrieved.   Within these bills, subassembly bills can be identified for the next lower level.   This process is repeated level by level until no more subassemblies are found. The index approach is superior but requires additional file-maintenance cost as changes occur.

Prior to today's computer techniques, single-level bills of material were difficult to use. However, the computer user has a variety of sound methods for maintaining an index of single-level bills of material inside the computer. This overcomes the problems of indexing and permits the computer user to take advantage of the significantly small file size and ease of file maintenance inherent in this format.

The single-level bill, irrespective of indexing, is the most useful format for issuing subassembly orders and parts requisitions. Since the contents define only one level of assembly, it may also be useful for maintaining assembly routing information and standards. In accounting, it is useful for purposes of accumulating actual cost for comparison to standard. With an indexing capability, it provides a highly useful format for calculating level-by-level gross and net requirements, assembly scheduling, component allocation, and product cost, as well as reference documentation for design and manufacturing engineering.

To the computer user, and to a more limited extent the punched-card user, perhaps the most important advantage of the single-level bill format lies in the very heart of the problem of the variety of format and content required by the many users. Since no one format is universally useful, the ability to

Component part no.	Assembly used on next level	Description	Quantity
44601	C2841		1
	D1458		1
C2841	B3055		2
	E2828		1

Fig. 20 Single-level where-used format.

prepare different formats from the same basic information becomes a paramount consideration.

On close examination of the single-level bill-of-material contents together with an appropriate indexing technique, it should be apparent that the product-structure format can be prepared by linking together a series of single-level bills. Similarly, a product-summary forecast can be prepared by summarizing the single-level bills for a given product without regard to levels of assembly.

The single-level bill defines the product in terms of its most basic building blocks. This format is in effect a common base from which other formats can be readily prepared through the use of file-organization techniques that are particularly feasible when a computer is available.

The single-level bill has a companion single-level format which is where-used or upward oriented in terms of the product-structure data. It is commonly referred to as "next level" or "single-level where-used." In Fig. 20 each component is listed showing only the next higher level of assembly on which it is used. Referring back to Fig. 19 and scanning the components column, 44601 is a component of subassembly C2841 and also of D1458. The next-level where-used format simply changes the orientation of the information from an assembly-contents or downward point of view to a where-used or upward perspective. Part 44601 is used directly on subassemblies C2841 and D1458 with a quantity of one per each usage.

There are two primary advantages inherent in this format.   When an engineering change is made to a component, the impact of the change, on both cost and compatibility throughout all products, must be analyzed in terms of where the component is used.   In addition to providing this capability, as in the case of the single-level bill, the next-level where-used formats can be generated.   For example, the indented where-used trace is a series of next-level where-used formats linked together by means of an indexing technique.

All where-used formats must be supplemented by some form of product-oriented format.   They are normally used in conjunction with a product-structure format since they are unsuited to those production and material control functions associated with the manufacturing process such as parts requisitioning and assembly ordering.

These formats have been used successfully for calculating gross and net requirements principally where sequential data processing techniques and files are employed.   Requirements calculation with where-used formats was discussed in an earlier section of this chapter.   Other uses include drawing-location index, allocation of back-ordered components to assembly orders, and analyzing the impact of component shortages upon existing assembly schedules and requirements.

The choice of format is indeed important and sometimes difficult, due to the variety of formats and the pros and cons of each in terms of their usefulness and the ability to maintain them.

In general, a good format

1. Defines all levels of assembly and each assembly's contents

2. Is as compact as possible to minimize file size and maintenance cost

If no levels of subassembly exist in the manufacturing process, then the product-summary or matrix formats have broad application.   The trade-offs between the two are dependent upon the commonality of components and the numbers of different products required in a given matrix format.   As the number of products or components increases or the number of common components decreases, the matrix becomes unwieldy and the product-summary format becomes more desirable.

Here are some pointers for selecting the best format to use to plan and control:

1. *Manual Systems.*   Select the format that will best serve the most important uses.   Although the single-level bill offers significant advantages, a computer is required to exploit the full potential of this format and to overcome its inherent disadvantages if there are a large number of products made from standard options and features.

2. *Computer Systems.*   The logical choice here for most applications would be the single-level bill format.   Compact file size, ease of file maintenance, and the ability to generate other formats offer clear-cut advantages over other formats.

3. *Punched-card Systems.*   The ability to sort bills of material maintained in punched cards from essentially one format to another would seem to show more advantage for the single-level bill format.   Simple sorting methods permit the creation of the next-level where-used format which facilitates analysis and entry of changes to the file.

Bill-of-material Structure: Multiple Levels of Assembly.   In the case of a complex product it may not be enough to decide upon the proper format alone.   Where the end product is assembled from a wide variety of options and standard components, the data contained in bills of material may have to be restructured for a number of reasons prior to organizing the file to get the most useful format.   A good format incorporates the structure of the product in terms of the way it is manufactured. A structure based upon the way the product is assembled may not lend itself to forecasting optional features and calculating subsequent gross and net requirements.

The need to forecast options rather than end products is illustrated in Fig. 21 for assembling a product within product group X. It must have one of the 10 variations of component A, one of the 8 variations of component B, one of 6 variations of component C, and either a component D or a component E.

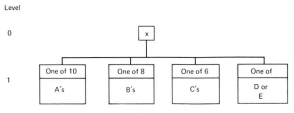

Fig. 21   Forecasting options.

The number of possible products that can be assembled is extensive:

$$10 \times 8 \times 6 \times 2 = 960$$

Number of individual options:

$$10 + 8 + 6 + 2 = 26$$

A fundamental characteristic of forecasts is that the larger the group of items forecast, the more inherently accurate the forecast will be. Since 960 possible products are made up from combinations of 26 standard options, it is far more effective to forecast the level 1 options than to attempt to forecast the 960 individual products. The automobile industry represents an extreme example of this point, since when all allowable combinations of options are totaled, there can be in excess of a million possible end products in some car product lines. The problem exists, but is not recognized, in many other industries, and a common symptom of an improperly structured bill is the complaint, "It's impossible to forecast all the variations possible in our product."

One way to overcome this problem effectively is to forecast *total* product sales (one large group) within a given product line without regard to variations in options, and then forecast the individual options as percentages of the total. These percentages are then calculated against the total product sales forecast, to get the number of each option from which the component-requirements forecast can be extended.

Because of the large numbers of possible products in the automobile industry and many others, bills of material do not exist for level 0 or such end items as the actual finished automobile. Since bills of material do not exist, it then becomes necessary to develop coding techniques to identify which level 1 items are called for when a customer specifies a product made up of a certain combination of options. A superstructure or coding scheme outside of the regular bill-of-material file must be established to bridge this gap. This may only be a convenience in some manual methods, but it is essential to automated order-entry systems which link detail order specifications directly to the bill-of-material file.

Another problem which again points out the need to modify the bill-of-material structure exists when the forecasting input to the materials planning system is incompatible with the manner in which the product is assembled. The following example illustrates this problem.

In the previous example, there were eight variations or eight different single-level bills of material for type B assemblies. Examining these bills of material, in Fig. 22 it can be seen that the eight variations of B are the result of different combinations of B's major components M, P, W, H, L, and T.

Each product always contains one of the eight variations of assembly B. A forecast is received which specifies that 100 of the product type X are required. The percentages by option are given as follows:

$$75\%M–25\%P$$
$$60\%H–40\%L$$
$$20\%T–80\% \text{ no } T$$

Given this forecast, how many of each of the eight combinations of features which make up a B must be exploded to plan requirements for lower-level components?

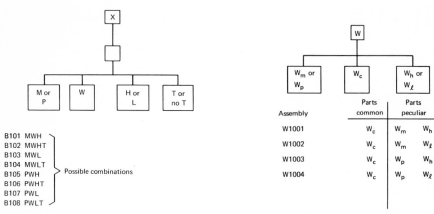

| B101 MWH |
| B102 MWHT |
| B103 MWL |
| B104 MWLT |
| B105 PWH | Possible combinations |
| B106 PWHT |
| B107 PWL |
| B108 PWLT |

Fig. 22 Variations in option B.

Assembly	Parts common	Parts peculiar	
W1001	W_c	W_m	W_h
W1002	W_c	W_m	W_ℓ
W1003	W_c	W_p	W_h
W1004	W_c	W_p	W_ℓ

Fig. 23 Bill-of-material variations.

There is no precise way to determine how many of each of the different type B assemblies are needed. However, we know from the forecast how many of each major component to make: 75 M's, 25 P's, 100 W's, etc. In this instance, level 1 type B assemblies must be bypassed for purposes of calculating gross and net requirements. This results in one bill structure which applies to forecasting options and materials planning, and another which reflects the way in which the product is manufactured to be used for exploding actual parts used from inventory, etc. These different versions of product structure are often designated "planning" bills of material and "manufacturing" bills of material.

Figure 21 showed the contents of each of the eight possible type B subassemblies. Based upon the component makeup of each of its major second levels, another problem may still exist. Assume that any B is assembled by starting with a W (common to all B's) and attaching either an M or a P unit to one end and either an H or an L to the other. (T has been dropped as it has no direct bearing on this example.) M, P, H, and L are unique standard assemblies each having its own single-level bill of material. However, W assemblies are composed of four distinct, single-level bills, one for each of the possible combinations of M, P, H, and L with W. In each bill for W there are parts which are only used in combination with L. There are other parts included in the W bill which are only used when it is attached to a P, etc.

We could think of W as an engine block and M and P as different carburetors each requiring its own special intake manifold; and of H and L as being two different transmissions that require different flywheel housings. The manifold and flywheel housings are actually parts of the *engine* bill of materials. Figure 23 shows the problem where the W bills actually contain parts that are used *only* when an M is attached (designated W_m in the figure). Other parts in the W bill of material are used only when it is attached to a P, H, or L. The common parts that are *always* included in a W bill are designated W_c in the figure.

This structure is suitable for manufacturing because four different W's may be ordered, scheduled, produced, and accounted for. In terms of forecasting, the common parts represent no problems since 100 B's have been forecast and thus 100 sets of common W components will be required. The parts used only with M, P, and H, and L do present some trouble. The number of each required must be determined from the forecast quantities of option M, P, H, and L.

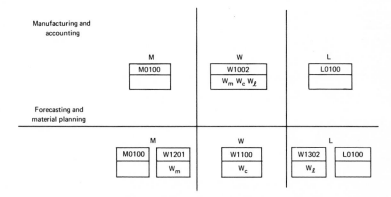

Fig. 24   Structure variations at level 2.

Removing the parts peculiar to the W bills and adding them to the respective M, P, H, and L bills, leaving only one W bill of parts common to all combinations, would be a solution to the forecasting and gross-to-net requirements problem. Expressing this in terms of the engine example, the intake manifolds and flywheel housing would be added to the carburetor and the transmission bills with which they are associated for forecasting purposes only.

Obviously this planning bill of material would have to be maintained in addition to the manufacturing bill which would still be required for parts requisitioning, accounting, etc. For manufacturing and accounting purposes, the original structure remains, and for the planning functions of forecasting and calculating level-by-level component requirements, an alternate structure must be available.

Conceptually, the different structures for manufacturing and planning purposes are shown in Fig. 24 for product X when options M and L are to be attached. W1002 is the assembly part number used when assembling a bill with options M and L. Its bill of material lists all components required to make one unit of assembly W1002. For the purpose of entering forecast data and planning material requirements, W1002 does not exist and its components have been grouped into three categories: parts peculiar to M, L, and parts common. New numbers have been assigned these component groups for planning purposes only and will not appear in manufacturing documents and accounting procedure. In effect, W1002's components have been grouped, given pseudo assembly numbers, and promoted from level 3 to level 2. Manufacturing instructions and parts requisitions will not be issued to assemble W1201, W1100, or W1302. They exist only to facilitate forecasting and material planning functions.

Another type of artificial, nonengineering part number is commonly referred to as a "kit" or "bag" number. To reduce the large number of individual small components, such as brackets, bolts, etc., that are usually level 1 items used in final assembly of the product, they are grouped and given an assembly number and demoted to level 2. This facilitates order entry by reducing the number of level 1 items which must be associated with a given customer order. Figure 25 illustrates the structure before and after the assignment of kit numbers.

Kit numbers are typically an integral part of the regular bill-of-material structure. But, unlike other assemblies, they have no routing or assembly standards, and for purposes of costing, only the material cost is included at level 1 since the assembly labor cost is accounted for during final assembly.

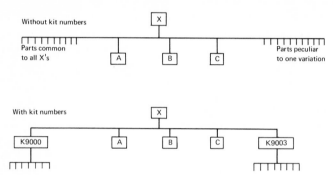

Fig. 25 Kit numbers.

Bills of Material: Summary. A bill-of-material file should be capable of satisfying several major functional objectives:

Production planning should be able to use the bill of materials for:
1. Forecasting optional features
2. Gross- and net-requirements planning
3. Capacity planning
4. Customer order entry

Manufacturing control should be able to use the bill of materials for:
1. Issuing parts requisitions for all levels of assembly
2. Preparing assembly orders, labor standards, and assembly instructions
3. Accounting for all materials and components
4. Product costing

The bill of materials should be useful to the engineering department, of course, but the engineers usually are the originators and will generally put the bill of material in a form that is useful for engineering at the outset. Since change is a way of life in most manufacturing companies, the bill-of-material file should also be in a form that lends itself to maintenance.

Various format approaches were discussed above. The product-structure formats in general lend themselves to most manufacturing control activities since they reflect the way the product is put together. Where there are many common parts, this format is difficult to maintain, however. The single-level format, on the other hand, lends itself better to maintenance, but requires a great deal of cross-referencing or indexing, which is awkward and time consuming in a manual system.

In a self-designed computer system, single-level bills make a great deal of sense since indexing is readily handled by the computer. But an important point to bear in mind is that merely storing existing bills of material in a computer system cannot overcome the selection of the wrong basic format or the lack of proper structure. The structure must be reworked in many cases to facilitate option forecasting and the like.

Lack of accurate, complete definitions of bill-of-material data will adversely affect performance in terms of extra costs and confusion in most functional areas of a company. Its symptoms which often are not recognized are excessive inventory, poor delivery performance, and needless confusion because the proper data are not available to run the control system effectively.

Improving the quality and availability of bill-of-material data can definitely help to improve performance. To achieve these improvements, the following steps are suggested:

1. Understand the complex nature of the many problems and trade-offs associated with the use of bill-of-material data in terms of your product in your company's environment. Consider:

  a. Multiple users, many different uses

  b. Duplicate files

  c. File-maintenance costs

2. Select the basic format which will be most useful to the most important and frequent users considering the amount and type of data processing capabilities available.

3. Study and re-redefine the structure of products to best accommodate present and future requirements in conjunction with anticipated data processing capabilities.

DESIGNING AN EFFECTIVE INVENTORY SYSTEM

There are many inventory control techniques available to the systems designer, and in the past there have been considerable partisan attitudes on the part of many practitioners—some preferring requirements planning techniques, others preferring order-point techniques, some claiming that the ABC "system" will not work in their company, etc.

A professional approach to inventory management demands that the designer and practitioner understand all the techniques that are available and have a reasonable understanding of the proper application of each technique. One of the most important concepts that has been developed in recent years to provide criteria for choosing the proper technique is the independent–dependent-demand inventory concept.[3]

The independent–dependent-demand concept suggests that when items have demands which are independent of any other item, such as finished-goods items, service parts, etc., it is necessary to forecast their demand using techniques like exponential smoothing. This forecast should then be the *forecast* that is used over lead time for reordering. Where demand is dependent (related to demand for other items), this demand should be *calculated* through a bill-of-materials explosion from a higher-level forecast. In general, it is recommended that demand for dependent items not be forecast when it can be calculated from items at a higher level. This concept would indicate that finished-goods items and service parts should use reorder-point techniques and the square-root

EOQ approach, while components that go into higher-level assemblies or semi-finished items should have their requirements calculated through requirements planning techniques.

Experience of a great many practitioners in many companies has shown this to be sound counsel. In fact, the statistical order-point techniques have too often been described without defining their proper application. Some practitioners assert that they use order points to control the components going into higher-level assemblies so that all components will be available when an assembly order is created. An electric-motor manufacturer, for example, might well feel that he should use order points on each of the components going into the motors so that he would have the components available to custom-assemble a motor to the customer's requirements when an order is received. The fallacy of this thinking should be evident to anyone with even a superficial knowledge of statistics.

When components are ordered independently, the service level for *all* components will be much lower than the service level for the *individual* components. This phenomenon is one that is well known to statisticians; it simply illustrates the laws of probability in action. *If any individual component is likely to be on hand 95 percent of the time that it is required, any two components will be likely to be on hand simultaneously 90 percent of the time* ($95\% \times 95\%$). If the service level on each of three independently ordered components is 95 percent, the cumulative service level or the chances of having all three available to satisfy a random demand is 86 percent. If an assembly has 10 components and each of them is ordered independently to maintain a 95 percent service level, the cumulative service level for all 10 components will be down around 56 percent.

Obviously, the electric-motor manufacturer can hardly expect to succeed in maintaining a good level of service to his customers when he orders each component independently. In fact, if it weren't for expediters trying to get the right components through production based on assembly shortages or the projected assembly shortages, he probably couldn't even be in business. This is an excellent example of a company succeeding *in spite* of its system rather than because of it. The requirements planning approach is simply an attempt to forecast assembly requirements, much as the expediter does over a short period of time, far enough into the future so that this information can be used to generate component reorders.

This doesn't mean that the order-point–EOQ techniques don't have a proper application. So many companies have used intuitive approaches in determining order points that dramatic improvements can be made when statistical order points are properly applied. The use of economic lot sizes can reduce either inventories or ordering costs when they are properly applied to independent-demand items. The important point is that the practitioner and system designer must recognize where the tools apply and apply them in a system that is best suited to the individual company's requirements.

Some examples of proper system design are considered below:

1. A company manufactures a simple one-piece product which is machined and carried in finished-goods inventory. Many of the items go through similar setups.

This company should consider statistical order points and square-root economic order quantities. It might be advantageous to consider joint replenishment for the economic lot sizes as described in Chapter 16. Before applying the economic-ordering concept, however, the basic principle behind the LIMIT approach should be considered: What are the current lot sizes? What aggregate inventory levels and ordering-costs levels do they generate? What will the new lot sizes be? How can the economies of EOQ actually be *realized*?

2. A manufacturer of electric motors must maintain components on hand since his assembly lead time must be short to respond to customers' requirements and thus be competitive. He does not stock any finished motors but only components.

This company should review the bill-of-materials structuring very carefully since there are many combinations of components that can be put together in an electric motor and it would be impossible to forecast all the possible combinations. Materials planning should be used to forecast component requirements, the time-series order-quantity calculation described earlier should be used to calculate lot sizes, and perhaps on a daily basis a component allocation program would be run to get optimum use out of the components currently on hand.

3. A company wishes to effectively replenish branch warehouses. Since any splitting of inventories requires a higher level of reserve stock, this company should try to hold as much of the inventory safety stock as possible in a central location. If the warehouses are replenished periodically by truckloads, a periodic-review inventory system should be designed to replenish the independent-demand items. Individual lot sizes for replenishing the branch warehouses probably don't make a great deal of sense. It is extremely important, however, to determine the most economical replenishment period based on ordering costs, inventory costs, and transportation costs. Less-frequent shipments to the warehouses can frequently save a great deal of shipping costs but mean larger lot sizes. Looking at the lot sizes that are used to replenish the warehouse from an aggregate point of view, some items will be replenished every replenishment period, some every other replenishment period, some every third replenishment period, to keep the number of replenishment orders and the corresponding lot-size inventory properly balanced from an aggregate point of view.

4. A company carries a number of assembled products in finished inventory and must order components to make these products.

The items in finished inventory are independent-demand items and an order-point technique based on the assembly lead time only could be used to replenish the finished inventory. The requirements planning system could then be combined with the order-point system to order the dependent-demand components. Consider the following example:

$$\text{Item X assembly lead time} = 5 \text{ weeks}$$
$$\text{Weekly forecast} = 100 \text{ units}$$
$$\text{Order point} = 700 \text{ units}$$
$$\text{Order quantity} = 1,000 \text{ units}$$

Assume that there is currently an inventory level of 900 units in finished inventory. In order to forecast component requirements, the system can estimate that (the current planning period is week 1) there should be a requirement for 1,000 in week 3 because the current inventory level is 900 units, the order point is 700 units, and the weekly forecast is 100 units. Since the order quantity is 1,000, it should last for 10 more weeks and another assembly order should be placed in week 23. In this manner, the independent-demand inventory system for the finished assembled product can be used to predict when the component requirements will be, thus providing the master schedule for materials planning. This approach combines both the independent and dependent inventory control techniques where they best apply.

5. A company makes many finished products from a small number of semi-

finished products. The final configuration of the product depends on painting, packaging, branding, etc.

These semifinished items once again are *dependent*-demand items, and the inventory of semifinished items should be replenished by trying to plan when each of the finished items will need to be reordered and projecting semifinished inventory levels out into the future on a time-series basis. While this semifinished item can hardly be considered a "component," it is a dependent-demand inventory item and a materials planning technique will be most effective in controlling it.

A great many inventory management techniques have been discussed in this chapter and in Chapter 16. Probably the most important technique is the one that most practitioners tend to ignore: the concept of ABC. In looking at any inventory, it is important to separate the vital few from the trivial many. Aggregate dollar reports showing what the levels of inventory purchased commitments should be to maintain these inventory levels, what the levels of manufacturing should be, etc., are an important part of an overall inventory management system. In some companies, the inventory manager actually gets brief summary reports listing the inventory levels for the vital few product lines and even the vital few components or products within these lines. The basic ABC principle, often thought of as a "system" or "technique," is probably the most important inventory management tool available to the system designer.

REFERENCES

1. For discussion of least unit cost versus total cost, see Thomas Gorham: "Dynamic Order Quantities," *Production and Inventory Management,* vol. 9, no. 1, pp. 75–79, 1968.
2. H. M. Wagner and T. M. Whitin: "Dynamic Version of the Economic Lot Size Model," *Management Science, vol.* 5, no. 1, pp. 89–98, October, 1958.
3. This concept was developed by Dr. Joseph A. Orlicky, Manufacturing Industry Consultant, Data Processing Division, International Business Machine Corp., White Plains, N.Y.
4. *Requirements Planning Manual* H20-0487, International Business Machine Corp., White Plains, N.Y.

BIBLIOGRAPHY

Greene, James H.: *Production Control: Systems and Decisions,* Richard D. Irwin, Inc., Homewood, Ill., 1965.
Magee, John E., and David M. Boodman: *Production Planning and Inventory Control,* 2d ed., McGraw-Hill Book Company, New York, 1967.
Management Operating System Inventory Management and Materials Planning Detail, no. E20-0050, Data Processing Division, International Business Machines Corp., White Plains, N.Y.
Plossl, G. W., and Oliver W. Wight: *Production and Inventory Control: Principles and Techniques,* Prentice-Hall, Inc., Englewood Cliffs, N.J., 1967.
The Production Information and Control System, no. E20-0280, Data Processing Division, International Business Machines Corp., White Plains, N.Y.

Chapter **18**

Inventory Control in the Department of Defense

EDITOR:

Paul J. Hyman *Assistant Staff Director, Materiel Management Systems Division, Office of the Assistant Secretary of Defense (Installations and Logistics), Washington, D.C.*

CONTENTS

Inventories in the Department of Defense generally are divided for management control into two groups. The first group is composed of weapons and ammunition, aircraft engines, certain kinds of vehicles, electronics and communications equipment, and other major "end items" referred to as "principal items." At the end of the 1967 calendar year the value of these items exceeded $19.5 billion—weapons and ammunition comprising over half. The second group are those several million items referred to as "secondary items"—the repair parts and consumables which comprise the greatest investment in distribution system inventories ($23 billion on Dec. 31, 1967) and present the greatest challenge to inventory management by virtue of the several million stock numbers and part numbers involved.

For the most part, the principal-item segment of the supply system has long been under intensive management in each military service. The unit value of these items is high. Many of these items have a relatively long service life, and they are often subject to worldwide control by piece. For example, aircraft engines have long been controlled on a serial-number basis, with transactions reporting on each significant event in the life of an engine.

Since the major problems of inventory management are presented by the large numbers of secondary items which have high and fluctuating usage rates, it is the objective of this chapter to zero in on the management and control of these items. This chapter is intended to give the reader two perspectives of the inventory control in the national defense establishment—organizational and procedural. First will be presented a survey of the organizational and administrative arrangements for inventory control which have been adopted by each of the major Defense components—Army, Navy, Air Force, Marine Corps, and the Defense Supply Agency (DSA). Second, a sampling of significant programs and techniques used in the day-to-day operation of military supply systems will be discussed.

ORGANIZING AND MANAGING
THE SUPPLY SYSTEMS

In general each of the military supply systems, including DSA, is organized on a functional basis. Each has specifically identified organizational elements for determining requirements (both qualitative and quantitative); effecting procurement; providing for the physical acts of receipt of materiel, its storage, and shipment to the customers of the system; performing major overhaul or rebuilding of equipment; and disposing of items either no longer needed or unfit for further use. Once requirements have been determined and materiel has been procured, the supplies are the responsibility of the distribution system until issued to the ultimate user. Supplies ordinarily remain in the hands of users until they are consumed or become unserviceable or obsolete. Unserviceable supplies may be restored to serviceable condition by repair or maintenance and may find their way back into the distribution system; or obsolete items may be disposed of.

In spite of the commonality of general supply functions, each of the services and DSA have organized differently for the management of these functions. Some of these differences stem from basic differences in missions, while others have their foundation in the way each has organized its other functions such as research, development of weapons, and maintenance of equipment.

OSD Management and Control. Policy guidance to the military departments and DSA in the implementation of their missions is furnished by the President through the Secretary of Defense. Created by the National Security Act of 1947, the Office of the Secretary of Defense (OSD) has grown steadily in power and stature. Today, no function in any part of the Defense Department or in any of its component agencies can be performed independently of the direction, authority, and control of the Secretary of Defense. For example, in the area of supply management, Section 2202 of Title 10 of the *United States Code*, entitled "Armed Forces," enacted into law Aug. 10, 1956, stipulates:[1]

Notwithstanding any other provision of law, an officer or agency of Defense may obligate funds for procuring, producing, warehousing, or distributing supplies, or for related functions of supply management, only under reguations prescribed by the Secretary of Defense. The purpose of this section is to achieve the efficient, economical, and practical operation of an integrated supply system to meet the needs of the Military Departments without duplicate or overlapping operations or functions.

The Defense Secretary directs the continuous and comprehensive implementation of this legislative mandate. The principal staff assistants to the Secretary of Defense are charged with "monitoring and reviewing the implementation" of the above-quoted legislative provision, "including the maintaining of such records and the making of such reports to the Secretary of Defense as may be necessary to keep him informed of progress in its implementation."[2]

The principal assistant and adviser to the Secretary of Defense on all supply and logistics matters is the Assistant Secretary of Defense (Installations and Logistics). In consonance with existing operating principles and concepts, the Assistant Secretary of Defense (I&L) has developed integrated supply systems for the Department of Defense (DOD) as a whole, while at the same time providing for deviations based on differing roles and missions. Essentially the emphasis has been on program development designed to accomplish improvements in the supply systems. Recognizing that uniformity for uniformity's sake alone may be harmful, the programs call for only that degree of uniformity which is necessary to produce efficiency, effectiveness, and economy. And because DOD programs and policies are designed to enhance operational effectiveness, they are developed in close collaboration with the military departments.

The office of the Assistant Secretary of Defense [ASD(I&L)] is charged with the development of policy in the logistics area with day-to-day coordination with the military departments, furnishing guidance in governing planning and program developments, evaluation, and surveillance. The primary objective of DOD policy guidance is to assure that DOD supply systems provide prompt and adequate supply of materiel essential to missions, are rapidly convertible from peacetime to emergency or wartime operations, are simple and flexible, are responsive to emergency and war plans, have adequate communications, are protected, and provide for rapid determination of requirements.[3]

The ASD (I&L) is organized on a functional basis with staff elements for the development of materiel requirements, procurement, production, inventory management, maintenance, storage and distribution, communications, supply cataloging, transportation, standardization, quality control, and other logistics services. These elements work closely with their counterparts in the offices of the materiel secretaries of the military departments, the principal logistics staffs of military service headquarters, and specific program directors in the Defense Supply Agency. The ASD (I&L) also coordinates with other DOD agencies having collateral or related functions and maintains liaison with appropriate agencies outside the Department of Defense on supply and logistics matters.

The recent formalization of agreements concerning Defense Supply Agency-General Services Administration (DSA-GSA) division of responsibilities serves as an example of logistics policy development by the Assistant Secretary of Defense (I&L). The division of responsibility for DSA and GSA as it pertains to support of the military services and other federal agencies was clearly delineated. In brief this policy states that GSA will provide direct support to all military services on items that are commercial in nature and similar to those produced by industry for general consumption by the civilian economy. The role of DSA in this agreement is to act as coordinator between GSA and the military services to ensure consistency of policy and procedures governing centralized supply management. On the other hand, DSA will support other federal agencies on items it stocks, so as not to duplicate the GSA range of items. In this connection GSA acts as coordinator between DSA and federal civil agencies to ensure that interests are protected and supply requirements met.

Numerous other programs designed to improve supply management policy, practices, and procedures throughout the Department of Defense are generated and sponsored by the Assistant Secretary of Defense (I&L).

The increasing reliance on automatic data processing systems for inventory control has resulted in ASD(I&L)-fostered joint programs to assure compatibility and standard techniques in the processing of supply information. It is an objective of these standard techniques to permit the output of one supply data system to be communicated and utilized as the direct input (with minimum clerical intervention) to other related data systems. For example, through ASD(I&L) efforts in 1962, 16 different documentation systems for the receipt and issue of supplies were replaced with a Military Standard Requisitioning and Issue Procedure (MILSTRIP). Prescribing standard codes, definitions, document formats, and related processing rules, MILSTRIP provided impetus to the application of computers to many areas of interservice supply communication. The increased use of computer processing as a substitute for clerical labor has saved a considerable amount of time (there are over 400 million requisition-system documents processed annually in DOD) devoted to processing supply transactions and permitted a rechanneling of manpower to more productive pursuits. Several other standard logistics data systems have been developed under the auspices of the ASD(I&L) and have similarly contributed to the establishment of a common language for rapid communications among supply activities and customers. Examples of joint systems are:

1. Military Standard Transportation and Movement Procedures (MILSTAMP) provide simplified, uniform documentation and coding for automated information systems controlling the movement of cargo into and through all segments of the Defense transportation system. The Transportation Control and Movement Document is established by MILSTAMP as the multipurpose document which is used as a basic movement and control document, terminal-handling document (e.g., dock receipt), cargo manifest, or tracing document. When MILSTAMP became operational in 1963, it replaced a score of different forms, formats, and codes for transportation documentation.

2. Military Supply and Transportation Evaluation Procedures (MILSTEP) utilize the standard codes and forms produced by the MILSTRIP and MILSTAMP systems as input for the purpose of evaluating supply and transportation performance against the order and shipping-time standards. These input data are mechanically manipulated to produce standard output reports by military service and by distribution system to reflect, by issue priority, the elapsed time for requisition submission, supply source (i.e., depot, inventory control point) processing, cargo-handling time, and in-transit time. They also provide the capability for detailed analyses of any of the aforementioned time segments to permit the application of management-improvement techniques in reducing the order and ship times from the date the requisition was submitted until the date the materiel is delivered to the consignee.

3. Military Standard Transaction Reporting and Accounting Procedures (MILSTRAP) standardize machine-sensible codes and formats for the interchange of data among inventory managers and storage depots to permit the posting to accountable records of all types of transactions, i.e., receipts, issues, and the adjustments which affect the on-hand balances. The coding system has been structured also to accommodate the income, expense, and inventory accounting classifications for investment analysis and appropriated-fund accounting systems.

4. Military Standard Contract Administration Procedures (MILSCAP) provide the procedural standardization necessary to improve the flow of data through joint contract administration activities to buying office, ICP, contractor, and user activities. To support contract administration, production, quality assur-

ance, financial accounting, and disbursing, uniform manual and mechanized documentation procedures will be implemented. These uniform procedures will also simplify requirements placed on contractors for data.

Other ASD(I&L) programs have accomplished significant improvements in the utilization of stocks held by all depots and retail supply activities by computer matching of potential excess and transferable retention stocks against DOD-wide materiel requirements and thus identify useful applications of assets in long supply. An inventory-item reduction program has been established to systematically remove items of supply which are inactive and no longer required in support of assigned missions.

A program of provisioning screening has been established under ASD(I&L) auspices to automatically screen manufacturers' parts numbers and other identifying numbers against data maintained in the Master Federal Catalog File in order to identify support items prior to their entry into the Defense supply system during the provisioning of repair parts for new weapons. During fiscal year 1968, 6.3 million part numbers were screened in this program, of which 41 percent of items matched existing numbers on file having assigned federal stock numbers (FSNs).

The Defense Supply Agency. When reviewing the organization of the Defense Supply Agency from the viewpoint of supply management it must be remembered that it manages what might be viewed as a wholesale supply system. It does not manage a complete "cradle to grave" operation as is found in the military services. DSA's role of providing technical supply support of military operations of its customers is basically confined to the supplying of maintenance-support items which are more of the commercial type. They are considered to be the "bits and pieces" of the weapons systems, as opposed to major assemblies, components, and items of equipment which continue to be the responsibility of each service. Thus, responsibility for many of the more technical decisions concerning the level of support required, wear-out factors, degree of essentiality, insurance-item requirements, etc., remains with the using military service. Even in the more common supply items such as clothing, subsistence, and fuel, support by DSA is provided at the wholesale level with final distribution to the end user being made through the retail supply system of the applicable military service. On the other hand, DSA does perform a number of important common service functions and administers a number of programs that are essential to the effective operation of the supply system of each military service. These service functions, assigned by the Secretary of Defense, affect not only DSA-managed items but all items managed by every element of DOD, and thereby serve to bring together a unified DOD supply system.

HISTORY: The Defense Supply Agency is the logical result of an evolutionary process by which the Department of Defense has applied the concept of integrated management in the area of common support. The elimination of undesirable duplication in the supply systems of the military departments has been a major effort since the establishment of the National Military Establishment (later redesignated Department of Defense) in 1947. A number of steps were subsequently taken to integrate common supply needs of the Department of Defense, often upon the urging of Congress, sometimes by the military services themselves, and sometimes upon the recommendations of other informed groups. Among these steps was the development of the Federal Catalog System, including federal supply classification of commodities, which established the foundation for common description and identification of items essential to interservice and common support. Other early "foundation" programs were item standardization, single-department procurements, interservice supply support, utilization of one service's excesses by the other services, and the application of the "single manager" concept to a number of common supply and service areas.

"Single manager" agencies established within the military departments at the direction of the Secretary of Defense, starting in 1955, began to reduce supply inventories and operating costs while maintaining effective support of the Army, Navy, Air Force, and Marine Corps. After a survey of what these agencies accomplished, and the possible extension of integrated management into other areas, the Secretary of Defense established the Defense Supply Agency in 1961 to manage the procurement and distribution of common supplies and to perform related services.

In establishing the DSA system, the single managerships already in existence were inherited from the Army and the Navy, i.e., subsistence, clothing and textiles, medical, petroleum, automotive (later returned to the Army), industrial, construction, and general supplies. These formed the nucleus for an integrated manager plan under which each commodity center was designated to perform all supply management functions for that commodity. This assignment embraced a complete supply cycle including standardization, cataloging, requirements determination, procurement, inspection, inventory management, stock positioning, receipt, storage issue, transportation, and disposal.

DSA became operational on Jan. 1, 1962. Conversion of the departmental single managers to field activities of DSA encountered no major problems. They were taken over in place with assigned personnel, funds, equipment, and facilities. Their operations continued without interruption under a new and shortened chain of comman l. This was also true of the operational elements of the Armed Forces Supply Support Center, a common service activity, and the property disposal activities of the military services which were assumed by DSA and assigned to a Defense Logistics Services Center.

The Secretary of Defense established two primary objectives for DSA:

1. To ensure effective and timely support to the military services in the event of mobilization, war, or other national emergency, as well as in peacetime

2. To furnish this support at the lowest feasible cost

In commenting on his decision to establish the Defense Supply Agency, Robert S. McNamara, who was the Secretary of Defense, set forth the following challenge to the new organization:[4]

One of the most productive fields for the economic application of centralized management is in the provision of common supplies and related services to all the military departments. After a rather comprehensive study of this entire problem, we came to the conclusion that considerable economy and efficiency could be gained if all the common supply management activities were consolidated into a single agency. Accordingly, a new Defense Supply Agency was established and placed directly under the Secretary of Defense. I am confident that in the long run it will improve supply support to the operating forces while materially reducing the cost to the taxpayer.

The DSA mission is to provide effective and economical support to the military services, other DOD components, federal civil agencies, foreign governments, and others as authorized for assigned materiel commodities; to perform logistics services directly associated with the supply management function, and other support services as directed by the Secretary of Defense; and to administer the operation of DOD programs as assigned.

The military services determine their gross requirements for items managed by DSA, and with the Joint Chiefs of Staff, establish priorities. DSA supply centers compute net materiel requirements, procure supplies from commercial sources, and sell to the military services at cost plus surcharges for transportation and foreseeable losses.   Reimbursements from customers replenish the DSA Stock Fund, which is a revolving fund that provides the working capital for DSA procurement actions without annual appropriation.

ORGANIZATION: The operations of DSA are oriented primarily toward logistic support of the several military services and encompass a variety of responsibilities.   Important aspects of the DSA mission include:

1. Management of assigned items of materiel

2. Procurement of common supplies and common services

3. Operation of a distribution system for assigned supplies in the United States

4. Provision of contract administration services in support of the military departments and other DOD components, the National Aeronautics and Space

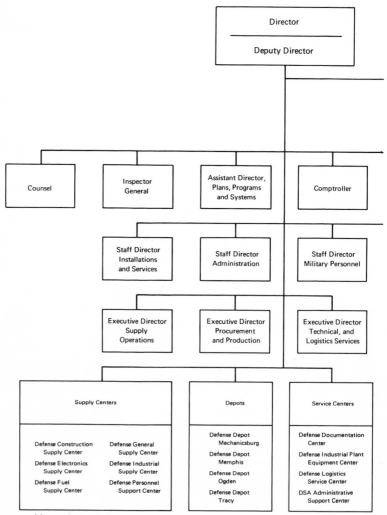

Fig. 1   Defense Supply

Administration, other designated federal and state agencies, and friendly foreign governments

5. Logistics systems analysis and design, procedural development, and the maintenance of assigned supply and service systems

6. Scientific and technical documentation, including acquiring, storing, announcing, retrieving, and distributing formally recorded information

7. Administration and supervision of a number of programs as directed by the Secretary of Defense (of primary interest to supply managers are the DOD Coordinated Procurement Program, the Defense Materiel Utilization Program, the Federal Catalog System, and the DOD Excess, Surplus and Foreign Excess Personal Property Disposal Program.)

DSA Headquarters, with its field activities, is jointly staffed by Army, Navy,

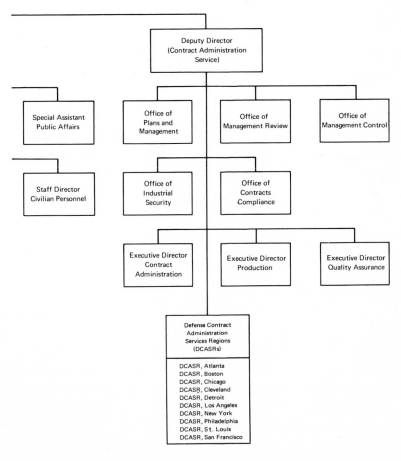

Agency organization.

Air Force, and Marine Corps military personnel and civilian personnel. Headquarters organization consists of the Director, Deputy Director, and a central staff which provides common administrative, professional, technical, and managerial support, and mission elements which exercise staff supervision over the execution of mission operations. The DSA Headquarters staff shown in the accompanying chart (Fig. 1) assists the Director in the exercise of direction and control over the Agency as a whole, and is responsible for policy development, broad planning, and staff supervision of the total mission of the Defense Supply Agency.

The DSA field organization consists of 25 primary-level field activities. These are categorized as Defense supply centers, Defense depots, service centers, and Defense contract administration services regions. In addition, there are a number of headquarters field-extension offices controlled by specified headquarters staff elements.

DEFENSE SUPPLY CENTERS: The Defense supply centers (DSCs) perform inventory management under the supervision and technical guidance of DSA Headquarters. Each is a functionally integrated unit, with complete responsibility for the performance of all inventory management functions for the full range of items assigned to it—providing for necessary catalogs, computing the wholesale stock requirements to support the anticipated needs of all customers, initiating appropriate procurement or repair action, positioning stocks in accordance with expected need, determining retention limits, and initiating disposal action for excesses. Each is expected to provide responsive support to all users and at the same time permit economies inherent in integrated management.

The six Defense supply centers and their general areas of responsibility in supply management are discussed below.

1. Defense Personnel Support Center (DPSC), largest of the DSA field activities, was established July 1, 1965. This center was formed by the consolidation of the Defense Clothing and Textile Supply Center, the Defense Subsistence Supply Center, and the Defense Medical Supply Center. In addition to supplying the personnel needs of the military, this center provides certain common items to the Civil Defense Program, the Military Assistance Program, the Veterans' Administration, the Public Health Service, the Office of Economic Opportunity, Department of Health, Education, and Welfare, and other federal civil agencies.

2. Defense Electronics Supply Center (DESC) was established in 1962 in facilities formerly occupied by the Dayton Air Force Depot and Gentile Air Force Station to provide integrated management of assigned electronic and electrical repair parts. In addition to support of the military services, this center's mission includes support of such federal activities as the Coast Guard, Federal Aviation Agency, Maritime Administration, National Aeronautics and Space Administration, the Post Office Department, and the General Services Administration.

3. Defense Industrial Supply Center (DISC) manages industrial-type items including bearings, block and tackle, rigging and slings, rope, cables and fittings, hardware, metal bars, sheets and shapes, and electrical wire and cable.

4. Defense Construction Supply Center (DCSC) is the principal source for items ranging from common commercial varieties of lumber, gardening implements, and plumbing accessories to complex repair parts for mechanical, construction, and automotive equipment, and repair parts for military aircraft, ships, submarines, combat vehicles, and missile systems.

5. Defense General Supply Center (DGSC) provides a variety of item categories of a general nature. Important product groups include materiels-handling equipment, rubber fabricated materiels, photographic supplies, cleaning equip-

ment and supplies, packaging materials, and electrical hardware and supplies. DGSC serves as the National Inventory Control Point for fallout-shelter supplies and other Civil Defense-owned materiels which are distributed throughout the United States and its possessions in support of the National Civil Defense Program.

6. Defense Fuel Supply Center (DFSC) procures petroleum products and coals for the military services and arranges for storage and handling of government-owned fuel and for refueling services of government aircraft. DFSC also procures packaged petroleum products and chemicals for which DGSC performs the inventory control and distribution functions.

The DSA centers took over inventory control functions for assigned commodities previously performed by the single managers. Their primary functions are to compute replenishment requirements for assigned items, maintain complete records of inventory status and transactions, receive and edit requisitions, and direct shipment of supplies to the customers. Other personnel at the typical center are engaged in such related activities as cataloging, standardization, procurement, and installation management.

The DSA supply system is geared to centralized control and is operating under a highly mechanized system using the MIL systems (MILSTRIP, MILSTAMP, MILSTRAP, MILSTEP, etc.) and the Automatic Digital Communication Network (AUTODIN) for transmitting data to and from the supply centers, depots, and customer activities. The system provides for each commodity a single point for handling customer requisitions and inquiries.

DSA SERVICE CENTERS: The Defense Supply Agency service centers consist of the Defense Logistics Services Center (DLSC), the Defense Industrial Plant Equipment Center (DIPEC), the Defense Documentation Center (DDC), and the DSA Administration Support Center (DSASC). DLSC administers the DOD-wide cataloging, materiel utilization, and surplus property disposal programs. DIPEC performs centralized management of idle equipment and supervision of the disposal of excess industrial plant equipment; DDC is responsible for the operation of the management-information system in the field of scientific and technical documentation and information; for acquisition, storage, announcement, retrieval, and secondary distribution of scientific and technical documents; and for primary distribution of foreign technical reports. DSASC provides administrative support and common service functions to DSA activities within the Washington, D.C., metropolitan area.

DSA DEPOTS: When DSA assumed operations, the items assigned to it for management were stored in 77 major distribution depots operated by the military services. DSA immediately initiated a study, with the assistance of the military services, looking toward the design of an integrated distribution system for materiel under its management. The project sought to develop the system around selected installations which would effectively and economically serve all DSA customers; provide a basic, uniform, and integrated inventory control concept to be employed by all DSA materiel managers; and identify personnel and equipment resources required to operate the proposed distribution system.

The study surveyed sources of customer demand and of production. Ten thousand traffic rates were compiled and fed into a computer to select preferred locations for stockage in order to eliminate backhauling and crosshauling and to place supplies to best advantage in areas of military concentrations. Completed in April, 1962, the study listed the following operational objectives: centralized inventory control by commodity, customer requisitions submitted to one central location for each commodity where the requisition would be edited against system-wide asset availability, supply information provided to the customer from one point only for each DSA commodity, maximum specialization in the use of electronic data processing equipment, minimum storage installations strategically located throughout the United States to provide effective and economical support of all DSA customers, and capability for rapid expansion, if required in an emergency.

The services examined the proposals in light of their supply systems and the needs of their operating forces in the United States and overseas. With appropriate modifications to meet the specialized requirements of the military departments, the DSA distribution system was approved by the Secretary of Defense. The system consists of a depot storage pattern based on the concept of positioning stocks close to the concentration of military customers and ports of embarkation in the United States. Although the numbers have changed at various times since 1962, there were in 1969, 7 principal distribution depots, 4 specialized support depots (SSDs), and 10 direct supply support points (DSSPs).

Army Supply Management. There are many different levels of installations and units and many different phases of the Army supply system. In a support function so vital to combat, there cannot be a sharp break among the various parts of the supply system. However, two large segments of the Army supply system are discernible. They are the "Wholesale Logistics" element and the "Army-in-the-Field" element. These are imperfect terms. They are useful, however, in delineating generally between two broad areas of logistics operations.

The *Army Dictionary* defines "Army Wholesale Logistics" as "the Army logistics system less Army-in-the-Field logistics; includes complete logistic support of the Army Wholesale Logistics complex itself, and of special Army activities retained under direct control of Headquarters, Department of the Army." The same source identifies "Army-in-the-Field" logistics as "that portion of the Army logistics system which pertains to functions internal to theaters of operations, units and organizations deployed in oversea theaters, and Army-in-the-Field units in the Continental United States (CONUS)."

The responsibility for the operation of the wholesale-logistics system is vested in a single commander, the Commanding General of the Army Materiel Command. This assignment provides a clear-cut channel for business contacts with the Army and presents a single source of wholesale Army supply support to users.

Responsibility for "retail supply" is assigned to supported commanders, i.e., the using units. For example, the retail element of supply in Europe is under the Commander in Chief, United States Army Europe, and the retail supply at administrative posts in the United States is under the Commanding Generals of the Continental Armies, who report to the Commanding General, United States Continental Army Command. This arrangement makes Army supply immediately responsive to the needs of the supported commander—an important precept in Army logistics philosophy.

The Army supply system, like that of the other military departments and DSA, is governed by broad policies established by the Secretary of Defense. The Secretary of the Army, like the other departmental secretaries, is responsible for implementing all DOD directives and instructions which deal with the military supply system—procurement, production, cataloging, standardization, warehousing, distribution, maintenance, disposal, transportation of supplies or equipment, and related functions.

The Secretary of the Army is aided in supply and logistics matters by the Assistant Secretary of the Army (Installation and Logistics). Within the Army staff, the Deputy Chief of Staff for Logistics (DCSLOG) is the principal adviser to the Chief of Staff on logistics matters.

THE 1962 REORGANIZATION: Traditionally, the burden of operating the Army supply system had been borne by technical services organized around commodity groupings: the Ordnance Corps, the Quartermaster Corps, the Corps of Engineers, the Signal Corps, the Transportation Corps, the Army Medical Service, and the Chemical Corps. These technical services accomplished their supply missions through operating organizations that determined requirements and procured, received, stored, issued, maintained, and disposed of the items for which they were individually responsible. Over the years the Army has taken a number of steps to establish clear lines of authority and accountability for the interrelated functions involved in supply management. Perhaps the most important of these steps was the establishment of the position of Deputy Chief of Staff for Logistics (DCSLOG) in 1954, with clear-cut responsibility and authority for logistics planning and for direction of supply operations. Despite notable progress in coordinating supply responsibilities and eliminating unnecessary variations in procedures, the technical services concept stood in the way of a fully effective integration of the Army supply system.

This roadblock was removed by a major reorganization in 1962, which completely realigned the Army supply system. The Army within CONUS was formed into three major commands: the Army Materiel Command, the Continental Army Command, and the Combat Developments Command. The traditional technical services were reduced or eliminated, and all their former materiel functions were centralized within the new Army Materiel Command. The DCSLOG was relieved of commandlike responsibilities for the technical services, and his planning and policy responsibilities were remphasized.

Responsibility for the supervision of individual and unit training for all military personnel in CONUS was centered within the Continental Army Command (CONARC). The consolidation offered opportunities for substantial improvement in the efficiency and effectiveness of the overall Army Training Establishment. A natural outgrowth of organizational and doctrinal trends in the direction of combining combat and combat support elements, CONARC affords Army components of unified and specified commands a single point of contact for obtaining the trained units which they require. The reorganization did not change the basic responsibilities of the Continental Armies or the Military District of Washington, which are subordinate commands of CONARC. They continue to be responsible for support of civil powers in emergency or disaster situations, support of civil defense, defense of CONUS against ground attack, and for execution of CONARC's remaining missions within their geographic areas. As part of the reorganization, CONARC was stripped of all its development functions, with the materiel test boards going to the Army Materiel Command and the combat developments elements of CONARC schools becoming field agencies of the new Combat Developments Command.

A far-flung organization, the Combat Development Command (CDC) serves as the proving ground for ideas on the best organization, equipment, and tactics for the land forces in any type of combat now and in the foreseeable future. Its mission is to find and recommend answers to three basic questions: (1) How should the Army be organized? (2) How should the Army be equipped? and (3) How should the Army fight? Also for consideration and CDC proposals for the integration of the new concepts into the Army based on realistic cost analyses.

THE US ARMY MATERIEL COMMAND: Our primary concern here, of course, is with the Army Materiel Command (AMC). The wholesale supplier for the Army, AMC assumed the missions formerly assigned to the technical services. These encompass the development, testing, cataloging direction, quantitative

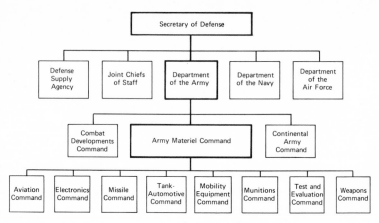

Fig. 2   Army Materiel Command organization.

requirements determination, procurement, production, distribution, supply control, inventory control, maintenance direction, and disposal of surpluses of Army
supplies and equipment.   AMC accomplishes its job through seven commodity
commands, a Test and Evaluation Command, and a number of project managers,
as indicated in the organization chart in Fig. 2.

The seven commodity commands, each responsible for integrated materiel
management in a specific commodity area, are:

1. The Aviation Materiel Command, responsible for aeronautical and air delivery equipment

2. The Tank-Automotive Command, responsible for tactical wheeled and general-purpose vehicles

3. The Mobility Equipment Command, responsible for construction and bridging equipment and power generators

4. The Missile Command, responsible for free rockets, guided missles, ballistic
missiles, and related equipment

5. The Weapons Command, responsible for weapons, combat vehicles, and
fire-control equipment

6. The Munitions Command, responsible for ammunition, rocket and missile war-
head sections, chemical, biological, and radiological materials, and pyrotechnics

7. The Electronics Command, responsible for communications equipment, electronic warfare equipment, photographic equipment, automatic data processing
equipment, and meteorological equipment

The United States Army Test and Evaluation Command is not a commodity
command but is responsible for engineering and service tests.   It provides test
and evaluation support to the sponsoring commodity commands and project
managers, and participates in planning and preparing for troop tests involving
Army materiel.

Project managership is a vital part of the AMC organization and concept of
operation.   The project manager is responsible for managing a high-priority
weapon system or major item of equipment from research and development
through all stages until delivered to the using units.   He has direct access to
the AMC commander and is authorized to deal directly with all echelons in
pursuing his mission of placing the project item in the hands of using units
with minimum delay and cost.   A principal advantage of this approach is the
focusing of all aspects of a project from development to delivery of an item

in the hands of a single responsible individual. Although clothed with considerable authority, the project manager depends to a large degree on coordinating the efforts of others.

The key activities in the operating organizations of the AMC's major subordinate commands are the National Inventory Control Points (NICPs) and the Army depots. The NICPs are responsible for the worldwide management of items specifically assigned to them. This responsibility includes requirements computation and direction of procurement, distribution, overhaul, and disposal. As a result, all wholesale functions of inventory management of an item are centralized at one place. In addition the Army has established Army Inventory Control Points (AICPs) or an army retail manager as a branch at several of its NICPs to provide technical, supply management, and cataloging services to the Army for items for which wholesale management has been assigned to the Defense Supply Agency or the General Services Administration.

ARMY MATERIEL MANAGEMENT: Prior to the 1962 reorganization, the Army had a multiplicity of logistics support systems operated by the seven technical services in support of the Army in the field. While each was workable and had successfully supported the Army through a number of national emergencies, somewhat different methods for processing requisitions and for stock control and accountability posed problems for the customer in filling his total requirements. Some of the support systems were completely centralized, with supply control, stock control (maintenance and accountable records), and the processing of requisitions performed at an NICP. Others had only supply control at the NICP, with requisitions from CONUS customers going directly to the depot which maintained the accountable stock records.

With the establishment of the Army Materiel Command, the development of a single Army distribution system became imperative. A study entitled "The Army Supply and Maintenance Systems Study" (TASAMS) recommended the removal of accountability and stock control functions from the supply depots and the placement of these functions in the NICPs, and the realignment of item management from the then-existing 11 NICPs.

A Department of the Army letter dated July 25, 1963, approved the "centralized-by-commodity" concept proposed in TASAMS. The interrelated functions of determining the types and quantities of items to be brought into the system, obtaining them, controlling them, and eliminating them when necessary, the Army believes, can be performed effectively only when the supply manager has accurate working information. The NICP is the organization to coordinate this information. To further the close relationship among the various elements of supply management, the NICPs have been placed under the control of the Army Materiel Command.

Under the Army's "centralized-by-commodity" concept, requisitions flow directly from the overseas commanders and CONUS customers to the NICP handling the commodity desired. Materiel release orders are forwarded electronically by the NICP to the appropriate storage depot. The depot then ships the desired materiel to the customer.

There are two exceptions to this direct customer–supply-manager relationship. The first concerns supply under the Military Assistance Program (MAP). The Military Assistance Advisory Groups (MAAGs) that assist in the initiation of MAP requisitions are usually small elements that may not be capable of maintaining the extensive catalogs required. For this reason and because of funding considerations, a separate MAP requisition processing point has been established to receive, process, and fund all MAP requisitions and forward them to the appropriate NICP.

The other exception concerns overseas requisitions. In the overseas Army commands, the theater commander under certain considerations has been authorized to establish inventory control centers (ICCs) to process requisitions before forwarding them to the CONUS supply source.

The commodity manager at an NICP receives the information necessary for his decision. This includes stock-status information, detailed analyses of depot issues and receipts, repair and rebuild schedules, demand analyses, procurement status, reports of stocks with the troops, and stock fund and financial inventory accounting reports. In addition, liaison visits to depots, installations, Army terminals, and overseas areas provide additional firsthand information to the NICP and the individual commodity manager.

Extensive use of high-speed data processing and transmission equipment has made possible the concept of centralized inventory management. The customer, the storage depots, and the NICP are tied together by communications networks. This makes it possible for the NICP to process requisitions and maintain on a current basis the records required to make supply decisions.

Under the principle of integrated materiel management, a designated Army commodity manager administers the related logistics mission, subject to the policies, programs, and control actions over principal and major secondary items directed by higher authority. Such management includes initiation of actions requiring the timely identification of items and preparation of manuals leading to the cataloging of items (cataloging direction); computation of quantitative requirements (requirements determination); authority, within limitations of approved programs, to require procurement (procurement direction); control of stocks in, due into, or planned for the distribution system on a quantitative and monetary basis (distribution direction); authority to require overhaul (overhaul direction); and authority to require disposal (disposal direction).

THEATER OF OPERATIONS: Army logistics is viewed as the bridge between combat troops and the resources of the Nation. The logistics system's effectiveness is measured by its ability to support the fighting units in sustained combat. It must be capable of supporting both nuclear and nonnuclear operations. Its sufficiency has a direct impact upon the Army's capability to maintain both its forces overseas and the strategic forces in the United States, to equip and support air defense units at home and abroad, and to support both our Reserve components and the active units of our allies.

The general organizational pattern for Army logistics outlines a flexible structure which may be modified as necessary to suit any given situation in varying combat environments. Pending the establishment of a theater communication zone, a logistical command may be attached to a field army to assist in controlling supply operation. Combat service support units, organized into brigades, groups, or battalions, are directly responsible to the field army support commander, who in turn is responsible to the field army commander for providing adequate support to the field army. Each combat service support unit is individually structured so as to be responsive to field army requirements for the items and services for which it is responsible. A fixed organization is not prescribed for the field army; hence, numbers and types of logistical support units are determined by the mission, combat and combat support units, availability and use of nuclear weapons, terrain and weather within the area of operations, and composition and capability of the probable hostile forces.

Navy Supply Management. The unique characteristics of the Navy as it exists and operates today determine to a large extent the dimensions of its supply management. The Navy is a composite warfare system, a mix of some 900 ships and submarines, over 8,000 aircraft of every kind and configuration, missiles, and 260 supporting shore stations, all manned by over 760,000 military personnel and more than 398,000 civilians contributing their special skills and talents to a capable and highly mobile force. Just as the Navy itself is a composite warfare system, a system which keeps it supplied is also a composite of material, personnel, and facilities, processes and organizations, and different levels and varieties of activities, all in motion together and all merging in the common—and basic—objective of meeting the requirements of the customer.

EVOLUTION OF CHANGE: The reorganization of the Navy at the departmental level has been undergoing changes in recent years that may be considered as evolutionary in nature. Departures from the traditional structure have been effected in stages rather than one overall reorganization. There are those who propose further changes to achieve the optimum organization. Further reorganizations no doubt will come, but whether they are necessary today or will result from future advances in technology or changes in requirements of the operating forces is a debatable issue.

Prior to 1963 the basic organization of the Navy Department was bilinear in nature, i.e., the *users* of materials and services constituted one side of the structure, and the *producers,* buyers, or manufacturers of those things that satisfy the requirements of the users constituted the other side, both reporting to the Secretary of the Navy. Heading the *user* organization was the Chief of Naval Operations (CNO), who commanded all functions and activities of the operating forces of the Navy, and in that capacity determined the broad material requirements of these forces, including weapons or weapons systems, supplies, facilities, maintenance, and supporting services. When the military hardware was provided in response to his requirements, he was responsible for its use. The CNO had no responsibility for development, production, or procurement of the hardware or for the supporting supplies and facilities. These functions were assigned to the *producers,* the various material bureaus whose chiefs also reported directly to the Secretary of the Navy. Although the structure of these bureaus had changed from time to time, they generally were organized along broad material categories such as ships, aircraft, ordnance, and facilities. In addition, separate service bureaus with responsibilities in functional areas such as personnel management, medicine, and supply management also reported to the Secretary of the Navy.

As a result of a management review conducted in 1962 certain changes were prescribed. A Navy Material Support Establishment was formed to coordinate the activities of the various bureaus. It was still a bilinear organization with the Chief of Naval Operations responsible for *user* logistics and a Chief of Naval Material who reported to the Secretary of the Navy responsible for coordinating the *producer* logistics functions of the various bureaus.

It became apparent that further adjustments in concepts and procedures were necessary. Progressive changes culminating in the implementation of General Order Number 5 effective May 1, 1966, resulted in the present organization which will be discussed below. In effect the new changes abandoned the bilinear system; all responsibilities for logistics support of operating forces as well as all the organizations that provide this support now come under the Chief of Naval Operations.

DEPARTMENTAL MANAGEMENT: In any discussions of the organization of the Department of the Navy it is important to keep in mind that here, unlike the other military departments, in effect two military services are being administered. The Secretary of the Navy under the direction, authority, and control of the Secretary of Defense is responsible for the policies and control of both the Navy and the Marine Corps. Although supply management in the Marine Corps will be discussed separately, it should be noted that the departmental administration emanates from the Secretary of the Navy and his staff.

The Secretary of the Navy is assisted by a number of civilian and military executive assistants. Two of these are of direct interest to the subject of supply management. The Assistant Secretary of the Navy (Installations and Logistics) is held responsible for the department-wide policy supervision of all matters related to production, procurement, supply, distribution, and disposal of material. The second and principal assistant is the Chief of Naval Operations who is now responsible for both user and producer logistics in the Navy. The producer agencies formerly reporting to the Secretary of the Navy are now responsible to the Chief of Naval Operations through the Chief of Naval Material.

The Chief of Naval Operations is responsible for the overall direction of the Navy's material programs and for the broad formulation of material requirements, taking into consideration the constraints of approved force levels and budgetary limitations contained in the Five-Year Defense Program. All the Navy material requirements derive from operational concepts, program direction, logistics guidance, and support policy stated by the Chief of Naval Operations. The logistics guidance and supply support policy is expressed in numbers of days' endurance to be provided to support designated forces at prescribed tempos of operations or consumption rates. Further guidance for achieving the material objective is provided in the form of program priorities and order of precedence for competing programs of near equal importance. All material requirements, of course, are based on recommendations and needs of the operating forces. Most of the staff assigned to the Chief of Naval Operations consists of personnel who have had recent operational experience and understand the needs of the fleet.

These requirements are stated in general terms and are then passed to the Chief of Naval Material (CNM). The CNM is supported by technicians in the various systems commands of the Naval Material Command who provide advice concerning the feasibility of meeting these requirements. Five of these systems commands are hardware oriented, while the remaining one is functional in mission. The hardware system commands are Ship, Ordnance, Air, Facilities, and Electronics, while the functional command is the Supply Systems Command.

The technicians in the appropriate systems commands analyze the general requirements, develop specific programs, provide alternatives for filling the requirements, and prepare supporting cost analyses to justify budgetary requests. This information is then returned to the program manager under the Chief of Naval Operations for selection of the final course of action and submission of appropriate budgetary and program data. After approval of the program, responsibility for implementing action, including design, development, procurement of not only the hardware but supporting equipment, facilities, repair parts, and supplies, rests with the appropriate systems commander.

The Navy material requirements reflect the coordinated efforts of representatives of the CNO, the CNM, and the fleet commander. Each potential requirement for material is the concern of a sponsor in the CNO's staff, a program manager in the Navy Material Command, and a customer or user in the operating forces. It is through close cooperation, extensive exchanges of information, and continuing program evaluation that material needs are developed and the required hardware produced.

To facilitate this continuity of management on certain essential weapons systems, the concept of project manager has been adopted. At present the Navy has 12 project managers appointed by the Chief of Naval Material to integrate the diverse functional areas within and between the systems commands and to serve as focal points of decision, direction, and control on these projects. The authority and resources available to each project manager vary but are fixed by an individual CNM charter. A weapons system may be designated for project managment during any part of its life cycle, and conversely, will be disestablished when the need no longer exists. The basic aim in the Navy's project management is to place on one person the responsibility for a given project, to grant him the necessary authority, to provide him with adequate control over resources identified with that project, and to put him in a position to obtain the support necessary to ensure optimum performance.

Within the Naval Material Command five technically oriented systems commands are responsible for meeting those material support needs of the operating forces of the Navy and the Marine Corps that are within the assigned "material support" areas of each command. The Air Systems Command provides Navy and Marine Corps aircraft, including components, fuels, and lubricants. The Electronics Systems Command is responsible for shore electronics, certain shipboard and aircraft electronics equipment, and the Navy's space programs. The Ordnance Systems Command provides surface and underwater ordnance, air-launched mines and torpedoes, and small arms. The Ship Systems Command provides ships, submersibles, amphibious craft, boats, and shipboard components not otherwise assigned. The Facilities Engineering Command provides functional service to the operating forces of the Navy and the Marine Corps in the general area of shore facilities and related material and equipment. The functions of these technical systems commands encompass research and development, design, test and acquisition of hardware, establishment of specifications and inspection standards, and planning for fitting out, supply, maintenance, conversion, and overhaul of the assigned material. The Navy Supply Systems Command (NAVSUP) administers the Navy supply system. It is responsible for the development and direction of that system, including the promulgation of Navy supply management policies and methods to activities of the Navy and Marine Corps. These include cataloging, inventory management, field purchasing, distribution, materials handling, traffic management, transportation, packaging and preservation, receipt, storage, and disposal of naval material. Of the 4 million items in the DOD supply system, about 1.6 million are Navy-interest items and about half are managed and controlled by NAVSUP through its inventory control points. The technical systems commands, however, are also involved in the operation of the Navy supply system in that they exercise supply management over some 28,000 principal items of material such as missiles, aircraft engines, ordnance, shipboard machinery, and electronics equipment. The remaining items are managed by DSA or GSA.

OTHER ECHELONS OF SUPPLY SUPPORT: The prime characteristics of the operating forces, their readiness, mobility, and endurance, prescribe the form of support which the Navy supply system must render. Conceptually, Navy fleet supply support is based upon three echelons of supply: (1) the combat ship, (2) the mobile logistic support ships and overseas bases, and (3) the CONUS depot system.

The first of these echelons is the material specified in the individual ship's *allowance list* and carried on board the ship itself. The allowance list, similar to the Army Table of Organization and Equipment (TO&E), is tailored to the individual ship based on the ship's equipments, military essentiality of ship's systems, and composition and size of the crew. The depth of material on the ship's allowance list is usually computed to provide balanced support for a period of three months. This objective must be modified in the case of large, bulky, consumable items such as food, fuel, and ammunition, when space constraints do not always allow a full three months' supply to be carried. The allowance list also provides for "insurance" items. These are repair parts for which demand cannot be accurately predicted, but without which the ship's mission could be impaired. The objective of the allowance list is to maximize endurance and provide balanced support for a specified period.

The second echelon of combat supply support consists of the ships of the mobile logistic support forces, including tenders, oilers, repair ships, and fleet issue ships. This force is augmented by a very few overseas depots. These fleet issue ships, carrying cargoes of consumable items tailored to the combat forces they support, can rendezvous with a task force in the forward area, and by ship-to-ship or helicopter transfer, can keep the fleet at sea and on station for extended periods of time. This second echelon of fleet support backs up the first echelon of allowance list material which is carried in the combatant ships.

The material carried in these mobile logistic support ships is prescribed in accordance with load lists which reflect support mission and types of ships supported. These load lists, like the ship's allowance lists, prescribe both the range and depth of material to be carried aboard the individual mobile support ships. They do not duplicate those insurance items included in the combatant ships' allowance lists. Instead they supplement the combatant ships' endurance by providing a source for fuel, ammunition, provisions, repair parts, and general consumable items. The combination of the first and second echelons of combat supply support satisfies the Chief of Naval Operations policy that the deployed fleet will be self-sufficient to permit operations in combat for from three to six months without the necessity of resupply from the continental United States.

The third echelon of supply consists of the materials located predominantly at the tidewater centers and depots in the United States. These supply activities serve as the material reservoir and act as pipelines between industry and other supply systems and the fleet. Centers and depots issue Navy-, DSA-, and GSA-managed material to the mobile logistic support forces and directly to the operating forces.

In addition to fleet support, the centers and depots provide support to the activities of the Shore Establishment: the air stations, ordnance plants, shipyards, training stations, and smaller shore activities. The scope of the supply departments at shore activities varies, depending on the size and mission of the activity; it can range all the way from a small retail outlet called a "ready supply store" (similar to the Army self-service store) to a large supply department at a shipyard or an air station. The centers and depots likewise provide support to the Marine Corps, Coast Guard, units of other military services, and to friendly foreign countries under the Military Assistance Program.

The Navy supply system functions on the basis of centralized control of assets. The nerve centers of the Navy supply system are the inventory control points (ICPs). As the Navy supply manager, the Chief of the Supply Systems Command commands the ICPs.

It is basic Navy policy that the inventory management of Navy material will be assigned to the ICPs under the Supply Systems Command. Only those items for which acquisition and continued control are essential to the discharge of peculiar missions will be managed by the technical systems commands of the Navy Department. The specific guidelines that apply in implementation of this policy are:

1. The Supply Systems Command will manage items procured for other than immediate use. These items consist of equipments, components repair parts, consumables, installation material, and items required for test and repair pur-

poses. This includes not only items required in support of equipment and systems installed and in use, but reparables which are returned for overhaul, repair, or modification and return to storage for further distribution.

2. Item management by the other system commanders, therefore, is limited to items in a research and development stage; items requiring administration and control in the programming, procurement, and production of weapons or weapon systems; items of such technical complexity that engineering decisions must be made prior to issue; and items to satisfy one-time requirements in that they are not procured for stock and general issue.

At present there are three Navy inventory control points. Their basic assigned material responsibilities are:

Inventory Control Points	*Material Responsibilities*
Aviation Supply Office (ASO)	Equipment and parts peculiar to naval and Marine Corps aviation; photographic and aerological equipments and parts
Ships Parts Control Center (SPCC)	Ships' hull, submarines, machinery, ordnance, and vehicle equipments and repair parts
Electronics Supply Office (ESO)	Electronics equipments and repair parts

The Navy has established four retail offices to exercise financial control and retail management of material managed at the wholesale level by DSA and GSA. These offices provide DSA with certain Navy program requirements, and develop and publish working procedures for management of retail stocks. Retail-stock levels are monitored by using financial inventory control data and by field-service visits rather than through an individual-item reporting system.

For those 700,000 items which are centrally managed by DSA or GSA, certain functions must continue to be performed by the Navy. These functions include the computation of requirements for initial outfitting of fleet units and the preparation and maintenance of allowance lists, the computation of requirements for war reserve stocks and their prepositioning, physical stocking and issue of DSA on a reimbursable basis, the management of DSA items within the Navy distribution system ashore and afloat, and furnishing DSA with technical data pertaining to DSA-managed items used by the Navy.

The basic responsibility for providing supply support to meet total user needs for most of the Navy supply items thus rests in the inventory control points. These ICPs determine the depth and range of items to be carried at specific locations, position these inventories at the major stock points, and determine, in collaboration with the material bureaus and customers served, the individual support missions that these stock points will carry out. In addition to the centers and depots subject to NAVSUP control, the supply departments of major air stations, shipyards, and construction centers are significant elements of the Navy supply system for receipt, storage, and issue of material on a Navy-wide basis.

Inventories of material also are located at secondary stock points, smaller air stations, training stations, naval bases, and ordnance plants which hold stocks primarily for their own use. They generally determine their own requirements and do not support any significant number of activities other than themselves. The ICPs do not control these inventories. Consequently, ICPs do not utilize the stocks held at these points to meet needs elsewhere and do not have the same control over the operations of these points that they do over the major points.

The Marine Corps Supply System. The United States Marine Corps' amphibious role, its status as a force in readiness, and the relatively small size largely shape its supply system. The Marine Corps is characterized by a high order of mobility of the combat elements of the landing forces. To attain this degree of mobility the Marine Corps must have a supply system that is austere, simple, balanced, and immediately responsive to the needs of the combat elements. The requirement to project the supply system of the landing force from sea to a land environment without loss of momentum is peculiar to amphibious operations. The Marine Corps supply system is especially designed to meet this need by providing prescribed loads of equipment and supplies with individuals and units and by arranging for rapid response for resupply actions. An additional factor that shapes the design of this system is the close relationship of the Marine Corps to the Navy and the Navy's responsibilities for supporting Marine Corps aviation with common items of equipment and repair parts.

The Commandant of the Marine Corps commands the Corps, and this command includes the task of logistics administration and control. The Assistant Chief of Staff, G-4 under the direction of the Commandant is responsible for Marine Corps logistics plans, determination of requirements, program objectives, and programs relating to material readiness. He interprets logistic directives from higher authority and prepares implementing instructions. He is responsible for planning, coordinating, and supervising the material program that produces new equipment required for support of operations concurrent with the evolution of new tactics and techniques for assault warfare. The Deputy Chief of Staff (Air) coordinates Marine Corps aeronautical requirements with the Chief of Naval Material who is responsible for planning logistics support of both Navy and Marine air units insofar as common equipment, parts, and maintenance are concerned.

The Quartermaster General of the Marine Corps, as head of the Headquarters Supply Department, is responsible to the Commandant for the Marine Corps supply system. Among his many responsibilities are the computation of material requirements for peacetime operating forces and mobilization plans and the procurement, warehousing, distribution, shipment, repair, and issue of all equipment and supplies for the Marine Corps, except items specifically assigned to the Navy for support of the Marine Corps.

In the past the Marine Corps supply system was oriented around a distribution system on each coast connected by National Inventory Control Points at Headquarters, Marine Corps, and at Philadelphia. A supply center on each coast performed as an inventory control point within each coastal complex and each supply center controlled three storage activities. Thus, there existed a layering of inventory control points. A typical requirement would be submitted by the user to the assigned service unit. From there it might be referred to a storage activity and then to the coastal supply center and eventually to the appropriate National Inventory Control Point.

With the availability of improved and faster communications media and more effective transportation modes, the Marine Corps supply system has been restructured and streamlined. The Marine Corps supply system has been reoriented to centralized inventory management and decentralized supply distribution to provide the responsive support required by its customers. This centralized management of inventories was implemented when the Marine Corps Unified Material Management System (MUMMS) became operational in 1967. Through use of the most modern computer equipment, all facets of inventory management are being performed on a real-time basis by a single inventory control point located at the Marine Corps Supply Activity, Philadelphia. Inventories at eight strategically located remote-storage activities are managed on a one-warehouse basis. Requirements are received directly from operating field units and immediately compared by the computer with running inventory balances at all the storage locations. Shipment is directed from the nearest site, and balances retained within the computer memory are immediately updated in order to permit responsiveness to the next request.

In addition to the inventory control and distribution function, such other auxiliary operations as catalog preparation, procurement documentation, billing of customers, and financial accounting are fully automated under MUMMS. The distribution of supplies to using units is accomplished through eight CONUS storage activities located on the two coasts. From there the supplies flow through service units and aircraft groups, as well as the Marine Corps posts and stations which perform the supply function for Marine battalions and aircraft wings or squadrons in training or combat.

Air Force Supply Management. A distinguishing characteristic of the Air Force supply system is its use of a limited number of storage depots that are colocated with inventory control points and overhaul and maintenance functions. Effective supply support is obtained from these few specialized storage locations through the use of high-speed data processing, communication, and transportation systems to move items from the Air Force depots directly to its worldwide customers.

HEADQUARTERS ORGANIZATION: Logistics objectives and general policy guidance for the operation of the Air Force supply system are established at Air Force Headquarters by the Secretary of the Air Force and the Chief of Staff. The Air Force Secretary's principal aid in materiel management matters is the office of the Assistant Secretary of the Air Force for Installations and Logistics with deputies specializing in production, procurement, supply, and transportation. Responsibilities of the Air Force Chief of Staff, supervising and planning for supply management, are centered in the Deputy Chief of Staff for Systems and Logistics, his assistants, and the directorates under his control. This group is essentially a planning and policy-making staff charged with the task of promulgating guidance for the supply plans and programs organized throughout the Air Force.

Under the Deputy Chief of Staff for Systems and Logistics, a separate Directorate of Supply and Services has responsibility for the issuance of policy directives for supply management and participating in the review of quantitative materiel requirements.

THE MAJOR COMMANDS: Below the headquarters level, the Air Force is organized into a number of major commands. Some of these commands, the Strategic Air Command, the Tactical Air Command, and the Air Defense Command, carry primary operational responsibilities for the Air Force. Other commands, such as the Air University, Air Force Communications Service, Air Training Command, and Military Airlift Command, support the operational commands with education, communications, personnel training, and airlift, respectively.

The two commands most directly associated with materiel acquisition and subsequent supply support are the Air Force Systems Command (AFSC) and the Air Force Logistics Command (AFLC). The Air Force Systems Command is responsible for research and development and acquisition of new aircraft, missiles, and command and control systems. Basically its mission is to advance aerospace technology, develop operational aerospace systems, and acquire systems and supporting materiel to accomplish the Air Force mission.

AFSC's responsibilities for system and materiel management generally phase out toward the end of the acquisition period, usually with the first delivery of the weapon system to the operational commands. At this time AFLC assumes responsibility for the system's support under the concept of system support manager (SSM) and continues the support until the weapon leaves the usable or operational inventory.

The introduction of a system into the Air Force is viewed as a "life cycle" that can be logically divided into the following four phases: (1) *conceptual,* wherein the fundamental idea for a system is formed; (2) *definition,* wherein the idea formed in the conceptual phase is brought into specific and tangible substance including all the physical and supporting resources needed; (3) *acquisition,* when the development, production, and in some instances, initial or interim operational capability or testing take place; and (4) *operational,* when the system is committed to the using activity. During each of the four phases, both AFSC and AFLC have specific roles and responsibilities that vary in magnitude as the system travels through its "life cycle," each requiring coordination to ensure unity of effort.

The coordinated effort between AFSC and AFLC begins during the definition phase and carries through the acquisition phase. The decisions made during these phases have a profound effect on the type, depth, and eventual cost and effectiveness of the system's support. When AFSC establishes a systems program office (SPO) to direct the management and development of the prospective system, AFLC assigns logistics personnel to the SPO to develop support phasing. Soon thereafter, AFLC designates an air materiel area (AMA) to assume responsibility for the new system's support, and the AMA appoints a systems support manager (SSM). In addition to the representation at the SPO level, AFLC has members assigned to AFSC divisions over and above the SPO levels. AFLC deals on a daily basis with the many research and development activities of AFSC and assists directly in the preparation of systems documentation, the selection of contractors for system definition, and the evaluation of contractor's orders for further definition of production contracts.

The initial contacts between AFSC and AFLC are used to develop later follow-on support plans. These weapon system logistics plans permeate the entire structure of logistics, beginning with the systems program director (SPD) at Headquarters USAF level down to the systems support manager and to the item managers throughout AFLC.

The weapon system logistics plans lead directly to the scheduling of the various logistics activities, such as the purchase of repair parts and the modification, overhaul, or repair of the equipment. Under these schedules the Air Force contracts with industry for spares, programs aircraft, engines, and accessories into overhaul and modification shops, and places with industry work that cannot be accomplished within Air Force facilities. As these actions are taken, feedback information is provided to the logistic support project manager, the SSM, who can determine whether schedules are being met and what measures may be needed to overcome delays.

In addition to supply support of new weapons systems, AFLC assumes the overall logistics support of the Air Force. Logistics support in this sense includes the central procurement of bulk materiel, the storage and distribution of wholesale stocks, and the depot-level repair of the technical equipment and materiel used by Air Force units.

The operating agencies of AFLC are the air materiel areas (AMAs). The supply management functions of the AMAs include inventory control, purchasing, storage, and distribution of centrally procured stocks. In addition, they provide technical assistance within their geographical area of responsibility, and have extensive depot-level maintenance facilities for major overhaul of aircraft, engines, and missiles.

EVOLUTION OF THE AFLC AND AIR-MATERIEL-AREA CONCEPT: Perhaps the most striking example of adaptation to changes in the management of logistics is found in the evolution of the Air Force Logistics Command (AFLC). Since the inception of the Air Force in 1947, its logistics management has undergone constant change not only in philosophy, but also in the techniques employed. In the past the logistics support was based on a group of rather archaic, manually operated, general-purpose, geographically oriented depots. Today, support is furnished from a streamlined, functionally organized, automated complex of specialized, operations-oriented air materiel areas.

After 1947, the Air Force supply system was based in general depots. Each had as its primary responsibility the support of all the bases within its assigned geographical area; hence the name "air materiel area," or AMAs. Each AMA attempted to stock all the items that its area customers might need, whether the items were for a B-29, a C-47, or a P-51. With the increased numbers and complexities of the new weapons systems, the general depot arrangement could not respond effectively. The chief difficulty was the lack of a central point of inventory control and slow communication between the depots and headquarters. The Air Force soon found itself with bloated inventories, uneconomical utilization of resources, and less than satisfactory support.

In an attempt to modernize its logistics management, the Air Force created a bizonal system of supply. The Air Materiel Command (the predecessor to AFLC) divided the responsibility for the management of the commodity classes among the then-existing air materiel areas and general depots. The country was divided into two zones, with the Mississippi River as the approximate line of division. Each of the zonal depots stocked items in certain specified classes. Most commodity groups or classes were stored in "matching" depots; that is, one in the zone west of the Mississippi River and one in the zone to the east.

In this fashion the depots functioned as commodity specialists, each supporting the individual bases within its geographic zone of responsibility and certain overseas installations for designated classes of items. The assignment of commodities to specific depots was predicated on a number of factors, such as the existing work loads, the proximity to the sources of supply, and the maintenance skills and facilities available. The separation of stocks between the zones provided for some measure of dispersal in that the destruction of facilities at one location would not eliminate the entire wholesale stocks.

When this system was first adopted, the depots functioned simply as supply, storage, and distribution points. In 1950, Headquarters Air Materiel Command (AMC) designated one of these two depots for each commodity class as the "prime" or management depot with the worldwide distribution responsibility and the opposite depot as "zonal." The prime depot could place shipping orders against the assets of the opposite zonal depot if its own stocks were in short supply. Although this method of distribution was an improvement over the earlier versions, problems arose because the depots continued to operate somewhat independently. For example, a prime depot did not have control over the receipts and issues at the zonal depot and could not fully manage all of the transactions that affected the inventory on an item. Further complications developed because the operating functions of budgeting, requirements determinations, and procurement were still retained at AMC Headquarters.

During the Korean War it became evident that performance of the operating functions at Headquarters AMC was interfering with the staff's effectiveness as a planning and policy-making body. The computation of requirements and the initiation of purchase requests as well as many maintenance functions were still handled at the headquarters. The great mass of correspondence to and from the AMAs and depots overtaxed the capabilities of the headquarters. Accordingly, early in 1952 AMC decentralized many of its functions to the air materiel areas. Key personnel were moved to form the nucleus of the expanded supply management organization in the field.   Each supply depot was given the responsibility in its prime commodity classes for budgeting, forecasting requirements, initiating purchase requests, and handling the receipt, storage, issue, and disposal of supplies.   By 1957, the Air Force had achieved a gradual conversion from the bizonal supply system to a single-point distribution system.   Under this arrangement the prime depot or AMA received all base requisitions and functioned as the worldwide inventory control point for its assigned commodities.

The streamlining of the Air Force supply system has continued to this day, as evidenced by the recent closing of four air materiel areas.   The Air Force now has only five "hard core" logistic support areas, shown in the accompanying

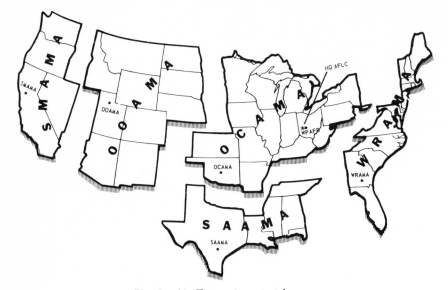

Fig. 3   Air Force air materiel areas.

map (Fig. 3).   The reduction in the number of field facilities is impressive when compared to the 15 AMAs and depots operated in the mid-1950s.

Along with the reduction of CONUS AMAs, the Air Force has phased out its overseas depots, the last one closing in 1960.   All overseas Air Force units now receive supply support directly from the AMAs with high-speed transmission of requisitions and use of electronic computers and appropriate transportation media, including airlift when justified.

The AMAs accomplish their supply management responsibilities through system support management (SSM).   Under this approach an AMA is responsible for the management of all elements of support required for designated weapons systems.   The AMAs also perform item management on a centralized worldwide basis, with responsibilities for requirements determination, procurement, storage, and issue of items in specified federal supply classes (FSCs) or the federal supply groups (FSGs) or by materiel management codes (MMCs) wherein the aggregation of items is based on the peculiarity or commonality of the next higher assembly of which the item is a part.

Since the introduction of systems management, most of the items have been assigned to a single AMA for inventory control.   Items peculiar to a particular system or weapon are controlled and distributed by the AMA to which that system or weapon is assigned.   Items used on more than one aircraft or missile are usually assigned to a single commodity manager including Defense Supply Centers for support of all weapon systems.

The system support management assignment is quite stable.   Many of the management assignments are made by a major system manufacturer.   Thus, Oklahoma City Air Materiel Area (OCAMA) is the SSM for the B-52 and the KC-135, both manufactured by Boeing; San Antonio Air Materiel Area (SAAMA) for the B-58 and the F-102, both manufactured by Convair.   Further, this system has concentrated particular "types" of weapon systems at specific depots, i.e., transport aircraft generally are assigned to Warner-Robbins Air Materiel Area (WRAMA); bombers, tankers, and aircraft engines to OCAMA and SAAMA; trainers to SAAMA; ballistics and air-launched missiles to Ogden Air Materiel Area (OOOAMA); and fighter aircraft to Sacramento Air Materiel Area (SMAMA).

INVENTORY CONTROL TECHNIQUES

Basic Supply Information.   SOURCES, TYPES, AND COLLECTION OF DATA: Control of the inventory and supply support of new materiel entering the system can be effectively performed only when management has adequate tools with which to work.   The basic functions of requirements management include the analysis of data and the projection of demand.   The accomplishment of these duties with any degree of effectiveness is dependent upon the adequacy and accuracy of the available supply-history data.   To forecast future demands, information on past demands must be collected, wherever possible, on each selected item of supply.   These data must be refined, interpreted, and adjusted in the light of changes in troop dispositions, defense policy, and the impact of new weapons on the supply system.   In turn, proper reporting of information is dependent upon uniform understanding of supply terms, the classification of data, and the importance attached to timely and accurate reporting.   Incorrect data result in distortions and inaccuracies in the forecasting of requirements.   It has often been said that "the power of adequate decision lies in being properly informed." Nowhere in the logistics system is this more true than in the area of requirements management of secondary items and repair parts.

In the Department of Defense "secondary items" is the term used to refer to reparable components and assemblies (e.g., helicopter blade assemblies, truck transmissions), consumable repair parts (e.g., spark plugs, electron tubes), bulk items and materiel (e.g., sheet aluminum, gasket materiel), expendable minor items (e.g., soap, canned beans, socks), which are contrasted to principal items such as trucks, aircraft, and small arms.   The following discussion of inventory management techniques in the Department of Defense is concerned primarily with secondary-item management.

The methods of collection and reporting of necessary supply information in order to make clear evaluation and accurate demand projections will be discussed below.

Defense materiel managers collect and utilize three basic types of supply history: issue data, demand data, and consumption data.   The supply history is used in varying degrees, depending primarily on the relative availability of the type of information.

1. Issue data are the most readily available types of information, since more accurate records are kept on issues (e.g., sales transactions) than on any other type of supply transaction.   Issue data provide supply history indicating a transfer of materiel to an authorized requisitioner.   This is ordinarily supplied in

a consolidated report form, and is generated wherever issues are made—depots, stations, or units.

2. Demand data are "[those] data which reflect requests for supplies, regardless of what is issued." They provide a more accurate basis for computation since they compile information on materiel requested as a true demand and recognize that materiel issued might well be a substitute item.

3. Consumption data consist of information compiled on materiel expended, whereby items are consumed and are lost to the system. Their main function is to provide an indication of the rate at which materiel already issued will be consumed so that consumption rates may be computed or rate of replacement may be anticipated.

The inventory control points in each military service have differing policies for data collection, based on the commodity characteristics of the items. Some use only issue data taken from stock accounting records. Others collect demand histories from various echelons, either CONUS depot or lower echelons closer to the user. Some agencies have instituted the collection and reporting of consumption data on a selective basis from supply units in the field. The amount and scope of data collected are based on the materiel reported upon. Extensive supply histories can be easily secured and effectively utilized on items consumed in a regular manner. Shorter, recent histories often are used on items consumed in an irregular manner.

There are advantages and disadvantages in the collection and application of each type of data which require careful consideration and possible adjustment before use. Issue data do not present a true picture of demands and if used without adjustments would result in inflated stock levels for substitute items and lower levels for desired items. Demand data require a more complex system for collection and reporting since information is necessary as to time period, geographical location, and the recording of demand against the preferred item, though a substitute is issued. These data are only accurate at the level at which they are collected—information as to whether the requirement represents true demand beyond that point is unknown. Demand data are, however, more accurate than issue data. Consumption data, secured at the user end of the pipeline, can present imposing problems if the data are not collected on a selective basis.

Maintenance data collection systems on the repair and use of major equipments, e.g., vehicles, prove a useful source of data. Each service has developed these data collection systems. For example, in the Army demand and consumption data are provided to personnel engaged in requirements computations through the Army Equipment Records System (TAERS), established by AR 750-5 and implemented in TM 38-750, by depot overseas stock-status reports and Army supply-status reports (AR 711-5). Although basically intended to provide information related to maintenance and materiel readiness, TAERS reports provide information on parts consumption by maintenance and repair echelons. The information is transmitted to a central data agency which furnishes the compiled data to the Army commodity commands.

RECURRING AND NONRECURRING DEMAND: Demand classifications are divided into "recurring" and "nonrecurring."

1. Recurring demand is a replacement demand of a repetitive nature made to replenish materiel consumed or worn out in operation. Recurring demand comprises the bulk of demand for replacement supply and must be clearly established so that forecasting can be effectively performed.

2. Nonrecurring demand is a demand made on a one-time basis with no repetitive subsequent demand contemplated within the next 12-month period

for the same purpose. This includes initial demands to satisfy initial allowances, pipeline increases, special projects, and demands from depot maintenance for rebuild of end items not subject to rebuild again in the foreseeable future.

The degree of refinement in demand reporting is based on the value and activity of the materiel. The distinction between recurring and nonrecurring demand is unnecessary for items having regular consumption history or low dollar demand, and requirements projections may be made on the basis of gross demand. When demands are segregated, comparison of both types of demands with previous experience is necessary for accurate forecasting and the phasing of supply action.

Nonrecurring demand is not utilized in computation of local stock levels; ICPs, however, record issues as either recurring or nonrecurring (as indicated on requisitions), and data are reported along with issue and demand history, for consideration in reviews. Management of high- and very high-dollar-value items requires a greater refinement in reporting, and segregating categories of particular significance, such as "rebuild," "initial," or "programmed" demand.

1. Programmed demands represent those requirements which are known far enough in advance to permit accurate forecasting. These may encompass prior stockage of repair parts to accomplish a rebuild or overhaul program, equipment issue to newly activated units, or modification in mission or equipment with consequent demands. Where programmed demands are received for items having no past issue experience, computations are often based on engineering estimates. Because these estimates are published in technical manuals, they are often called "book demands."

2. Unprogrammed demands are those which occur through creation of special situations, are brought about through changes in world situations, or are occasioned by natural disasters.

Although unforeseeable demands cannot be programmed, a level of demand to anticipate such contingencies may be established, based on experience. Even emergencies may recur, and unforeseen demands can be stabilized and factored by considering a long period of time. Care must be exercised to ensure consideration of recurring seasonal demands over an extended base period, thereby securing a separate demand for each cycle. If the quantity of an item consumed in normal operation is to be determined, it is essential that abnormal or one-time issues be distinguished in computations.

The analysis of demand, distinguishing between recurring and nonrecurring requirements, taking all known factors into account, results in an average demand figure. Management should assign supply analysis personnel to a related group of items insofar as possible to permit them to gain experience in the behavior of a given commodity.

ANALYSIS OF HISTORICAL DEMAND DATA: An accurate forecast of future demand must consider the experience or past history of the item. Although consumption demand data are available for requirements computations in the field, requirements analysis at the ICP level is dependent for the most part on issue and demand data from one or more levels between the consumer and the ICP. In many cases the collection and use of data from many sources and levels on a worldwide basis are necessary for an adequate demand projection. Demands which are not expected to recur or which will be separately programmed must be segregated from normal demands and considered individually as to their impact. At this point, analytical judgment and past experience with the commodity must be brought to bear.

Inventory losses, as indicated in transaction reports, do not always result from a demand. Adjustments in stock balances caused by disposal or transfer, that are listed in such reports, are not actual issues to consumers; thus a discrepancy between issue data and available demand data requires analysis. The causes for discrepancies may be found in:

1. Reports of demand and issue from varying levels with differing reporting time periods or cutoff dates
2. Failure to make issue due to temporary shortage of materiel
3. Issue of substitute materiel for supplies actually requisitioned

Differences in patterns of demand may be reconciled by comparison of stocks due out and due in and by considerations of the relative age of the demand. If the trend of back orders has steadily increased or decreased, it may be considered as a basis for a corresponding increase or decrease in demand rate. If the material due in will compensate for a sporadic fluctuation, the demand rate need not be altered. The relationship of issue of known substitutes to a decrease in a preferred item assists in computation when a wide variance in data arises. If the pattern indicates increased issue experience of substitutes and decreased issue of the preferred item, the combining of demands will develop a demand equivalent for projection. In either case, care must be exercised to assure that increased back orders are indicative of a trend or that substitutions can be interpreted as a legitimate demand for the item being studied and are not a "true" demand against the substitute in its own right.

Demand analysis brings to bear the indispensable judgment and skill of management in the determination of the extent to which related factors affect the basic rate of demand. To effectively perform this function, management must rely on proven concepts, experiences, and statistical methods. Changes in defense policies, troop dispositions, and new equipment must be considered and applied in combination with historical demand data. Procedural patterns cannot be so stringent as to restrict the use of judgment. Management must avoid the treatment of demand histories as a consistent pattern or formula from which a forecast can be derived by mathematical computation alone.

DEMAND FORECASTING: The techniques of combining back orders with issues or other normal methods of projecting future demands present to management only a tentative figure which may be subjected to further refinement by statistical methods or which will require adjustment because of the impact of such other demand factors as troop deployments, troop levels, weather conditions, geographic areas, seasonal influences, and the number of end items in the supply system (end-item density). Because of the continuous introduction of new items and the dropping of obsolete items as weapons systems are modified or phased out, there is a high degree of volatility in consumption and demand rates for many items.

Any change in the density of end items in the field causes changes in demand pattern for supporting repair parts. Initial supplies of repair parts to support a new item are distributed on the basis of the total number of an end item planned for each theater or area. Engineering estimates, formulated during the development stage, are multiplied by the planned density to determine the quantities of parts to be supplied. Once materiel is with troops, and demand experience is accumulated, projection of demand becomes susceptible to program-change factors. These factors are established by dividing the future known density figures for the end item by the current density figure, thus deriving a trend, expressed in decimal equivalents, for each year. The demand rate is multiplied by the forecast program-change factor, applied separately to theaters, reflecting the relative change of end-item density. Use of the program-change factor results in providing computations with contemplated changes, but consideration must still be given to accuracy of density figure, age of the end item, and differing rates of deterioration and repair in varied areas and under diverse conditions.

Certain statistical techniques have been developed and are used by management to arrive at basic quantitative requirements to which density factors, troop dispositions, etc., can be uniformly applied.

Management uses such statistical techniques as exponential smoothing, the method of least squares, semiaveraging, and moving averages in analyzing trends to achieve the most accurate projection of demand. Their accuracy, as in any statistics, depends on the validity of the historical data. Extensive application of electronic computers in the requirements computation process at inventory control points has enabled these techniques to be used in the automatic preparation of "supply control studies" on each item of supply.

Management separates demand history into months or quarters, comparing the activity within these periods to detect trends, and assesses their impact to determine necessary adjustments. Simplified graphing furnishes a convenient method of revealing trends and is most accurate when the period of demand history is of sufficient length to indicate both seasonal variations and random fluctuations for the item. The trend line may be indicated on a graph by drawing an intermediate line through the demand plotted by month or quarter. More mathematical accuracy is obtained by the use of the semiaverage or least-squares techniques.

Semiaveraging divides the base time period into two parts, securing an arithmetic means for each period. This point is indicated midway in each part of a graph and a line is drawn across the points. Figure 4 portrays the application of this technique.

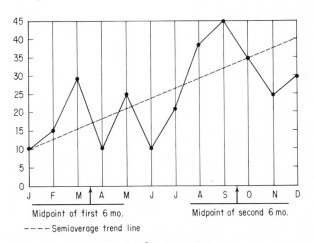

Fig. 4 Semiaveraging.

The least-squares method of computing trend lines is founded on basic algebra and calculates the equation of a straight line for any particular set of data, using the equation to forecast probable future data. Figure 5 illustrates the application of the theory. A trend line (or line of best fit) is computed so that the sum of squared deviations above and below the line is smaller than it would be for any other line fitted to the same data.

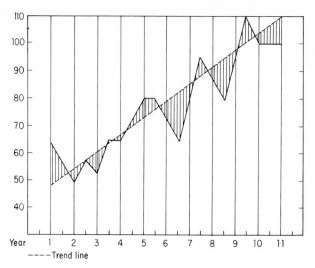

Fig. 5 Least squares.

Trend lines are constructed for the purpose of extrapolation, which is, in requirements computation, the projection of experienced demand rate into the future. While the trend line constructed from past data may not be representative of a future pattern, the problem is minimized by extending forward from the original data only so far as is necessary or until the next scheduled study.

Neither the moving-average method nor trend techniques take into account the short-term fluctuation of demand rate above or below the average demand rate, though statistical methods will indicate the probable degree of fluctuation. The most significant application of statistical techniques is to the safety level which is established to provide a degree of protection against temporary fluctuations in demand.

The term "exponential smoothing" is descriptive of a statistical method for determining average demand. This method is used in computer applications. It takes its name from the fact that a numerical figure, or exponent, is used in making computations to give proper consideration to fluctuations in data. In exponential smoothing, past demand experience is condensed into a single number representing previous demands for an item. The established number then becomes the basic figure against which a succeeding demand figure may be applied. In computing a new average demand only a fraction of the old and the new data is used to obtain a smoothing effect, giving as a general rule greater weight to current data and less weight to older demand history. The fractional value applied to the data is called a "smoothing constant," which must be a fraction between 0 and 1. The weight given to new data determines the weight to be applied to past data—if 0.1 is applied to recent data (three months' experience), then 0.9 is applied to the older data. If 0.2 is used for the new data, 0.8 is applied to the older data. For instance, the average of three past demands of 4, 2, and 12 would be 6. If a new demand of 8 were received, the old average of 6 would be considered along with the new demand to form a new average. Any weight could be assigned to the 6 and 8, so long as the sum of the weights equaled 1. If a weight of 0.1 was assigned to the new demand and a weight of 0.9 to the old average, the computation of a new average would be

$$\tfrac{1}{10}(\text{new demand}) + \tfrac{9}{10}(\text{old average})$$

or

$$\tfrac{1}{10}(8) + \tfrac{9}{10}(6)$$

thus

$$0.8 + 5.4 = 6.2 \ (\text{new average})$$

If the analyst felt that the new average should be closer to 8, he could increase the weight given to the most recent demand from 0.1 to 0.2 and could lower the weight given to the old average from 0.9 to 0.8:

$$\tfrac{2}{10}(\text{new demand}) + \tfrac{8}{10}(\text{old average})$$

or

$$\tfrac{2}{10}(8) + \tfrac{8}{10}(6)$$

thus

$$1.6 + 4.8 = 6.4 \ (\text{new average})$$

Exponential smoothing is generally used in establishing an average demand figure for items having relatively stable demand patterns. When the technique is used it eliminates the requirement for data files maintained for the purpose of establishing average demands. The analyst needs only two sets of data—the figure representing past demand experience and the figure representing demand in the quarter just ended—to compute a new average demand figure. Past demand history is never completely lost—the value assigned to it merely diminishes. The value of the smoothing constant applied to current data determines whether changes in supply levels will be slow or rapid. An increase in its value from 0.1 to 0.3 results in the quicker response, while a lower constant permits a smooth and gradual response to a change demand. Computer applications at inventory control points perform these calculations in preparing the supply control studies that are used by supply analysts in making decisions to buy, or dispose, of stocks.

Supply Management Tools. FACTORS INFLUENCING DISTRIBUTION-SYSTEM STOCK LEVELS: There are many factors which enter into the computation of requirements. Factors that determine the most efficient level at which inventory should be maintained are the same in both private enterprise and the military services, though values assigned to various costs and benefits of the two systems may differ.

One of the basic inventory theories is that it is not always the most desirable policy to carry the smallest possible level of supply, since the cost of multiple procurements, receipts, postings, and audit actions involved would be excessive. Since demand can never be projected with absolute accuracy, a safety level must be maintained which will satisfy unanticipated demands. The length of time between placement of an order and receipt of supplies requires that stock be on hand during that period to satisfy current demands.

Management must consider the total situation involving supply, maintenance, procurement, storage, etc., that will have an impact on the item being studied before arriving at a firm requirement. Some of the factors that influence the final decision are:

1. The actual inventory already on hand and available storage capacity
2. The lot sizes in which new supplies may be ordered
3. The cost of storage and security
4. The cost of processing an order
5. The lead time involved in procurement
6. Whether the requirement is to satisfy initial or replacement demand
7. The cost of maintenance
8. The possibility of obsolescence

9. The storage life and any special characteristics of the item

10. The nature of the supported item if the materiel being procured is a component of another item

11. Anticipated technological changes which may increase or decrease the demand

12. The cost of being unable to meet demands

Many of the factors affecting the quantity of materiel entering into or remaining in the system may be adjusted by personnel engaged in requirements computations.

The date at which supply levels reach the reorder point or the time established for review of stock status of materiel has an influence on the quantitative requirement. Since it is impractical and uneconomical to review all the vast number of items in the supply system more frequently, established reviews are generally conducted at intervals of 3, 6, or 12 months, depending on the dollar value of annual demand. The review provides the opportunity to examine past issue and demand experience, predicts the demand for the next period, and adjusts stock by appropriate action. In addition to the normal review, an item is also reviewed when it reaches a level of supply designated as the reorder point. This safeguard reduces the effect of unusual demand but does not warn of falling demand and the resulting accumulation of excesses. Potential excesses are generally indicated at normal review periods. The most economical length for the interval between review periods is determined primarily by the frequency of issue and the dollar value of demand. Fast-moving stocks require more frequent review and reorder than slow-moving stocks if a wide variance in demand makes it impractical to order in large quantities.

Generally speaking, an item with high dollar demand is reviewed more frequently than one with a low dollar demand. The principle of management by exception should be exploited in the application of criteria for triggering an item review. In this way only those matters that are the exception to established limitations and procedures receive the full and prompt attention of inventory managers. Management effort can be focused on nonroutine or unexpected occurrences, as item behavior exceeds computer-programmed parameters—e.g., reorder points, demand projections. Logistics computer applications make extensive use of such "exception printout" techniques. Supply control procedures, programmed for computers wherever possible, provide the analyst with the essential data necessary to review demand and adjust levels as required.

Inventory may be maintained at a higher level if there is a large setup cost by the manufacturer which makes it more economical to order a fairly large amount. Large inventories may also be justified for items which are small, having low storage cost; nonperishable; subject to wide variations in demand; or unlikely to become obsolete. Low inventory levels may be desirable if procurement costs are slight, storage cost is high, lead time is short, or demand is constant. The inventory level should always be increased if a shortage of the item would materially affect capability to accomplish a mission, i.e., the military essentiality of an item.

Consideration of the variable factors above, the procedures utilized, and the actions and reactions within the systems makes it abundantly clear that procedures cannot always be applied rigidly or mechanically. The judgment and experience of management must govern and may override procedures in the interest of efficient planning and control. The greater the military essentiality of the item, the dollar value of demand, etc., the greater should be the dependence on human judgment and experience in the man-machine systems that comprise modern inventory control systems.

THE ECONOMIC-ORDER PRINCIPLE: The ultimate goal of requirements computations and materiel management is to have the right amount of supplies available to permit operations in support of plans. This must be accomplished at the lowest cost that can be attained without endangering the military mission. Procurement costs vary with the number of orders placed. The principle of optimum frequency of reorder requires that items with low dollar demand should be ordered less frequently than items with high dollar demand. Procurement cost therefore can be reduced by the placement of large orders. This increases the inventory cost and the carrying cost. On the other hand, carrying cost can be reduced by maintaining a smaller inventory. This goal can be achieved by placing small orders frequently—resulting in higher procurement costs. *Ordering, therefore, creates procurement costs, while possession creates carrying costs.*

Economic-ordering principles are employed by all Defense activities in achieving a practical balance between the cost of frequent orders and the cost of maintaining stocks on hand. Expressed in its simplest terms, the principle equates the cost to order to the cost to hold. This is the point at which the combined costs are at a minimum, and the size of the order to be placed at that time is called the "economic order quantity" (EOQ). To arrive at an economic order quantity it is necessary to consider as a minimum:

1. The annual requirement for the item
2. The annual variable cost of ordering
3. The annual variable cost of carrying inventory
4. The unit price of the item

Various formulas are employed to arrive at the EOQ in each DOD component. In general such formulas as the following attempt to equate the cost to order and the cost to hold. This principle may be expressed by

$$Q = \sqrt{\frac{2AC}{H}}$$

where Q = economic order quantity, in dollars
A = annual value of demand, in dollars
C = cost to order, in dollars
H = cost to hold, expressed as a percentage per year

Decisions as to when to order and how much result in control over the inventory. The EOQ answers the question of how much to order and in so doing establishes the frequency with which orders are placed.

Manufacturers often offer quantity discounts, sometimes in increments, depending on the amount purchased. A reduced price encourages the buying of a large quantity, with a concurrent reduction in cost to reorder. When discounts are available it becomes necessary to compare the optimum-buy quantities at different price ranges with associated costs at unit-price ranges to calculate the best purchases.

EOQ is applicable both to single items and to any group of stock items with similar holding and procurement costs. Its use causes the sum of the two costs to be lower than under any other system of replenishment. Figures 6 and 7 present a comparison between constant-level replenishment and EOQ replenishment for nine hypothetical items which resulted in less inventory and lower total costs. In Fig. 7, the ratio of costs to average investment is the same for each item, and minimum costs are achieved only when costs bear the same relationship to investment for each item.

SELECTIVE MANAGEMENT: Selective management is a philosophy of inventory control which provides precise control over items selected for close attention

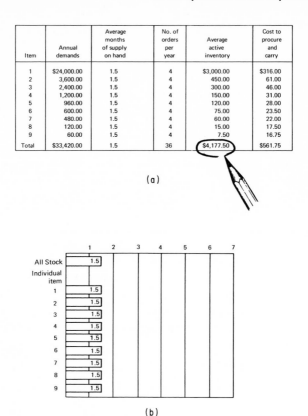

Item	Annual demands	Average months of supply on hand	No. of orders per year	Average active inventory	Cost to procure and carry
1	$24,000.00	1.5	4	$3,000.00	$316.00
2	3,600.00	1.5	4	450.00	61.00
3	2,400.00	1.5	4	300.00	46.00
4	1,200.00	1.5	4	150.00	31.00
5	960.00	1.5	4	120.00	28.00
6	600.00	1.5	4	75.00	23.50
7	480.00	1.5	4	60.00	22.00
8	120.00	1.5	4	15.00	17.50
9	60.00	1.5	4	7.50	16.75
Total	$33,420.00	1.5	36	$4,177.50	$561.75

(a)

(b)

Fig. 6   (a) Constant level replenishment (old); (b) average months' supply on hand.

because of their high dollar value, and provides for eliminating all but the most necessary details in the management of low-dollar or low-volume materiel.   It is a dynamic and positive way to improve materiel requirements management.   The cost of management has a direct relationship to the importance and the cost of the item.

Department of Defense instructions prescribe four standard degrees of management intensity, based upon the value of annual demands or planned issues as follows:

Management Intensity Grouping	Value, Annual Demand
Very high	Over $500,000
High	Over $50,000 to $500,000
Medium	Over $5,000 to $50,000
Low	$5,000 or less

For the top two groups, the most intensive management review and analysis are prescribed, including obtaining asset information on a worldwide basis, as fully as practicable, and the use of high-speed transportation whenever economically advantageous.   Periodic management review may result in the movement of an item between groupings.

The most intensive management system today covers 77,000 recoverable Air Force items, primarily aircraft and missile parts and components.   This system,

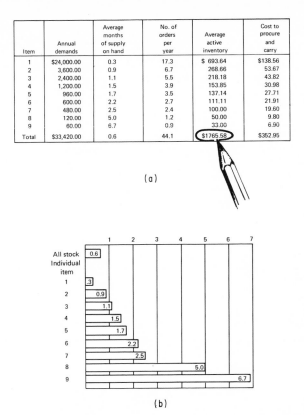

Item	Annual demands	Average months of supply on hand	No. of orders per year	Average active inventory	Cost to procure and carry
1	$24,000.00	0.3	17.3	$ 693.64	$138.56
2	3,600.00	0.9	6.7	268.66	53.67
3	2,400.00	1.1	5.5	218.18	43.82
4	1,200.00	1.5	3.9	153.85	30.98
5	960.00	1.7	3.5	137.14	27.71
6	600.00	2.2	2.7	111.11	21.91
7	480.00	2.5	2.4	100.00	19.60
8	120.00	5.0	1.2	50.00	9.80
9	60.00	6.7	0.9	33.00	6.90
Total	$33,420.00	0.6	44.1	$1765.58	$352.95

(a)

(b)

Fig. 7 (*a*) EOQ replenishment (new); (*b*) average months' supply on hand.

installed in November, 1967, requires daily transaction reporting on a worldwide basis. The Navy has for some time maintained worldwide visibility over 6,000 items having an annual demand of $50,000 or greater. The Army is currently developing such worldwide procedures, based upon a test of 1,780 high-value items.

The principle of management by exception is applicable at all levels of supply but is ideally suited to the distribution-system management of secondary-item repair parts because of the categorization of materiel from low to very high dollar values. The principle is applicable to the above categorization since routine procedures are established for low- and medium-dollar-value items and only exceptions (e.g., an item reaching a reorder point prior to the time of a scheduled review) are singled out for analysis. Requirements for low-dollar-value items may be completely mechanically computed. Those of medium value are also mechanically computed unless designated as requiring a supply control study (exceeding established limits). Higher-dollar items receive detailed attention and consider assets stocked in oversea depots, and may even consider those items in the hands of units worldwide.

THE SUPPLY CONTROL STUDY: The supply control study serves as the focal point for gathering all supply intelligence on an item of supply in order to support materiel management decision making. Supply control studies may be called for when assets on a given item are not in balance with expected demand patterns—resulting in appropriate action to (1) initiate procurement or repair, (2) terminate procurement or rebuild programs, or (3) dispose of surplus items. Defense policy calls for inventory managers to update supply control studies monthly for all items with an annual procurement value of over $1 million. Studies for items with an annual procurement value of $5 million are submitted to the Office of the Secretary of Defense for review.

Supply control studies may also be prepared (1) as part of the backup data for future buying programs used in budget justification, (2) on a cyclic basis for certain high-investment items, and (3) as a diagnostic tool for items "in trouble," i.e., where demand far exceeds supply availability. They may be prepared manually or by computer, but in most processing methods, the supply analyst depends heavily on computer output.

In the preparation of a supply control study, any estimate of future demands for an item is generally based on the assumption that the pattern of recurring demands established during the most recent control period will be repeated during the control period which follows. Identified nonrecurring demands are excluded from projections except for computing average demand for low-dollar-value items. This approach is best for determining levels for normal replacement demand, but must be modified in situations where there is a seasonal demand or abrupt change in requirements for any reason. Supply levels must be reviewed regularly to adjust to fluctuations of demand, modification of maintenance policies, changes in the tactical situation, and many other compelling factors. Review of supply levels is often accomplished by computer, as part of inventory management systems such as the one discussed in the final section of this chapter.

The terminology, general procedures, and considerations of the various factors which influence requirements computations are covered in the following list.

1. *Requirements Objective* (*RO*). The maximum quantity of materiel to be maintained on hand and on order, at any one time, to sustain current operations and objectives constitutes the requirements objective. It consists of the sum of requirements represented by the reorder-cycle quantity, the procurement lead-time quantity, safety-level quantity and protectable mobilization reserve-materiel objectives or emergency level of supply, and prepositioned war-reserve requirements, as appropriate.

2. *Reorder Cycle.* The reorder cycle is the interval between successive reorders or procurement actions. The quantity of materiel required to satisfy demands received during this interval is referred to as the "reorder-cycle quantity" or "operating-level quantity."

3. *Procurement Lead Time* (*PROLT*). This is the span of time from the date of a supply control study resulting in procurement to the receipt of the first shipment in the supply system. It comprises administrative lead time (ALT) from the date of a supply control study to the award of contract, production lead time (PLT) from award of contract to completion of manufacture of the items for the first scheduled shipment, and delivery lead time (DLT) from completion of manufacture to receipt of first shipment into the supply system.

4. *Base Period.* This is the period of time, normally expressed in quarters of a year, over which program data, demands, and returns are considered in the computation of factors and rates. Normally the base period will include eight quarters of average quarterly demand (AQD) of the two years' history immediately preceding the quarter in which the supply control study is being made.

5. *Reorder Point.* It is essential that a point be established in the stock level that will assure the ordering of additional stocks which will be received

before the stock on hand is depleted. This is known as the "reorder point," defined as that point in time at which a supply review will be made or at which an order for supplies is prepared. Replenishment action at that time avoids exhaustion or the use of safety stocks. A reorder point is established at any level which controls materiel and is responsive to customer demand—ICPs or retail property offices. The reorder point on each item assures that supplies are ordered in sufficient time to maintain a constant flow and considers the transit-time period between the ordering activity and the supplier. The reorder point is generally expressed in days of supply.

6. *Safety Level.* The safety level represents that quantity of materiel, in addition to the reorder-cycle quantity, required to be on hand to permit continued operations in event of minor interruption of normal replenishment or unpredictable surge in demand. Normal demand rarely occurs at a constant rate and may exceed an expected average during any given segment of the period. Thus, the safety level actually functions to permit continued supply support to consumers despite abnormal demand or any extension of procurement lead time, i.e., late deliveries. Occasional or even frequent use of a portion of the safety level represents a normal, healthy, and efficient supply situation.

7. *Variable Safety Level.* The term "safety level" does not always represent a constant factor to be automatically applied in computations. While it provides protection against stock depletion caused by abnormal fluctuations in either demand or lead time, it may be applied on other than a cyclic basis. The quantity of materiel carried as a level may vary, based on many influences including, among others, the frequency of demand, the size of the average requisition, the length and predictability of lead time, and reorder frequency. A safety level of 10 days of supply may be entirely satisfactory for one item based on demand, yet a safety level of 60 days of supply may be entirely inadequate for another item. It is the policy of the Department of Defense to establish variable safety levels for repetitive-demand consumable-type items.

Safety level is stated in terms of "days of supply" for average expected demands over a given time period. In the computation of a variable safety level it is necessary that accurate and up-to-date records be maintained on actual lead times and demands. Demand characteristics, lead-time variations, etc., are analyzed, and safety levels are computed which provide a desired level of demand and lead-time protection. This permits establishment of varying levels of safety stocks for individual items based on item characteristics, i.e., larger stocks for items having irregular demand and smaller stocks for items having regular and predictable demand and lead-time patterns.

The variable safety level is a means of providing a predetermined level of protection against stock depletion. Its effectiveness can be determined by accumulating data on the number of items in a similar group which are out of stock at the time replenishment is received. The fraction of the total supply that is not on hand at that time will indicate the adequacy of safety levels and provide the guidance for adjustment.

Supply control studies are made whenever assets are not in balance with forecasted demand in any time frame of the RO period. These imbalances are usually occasioned by unusual demand on the supply system. The recomputation of requirements, considering the causes of the fluctuations and their probable continuance, results in the establishment of a revised safety level, as well as adjustment to the AQD. Stock imbalances may require recomputation of demand rate and changes in variable-safety-level quantities based on changing demand characteristics, lead-time factors, etc., at each supply control review.

Impressive savings can be realized from shortening procurement lead time, the net result being a contraction of the study-period time and reduction of the investment in safety-level and lead-time quantities.   Management will designate levels, in accordance with selective-item management principles, at which approval authority for shortening of procurement lead time or reduction of quantitative levels may be exercised, based on dollar values involved.   Management, in review of selected supply control studies, must look for abnormal or subnormal forecasts of requirements.   Past and current demands should be scrutinized and compared with projections to verify wide deviations.   If the causes of an out-of-balance position are not satisfactorily explained by the data provided by the study, they must be sought out by the supply analyst.   Each demand may be analyzed in an attempt to detect large quantities erroneously categorized as recurring demand.   Consumption and usage factors may be double-checked to assure that maintenance and manufacturer sources of information agree on the factors used for a given item.   Action must be taken to rectify any underlying erroneous factors which cast a doubt on the action recommended by the supply control study.

THE SAWTOOTH DIAGRAM: As a management tool which may be used for the projection of future requirements, the demand history of any item and related factors may be portrayed in graphic form, presenting seasonal trends, time lags, and statistical data for consideration.   The main facts are emphasized, a mass of related material is summarized, and facts are often disclosed which have been overlooked.

The theory and application of the factors of management control are presented in the "sawtooth design," which illustrates the use of the tools of requirements management, from the basic time and quantity relationship to the use and adjustment of requirements objectives.

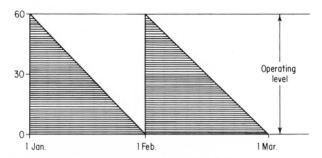

Fig. 8   Operating level.

Figure 8 illustrates stock status for a two-month period when issues and receipts are regular.   Demands total 2 units per day or 60 per month.   They are completely consumed in one month, and receipt of replenishment brings the depleted quantity back up to the operating level of 60 units on February 1. The operating level is conveniently indicated by a horizontal line drawn from the appropriate point on the vertical scale.

Figure 9 adds to the operating level a 15-unit buffer, called the "safety stock," to guard against stock depletion.   If an unusual demand occurs or the delivery arrives late, supply would be unable to meet demands for a few days if safety stock was unavailable.   The safety level provides a cushion for unexpected demands and prevents the supply activity from being out of stock.   The incompleteness of the information on which estimates are based makes the safety

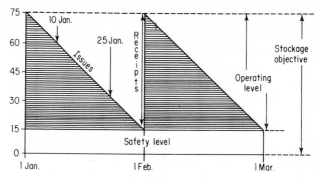

Fig. 9 The stockage objective.

level a useful device to help the supplier give good service. The stockage objective, or the maximum amount permitted to be on hand at any given time, is the sum of the safety level and the operating level.

Figure 10 portrays the element of procurement lead time, which is the time between the date of a supply control study, submission of an order for supplies,

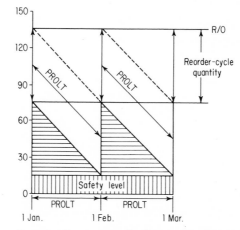

Fig. 10 Procurement lead time (PROLT).

and the receipt of the items into the system. In this figure the procurement lead time equals the time required to deplete the operating-level quantity. This is not always true, since the PROLT might be two months, with one month required to deplete the operating-level quantity, in which case the RO would require an additional quantity to be ordered, as indicated by the broken line in Fig. 10.

Figure 11 indicates a signal point at which to reorder, when the total stock on hand plus the amount of order drops below an established figure. The figure illustrates the use of safety stocks to satisfy an unusual demand with submission of an order for a definite quantity when the point is reached. The quantity on hand one week before the end of February, when combined with the new order which must be submitted, brings the total assets up to the new requisitioning objective.

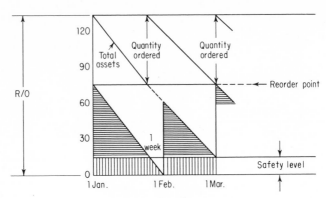

Fig. 11   Reorder point.

Figure 12 consolidates previous illustrations and indicates a regular pattern of supply operations over an eight-month (240-day) period. The graph portrays the issue of 1 unit per day, and the quantity on hand drops to the safety level, at which time replenishment stock arrives. The assets are then at the reorder point and replenishment action is taken. A procurement lead time of 60 days is shown with orders every 30 days, making 30 on order and due in at the time another order is placed.

The sawtooth diagram provides a valuable visualization of the impact of various factors on inventory levels and can be used to compare alternative stock-level control policies. The diagram is especially useful in planning for supply of a large number of items and when procurement is relatively uncomplicated. General rules regarding levels of supply can be established for a variety of items without considering the number of units of each item required to make up those levels.

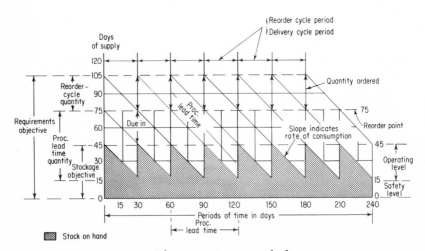

Fig. 12   The composite sawtooth diagram.

AUTOMATED INVENTORY CONTROL SYSTEMS: The reliance of inventory managers on electronic computers can be fully appreciated by examining the content of a typical automatic data processing system used to support the functions of inventory control point and commodity command. Figure 13 indicates the title of the files in one military service's inventory management system. The media

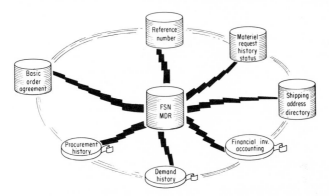

Fig. 13   Major files in the inventory management system.

for storage of the files are represented by appropriate data processing symbology. The storage media employed include, among other things, high-speed immediate-access disk storage and magnetic-tape storage. The following paragraphs offer a limited description of the files in the system. These brief descriptions are considered adequate to offer a basic understanding of file purpose, control, and content necessary to appreciate the scope and potential of automated inventory control systems.

Reference-number File. This is a cross-reference file which provides an index to the federal stock number (FSN) master data record and a base for validation of all input to the system. It contains every number in use within a particular commodity command, whether it be a manufacturer's part number, an obsolete stock number, a substitute or interchangeable number, or a current stock number. It is established in reference-number sequence regardless of the type of number that is involved. This file is the key to real sophistication of processing transactions against the FSN master data record because it provides an avenue for direct entry into the master record regardless of the number that is on the input transaction—e.g., requisition, receipt report, etc.

Materiel-request History and Status File. This file has as its key data element the MILSTRIP requisition-document number as assigned by any Army customer or other service customer as may be appropriate. It reflects complete information concerning a requisition document from the time of its entry into a commodity command until it is finally satisfied, transferred, canceled, or otherwise resolved. It will be used to screen duplicate requisitions, to accomplish supply performance reports for higher headquarters, to answer status requests from field customers, and finally, for billing purposes to charge customers for supplies delivered.

Shipping-address Directory. This file will have the six-position coded identification of customers and contractors as its key data element. The file will contain the code, the name, and the in-the-clear address of all customers and manufacturers with whom each respective commodity command does business. The file will be used to validate input transactions and also as a source for conversion of coded information to in-the-clear address information for contracts and other appropriate communications.

Basic-order-agreement File. This will be a small file containing the contract number for open-end or basic-order-agreement-type contracts and will be in the sequence of contract number. The appropriate manufacturer and the number of the last private manufacturer will be identified, and the number of the last delivery order issued will be carried in the file. The file will be used for automatic machine preparation of delivery orders.

The Financial-inventory-accounting (FIA) File. This file will be in stock-number sequence and will be accumulated daily as a result of the consummation of all transactions of an inventory accounting nature. Each transaction which completes processing will be merged into a daily file. This one symbol actually represents a number of files in that daily files will be merged weekly, weekly files merged monthly, and monthly files merged quarterly for preparation of financial reports and for extraction of demand-history information.

Demand-history File. This file will be developed as a result of the extraction of requisitions and filed return transactions from the FIA file. The file will be in the sequence of the stock number which was ordered or returned. The capability will exist for updating demand information by referring the stock number in the demand-history file to the reference-number file to bring demands up to a current status insofar as number relationships are concerned. The file will be maintained on a weekly cycle and will contain a full 24 months of experience for computation of the average monthly issue rate in supply control study preparation.

Procurement-history File. This file is sequenced by customer-order number, contract number, and contract-line-item number as appropriate to the current status of the procurement action. It will be initiated concurrently with the procurement request and will be updated to contain each significant transaction which affects the corresponding procurement-action record in the MDR, and will serve to provide a basis for all necessary external and internal management reporting on individual or summarized procurement actions. By its comprehensive nature, the record will provide the audit trail for procurement actions.

Federal-stock-number Master-data-record (FSN MDR) File. This file is the primary file in inventory management processes. Data residing in this file will be identified to virtually all functional areas of a commodity command. The file is developed on the "sector concept." Each sector is related to subordinate levels of the commodity command or to various combinations of ICP subfunctions.

The number and title of the sectors of the FSN MDR file have been listed in Fig. 14. Requirements for internal computer control fields have not been included. There are multiple entries in most of the sectors to accommodate the requirement for entry of numerous "lines" of data. The entry of several contracts for the same item and the entry of many scheduled deliveries for a single contract are good examples. These separate "lines" within this sector are referred to as "segments." There will be no limitation on the number of segments which can be entered into each sector. This assures the functional manager of unlimited data storage capability and removes the problem of exceeding file limitations.

The FSN MDR is stored in disk in the sequence of the prime FSN. This is the number that is referred to in some commands as the "preferred" item or "supply-controlled" items. All items which are substitute to the prime item are contained within the record of the prime FSN. All data pertinent to both prime and substitute items are combined in each sector. This method facilitates

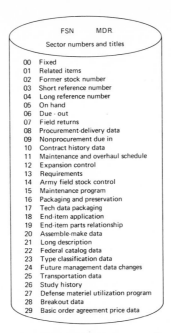

FSN   MDR

Sector numbers and titles

00 Fixed
01 Related items
02 Former stock number
03 Short reference number
04 Long reference number
05 On hand
06 Due - out
07 Field returns
08 Procurement-delivery data
09 Nonprocurement due in
10 Contract history data
11 Maintenance and overhaul schedule
12 Expansion control
13 Requirements
14 Army field stock control
15 Maintenance program
16 Packaging and preservation
17 Tech data packaging
18 End-item application
19 End-item parts relationship
20 Assemble-make data
21 Long description
22 Federal catalog data
23 Type classification data
24 Future management data changes
25 Transportation data
26 Study history
27 Defense materiel utilization program
28 Breakout data
29 Basic order agreement price data

Fig. 14   Content of the FSN master data record.

retrieval and processing where prime and substitute items are involved. Processing of customer requisitions is the best case in point. Substitute items may be issued in lieu of primes. When the ordered item is "out of stock," automatic issue of related items can be accomplished. Although an item can be designated as substitute for only one prime item, additional "alternate" item relationships can be specified in the end-item parts relationship sector.

The prime item will always be in the "fixed" sector. Substitute items will be in sector 01, and essentially sector 01 and the fixed are synonymous in their content. Sector 02 will contain former FSNs assigned to prime or substitute FSNs. Sectors 03 and 04 will contain all manufacturer codes and part numbers for prime and substitute FSNs. These represent all reference numbers which the system will be able to handle as input automatically.

SYSTEMS INTEGRATION: Each of the above files is available and called upon as appropriate for the full range of logistics data processing for supply accounting, cataloging, requirements computation, budgeting, etc. Using these data, the automated system interrelates masses of information on a given item supply. Additional support files may augment the system from time to time and are subject to the same logical and preplanned processing provided by the computer program. In this way, many diverse factors are considered and provide the inventory manager with a potent tool for inventory control decision making. This integrated and timely processing has not been economically feasible without electronic computers. When we recognize that these files contain millions of characters of information which can be manipulated in fractions of a second, the full power of automated inventory control is recognized. Review of stock levels on 200,000 different FSNs (a typical ICP item range) is not now an annual task, but can be managed as frequently as justified by economic criteria—perhaps daily if justified. In this processing, each item is assured the benefit of identical methodical computation and expert analysis—as preserved in the computer program. Thus, it is essential for the materiel manager to bear a significant responsibility for computer-program definition, if the full potential of automated inventory control is to be realized.

REFERENCES

1. *United States Code*, 1958 ed., vol. 2, 1959, pp. 1068–1087.
2. "Basic Regulations for the Military Supply System," *DOD Directive*, no. 4000.8, June 13, 1963.
3. "Requisite Characteristics for Wartime Readiness of DOD Supply Systems," *DOD Directive*, no. 3110.3, Nov. 7, 1960.
4. *Statement of the Secretary of Defense before the Committee on Appropriations*, U.S. House of Representative, 87th Congr. 2d Sess., January 20, 1962, pp. 153–154.

BIBLIOGRAPHY

Astrachan, Max, and Albert S. Cahn, (eds.): *Proceedings of Rand's Demand Prediction Conference*, Santa Monica, Calif., The Rand Corporation, January, 1963, 135 pp.

Clark, Andrew J., and Herbert Scarf: "Optimal Policies for a Multi-Echelon Inventory Problem," *Management Science*, vol. 6, No. 4, July, 1960.

Denicoff, Marvin, Joseph P. Fennell, and Henry Solomon: "Summary of a Method for Determining the Military Worth of Spare Parts," *Naval Research Logistics Quarterly*, vol. 7, No. 3, September, 1960.

Eccles, Henry E., RADM USN; *Logistics on the National Defense*, The Stackpole Company, Harrisburgh, Pa., 1959, 347 pp.

Haber, Sheldon E.: "A Comparison of Usage Data Among Aircraft Types," Logistics Research Project Serial T-174, George Washington University, Washington, September 1, 1964.

Hoffman, William H.: "An Approach to Improved Application of Economical Order Quantities," *Systems and Procedures Journal*, December, 1962.

U.S. Army, Field Manual 38-2-1: "Logistics Materiel Management Requirements," February, 1965.

U.S. Army Logistics Management Center, Defense Logistics Studies Information Exchange: *Annual Department of Defense Bibilography of Logistics Studies and Related Documents*, U.S. Army Logistics Management Center, Fort Lee, Va., January, 1969.

U.S. Congress House Committee on Post Office and Civil Service, *Report on the Use of Electronic Data Processing Equipment in the Federal Government*, Prepared by the Subcommittee on Census and Government Statistics, 86th Cong., 2d Sess., 1960.

U.S. Congress, Subcommittee on Defense Procurement, Joint Economic Committee, *Background Material on Economic Aspects of Military Procurement and Supply*, Joint Committee Print, 86th Cong., 2d Sess., 1960.

Chapter **19**

The Theory of
Inventory and Forecasting

EDITOR:

Robert G. Brown *Industry Consultant, International Business Machines Corp., White Plains, New York*

CONTENTS

This chapter provides a background in the mathematical and logical theory underlying the practical applications of inventory control systems given elsewhere in this handbook.

CONCEPTUAL FRAMEWORK OF THE INVENTORY SYSTEM

The routine day-to-day processing of inventory transactions is carried out by an inventory *control* system, which also generates the regular replenishment orders. The decisions about when to order and how much to order for each stockkeeping unit are governed by a pair of control numbers (such as an order point and an order quantity) which are from time to time revised within an inventory *management* system.

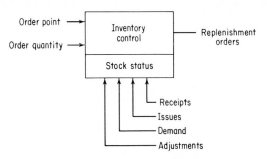

Fig. 1 Inventory control systems.

Inventory Control Systems. An inventory control system (see Fig. 1) is any means for processing transactions to maintain status files. The usual input transactions include demand, issues, and receipts which are posted to the status record:

1. Quantity on hand
2. Quantity on order
3. Backlog of unfilled demand
4. Available stock

The principle output transaction is the replenishment order.

The available stock is the sum of the quantity on hand, plus the quantity

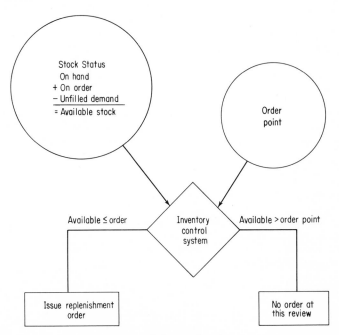

Fig. 2 Ordering decisions.

on order, less any unfilled demand. In our discussion of the theory of control and management it does not matter whether the files are kept in a manually posted ledger, on a computer, or even by the physical stock balance itself.

The decisions about *when* to order more stock, and *how much* to order, are governed by a pair of control numbers. The decision that *now* is the time to order can be determined in one of two basic ways. The first method (Fig. 2) is to compare the available stock to an order point, each time a demand transaction is posted and if the available stock is less than or equal to the order point, an order must be generated *now*. In the second basic method of ordering, replenishment orders are generated at regular intervals of time, such as every Friday or on the twenty-fifth of every month. An intermediate case uses an order point, but the total of all demand transactions is posted only at regular intervals.

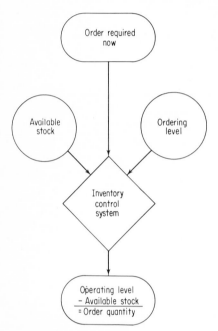

Fig. 3 How much to order.

If an order is generated *now* for either method of deciding *when,* there are two basic ways of determining the *quantity.* The simplest way is to order a preset quantity, such as 300 pieces or a two-week supply. When the normal demand quantity is for more than one piece, it is better to compute the order quantity (Fig. 3) as the difference between the available stock and a predetermined operating level. If the posting interval is long enough that the total demand posted is likely to be larger than one piece, the effect is the same. Suppose that now, when we have an opportunity to order, the available stock may be just above the order point, so that no order is actually triggered. At the next opportunity to order, the available stock may have dropped far below the order point. When the order quantity is the difference between the available stock and the operating level, any deficiency will automatically trigger an order for the difference..

These procedures can be combined, as in Fig. 4, in a variety of ways:

1. Order a preset quantity when the available stock drops to the order point.

2. Order up to the operating level when the available stock drops below the order point.

3. Order up to the operating level at regular intervals.

4. Order a preset quantity at regular intervals.

Only the last combination presents an impractical system when there is any uncertainty about demand for the item.

Inventory Management Systems. The inventory management system (Fig. 5) provides for the routine recomputation of the numerical values of the order point and either the order quantity or the operating level, as required by the control system. The principal inputs to the inventory management system are:

1. The forecast of future requirements for the item, expressed as a probability distribution

How much to order

	Preset quantity	Difference between operating level and available
Compare available with order point	(1) Simplest system, small demand continual posting	(2) Lumpy demand or long intervals between posting
Compare ordering date with calendar	(3) Not feasible	(4) Coordinate orders for many items

When to order

Fig. 4 Ordering rules.

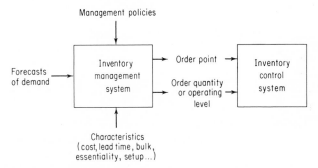

Fig. 5 Inventory management systems.

2. Measurable characteristics of the item in question, such as cost, lead time, bulk, essentiality, setup time, and so on

3. Management policies in the form of numerical values for the carrying charge, the level of customer service, and the rate of response to changes in customer demand

This information is used in appropriate formulas, representing decision rules, to evaluate the current numerical values of the order point, order quantity, and operating level. The remainder of this chapter is devoted to a discussion of the theory leading to these decision rules. The principal change in information about an item is usually the forecast of demand in the immediate future, so that the recomputation cycle of the control numbers is related to the interval for revising the item forecasts.

ORDER-QUANTITY FORMULAS

In the case where future demand is known with certainty, the basic order-quantity formula is computed by the economical order quantity (EOQ). There are a number of modifications and extensions. The following discussion covers the variants for:

1. The quantity is delivered over a finite period of time.
2. There is a premium on the space occupied by bulky items.
3. Price discounts are offered for ordering larger quantities.
4. Several related items can be ordered at one time on the same basic setup.
5. It is possible to coordinate the schedule of lots at different manufacturing levels.

The Basic EOQ.[*] Suppose that stock will be used at the known, uniform, annual rate of S units per year. We plan to replenish the stock in lots of Q units at a time. It costs A to process an order for any quantity (including direct setup costs). Each unit has a cost, for inventory valuation, of v dollars. Since demand is known, it is conceptually possible to schedule the delivery of each lot when the stock on hand has dropped to exactly zero. When the entire lot is delivered at one time, the maximum stock level is Q pieces. Thus the maximum stock level is Q just after delivery and the average working stock is $\frac{1}{2}Q$ pieces, worth $\frac{1}{2}Qv$ dollars. If we let the carrying charge be r dollars per dollar per year, the cost to carry the working stock is $\frac{1}{2}Qvr$.

The annual cost to process replenishment orders is AS/Q; hence the total annual cost (Fig. 6) that depends on the quantity ordered is $C(Q)$ where

$$C(Q) = AS/Q + Qrv/2$$

The order quantity which minimizes these total costs is the economic order quantity, EOQ, where

$$\text{EOQ} = \sqrt{2AS/rv}$$

which is the solution to $dC/dQ = 0$. The minimum total annual cost is

$$C(\text{EOQ}) = \sqrt{2ASrv}$$

SENSITIVITY: The EOQ formula is very robust. An appreciable percentage change in the value of any of the factors will increase the total annual costs by a very small percentage. Suppose we use the *apparent order quantity,* EOQ′, computed from the wrong setup cost $A' = (1 + m)A$. By direct substitution we see that

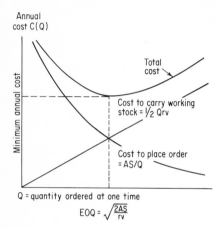

Annual cost C(Q)

Minimum annual cost

Total cost

Cost to carry working stock = ½ Qrv

Cost to place order = AS/Q

Q = quantity ordered at one time

$$\text{EOQ} = \sqrt{\tfrac{2AS}{rv}}$$

S = annualized rate of usage (units per year)
A = cost to process an order (dollars per order)
v = unit cost (dollars per unit)
r = carrying charge (dollars per dollars per year)
Q = quantity ordered at one time (units per order)

Fig. 6 Economical order quantities.

$$\text{EOQ}' = \sqrt{2(1 + m)AS/rv} = \text{EOQ}\sqrt{1 + m}$$

The actual total annual costs are

$$
\begin{aligned}
C(\text{EOQ}') &= AS/\sqrt{2(1 + m)AS/rv} + \tfrac{1}{2}rv\sqrt{2(1 + m)AS/rv} \\
&= \sqrt{ASrv/2(1 + m)} + \tfrac{1}{2}\sqrt{2(1 + m)ASrv} \\
&= \sqrt{ASrv/2}\,(1/\sqrt{1 + m} + \sqrt{1 + m})
\end{aligned}
$$

Thus the ratio of the annual costs, with the incorrect lot size, to the true minimum costs is

$$C(\text{EOQ}')/C(\text{EOQ}) = \tfrac{1}{2}(1/\sqrt{1 + m} + \sqrt{1 + m})$$

If $m = 1$ (so that the assumed setup cost is twice the correct value), EOQ′ (Fig. 7) is approximately 41 percent larger than the true EOQ, but the total annual costs increase by a factor of only 1.06, a 6 percent increase.

[*] See the complete glossary of terms at the end of this Chapter.

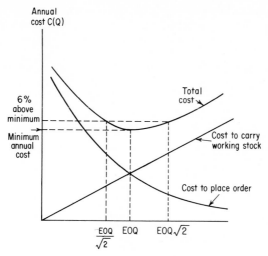

Fig. 7 Incorrect lot size.

Approximation for Tables. Because of this insensitivity, it is practical to set up tables of order quantities where the time supply ordered is the same for all items with the dollar value of annual usage in an interval from half the correct value to twice that value. The number of months that an average lot will last is

$$T = 12Q/S = 12\sqrt{2A/rSv}$$

Thus within a group of items that all have the same setup cost A, the EOQ for all items with the same annual dollar value of usage Sv will last the same number of months. Because of the robustness of the EOQ formula, it is safe to order the same number-of-months supply for all items with usage values between $0.5Sv$ and $2Sv$. A table of half a dozen different standard time supplies is usually sufficient to span an entire inventory.

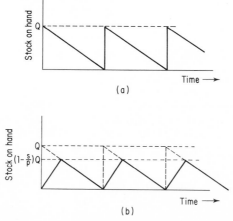

Fig. 8 Delivery rate: (a) instantaneous delivery; (b) finite delivery.

Extensions to the Basic EOQ Formula. There are several real cases where the facts do not agree with the assumptions used in deriving the EOQ formula.

FINITE DELIVERY RATE: If the entire lot is not delivered at one time (Fig. 8) but is delivered at the finite rate P (annualized to pieces per year), then the maximum stock on hand is not Q but is $(1 - S/P)Q$ because of the withdrawal of some of the earliest deliveries before the lot has been completed. Since the working stock is correspondingly lower, the quantity ordered can be increased to

$$ROQ = \sqrt{2AS/(1 - S/P)rv} = EOQ/\sqrt{1 - S/P}$$

Obviously the rate of delivery must be less than the rate of withdrawal $S < P$.

SPACE OCCUPIED: Suppose that each piece in stock occupies c cubic feet of space per unit, and there is a premium R dollars per cubic foot per year. Then the annual-cost equation has an additional term $C(Q) = AS/Q + \frac{1}{2}Q(rv + Rc)$. The order quantity that minimizes this total cost is

$$EOQ = \sqrt{2AS/(rv + Rc)}$$

QUANTITY DISCOUNTS: There are a variety of ways in which a discount in unit cost is offered by the vendor in return for larger order quantities. If a larger quantity is ordered at one time, there will be a smaller annual cost of processing the replenishment orders and a larger number of pieces in the working stock will more than offset the decrease in annual cost of processing orders. Thus there is a maximum quantity that can economically be ordered to qualify for a quantity discount.[1]

Let the discounted price be $v_1 = (1 - d)v_0$ where v_0 is the normal list price. Let Q_0 be the economical order quantity computed from the normal list price, and and $Q_1 > Q_0$ be the quantity necessary to order to qualify for the discounted price.

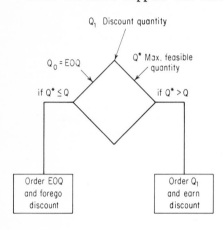

v_0 = list price (dollars per unit)

v_1 = quantity price (dollars per unit) for at least Q units

d = $1 - \frac{v_1}{v_0}$ = discount fraction

Q_0 = normal EOQ (units per order)

r = carrying charge (dollars per dollars per year)

$Q^* = \frac{2dS}{r} + (1-d)Q_0$ = maximum feasible order

Fig. 9   Quantity discounts.

The maximum quantity (Fig. 9) that one could economically order is $Q^* = 2dS/r + (1 - d)Q_0$. Therefore if $Q_1 \leq Q^*$, order Q_1 and get the lower price. But if $Q_1 > Q^*$, order Q_0 because the decrease in unit price is not sufficient to offset the higher carrying charges. This result is valid providing that $rQ_0/S < 0.1$.

MULTIPLE-ITEM FAMILIES: There may be a major setup cost A incurred for a whole family of related items (or the header cost of preparing an order for several items supplied by one vendor), and minor setup costs a_i associated with ordering the ith item in the family. All items in the family should be coordinated and ordered jointly at intervals of T months, where

$$T = 12 \sqrt{\frac{2(A + \Sigma a_i)}{r\Sigma S_i v_i}}$$

The summations of minor setups and annual dollar value of usage span all items in the family. Some items where $S_i v_i$ is a very small fraction of the total value of usage for the family can be ordered every other cycle, or every third cycle, in quantities sufficient to last until the next time that item is due to be ordered with the rest of the family. The cycle multiple for such coordinated items[2] is approximately $k_i = \sqrt{2a_i/rS_iv_i}/T$.

COORDINATED LOT SIZES FOR SUCCESSIVE MANUFACTURING LEVELS: Consider the case of machined parts which are made in lot quantities from a supply of standard castings. If the replenishment of the castings can be coordinated so that the new lot arrives just when the next machining lot is due, there can safely be a period of time when there are no castings on hand and none required

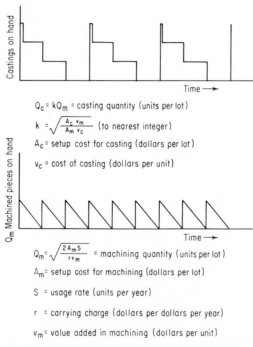

Castings on hand

Time →

$Q_c = kQ_m$ = casting quantity (units per lot)

$k = \sqrt{\dfrac{A_c\, v_m}{A_m\, v_c}}$ (to nearest integer)

A_c = setup cost for casting (dollars per lot)

v_c = cost of casting (dollars per unit)

Q_m Machined pieces on hand

Time →

$Q_m = \sqrt{\dfrac{2A_m S}{r\, v_m}}$ = machining quantity (units per lot)

A_m = setup cost for machining (dollars per lot)

S = usage rate (units per year)

r = carrying charge (dollars per dollars per year)

v_m = value added in machining (dollars per unit)

Fig. 10 Coordinated lot sizes.

(Fig. 10). In that case, the quantity to be machined at one time should be computed as an EOQ of the following form:

$$Q_m = \sqrt{\frac{2(A_c/k + A_n)s}{r(kv_c + v_m)}}$$

The castings should be ordered in lots which are multiples of the machining lot. The multiple is the postive integer closest to $k = \sqrt{A_c v_m/A_m v_c}$ where A_m several items supplied by one vendor), and minor setup costs a_i associated ing the supply of castings, v_m is the value added in machining, and v_c is the material cost of the castings.[3]

This relationship does *not* hold if the replenishment of the castings supply cannot be coordinated to arrive just as the next machining lot is scheduled. If the two manufacturing levels are not coordinated, then the machining lot quantity must be computed by the EOQ formula using total costs, including material costs.

Operating Levels. The various order-quantity formulas derived above represent the average quantity ordered at one time. If you use an inventory control system that orders a predetermined quantity whenever it is time to order, the appropriate formula can be used to determine what that quantity is.

If you use a system where the quantity ordered is the difference between the current available stock (which will be at or below the order point) and the operating level (Fig. 11), you still want the average order quantity Q to

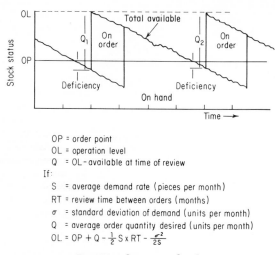

OP = order point
OL = operation level
Q = OL - available at time of review
If:
   S = average demand rate (pieces per month)
   RT = review time between orders (months)
   σ = standard deviation of demand (units per month)
   Q = average order quantity desired (units per month)
   $OL = OP + Q - \frac{1}{2} S \times RT - \frac{\sigma^2}{2S}$

Fig. 11 Operating levels.

be given by the appropriate formula. Therefore the operating level should be set at $OL = OP + Q$. The deficiency at any opportunity to order is the difference between available stock and the order point. In the case of a uniform demand rate S (pieces per unit time) and an interval between opportunities order RT (for review time, expressed in the same time unit), the average deficiency at the time an order is placed is $\frac{1}{2}S \times RT$. When the demand is variable with a standard deviation σ, the average deficiency is $z \cong \frac{1}{2}S \times RT + \sigma^2/2S$. The derivation of the last equation has not yet been published, and is valid for any demand distribution provided that the operating level is enough higher than the order point that there will be several review periods in which no order is placed.[4]

Thus the approximate expression for the operating level is $OL = OP + Q - \frac{1}{2}S \times RT - \sigma^2/2S$, where S, RT, and σ are all based on the same units of time.

FORECASTING TECHNIQUES

In any inventory there are a few items which have a high rate of usage and a high unit cost. These important items (usually designated as class A) may account for more than half the total value of usage in the inventory. These items deserve very careful management, and especially careful estimates of future usage. There are also a great many items with very low individual usage and low unit value (usually designated as class C items) which in total account for only a few percent of the total value of usage. Very little effort should be devoted to making forecasts of requirements for these class C items—the safety stock that is ample to cover all contingencies is cheaper than the effort necessary to obtain a more precise estimate. The intermediate class B items justify reasonable, but routine, effort in forecasting demand and in managing the inventory. For further discussion of the ABC inventory system, see Chapter 16.

The bulk of this section will be devoted to the statistical forecasting techniques (Fig. 12) usually appropriate for class B items. The same techniques should

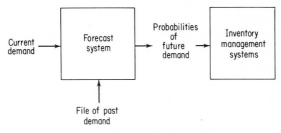

Fig. 12 Statistical forecasting.

be applied routinely to class A items as well, but the results should be screened carefully by competent management authority. Later in the section (see "Exogenous Information," p. 19-15) we shall discuss briefly how adjustments should be made to take account of available information about price changes, new products, competition, changes in the national economy, promotion and advertising plans, and similar exogenous variables.

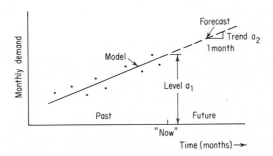

Fig. 13 Forecasting model.

Simplified procedures for obtaining the necessary forecast factors for class C items will be discussed at the end of this section.

Models and Coefficients. If one can discern a regular pattern in a history of demand, that pattern can be projected as a forecast of the expected future demand. In many basic manufacturing industries the pattern is adequately expressed, over any short interval of time t, by a linear function (Fig. 13) of time $\hat{x}_t(T) = a_1 + a_2 t$. The geometrical interpretation of these two terms is that a_1 represents the level of demand at time T when the forecast is being made, and a_2 represents the trend of demand per unit of time in the recent past that is expected to continue into the immediate future. Obviously, over any long history of demand, the numerical values of the level a_1 and the trend a_2 will depend on the time T when the forecast is prepared.

For inventories that feel the effects of consumer demand, there is frequently a significant seasonal pattern that repeats cyclicly from year to year. (There are also some cases where it may be important to consider the cyclic pattern of demand within a month, such as for accounts receivables, or by day of the week as for volume of mail received. These cases can be handled by an extension of the concepts discussed here in terms of demand patterns by month of the year, which repeat from year to year.)

There are two general methods in common use for expressing the model of the cyclic seasonal variations. The first method prepares a set of seasonal indices, with one value for each month of the year. The deseasonalized monthly demand is one-twelfth of the total annual demand, and the seasonal index (Fig. 14) represents the expected demand in a particular month as a ratio to the deseasonalized monthly demand.[5]

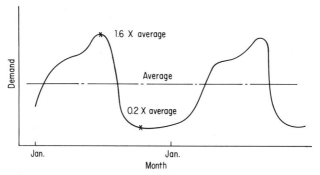

Fig. 14 Seasonal index.

Another representation if regular seasonal variation is by the Fourier series representation in terms if trigonometric functions $\sin 2p\pi t/12$ and $\cos 2p\pi t/12$, for the tth month, for $p = 1, 2, 3 \ldots$. These models are particulary well suited for modern electronic computers and for demand patterns that are reasonably well represented by sinusoidal cycles.

In either case the particular demand pattern is represented by estimates of the values for a set of seasonal coefficients, which may be either indices or the coefficients of the sinusoidal terms in a Fourier series.

In many manufacturing and wholesale applications the necessary and sufficient model for forecasting is $\hat{x}_t(T) = a_1 + a_2 t + a_3 \sin 2\pi t/12 + a_4 \cos 2\pi t/12 + a_5 \sin 4\pi t/12 + a_6 \cos 4\pi t/12$. At least some of the items in the inventory will have a trend, so that the term $a_2 t$ is necessary. There will also be some items with a seasonal cycle in demand, which require the last four terms in the model. Usually one finds that, except for retail consumer demand, four terms of the Fourier series are sufficient. Other models are possible.[6]

If there appears to be a quadratic trend, especially with seasonal swings with growing amplitude, it is sometimes helpful to take logarithms of the data (provided that the minimum value is much larger than zero) before attempting to develop the forecast model. Instead of plotting demand on a regular scale, plot it on semilog paper. If the latter graph seems to have a pattern that is easier to describe, then the computations should be done with the logarithm of demand, rather than actual demand.

Initial Estimates of the Coefficients. It is practical to use the same model for all items in the inventory. The effect of an insignificant term on the forecast is negligible when the value of the coefficient is small enough to be rejected by a statistical test of significance. Thus the forecast for each item can be computed once the values for the six coefficients $a_1, \ldots, a_6$ are known. The generally accepted method for computing estimates of these coefficients from the available history is by least squares.

LINEAR MODELS: Consider first the case of the linear $\hat{x}_t(T) = a_1 + a_2 t$. This model is appropriate when there are no significant seasonal cycles, or for deseasonalized data where the monthly pattern is to be generated by seasonal indices. To fit a linear model to a series of N past observations (N should be at least 10, for stability) proceed as follows. Form the sums Σx_j and $\Sigma j x_j$ where $j = 1$ for the oldest observation, $j = 2$ for the following observation, and so on, until $j = N$ for the most recent observation. Then the two coefficients in the model are the level $a_1 = A\Sigma x - B\Sigma j x$, and the trend $a_2 = -B\Sigma x + C\Sigma j x$. The constants in these equations are $A = 2(2N + 1)/[N(N - 1)]$, $B = 6/[N(N - 1)]$, and $C = 12/[N(N^2 - 1)]$. Note that if there are several items to be processed, and the number of months N of history is the same for all of them, the constants A, B, and C need be determined only once. The sum and the weighted sum of the past demand must, of course, be computed for each item.

SEASONAL MODELS (Fig. 14): The general procedure for fitting any model by least squares involves the solution of a set of simultaneous linear equations, which may be expressed mathematically as the inversion of a positive definite matrix. Matrix inversion is a time-consuming process, even on a computer. But if the same seasonal model is to be fitted to many different items in the inventory (letting some of the coefficients be zero if appropriate) it is possible to evaluate one matrix, corresponding to that model, invert it once, and use the inverse as a table of program constants. For the model $\hat{x}_t(T) = a_1 + a_2 t + a_3 \sin 2\pi t/12 + a_4 \cos 2\pi t/12 + a_5 \sin 4\pi t/12 + a_6 \cos 4\pi t/12$, the least-squares computation can be organized as follows:

First form six weighted sums of historical data. The six sums are based on the most recent observations of X_t, $t = 1, 2, \ldots, 36$. Use 36 months of data, to provide a reasonable stability in estimating the seasonal cycles. The time index $t = 1$ for the earliest observation, and increases to $t = 36$ for the most recent observation. These six sums are components of a column vector Σxf The column vector of estimates for the coefficients is the matrix product $a = G \times f$ where the matrix G for this model and for 36 months of history is:

0.124341	−0.005220	−0.019480	0.005220	−0.009041	0.005220
−0.005220	0.000282	0.001053	−0.000282	0.000489	−0.000282
−0.019480	0.001053	0.059485	−0.001053	0.001824	−0.001053
0.005220	−0.000282	−0.001053	0.055838	−0.000489	0.000282
−0.009041	0.000489	0.001824	−0.000489	0.056402	−0.000489
0.005220	−0.000282	−0.001053	0.000282	−0.000489	0.055838

If there are not 36 months of actual history available (such as in the case of a new product just being introduced), use the available predictions, together with the patterns of analogous products, to construct a *pseudo history* for the next 36 months based on the best estimates available, and use the process described above.

Periodic Smoothing and Forecast Revision. At convenient intervals of time the forecasts must be revised in the light of current data. The interval should be chosen with a view to the typical lead time over which the forecasts will be required. As a general rule of thumb, if it is possible, revise the forecast at least three times per lead time, but not oftener than 10 times per lead time.

Linear Models. If the forecasts are to be revised once a month, let $x(T)$ be the actual demand in the most recent month, and let $a_1(T - 1)$ and $a_2(T - 1)$ be the estimates of the level and the trend as of the end of the previous month. These coefficients were used to provide an estimate of the demand in the most

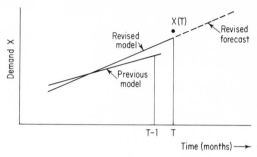

Fig. 15 Linear model.

recent month $\hat{x}_i(T) = a_1 + a_2 1$. The new estimates (Fig. 15) of the level and the trend are

$$a_1(T) = a_1(T - 1) + a_2(T - 1) + h_1[x(T) - \hat{x}_1(T)]$$
$$a_2(T) = \qquad\qquad a_2(T - 1) + h_2[\hat{x}(T) - \hat{x}_1(T)]$$

The origin of time in these forecast models is always taken to be the current month, so that a forecast as of the end of a lead time t is always $\hat{x}_i(T) = a_1 + a_2 t$.

If the model of the demand is a straight line, the slope of that line, called the "trend," is the same no matter where the origin is taken. But the intercept of the line changes as we advance the origin in successive months. In the equations for revising the coefficients, the first equation increases the level (intercept) by the amount of the trend each month, but the second equation says that the new trend is approximately equal to the previous trend. Note that the initial estimates of the coefficients in the discussion concerning linear models places the origin of time before the data used. Therefore, as part of the initialization process, simulate the smoothing process N successive times to move the origin of time to the latest available observation, before starting the actual revision process.

The last term in each equation makes an adjustment proportional to the forecast error, the difference between the current actual demand and the previous forecast of what the demand would be. The two smoothing constants are

$$h_1 = 1 - \beta^2$$
$$h_2 = (1 - \beta)^2$$

These factors are derived from a discounted least-squares model of the demand.

The discount rate β is the complement of the smoothing constant α usually asociated with exponential smoothing,[7] $\beta = 1 - \alpha$.

A great deal of work has been spent in trying to determine the "optimum" smoothing constant, to no avail. The value cannot be determined by simulation, since the sampling error in any finite time-series simulation is larger than the theoretical effect of different values of the discount rate.

For normal smoothing in most industrial applications quite satisfactory results have been obtained with $\beta^2 = 0.9$, which leads to $h_1 = 0.1$ and $h_2 = 0.00263$. Normal smoothing is appropriate when there is at least 10 months of history available to estimate the coefficients initially. A faster rate of response is sometimes warranted (such as when the initial estimates of the coefficients had been based on a limited span of history) and then one can conveniently use $\beta^2 = 0.75$, which corresponds to $h_1 = 0.25$ and $h_2 = 0.01795$.

Seasonal Models. The coefficents $a_1, \ldots, a_6$ for the seasonal model may also be revised every month in the light of new information. There are six equations, in which the first terms move the origin of time to the current month, and the last term is a smoothing correction, proportional to the forecast error.

$$
\begin{aligned}
a_1(T) &= a_1(T-1) + a_2(T-1) && + h_1e \\
a_2(T) &= a_2(T-1) && + h_2e \\
a_3(T) &= 0.86603a_3(T-1) - 0.5a_4(T-1) && + h_3e \\
a_4(T) &= 0.5a_3(T-1) + 0.86603a_4(T-1) && + h_4e \\
a_5(T) &= 0.5a_5(T-1) - 0.86603a_6(T-1) && + h_5e \\
a_6(T) &= 0.86603a_5(T-1) + 0.5a_6(T-1) && + h_6e
\end{aligned}
$$

The error $e = x(T) - \hat{x}_1(T-1)$. The values $0.86603 = \sqrt{3}/2$ and 0.5 are based on sine waves with 12 (monthly) observations per cycle (year).

It is not convenient to give a closed expression for the smoothing constants $h_1, \ldots, h_6$. Values have been computed and tabulated for normal smoothing and for a fast rate of smoothing.[8]

	Normal Smoothing	Fast Smoothing
h_1	0.03519	0.06742
h_2	0.0003256	0.001245
h_3	0.002104	0.008039
h_4	0.03508	0.06663
h_5	0.002851	0.01085
h_6	0.03499	0.06595

In the cases of both the linear and seasonal models, this method of smoothing is called "adaptive smoothing," an extension of exponential smoothing. The formulas for revising the estimates of the model coefficients are derived[9] from a criterion of discounted least squares, which minimizes the sum of the squared residuals, weighted by a geometrically decreasing factor β^j.

The way in which the coefficients were computed for the seasonal model initially put the origin of time at the beginning of the historical period. One way of moving the origin to the most recent observation, where it is assumed to be for the routine forecast revision, is to simulate the smoothing process, month by month, throughout the 36 months.

Exogenous Information. The forecast models discussed above simply extrapolate the linear or seasonal pattern that has been apparent in past demand. Frequently someone in the organization will have information (Fig. 16) about planned promotions and advertising campaigns, announcements of price changes, competitive actions and strikes, changes in the level of disposable income, and other data that in some way may be relevant to changes in the pattern of item demand. It is appropriate to report a summary of the detailed forecasts, for example, accumulated by product line or by district, to be reviewed in the light of this semiquantitative, badly organized, exogenous data. A skilled person, with considerable experience, will be able to suggest percentage changes to some of the aggregate forecasts. The computer system should be capable of prorating these changes to the forecasts of each item in the corresponding aggregate. Keep track of the errors (see next paragraph) both in the routine statistical forecast and as a result of the changes introduced from the reviewers.

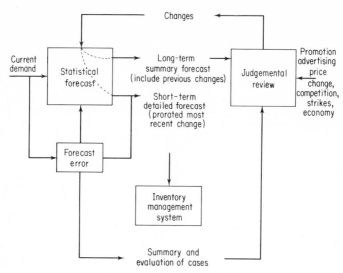

Fig. 16 Exogenous models.

Report these errors back to the people making changes, to encourage further changes that improve the forecasts and to discourage changes that have little effect or an adverse effect on the accuracy.

Forecast Errors. No forecast will be reliably perfect. It is important to have an estimate of the distribution of errors (Fig. 17) in the forecast. Some items are easier to forecast than others, and a smaller margin for error is required. Over the past 10 years most of the really significant improvements in inventory management can be ascribed to a better balance of stocks, based on estimates of the error distribution. Some items that are hard to forecast require larger safety stocks to assure reasonable service; but other items can safely have smaller stocks, without jeopardizing the level of service. The net effect is an overall reduction in investment and an improvement in customer service. Note that the important concept is the distribution of forecast errors, rather than the distribution of demand. If the forecasts are revised at least three times per lead time, then the distribution of forecast errors can be approximated safely by the normal distribution (Fig. 18). In retail inventories, where lead times are

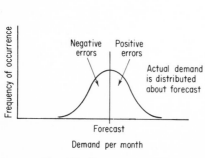

Fig. 17 Forecast errors.

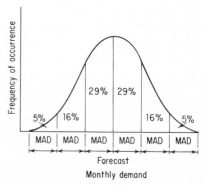

Fig. 18 Normal distribution.

short and customer demand tends to be Poisson, it may be necessary to conduct a special study to determine what the distribution of forecast errors is.

MEAN ABSOLUTE DEVIATION: The mean absolute deviation (MAD) is a measure of the scatter of the forecast errors, the average of the absolute magnitudes of the errors. Initially it is estimated (Fig. 19) from the average of the magni-

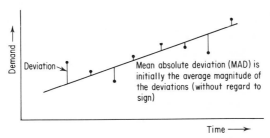

Fig. 19   Mean absolute deviation.

tudes of the residuals. The differences between the historical data and the forecast model are generated from the initial estimates of the coefficients.

In each period, when you revise the forecast-model coefficients, the first step is to compute the forecast error $e(T) = x(T) - \hat{x}_1(T-1)$. The new value of the mean absolute deviation is obtained by exponential smoothing of the absolute values of these errors. $\mathrm{MAD}(T) = 0.1|e(T)| + 0.9\ \mathrm{MAD}\ (T-1)$.

In some highly seasonal patterns the proper measure of variability appears to be the ratio of the absolute error to the current forecast, rather than simply the error itself. That is, in peak periods demand may vary around the forecast by ±10 percent, and in the slow periods the demand is also within ±10 percent of the forecast. But the quantity that corresponds to ±10 percent can be quite different in the two periods of the year.

It is common to find in any inventory that there is a consistent relationship between the mean absolute deviation and the average level of demand. To find this relationship in your inventory, prepare a graph on log-log paper (see Fig. 20). One axis represents the average level of demand (a_1 in the model) and the other axis represents the mean absolute deviation. Plot one point for each item analyzed, or at least for a large enough sample to span the en-

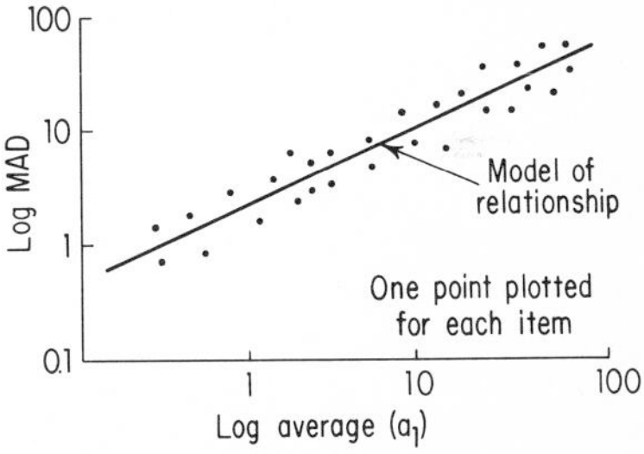

Fig. 20   Relationship between MAD and average level of demand.

tire inventory. You should find that the points tend to cluster around a straight line.

This line may be used to estimate the initial value of the mean absolute deviation for a new item, for which there is no past history, when you have to start with a subjective prediction of the average rate of usage.

STANDARD DEVIATION: Most of the theoretical work on safety stocks is based on the standard deviation of the forecast errors over the replenishment lead time. The mean absolute deviation is a measure of the scatter of errors on a monthly basis. The standard deviation, used as a basis for safety stocks is $\sigma = 1.25(0.659 + 0.341L)\mathrm{MAD}$. The lead time L is measured in multiples of the forecast revision interval, and the factor 1.25 converts the mean absolute deviation to the standard deviation in a normal distribution. The factor in parentheses is an empirical approximation to a number of theoretical functions that relate the standard deviation over a lead time to the standard deviation in one month. Note that because of the serial correlation introduced by the forecasting process, successive forecast errors cannot be considered to be statistically independent, and the standard deviation does *not* increase as the square root of the lead time.

TRACKING SIGNALS: A formal computing system will calculate bad forecasts as cheerfully as it will calculate good ones. Therefore it is necessary to build in some sort of tracking signal to detect the possibility of a consistent bias in the forecasts and report the information to someone who can determine whether the pattern of demand for that item has changed significantly, and if so, how. There are two methods for measuring bias in common use. One depends on the cumulative sum of the errors (cusums), taking account of the algebraic sign. The other depends on the exponentially smoothed average errors.

1. *Cusums.*[10] If the average error is zero, the forecasts are unbiased, and the sum of the errors (Fig. 21) will tend to vary around zero. If there is

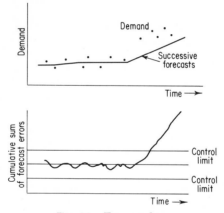

Fig. 21 Forecast bias.

a consistent bias to the forecasts, then the errors will tend to have the same sign for several successive months, and the sum will tend to grow. If the sum grows to exceed (in either direction) about five or six times the mean absolute deviation, that can be taken as a sign that the pattern of demand should be investigated. There has been considerable theoretical work done on determining the significant limits for specified detection probabilities with random demand. In practice it has been found best to adjust the limits empirically. If too many items are being reported out, set the multiple a little larger. If there are not enough items being detected early enough, make the limits narrower. Woodward and Goldsmith develop a more elaborate V mask, which is being used experimentally with some success in a few organizations.

2. *Smoothed Error.*[11] The cumulative sum remembers large errors forever. Therefore Trigg has proposed that the errors, with algebraic sign, be exponentially smoothed: $z(t) = 0.9z(t-1) + 0.1e(t)$, $z(o) = 0$. Then 5 percent detection limits appear to be about 0.2 to 0.4 times the mean absolute deviation. Again, there has been some theoretical work done on the distribution of the

smoothed error, under somewhat artificial assumption. In practice one can vary the constant to have a sufficient, but not unmanageable, number of items to investigate each month.

Replenishment Lead Times. The replenishment lead time is an interval of time that begins at the date when a transaction is posted to the inventory status that triggers a replenishment order. The lead time ends on the date when the corresponding receipt is posted. If the records can be posted only at intervals of some review time, the factor L used in computing the standard deviation of forecast errors must include the replenishment lead time plus the ordering review time, since there is no opportunity to order between posting reviews. In the equations, L is expressed in multiples of the forecast-review interval, which may not be the same length as the order-review interval.

The lead times may vary. If the variation is regular (e.g., seasonal), then use the lead time appropriate to the immediate future—how long will it take the next order placed to arrive? Sometimes the variation is unpredictable. If lead times vary at random, and the variations are statistically independent of the variation in the rate of demand, then the effect is to increase the standard deviation used in computing the safety stocks. Let $\hat{x}$, σ_x^2 be the mean and variance of the demand during one month, and $\hat{t}$, σ_t^2 be the mean and variance of the lead time, in months. Then the mean demand in the lead time is $\hat{x}\hat{t}$, and the variance of the demand during a lead time is $\sigma^2 = \sigma_x\sigma_t + \hat{t}\sigma_x^2 + \hat{x}\sigma_t^2$.

However, in most actual applications, when the variability of the lead time is large enough to be significant, there is some assignable cause. Analyze your information and review the data with the vendor (or other source of supply). Usually the source of the variation can be found and eliminated, or reduced to the point where the variability is insignificant. Elimination of the variability is much more productive than the theoretical increase in the standard deviation to take account of it, because (1) the theoretical model may be inappropriate to the real model of variation, and (2) when variability is reduced, the average is usually reduced as well.

Forecasts for Class C Items. For approximately half of the items in the inventory, those with the lowest usage, it is generally not warranted to go to the effort of analyzing the forecast model and estimating coefficients to the degree described above for class A and class B items. The usage is so low that on the one hand no pattern, other than the average rate, can be discerned, and on the other hand, the dollar value of usage for all the class C items combined is only a few percent of the total value.

For these items it is usually adequate to revise the forecast once a year or so, on the basis of the average demand during the past year. The mean absolute deviation should be based on the general relationship found between the average demand and the mean absolute deviation for all items in the inventory.

Safety Stocks and Order Points. The order point is the sum of two terms (Fig. 22): (1) the forecast of expected demand during the lead time and (2) the safety stock. The forecast model is evaluated for each month during the next replenishment lead time plus one review period, and the results summed. If the lead time, including the review period, is not an integral number of months, the forecast for the last month in the period can be appropriately prorated.

The second term in the order point is the safety stock, which is computed as the product of safety factor and the standard deviation of the forecast errors over the relevant lead time. The following discussion is devoted to the development of the theoretical basis for computing the safety factor k.

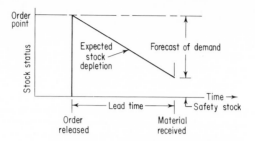

Forecast = sum of forecasts for each month in lead time
+ Safety stock = (safety factor) X (standard deviation over lead time)
                = Order point

Fig. 22 Safety stocks and order points.

Measures of Service. The demand during the next lead time will be a sample from a probability distribution. The mean of the distribution is the forecast of expected demand during the replenishment lead time plus inventory control review period. The standard deviation of the distribution is $\sigma = 1.25\text{MAD}(0.659 + 0.341L)$, where L is the number of forecast-review intervals in the total lead time. Provided that the lead time L is at least three times as long as the interval between forecast revisions, the form of the distribution can be approximated satisfactorily by the normal distribution (Fig. 23).

The order point defines a critical point within the range of that distribution; it exceeds the mean by the amount of the safety stock $k\sigma$ (the safety factor is k). The significance of this critical point is this: If the next sample drawn from the distribution of future demand is below that critical point, there will be some stock left on hand by the time the next order arrives. If the sample is above that critical point, there will be a shortage. The probability that there will be a shortage, and its expected size, can be computed for any safety stock. Usually, of course, one specifies the probability and computes the required safety stock from it.

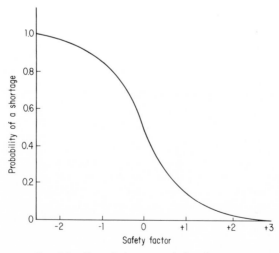

Fig. 23 Cumulative normal distribution.

PROBABILITY OF A SHORTAGE: Let

$$p(x) = \frac{1}{\sqrt{2\pi}\sigma} e^{-(x-\mu)^2/2\sigma^2}$$

be the normal probability density function, where μ is the mean and σ^2 is the variance. Then

$$F(k) = \int_{\mu+k\sigma}^{\infty} p(x)\, dx$$

is the probability that a shortage will occur, if the safety factor used in computing the safety stock is k. If total annual usage is S pieces per year, and the stock is replenished in lots that average Q pieces per lot, then the expected number of shortage occurrences per year is $SF(k)/Q$, since there are S/Q opportunities for a shortage and a chance $F(k)$ at each opportunity.

In manufacturing operations it is frequently possible to expedite a reasonable number of orders and thus avert a potential shortage. Suppose that a shop can expedite 200 orders in any month, if those orders would otherwise be so late as to be likely to cause a shortage. (This assumes that there is some mechanism in the inventory control system that can detect demand that is significantly higher than was expected when the order was released, and that can report the critical items to the shop.) If there are 10,000 items in the inventory, the average number of shortages per item per year is $200 \times 12/10{,}000 = 0.24$. The minimum total number of potential shortages to be expedited will be achieved if the safety factor for each item is computed to satisfy $S_i F(k_i)/Q_i = 0.24$, or the probability of a shortage is $F(k_i) = 0.24 Q_i/S_i$. Thus for an item ordered every 2 months $Q/S = \frac{1}{6}$, $F(k) = |0.04$, and the safety factor $k = 1.75$ (from a table of the normal distribution). An item ordered once a year would require $F(k) = 0.24$, or a safety factor $k = 0.70$.

It is clear that high-value items that are ordered frequently will have a lower probability of a shortage, and hence a higher safety factor. Low-value items that are ordered occasionally in large lots will have a higher probability of a shortage per order cycle, and a correspondingly lower safety factor.

EXPECTED QUANTITY SHORT: The partial-expectation function[12]

$$E(k) = \int_{\mu}^{\infty} (t-k)p(t)\, dt$$

can be used to determine the average quantity short. If the safety is k, the expected shortage is $\sigma E(k)$. The total value of demand not satisfied immediately from stock on hand during one year is $\sigma v E(k)S/Q$. The total demand is S. If it is desired to meet a fraction P of the demand from stock on hand, then $\sigma E(k)S/Q = (1-P)S$, or the safety factor is computed to satisfy $E(k_i) = (1-P)Q_i/\sigma_i$. This basis for selecting the safety factors will distribute the safety stock somewhat differently among items in the inventory. For a more complete discussion of several alternative logical bases for computing the safety factor, see Prichard.[13]

Table 1 give values of the probability $F(k)$ and the partial expectation $E(k)$ corresponding to values of the safety factor k.[14]

BACK ORDERS AND LOST DEMAND: In the manufacturing and wholesaling environment, it is quite common to back-order the demand that cannot be filled immediately from stock, so that the demand will be filled as soon as the next shipment arrives. In that case the mathematical theory treats the back order as a negative

TABLE 1   Values of the Safety Factor, Probability of a Shortage, Partial Expectation, and Their Ratio from the Normal Distribution

Safety factor, K	Probability, $F(K)$	Partial expectation, $E(K)$	Ratio, $T(K)$
0.0	0.5000	0.3989	0.7979
0.1	0.4602	0.3509	0.7626
0.2	0.4207	0.3069	0.7294
0.3	0.3821	0.2668	0.6982
0.4	0.3446	0.2304	0.6688
0.5	0.3085	0.1978	0.6411
0.6	0.2743	0.1687	0.6150
0.7	0.2420	0.1429	0.5905
0.8	0.2119	0.1202	0.5674
0.9	0.1841	0.1004	0.5456
1.0	0.1587	0.0833	0.5251
1.1	0.1357	0.0686	0.5058
1.2	0.1151	0.0561	0.4875
1.3	0.0968	0.0455	0.4703
1.4	0.0808	0.0367	0.4541
1.5	0.0668	0.0293	0.4387
1.6	0.0548	0.0232	0.4241
1.7	0.0446	0.0183	0.4104
1.8	0.0359	0.0143	0.3973
1.9	0.0287	0.0111	0.3849
2.0	0.0228	0.0085	0.3732
2.1	0.0179	0.0065	0.3621
2.2	0.0139	0.0049	0.3515
2.3	0.0107	0.0037	0.3415
2.4	0.0082	0.0027	0.3318
2.5	0.0062	0.0020	0.3227
2.6	0.0047	0.0015	0.3141
2.7	0.0035	0.0011	0.3057
2.8	0.0026	0.0008	0.2978
2.9	0.0019	0.0005	0.2905
3.0	0.0016	0.0004	0.2830

stock on hand, and the average safety stock (the average of the quantities on hand when a replenishment shipment is received) is simply $k\sigma$.

In retail stores, and some other applications, no record is kept of demand that cannot be filled immediately. Shortages represent lost demand, and the minimum stock on hand at the time of receipt is the actual stock, which can only be zero or positive. In these cases, the investment in safety stock is $\sigma[k + E(k)]$, larger by the amount of demand that was not satisfied.

Interaction between Safety Stock and Working Stock.   When the standard deviation of forecast errors is large compared with the normal order quantity, it is possible to give the desired level of service at lower cost by increasing the order quantity, and hence the working stock, to get a reduction in the annual cost of ordering and a reduction in the average investment in safety stock.

Let the service policy be that a fraction P of the demand is to be met from stock on hand, and demand that cannot be filled immediately will be back-ordered. Find a dummy safety factor from Table 1 that satisfies

$$F(k) = 2(1 - P)$$

and get the corresponding value of the ratio $E(k)/F(k) = T(k)$.

If $P = 0.96$ (4 percent of demand may be back-ordered), $F(k) = 2(0.04)$ $= 0.08$, which corresponds to $k = 1.40$. $E(1.40) = 0.037$, and $T(1.40) = 0.46$. Next compute the modified order quantity:

$$Q = \sigma T(k) + \sqrt{\sigma^2 T^2(k) + 2AS/rv}$$

This quantity is larger than the conventional EOQ, depending upon the size of the standard deviation σ and the desired level of service that determines $T(k)$. Finally compute the safety factor k to satisfy $E(k) = (1 - P)Q/\sigma$. Since the order quantity Q is larger than an EOQ, the partial expectation is larger, which results in a correspondingly smaller value of the safety factor.[15] This correction is not warranted except in cases where the standard deviation of the forecast errors is more than three times as large as the conventional order quantity.

ALLOCATION

Frequently it is necessary in an inventory control system to divide a lot into several equitable sublots. A production batch of paint or cereals may be allocated to a variety of package types. A manufacturing lot of grinding wheels may be allocated among several field warehouses. The total capacity of a truck-load may be allocated among several different items that are being shipped to the same destination. In contrast to the order-quantity formulas developed earlier, the required quantities here must be computed subject to the restriction that the totals of several quantities add up to a specified total.

Equal Runout Time. If the requirements for each of the items are reasonably well known, with little uncertainty, the proper allocation would be quantities q_i for the ith item such that the resulting available stock (including what is already on hand and on order) will last the same length of time for all items. That makes it possible to defer as long as possible the next replenishment of stock.

Let I_i be the available stock of the ith item, before the allocation, S_i be the rate of usage (for example, in pieces per year), and Q be the total amount to be allocated. The time that the resulting stock will last is $T = (Q + \Sigma I_i)/\Sigma S_i$. Since the available stock for each item must last the same length of time, $q_i = S_i T - I_i$, provided this quantity is not negative. If the present available stock is too large, omit that item from the computations, find a new runout time T for the remaining set, and recompute the new quantities q_i.

Minimum Remnant Stocks. When the individual item demands are uncertain, then some item will run out of its stock before the rest do. When any item runs short, it is necessary to obtain a supply to replenish that stock. When the first item is replenished, the other items will have some stock left on hand; this stock is called "remnant stock." The condition for minimizing the total remnant stock in the system is that the probability that a given item is the first one to require replenishment be proportional to the fraction of the total demand contributed by that item (or warehouse location).

The allocation quantities are computed so as to make the resulting available stock last different lengths of time for different items. We do so by using usage rates larger than the average. The apparent usage rate for the ith item will be $x'_i = \hat{x}_i + k_i \sigma_i$ where $\hat{x}_i$ is the average rate of usage, and σ_i is the standard deviation. The factors k_i are computed to satisfy the probability equation $F(k_i) = 0.62\hat{x}_i/\Sigma\hat{x}_i$. That is, the probability F is proportional to the fraction of total demand in the ith item; the constant 0.62 is a reasonably robust approximation to the theoretically true value.[16]

First compute the ratio of the demand for each item to the total demand for all items involved in the allocation. Then find the factors k_i that give a probability of runout equal to 0.62 times the item's fraction. The quantity to devote to the ith item is provisionally $q_i = \hat{x}_i T + (0.824 + 0.426T)k_i\Delta_i - I_i$, where Δ_i is the mean absolute deviation (the numerical constants come from the relationship of the standard deviation to various time intervals). By simple algebra we get the interval

$$T = \frac{Q + \Sigma I_i - 0.824\Sigma k_i\Delta_i}{\Sigma\hat{x}_i + 0.426k_i\Delta_i}$$

If none of the quantities is negative, the allocation is complete. If this computation appears to allocate a negative quantity to some item, because of a high available stock already, omit that item from the group and repeat the computations.

Reduced Quantities to Meet Capacity. A related allocation problem arises in the case where quantities may be determined for each of several items, on the basis of their own characteristics, but the total quantity exceeds some available capacity. A common example is the case where the shop capacity is not sufficient to accommodate EOQs (with appropriate modifications) for all the items that have to be made in one week.

Let Q_i be the order quantity desired for the ith item, and the direct manufacturing time be h_i hours per piece. The annual usage is S_i, and the unit cost (for inventory-valuation purposes) is v_i. Compute a multiplier factor

$$\lambda = \frac{H + \Sigma Q_i h_i}{\Sigma S_i h_i^2/v_i}$$

where H is the total number of hours of work to be taken out of the schedule. The reduction for the ith item is $y_i = \lambda S_i h_i/v_i - Q_i$. If all these quantities are positive, the reductions are feasible. If this computation leads to a negative reduction for some item, there will be at least one other item where the reduction is larger than the original lot, which is obviously not feasible. Reduce that lot to the minimum feasible lot, take credit for the number of hours saved, and repeat the computations with a smaller number of candidates.

AGGREGATE MEASURES

In the formulas for the order quantities there appeared the factor r which is management's carrying charge on investment tied up in working stocks. In the safety-stock formulas there appeared a factor P for the fraction of demand that is to be filled from stock on hand. We shall now turn our attention to the problem of getting a meaningful specification of numerical values for these management policy variables.

Exchange Curves. If one were to use a large value for the carrying charge r, it would appear expensive to carry working stock, so that the EOQ formula, and any of its extensions, would tend to order more frequently in smaller quantities. The result (Fig. 24) would be that the company would have a small investment in working stock, but a fairly high annual expense of processing replenishment orders. In contrast, if a low value were used for the carrying charge, there would be a high investment in working stocks, but a lower annual cost of processing replenishment orders. For each of several values of the carrying charge r one could compute the total investment in working stock for all items, and the total annual expense of processing replenishment orders. One

Fig. 24   Exchange curve.

point could be plotted for each case.   These points would lie along a smooth curve, the "exchange curve."

Similarly, suppose management wanted to fill a high fraction of demand from stock on hand.   There would be a large investment in safety stocks, but a low expected value for the demand that had to be back-ordered.   For a lower specification of the service percentage, the safety stocks would be lower, at the cost of a larger amount of demand back-ordered.   Again, one could compute the total investment and the total value of shortage for each of several possible specifications of demand, and plot them along a smooth exchange curve.

In each of these cases we have an exchange curve that specifies the possible trade-offs available to management, where an additional capital investment in stocks can gain some reduction in operating expense or effort.

WORKING STOCK VERSUS SETUP COSTS: If the order quantity for the ith item is $Q_i = Q_i(r)$, and the unit cost for inventory valuation is v_i, then the average working stock is $\frac{1}{2}Q_i v_i$, and the total investment in working stock for all items is $\frac{1}{2}\Sigma Q_i v_i = Qv(r)$.   If the ith item is used at the rate of S_i pieces per year, and the cost of processing one replenishment order (including machine setups) is A_i, then the annual expense of processing all the replenishment orders is $\Sigma A_i S_i / Q_i = C(r)$.   A series of values for $Qv(r)$ and $C(r)$ for different values of the carrying charge enable one to plot the exchange curve.   Management can usually find the place on the curve where the trade-off between capital investment and operating cost is most attractive.   That point determines the appropriate value to use for the carrying charge.   The exercise should be repeated, and a new decision taken, about once a year, or whenever there appears to be a significant change in the economic incentives on the plant.

SAFETY STOCK VERSUS SHORTAGES   In the case that demand which arrives during a shortage is back-ordered, the value of the safety stock is $v_i k_i \sigma_i$, where $k = k(P)$ is the safety factor and σ is the standard deviation of the forecast errors over the appropriate lead-time period.   The expected number of item shortages per year is $S_i F(k_i) / Q_i$.   Hence for each of several reasonable values of the service policy P one can compute the total investment in safety stock $I(P) = \Sigma v_i k_i \sigma_i$ and the total number of shortages $Z(P) = \Sigma S_i F(k_i) / Q_i$.   These values can be plotted to form the exchange curve that shows management clearly how much has to be invested to achieve a given level of service.   The specified policy should be reviewed annually, or whenever there is a significant change in the degree of competition.

Evaluation. The estimates for the points along these exchange curves can sometimes be obtained by making use of the lognormal distribution of usage rates in any inventory; it is possible to handle more general situations by means of a stratified sample; and for most accurate investigations, the entire inventory should be enumerated on a computer.

LOGNORMAL MODELS:[17] In any homogeneous inventory, the distribution of usage rates Sv (in dollars per year) can be adequately described by a lognormal distribution (Fig. 25). The mean of the distribution is the average dollar sales

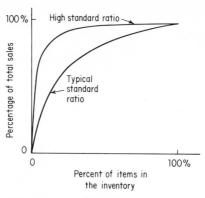

Fig. 25   Distribution of usage rates.

value per item, and the dispersion can be measured by the *standard ratio*. The standard ratio tends to be characteristic of entire industries—consumer goods usually have a low standard ratio, near 3; general manufactured goods have a standard ratio of about 10; and highly technological industries, such as computer manufacturers and airframe manufacturers, may have a standard ratio as high as 25. The standard ratio is designated by ρ (rho), and for theoretical computations one uses the parameter $\sigma = \ln \rho$ (natural logarithm). In practice what is needed is a correction factor $J = \exp (\ln^2 \rho/2)$.

The average value of any power of the dollar-usage rate can be estimated simply from that power of the average dollar, multiplied by a power of the correction factor: $\overline{(Sv)^k} = \overline{Sv}^k J^{k(k-1)}$. This result is particularly helpful for estimating consequences of using the EOQ formula, where the dollar value of an order $Qv = \sqrt{2ASv/r}$ is proportional to the square root of the dollar value of usage. Hence the sum of the working stocks for N items would be

$$N \sqrt{\frac{2A}{r}} \sqrt{\overline{Sv}} \, J^{1/2(-1/2)}$$

The disadvantage of this method of estimating is that it is impractical to take account of limitations on the maximum and minimum order quantities, or the extensions to the formula required because of quantity discounts, finite delivery rates, and so on.

STRATIFIED SAMPLES: Make a listing of all items in the inventory, ranked according to the dollar value of a year's usage. This distribution by value will have adjacent items with similar usage values. Quite useful estimates of the aggregate consequences of any policy can be estimated by dividing the inventory into a dozen or so ranges of usage value. Within each interval all items can be analyzed in terms of an item with the average usage value. The total consequences of that group will then be the value of stock, number of shortages, and cost of processing replenishment orders, for the average item, multiplied by the number of items in the group. These analyses are more accurate than the lognormal models, since it is possible to take account of limiting policies that affect items with very high sales values and with very low sales values.

COMPUTER ENUMERATION: For detailed analysis, now that computers are generally available, it is usually worthwhile to write a simple program that computes the safety stock, working stock, and total investment; the number of shortages and the expected value of the back-ordered demand; and the annual cost of processing replenishment orders. The necessary item characteristics have to be on a computer file anyhow for the inventory management system. This file can be processed through the analysis program to get quite reliable estimates of the exchange curves as a function of the policy variables, taking proper account of all the limitations imposed, item by item.

Comparative evaluations have been made that show that the stratified sample usually produces aggregate estimates within about 10 percent of the results of those obtained by a complete enumeration.

LIST OF SYMBOLS

A	Cost to process and order, including setup cost (dollars/lot)
a_i	Setup cost among items in a family (dollars/lot)
a_i	Coefficients in forecast model (pieces/time)
c	Bulk (cubic feet/piece)
d	Discount (dimensionless)
$e(T)$	Forecast error (pieces/unit time)
$E(k)$	Partial-expectation function (dimensionless)
EOQ	Economical order quantity (pieces)
f	Vector of fitting functions (time)
$F(k)$	Probability of a shortage (dimensionless)
g	Data vector (pieces/time)
G	Covariance matrix (dimensionless)
h_1, h_2	Smoothing constants (dimensionless)
h_i	Work load (hours/piece)
H	Total number of hours (hours)
I_i	Available inventory (pieces)
J	($= \exp \ln^2 \rho /2$) Correction factor (dimensionless)
k	Safety factor (dimensionless)
L	Lead time (dimensionless)
m	Fractional change (dimensionless)
MAD	Mean absolute deviation (pieces/unit time)
N	Number of past observations (dimensionless)
OL	Operating level (pieces)
OP	Order point (pieces)
P	Annualized production rate (pieces/year)
P	Fraction of demand filled from stock (dimensionless)
$p(x)$	Probability density function (dimensionless)
Q	Order quantity (pieces/lot)
q_i	Quantity allocated to ith item (pieces/lot)
r	Inventory carrying charge (dollars/dollar/year)
ROQ	"Rate" order quantity (pieces/lot)
R	Premium charge on space (dollars/cubic foot/year)

RT   Review time (time)
S   Annualized usage rate (pieces/yr)
t   Short interval of time
$T(k)$ Ratio of partial expectation to probability (dimensionless)
T   Time a lot lasts (months/lot)
v   Unit cost for inventory valuation (dollars/piece)
$x(T)$ Demand observed at time T (pieces/unit time)
$\hat{x}_t(T)$ Forecast made at time T for t periods ahead (pieces/unit time)
$z(T)$ Smoothed error (pieces/unit time)

α Smoothing constant of exponential smoothing
β Discount rate ($= 1 - \alpha$)
Δ Mean absolute deviation (pieces/unit time)
μ Mean of a distribution
ρ Standard ratio of a lognormal distribution
σ Standard deviation (pieces/lead time)

REFERENCES

1. For a more extended theoretical treatment, see R. G. Brown, *Decision Rules for Inventory Management*, Holt, Rinehart and Winston, Inc., New York, 1967, especially chap. 15. The IBM IMPACT system has developed efficient computation routines for evaluating alternative strategies.
2. *Ibid.*, chap. 5.
3. *Ibid.*, chap. 6.
4. See E. Naddor, *Inventory Systems*, John Wiley & Sons, Inc., New York, 1966, chap. 15; and K. J. Arrow, *et al.. Studies in the Mathematical Theory of Inventory and Production*, Stanford University Press, Stanford, Calif., 1958, chaps. 8 and 9.
5. R. G. Brown, in *Statistical Forecasting for Inventory Control*, McGraw-Hill Book Company, New York, 1959, chap. 5, uses a base series which is in effect the reciprocal of the seasonal index described here. There is an inherent instability in a base series defined that way for demand patterns with low periods when the demand fluctuates near zero. The ratio of demand for a particular month to the deseasonalized average is much less sensitive to these fluctuations.
6. See R. G. Brown, *Smoothing, Forecasting, and Prediction*, Prentice-Hall Inc., Englewood Cliffs, N.J., 1963, chaps. 4 and 11.
7. Brown, *Statistical Forecasting for Inventory Control* and *Smoothing, Forecasting, and Prediction*.
8. Brown, *Decision Rules for Inventory Management*, chap. 11, gives the mathematics for computing values for other models.
9. Brown, *Smoothing, Forecasting, and Prediction*.
10. *Ibid.*, pp. 281–290; and R. H. Woodward and P. L. Goldsmith, *Cumulative Sum Techniques*, Oliver & Boyd Ltd., London, 1964.
11. D. W. Trigg, "Monitoring a Forecasting System," *Operational Research Quarterly*, vol. 15, no. 3, pp. 271–274, September, 1964.
12. See Brown, *Smoothing, Forecasting, and Prediction*.
13. J. W. Prichard and R. H. Eagle, *Modern Inventory Management*, John Wiley & Sons, Inc., New York, 1965, chap. 9. See also Brown, *Decision Rules for Inventory Management*, chaps. 13 and 17.
14. For more extensive tables, see Brown, *Decision Rules for Inventory Management*, chap. 8.
15. The derivation is given in *ibid.*, chap. 16.
16. See *ibid.*, chap. 20.
17. Brown, *Statistical Forecasting for Inventory Control*.

Systems for Production and Inventory Control

Chapter **20**

Systems Analysis and Design

EDITOR:

George Trollope *Director of Information Services, U.S. Electrical Motors, Milford, Connecticut*

CONTRIBUTORS:

Jay Ellison *Supervisor, Systems Analysis, McDonnell Douglas Corporation, St. Louis, Missouri*

Stuart Farrell *Director of Management Information Systems, Maritz, Inc., St. Louis, Missouri*

Prof. Donald W. Fogarty *Department of Industrial Engineering, Saint Louis University, St. Louis, Missouri*

Irwin Jarett, Ph.D. *Chairman, Department of Accounting, Southern Illinois University, Edwardsville, Illinois*

CONTENTS

"**S**ystems" is the function of analyzing, designing, and implementing methods to accomplish management objectives. Given managements' objectives, systems determines how to accomplish these objectives, systems designs the means to carry out the functions of management.

The primary function of a systems staff is the analysis, design, and implementation of new and improved methods of operation. Systems staffs may also be responsible for all or part of the following duties:

1. Planning and charting organization structure
2. Maintenance of policy and/or procedure manuals
3. Design and control of forms
4. Control of records, records storage, disposal, and security
5. Selection and standardization of office equipment
6. Layout of office space
7. Research and education on new techniques and equipment

The Systems Evolution. The formal development and utilization of systems have rapidly increased in recent years. Most large organizations today have staff personnel responsible for performing systems functions. Many smaller organizations now have systems analysts or employ consulting services for this purpose.

Since the 1940s rising clerical costs have made it imperative that businesses study their clerical procedures to control costs. New techniques were applied to simplify the work and standardize the procedures. Then, in the 1950s, there was increased evidence of the data processing revolution which mechanized clerical procedures. The first phase of the data processing revolution was the use of punched-card equipment to process data faster and more economically. Punched-card systems were installed to process large volumes of accounting transactions and produce reports for the use of operating personnel. The second phase, which we are in today, is the use of electronic computers. The early computers were also put to work processing data faster and more economically. However, as more experience is gained and new generations of computers are created, computers are being utilized in the system to control the operations. The information developed in the processing of data is used for management control purposes. Voluminous reports are replaced by exception reports which are produced only as required by management.

Impact of the Systems Concept. Computers have been a key factor in the development of the *total-systems concept*. The total-systems concept is an approach which considers the entire organization as a system and provides accurate and timely data for decision making. Often these total systems are developed by integrating subsystems into one operating system. The total-systems concept does not always require the use of computers. Total systems can be developed using manual methods. The computer has provided the *tool* for efficiently performing operations on the great masses of data inherent in large organizations. Also, computerization is not necessarily cheaper, but for a company to remain competitive it may be a necessity and should be considered as a tool for making profit rather than a tool for reducing costs.

Management-information Systems. Management-information systems is another recent development which is growing in importance. Essentially it is the recognition that information is developed primarily for the use of management. In a management-information system the basic operating data are made available not only for operating control and management control, but also for the planning of the business strategy. To accomplish this, information is organized by means of a "data base." Rather than having basic elements of information scattered throughout several application areas, the basic information is maintained only at one place in the data base. Any application requiring the use of this data has access to the data base.

Another facet of management-information systems is the change in the method of utilizing the data base. Since management desires to use the data for strategic planning, and all the problems of strategic planning cannot be foreseen, the method of reporting to management is likely to be varied and will require great speed. It is possible for a manager to have operating data displayed before him on a screen by pushing a button.

Finally, in very recent years there has been a rapid growth in the employment of new "scientific management" techniques. The disciplines of mathematics, physics, industrial engineering, and other sciences have been combined to provide new techniques to aid management in decision making. These methods often require considerable data and systems for their effective development and implementation.

SYSTEMS ANALYSIS AND DESIGN PROCEDURE

In performing a systems analysis and design, it is axiomatic that the study should be performed in a systematic manner. The *five basic steps* are:

1. Planning
2. Fact finding

3. Evaluation of the facts
4. Designing the system
5. Implementation

These steps, which comprise a logical procedure, follow closely the basic rules of problem solving: observing, analyzing, evaluating, implementing, and follow-up.

The system designer will do well to adopt and incorporate the five basic steps in any system designing with which he is involved. Each one of the steps will be discussed.

Planning. Defining the specific objectives of the study is the most important and difficult part of any systems project. Many system reviews start without clearly defined objectives, thus leading to confusion, excess time, and usually inadequate results. Therefore, the following discussion concentrates on showing how objectives might be determined and on planning to meet them.

The key to the successful completion of any systems project is a formal step-by-step, detailed work program. The work program should define each of the steps to be followed in the study and the objectives to be met. For convenience the work program will be discussed under the following steps:

1. Preliminary review and tour of the area
2. Review of policies, procedures, and organization chart
3. Obtaining management's cooperation
4. Establishing objectives and a timetable

   A. Organization and management
      1. Review overall company objectives and policies.
      2. Obtain and review organization chart.
      3. Evaluate the organization's efforts regarding intermediate- and long-range planning.
      4. Review overall operations with emphasis on policy and major operational problems.
   B. Financial
      1. Obtain and review current major financial data for content and form.
      2. Review financial and budgetary controls.
      3. Review cost-reporting system.
   C. Information processing and reporting
      1. Review system documentation and utilization efficiency of present EDP installation. Emphasize scheduling and system economics.
      2. Define reports currently being prepared, their disposition, intended and actual use, and frequency.
      3. Review company requirements for sales and marketing information.
      4. Review the sufficiency and use of performance evaluation measures and reports.
   D. Summary and conclusions
      1. In which of the above or related areas are significant improvements possible?
      2. Are these changes justifiable in terms of estimated costs and savings?
      3. What intangible factors should be considered?
      4. How might the implementation of these improvements be approached?

Fig. 1 Topical headings for preliminary review work program.

PRELIMINARY REVIEW: It is usually necessary to make a preliminary tour of the area(s) to be studied, if the systems assignment is to be clearly understood. When the actual systems project is extensive, it may be necessary to prepare a general work program for the preliminary review. Figure 1 is an example of the topical headings found in a work program to support an extensive eight-week preliminary review.

REVIEW OF POLICIES, PROCEDURES, AND ORGANIZATION CHART: There are many types of systems projects. They range from very simple work-improvement studies that are confined to a single homogeneous department to the extensive and more difficult design of a "total management-information system."

If the systems project is limited to a restricted area, it is probable that the systems analysis will start at the detailed level. This approach is referred to as "from the bottom up." Working from the bottom up simply means that the analyst begins by reviewing each of the various tasks, functions, paper-work flows, and former reports, in detail. After this detailed review, the analyst will have a thorough knowledge of the current work load and procedures in the department. His objective will most likely be to simply improve the timing of the data flows and the way data are manipulated, without basically changing the data content. This is accomplished by improving the way data are recorded, processed, and distributed.

At the other end of the scale is the "total management-information system," where the specifc objective is to determine the information management needs to run the company and then create a system designed to meet these needs. New forms of data and data analysis may be developed utilizing new techniques and equipment. This method of starting with the information needs of management and working to the systems requirements is considered "from the top down."

In most studies, some combination of both the "bottom up" and "top down" proves most successful. The steps described in the following material are equally applicable to developing either approach. The only difference is the amount of detail required in the work program and the amount of effort required to complete the study.

An organization chart is one of the most significant pieces of information required in the initial phase of the study. If there is no formal organization chart, one should be developed as part of the project (see Chapter 2).

Figure 2 shows the various personnel on the chart ranked according to both salaries and responsibilities. This type of chart has two major advantages: It shows the organzational structure of the department; and it identifies the salary structure of the people in the department. The information on salary structure will be required later in the study when costs and benefits of various alternatives are considered.

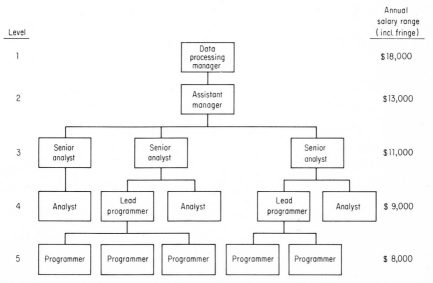

Fig. 2 Organization chart: data processing department.

OBTAINING MANAGEMENT'S COOPERATION: Once the detailed work program and priority of assignments have been established, another meeting should be held with the department heads to agree on a means of reporting project progress. In a long project, reports should probably not be made more often than once a month nor less frequently than once every two months. A smaller systems study might have reporting dates at the middle or end of the fact-finding phase and some time before the final design alternatives have been committed to paper. It is imperative that the management of each group or department be involved and committed to the success of the project. The final report that comes out of the systems study should not be a "surprise" to any of the people in the department. All the ideas, recommendations, concepts, philosophies, and so forth should have been cleared with them prior to inclusion in the report. One of the quickest ways to assure failure of a new system is to spring a surprise on department heads at the time the report is delivered.

An entire book could be written on the means and methods of communicating with management during a systems project. It is virtually impossible to have too much communication with the top management of a department during the project. Every effort should be made to explain progress and results as they occur.

In addition the employees should be kept informed through the use of meetings, seminars, training sessions, and other communication techniques. On long projects, a monthly bulletin can be established to specifically report on the progress of the study. At the beginning of the project, the employees will probably be worried about their jobs, how much their jobs are going to be changed, and exactly what the study hopes to accomplish. Every effort should be made to answer their questions. Most people will cooperate effectively if they are aware of what is happening. A lack of cooperation can often be traced directly to a lack of understanding.

In all cases the functions and departments under study should be involved by providing staff to help in the project. It is a very serious mistake for any systems group to try to perform a study without someone from the department(s) under study actually participating on the team. Departmental participation provides training for the people in the departments and gives them a feeling of responsibility toward the success of the new system.

Once the preliminary review is completed, it is essential that specific objectives be developed to describe the purpose of the study, the expected results, and generally how the study should be done. A supporting letter or memo as shown in Fig. 3 should be written to the highest management personnel involved, outlining:

1. The objectives
2. Estimated participation expected from the department
3. Estimated cost of the project
4. Expected payoffs

Prior to actually starting the work, this document should be reviewed and approved by the department head who has ordered the study to be made. If the project involves a broad management-information system, the top executives of the company should discuss the document in detail. Depending upon the size of the systems project, this document may be a one-page letter or a many-page booklet. The more extensive the scope of the study, the more details necessary to accurately itemize what the project is to accomplish.

ESTABLISHING A PLAN: Many projects have failed because the scope of the study was not clearly defined in the beginning and the systems analyst was required to continue to expand the project until he was unable to complete the work in the required time and within the budget. The final agreement

Mr. George Manager
Vice President and Comptroller
Any Company, Inc.

Dear Mr. Manager:
This letter will confirm our discussions of last Friday, relative to the computer feasibility study for our company.
This study will include a comprehensive review of all significant accounting, clerical, and related functions within the company. The specific objectives of the study will be as follows:
1. Recommend a course of action with respect to mechanization. If mechanization is not recommended at this time, the data provided by the study will be summarized so that they can be periodically updated as conditions change and as new equipment is announced.
2. Recommend interim improvements in accounting, reporting, and clerical procedures. This would specifically include an evaluation of the potential for further clerical-cost reductions. Many of these improvements could probably be implemented during the next few years, prior to the possible installation of mechanized procedures.
3. We plan to summarize our recommendations in the form of a specific program for improvement and, possibly, mechanization. During the course of our study, these recommendations will be discussed at length with you and concerned personnel.
We plan to commence this study in late May, and approximately six weeks will be required for completion. You have indicated that you will assign a man to work with us on a full-time basis during this period. We estimate the costs of the project will be in the range of _____.
We appreciate your confidence, and we will give this assignment our very best efforts.

Very truly yours,

Systems Department Manager

Fig. 3 Supporting letter to management.

by top management to the project description should be confirmed in writing. Verbal commitments should definitely be avoided on this particular point.

Once the objectives have been specifically agreed upon, a detailed work program can be developed. This work program should include a step-by-step description of the work that is to be performed by the project staff. These steps should be as detailed as possible without establishing biases or preconceived notions. The program steps should act as a checklist as well as give specific instructions for the types of analysis and work to be performed. Each program step should be a complete project within itself and should not cover an extended period of time in relation to the total time of the project. For example, if the entire study will cover only one week, then each program step will probably cover a period of three or four hours. If the project is of one or two years' duration, then one week might be the time element assigned to the individual steps. Naturally, these steps can be subdivided for greater clarity. Figure 4 is an example of one page of such a work program.

Each program step should identify:
The starting date
Elapsed time required
Expected completion date
Number and level of systems men required for that step
The individual responsible
Project priorities must also be established. If the project is exceptionally large, with many steps, then a project network should be established (see Fig. 5). The network is then utilized as a control for the project and as a basis for reporting progress to management.

WORK-PAPER CONTROL: Most systems projects create a great deal of paper. Some of these papers are extremely important and can affect the success or

Project description	Responsi-bility	Estimated man-weeks, analysts programmers	Scheduled start	Dates complete
1 5.4 Identify and analyze the specific problems involved in accounting for manufacturing overhead expenses.	WJS	1.75	5/10	5/20
1.5.4.1 Define, categorize, and analyze manufacturing expenses.		0.5	5/10	5/12
1.5.4.2 Determine which manufacturing expenses are fixed and which are variable.		0.25	5/12	5/13
1.5.4.3 Establish bases and methods for reflecting variable manufacturing expenses in product costs. Compare to present absorption methods.		1.0	5/14	5/20
1.5.5 Define, categorize, and analyze distribution and administrative costs on various bases of cost significance, including: a. Expense control b. Product and sales-effort evaluation c. Merchandising efficiency	WJS	1.5	5/21	5/30
1.6 Identify specific problems and policy deficiencies found in the current accounting system. Isolate cause and effect of each problem. Include the following for investigation: a. Intercompany transfer price problem b. Costing and accounting for special items	DML	2.0	6/1	6/12

Fig. 4   One page of work program.

failure of the study.   Other papers become superfluous and only add confusion. It is necessary to develop adequately indexed work papers and to control their content.   One example of work-paper indexing for a large project is shown in Fig. 6.   Coding of the work papers should not be taken lightly, and each project will require a coding or referencing structure adapted to that particular job.

The example given highlights the selected sections from the work papers of a large project.   Each project manager will have to develop and control work papers according to the nature of the individual project.

Fact Finding.   The great majority of systems studies are concerned with operating systems in ongoing enterprises.   This discussion concerns the methods of determining the operational characteristics of the present system.   In particular, the fact-finding phase of the system-analysis procedure attempts to determine the following with regard to the present system:

1. What is done?
2. When is it done, in what sequence?

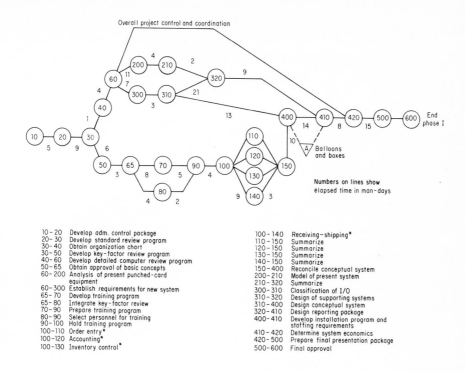

10-20	Develop adm. control package	100-140	Receiving–shipping*
20-30	Develop standard review program	110-150	Summarize
30-40	Obtain organization chart	120-150	Summarize
30-50	Develop key-factor review program	130-150	Summarize
40-60	Develop detailed computer review program	140-150	Summarize
50-65	Obtain approval of basic concepts	150-400	Reconcile conceptual system
60-200	Analysis of present punched-card equipment	200-210	Model of present system
		210-320	Summarize
60-300	Establish requirements for new system	300-310	Classification of I/O
65-70	Develop training program	310-320	Design of supporting systems
65-80	Integrate key-factor review	310-400	Design conceptual system
70-90	Prepare training program	320-410	Design reporting package
80-90	Select personnel for training	400-410	Develop installation program and staffing requirements
90-100	Hold training program		
100-110	Order entry*	410-420	Determine system economics
100-120	Accounting*	420-500	Prepare final presentation package
100-130	Inventory control*	500-600	Final approval

* Key-factor analysis performed by
individual departments with
assistance of team members.

Fig. 5 Project network.

Section	Description
A.	General flow of application with brief overall written descriptions (balloons and boxes).
B.	Brief written description of each run. Comment on run input, output, processing rules, and error processing. Comment on memory requirements, programming language, status of documentation, any other pertinent points.
C.	Input documents, volumes on each, and source. Comment on generations, flow, and validating problems. Comment on input scheduling (see section H).
D.	File layouts and volumes of each file.
E.	Output reports, including volumes, frequency, and distribution.
F.	Controls. Comment on all controls—input, output, processing. Comment on clerical processing of rejects and controls to assure that rejects are reprocessed.
G.	Scheduling. Record run time for each run in system. Record frequency of run. Include special or infrequent periodic runs. Estimate weekly and monthly computer time required.
H.	Use comments on problems. Are results used? Are duplicate records maintained? Do the users have confidence? Are there major difficulties with input? with changes? with connections?
I.	Summary comments. Brief overall summary and recommendations. Written summary should be concise. Recommended flow should be concise—but not perfected to minute detail.

Fig. 6 Work-paper indexing system (for computer study).

3. Who does it?
4. How is it done?
5. Why is it done; what is the purpose?
6. How consistently is the procedure followed?
7. What is the volume of work?
8. How many man-hours and machine-hours are required per period?
9. How much does it cost?

The source of information concerning a system that will be useful in a particular study is problematic. However, investigation of the following sources will usually prove fruitful.

1. Standard procedures manual
2. Other written operating instructions and procedures
3. Minutes of meetings, reports, files, etc.
4. Interviews with the personnel involved

The sources should be contacted in the order indicated. The standard procedures, if available, will allow the analyst to become familiar with the general and perhaps the detailed nature of the procedure including its objectives. All of the first three sources should provide the analyst with sufficient knowledge to discuss the procedure intelligently and thus decrease the time required for interviewing personnel. It is axiomatic that the systems analyst must be thorough yet very tactful in his investigation.

The fact-finding phase should culminate in a well-documented flow chart of the process.

Although many variations in flow-charting symbols and methods exist, there

Processing: A group of instructions which perform a processing function of the system.

Input-output: Any function of an input-output device (making information available for processing, recording processing information, tape positioning, etc.).

Decision: The decision function used to document points in the program where a branch to alternate paths is possible based upon variable conditions.

Predefined process: A group of operations not detailed in the particular set of flow charts.

Terminal: The beginning, end, or a point of interruption in a program.

Connector: An entry from, or an exit to, another part of the program flow chart.

Off-page connector: A connector used instead of the connector symbol to designate entry to or exit from a page.

Flow direction: The direction of processing or data flow.

Fig. 7 System flow-chart symbols.

is a trend toward standardization. Figure 7 contains symbols in common usage today. A typical flow chart using some contrived symbols is shown in Fig. 8. Chapters 22 and 23 contain examples of systems.

After the system has been charted, it is usually a good idea to obtain the concurrence of operating personnel regarding the accuracy of the flow chart and its documentation.

Evaluation. Once the nature of the system has been determined, it must be evaluated. The following questions must be answered:

1. Does the system supply adequate information of sufficient accuracy and in sufficient time to permit management utilization of the information for planning and control purposes? In brief, is the system effective?

2. Considering the objectives, is the system relatively simple, easy, and economical to operate?

3. Does the system permit management by exception, generate corrective action when necessary, and provide for the determination of the causes of performance variances?

If the answer to any of these questions is negative, the system must be redesigned. Even if the answers are affirmative, an evaluation of the system may lead to substantial improvements. The principles and methodology of systems design are directly involved in systems evaluation, which asks the question: "How well is the system designed?"

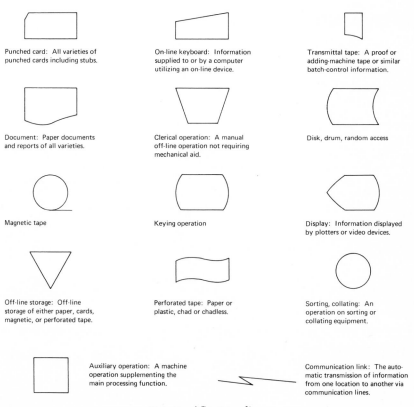

Fig. 7 (*Continued*)

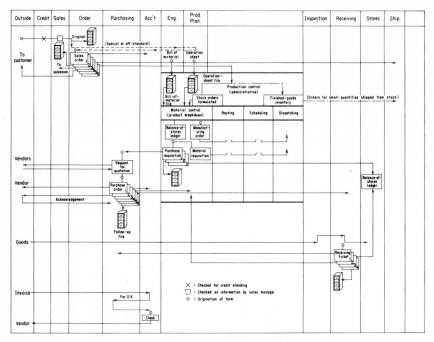

Fig. 8 A procedure for processing customer's order.

EVALUATION CRITERIA: A few of the guides to systems design are particularly helpful in systems evaluations.

1. Systems should be integrated both functionally and technologically. Concerning functional integration, the system should include all the information required by the various management departments. For example, it is normally better to have one shop—reporting system including the data required by production control, accounting, and other departments rather than individual reporting systems for each department. With regard to technological integration, the system should be designed so that the transfer of data between manual and nonmanual systems is accomplished with minimum cost of equipment, time, and accuracy.

2. The output requirements of the system, data required for planning and control, should be determined first; the available sources of input data are determined next; and then the alternative methods of processing the input data are evaluated in terms of cost, timeliness, and accuracy.

3. Data should be recorded in machine processing language as close to the source as economically feasible. Mark-sensed cards and input terminals on the shop floor are two methods of accomplishing this.

4. The system should be designed with a degree of flexibility capable of handling future growth and revision. The experience of most firms indicates that the ultimate in human foresight is not capable of anticipating all future requirements and changes in operating conditions. Many excellent checklists of discerning questions regarding systems are available in the texts included in the bibliography at the end of this chapter. The list contained in Fig. 9 is a proposed checklist.

_____Can any forms be eliminated?
_____Can any step be eliminated?
_____Can any other person do the operation better?
_____Can any steps be combined to advantage?
_____Can any steps be subdivided to advantage?
_____Can the sequence of steps be improved?
_____Can spot checks be substituted for 100 percent inspection?
_____Can the originator of a form furnish more information, and on a better form?
_____Are work loads balanced?
_____Could a lower-paid employee do the operation?
_____Can delays be eliminated or utilized for other operations?
_____Can the travel distance be reduced?
_____Can bottleneck operations be scheduled better?
_____Can forms be presorted while completing an operation?
_____Can any filing operation be eliminated? Why save this form?
_____Is a record being kept in more than one place?
_____Can any employee offer suggestions to improve the procedure?

Fig. 9 Systems evaluation checklist. (*From James H. Greene, Production Control: Systems and Decisions, Richard D. Irwin, Inc., Homewood, Ill., 1965, pp. 264 and 265.*)

FORMS EVALUATION: The nature of the forms used in any system affects the efficacy of the system to a substantial degree. Therefore, the design of forms is frequently a major portion of the systems design task.

The primary purpose of the form is to serve as a means of accurate and timely communication that costs less than the value of the service rendered.

Form analysis seeks the answer to the same questions as systems analysis does, namely: "Who, what, where, when, how, and why?" Many checklists of questions attempting to obtain these answers, such as shown in Figs. 9 and 10, are contained in the books in the Bibliography.

The costs of forms can be divided into paper, printing, and utilization costs.

_____Is this form necessary, or is its purpose served by another form?
_____Does this form have a title which really describes its purpose?
_____Are there adequate instructions on the form for its general use?
_____Are sorting symbols in the most convenient place?
_____If the form is a traveler, does it need a space for addressor and addressee?
_____Is the form of a suitable size for filing?
_____Are there adequate margins for binding?
_____Can both sides of the form be used?
_____Will the forms get dirty? If so, how should they be protected?
_____Is common information grouped in blocks? Is all the information used by one person or department placed in one location?
_____Are data which could cause serious transcription errors separated on the form?
_____Is the information in convenient sequence for transcription?
_____Can more common information be printed on the form, rather than filled in?
_____Are spaces adequate for the information to be filled in?
_____Do the printed lines conform to typewriter spacing?
_____Is print arranged for a minimum number of typewriter stop settings? (Stop settings should conform to other business forms in use.)
_____Would horizontal or vertical lines help reduce errors?
_____Can check boxes be used as a substitute for written-in information?
_____Can any wording be misinterpreted?
_____Can a common sketch, with fill-in spaces for specifications, be substituted for blueprints or other descriptive material?
_____Is all the information necessary?
_____Does the form create a good appearance? Would it create a good mental attitude in the user?
_____Will colored paper help in identification or filing?
_____Can the employee who uses the form suggest improvements?

Fig. 10 Forms design checklist. (*From James H. Greene, Production Control: Systems and Decisions, Richard D. Irwin, Inc., Homewood, Ill., 1965, p. 267.*)

In designing and purchasing forms, it should be remembered that the costs of filling out and reading the form are usually many times the cost of printing the forms. Savings in paper and printing are frequently lost many times over in the time required to complete and read poor forms.

Although a more thorough treatment of this subject can be found in T. Radamaker, *Business Systems* (see Bibliography) a few salient principles of forms design should be noted:

1. Adequate space should be provided for insertion of data.

2. The user should be able to easily read and understand the form.

3. Data input should flow from left to right, and the position of data on the form should correspond to its location on other forms.

Systems Design. The necessity of an ordered approach to the systems project and the clear definition of objectives have been stressed above. The emphasis on objectives is continued throughout the design and implementation phases.

An integral part of the objectives of the new or revised system should be the general nature of the system's output. However, at this preliminary point, the format, frequency, and distribution of the output are usually not certain.

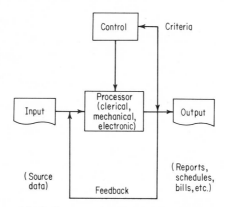

Fig. 11 System block diagram (input, output, processor, and control).

If the system is viewed as a processor that will provide the requisite output, the next determination is the nature of the input required by the processor system to get the desired output (see Fig. 11). Most processing systems consist of a combination of the following operations:

A. Computing

B. Classifying or distributing (sorting)

C. Summarizing

D. Recording (collecting or retrieving)

E. Storing

The problem in design is what input is to be manipulated in which of the above manners to produce the output required by the objectives of the system.

CLASSIFICATION OF INPUT AND OUTPUT: Except in the case of very simple direct systems, it is necessary to be selective in design. The required input and output must be broken down into parts suitable for analysis by category. The input and output data might be classified by type, such as fiscal, statistical, or production control information; or if the data are homogeneous, they may be classified according to the nature of the objects, people, or processes to which they refer. Figure 12 illustrates an example of such categorization.

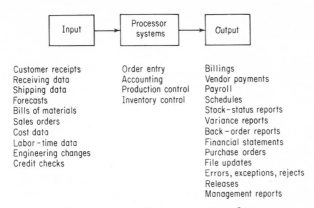

Fig. 12   Categorization of input, output, and processor.

CRITICAL FACTORS: When related to the stated objectives of the system, critical factors such as costs, timing, and accuracy tolerance of output can be brought into focus.   These critical factors are the criteria that will determine the success or failure of the system.   The system is composed of input, processing, and output.   Therefore, each element and category of input and output data and each operation in processing must individually be assessed in view of these criteria.   The rationale of this approach is to identify the key factors that will determine the overall success or failure of the system, gearing the emphasis in the design phase to these key factors.   For each key factor it will be necessary to state success or failure benchmarks that can be compared to measurable performance.   The basic thesis of this concept is that, of the multitude of operations that may be performed in the system and the numerous reports produced, only a relative few are crucial to the overall success or failure of the system.

An example of a key factor regarding a production control system is the ability of the system to predict and report parts or material shortages in sufficient time to prevent the shutdown of a production line.   That is, will the system alert production control to the fact that parts will not be available unless corrective action, expediting, is taken?   If expediting cannot obtain the parts or material in sufficient time, another product can be scheduled for production.

DESIGN OF CONTROLS: It is not enough to simply define key data and operation factors.   Information and functional elements in themselves provide no control. Control is exercised in terms of actions or decisions by individuals using the system.   The control problem has two basic aspects: first, the previously mentioned benchmarks for the success-failure criteria; and second, the need to relate these performance standards to specific responsibilities.   Thus it is necessary to identify who is to be responsible for actual performance.   For example, someone must be assigned the duty of taking the necessary action when the system reports parts or material shortages.

Implementation.   Implementation is the act of placing the new or revised system method into actual operation.   It is the physical process of changing the old method and starting the new method.   Implementation is not the most important step in the systems improvement process, but it has considerable effect on the attainment of the desired results of the system.   Poor implementation can reduce, eliminate, or even reverse the value of an otherwise excellent system design.   Proper implementation will produce the results desired of the system and may enhance the system itself or related systems.

Unfortunately, implementation is one of the most difficult aspects of the systems analyst's job, and normally requires an ability to work with details. Often special one-time procedures must be developed which will not be a part of the system after operation has begun. Therefore, the effort expended in this area of implementation is frequently minimized to the extent that the full potential of the system is not achieved.

Implementation involves all the effort that is required to prepare, install, and review the new system. Whether it is the implementation of a simple procedure change or an entire computer system, these three basic elements must be included.

PREPARATION: When the expected results of a system are not achieved, the responsibility lies either with the systems analyst or the operating personnel. Assuming the system design was reviewed and approved by all concerned, it is usually the operating personnel who are first suspected of not achieving the expected results. Often this is traced back to the lack of a well-planned and executed implementation procedure. Therefore, the operating manager must, for his own benefit, actively participate in the implementation phase. Not only should he thoroughly understand the system as it will eventually operate, but he should take a part in the planning of how to install the system and understand what effort will be required of the operating personnel. The operating manager then must follow up and carry out his responsibility in the implementation phase.

Preparation for implementation must begin during the actual systems study. As the systems analysis and design phases occur, consideration must be given to the possible implementation requirements and methods. To be of operational value, a good system design must be capable of being effectively implemented.

The installation or conversion must be carefully planned. The need for planning will increase with the complexity of the system, but should be performed prior to any installation to assure effective implementation.

Preparation involves making a plan for installation and establishing a schedule to carry out the plan. These plans and schedules may be included in the original system proposal to management. If not, management may not approve the system before there is a plan describing how and when installation will take place. Management's awareness and recognition of the installation plan may be required to overcome the myriad problems which arise as the system becomes operational.

The preparation plans should cover all aspects of the installation, including consideration of all or part of the following:

1. Personnel required during the installation, both from the operating staff and temporary help from other sources

2. Equipment required either on a permanent or temporary basis

3. Procedures required to carry out the jobs which may even be performed only once in the installation

4. Forms and supplies which will be required either temporarily or as an eventual part of the system

5. Physical arrangements or site preparation where there is a rearrangement in the office layout or where space must be provided for additional equipment

6. Education and training of the operating personnel and management

7. Controls which will be required to feed back error conditions so that corrective action can be taken

The plans should be scheduled in a manner as required by the complexity and importance of the system. A very simple system may have two or three time periods set as checkpoints for the installation. At the other extreme, a large and complex project may utilize the techniques of PERT charting and critical-path analysis. The important element in the schedule is that it must be used to evaluate performance as the installation progresses. Without a schedule, the installation may drag out over long periods of time and conceivably become stalled at some intermediate point in the plan.

INSTALLATION: For any useful systems design there is a time when the system is put into use. This is often called the "installation of the system." It should not be confused with the installation of equipment, which may be a part of the system or an independent project concerned only with the equipment. Installing the system is a physical act of beginning new methods or altering old methods to new methods. Implementation may be accomplished by two basic methods: "cutover" and "parallel." Further variations of these two basic methods will also be described.

The cutover method is the direct and simple conversion at a specific time from the old to the new system. It is usually the least expensive. However, it is the most "dangerous" in that the element of risk is great, depending upon the effectiveness of the new system and the ability to recover the old if the new fails. In actual practice, the use of the cutover installation has an effect of making more certain that the new system will work. It places the responsibility on all individuals involved to pretest the system and have complete assurance of its success. Under this approach, responsibility for the new system must be shared by the designers and the users.

Parallel conversion is the start-up of the new system before elimination of the old system. This provides a period of time during which both systems are operating. The purpose for this is to measure the effectiveness of the new system before actually converting to it. The obvious advantage is that this is a safer procedure to follow, and therefore, reduces risk to the business operations. Also, it allows changes or adjustments to be made before involving the operating personnel. This is a more expensive method during the period in which both systems operate. In some cases, it may be impossible to operate in parallel due to time, space, or staff limitations.

Parallel conversions are often easier to sell to management, or are offered when management is unwilling to make a decision and some proof is required to convince management. The choice of a parallel conversion may lead to poorer system design or preparation for conversion, since there is to be this "safe" period of operation. It has disadvantages from the operations standpoint in that it may lessen the user's concern and involvement. In a parallel conversion, it is also possible that both systems may continue to run for longer periods than planned. There is no general agreement among systems personnel regarding the relative merits of the cutover and parallel methods of installation.

The basic installation approach may be modified by three other choices:

1. Converting segments of the system by phases
2. Converting segments of the operating areas by phases
3. A combination of the first two, converting segments of the operations with segments of the system

By phasing in segments of the system, the overall system is divided into phases which may be installed separately. Installation may be forward or reverse to the flow within the system depending upon the ease of installation. This may cause temporary inefficiencies in the system. Care must be taken not to have the system canceled during the phasing-in period when cost reductions are achieved in the early phases of the installation.

Phasing may also be approached by converting segments of operating areas where there are multiple-operating groups performing the operation to be converted. This occurs in larger companies where several divisions or branches are performing similar operations. One division is selected to install the system first and others follow at specific intervals. This is an excellent approach in that the best environment can be selected for the first conversion on the basis of size, need, expected results, expected cooperation, and abilities of the division selected. The experience and success of the first installation will accelerate succeeding conversions.

In major system installations, combinations of phasing in can be done by segments of the system within segments of operations. The branch or division operation is selected for conversion, and the system is installed by dividing it into phases which are installed sequentially. Succeeding branch or division operations are likewise converted, or perhaps the system phases may be altered based upon experience within the first operation.

REVIEW: After the system has been installed, there is one last function required for an effective system. This is to perform a periodic review of the system in operation. The purpose of the review is primarily to assure that the system is meeting the objectives for which it was designed. The periodic review is one of the most ignored functions, but may mean the success or failure of the system. It may produce additional benefits from the system or lead the systems analyst to recommend other improvements in the system.

During the review, the systems analyst will determine first if the system is being operated according to the established procedures. If the procedures are not being followed, or alterations have been made in the procedures, these changes must be evaluated and accepted or rejected. In addition, any problem areas in procedures must be resolved. Second, the systems analyst will determine if the system is producing the expected results. If not, then he will investigate and modify the operation of the system to attempt to achieve these results.

These reviews should be conducted on a periodic basis after the time of installation. The frequency of review must suit the need for review. If the system is routine or simple, less review is required. If the system is complex or radical, frequent and complete reviews will be required. These reviews may be conducted on a formal schedule or at random intervals depending upon the size of the review and the duration of time since the installation was made. As the time since installation increases and the system operates more effectively, the frequency of reviews can be reduced until the point where they are no longer needed.

COMPANY MANUALS

Purposes and Benefits of Manuals. The basic purpose and benefit of any company manual is to serve as a *tool of communications*. The manual represents one important means of communicating management decisions concerning organizational structure, company policies, administrative procedures, and technical processes.

Emphasis today is placed on using manuals to carry and maintain information, and they are now designed emphasizing readability, simplicity, and flexibility. This means that manual development is no longer just a one-time job of putting policies into permanent book form, for it is now looked upon as a means of keeping personnel informed of changing management decisions, policies, and procedures.

Although serving as a tool of communication is the basic purpose and benefit of a manual, it is by no means the only one. Some of the others are as follows:

1. *Serve as Reference Guides.* Many company personnel have need for almost daily reference to written policies and procedures in the normal course of business functions. This is especially true in larger companies where the lower levels of management seldom have actual contact with those in higher management. Because of this, they must be kept informed by the written word which, in turn, serves as their reference guide.

2. *Clarify Organizational Structure and Responsibility.* Certain types of manuals show "who reports to whom" and "who is responsible for what" throughout the company. They can also establish the scope of operation for any given job or position within the company and show interfaces between company functions.

3. *Provide Uniformity in Interpretation and Administration.* There is no substitute for putting company policies down on paper. By so doing, everyone will be or should be thinking alike on any given policy. Handing down verbal directives from one person to another often causes misinterpretation, and in some cases, costly errors simply because all people do not obtain the same meaning from the same words, and like a rumor, verbal exchanges are often distorted in passage.

4. *Coordinate Activities.* A manual will show everyone involved in a procedure exactly what he is expected to do and why. It also shows who does what both before and after one person's actions are performed. In this way, all actions are coordinated with no loose ends.

5. *Eliminate Duplicate Functions.* System tools, such as flow charts and other types of analysis and work-simplification techniques, applied to functions under study will pinpoint and help eliminate duplications of effort.

6. *Provide Consistent Review and Improvement.* Assuming that manual data are referred to and adhered to, thinking will be stimulated toward improving operations. This is particularly true when supervisory personnel are asked to recommend changes to policies or procedures if experience shows that current instructions are impractical.

7. *Provide an Internal Auditing Base.* Systems and auditing work is invariably more effective and is done quicker when proper manuals are available to guide those doing this type of work.

8. *Shorten Training Period for New Employees.* When comprehensive, easy-to-read procedures are available, there is bound to be a reduction in training time; again the idea of the verbal versus the written instruction. Further, a procedures program will expedite the interchange of employees from one job to another. This applies whether transfers are for temporary employment a part of a deliberate program to develop versatility, or permanent job changes.

9. *Eliminate Snap Decisions.* Under an organized method for issuing new procedures or getting changes made in an existing procedure, snap decisions are largely eliminated. The change-making process is formalized. Changes can, therefore, be made only after a careful study of the facts. This study results in specific recommendations which can be carefully weighed and approved by management.

Classification of Manuals. Manuals are designed to serve specific functions. Although there are other types of manuals in use with other names, most manuals can be classified as one of the types listed below. Some companies will combine a number of manuals. Other companies will maintain separate manuals.

1. *Policy Manuals.* In this form, the manual is a compilation of rules of conduct for the office or company at large. It is sometimes referred to as a "handbook" or "rule book." Its purpose is twofold: (*a*) to provide for uniform interpretation and application of company rules, and (*b*) to provide new em-

ployees with a source of information about their responsibilities, rights, and privileges. Policy manuals may have extensive distribution throughout the company or may be limited to top executives only, depending on their content and purpose.

2. *Procedures Manuals.* These cover standard practices or routines for handling various administrative operations. They may take a number of different forms. On one hand, they are broad in scope, designed to bring together all company procedures and routines in one manual. This type is usually called a "corporate" or "control procedure manual." On the other hand, they may be designed to cover a specific operation or function. This type is called an "operating" or "operational manual." A manual, with standard forms, describing in detail production and inventory control procedures is an example of this type. There are some manuals that are combination policy and procedure manuals.

3. *Organizational Manuals.* These include a definition of the duties and various functions of several departments, units, or individual positions in the company and show the relationship of one to another. Organizational charts are used most often to graphically show these relationships. This type of manual is in less frequent use than either a policy or procedure manual. It is usually used only in large companies. Nevertheless, it is valuable in showing where authority and responsibilities lie and also in defining exactly the functions of each major and subdepartment.

4. *Technical Manual.* As its name implies, this manual covers a technical function or operation, or a group of such functions or operations. Consequently, the information contained is of a highly technical nature. Examples of this type of manual would be a drafting manual, a process specifications manual, or an engineering standards manual.

Prerequisites of Manuals. Policies and procedures cannot be written in concise and effective form unless they are clearly defined and standardized before issue. Consider seniority rights, for instance. Definite decisions must be made on how seniority applies to layoffs, reemployment, promotions, and the like. Unless all such questions are answered beforehand, a manual cannot be compiled that will serve as a guide when these questions arise in the future.

Company procedures should also be simplified before being formally issued to provide the basis for efficient operation. This is one of the main areas in which a systems staff can contribute to the company's overall operations.

Policies and procedures must be so defined that when they are written the resultant manual will provide uniform and efficient standards. Such standards are needed before any effective form of executive control is possible. Manuals supply a tool to management by describing such standards.

Manual Format. Most manuals should consist of the following sections:

1. *Heading.* The heading of a procedure usually contains the title of the procedure, the procedure number, the date the procedure was originally issued, and its latest revision date if it has been revised since the original issue. The procedure number is often determined by separating the manual into sections which represent various functions of the company, such as general administration, procurement, contracts, production control, engineering, etc. If this is done, each section is assigned a numerical series. Then all procedures within the series are appropriately numbered.

2. *Table of Contents.* This is simply a list of the principal parts in the sequential order that they appear in the manual.

3. *Directions.* Quite often, personnel involved in a procedure must have some background knowledge, reference information, or directions before the

operating steps of the procedure can be taken. It's this type of information that is put into a brief directions or general-information section depending upon the type of manual and procedure. This section should not contain any actual operating steps.

4. *Policy or Purpose Statement.* What is the policy or purpose? For procedures, it is a decision or dictate that "the" or "a" top executive makes regarding a particular function or action. Such statements should be in writing and must be exact to be effective. If the policies aren't consistent, there actually is no policy.

Usually the best place for a concise statement of policy is right at the beginning of the procedure. An example of a policy statement is: "Machine- and man-loads will be revised weekly for the coming month."

5. *Divisions Affected.* Many procedure writers use this section to show exactly which divisions of the company are affected by the procedure at hand. This immediately tells employees if they are or are not affected.

6. *Body.* The main body of the manual contains those subsections that describe the procedure or policy in detail. They are:

a. *Definitions.* The main reason for this section is to define any abstract or technical terms involved in the procedure so that all concerned are speaking the same language.

b. *Responsibilities and Handling or Operating Steps.* This is the section that tells who does what. Strongly recommended for this section is the *playscript style* of writing. This style lists the *actors*, those persons responsible for taking action, in the lefthand column, and shows the action to be taken to the right of the actor's name. By writing the section this way, we can start at a logical beginning and then move step by step through the process. The section can either go into minute detail for an operating procedure or be written in a general way for a company procedure.

All the action steps in this section should begin with an active verb. This not only sets up the action but cuts down on unnecessary words. The playscript style forces the procedure writer to make sense. All the steps must be related in direct sequence and should cover a logical cycle. An example of the playscript style, taken from a hypothetical procedure that could be titled "Processing of Absence," is as follows:

SUPERVISOR   1. Instruct employees to furnish reason for any absence before end of first day's absence.

TIMEKEEPER   2. Present clock card daily denoting partial or full day's absence to supervisor.

SUPERVISOR   3. Indicate reason for absence and sign. (etc.)

c. *Forms Section.* This section lists all the forms used in carrying out the procedure. The full names of the forms and their numbers should be used to avoid confusion. Sample forms, blank and relating to various stages of the process, should also be included in this section. The combination of a narrative description of a sample execution of the procedure and the posting of sample data on the appropriate form will enhance the understanding of the procedure.

7. *Appendix.* This section is used for any reference materials or exhibits that would severely interrupt the train of thought in the main body.

8. *Index.* Every manual should contain a subject index listing in alphabetical order every topic discussed in the manual and page(s) on which each is discussed.

Manual Preparation. Manuals are frequently prepared by individuals from the systems or some similar department. It is highly recommended that individuals from the departments in the organization affected by the manual participate in its preparation. Adherence to this policy produces both technical and social-psychological benefits. The individuals involved in the day-to-day implementation of the procedure have greater knowledge of the procedure and all the variable conditions under which it must operate. Their participation reduces the possibility of unrealistic procedures in terms of personnel, equipment, and operating conditions. If changes in the procedure are proposed by the systems man, an outsider, their acceptance and utilization is more likely if departmental representatives have participated in the evaluation.

Distribution and Control. All manuals should obviously be issued only to those employees with a true "need to know." The person controlling the distribution should be sure that everyone in the company doesn't have a manual "just because." Writing, printing, issuing, and maintaining manuals is a costly business. This is why distribution should and must be carefully controlled.

As stated earlier in the chapter, company manuals are an important means of communication between management principals and other employees. As such, they are worthy of and must have constant attention from competent employees to assure clear documentation, continuous maintenance, and control of distribution. Only through this type of handling will they serve in the efficient manner for which they were designed.

Standard procedures and revisions should not be distributed until they have been approved by the departments affected and the executive responsible for the preparation and maintenance of manuals.

THE SYSTEMS STAFF AND ORGANIZATION

To be effective in any organization, the systems staff must have competent personnel and the support of top management. The necessity of competent personnel is obvious, and every effort should be made to select and obtain qualified personnel. The support of top management must be obtained because systems frequently cross departmental lines. Without authority in affected departments, the systems study may be impeded, and the resulting system is likely to be less effective.

The systems staff must have organization responsibility to a high level of management. Everyone wants to report to a high executive officer to obtain authority and prestige. Unfortunately, top executives seldom have sufficient knowledge of techniques, or time, to effectively administer the systems functions. A systems staff reporting to lower levels of management is likely to lose the corporate viewpoint and the authority to cross departmental lines. If the systems staff reports to a functional executive, it may become specialized in that same functional area. The solution is usually a compromise of the two extremes, but should not fall below the upper-management circle.

The most common type of organization is the central staff, especially in the smaller business. As businesses grow, there is usually a tendency to decentralize either divisionally, geographically, or functionally. Decentralized systems staffs are usually more effective in working with the operating problems. However, they may lose sight of corporate objectives and require coordination corporate-wide. Functional decentralization tends to create specialists by functional areas, but does not always meet corporate needs because of the more narrow approach to problems.

Depending upon the size and needs of the divisions of a business, a combination of decentralized and centralized systems staffs may be employed to meet both divisional and corporate needs. The decentralized staff can fulfill divisional or functional needs. The central staff can coordinate the decentralized staff effort and provide direct effort in those areas which cannot maintain their own staff.

Within the systems staff there are many methods of organization. Most common is the specialist organization where staff members are specialists by area or by type of operating system. Another method of organization is the "team" approach, where staff members are assigned to work in teams on specific projects. Large systems organizations frequently have specialists on their staff to maintain charts, manuals, control forms, prepare proposals, etc.

It is not likely that one person will possess all the desired qualities and aptitudes of a systems analyst. But there are certain basic qualities that should be found to some degree in a practicing systems analyst:

1. A creative nature
2. An inquiring-type mind
3. The ability to work with details
4. The ability to communicate ideas
5. A sense of salesmanship

In addition to the basic qualities, the systems person must acquire knowledge and experience to match the requirements of the job he must perform. Formal education is desirable to provide a basic knowledge of business methods and to develop a logical approach to problem solving.

However, only with actual experience in the application of systems methods will the analyst become proficient in the profession of systems. The value of this experience increases where the analyst is called upon to specialize in his work or within the organization.

Where the application of data processing equipment is involved, there is a particular need for the systems analyst to be familiar with the capabilities and limitations of such equipment. The degree of familiarity with data processing equipment depends upon the size and method of organization of the systems and data processing operating functions.

The securing of capable systems analysts is a major problem. Obviously there are two sources, external and internal. External candidates must be fully evaluated and require familiarization with company policies, methods, and operations. Internal personnel who do not require systems training are seldom available. Generally, it is best to develop systems analysts internally unless there are time restrictions or a lack of suitable candidates.

In most firms the production control department should have one man with the assigned duty of working with the systems department in reviewing proposed new systems and system revisions and implementing them after approval. In a small firm this individual may well be the manager of the department. In the larger firm he should have the duty of involving the representatives of all sections within the production control department in the appraisal of system changes and new systems and in the implementation of them if approved.

BIBLIOGRAPHY

Gallagher, J. D.: *Management Information Systems and the Computer.* American Management Association, New York, 1961.

Gillespie, C.: *Accounting Systems: Procedures and Methods,* Prentice-Hall, Inc.. Englewood Cliffs, N.J., 1961.

Greene, James H.: *Production Control: Systems and Decisions,* Richard D. Irwin, Inc., Homewood, Ill., 1965.

Lazzaro, V.: *Systems and Procedures: A Handbook for Business and Industry*. Prentice-Hall, Inc., Englewood Cliffs, N.J., 1959.

Knox. F. M.: *Design and Control of Business Forms*, McGraw-Hill Book Company, New York, 1952.

Malcolm, G., and A. Rowe, (eds.): *Management Control Systems*, John Wiley & Sons, Inc., New York, 1960.

Optner, S. L.: *Systems Analysis for Business and Industrial Problem Solving*, Prentice-Hall, Inc., Englewood Cliffs, N.J., 1965.

———: *Systems Analysis for Business Management*, Prentice-Hall, Inc., Englewood Cliffs, N.J., 1968.

Prince, T. R.: *Information Systems for Management Planning and Control*, Richard D. Irwin, Inc., Homewood, Ill., 1966.

Radamaker, T. (ed.): *Business Systems*, Systems and Procedures Association, Cleveland, Ohio, 1963.

Scheele, E. D., W. L. Westerman, and R. J. Wimmert: *Principles and Design of Production Control Systems*, Prentice-Hall, Inc., Englewood Cliffs, N.J., 1960.

Chapter **21**

Nonautomated Systems

EDITOR:

Saul Kessler   *Project Manager, Materials Management Systems, Western Union Telegraph Company, New York, New York*

CONTRIBUTORS:

R. Leonard Allen   *Director of Inventory Control, Western Union Telegraph Company, New York, New York*

Dr. Clifford M. Baumback   *Professor of Industrial Management, The University of Iowa, Iowa City, Iowa*

Donald F. Hess   *Principal, Donald F. Hess Associates, Lancaster, Pennsylvania*

Lamont La Robardier   *Manager, Administrative Services Division, Arthur Andersen & Company, New York, New York*

CONTENTS

The purpose of this chapter is to describe the methods of manually performing the four phases—ordering, action, feedback, and recording—of a complete production control system. In this age of the computer we find that more than 70 percent of the companies surveyed still rely on manual methods for performing most production control functions.* One can assume that most companies will want to computerize these functions when it is economically feasible. There are situations, however, where a company will prefer to remain with manual systems.

When is a nonautomated production control system preferable?

1. When a manual system meets the test of shipping on schedule at a profit, and can do it for less cost than a computer, why automate at all? The nature of the business, its size, and the volume of transactions may not warrant a computer.

2. When the information necessary for the *data base* does not yet exist, the benefits to be derived from data processing are limited. A good data base requires bills of material, operational routings, labor standards, lead time, and so forth.

3. When there is no system, or when the system is being developed but not all functions are being performed, then the system may not be ready for the computer. It is often advisable to wait until the manual operations are proven.

In covering the basic components essential to an effective nonautomated system, this chapter will help speed the day when the manual system will be ready for conversion to a computer.

The functions of a complete production control system are interrelated. When performed properly these functions can be considered as a complete system with four distinct phases (see Fig. 1):

1. *Order Generation Phase.* Introduces the work into the system according to plan. It provides the paper work which describes the performance of the work in terms of *what, when, how,* and *how much.*

2. *Order Action Phase.* Sends the paper work and the materials to the right place at the right time, so that the work is done as ordered.

3. *Feedback Phase.* Reports the progress of the work. It shows actual versus scheduled status of the order. The information provided leads to the corrective action to be taken if the order falls behind schedule.

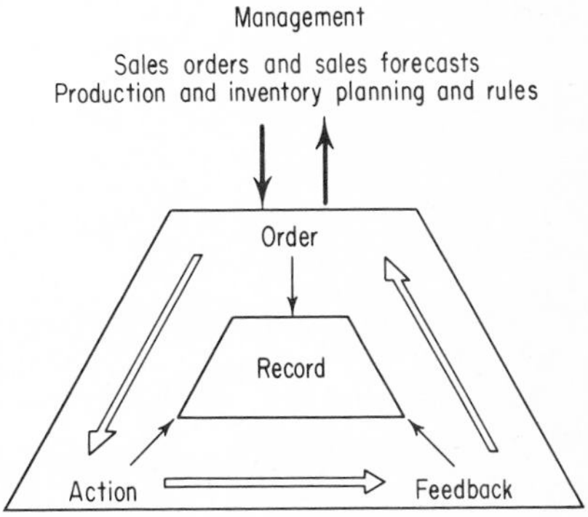

Management

Sales orders and sales forecasts
Production and inventory planning and rules

Order

Record

Action   Feedback

Fig. 1 The phases of a complete production control system.

* See "APICS *Factory* report," Chap. 30 of this handbook.

4. *Record Phase.* Compiles the information needed for planning, control, and making decisions. Without proper records and the data they provide, there is no basis for a system.

This chapter will discuss each of these four phases of the nonautomated system.

ORDER GENERATION PHASE

The purpose here is to discuss the procedures for introducing work into a production control system. An effective production plan, although a very important prerequisite, does not provide adequate input control on a day-to-day basis. Hence, if the production plan is to be fulfilled, the need exists for routine procedures to handle the influx of demand on production facilities in an orderly manner.

Order Entry. Order entry is the introduction of requirements into the production cycle. These requirements may be derived from either customer orders or internally generated forecasts and are usually expressed in quantities for a specified time period.

Production and inventory control functions are both subsequent to and dependent on a detailed and controlled order-entry routine, and the emphasis upon this routine should correspond with the emphasis on the production control functions.

INTERNAL DEMAND: The routine for internally generated forecasts is for a sales or marketing group to release on a formal basis their projection of product demand for specified time periods. This product demand is processed by production control to develop raw-material, parts, and assembly demand in conformance with established inventory policies.

EXTERNAL DEMAND: Order entry for customer orders follows a different routine and time sequence and includes additional elements of control. Generally a customer's order will require acceptance and acknowledgment, clarification and engineering, and will eventually be released to production control in a standard format.

In addition, there may be financially related elements to order entry such as credit checks. These are excluded from this discussion since they do not generaly relate to production control.

Requirements Generation. Requirements generation is the determination of the quantity required for each item within a particular time for the designated end use. The determination of items, quantity, and time begins with the *end-use requirement* and the sequential requiremnts at all the various dependent levels of manufacturing.

Gross requirements tempered by inventory policies result in net requirements to be scheduled.

Forms Required. Assuming that requirements have been generated, the next step is to provide detailed instructions to the manufacturing facility which specify *what* to produce, the *quantity* to be produced, and *how* it is to be produced. To accomplish this it is necessary to translate requirements data into the operational formats used by the manufacturing facility. A great variety of forms may be used for transmitting manufacturing instructions. Together they are frequently referred to as the "route file" or production control "package." Following are some of the more common forms:

Shop Work Order. A document conveying authority for the manufacture of specific parts and/or products in specific quantities usually by specified completion dates.

Purchase Requisitions. Documents conveying authority to the purchasing department to purchase specified materials in specified quantities which are to arrive by a specified date. This form is required when raw materials are not drawn from inventory.

Stores Requisition. Authority to withdraw materials from the inventory.

Purchase Orders. Documents conveying authority to vendors to ship specified materials in specified quantities within a specified time, for an agreed price.

Labor Tickets or Labor Vouchers. Reports entered by operators or by their supervisor detailing time spent on each individual shop work order.

Move Tickets. Documents authorizing the movement of a particular item from one plant location to another. These are used to control movement of material in the plant and as the medium for reporting progress against production schedules.

Process Chart. A chart which specifies the exact step-by-step method by which a particular operation is to be performed.

Route Sheet. A document which specifies the operation sequence to be used in manufacturing a particular part along with other necessary information such as raw-material specifications, quality specifications, jigs and fixtures required, and the standard time allowance for each operation.

Assembly-material List. A bill of materials in a format suitable to show all the components required in assembly operations.

Product Description. A graphic description of the product which is often called an "engineering print," or "blueprint."

These last three forms, the route sheet, assembly-material list, and product description, specify in detail the manner in which an end product is to be manufactured. They are usually maintained in a master file by the manufacturing-engineering function and copies are released to the shop accompanying the shop work order.

ORDER ACTION PHASE

Functions and Scope. *Dispatching* is the coordinated release of work to productive operations in accordance with previously determined *schedules* which are planned to deliver components to assembly when they are needed and the final product to the customer as promised.

This coordinated release of work is accomplished through the issuing of previously written material requisitions, work orders, and product and process descriptions for each component part and subassembly of the final product. Therefore, correct timing of release to each work station in the sequence of operations is the essence of dispatching. To accomplish this objective of correct timing, it is necessary that the following functions of control and reporting be performed:

1. Scheduling and assigning individual jobs to individual machines within a work center or a battery of similar machines.

2. Movements of materials and parts or subassemblies from one work station to the next one.

3. Issuing the route file or "package" of instructions and papers for reporting the actual time required for each job at each machine and collecting reusable instruction sheets or engineering prints after the job is completed at each machine.

4. Recording and reporting the actual elapsed time required for each job at each machine for comparison with schedules and job standards, and analysis of progress. Determine delays and their causes, and the efficiency or effectiveness of the man, machine, work center, and department.

5. Analyzing progress and delays and their causes and "expediting" or finding

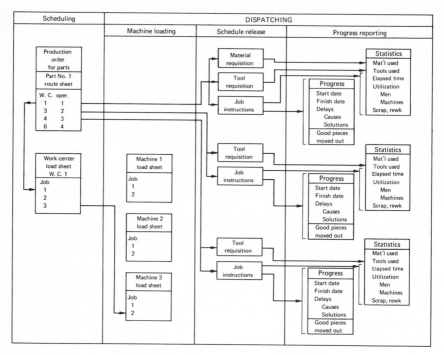

Fig. 2   The dispatching cycle and functions.

alternative solutions to unexpected problems that delay scheduled progress because of machine repairs, lack of materials, lack of parts, etc.

These functions are shown schematically in Fig. 2 and described in detail in subsequent paragraphs, but before we discuss these details it is important to understand the overall controls of scheduling which govern the release of work that is coordinated by dispatching.

Scheduling. Scheduling sets up the manufacturing plan for each product by issuing *production orders* for each component part and *assembly orders* for subassemblies and products. Completion dates are established that will assure delivery of the product when it is needed by either the customer or the finished-goods stock room.

Coordinated timing of these production and assembly orders is extremely critical to "on time" delivery of the product. The coordinated plan of timing is prepared in scheduling from the time required for each operation on the route sheet for each part. The estimated date it can be completed in each work center is based upon the balance of the "load" hours of jobs preceding it and the man-machine-hours available in each of the work centers through which it must be processed.

When many production orders need to be run at the same time on the same machines, to be finished when required, scheduling must determine the priority for each job and give it to dispatching to be carried out in the shop.

ORDER PRIORITIES: Order priorities start in the sales or customer service department where the orders for products can be assigned a three- or four-digit priority number, called a "flow control number," that represents various degrees of importance and urgency.[1]

Two more digits can be added to the priority number in scheduling to indicate the number of operations and the total production time required to process the part. The combined five- or six-digit priority number is written on each production-parts order, subassemblies order, or assembly order. This concept of assigning a flow control number is as follows:

		A	B	C	C		D	E

Start week—week number to start on the job.   (1 through 52)
    A—Importance of customer or product—ABC determination
        B—Value of the order
            C—Degree of urgency for customer or stock orders
                D—Number of operations in sequence for part
                    E—Total time of all operations for order

The first three digits, ABC, of the priority code indicate the degree of importance of the customer or product. The greater the importance, the lower will be the priority numbers.

The next digit, D, of the priority code can represent number of operations, and the last digit, E, can represent operation hours. If jobs with lowest numbers have the smallest number of operations and hours, the small lots will speed through the production processes with the result of fewer lots in process and a smaller total work in process. However, when it is desirable to work on the larger lots with more operations first, the result will be more lots in process with a higher total work in process.

The flow-control-number method has several advantages over the traditional method of calculating start and finish dates for each operation in the sequence:

1. It is flexible. The priority number can be changed without recalculating start and finish dates on all subsequent orders in each work center.

2. Calculation of start and finish dates for each operation can be eliminated.

3. It is a means of communicating priorities to all those involved, from the sales department to the machine operator, because the only instruction that needs to be given to the scheduler, dispatcher, foreman, and machine operator is "select and work on the lowest number first."

This method of assigning priorities greatly simplifies the perpetual dilemma of "which job first" that continually confronts the scheduler and the dispatcher in loading work centers or specific machines. It also accomplishes a fast flow of work in process with a minimum of paper work by assuming that if the job is started on time, exception reporting of all jobs that remain in any work center more than 48 hours plus operation time will keep it moving rapidly through production. Such exceptions are reported daily by the foremen for each work center on the form shown in Fig. 3.

DELAY REPORT						
Work Center Number			Date			
Machine Description						
Priority Number	Order Number	Lot No.	Part Number	Mach. No.	Date Rec'd.	Reason for Delay

Fig. 3   Delay report.

PLANNING AND SCHEDULING TOOLS: There are a wide variety of planning and scheduling tools which can be incorporated into a typical system as the need exists. Among the more common are the following:

1. *Tabular Scheduling Tools.* A common way of preparing a schedule is to tabulate the product quantities or other information by dates.

  a. *Master Schedule:* The primary output of the production planning function, consisting of the quantities of each individual and product group to be manufactured in specific periods (usually monthly). It is normally used to plan facilities and overall manpower requirements and to time production releases and measure actual versus forecasted demand.

  b. *Planning Record:* A record of basic planning data for a particular product or product component. It is used for reference purposes during the planning process. Usually contains such data as order quantity, load factors, planned capacity, and historical records of previous planning activities.

  c. *Lead-time Tables:* Reference tables used for assigning schedule dates to orders based on the buildup of individual lead times of all the order processing and manufacturing operations required to produce the order.

  d. *Man- and Machine-loads:* Accumulations of the work backlogs by time periods for each individual work station and machine. This is a detailed scheduling method used primarily to gain maximum output from critical or bottleneck operations.

  e. *Detailed Scheduling:* The assignment of schedule dates to each operation or group of operations necessary to produce a specific manufacturing order. The degree of detail designed into the system should be consistent with *progress-reporting requirements* as outlined later in the chapter.

2. *Graphical Scheduling Tools.* In more complex applications, graphically oriented scheduling methods may be effectively utilized. Some of the more common are:

  a. *CPM and PERT* (see Chapter 13): Project-oriented planning and scheduling techniques utilizing networks which show the interrelationships of each and every activity making up the project. The critical path, which is the longest sequence of events in the network, focuses on those activities most "critical" for the on-time completion of the project and hence meriting close control.

  b. *Product Tree:* A graphic representation of end-product structure showing the components and subassemblies at each level. Usually used for instructional and analytical purposes only.

  c. *Gantt Chart* (see Chapter 13): A control chart utilizing horizontal lines to show the relationship between planned and actual performance. It is especially applicable in machine loading, where one line represents capacity and the other the accumulated load, and in measuring job progress, where one line represents schedule and the other actual performance.

  There are a number of commercial devices predicated on the Gantt-chart principle which are not systems in themselves but may be used in conjunction with planning and scheduling systems as visual aids. For the specific devices available, refer to "Commercial Record-keeping Equipment" discussed later in this chapter.

  d. *Line of Balance* (see Chapter 13): A project-planning and progress-reporting technique using a lead-time offset chart and a chart of required final-assembly completions to graphically plot a third bar chart showing the number of each component that should be completed to date. The bar chart forms a descending line called the "line of balance."

SCHEDULE COORDINATION: This precedes the issue of schedules and the release of work to the production operations.

Dispatching prepares requisitions for the raw materials required for each part on the production order and checks with raw-material stores to see that the materials are available. It prepares requisitions for the tools required and checks with the tool cribs to be sure that sufficient tools are available to perform all the operations without delay. It prepares requisitions for gauges to be withdrawn from the gauge cribs and set for inspection. It collects and prepares all the papers necessary to give adequate instructions for performing all the operations in sequence. These include drawings, detailed setup sheets, inspection sheets, and instructions for each operation including start and finish dates.

When all this information has been prepared and it is known that all materials, tools, gauges, and instructions are available and ready for use, dispatching issues the necessary requisitions and instructions to the plant. As the jobs are completed at each of the operations, production clerks issue time tickets, inspection tickets, and move tickets.

Records are made of materials and tools used; job progress and delays; direct-labor start, finish, and elapsed time; acceptable pieces produced and pieces rejected for rework or scrap; and the utilization of the time of operators and machines. From this mass of details, dispatching prepares condensed reports that summarize the production output and utilization of men and machines for each work center, department, and the plant as a whole. Man and machine utilization percentages are then applied to the man-hours currently available in each work center to determine the number of hours available for loading jobs.

SCHEDULE RELEASE AND CONTROL: As shown in Fig. 4, when a complete system of schedule release and progress reporting is used to control all the operations

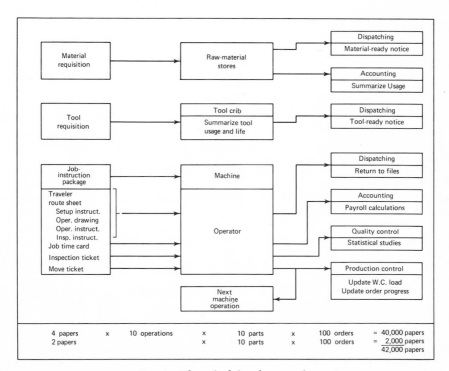

Fig. 4 The schedule-release cycle.

in a plant, it requires a tremendous amount of paperwork. With only 10 operations on each of 10 parts for a product, and with 100 orders in progress at one time, 42,000 papers are generated by a complete system of release and progress reporting. These systems usually report too much information too late, because of the duplications of progress reporting at each work station and the delays in transmitting information.

A satisfactory degree of control can be maintained with a minimum of paper work by reporting progress at the critical operations or major work stations in a sequence with *exception reports* of jobs not completed on time.

Whether dispatching should be centrally controlled or decentralized depends upon the size of the plant, the volume of parts and products flowing through it, and the type of communications used in the system. Generally small and medium-size plants will have strong central control of machine-loads and will issue instructions to foremen for assignment of jobs to men and machines. Larger plants usually have decentralized control with a dispatcher in each department carrying out all the functions.

MACHINE LOADING: This is a method of controlling the activity of each productive machine and therefore the productive output of every department. Essentially it is the determination of the priority and assignment of every job.

Machine loading starts with the production order for parts (Fig. 5), *route*

Part Number					PRODUCTION ORDER FOR PARTS				Priority Number						
Part Description									Production Order Number						
Drawing Number									EOQ Completed Order Quantity						
Date Wanted									% Scrap Allowance						
Date Issued					Lot No.		Quantity		Production Order Quantity						
Dept. No.	W. C. No.	Mach. No.	Oper No.	Operation	Schedule Allowncs			Oper. Piece Time	Job Hours		Critic Ratio B	Sched. Dates		Act. Dates	
					Setup	Move	Que		Oper.	Total		Start	Finish	Start	Finish

Fig. 5   Production order for parts.

sheets, or *traveler* which lists the operations in the sequence they are performed on a part, the time required to complete the order quantity at each operation, the setup, move, and queue time allowances for each operation, and the estimated start and finish dates for each operation in the sequence.

This is the master production plan for each part, and the operation standard time is posted to the proper load sheet for each work center and machine that will perform each operation in the sequence. Standard times need to be adjusted to the actual performance of the work center or department. This is done by determining the percentage of machine efficiency (shift-hours minus total downtime for all reasons) and the manpower utilization (direct-labor-hours on jobs as a percentage of clock-hours). Multiplying these two percentages produces a man-machine-hour utilization percentage that is then applied to the shift-hours of the men to determine the total hours available for loading jobs on the work center or machine. Fifteen to twenty-five percent of these available hours are then set aside and reserved for rush jobs as shown in Figs. 6 and 7. The calculations are shown in Table 1.

When there is a battery of more than one machine of the same or similar capability in a "work center" the overall control of the load-hours and machine-hours available for loading in the work center is kept in scheduling on a form

WORK CENTER NUMBER		21			CURRENT OPERATIONS		1st	2nd	3rd
Machine Description:					Number of men		11	4	0
11 - 2" Screw Machines			WORK-CENTER LOAD SHEET		Shift hours		8	8	0
Std. Machine Capacity:	1st	2nd	3rd		Man-hours avl. at 80% util.		352	128	0
5 day week: cum. shift hours	8	16	22.5		Man-mach. hours avl. at 72%		316.8	115.2	0
Cu. Mach.-hours Avl. at 90% Eff.	396.0	792.0	1113.8		Cum. man-mach.-hours avl		316.8	432.0	432.0

Part Number	Part Description	Operation		Production Order		Setup Hours	Machine Hours			Prev. C.R. B	Priority Number	Start Date
		No.	Seq.	Number	Quantity		Job	Avl.	Rush			
								367.2	64.8			

Fig. 6 Work-center load sheet.

similar to Fig. 6. There is a copy of the form for each work center in the plant. From this scheduling one can estimate the completion date for all the component parts of a product and give an estimated delivery promise to the sales department for incoming orders.

Loading individual machines within each work center is done by dispatching using one of the basic methods shown in Figs. 8 and 9. All accomplish the same results of reserving future time for specific jobs on a specific machine, using one load sheet for each machine and one line or pocket on the control board for each job.

One copy of the production order for parts is kept in the production control office and another copy is the *traveler* that moves with the work from one operation to the next. Progress of the job is reported from each work station in the sequence by move tickets when the job is completed at one work station and moves to the next one. The completion date is then recorded on the control copy and the traveler. Types of control boards are summarized in Fig. 10.

PRODUCTION RELEASE: As previously described, dispatching prepares all the papers necessary to requisition materials and tools and instruct the operators, and reports the progress of the job, operator's time spent on the job, and the quantities of good pieces and rejections at each of the operations. Dispatching coordinates the timing of the release of these papers in such a manner as to accomplish the schedule on time but not overburden any of the work stations with a multitude of orders for future jobs. This is accomplished by holding the package of instructions and reporting papers in dispatching until "just before" the time they are actually needed at each work station. Each station should have ahead of it at any time only the papers for the next three to five jobs or about three days' work. This practice in itself will reduce the number of jobs

W. C. No. 21 Mach. No. 10 Mach. Desc. 1½" Turret Lathe

Current Operation 2 Shifts 6 days per week 96 hours per week

Mach. Eff. 90% Manpwr. Utl. 80% Mach. Load 72% 69.12 hours available

Part Number	Production Order		Setup hours	Machine Hours			Prev. C. R. B	Priority Number	Sched. Dates	
	Number	Quantity		Job	Avail.	Rush			Start	Finish
W. E. 7-16 Available					58.76	10.36				

Fig. 7 Machine load record.

TABLE 1   Calculations for Figs. 6 and 7

	Fig. 6 Work-center load sheet			Fig. 7 Machine load record		
Normal capacity:						
Number of machines..................	11			1		
Cum. shift hours:						
1 shift............................	8			8		
2 shifts...........................	16			16		
3 shifts...........................	22.5			22.5		
Gross shift hours available in five-day week:						
1 shift............................	440			40		
2 shifts...........................	880			80		
3 shifts...........................	1237.5			112.5		
Current operating efficiency:						
Utilization of machines: 90 percent						
Utilization of manpower: 80 percent						
Efficiency for scheduling: 72 percent						
Current operations:						
Normal machine capacity available at 90 percent in five-day week:						
1 shift............................	396.0			36.00		
2 shifts...........................	792.0			72.00		
3 shifts...........................	1113.8			101.25		
Current manning:	Men	Hours	Days	Men	Hours	Days
Shift 1............................	11	8	5	1	8	6
Shift 2............................	4	8	5	1	8	6
Shift 3............................	0	0	0	0	0	0
Gross hours available:						
Shift 1............................	440			48		
Shift 2............................	160			48		
	600			96		
Machine-hour available at 90 percent........	540			86.4		
Man-hours available at 80 percent..........	480			76.8		
Net man-machine-hours available for loading at 72 percent:						
Total..............................	432.0			69.12		
15 percent for rush jobs.................	64.8			10.36		
85 percent for normally scheduled jobs.....	367.2			58.76		

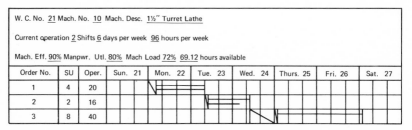

Fig. 8   Gantt-chart machine load.

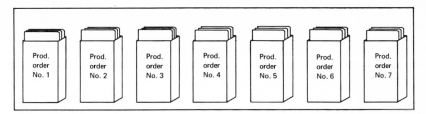

Fig. 9 Pocket-type boards.

at each machine and consequently the total work-in-process inventory. The use and flow of the requisitions and papers in the "package" sent to each work station were shown in Figs. 2 and 4. Examples of requisitions for tools and materials are shown in Figs. 11 and 12, and examples of the papers used for reporting the results at each work station are shown in Figs. 13, 14, and 15.

Material Control. FUNCTIONS AND SCOPE: Material control has the responsibility for maintaining a supply of raw materials, purchased parts, and supplies in appropriate quantities for the current level of shipments of incoming customer orders. Material control is closely tied in with the production planning and scheduling because it receives material specifications, quantity requirements, and delivery dates from the scheduling department's bills of material and production orders. It can, however, operate somewhat independently by maintaining inventory levels that will satisfy the requirements of the production schedules. Usually the material control supervisor will report to the production and inventory control manager and will be responsible for two major functions:

1. *Planning and controlling inventory levels,* which includes the record keeping and the necessary analysis of the records to maintain optimum inventory levels. It also includes the requisitioning and expediting of materials, parts, and supplies necessary to replenish the inventories with the proper quantities at the appropriate times.

2. *Physical control of inventories* from arrival at the plant until issued for use in production. This includes control of the receiving and materials stores departments. It embraces the complete cycle of physical control and responsibility for quantities ordered, received, stored, and issued. It also includes responsibility for adequate protection in storage against fire, theft, deterioration, explosion, rust, etc. The relationship of these functions is shown in the *material control cycle* in Fig. 16, which depicts the sources, flows, and use of information needed to control materials inventories.

ELEMENTS OF MATERIAL CONTROL: Maintaining a constant supply of materials with adequate but not excessive inventories includes the following elements:

1. Forecasted rate of usage
2. Usage during the procurement lead time
3. Inventory reserve
4. Safety stock or "cushion" when usage exceeds the forecasted rate

Gantt-chart type:	Pocket type:
Tape and peg boards	IBM card racks or wooden pocket racks
Index-visible boards	Hook boards
Racks with movable data units	Pocket or grooved-strip boards
Pictorial boards	Spring-clip panel boards

Fig. 10 Types of control boards.

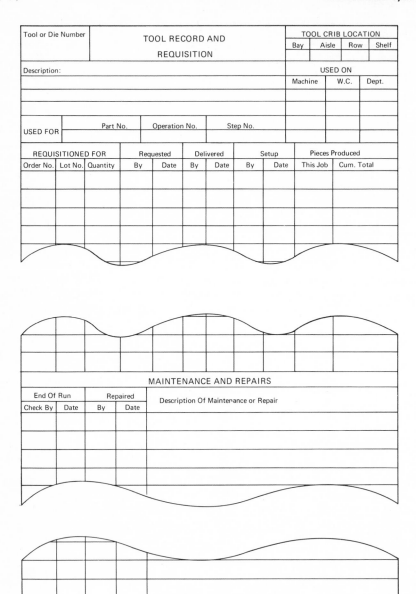

Fig. 11   Tool record and requisition.

5. Economic order quantity
6. Actual inventory balance
7. Reservations or assignments for scheduled production orders
8. Unshipped balances of open-purchase orders
9. Available balance which is the actual inventory balance minus assignments plus open-purchase-order balances

Requested by:			MATERIAL STORES REQUISITION			Requisition No.			
Approved by						Date Written			
						Date Wanted			
Order No.		Lot No.		Account No.		ISSUE		CREDIT	
DELIVER TO:			Department		Work Center		Machine		
Quantity	Unit		Description			New Bal. Bin Tag	Unit Cost	Amount	
Issued by:		Date	Received by:			Date	Extended by:		Date

Fig. 12 Material stores requisition.

Forecasted rate of usage can be obtained from a moving average of usage for the past 3, 6, 10, or 12 months. If material is assigned several months in advance for future production orders, a moving average of this assigned material will indicate a change in the trend of the forecast much sooner than waiting for the actual usage to occur and become a part of the moving average. Exponential smoothing of either actual usage or assignments will add the monthly trend and an error correction to the moving average and consequently improve the accuracy of the forecast.

Usage during the procurement lead time depends upon a reasonably accurate forecast and a reliable statement of the procurement time. Lead time extends from the time the need for replenishment is recognized until the material is delivered to stores.

Employee's Name		Clock No.		JOB TIME CARD			
Department	Work Center			Machine			
Part Number	Part Name			Account No.			
Operation Number	Operation Name				Sequence No.		
Order Number	Lot Number			Pieces Produced			
Order Quantity	Lot Quantity			Total	Good	Reject	
START Date Time		Std. Cost Per 100 Pcs.			$		
STOP Date Time		Employee's Hourly Rate		Favorable		Unfavorable	
ELAPSED TIME		Employee's Earnings		Approved by:			

Fig. 13 Job time card.

	Order	Lot	INSPECTION REPORT		Date		
Number					Part No.		
Quantity			No.		Part Name		
Incoming Material			Incoming Part or Subassembly		Subcontracted Operations		
Quantity		Description			Vendor's Name		Number
Purchase Order Number				Item No.		Date Received	
Prod. Oper. No.			Operation Name				Sequence No.
Department No.			Work Center No.			Machine No.	
Employee Name							Clock No.
Quantity		REASON FOR REJECTION		DISPOSITION			(Check One)
				Put In Stock			
				Return To Vendor: For Credit			
					For Replacement		
				Repair And Charge To: Vendor			
					Dept. No.		
				Scrap And Charge To: Vendor			
					Dept. No.		
Inspector				Inspect. Supvr.			

Fig. 14   Inspection report.

The vendor's delivery time is the most important element of lead time, but there are others frequently overlooked. Some elements overlooked are the time lag between the date of inventory status report and writing the purchase requisition, time required by purchasing to select a vendor and write a purchase order, mail time, vendor's time to acknowledge an order, transit time of the materials, receiving and incoming inspection time, and time to deliver the material from receiving to stores. Omission of any of these elements from the stated lead time used for inventory replenishment means that materials will not be available when planned. This lateness will actually be built into inventory plans, and will have to be made up by expediting the manufacturing operations. Regular monthly review of lead times with the purchasing department and prompt notification of changes are absolutely essential when replenishments are based on lead time.

Lower inventory levels can be carried by using smaller order quantities repeated more frequently and timing the replenishment order with a reorder point

	FROM	MOVE TICKET		TO		
Department No.			Department No.			
Work Center No.			Work Center No.			
Machine No.			Machine No.			
Last Operation No.			Next Operation No.			
Released By			Received By			
Date			Date			
CONTAINERS				DESCRIPTION		
Number	Type	Quantity	Unit	Part Number	Order Number	Lot Number

Fig. 15   Move ticket.

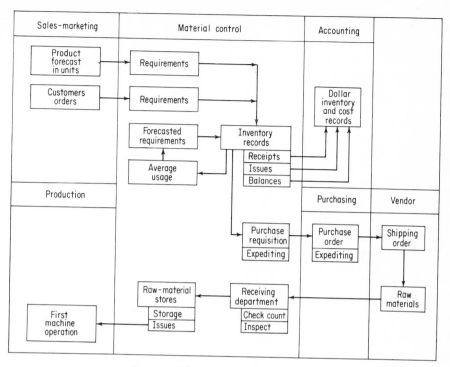

Fig. 16 The material control cycle.

established on *available supply*. In this manner, the purchase orders replenish the supply pipeline to back up the smaller inventory.

Available-supply ordering procedure is explained as follows:

Actual inventory on hand − Assignment for scheduled production order = Available inventory for future assignment

Available inventory for future assignment + Unshipped balances of open-purchase orders = Available supply

When available supply minus reorder point is equal to or near zero, place an order.

All the elements for maintaining a constant supply of materials should be incorporated into one record as shown in Fig. 17 so that all the information needed to make a replenishment decision can be reviewed at a glance. This record provides an exponential smoothing of material assignments for a forecast of monthly usage which is used to revise the calculations of order quantity, reserve, and reorder point. It also provides an available-supply balance from which the reorder point can be subtracted mentally to determine whether another order needs to be placed.

Delinquent orders are controlled best in a nonautomated system by simply filing a copy of the purchase order by the day of the month of the earliest promise date. The vendor should be called on that day or a follow-up card mailed several days in advance with the question: "Did you ship our order?" A space to indicate when he will ship if he hasn't done so may be included on the card. A *speed-reply* type of follow-up form such as shown in Fig. 18 can be used instead of the postcard or phone call.

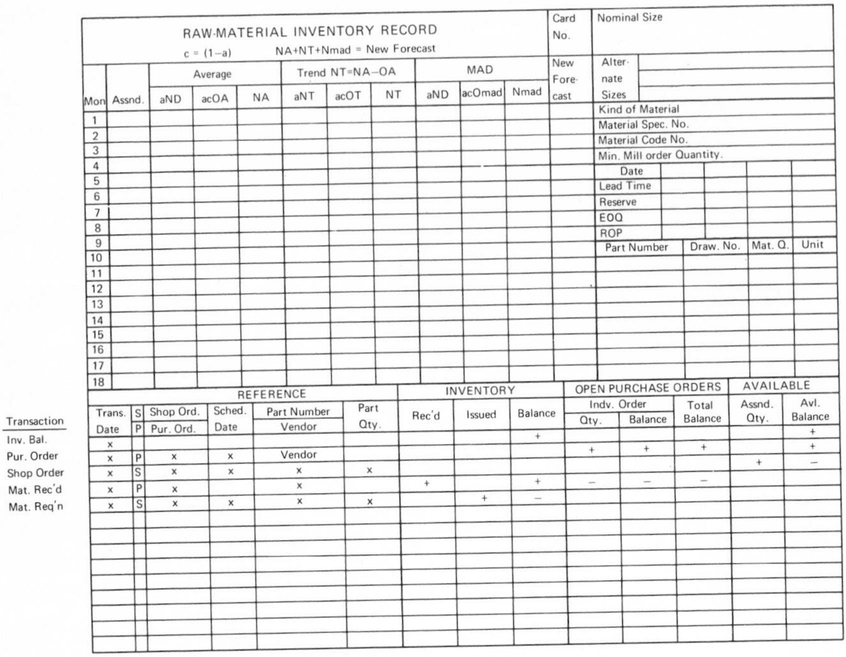

RAW-MATERIAL INVENTORY RECORD

$c = (1-a)$ $NA+NT+Nmad = \text{New Forecast}$

Mon	Assnd.	Average			Trend NT=NA−OA			MAD			New Fore-cast		Card No. / Nominal Size info
		aND	acOA	NA	aNT	acOT	NT	aND	acOmad	Nmad			

Right-side panel:
- Card No.
- Nominal Size
- New Fore cast
- Alternate Sizes
- Kind of Material
- Material Spec. No.
- Material Code No.
- Min. Mill order Quantity
- Date
- Lead Time
- Reserve
- EOQ
- ROP
- Part Number | Draw. No. | Mat. Q. | Unit

Rows: 1–18

	REFERENCE					INVENTORY			OPEN PURCHASE ORDERS			AVAILABLE	
Transaction	Trans. Date	S / P	Shop Ord. / Pur. Ord.	Sched. Date	Part Number / Vendor	Part Qty.	Rec'd	Issued	Balance	Indv. Order Qty.	Indv. Order Balance	Total Balance	Assnd. Qty.	Avl. Balance
Inv. Bal.	x								+					+
Pur. Order	x	P	x	x	Vendor					+	+	+		+
Shop Order	x	S	x	x	x	x							+	−
Mat. Rec'd	x	P	x		x		+		+	−	−	−		
Mat. Req'n	x	S	x	x	x	x		+						−

Fig. 17 Raw-material inventory record.

KITTING: When parts are being withdrawn for subassembly or the final assembly the storeroom personnel will frequently perform the function of "kitting." This is simply gathering together in a "kit" all the components or subassemblies required for the assembly operation. The instructions for doing this are an assembly order containing a list of all parts required for the assembly. One copy is used by the storeroom as a requisition so the quantity of parts may be deducted from the storeroom inventories. Dispatching controls the timing of the "kitting" by its release of the assembly order to the storeroom.

Performance Evaluation. Overall evaluation of the performance of production and inventory control in a plant may be measured by:

1. Number of on-time deliveries compared to a competitor's delivery times
2. Actual deliveries made within the quoted delivery time
3. Inventory size
4. Investment and turnover

On-time delivery is usually measured as a percentage of on-time shipments for items or orders, units of product, and dollar value, which are also measured by the age of the late shipments in days or weeks.

The size of inventories is measured against "what the inventories should be" as established by the inventory policies. The maximum inventory of an item would be the sum of the order quantity and the reserve or safety stock. Any actual inventory quantities that exceed this measure are surplus, and the reason for the surplus should be explained. The average inventory quantity is stated as the sum of one-half the order quantity plus the reserve or safety stock.

Comparing actual inventories with the calculated average should be done only on the total of all inventory items, since each item will be at a different inventory level. Some items will be almost at maximum because an order was just received, while others will be almost down to the safety stock with an order due to be delivered. Because of these variations in the inventory levels of individual items which offset each other, the total of actual inventory of all items should be very close to the calculated average of all items.

If on-time delivery is the key measurement of performance for overall plant operations, each department and work center must be measured in the same manner. On-schedule performance is the key measure for the number of jobs or production orders and the quantities of parts produced as scheduled. When these are expressed as percentages of the schedule, all departments have the same unit of measure and can be compared with each other on a daily report listing all departments. Daily reports of performance and causes of delays and shortages are essential for planning and taking prompt corrective action in each department or work center of the plant. Other measures of productive operations that affect performance to schedule include utilization of manpower and machines, performance to job time standards, and amount of overtime used to accomplish the schedule.

FEEDBACK: PROGRESS REPORTING

Though work may be started (dispatched) on schedule in accordance with the production plan, this in itself provides no assurance that the work will

COMPANY NAME Street Address City, State, Zip Code Telephone Number			1. Please rush prices requested.
			2. Please acknowledge our order.
			3. Please send ACCEPTANCE COPY of our order
			4. CHANGE ORDER as noted below and acknowledge.
PURCHASE ORDER FOLLOW-UP		Date	5. Release shipments as shown below.
		Number	6. Ship this order to address below.
Vendor		Number	7. Please be sure to ship via:
			8. When are you shipping? Goods urgently needed.
			9. Can you meet our shipping date?
			10. Can you give a more specific shipping date?
PLEASE REPLY TODAY BY:		Telephone	11. Goods not received. Please trace shipment.
Wire	Letter	Return this form	12. If goods were shipped, mail invoice today.
WE REQUIRE INFORMATION ABOUT:			13. When will you ship the balance of our order?
Quotation Request Number	Purchase Order Number		14. Please send us a shipping notice;
			15.
Our Comments:			Your Reply:

Fig. 18   Speed reply.

be completed on schedule. The control of production output requires a regular feedback of information concerning the progress of work in process, so that corrective action may be taken when and where required. Without this feedback there is a loss of production "control."

As emphasized repeatedly throughout this handbook, production control is primarily an information system. Any such communication system must provide adequate, timely, and pertinent information on the progress of work in process to at least the following functional groups or departments in the organization:

Production control—for expediting and/or replanning the work, where necessary

Accounting—for recording the labor and material expenditures. and factory overhead allocations, for the various job orders or products

Manufacturing—for guidance in making plant operating decisions, particularly in problem areas requiring attention

Sales—for reporting unavoidable schedule changes to customers and distributors

Progress reporting is more complicated in job shops because there are many orders, all different, in process at the same time. In such shops the status of individual orders must be known at all times. Order control requires follow-up of both purchased materials and work in process.

Purchase Orders. Purchase orders are written by the purchasing department on the basis of information provided by the production control department on the anticipated usage of various raw materials and purchased components. For follow-up purposes, a copy of each purchase order is usually filed by date. Sometime in advance of the promised or expected date of delivery the vendor is contacted by mail or phone to ascertain the status of the purchase order and the probabilities of delay. If a delay is imminent, the production control department is informed of the expected length of the delay so that production orders can be rescheduled if necessary. This same vendor follow-up procedure is used also in the continuous type of manufacturing.

Upon receipt of the purchased goods, they are inspected and a receiving report is issued by the purchasing department. In a job shop, validated copies of the purchase order and receiving reports provide the information needed in making the appropriate entries in the balance-of-stores ledger. In a mass-production plant these documents are used in posting to a cumulative record which compares each vendor's shipments and supply commitments.

Shop-order Paper Work. Each production order in a job shop is routed, scheduled, and dispatched separately. Thus an effective follow-up procedure must provide information on the progress of individual orders. Such an order control system requires a report on the completion of each operation on the order. This requires a considerable amount of "paper work."

In good systems design prewritten forms serve multiple purposes. Thus, in the typical job shop, the labor vouchers that are used in dispatching a job may be used also as notification of the completion of the job. The department foreman simply initials the voucher and returns it to the dispatcher who, in turn, returns it (or copies of it) to the accounting and production control departments. The dispatcher, having thus been informed of the completion of the job, authorizes the movement of the work to the next production center in sequence. After this move order has been initialed and returned to him, indicating that the work has in fact been moved, the foreman then issues the labor voucher for the next operation, and the cycle of events is repeated.

On critical operations where inspections are required, the production control department also receives a copy of the inspection report, so that the necessary "paper" may be generated for rework operations or for the replacement of scrapped materials.

The labor vouchers and inspection reports received from the shop are translated by the production control department into progress reports, which usually take the form of either a Gantt chart or some variation such as a mechanical peg-board. In this manner the status of any order in the shop can be immediately ascertained. This same information can also be used in maintaining machine-load charts.

For control purposes it is important to receive information not only on the *completion* of each operation, but also on the *elapsed time* taken to complete the operation—to provide a check on the accuracy of the scheduling, as well as for purposes of factory overhead-cost allocation. This elapsed-time information is usually added to the labor voucher by the department foreman.

Labor vouchers, inspection tickets, and move orders, as noted, are the principal forms used in reporting the progress of work in process in a job shop. A stores issue slip, on the other hand, forwarded to the production control department, serves as notification that the work has been started in process. (A copy is also sent to the accounting department, so that the material costs of the order may be recorded.) If the work must be delayed for lack of material, a shortage slip is issued and the work is rescheduled as necessary. Similarly, a *finished-stock delivery slip* is used to convey the information that *all* the operations on an order have been completed and that the work no longer is in process.

Progress reporting, however, does not end here. In addition to completed orders, progress charts must also be maintained for shipments. Thus the production control department must receive copies of all shipping orders for a job shop, and service is measured by the promptness with which orders are shipped to customers in relation to scheduled delivery dates.

Information Transmission. Work-progress information may be transmitted in a number of different ways. Among the more common methods are the following:

PREWRITTEN FORMS: A wide variety of paper forms are required in the dispatching of production orders in a job shop, such as labor vouchers, inspection tickets, move orders, material requisitions, and so forth. Each of these forms can also be used in reporting work accomplishment, simply by generating the additional copies required for that purpose. The use of paper forms for multiple purposes is an important principle of systems design.

This method of progress reporting minimizes the amount of time spent by operating personnel on clerical work. (Usually only a signature, or a hand punch, is required.) Prewritten forms prepared on a typewriter or duplicating machine also lessen the danger that inaccurate information will be transmitted or that the information will be misread or misinterpreted. This is a basic communications system used in most job shops.

ORAL COMMUNICATIONS: TELEPHONE AND INTERCOM: Work accomplishment may be reported orally as well as in writing. Oral reports can be transmitted more rapidly than written reports, and there is a two-way flow of information. However, there is no record of the information transmitted, and errors in interpretation of the information are likely. For these reasons most plants use telephone and intercom equipment only in emergency or rush situations, and as an adjunct to some other, basic method of progress reporting.

ELECTROMECHANICAL AIDS: A number of commercial electromechanical devices are available which expedite the two-way flow of work-progress information, yet possess none of the disadvantages of the telephone or intercom. These devices, however, serve only as *aids* to store and convey information, and their use cannot compensate for a poorly conceived communications system. Some of the more common ones are described and illustrated below.

1. *Pneumatic Tubes.* Where production facilities are widely scattered, much time can be saved by placing the work-progress report in a capsule and "shooting" it by air in a pneumatic tube, rather than relying on the in-plant messenger service. Rapid two-way written communication is facilitated by installing the tubes in pairs: one for propelling the capsule in one direction, the other for propelling it in the opposite direction.

The main disadvantage of this aid to progress reporting, other than its relatively high initial cost of equipment and installation, is its inflexibility. Information can flow only over a limited number of fixed paths.

2. *Teletype* (see Chapter 25). The Teletype (or Flexowriter) can be used in progress reporting as well as in order preparation. Unlike the telephone, which transmits messages and reports orally, the Teletype provides a written record of the two-way communication. It is commonly used for progress reporting and other production control communications in the mass-production industries.

3. *TelAutograph* (see Chapter 25). The TelAutograph transmits information over electric wires; hence, as in the case of the telephone, intercom, and Teletype, the information is received instantaneously. However, unlike the latter devices, the TelAutograph can transmit graphical matter as well as verbal messages. And, like the Teletype, a permanent record on paper is provided at both the sending and receiving ends.

Separate transmitting and receiving units are required. The information to be conveyed is written or drawn by use of a stylus mounted onto the transmitting unit. The exact stylus movement is instantaneously recorded on paper, both on the transmitting unit and the receiving unit.

In most TelAutograph installations the sending units are located in the various work centers, and the receiving units, in the centralized production control office; thus, two-way communication is not provided. This deficiency can be overcome, of course, but only by increasing the cost of equipment and installation.

4. *Telecontrol* (see Chapter 25). Telecontrol equipment provides a continuous and automatic form of progress reporting, rather than an intermittent oral or written report.

There are two major units in the telecontrol system: (*a*) a control box, located at each production machine; and (*b*) a centralized control panel, located in the production control department, to which the individual control boxes are wired. By means of actuators in the control boxes, each machine's production is counted automatically on individual counters on the control panel. The counters record not only the number of units produced, but also the number of units remaining to complete the job order or production run.

Also wired to the control panel, in addition to the counters, are time clocks for the individual machines. Each machine is assigned two time clocks: one to register the elapsed production time, and the other to register downtime. Downtime, however, can be registered only when the foreman turns a key-operated switch on the control box.

Each machine also has a green light and a flashing red light connection on the control panel. The steady green light indicates that production is progressing normally, but in the event of trouble the machine operator can actuate the red warning light for his machine by pulling a toggle switch on the control box. The foreman is then alerted by means of a public address system. The foreman may communicate directly with the production control department by plugging a phone headset, which he carries with him at all times, into a phone jack on the control box.

FREQUENCY OF REPORTING: Work-progress information is useful for production control only to the extent that the information transmitted is *timely*. There can be no control over past events, only over those which are likely to occur if preventive action is not presently taken.

There are two basically different methods of establishing the time and frequency of progress reports: (1) at fixed time intervals, and (2) at the completion of assigned tasks. In the continuous type of manufacturing process (or mass-production industries), daily or even hourly reports are necessary to maintain production schedules on a current basis. Fixed-interval reporting is the rule also in some job shops manufacturing standard or stock items. However, in most job shops, because of the diversity of production and the conflicting process requirements, it is more common to make reports at the completion of each operation on each manufacturing order. In this way prompt action can be taken on the tooling and scheduling problems which are more likely to occur in this type of plant. Prompt reporting and corrective action is particuarly important where the product is made to customers' order.

The latter type of progress reporting, of course, does not preclude the making of fixed-interval reports as well. In most job shops daily reports on the status of the jobs still in process are also made.

RECORD KEEPING

Records must be kept in the production control system to give the manager data with which to make decisions. In addition, records are regularly used to compile various reports, summarizing data necessary to keep others informed, or as inputs to other department's records.

Good records and record-keeping systems must meet three requirements:[2]

1. Preserve essential facts comparing the value derived from the record made with its cost of maintenance.

2. Have data arranged in an orderly fashion so that they can (*a*) be consulted with a minimum of effort and (*b*) be posted quickly and simply.

3. Eliminate or summarize data that are not essential or significant due to their age.

The manager using records to reach decisions may need one of four types of records in production control:

1. Basic information records such as bills of materials and route sheets

2. Availability of material, capacity, or tooling records such as perpetual inventory records and machine loading

3. Performance records such as manufacturing-order progress, delivery performance, and department or plant schedule performance

4. Historical records such as sales, scrap, and man or machine efficiency

With the exception of the first type of record, basic information, most of these records are production control's responsibility to design and maintain. A description of the functions, design, and maintenance of these records follows.

Basic Information Records. This category includes all the design information required to produce the product. In a metalworking plant it usually originates from product design engineering and process or manufacturing engineering in the form of:

1. Drawings or blueprints

2. Bills of materials and material specifications

3. Route sheets; e.g., operations and their sequence, time allowances, equipment, tools, jigs and fixtures

This basic information is primarily used in the order generation phase described previously.

Production control, using forecasts or customer orders, must convert the basic design information into demands upon the plant in terms of material, labor, and equipment capacity and special tooling. These demands are then either explicitly or implicitly compared with records of availability to determine required action.

Inventory Records. Inventories controlled may be of many types. The categories of material usually controlled are:

1. Raw material and purchased parts
2. Semifinished and finished components
3. Finished goods

In addition, some systems control work in process using a perpetual inventory record. This record seldom shows a significant balance as the inventory is not held and stored at this stage. However, the record may be useful for:

1. Keeping track of overruns and underruns
2. Furnishing a complete history of component activity
3. Recording component control information
4. Interfiling basic information such as bills of material and route sheets

FUNCTIONS OF PERPETUAL INVENTORY RECORDS: There are only three *basic* functions of the perpetual inventory record. The record should contain information used to:

1. Show material availability for use on incoming orders
2. Signal when to order
3. Determine how much to order

The three basic functions are carried out through decision rules and the comparison of control quantities (units or time) with various inventory balances. In

TABLE 2   Information Recorded on Perpetual Inventory Records and Its Purpose

Information	*Purpose*
1. Identifying information:	
Material or part name and number	
Specifications or descriptive ordering information	
Final assembly, next assembly, or other where-used information and quantity	To aid in estimating future usage and in phasing products in and out.
Unit of measure and conversion factors	
Location in stock room	To eliminate need for locator records.
Phase-out and obsolete information	
2. Control quantities:	
Order quantity	Determines how much to order.
Reorder point	Signals when to order.
Expedite point	Signals expediting or order increase desirability.
Safety stock	Used in calculating reorder point.
Lead time	Used in calculating reorder point.
Maximum point	When exceeded signals desirability of open-order delay, decrease, or cancellation.
Historical usage information } Seasonal and trend factors }	Forecasting expected usage.
Other control data—unit cost, setup cost, carrying percent, A, B, C category, service level, forecast error, labor leveling factor, scrap rate	Are all useful in setting control quantities.

TABLE 2 *(Continued)*

Information	*Purpose*
3. Balances:	For comparison with control quantities. When the control quantity is passed by the balance quantity, then action is usually required.
On-hand balance (Figs. 19 to 24)	The actual physical quantity in the storeroom. Transactions affecting: + receipts, − issues.
On-order balance (Figs. 20 and 21)	The net quantity on open order. Transactions affecting: + orders, − receipts.
Available balance (Figs. 21 to 23)	The quantity remaining when on-hand and all open orders are reduced by reservations. Transactions affecting: + orders, − reservations.
Reserved balance (Figs. 20 and 21)	The net quantity on open, that is, unissued reservation. Transactions affecting: + reservations, − issues.
Free-stock balance	That portion of the physical on-hand balance that is not reserved. Transactions affecting: + receipts, − reservations.
Time-phased balances (Fig. 23)	This is usually the expected on-hand balance in any future period.
4. Transactions:	The updating of balances and the furnishing of factual historical data.
Orders—information recorded: date posted, entry reference, quantity ordered, required or promised date, date received complete or check mark (✓) to indicate receipt	Date received complete or checkmark (✓) is helpful in causing adjustments to available balance if receipts vary from orders, identifying open orders for changes thereto, and aiding in physical inventory reconciliation. Required dates are used to anticipate timing of future balances, a start toward time-phased balances.
Receipts—information recorded: date posted, entry reference, quantity received or returned	Updates several balances.
Reservations (syn. assignments, allocations)—information recorded: date posted, reserving order number, quantity reserved, date reserved quantity is needed, date issued complete or checkmark (✓) to indicate issue	Ability to indicate future usage. Date issued complete and checkmark (✓) postings are helpful in causing adjustments to available balance if issues vary from reservations, selecting reservations not covered by stock on hand for release, and aiding in physical inventory reconciliation. Required dates are used to anticipate timing of future balances, a start toward time-phased balances.
Planned reservations (quantities required for orders not on hand but forecasted)	This provides a good indication of future usage and is often used in time-phased balances as calculated by exploding a forecast.
Issues (syn. withdrawals, disbursements)—information recorded: date posted, entry reference, quantity	Updates several balances. Issues can be posted when the reference document is sent to the storeroom (called "preposting" or "planned issues") or following storeroom disbursement (called "post-posting") or a combination of the two.
Adjustments (returns to stock, scrap, inventory write-off or write-on)—information recorded: date posted, entry reference, quantity	Updates several balances.
5. Record proof	To ensure posting accuracy.

addition, the inventory record can perform several corollary functions useful in handling exceptions. All aditional functions require more posting effort, and hence cost, a factor considered by most ABC analyses.

INFORMATION RECORDED AND ITS PURPOSE: Table 2 lists information recorded in perpetual inventory record cards. Also, the purpose of the information in

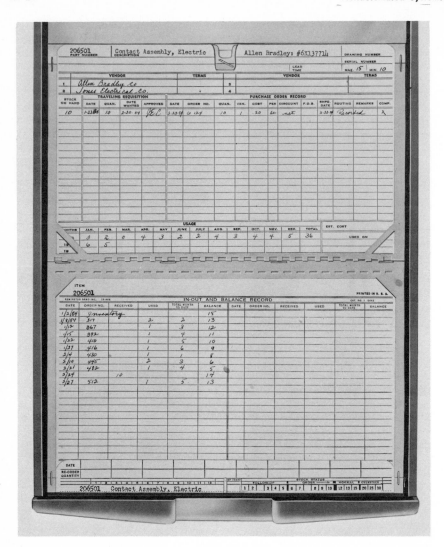

Fig. 19 Inventory record: on-hand balance inventory record with traveling requisition and purchase-order record.

helping to fulfill the basic functions of the record is explained. In actuality, few records would contain all the information shown in the table due to posting cost, redundancy, and other local considerations. Figures 19, 20, 21, and 22 illustrate various record-keeping formats.

The important job of the system designer is to relate the additional cost of more record keeping with the return expected. In this regard, the number of transactions and balances required to support various basic perpetual-inventory-record balances is an indication of cost; whereas the return expected is the record's ability to adequately perform the basic functions usually required of the perpetual inventory record. For example, low-value material, material

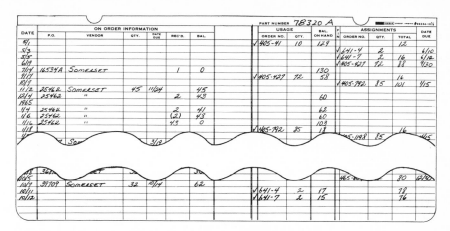

Fig. 20 Three-balance inventory record.

Inventory record card (Fig. 21)

ITEM .128 RD. | QUALITY BRASS | COLOR | UNIT LBS.

DATE OF ORD.	ORDER NO.	AUTH-ORIZER	QUAN.	1ST DEL. PROMISED	DATE COMPL'T'D	UNIT COST	SOURCE	REMARKS
1/2/68	2037	HW	5,000		1/29/68	.7640	CHASE	
1/7/68	2038	HW	5,000				AMERICAN	

DATE	ORD. PT.	EXP. PT.	ORD. Q.	PERIOD	AV. COST	SET-UP	PERIOD	AV. COST	SET-UP	DATE	ORD. PT.	EXP. PT.	ORD. Q.

ARMBRUST CHAIN CO. | RECORD OF ORDERS | WHEELDEX FORM 81476-1A

Four-balance inventory record (Fig. 22)

ITEM .128 RD. BRASS — STOCK CONTROL RECORD — ARMBRUST CHAIN CO. WHEELDEX FORM 81476-2

PROOF: A + B = C + D

DATE	REF. NO.	ORDERED	REC'D	RE-SERVED	RESERVATION CANC'L'D	SHIPPED	RET'D TO STOCK	CASH SALE	AD-JUST-MENT	SCRAP	A ON ORDER	B ON HAND	C RESERVED	D AVAILABLE
12/13/67	INV.										0	5,000	0	5,000
1/2/68	2037	5,000									5,000	5,000	0	10,000
1/9/68	19971		7,500								5,000	5,000	7,500	2,500
1/10/68	19971					5,000					5,000	0	2,500	2,500
1/16/68	19972		5,000								5,000	0	7,500	-2,500
1/17/68	2038	5,000									10,000	0	7,500	2,500
1/22/68	2037		2,500								7,500	2,500	7,500	2,500
1/29/68	2037		2,500								5,000	5,000	7,500	2,500
1/31/68	19971					2,500					5,000	2,500	5,000	2,500

Fig 21 Inventory record card (containing summary usage and control information).
Fig. 22 Four-balance inventory record with traveling requisition. (*Courtesy of Armbrust Chain Co.*)

with little obsolescence, or material without significant lead times may yield little return from the additional record-keeping cost.

The relative ability of the basic balance and various balance combinations, interacting with control quantities guided by decision rules, to perform the functions of the perpetual-inventory-record system is shown in Table 3.

RECORD-KEEPING EFFICIENCIES: The proper selection of information and balances to be included in the perpetual-inventory-record design has been discussed without consideration of record-keeping alternatives and other efficiencies. There often are effective alternatives, lowering the record-keeping costs while at the same time retaining much of the control:

1. Combinations with Other Records. (a) Traveling Requisition, Purchase-history Record, Order and Receipt Record. This can eliminate posting receipts and orders to perpetual inventory record if the TR is filed with this record. If vendor and price information is carried, the purchase-history record can be eliminated. Figure 23 illustrates a typical combination of these records. (b) Storeroom Records. Quantity in and out records in the storeroom are seldom justifiable as they duplicate the perpetual inventory record.

2. Visible Aids on Record Cards. Visible aids incorporated into the record card are limited only by the designer's imagination. Generally the gain must be carefully evaluated where visibility requires additional posting, filing, or tab setting beyond the basic record-balance requirements.

Some of the more successful visible aids are: (a) Color. For example, the presence or absence of a color-coded record card. (b) Visible Balance. For example, control balance and control quantity showing in a margin. (c) Filing Sequence. Figure 24 illustrates a combined use of these three aids. (d) Slides. For example, a slide (d) on the margin which is scaled to represent inventory balance in relation to min and max or when material is due or when material was last issued. Figure 25 illustrates this application.

3. Record Card Access and Posting Efficiency. Housing and retrieving records is covered under the section "Commercial Record-keeping Equipment" below. Efficient card design should consider: (a) a minimum of hand movements occur for each access to the record; (b) line and column of adequate size; (c) card size to enable lines to be followed easily from left to right; (d) fixed or semi-permanent information on a separate card to prevent recopying information.

4. Elimination of Records. This is usually done on items of low unit value or annual cost where costs of control cannot be justified. Here physical control is used to replace paper control through: (a) physical reorder point using two-bin system or other segregated reorder point; (b) physical inventory on fixed-time-interval basis; (c) *kitting* by physically reserving material in advance of expected issue.

Machine and Manpower Records. The development of material requirements from "basic information" is followed closely in importance by the development of capacity requirements. Availability of capacity information leads to realistc scheduling, of both men and machines, and measured change in plant capacity.

CAPACITIES CONTROLLED BY LOADING RECORDS: Plant capacity can be controlled in great detail or in very broad terms. Some of the types of capacity controlled are (1) individual men or groups, (2) individual machines or groups, (3) work centers, (4) departments, and (5) total plant.   •

Decisions must be made concerning which capacities are to be controlled. In this regard, it is often advisable to control capacity, on both an overall basis and a detail basis. For example, the master schedule would control total plant load on a rough basis whereas work center schedules would control work-center load on a detail basis. The rough loading may be done in units other than

TABLE 3 Relative Abilities of Basic Perpetual Inventory Records to Perform Certain Functions

Basic perpetual inventory record balances	Functions performed by perpetual inventory records										Relative cost (in posting req'd)	
	Present balance		Future balance‡			Ease and flexibility of maintenance and use						
	Stock position (on hand)	Free-stock position (on hand—res'v'n)	Stock position (available)	Usage forecast	Physical inventory reconciliation	Evaluating orders for qty. or sched. change*	Comparing balance to ROP	Properly calculating ROP to suit balance§	Relieving back-ordered res'v'n	Keeping balances accurate*,†	Transactions	Balances carried
1. On-hand balance, Fig. 19	Exc.	....	....	Poor unless predictable usage—then good	Exc.	....	Poor unless no open orders	Exc.	....	Exc.	2	1
2. Available balance, Fig. 24	....	....	Good	Good	Poor*,†	Fair	Exc.	Fair	....	Fair	2	1
3. On-hand–available balance, Fig. 24	Exc.	....	Good	Good	Exc.	Fair	Exc.	Fair	Fair	Fair	4	2
4. On-hand–available–free-stock balance	Exc.	Exc.	Good	Good	Exc.	Fair	Exc.	Fair	Fair	Fair	4	3
5. On-hand–on-order–free-stock balance	Exc.	Exc.	Fair, must add balances	Good	Exc.	Good	Fair, must add balances	Fair	Fair	Fair	4	3
6. Time-phased available balance, Fig. 23	Exc.	Good	Exc.	Exc.	Exc.	Exc.	Exc.	Good	Fair	Fair	4	7 assuming 6 periods

* Checkmarks can be placed next to an order and receipt transaction indicating complete receipt. This is helpful in making adjustments to available balance if receipts vary from orders, identifying open orders for quantity or schedule change, and aiding in physical inventory reconciliation. All ratings are improved by this technique.

† Checkmarks can be placed next to a reservation and issue transaction indicating complete issue. This is helpful in making adjustments to available balance if issues vary from reservations, selecting back-ordered reservations for release upon material receipt, and aiding in physical inventory reconciliation. All ratings are improved by this technique. (See Fig. .20)

‡ The relative abilities assigned in these columns assume a significant and largely predictable time lapse between reserving and issuing.

§ The problem here is that reservations are made in advance of issue and cause available balance to be reduced as if the issue had occurred. Unless the reorder point is adjusted for this difference between reservation and issue, the lower available balance will cause premature ordering.

DATE 3/1 COMMODITY EVAP. COILS

Part Number / Where Used	Std. Cost / Qty.	Part Ordering Data (Mo. Sply)	Posting Description	End Previous Month	March Month	April Month	May Month	June Month	Action Taken
301-9527 / U48-1/c / UM/DM 36-1/c	8.78	Ld. Tm. 1.3	P. O. No/Vndr		ABC 6321	ABC 6380	ABC 6380 / ABC 6520		RESCHEDULED
	2	Rv. Tm. 1.0	Qty./Date		971 3/22	320 450 4/20	130 5/22 / 205 60 5/22		1. Order, cancel, and reschedule here (over reorder period),
	2	Rodr. Pd. 2.3	Resvn & Fcst		525	810	425		2. to make ending balance,
		Sfty Stk .2	Avail. Bal.	553	999	639 509	949 274		3. equal or close to reorder point
		EOQ 1.0	Rodr Pt = 1 + SS = 1.2	630	972	510	278		
301-9753 / UM/DM 54-1/c	10.55	Ld. Tm. 1.8	P. O. No/Vndr		XYZ 6370				
	1	Rv. Tm. 1.0	Qty./Date		75 3/28		65 5/28		ORDERED 65
		Rodr. Pd. 2.8	Resvn & Fcst		22	48	27	34	FOR 5/28
		Sfty Stk .5	Avail. Bal.	43	96	48	86	52	
		EOQ 2.0	Rodr Pt = 1 + SS = 1.5	33	72	41	51	51	
301-9755 / UM/DM 60-1/c	15.00	Ld. Tm. 2.7	P. O. No/Vndr				KLM 6510 →	KLM 6510	RESCHEDULED
	1	Rv. Tm. 1.0	Qty./Date		53 3/20		43 5/23 →	43 4/20	5/23 TO
		Rodr. Pd. 3.7	Resvn & Fcst		24	19	15	16	6/20
		Sfty Stk 1.0	Avail. Bal.	36	65	46	74 31	58	
		EOQ 2.0	Rodr Pt = 1 + SS = 2.0	48	38	30	32	42	

Fig. 23 Time-phased available balance.

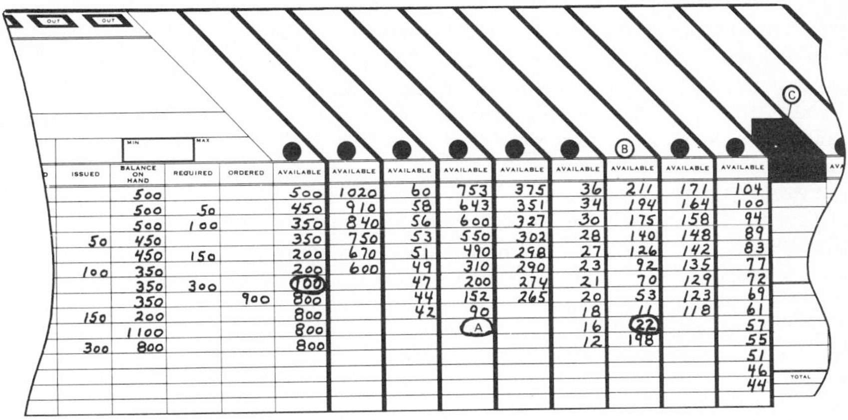

Fig. 24 Vertical visible record card with visible aids. (*Courtesy of VISIrecord, Inc., Copiague, N.Y.*) Visible aids used on this format are: (*a*) visible balance, part not ordered; (*b*) color absence caused by traveling requisition removal; (*c*) filing sequence with TR filed ahead of inventory record indicating open order.

load-hours (such as dollars, pounds, feet, etc.), but detail loading is generally done in more exact units, usually load-hours.

FUNCTIONS OF LOADING RECORDS: The operations of loading records are less complex than material records, but the number of transactions and changes are typically much greater. The basic functions of loading records are threefold:

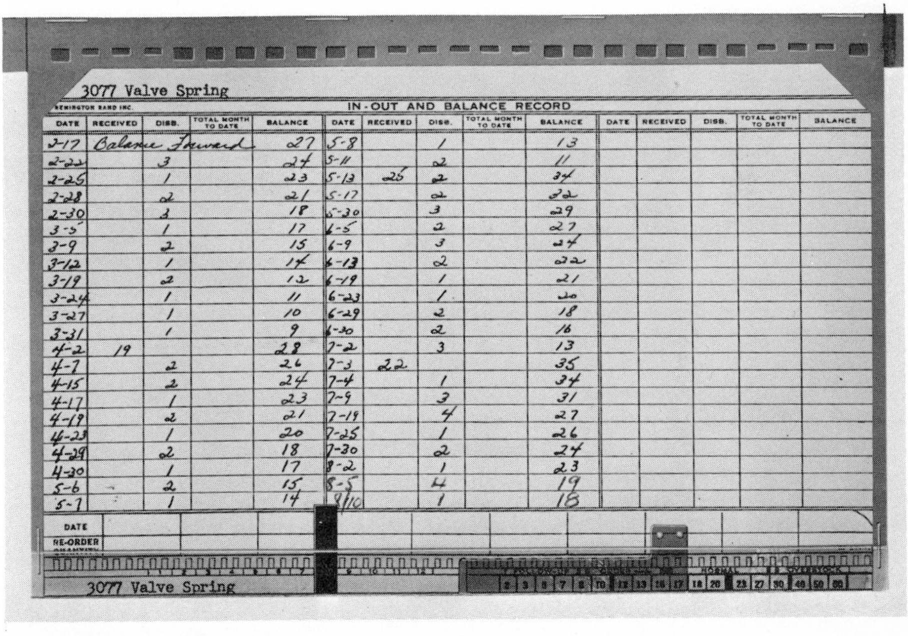

Fig. 25 Application of visible record: Kardex record, tab visible aids. (*Courtesy of Remington Rand Office Systems.*) Tab visible aids show: (*a*) month of last disbursement (to detect slow moving); (*b*) quantity on hand (quantity scale selected for proper reorder point and other control quantities).

(1) show capacity availability for use on new orders, (2) show early enough when capacity is insufficient or excessive to allow orderly capacity or schedule changes, and (3) indicate magnitude of these changes.

These functions are closely comparable to the perpetual inventory record discussed earlier, and therefore, the record design will tend to have many similarities.

TYPES OF LOADING RECORDS: Various types of loading records are kept depending upon what capacity is being controlled and the accuracy and timeliness of the information required. Table 4 describes representative types of loading records and their respective abilities to perform the major capacity control functions. Figures 26 and 27 illustrate typical loading records.

All these load-record-keeping systems have two elements which increase their complexity beyond the tabulated descriptions.

First, units of measure must be comparable, for example, a *load-hour* (or other measure of load) often varies from a *capacity-hour* due to inefficiencies in production or inaccuracies in estimating. Either load-hours or capacity-hours must be adjusted by some factor before meaningful comparisons can be made and capacity controlled from these comparisons.

Second, load status must be defined. In material control terms, *load* represents a reservation of capacity. However, this reservation may be of three distinct types: physically present, not yet present but in process, and only forecasted. Having the load record show the status of all three loads requires more detail and cost.

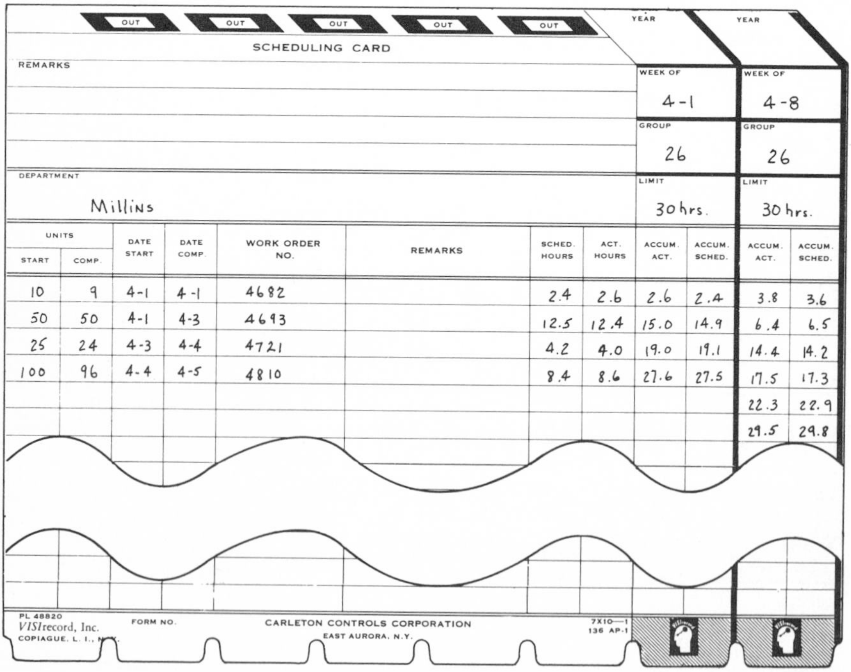
OUT OUT OUT OUT OUT

SCHEDULING CARD

YEAR | YEAR

REMARKS

WEEK OF 4-1 | WEEK OF 4-8

GROUP 26 | GROUP 26

DEPARTMENT Millins

LIMIT 30 hrs. | LIMIT 30 hrs.

UNITS START	UNITS COMP.	DATE START	DATE COMP.	WORK ORDER NO.	REMARKS	SCHED. HOURS	ACT. HOURS	ACCUM. ACT.	ACCUM. SCHED.	ACCUM. ACT.	ACCUM. SCHED.
10	9	4-1	4-1	4682		2.4	2.6	2.6	2.4	3.8	3.6
50	50	4-1	4-3	4693		12.5	12.4	15.0	14.9	6.4	6.5
25	24	4-3	4-4	4721		4.2	4.0	19.0	19.1	14.4	14.2
100	96	4-4	4-5	4810		8.4	8.6	27.6	27.5	17.5	17.3
										22.3	22.9
										29.5	29.8

PL 48820 *VISIrecord*, Inc. COPIAGUE, L. I., N.Y. FORM NO. CARLETON CONTROLS CORPORATION EAST AURORA, N.Y. 7X10—1 136 AP-1

Fig. 26 Scheduling card: load scheduled by period on ledger cards. (*Courtesy of VISIrecord, Inc., Copiague, N.Y.*)

TABLE 4   Types of Loading Records and Their Effectiveness

Type of loading record	Description of loading record	Effectiveness of loading record
Load maintained on ledger cards: 1. Capacity available by schedule period (Fig. 26)	The comparison of load with capacity by schedule period is done on a perpetual work-center loading record similar in most respects to the "time-phased balance" described for material. New capacity is posted for each period and new orders deducted from this capacity.	Loading-record functions are performed well particularly if guidelines are established indicating impending overload or underload. Approaches to simplification are many, such as: keeping records on only key work centers, start or primary work center, or loading only those parts causing heavy demands.
2. Backlog in periods	The comparison of total load or backlog with one period's capacity yielding backlog in periods. Total load is kept on a perpetual record adding new orders and subtracting completion. Some ledger cards are designed with tabs that can be set to represent backlog in periods.	Providing the backlog is within certain minimum and maximum boundaries, there is adequate capacity available for orders with no need for adjustments. Backlogs falling below or above these guidelines signify action required but fail to indicate the magnitude of the change.
3. Backlog in load-hours	Similar to the backlog method, a perpetual record of total load is maintained.	Total load is not converted to backlog in periods but simply compared with minimum and maximum guidelines.
Load maintained in files: 4. Backlog file	Work orders representing load are contained in a file by load center. File can be kept in folders, drawers, bins, clipboards, hook boards and so on.	This is the simplest loading method and requires a regular sight-check of orders to roughly estimate load. It is primarily a sequencing method.
5. Backlog file—periodic add up	This method is an extension of the backlog file: The load is simply added up periodically by locating all documents representing load. The load is usually posted by periods and compared with capacity by period so that the report is similar to the "capacity available by schedule period."	The method has drawbacks in that load or capacity may change drastically between reports and the location and adding up of all relevant documents may be costly. In addition, scheduling must be done without confirmed knowledge of capacity availability. This method is often satisfactory to a small plant where document location is not difficult and load or capacity changes are well known.
Load maintained on graphs: 6. Manual graph of capacity availability (Fig. 27)	Any of the ledger methods preceding can be graphed using one of several Gantt-chart approaches. The charts are typically drawn periodically to aid in decision making.	Schedule changes cannot be handled easily. The graph is difficult to keep current.
7. Display board of capacity availability	This method keeps track of load by creating a bar from cards cut to measured load length, strings or tapes extended, or other techniques. The techniques generally require special equipment. (See "Commercial Record-keeping Equipment" section.)	More ease and flexibility in rescheduling load, and if the perpetual posting is eliminated, a display without significant additional cost is created. In practice, though, the perpetual load is often kept using one of the ledger methods so that the cost of chart upkeep must be mainly paid for by improved decisions due to the display.

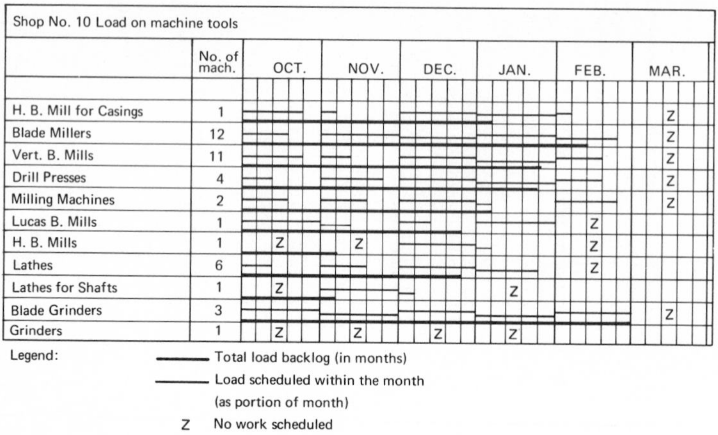

Shop No. 10 Load on machine tools

	No. of mach.	OCT.	NOV.	DEC.	JAN.	FEB.	MAR.
H. B. Mill for Casings	1						Z
Blade Millers	12						Z
Vert. B. Mills	11						Z
Drill Presses	4						Z
Milling Machines	2						Z
Lucas B. Mills	1					Z	
H. B. Mills	1	Z	Z			Z	
Lathes	6					Z	
Lathes for Shafts	1	Z			Z		
Blade Grinders	3						Z
Grinders	1	Z	Z	Z	Z		

Legend:
———— Total load backlog (in months)
———— Load scheduled within the month
(as portion of month)
Z   No work scheduled

Fig. 27 Gantt load chart of machine shop. (*From Wallace Clark, The Gantt Chart, The Ronald Press Company, New York, 1922.*)

Tooling Records. Machine and manpower requirements are developed from "basic information" and compared with capacity. The need for tooling and special equipment also is contained in "basic information" and is ignored—at the peril of the production control manager. Most often the time requirements on tooling are intermittent and erratic, not requiring one of the sophisticated methods described for capacity control. However, the existence and proper functioning of tools or the timely ordering and receipt of a new tool must be continually monitored.

The production control problem with tooling and special equipment design and procurement is usually associated with changes to new products or changes to existing products. These changes can be followed best by special assignments, personal attention, or other nonroutine control efforts which will encompass the problems of tooling and special equipment availability. However, where tooling availability is critical, a record of tooling status for each new order must be maintained and consulted.

Recording Peformance against Plan. PERFORMANCE AGAINST PURCHASE ORDER AND MANUFACTURING ORDER: Keeping open-order status for the plant or the vendor up to date is a constant demand upon the dispatching and expediting group. This feedback information from the "order" and "action" phases of the production control circuit was described previously.

PERFORMANCE AGAINST MASTER SCHEDULES: As finished products are completed the recording and summarizing of this progress against the master schedule will yield a performance measure. This can take many forms. For example, dollars or units produced against dollars or units scheduled might be used. Delivery performance as a percentage of orders on time or late is also used. Usually this performance report is of such importance that reasons for poor performance must be stated and analyzed.

Historical Records. Comparisons of performance against plan for a period of time will provide useful historical data. Some useful comparisons are:

1. Actual plant or department production versus anticipated production
2. Actual inventory levels versus anticipated levels
3. Standard man-hours versus actual man-hours
4. Standard machine-hours versus actual machine-hours

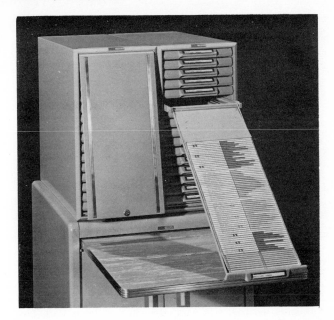

Fig. 28   Tray and exposed-bottom margin file.   (*Courtesy of Acme Visible Records, Inc.*)

COMMERCIAL RECORD-KEEPING EQUIPMENT

Equipment without Display as Main Purpose. TRAY AND EXPOSED-BOTTOM MARGIN FILE: One common type of commercial record-keeping equipment is the tray file shown in Fig. 28.   The records lie flat in the tray, each being retained in a pocket hinged at the top edge.   The bottom margin of each card is exposed, providing for fast recognition of the record desired.   Record posting is accomplished by sliding the tray out from the cabinet without removing it, resting the tray edge on a table or horizontal surface, and flipping open the cards using the exposed margin.   Posting is done directly without removal of the card record.   Though time is saved in not removing the record, the posting position of the record and its distance from the information to be posted must be considered in an evaluation of the equipment.   In addition the time to remove and refile individual records when required is relatively long.

Slides may be fitted to the exposed margin which, when set, may indicate inventory position, work-load backlog, open-order status, and so on.   A tray when open can be reviewed at a glance by noting the positions of the visible slides as shown in Fig. 25.

Mechanization of tray access is available which offers several advantages. The number of records contained per square foot of floor space is increased, and the trays are positioned horizontally at desk height for ease in posting. Figure 29 shows the tray sliding out in response to the clerk's selection.   Cycle time to select and position the tray may be greater than with some manual setups, however.

TUB AND VERTICAL VISIBLE FILE: The tub file mainly houses records arranged for vertical visible filing.   Here the righthand edge and usually a corner are visible with the records standing vertically in the tub.   No trays or pockets

Fig. 29 Mechanized exposed-bottom margin file: Vis-U-Triever. (*Courtesy of Remington Rand Office Systems.*)

are required, as shown in Fig. 30. Record posting is accomplished by opening to the row of cards desired, removing the card to be posted, posting at desk level, and then refiling. Though unfiling and refiling are required, the action is rapid and the posting is made in a comfortable position. The tub file is quite versatile in its ability to contain records of varying width and thickness. For example, interfiling of master bills of material, punched cards, punched paper tapes, and cards with address plates is quite common. The visible edge can be fitted with a slide for display purposes. However, posting and filing "flags" accomplished as a posting by-product usually make this cost unnecessary (see, for example, Fig. 23).

WHEEL FILE: This file provides access to cards through either manual or mechanical rotation of the wheel with cards attached. Cards are blind-filed in tray segments around the wheel periphery (Fig. 31) and are retained in place when rotated by a unique belt arrangement Virtually any size rectangular card, even the one previously in use, can be accommodated in this file, and the

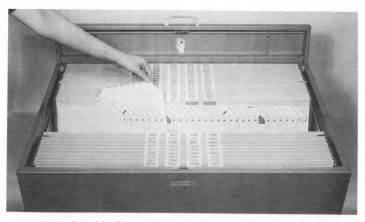

Fig. 30 Vertical visible file. (*Courtesy of VISIrecord, Inc.. Copiague, N.Y.*)

Fig. 31   Wheel file: Revo-File.   (*Courtesy of The Mosler Safe Company.*)

absence of special pockets makes filing very rapid.   Another wheel file retains the card in position by having each card die-cut at the top edge to snap over the retaining wheel frame.   Posting is accomplished by rotating the wheel to the desired card at desk level and posting direct.   No visible slides or edge controls are used.

A larger wheel file (Fig. 32) uses vertical filing in small tubs suspended between two wheels "ferris wheel" style.   Tubs are rotated to desk height and the posting is accomplished as in normal vertical filing.

Endless-chain conveyors are used to move the tubs in some models.   The

Fig. 32   Conveyor file.   (*Courtesy of Wheeldex, Inc.*)

Fig. 33   Hinged-panel file.   (*Courtesy of Acme Visible Records, Inc.*)

number of records housed per square foot is high and the relative ease of retrieving the record is good, though speed may suffer over less dense, manual vertical filing methods.

HINGED-PANEL FILES: Hinged-panel files (Fig. 33) have trays, panels, or other record-holding devices attached at the inside edge, much like leaves of a book. Cards are retained in the trays as in the tray file.   Other holding devices contain strips of data or receive a die-cut card.   Modifications of the hinged panels to resemble a large book are almost invariably desk top and do not post easily without record removal.   The individual strips of data are popular for cross-reference files, and when the leaves are hung vertically, accessibility to data is rapid.

OTHER TYPES OF RECORD-KEEPING EQUIPMENT: An almost limitless number of configurations of drawers, shelves, pockets, tubs, and other types of record holders are available.   These typically have few mechanical devices associated with the container itself.   In addition, a variety of "semiequipment" is available covering the spectrum from the step above a hand-posted ledger book to the equipment described in the preceding paragraphs.

Equipment with Display as Main Purpose.   This type of record-keeping equipment with display as its main purpose is generally used for displaying loading and capacity availability and for recording performance against plan.   Preceding sections have discussed both these subjects.

A third possible but unusual use of display boards is to show material availability.   Generally, equipment without display is preferred for this latter application.

The equipment described here is representative of those types commercially available.   Because each type has some unique principle it is described using the commercial name.

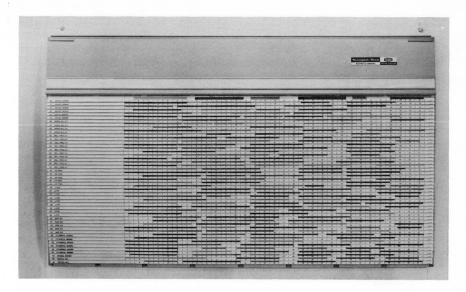

Fig. 34 Sched-U-Graph. (*Courtesy of Remington Rand Office Systems.*)

SCHED-U-GRAPH: The Sched-U-Graph (Fig. 34) is Remington Rand's device for making the Gantt chart a more convenient tool. This charting device has many varied applications and can be adapted to a number of uses.

The Sched-U-Graph is actually the famliar, exposed-bottom margin file enlarged to display-board size. This type of card file consists of a number of overlapping cardboard flaps as shown in Fig. 35. Each flap is bound with a plastic lip on the lower edge in which a card can be filed. The flap can be raised to expose the entire card, but in its normal position only the lower margin is exposed.

As in the Gantt chart, time or quantity is the common denominator. In the application illustrated, a time scale—consisting of a folded date strip—is placed in the plastic pocket. The span card, which is placed behind the date strip as shown, can be cut to any length desired, thus representing different periods of time. A colored plastic strip can be placed inside the pocket of the span card, which can be hidden behind shield cards as shown. Signals, consisting of movable colored plastic tabs, are available for the edge and can be slid along as desired.

Figure 36 shows the Sched-U-Graph being used as a Gantt progress chart but in a "product tree" arrangement known as SPERT (simplified PERT). The

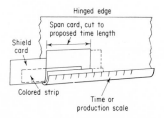

Fig. 35 Sched-U-Graph Detail. (*Courtesy of Remington Rand Office Systems.*)

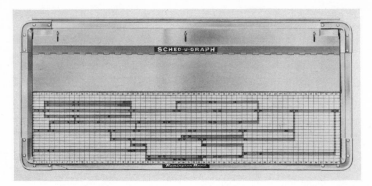

Fig. 36 SPERT application. (*Courtesy of Remington Rand Office Systems.*)

board displays the critical path, slack, events, activities, and progress against schedule.

Figure 37 shows the Sched-U-Graph used for machine loading and scheduling. On the left are cards representing and describing each work center, such as the radial drill and other machine tools. In the plastic slot for each work center is placed the operation record cards for the various orders presently being manufactured. Each operation record card is cut to the proper length to represent the time it should take to complete the job. A folded "day strip" is placed in each slot so that the dark edge of the operation record card, when placed in the slot, will appear as a bar. The white spaces indicate free time. The "today line" is represented by the vertical tab, while progress is indicated by tabs on each plastic strip.

One obvious advantage of the Sched-U-Graph is the ease with which schedule changes can be made. It is only necessary to reshuffle the cards. This is probably one of the most practical devices for charting, and it is quite readily applied to production scheduling, graphical inventory control, and similar applications.

PRODUC-TROL BOARD: The Produc-trol Board (Fig 38) is also suitable for Gantt charting and other bar-chart applications and is one of the forerunners in visual display equipment. On the left side of the illustration is shown a removable-card filing system. The flaps are bound on the lower edge to hold

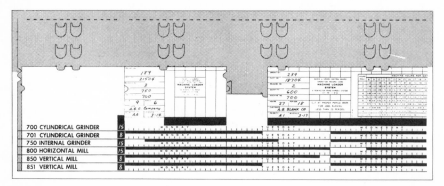

Fig. 37 Detail machine-load application. (*Courtesy of Remington Rand Office Systems.*)

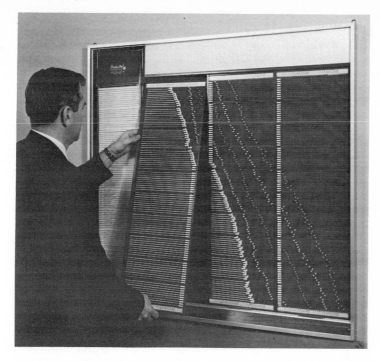

Fig. 38   Produc-trol Board.   (*Courtesy of Wassell Organization, Inc.*)

such forms as inventory cards, operation sheets, or other manufacturing records. Filing infomation can be placed at the bottom of the form in order to be easily seen.   The information on the records, as well as the records themselves, can be easily changed.

Adjacent to the card file is a board which resembles a king-size punch board. For each card in the file there are two rows of holes that extend across the board.   One row is equipped with an elastic string which can be stretched across the board to form a "bar."   The other row of holes is for colored pegs which mark off a span of holes representing time or quantity.   Across the top of the board is a channel in which a paper strip can be placed, imprinted to present time, quantity, or other desired information.   A vertical spring-loaded string can be used to indicate a "today line" or, in the case of inventory applications, a reorder point.

This control panel can be used to maintain machine schedules, as previously discussed, or the individual work orders can be placed in the file card holders. When this method is used the horizontal distance across the board represents the expected and actual time for each activity.   The pegs show when each individual operation will be completed, and the solid horizontal strings show what has been actually performed.   A vertical string, which is moved from day to day, represents the "today line."   If the horizontal strings representing the work orders are to the left of the today line, the work is behind schedule.   If they are to the right, the orders are ahead of schedule.   When the horizontal strings have passed one panel, the panel is removed and the others slid to the left.   This feature helps in keeping the board up to date easily as no shifting of pegs is required.

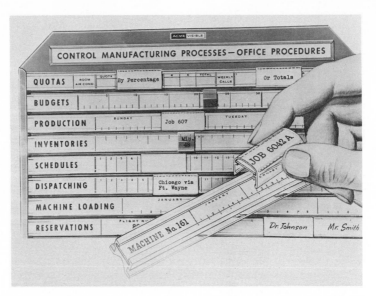

Fig. 39 Acme visible control panel detail. (*Courtesy of Acme Visible Records, Inc.*)

ACME VISIBLE CHART: Another versatile charting device is shown in Fig. 39. The horizontal bars consist of plastic strips. Inserts for the pastic strips can be printed to specification and exposed to permit hand posting. Colored signals, interior and overriding styles, snap on and off or slide freely, bypassing one another. The panels are available in various sizes.

ROL-A-CHART MAGNETIC VISUAL CONTROL BOARDS: The Rol-A-Chart (Fig. 40) offers the advantage of a continuous charting surface in the form of an endless, transparent plastic sleeve which can be moved horizontally each hour, day, or week. Scheduling data entered, whether written or coded in magnets, move with the sleeve to bring deadlines in alignment with the today line. The transparent sleeve is backed by a stationary grid which is used to represent time or quantity units.

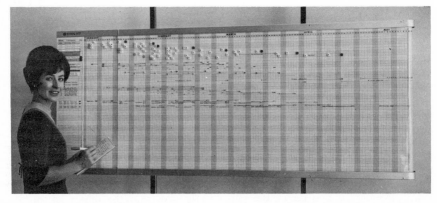

Fig. 40 Rol-A-Chart KING 100 magnetic visual control board. (*Courtesy of Wm. A. Steward Co.*)

On the left side of the chart is a stationary index panel on which the items to be scheduled are entered, such as customer orders, work orders, work centers, machines, or inventory items. A today line provides a present-time reference point and produces a "delinquent zone" near the index. The sleeve material and the index panel surface accept fiber-tipped pens or grease-pencil markings which wipe off readily. Ceramic magnets and plastic magnet strips, which also accept such markings, will adhere to both the index panel and grid section.

One hundred items can be listed vertically on the index panel. A selection of sleeve lengths and grid widths provides horizontal capacities from 84 to 364 half-inch spaces. The Rol-A-Chart is adaptable to the Gantt and other charting techniques which have been discussed.

Mechanized Posting Equipment. ACCOUNTING MACHINES: Posting information to a record card and computing new balances are often suitable applications for accounting machines of the adding-bookkeeping variety. This is particularly true where volume is high enough to justify equipment cost and too low to justify more sophisticated data processing equipment. Accounting machines can perform many functions to advantage:

1. Transactions keyed in by the operator will be legibly printed with date and transaction code shown, all in the proper column.

2. Balances will be automatically and accurately calculated and then printed in the proper columns.

3. Collated forms can record each entry in succession as a carbon copy. This record can be used as a proof of the preceding postings, a direct update to the inventory account represented, and a method of showing exceptions noted by the operator in posting.

4. "Programming" the machine can cause many operations to be performed automatically: printing dates, tabulating progressively to specified columns, stopping where operator is to enter data, computing from numerical entries, reprinting data in a different column, and returning the carriage at the end of the accounting process.

Figure 41 shows one electronic accounting machine of higher capability which accepts a punched-tape program. The prime advantage of the accounting machine is accuracy, and it is especially useful for automatic inventory-account updating. Another advantage is the ease with which a punched-paper-tape output can be created.

PAPER-TAPE PUNCHES: The Flexowriter automatic writing machine is illustrated in Fig. 42. This versatile typewriterlike unit operates from punched paper tapes, edge-punched cards, or tabulating cards to produce business documents, such as purchase orders, and simultaneously punch a tape containing all or selected portions of the information typed on the documents. This tape then can be used as source data for other documents. The keyboard is used only for entering new data that has not previously been recorded. The Flexowriter is widely used in numerical control applications or in repetitive writing assignments such as the preparation of production orders, engineering specifications, or other office records.

Notched Cards. For small systems the edge-notched card is often suitable. This card with prepunched peripheral holes is often used as a payroll card, inventory card, tool control ticket, or as an operation ticket as is illustrated in Fig. 43.

Each hole in the card represents one piece of information. To represent a piece of information the hole is either notched to the edge or left as is. For example, a hole notched to the edge might represent the second shift while an unnotched hole could represent the first shift. To separate cards representing

Fig. 41 NCR 400 electronic accounting machine: NCR 400 with tape program. (*Courtesy of National Cash Register Co.*)

the second shift from those for the first shift it is only necessary to pass a needlelike tool through the holes in the stack and shake out those with a notch representing the second shift. You will notice on the left edge of the card illustrated that two holes are used, however, to determine the shift.

The marginal holes on the periphery are known as "code positions" when as-

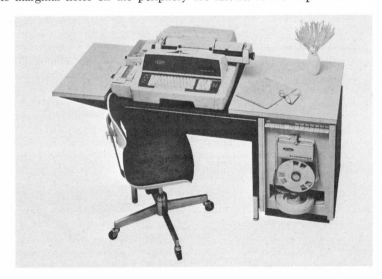

Fig. 42   Flexowriter, programmatic model.   (*Courtesy of Friden, Inc.*)

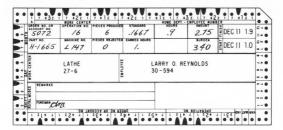

Fig. 43   Operation ticket.

signed to a particular type of information.   A "code field" is a one or more code positions used for one purpose such as a department number.

In coding it is frequently necessary to economize on space since there is a limit to the number of code fields which can be placed around the edge of the card.   A work-center number of three digits as shown on the upper edge of the card would require at least 27 positions if direct coding were used.   To overcome this difficulty it is common to set up a 7-4-2-1 code as shown.   The work-center number can then be represented by combining the numbers in the three sets of 7-4-2-1's to conserve a considerable amount of space.

This method of coding has one disadvantage in that several more sortings may be required.   This code is similar to the 8-4-2-1 code used in the computer but has the one advantage that fewer sorts are required.

The card can be used with the alphabet as well as numbers by using a simple method of coding.   The letter A is represented by a 1, the letter B by a 2, and so forth up to the letter M which is number 13.   At this point we run out of numbers and must start over.   To indicate that the letter is in the second half of the alphabet, another code position must be added.   This "N to Z" position is punched when the code field is being used for a letter between N and Z.   Of course there must be one NZ position for each letter field that is being punched.

One important advantage of the edge-notched card is that it can be used without expensive equipment.   However, there are pieces of equipment which can be used to make the task more efficient.   One device will notch, "groove," a whole stack of cards at one time.   This is useful when some common information, such as an order number, must be placed on a stack of operation tickets.   For high-speed notching there is a keyboard key punch.

The center of a card is available, of course, for handwritten information.   Usually the card is a preprinted form with spaces which can be filled in as desired.   One application is to print information on the card with an embossed card similar to the one used in the gasoline station for credit purposes.   At the same time the card is being printed it can also be notched.   Such a device is ideal for some production and inventory control applications.

In addition to the equipment described here there are other more sophisticated devices which are used for sorting, tabulating, and printing out information.   A company interested in applying this efficient card equipment should contact the vendors for the latest developments in equipments and applications.

Methods of Duplicating.   The need for the effective production control system to communicate the information it generates or collects is largely met by use of office copying machines.   These machines reproduce information at less cost than hand copying, and facilitate timely distribution of any number of required copies to points of use.

Copying-equipment technology growth continues to be very rapid. With more than 40 companies currently producing a variety of machines, sales have grown from $50 million to $1 billion in little more than 10 years. Detailed descriptions of specific equipment would soon become dated in a handbook. There are periodicals which regularly survey the copying machines on the market and provide comparative data on price, cost per copy, time it takes to make each copy, and kind of paper used. Other features compared are kind of process used, maximum size of the original, and kind of original which can be copied, e.g., photos, opaque, translucent, two-sided, etc. Help is available, if needed, in selecting the right machine through the Buyers Laboratory Inc., located in New York City. It is an impartial testing service which aids users in determining which copier to buy.

Although it is impossible to discuss all the different duplicating processes available, the production control manager should be aware of the processes suitable for his operations. The following gives an overview of common processes which he may wish to use.

SPIRIT DUPLICATING PROCESSES: This type of duplicating process goes under a number of popular trade names. The master, from which the printing is done, consists of a piece of paper upon which a layer of carbonlike material is laid down by making an impression with a typewriter or the sharp point of a drawing instrument. This master, with its mirror image, is attached to the drum of the machine (Fig. 44). The drum rotates in contact with the paper to be printed. As the drum rotates it is damped with spirits which loosens just enough of the carbonlike material to make a suitable impression. Since the printing material is removed in the process, the number of copies which can be made is limited.

For production control purposes the master may be stored and used from time to time. For example, a master operation sheet may be stored and used every time the manufacturing order is placed with the factory.

These machines have several modifications which make them especially suitable for production and inventory control purposes. For example, there are forms which are essentially packaged for such applications as time cards, operation tickets, and material requisitions. These tickets are temporarily bound together on the short edges and staggered so that the long edges just overlap by the width of the spaces on the operation sheet. This package form is run through the machine picking up the information for each separate operation on each of the individual cards. The package is then "exploded" by removing the edge binding them together. The cards can then be run through the machine again to pick up the common information. Such an application can help to reduce the number of errors as well as the cost. There are other devices which should be considered when it is time to purchase equipment. One such device is for attaching variable information to a form containing information which does not change from time to time. For example, purchase-order information may be changed on an operation sheet which is used time after time.

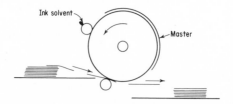

Fig. 44   Spirit duplicating process.

ENGINEERING-PRINT PROCESSES: Many companies use their engineering-print process for production control applications. They may use the same machine or eventually obtain their own table-top model.

The operation sheets or other forms are usually printed up on a translucent material. It is no problem then to print or type in the information required. This way of duplicating is especially attractive to those who wish to change the master frequently because information on the master is easily erased.

WET PHOTOGRAPHIC PROCESSES: Many of the so-called wet photographic processes are so sophisticated that the casual observer is hardly aware that there are any fluids involved. This is because the moisture is squeezed out before the copy is returned to the user.

These processes use the "reflex" method of printing which permits the light to pass through the negative and reflect from the opaque material being copied. This produces a mirror copy on the negative which is then placed in contact with a "receiving sheet" in a bath of developing fluids. When the negative and receiving sheet are pressed together an image is left on the receiving sheet. In some processes the negative may be used for several copies, but the quality decreases. The process is therefore suitable for only short runs.

OTHER DUPLICATING PROCESSES: A very common duplicating process uses an electrostatically charged plate which loses its charge in areas which are exposed to light during exposure. The charge of the plate is transferred to the paper being printed. The charged paper is then exposed to granular material of opposite polarity. This results in an image which is fixed permanently to the paper. Other equally suitable processes for short-run production control applications use heat-sensitive paper.

These are but a few of the duplicating processes with innovations coming out all the time. It would be impossible to more than touch on this subject in a handbook such as this. If you are called on to select a piece of equipment for duplicating, it can only be suggested that you familiarize yourself with what the latest developments present.

SUMMARY

The administrator of a production control department is responsible for handling and sorting a deluge of information. It is true that the computer will take over part of this burden, but there are situations in which it is not suitable. This chapter has emphasized the nonautomated system which can be supported by many mechanical devices to make the system more efficient. Even in the most sophisticated computer system, however, there is a need for displaying information which can be readily manipulated and understood by all the people involved. This chapter contains information needed by all production control personnel.

REFERENCES

1. R. E. McInturff, and J. B. Robinson, "Flow Control," *Factory* Magazine, January, 1963.
2. E. H. MacNiece, *Production Forecasting, Planning, and Control,* John Wiley & Sons, Inc., New York, 1961.

Chapter **22**

Punched Card Systems

COEDITORS:

C. Martin Antisdale *Production Control Manager, Consolidated Diesel Electric Co., Old Greenwich, Connecticut*

Prof. Donald W. Fogarty *Department of Industrial Engineering, Saint Louis University, Saint Louis, Missouri*

CONTRIBUTOR:

Paul F. Bocigalupo *Senior Systems Engineer, International Business Machine Corp., Waltham, Mass.*

CONTENTS

The objective of this chapter is to give the reader a basic understanding of *unit-record equipment*. This equipment serves as a necessary adjunct to more advanced data processing equipment such as computers. In many applications, unit-record equipment fills the interim between a manual system and a computer-oriented system. It enables a user to "get his feet wet" in processing data faster and usually more efficiently than can be done manually. This may be accomplished only if there is a coordinated effort to review the current manual procedures recognizing the need for improved information. Systems analysis and design are of paramount importance for gaining the maximum efficiency from the equipment utilized. The punched-card machines are merely tools to aid in doing a better job. The term "unit record," which is synonymous to "punched card," evolved from the practice of recording the facts concerning a single event on a single punched card. For example, the details concerning a customer order are punched on one card; and a single card is used to record an inventory withdrawal.

History of Unit-record Equipment. In 1745, Joseph M. Jacquard, a Frenchman, developed punched cards which were used to control the rise and fall of a loom harness. This was actually a move toward industrial automation.

The decade 1880–1890 is generally considered to be the pioneering development period for improving and mechanizing the processing of data. Prior to this time, Charles Babbage had invented his "difference engine." Cards in his machine carried a punched code to represent numbers. This code was intended to activate the mechanism of his "difference engine." Unfortunately, his invention was only partially successful because his design was more advanced than the technology of the period.

During the 1880s, Dr. H. Hollerith, a statistician with the United States government, became concerned over the compilation of the data collected during the 1880 census. The facts had been collected, but five years later the Bureau was still struggling to compile them. Dr. Hollerith developed a system assigning a definite meaning to each separate position on the card. This system, described briefly in a later section of this chapter, was successful as evidenced by its acceptance and application in such cities as Baltimore and New York and the State of New Jersey Bureau of Vital Statistics.

Punched cards and unit-record equipment had a vital impact upon American business during the first 40 years of the twentieth century. Automatic recording scales and time-recording devices were developed as the forerunners of machines to process the punched cards. Unit-record equipment has proved to be a valuable asset in such areas as accounting and payroll, sales and marketing statistics, and some limited applications in the engineering and manufacturing environment. Data availability and the reduction of clerical effort to maintain data were key factors in the acceptance of this equipment. The era of computer technology has relegated unit-record equipment to a peripheral status as opposed to the major role it played for many years. However, many small businesses utilize this equipment for their information needs, and it is recognized as a valuable tool for the processing of data.

THE PUNCHED CARD

Since the late 1800s, the punched card has been utilized to solve record-keeping problems. The development of the cards, and the machines to process them, began as the result of specific needs and has progressed to the point where they have been used in virtually every type of commercial and scientific application. The basic principle of punched-card accounting is that the data are recorded once in a card which is available, as required, to produce desired results by machine processing. The data are recorded in the card in the form of punched holes which become a lasting record. This record, the punched card, once punched and verified can be classified (sequenced) and summarized by machine processing to produce the required output data.

Punched-card Characteristics. One type of punched card is divided into 80 vertical areas called "columns" or "card columns." Other types of punched cards contain 90 columns. Because it is more common and for ease of illustration our further discussion will consistently refer to the general-purpose 80-column-type card (Fig. 1). Each of the card columns is numbered from 1 to 80. For each of the 80 card columns there are 12 vertical punching positions. Therefore, there are 960 punching positions available in each punched card.

The punching positions in the column are designated from the top to the bottom of the card by 12, 11 or X, Ø, 1, 2, 3, 4, 5, 6, 7, 8, and 9 (Ø is commonly used to distinguish zero from the letter O). The punching positions

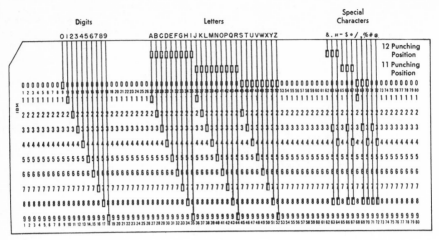

Fig. 1   A punched card.   (*Courtesy of International Business Machines Corp.*)

for digits Ø to 9 correspond to the numbers printed for each column on the card. It is common to reference a punched card by the phrases "12 edge" or "9 edge," and "face up" or "face down." The 12 edge of a card is the top edge and references the 12-punching position. The bottom edge or 9-punching position of the card is called the "9 edge." Machines always designate whether the cards are fed "12 edge first" or "9 edge first" and also whether the cards are "face up" or "face down." The printed side of a punched card is "face up," whereas "face down" means the opposite.

Punched-card Coding. The punched card is capable of accommodating up to 80 individual pieces of information because each card column can contain a digit, a letter, or a special character. Digits are recorded by holes punched in the digit-punching area of the card from Ø to 9. The figure illustrates digit punching, with a 1 punched in column 10 and a 9 punched in column 18.

The top three punching positions across the card (12, 11 or X, and Ø) are known as the "zone" punching area of the card. Alphabetic coding for the 26 letters is accomplished through the use of a zone punch and a digit punch based on a logical coding structure as illustrated in the figure. Punching position Ø, therefore, is the digit punch for zero when used by itself or becomes a *zone punch* when used in combination with other punching positions, as can be observed. The 12 zone punch in combination with digit punches 1 through 9 represents the letters A to I. Letters J to R are coded by the 11 or X zone punch and the digits 1 through 9. The last eight letters are S through Z and are coded with the Ø zone punch and the digits 2 through 9.

The special characters are recorded by using one, two, or three punches. The function of the special characters is to provide printed symbols as required, or to identify various cards and to cause certain operations to occur (through wiring or stored programs). The conversion of digits, letters, and special characters to and from the coding structure, described and illustrated in Fig. 2, is accomplished automatically by the various machines used to process data. Therefore, it is rarely necessary to refer to data in its code form.

Card Layout and Visual Identification. In normal usage, cards are printed with "field" headings (Fig. 2). A "field" is a column or columns reserved for the punching of data of a specific nature. The field can be from 1 to 80 columns

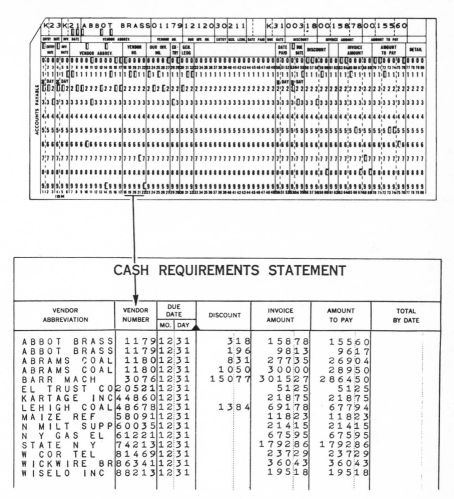

Fig. 2 Punched-card coding. (*Courtesy of International Business Machines Corp.*)

depending upon the length of the particular type of information. The field length is based on the maximum length of data that will be punched into the field. Card layouts and field assignments are usually made after analyses of the requirements.

Visual identification of different card layouts is accomplished through the use of "corner cuts" and color stripes. The two most common types of corner cuts are upper left and upper right—Figs. 1 and 2 illustrate this technique. Corner cuts assist in identifying the card as well as ensuring that all the cards in a group are facing the same direction and are right-side up.

CARD-PUNCH MACHINES

Data, frequently recorded first on handwritten documents, are recorded on the card in the form of punched holes through the use of a card punch (Fig. 3). The keyboard (*a*) on the punch unit is similar to that of a typewriter

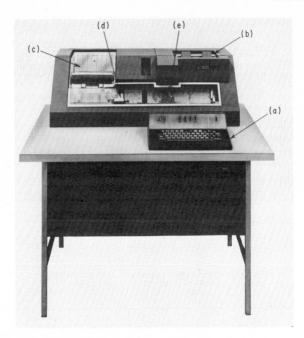

Fig. 3 Card-punch machine: (a) keyboard; (b) card hopper; (c) card stacker; (d) reading station; (e) punching station. (*Courtesy of International Business Machines Corp.*)

in that it is activated by depressing a key corresponding to the letter, digit, or special character to be punched in a card column. The keyboard may have a 64-character set. The card punch operates serially; that is, one card column is punched at a time. After one column is punched, the card is automatically positioned for the next column to be punched. Depending upon the card-punch model being used, the data punched also may be printed across the top of the card.

Key Punching and Duplication. As depicted in Fig. 3, the card-punch machine has two card depositories, b and c, and three card beds with two card stations, d and e. The cards pass from the upper-right card depository called the "card hopper" (b) into the card punching bed.

The card passes from right to left under the punch dies (e) at the punching station for the recording of the data. As the card is released from the punching station, it is moved to the reading-card bed. The card then progresses through the reading mechanism (d) at the reading station in phase, column by column, with the following card at the punching station. After the card following is released from the punching station, the card at the reading station is automatically moved to the card release bed and to the upper-left card depository called the "card stacker" (c).

Card duplication is possible because as a card passes under the reading station it is in phase with the card at the card punching station. Therefore, card duplication from card to card may be automatic and provides for ease of error correction. If an operator senses that she has made an error, she releases the spoiled card and duplicates on a new card up to the point that the error occurred, and then keypunches the correct data for the card column in question.

Other Functions. Other card-punch functions are possible under automatic or manual control. Card feeding may be automatic or manual. Filling in numeric card fields with zeros, duplicating and/or skipping card fields, and card clearance of the card beds can all be automatically accomplished.

Summary punching, the punching on a card of a sum determined by an accounting machine, can be accomplished by a card-punch machine modified to serve this purpose. One card is punched for each summary total so indicated from the accounting machine. This modified unit is cable-connected to an accounting machine to punch indicative information as well as accumulated totals into one card.

CARD VERIFICATION

After the data have been key punched into cards, the information should be checked for accuracy. There are two common methods of checking key-punch accuracy: visual or machine verification. Visual verification involves checking the printed punched data across the top of the card with the source documents. Another way is to obtain a printed listing of the data in the cards and then check it with the source documents. This process involves one or two people to read and verify.

Fig. 4 Card-punch verifying machine. (*Courtesy of International Business Machines Corp.*)

Machine verification is performed on a card-verifying machine (Fig. 4) which is similar in appearance to a card-punch machine. However, the first card station on the verifier is a verifying station rather than a punching station.

The operation is similar to card punching. Previously punched cards are placed in the card hopper and forwarded to the verifying station. The operator, preferably one who did not do the original punching, reading the source document, keys the data as is done in card punching. If the key depressed senses a hole in that position(s) of the column, the card advances one column. If no hole(s) is sensed, that card column is notched at the top of the card. If a card is properly punched (no card column contains an error notch), then the card verifier punches a verification notch on the right-end edge of the card. Therefore, all cards completely verified will contain this verification notch, as visual proof of machine verification. The error cards must be rekeypunched and sent through the machine-verification procedure.

INTERPRETING MACHINES

Not all cards are punched in the card-punch machine. Some are punched in the reproducing machine which does not *print* on the card the data that has been punched into it. These cards are usually *interpreted* in a special machine (Fig. 5) when visual reference may be required for data punched in the card.

Fig. 5   Interpreter.   (*Courtesy of International Business Machines Corp.*)

Machine Operation. Interpreting machines have the capability to translate holes punched in a card and print the corresponding letters, numbers, and special characters on the face of the card. These data can be printed in any sequence through the use of a wired control panel. Up to 60 positions of printing per line are possible, which normally appear across the top edge of the card. The cards, once printed, are stacked in their original sequence.

Other Functions. Printing can occur on any one of 25 lines on the face of the card through the use of the printing-line dial which selects the appropriate line. A selective line-printing device is optional and is useful in ledger-card-type applications.

Up to four selective card stackers are available to selectively stack cards after printing. Leading zeros can be controlled to suppress them from printing. All these functions may be included in one machine. It should also be noted that printing by interpreter is more readable than that done by the card-punch machine.

THE REPRODUCING PUNCH

Reproducing machines (Fig. 6) perform three primary functions: summary punching, gang punching, and reproducing. Reproducing-punch machines may also be called "document-originating machines." Document-originating machines perform all the functions of the reproducing punch but they have an added capability to end-print a line of eight numbers in one of two printing positions on the same card in which the data are punched or on another card. "End printing" refers to printing across the end column of a card, whereas regular printing is across rows. End printing is advantageous for easy identification when cards are placed in typical employee-time-card racks and similar storage devices.

Summary Punching. Summary punching is accomplished by interconnecting the reproducing machine and the accounting machine with a cable. As data are accumulated within the accounting machine, indicative information as well as summarized totals are sent to the reproducing machine, via the connecting

Fig. 6 Reproducing-punch machine. (*Courtesy of International Business Machines Corp.*)

cable, to be punched into a card. This is controlled through control-panel wiring in both the accounting machine and the gang-punch machine. Summary punching is described in greater detail below, in the section "Accounting Machines."

Gang Punching. Gang punching is the punching of data read from a lead or master card into subsequent detail cards. This can be illustrated by having a lead or master card which contains a date which you want punched into detail cards (these cards could be blank or contain punched data in columns other than those in which the date are to be punched). The lead card has a signifying punch which the machine senses, indicating that this card is the master card and should not be punched. Through control-panel wiring, the impulse from the card columns that contain the data are carried to punches so all subsequent detail cards are punched, one at a time.

Reproducing. A deck of cards with punched numerical, alphabetic, or special characters can be reproduced into another deck of cards. The punched cards are placed into a "read" hopper and pass under hole-sensing brushes which transfer the date to be reproduced to the punch dies via a control panel. Blank cards are placed in this "punch" hopper and pass under the punch dies to receive the data transferred from the reading mechanism as routed by the control-panel wiring. The control-panel wiring determines which columns are to be read from the original card and in what columns of the reproduced card these data are to be punched. An illustration of this operation would be to produce the stock numbers from card columns 1 through 6 of the master card into card columns 15 through 20 of the reproduced card. The master card might be an inventory stock status card and the reproduced card might be for cyclical physical inventory purposes.

Simultaneous reproducing and gang-punching operations are possible. In some cases, this will mean completing a job with fewer machine runs.

Associated with the reading station and the punching station is a set of sensing mechanisms which are used for the comparing operation. As a card is reproduced both the original and the duplicated cards pass into the second station. The original card is reread and is checked by comparing circuits. If no errors exist, the cards pass into their respective stackers. If an error has occurred, then an error indication light is activated and the machine stops so that the operator can determine the cause of the error. Comparing can also be accomplished on gang-punching operation.

Other Functions. An optional feature of reproducing machines is mark-sensed punching. This feature provides a sensing mechanism on the machine that will read cards that have been marked with electrically conducting lead pencils. These marks represent numerical or alphabetic information which the mark-sensing device converts to the corresponding holes in the proper column(s). An illustration of this feature would be having an employee mark-sense the quantity produced on a production labor card which would then be mechanically converted into punched data.

Other optional features include end printing and ticket converting. Both of these features are discussed later in this chapter.

SORTING MACHINES

Sorting machines (Fig. 7) can perform two functions: selection and sequencing. The sorter senses holes punched in selected card columns of a card. Through this mechanism cards can be selected from a deck or rearranged in a predetermined numerical or alphabetic sequence.

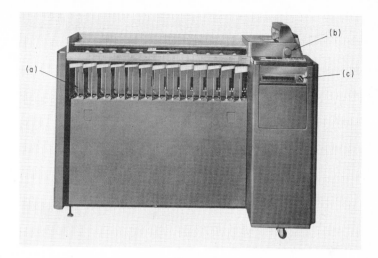

Fig. 7 Sorting machine: (*a*) sorting pockets; (*b*) column-selection knob; (*c*) sort-selection switch. (*Courtesy of International Business Machines Corp.*)

Machine Operation. A column-selection knob allows the positioning of the sensing device at the appropriate card column to be sorted. A sort-selection switch is provided to allow for the type of sorting desired (numerical, alphabetic, or alphameric sorting). Twelve digit-suppression keys permit suppress sorting on specific punching positions, that is, punches not to be sensed. There are 13 sorting pockets (*a*), which includes one pocket for each of the punching positions plus one reject pocket. A positive card-jam detection device automatically stops the machine if a card jam occurs. An editing feature rejects error cards into the reject pocket so the sorting may continue without stopping the machine.

An illustration of the selection process would be selecting cards which had a transaction code of 8 in card column 80. The cards would be placed into the card hopper face down, 9 punching row toward the machine. The column-selection knob (*b*) would be set to column 80. The sort-selection switch (*c*) would be set to numeric. All the digit-suppression keys would be depressed except 8, which would force all cards with a transaction code of other than 8 in card column 80 to fall into the reject pocket. Only code 8 would be selected from the deck of cards and would appear in pocket 8 (after depressing the start button).

If a deck of cards concerning inventory were to be sorted into numerical sequence by stock-room bin location, which was punched in card columns 1 through 3 of each card, then the operation would be as follows:

1. The cards would be placed in the card hopper, as previously explained.
2. The column-selection knob would be set on column 3.
3. The sort-selection switch would be set to numeric.
4. There would be no digit-suppression keys depressed.
5. After the sort on column 3 was completed, the cards would be removed from the pockets from right to left.
6. The column-selection knob would be moved to column 2 and the cards replaced in the card hopper for the column 2 sort.

7. Column 1 would then be sorted, after which the cards would be in sequence by stock-room bin location.

COLLATING MACHINES

Collators (Fig. 8) are machines that can automatically feed and compare two decks of punched cards. They merge or match the card decks filed in sequence and simultaneously select the unmatched cards from either file. The collator also checks the sequence of a card file to ensure correct ascending or descending order. A combination of these functions may be performed at the same time.

Fig. 8 Collating machine. (*Courtesy International Business Machines Corp.*)

Machine Operation. Pulling or filing cards automatically, interfiling cards in sequence, substituting new cards for old cards, and selecting predetermined cards in random sequence are functons that can be performed by collating machines through the use of proper control-panel wiring. It is possible to read special characters and alphabetic punched data as well as numerical data. Double punch and blank-column checking can also be accomplished on selected card fields.

Merging is the combining of two files of cards, already in sequence, into a single file. The cards in one file are compared with cards in the other file to determine which card should feed first into the merge pocket (stacker).

The matching function is performed by comparing two files of cards to determine that a card or group of cards in one file matches each card or group of cards in the other file. At the completion of a matching operation there can be four groups of cards: two groups of matched cards and two groups of unmatched cards. This operation is performed at a faster rate than merging because equals are fed from both feeds simultaneously.

Sequence checking of cards is accomplished by comparing each card with the card ahead to ascertain either an alphamerical or numerical sequence, depending upon the requirements. If a card is out of sequence within a file of cards, the card can be selected into a stacker pocket or the collator can be stopped. This operation can be performed in either feed hopper or in both feed hoppers simultaneously.

A particular card may be selected from a file of cards. The card selected can be an X or 11 punch card, a no X or 11 punch card, the first card of a group, a single card group, a zero balance card, a card with a particular number, a card out of sequence, or any other card conforming to a pattern set up by control-panel wiring.

An illustration of merging cards would be merging inventory issue and receipt transactions behind the appropriate inventory stock status card. Once these cards are merged, the merged file of cards can be run on an accounting machine to prepare an updated stock status report and summary-punch a new inventory deck of stock status cards to replace the old status cards.

ACCOUNTING MACHINES

Accounting machines have two basic functions: to print alphabetic and numeric data from punched cards in an orderly, meaningful, and desired format, and to provide data totals by proper classifications. The number of totals which can be accumulated at one time and the speed and processing capacity vary with the type and model of accounting machine.

The accounting machine illustrated in Fig. 9 has the capability to read cards

Fig. 9 Accounting machine. (*Courtesy of International Business Machines Corp.*)

and perform detail, group, and multiple-line printing from one card, for layout, arithmetic and storage operations, and summary punching.

Card Reading, Printing, and Forms Control Operations. Punched cards are read by two reading stations, which allows cards to be read as often as desired for such operations as multiple-line printing or cross-footing amounts from a single card. Once a card has been read the accounting-machine operations are determined by a control panel and the associated wiring.

Printing is accomplished through the use of 120 print wheels. Each print wheel has 47 different characters (10 numeric, 26 alphabetic, and 11 special characters). As data are read from the punched card, they may be printed through the use of control-panel wiring which identifies the card columns that are to be read and printed and what print wheels are to be used to print the data (print format).

Print forms may be positioned and controlled in the accounting machine automatically by the prepunched tape that controls the carriage and through control-panel wiring which directs the tape-control mechanism.

Arithmetic Operations. Arithmetic operations are performed in counters. Counter sizes and capacities vary with machines, but the described accounting machine has 112 counter positions which are arranged in 20 banks of 3, 4, 6, and 8 positions each. A 3-position counter can add up to 999, a 4-position counter up to 9,999, etc. If it is necessary to accumulate larger totals, for example, 12 positions, it is possible to join counter groups (a 4 and an 8, two 6s, etc.).

Counters add or subtract based on control punches within the individual cards. Generally, amounts to be subtracted (credits) are identified by an X (11) punch in a specific column of the card containing the credit amount. Therefore, cards without an X punch are cards that contain debits or amounts to be added.

Totals are determined through compare operations performed by the control-panel wiring to indicate when data classification groupings change. An illustration of group totaling would be an inventory transaction report. Issues, receipts, and adjustments would be in inventory part-number sequence. As the inventory transactions are read, they would be printed and accumulated. As the inventory item-number changes, the accounting machine could print totals of the different transactions by part number and space the information on the form for ease of reading. As the counters are read out for printing, they would be reset to be reused.

Storage Operations. This accounting machine has four storage units which are used to store numeric or alphabetic information. These data may be used for report and page headings and summary punching, which is described below.

Summary-punching Operations. Summary punching is the automatic preparation of one card with a total to replace the information contained in a group of detail cards. A summary card would contain the identification for the group and one or more totals accumulated for that group. The primary purpose of summary punching is to reduce the volume of cards and thus accelerate the preparation of reports, and thereby reduce processing time.

Summary cards are generally produced while preparing a detail report on an accounting machine. This is accomplished with a summary-punch machine that is cable-connected to the accounting machine and through the use of control-panel wiring on both machines.

An illustration of this function would be the preparation of an inventory stock status report and the creation at the same time of summary cards or balance-forward cards.

CALCULATING MACHINES

The electronic calculating punch machine (Fig. 10) logic may be compared to a manufacturing plant where raw materials (input factors) are received, manufactured into a product (calculation), passed on as output (punching) to a checking and inspection department (recalculation) for approval, and shipped to a customer or stocked in inventory (end of operation—card into card stacker).

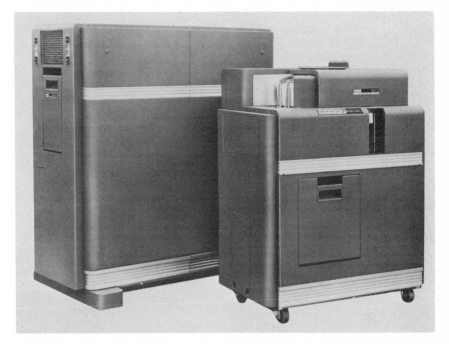

Fig. 10 Electronic calculating punch machine. (*Courtesy of International Business Machines Corp.*)

Calculators are machines which are capable of performing addition, subtraction, multiplication, and division operations. Data are read from a punched card into the calculator where computations are made. A series of mathematical steps are performed within one processing, and the results are punched into the same card. The electronic calculating punch performs these calculations utilizing control-panel wiring as the card-read punch reads and punches cards.

The control-panel-wired program for the mathematical steps is the forerunner to the stored programs used in computers. The logic used in computers is basically the same logic as used on the electronic calculating punch.

Calculating Operations. Group calculations can be accomplished on the electronic calculating punch machine, such as accumulation of factors from a group of cards and the punching of summarized or calculated results into the last card of the group.

All calculations and punching may be checked in the same operation where storage capacity permits. When storage capacity is limited, a separate run is required. Checking results within the same run involves reading the initial input factors and the result of the punched calculation back into the machine so that they may be recalculated and zero-balanced against the punched results. Performing the check in a separate run involves recalculating the original calculation and repunching the results and then checking the resultant card field for double punch and blank columns. If neither double-punch nor blank-column error detection occurs on the original or the check run, then the calculated result is accepted as correct. Reading, calculating, and punching require that the control panel in both the card read punch and electronic calculating punch machine be wired for that purpose.

Punched cards are placed in the card read punch hopper prior to the calculating operation. The cards are fed to the first reading station where input factors are read into the electronic calculating punch machine. During the time that the card passes between this reading station and the punch station where the results are punched into the card, the calculations are performed. The cards then pass to the second reading station where recalculations are performed. The cards then pass to the card stacker.

An illustration of this operation would be pricing an inventory. Each card would contain the inventory balance and the standard cost assigned to the item. These cards would pass through the card read punch with the operations being performed in the electronic calculating punch machine for the calculation of inventory balance times standard cost. The resultant inventory value would be punched into the card, which is then recalculated at the second reading station and stacked in the card read punch card stacker. These cards could then be run through the accounting machine to prepare the report.

COMPUTING ACCOUNTING MACHINES

Within the past several years there has been an advancement in the design of accounting machines. The added capability extends the arithmetic operations to multiplication and division, making possible the evolution of the computing accounting machine (CAM). These machines not only have the capability to compute but also have the ability to perform all the functions attributed to accounting machines.

The computing-accounting machine reflects the fact that a computing device has been added to the standard features on an accounting machine. The computing device can be used for addition, subtraction, multiplication, and division, and also allows for certain multiple computations to be performed in one machine cycle without interfering with other accounting-machine functions. These computations do not delay the processing of normal accounting-machine operations. If a series of computations is necessary, then additional machine cycles would be necessary.

The computing device contains six registers with 11 positions per register. When not being used for computations, these registers may be used for cross-footing amounts from various inputs, such as fields read from a card, counter output, storage-unit output, and output from the computing device. Data input to and output for the computing device are provided through the input and output mechanisms of the computing accounting machine.

The computing accounting machine has, in addition to the computing device, all the features of the accounting machine. The computing device imposes no restrictions upon the operation of standard and special accounting-machine features. Because the wired control panel is used to program the computing accounting machine, there is a physical limitation on the number of control-panel hubs available. Therefore, any combination of features is constrained by the number of control-panel hubs used with the computing device.

If the illustration, used above in discussing calculating machines, of pricing an inventory were to be done on the computing accounting machine, the calculations could be performed and the report prepared in one machine run. The result of the calculations, inventory value, could not be punched into the original data card, but normally would be summary-punched to prepare an output card. Therefore, in one machine run it would be possible to read the input cards, perform computations, arrange format and print a report with totals by class, and also summary-punch a new detail card and/or summary cards. This process could save at least one machine run and the resultant time involved.

OTHER UNIT-RECORD EQUIPMENT

Ticket-converting Device. A multipurpose machine, when attached to an accounting machine, is capable of converting information-punched tickets into cards, gang-punching the common data, and then summary-punching the balance or total cards. The detachable stub tickets are useful in controlling inventory in many retail merchandising applications. A similar device is available for use with the reproducing punch.

End-printing Devices. These machines, normally an added feature of the reproducing machine, convert punched information into bold printing across the end of the card simultaneously with gang-punching, reproducing, and mark-sensed punching operations. This end printing is similar to interpreting and makes quick reference to the card possible. Cards are printed in this manner for use in prepunched files where cards are stored on end or for use in attendance-card racks for convenient reference and selection.

Tape-punching Machines. This machine reads alphabetic and numeric information punched into cards and translates the information into various-width channel tapes. The tape may be utilized in turn for data transmission over long or short distances.

Tape-reading Machines. These machines utilize the process of converting numerical or alphabetic information from punched paper tape into punched cards. The machine may be set to read information from various-size channel tape. The machine can be programmed to punch into cards all or part of the data from tape.

UTILIZATION OF UNIT-RECORD EQUIPMENT

The equipment described in the preceding pages of this chapter will be only as valuable as the imagination of the people using it. Described below is an actual unit-record system which has been used successfully to control the work-in-process inventory of a major manufacturing company.

The Reason for Needing Unit-record Equipment. The manual system utilized was too slow in responding to the changing conditions needed for tight control over the work in process. A handwritten report of job status was issued biweekly listing everything in process with its due date. It was a huge clerical effort to obtain this report and the information was two days old at time of issuance. The expeditors were continually making up "hot" lists of priority items. The need for quicker information flow was urgent.

The objective of the systems redesign was to have a semiweekly job status report, no more than four weeks old when issued. This report would reveal the department location of each job and the date the job was due out of each department.   It would also serve as a departmental load report.

The System Utilizing Unit-record Equipment. Every lot of work issued to the plant had a punched card which indicated descriptive information such as the blueprint number, type of material, quantity, lot number, and a schedule time by department.   A manufacturing-day calendar and the department number were used as a combined four-digit number, two digits for each, to indicate movement of work from one department to the next.   Time-period calendar and digit-code correspondence sheets were issued to all users of the system so that the digit codes could be easily translated to calendar days.   Daily movement of the manufacturing lot was reported to production control and the corresponding punched card representing the particular lot of work was mark-sensed and manually moved from the tray for the first department to the tray for the next department.   The mark-sensing principle served to eliminate from the resultant report information about where the lot of work had been.

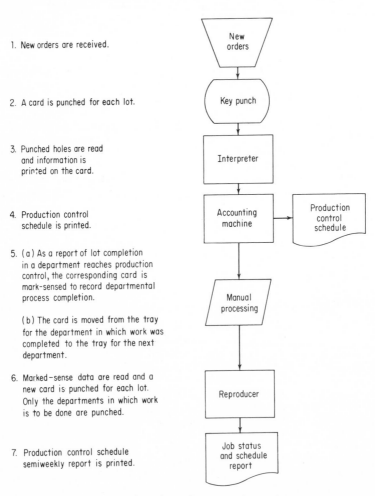

Fig. 11 Flow-chart shop reporting systems.

Completed processes were marked-sensed and not punched in the new card (see Fig. 11). The amount of time a lot was scheduled to stay in a particular department was determined by standard data available in industrial engineering and production control.

A report generated from the card file representing the status of the lots was issued twice a week to every department foreman. This report indicated all work in the particular department with a schedule of its due date out of the department and the due date for completion. Copies of this report were sent to production control personnel and factory management personnel for control purposes. Changes were incorporated daily and indicated on the next issuance of the production control schedule report. The result was a work-in-process status report twice a week with information only four hours old when the report was issued. Customer service improved because of factual delivery information and work in process was slightly reduced due to the systematic, orderly procedure of scheduling the lots of work utilizing standard data.

Figure 11 indicates the flow of information and the type of unit-record equipment utilized in this system. As the cards for the manufacturing lots are issued to the plant on a daily basis, working decks are punched and interpreted for those lots. These cards are processed through an accounting machine to obtain a listing. This listing is used in proofreading the original documents so that errors are detected and corrected immediately. The cards are then filed by department in the production control file. When a lot is completed in a department, it is reported to production control. The card for the completed lot is mark-sensed and moved from the tray for the department in which the job was completed to the tray for the next department. This manual operation eliminates the need for sorting and collating later. Twice a week the cards are sent to the data processing center by department sequence and are processed through the reproducing summary punch. This equipment updates the cards that have been mark-sensed by eliminating activity that has occurred. The cards are then fed into the accounting machine, and copies of the production schedule control report are printed. These copies are collated and ready for distribution within two hours after being received in the data processing center.

SUMMARY

The intent of this chapter is to acquaint the reader with the various types of unit-record equipment available. There are a variety of manufacturers and systems available, and it is suggested that the interested reader review more than one type of equipment before deciding which best meets his needs. Most manufacturers offer excellent advice regarding the multitude of problems that a customer may have. The application of this equipment covers all aspects of the industrial, educational, and governmental fields. The application described is one of many that have helped various businesses improve the performance of their operations.

Literature is available from manufacturers describing their equipment and its effective utilization. It is suggested that the services of these various companies be investigated for more detailed study regarding your particular application or problem area.

BIBLIOGRAPHY

Carter, Byron L.: *Data Processing for Small Business,* MacFadden-Bartell Corp., New York, 1966.
Hartkemeir, H. P., *Data Processing,* John Wiley & Sons, Inc., New York, 1966.

Lazzaro, Victor: *Systems and Procedures,* 2d ed., Prentice-Hall, Inc., Englewood Cliffs, N.J., 1968.

Martin, E. Wainright: *Electronic Data Processing Information,* Richard D. Irwin, Inc., Homewood, Ill., 1965.

Meacham, Alan D.: *Data Processing Wiring Guide,* American Data Processing, Detroit, Mich., 1962.

Optner, Stanford: *Systems Analysis for Business Management,* 2d ed., Prentice-Hall, Englewood Cliffs, N.J., 1968.

Rice, Donald E.: *Introduction to Data Processing,* Otterbein Press, Dayton, Ohio, 1962.

Chapter **23**

Computer-based Systems

EDITOR:

Joseph A. Orlicky *Industry Consultant, International Business Machines Corp., White Plains, New York*

CONTRIBUTORS:

E. V. Griffith *Program Administrator, International Business Machines Corp., White Plains, New York*

Roger W. M. Letts *Manager, Operations Analysis, Lederle Laboratories, Pearl River, New York*

Paul Schneider *Principal, A. T. Kearney & Company, Inc., Chicago, Illinois*

Leighton F. Smith *Management Consultant, Arthur Anderson & Company, Chicago, Illinois*

J. L. Sorensen *Management Consultant, Arthur Young & Company, Chicago, Illinois*

CONTENTS

In the manufacturing industries, the production and inventory control function has become a significant user of electronic data processing systems, commonly known as computers. Areas of planning, inventory management, and production-activity control represent opportunities for extensive computer applications because of the very large information-handling requirements inherent in the planning and control functions.

Computer applications in production and inventory control are bound to grow in both scope and sophistication due to an increasing complexity of products and their accelerating rate of change. Managements are exerting pressure for low inventory investment, uniform factory work loads, and high customer-delivery service, and in general a desire for the refinement and better responsiveness of existing systems.

The progressively lower cost of computer power and storage will enable even small manufacturing companies to utilize computers. It can be expected that practically everyone engaged in production and inventory control will, to some degree, become involved with computers and computer applications.

The purpose of this chapter is to provide basic orientation for the practitioner of production and inventory control, in the three broad areas of:

1. The machine: Concepts, as well as its functional and physical makeup
2. Computer processing methodology: Techniques and methods of utilization
3. Production and inventory control applications: Their range, their use, and the conversion from previous methods to computer processing

Definitions and brief explanations of the most commonly used terms and those basic functions for which the reader may seek reference information constitute this chapter. For pursuit of the various subjects in greater depth, a bibliography is provided at the end of the chapter.

COMPUTER AS A CONCEPT

The computer is a machine designed to duplicate, amplify, and extend certain *powers of the human intellect*. Despite its name, a computer is not just a device that performs arithmetic operations. Like the human mind, it has the ability to manipulate symbols and process information by receiving, storing (remembering), operating on, and outputting data. These information-handling operations are directed by a program of instructions which is stored in the computer's memory. This principle of using internally stored, alterable instructions to control the action of the machine is what sets the computer apart from any other mechanism ever created by man.

In addition to duplicating mental processes, the computer is also capable of performing clerical tasks that can be viewed as mechanical and physical, such as retrieval of records, posting and filing, i.e., record keeping, as well as transmitting, regenerating, and display of information. While the computer is relatively limited as compared to the human mind in its range of capability, and while it uses rather crude methods of internal processing, it has advantages of *speed, total recall, and complete accuracy.* Speed is the dominant characteristic, as computer circuitry typically handles signals at rates of millions per second.

The computer is also called an "electronic data processing system," because it is actually composed of several connected, interacting, and mutually dependent machines and devices operating in harmony under central control.

Another dimension of the computer concept is the relationship between machinery (hardware) and program (software). They are inseparable in that both, in combination, determine the total power of the computer, which has certain of its capabilities designed into its physical mechanism (wired-in capabilities) and others supplied through stored instructions (programmed capabilities).

In designing a computer, there are opportunities for trade-offs between these two types of capability. As a general rule, anything that can be programmed may instead be wired in, at an increase in hardware cost. This cost increment is then repetitively incurred with every unit being manufactured. Programmed capability, on the other hand, is more expensive to develop but once provided can be infinitely reproduced at nominal cost. Square-root extraction, for instance, could be provided through special circuitry (extra cost, fast execution) or through a string of instructions that will produce the same result (no extra hardware cost but slower execution) by utilizing the regular arithmetic devices.

Unlike other machines, all of which have a relatively limited, special purpose (e.g., locomotion, metal removal, bulk-material displacement), the computer is a truly *general-purpose* machine in its sphere of duplicating mental processes. Its application potential is universal in the sense that it can be employed wherever the human mind is at work.

To the extent that production and inventory control consists of mental and clerical procedures, it lends itself to potential computer applications. The computer, viewed as a production and inventory control tool, presents many opportunities for the improvement of production and inventory control performance. This will be particularly true in areas of planning and replanning, simulation of results of alternative courses of action, implementation of scientific techniques, and the rapid gathering and evaluation of production data—in short, doing things previously impractical or simply impossible.

COMPUTER SYSTEM CHARACTERISTICS

Stored Program. A computer is an information-handling machine that can execute instructions in a predetermined and *self-directed* manner. This self-direction is its outstanding characteristic. The fact that a computer does not depend on external instructions during the execution process, but instead has the ability to read and remember instructions, means that it need not be instructed as the job progresses. It can thus perform tasks of considerable complexity from start to finish without intervention.

The instructions for the execution of the data manipulation process are linked together into a logical arrangement called a "program." This internally stored program represents the series of steps that must be taken to produce a desired result. The computer has the ability to proceed automatically from one instruction step to another. Because its internal circuitry is so fast, it is important that it be able to *access* its instructions equally fast. The earliest computers had to read in their instructions from punched paper tape or a similar medium, with the result that the overall speed depended almost entirely on the time required to read these instructions, which, in turn, was dictated by the speed at which the medium could be moved physically. In modern computers, a stored program can be made available to the instruction-execution circuitry at the same speed at which the latter is able to function.

It is this speed of access to the instructions, plus the capability for program self-modification and conditional branching that makes the computer so versatile and prodigious for information processing work. Program "self-modification" consists, in essence, of executing an instruction that changes another previously executed stored instruction. Thus the program, in successive iterations or *loops,* need not be repetitive. So-called "conditional-branching" instructions cause the machine to determine whether a given condition exists, and depending on the outcome, to follow alternative instruction sequences or program paths. It is this ability to execute conditional branching instructions that enables the computer to perform *logical operations,* or to make decisions. Through the device of conditional branching, the program can loop back to execute a given set of instructions over and over again, using different data each time.

Central-processor Functions. The central-processing unit is the heart of a computer system, and it controls and coordinates the operations of all the interconnected devices that comprise this system. It regulates the movement of data in and out of the system, activates the appropriate programs, and executes the individual instructions. Functionally, the central processor is made up of the following four subunits:

1. Input-output control unit
2. Main memory unit
3. Central control unit
4. Arithmetic and logic unit

Input-Output Control Unit. In a computer system, all input-output devices are under program control, and none function automatically. Each step of an input or output operation is taken in response to an instruction of the program that is in control, either directly or indirectly through an attached input-output control device which is interposed between the central processor and the individual input-output devices. In the latter case it is said that the program "transfers control" of input-output operations to the intermediate device by instructing it to execute an operation and *returning control* upon completion. Thus, the central processor, in effect, delegates this type of work to the intermediate device which then, in turn, executes a series of *commands* that control individual input-output steps.

Within the central-processing unit, the circuitry and related internal devices that *interface* with external input-output machinery, including intermediate control devices, comprise the input-output control unit.

Main Memory Unit. The memory is the focal point of all data movement. It is that part of the central processor which stores information in a unit of hardware whose technology affords rapid access. The speed of access to memory is one of the prime determinants of the overall power of the system, and it is expressed in terms of *cycles* per second, i.e., rate of consecutive accesses. Depending on make and model, computer memories cycle upward of a million times per second. In the memory are stored:

1. All active instructions
2. Tables of reference data, as required
3. Blocks of data being processed

Because of the relatively high cost of its hardware, computer main memory is of limited size and the information included in the three categories above resides in it only temporarily. Information is being transferred in and out, as required, between memory and secondary storage or memory and input-output devices.

Main memory is organized in small subunits or *words*, each of which is uniquely identified by an *address*. The size of the word will vary with individual computer design, from 1 decimal digit or character up to about 12 such characters. Instructions in a program reference the contents of each word by specifying its address. The instructions, at the time of program execution also reside at specific address locations in memory, from which the central control unit automatically and successively retrieves them for purposes of execution.

Central Control Unit. The principal functions of this unit are to:

1. Receive and interpret instructions
2. Send appropriate signals to the executing hardware

An instruction is moved from memory into a *register* of the control unit, where the latter is said to "look at it" to determine what it is and how it must be executed. The signals generated that will cause the instruction to be executed include sending addresses to the memory unit causing it to read out or to store data, directing the arithmetic and logic unit to operate on the data, and initiating the flow of data between memory and input-output devices.

As instructions move into the control unit, so-called address registers are activated that keep track of the address of the last instruction and of the one to be retrieved next. Other registers monitor the substeps of both retrieval and execution operations, to assure coordinated function and the proper alternating between the *instruction state* (retrieve and interpret) and *execution state* (execute).

The central control unit also receives signals indicating some special conditions. Internal error-checking circuitry will generate special signals. Attached devices will send special signals at the termination of data transfers. External mechanisms, such as clocks or sensors, can be wired to provide special signals. Internal mechanisms of various sorts will send signals to the control unit to alert it to the occurrence of some special condition. On receiving a special-condition signal, the control unit may cause the central processor to stop, or it may interrupt the active program and transfer control to special sets of stored instructions designed to deal with the special condition being signaled.

Arithmetic and Logic Unit. This unit of the central processor performs the *mathematical operations* as well as the so-called *logical operations,* such as branching and decision operations, which means making choices between alternative sets of instructions. This is the unit that actually operates on and modifies information. Its circuitry will perform all the basic arithmetic functions but may, in less expensive models, use limited methods for accomplishing this. For instance, addition circuitry not only adds but, through *complements,* does subtraction as well. Furthermore, with the additional ability to *shift* (from decimal-point position) numbers, it can also be used to do multiplication and division. To achieve higher-speed arithmetic operations, other models have special circuitry to perform multiplication, etc. Logical operations are basically of two kinds:

1. Branch on condition
2. Compare

In the first instance, branching, as defined above, takes place if a condition exists. This condition is being *tested* at that point in the program. For example, the sign of a number may be tested, or the existence of a card in the reader, or the position of a switch that can be set externally.

In the second instance, two numbers are *compared* for magnitude, and depending on the outcome, alternative instruction sequences are executed. The testing, comparing, and branching capabilities of a computer system permit the construction of highly sophisticated programs to handle the most complex jobs.

Input-Output Devices. This family of devices, also known as "peripheral equipment," provides the means of entering data into, and removing data from, the system. Some of these devices have only one function—for example, input only, in the case of a card reader; or output only, in the case of a printer. Others combine both functions—for example, a console typewriter. Still others are, strictly speaking, *secondary storage* units, such as magnetic drums or disk files.

Input devices receive data from an outside source and *encode* it, or else receive it already encoded in *machine-readable* form, so that it can be manipulated by the computer. The group of these devices includes:

1. Punched-card readers
2. Paper-tape readers
3. Attached typewriters
4. Plastic-badge readers
5. Key-driven terminals
6. Optical-scanning devices
7. Magnetic-ink sensing devices
8. Various sensor devices
9. Voice-recognition devices

Output devices display data or record it on one of several media, either encoded (for subsequent use as input) or *decoded* and presented in *man-readable, recognizable* form. The group of these devices is varied and includes:

1. Card punches
2. Paper-tape punches
3. High-speed printers
4. Attached typewriters
5. Visual display (cathode-ray tube) units
6. Graphic plotters
7. Voice answer-back devices
8. Other signal-transmitting (lights, sound) devices

Secondary Storage. Devices in this category provide a means of storing large quantities of data and have three common characteristics:

1. Data are stored in machine-readable form.
2. Relatively rapid access to these data is provided.
3. It is a relatively inexpensive form of storage.

The technology used in the current family of secondary storage devices is the *magnetic surface* on which encoded data can be *written* and *read* by so-called *read-write heads.* These heads utilize the electromagnet principle to magnetize, or sense the polarization of tiny areas of the surface passing under the heads at high speed. The magnetic-tape unit, the magnetic-strip or data-cell unit, the disk file, and drum storage belong to this group of devices.

MAGNETIC-TAPE UNITS: These devices are capable of reading and writing, on a reel of magnetic tape as it is unwound and rewound. Data are written on the tape in *blocks* separated by blank *gaps.* One block at a time is read into main memory, and the gap signals to the system the end of the block and the reel stops. After the program has dealt with the block of data, another instruction will cause the reel to start unwinding and the next block will be read into memory.

Tape speed, or *data transfer* rate between the head and memory, is measured in terms of tens or even hundreds of thousands of characters per second. Since many millions of characters can be stored on a single reel of tape, this method of secondary storage is both low in cost and of unlimited capacity, because tape is reusable and the reels interchangeable. Both programs and data files can be stored on reels and kept in a *tape library.* The operator retrieves them for mounting on tape units as required. Until mounted, the tape-reel data is said to be "off-line," which means they are not immediately accessible by the computer.

Another limitation of magnetic tape is the necessity of *sequential* processing, because every data block must be read successively into memory, whether or not it is needed for the data processing job in question. Thus, a record that may be located physically in the middle of the tape can be read only after the reel has been unwound, in successive starts and stops, to that point. The delay inherent in accessing any specific record on tape makes this method of secondary storage unsuitable for applications requiring direct or *random* access to file records.

MAGNETIC-STRIP STORAGE UNITS: To overcome the inherent limitations of *sequential access* for magnetic-tape storage, devices in this category utilize what is in effect tape cut up into short strips. A *cartridge* containing a number of these strips (or magnetic cards of larger width which function as several strips of tape mounted side by side) is inserted into the storage unit, which can select individual strips directly and mechanically transfer each under the read-write heads.

Random access is thus provided, while retaining the read-write speed and low storage cost of magnetic tape. The delay between records, however, is much longer due to the mechanical operations of strip retrieval and return to cartridge. Machines in this category are considered *low-speed access* devices.

DISK-FILE STORAGE UNITS: These secondary storage units utilize rapidly rotating disks, on which data are recorded magnetically in a series of concentric *tracks*. A disk-file module may consist of one or several disks mounted on a common shaft. Both surfaces of the disk can be accessed. An *access mechanism*, or *arm*, equipped with read-write heads provides the motion between the rim and the center of the disk. Data records stored on the various surfaces and tracks can thus be accessed directly and either a whole track or a portion of it can be read into memory or, conversely, written.

The obvious limitation is the time that it takes for the physical movement of the access arm from track to track. Faster units are equipped with more than one arm per disk module, permitting simultaneous access to multiple tracks and overlapping of access so that while one arm reads or writes, another is in motion to the next position.

Modern disk storage units operate at very high speed, the data transfer rates being in the order of several hundreds of thousands of characters per second. The number of disk units that can operate *on-line* to a single computer system is limited, but maximum capacities are counted in billions of characters. Another feature is the removable disk module or *disk pack* which, like tape reels, can be stored off-line in unlimited quantities.

Disk storage units afford fairly high-speed random access to file records. Aside from access-mechanism motion delay, there is also the inherent *rotational delay* determined by the revolutions per minute of the disk module. These delays, which make up the record *access time*, are measured in thousandths of a second.

MAGNETIC-DRUM STORAGE UNITS: A cylinder rotating along its axis at very high speed represents the fastest method of secondary storage. Data are stored in tracks on the circumference of the cylinder, each track continuously passing under a stationary read-write head. There are as many heads as tracks, so there is no access motion delay but only rotational delay. The multiple heads, of course, increase the cost of the unit. The capacity of magnetic drums is limited, but the data transfer rates are upwards of a million characters per second.

These drums are used primarily to store programs rather than data files. In many computer applications, it is important to be able to bring a new program into main memory fast. To the extent that such programs can be stored on high-speed access drums, the main memory need not be as large.

It is the main memory that is the fastest of all storage devices, because it has no moving parts causing mechanical motion delays—but it is also the most expensive.

COMPUTER TECHNOLOGY

In concept, computer design logic is independent of the technology utilized in implementing it. The technology of the hardware varies and changes in time. The "state of the art" determines the specific technology selected by the computer manufacturer based on performance characteristics, reliability, cost, and size of components.

Character Representation. While technology may vary, all digital computers have one central characteristic in common, which is the capability to represent *characters*, numeric, alphabetic, and special, internally within the machine's components. The requirement of internal representation of characters and the ease of their manipulation is basic, and the universally employed method is that of *binary*, binary-based, or binary-coded characters.

There are many different schemes (codes) for character representation, but all define the various characters by means of strings of subcharacters or positions, each of which can have one of two values. These values are commonly represented as 0 and 1, but can also be thought of as "yes" and "no," "positive" and "negative," "on" and "off," etc. Under each code, the meaning of each combination of the two values is assigned by convention.

For instance, the letter K in the five-position Teletype code is represented as follows:

	Position				
	1	2	3	4	5
Code	•	•	•	•	•
or	1	1	1	1	0
or	yes	yes	yes	yes	no
or	on	on	on	on	off

In the seven-position U.S. Standard Code for Information Interchange (USASCII), the same letter is represented as follows:

	Position						
	1	2	3	4	5	6	7
Code	1	1	0	1	0	0	1

This general method of representing characters by way of groups of two-value or bistate symbols permits both internal storage and manipulation using electricity-related technologies, especially magnetics (bipolar devices) and electronics (pulse-switching devices), which lend themselves to character handling and character manipulation at very high rates of speed. As much of such manipulation is arithmetic, computers use the binary method of representing numeric values to take advantage of the simplicity and speed of *binary arithmetic*.

Binary Number System. The decimal number system that we normally use has 10 symbols (0 through 9). In this system, 10 is the base or *radix* because the positional value of a number is assigned in increments of the power of 10. Thus, the number 438 represents 8×10^0 plus 3×10^1 plus 4×10^2, or 8 plus 30 plus 400.

The binary (or base two) system of numbers uses only two symbols, 0 and 1; radix is 2 and the positional value varies with the power of 2. Thus, the number 111, expressed in *binary digits* or *bits*, represents 1×2^0 plus 1×2^1 plus 1×2^2 or 1 plus 2 plus 4, for a total value of 7.

	Positional value of bit						
	64	32	16	8	4	2	1
Binary representation	1	1	0	1	1	0	1

The above number 1101101 represents the value of 109, or the sum of 64 plus 32 plus 8 plus 4 plus 1. With only two symbols available, it took seven positions to express a value which in decimal requires merely three positions. Binary is less compact than decimal but its advantage lies in the extreme simplicity of its arithmetic. The logic of binary addition and multiplication, for example, is summarized in the following tables:

Rules for addition   Examples

	0	1
0	0	1
1	1	0*

Decimal	Binary
5	101
+6	+110
11	1011

*Carry 1

Rules for multiplication   Examples

	0	1
0	0	0
1	0	1

Decimal	Binary
5	101
×6	×110
30	000
	101
	101
	11110

Relatively simple circuitry can be devised to automate binary arithmetic, but that presupposes that data are expressed in straight or *pure binary*, such as the value of 30, or 11110, shown above. For computers used for commercial applications, it would not be practical to *convert* decimal input data to binary and in turn reconvert to decimal for output purposes. Internal representation is, therefore, *binary-coded decimal.*

Since a group of four bits can represent 16 states or combinations of ones and zeros, such a group can be so arranged as to represent the 10 states (numbers) in the decimal system. In the binary-coded decimal representation, each decimal position (and its value) is represented by a separate group of four bits. Thus, 30 would be written as 0011 and 0000 (the number three and zero, respectively). Such a system has a *mixed base*, and in doing arithmetic, it is necessary to convert from one base to another. For instance, when adding 5 and 6, the addition is:

$$
\begin{array}{r}
0101 \\
+0110 \\
\hline
1011
\end{array}
$$

The sum of 1011, which has the value of 11, must be *decimal-converted* to 0001, which represents the value of 1 to be retained in that position of the sum. There must also be a decimal carry of the value of 1 to represent the 1010 (10) carried to the next most significant position. Obviously, such a carry is not inherent in the binary-coded decimal system, but it can and must be provided by special circuitry.

Circuits and Their "Generations" Computer circuitry is the complex of paths that the signals generated by the computer-driving mechanism, or *clock*, must travel. These signals, depending on technology employed, can be *electrical* pulses in electronic computers, *light* in optical computers, *fluid* in hydraulic computers, and so forth.

The makeup of individual circuits varies with their function, but generally consists of an assemblage of components that *conduct* (wire), *regulate* (diodes, resistors), *switch* (transistors), *delay, amplify,* and *terminate* signals. It is the switching devices that permit the variety of internal signal manipulation and therefore character and data manipulation. The basic function of a switching device is to open or close a *gate*, or switch, in the circuit, thus permitting a signal either to travel through, block it, or direct it to an alternate path. It is fundamentally the switching devices that represent the technology being employed and determine the "generation" of a particular computer.

The relay, the vacuum tube, and the transistor have served the same function in, respectively, the electromechanical, electronic, and solid-state electronic technologies. With technological advancement, the device becomes smaller, faster, cheaper, and more reliable.

Integrated circuits, also known as "monolithic circuits," are fashioned into a single piece of material and represent an advanced solid-state generation. The various circuit elements are not assembled but are *deposited* onto this material by chemical, photographic, and similar processes. The microscopic dimensions attainable through these processes permit the *miniaturization* of circuits. This in itself enhances the speed of such circuits, because the electrical signals which propagate at a finite speed—the speed of light—have shorter distances to travel.

A still more advanced technology is the so-called *large-scale integration*, or LSI, which fashions multiple, connected circuits on one small *chip* of material. In the ultimate stage of LSI, a single chip could conceivably contain all the circuitry of one of the functional units of the central processor, or even the complete circuitry of all the units. In commercially available computers it is the cost, rather than the latest advancement in the state of the art, which dictates the choice of technology to be utilized.

Storage Devices. Retention, or storage, of digital data is a characteristic capability of a computer. Technologies employed to store the data vary and change with time, but functional distinction lies in whether storage is *primary* (called "memory"), which is directly accessible to the control and arithmetic units of the central processor, with very high read-write speed, or *secondary,* with lower access and read-write rates of speed, the contents of which can be read only into memory rather than directly into the control unit, as described above in the section "Secondary Storage."

The main memory acts as the working area of the computer where data and instructions are temporarily stored for instantaneous access by the central processor and where the results of arithmetic and logical operations can be stored at the same high rate of speed at which the central processor works. As jobs are completed, the memory-resident programs and data are typically transferred to secondary storage to make room for new programs and data.

In modern computers, the individual memory positions, generally one-character storage areas, are directly accessible and addressable. This contrasts with secondary storage where typically only a whole record, or block of records, can be accessed either directly (random-access storage devices) or sequentially.

After the initial variety of experimental technologies used in the first computers (magnetic slugs, drums, etc.), manufacturers have universally settled on magnetic cores (small ferrite toroids strung on wires) for main memories. Although core memories proved highly reliable, as well as being susceptible to considerable miniaturization, the manufacturing methods are rather clumsy, and their cost is therefore quite high. For this reason, they are bound to be superseded by devices which will lend themselves to further miniaturization and will minimize or eliminate the need for mechanical assembly.

Computer Design Logic. The "power" of a computer consists in so-called *throughput,* which is the capacity to perform an amount of work per unit of time. Aside from technology, quality, and speed of components, this capacity derives also from the approaches and methods of function, known as "design logic," incorporated in a particular model design.

For instance, characters of data can be transferred between memory and the central-processor control-unit circuitry in either a *serial* or a *parallel* fashion. Arithmetic can be performed in either binary or decimal mode utilizing either *fixed-point or floating-point registers.* Main memory design can utilize the *fixed word* or *field length* versus the *variable field length* principle. The former assigns a separate address only to relatively large strings, or blocks, of bit or character positions (typical word length is 32 bits); the latter partitions the memory into individually addressable characters or *bytes* (1 byte equals 8 bits).

Another design problem is devising an *addressing scheme* that permits addressing the largest number of individual memory locations while using the most compact address format. These are conflicting objectives. To the extent that memory is large and contains many unique addresses, programs tend to become bulky and occupy relatively more storage space, because memory addresses are part of each instruction.

Because of the disparity between the speed of the central processor and input-output devices, the central processor tends to waste too much time waiting for a given read-write operation to be completed. This problem can be solved by interposing a so-called *channel* between the central processor and the input-output units. The channel, actually a small, limited-capability, special-purpose computer, will accept, and store, *commands* from the central processor and will execute them by initiating, monitoring, and signaling the completion of input-output operations.   The independent control over the latter by the channel enables the central processor to do other work such as executing instructions of perhaps another program in the meantime.

Another example of alternative design logic is the so-called *scientific* versus *commercial* computer.   Scientific computation typically calls for limited input-output capability but high-speed arithmetic which is enhanced if done in binary mode using floating-point registers and fixed field length.   Commercial work, on the other hand, usually requires high input-output and data-handling capability plus variable field length, but only limited fixed-point arithmetic in decimal mode.   The best of modern, general-purpose computers combine all these capabilities, which are alternately called out through special instructions, depending on the type of job being run.

COMPUTER METHODOLOGY

Batch Processing and Continuous Processing.   Most of the data processing functions in the area of production and inventory control can be viewed as *file-updating* tasks, or more specifically, as collecting transactions, posting to master records, evaluating new status, and determining action indicated by the new status, as presented in output reports.

With strictly manual methods of processing data, the transactions tend to be collected and posted on a running basis.   With the advent of mechanical data processing techniques, utilizing at first punched-card equipment and later the first computing machinery equipped only with card and magnetic-tape input-output units, *batch processing* became the method universally adopted.   This method, tailored to the capabilities of the then-available data processing machinery, achieves efficiency of processing by letting transactions accumulate for a time until an economical run quantity, or batch, exists.   Transactions are then sorted into the sequence of the master file to which they will be posted.   Only then does the actual data processing operation, or *run*, take place by sequentially accessing file records and updating them.

This method proved to be quite satisfactory for most accounting work, which was typically the first to be automated.   From there it was carried over into production and inventory control applications as well.   There, however, it proved less satisfactory because records between processing cycles were out of date and output reports showed historical data, such as status conditions, as of some previous point in time and activity summaries cut off at, and reported only up to, such a point in time.

These deficiencies inherent in periodic processing of data in batches can be overcome by continuous, or nonbatch, processing methods permitting transactions to be entered in random sequence and at more or less random times.   Utilization of these methods has been made possible by developments in both the technology and the methodology of electronic data processing.   The introduction of random-access secondary storage devices and larger, faster main memories reduced the dependence on sequential-access techniques.   Advances in programming brought about new concepts of data processing operation, in particular *multiprogramming* and *time-sharing*.

More advanced production and inventory control computer applications therefore utilize continuous-processing techniques, at least to some extent, but particularly in the area of control of production, scheduling, shop-floor control, receiving control, etc.   Unlike batch processing, these methods are geared to the rhythm and dynamics of the operations they are designed to control.

Communications-oriented Systems.   Continuous-processing systems mentioned above are typically implemented using input-output units remotely located from the central processor, but operating *on-line* to it. Such units bear the collective name of "terminals," which range from simple keyboard devices to small processors. They can be linked to the system by means of private cabling or telephone lines if located in the plant, or use leased telephone lines and other facilities provided by common carriers where greater geographic distances are involved. Such systems are said to be "communications oriented." The on-line linkage implies *transmission* of data and immediate access between the peripheral device and the central processor, without any form of intermediate transcription and/or storage of data.

If the application which utilizes such on-line linkage is designed to provide *instantaneous response* (recognition, processing, and output) to the data transmitted, the system is said to operate in "real time." Real-time operation is characterized by lack of delay in system response. Lack of delay is a relative concept, for in reality, there must always be some delay, even though infinitesimal. This causes some confusion in the use of this term. A useful definition of "real-time response" postulates that it be fast enough for the purpose intended. Thus, a three-second response by an airline reservation system such as used by major United States airlines is considered satisfactory; a 10-second response might be suitable for on-line factory data collection or production monitoring; but anything more than a small fraction of a second would fail in an application where a computer guides a numerically controlled machine tool in contour milling.

Production and inventory control computer applications utilizing communications-oriented systems include on-line collection and real-time audit of shop feedback data, production monitoring, receiving-dock control, warehouse order entry and inventory control, plus inquiry programs dealing with inventory, shop-order, and open-purchase-order records.

Reports, Inquiries, and Management-information Systems. Computer system outputs are directed either to files in secondary storage, to other devices in the form of *machine-readable* signals, or to the system's human users. The wide range of *man-readable* (or usable) output possibilities is discussed above, under "Input-Output Devices." The bulk of user-directed data is presented in alphanumeric or graphic form, and it is either displayed on screens of special devices or printed, and sometimes drawn, on paper.

Printed outputs, technically known as "hard copy," predominate in the application areas of management, planning, and business controls. They can be categorized into:

1. Reports
2. Messages, such as action notices or replies to inquires
3. Special listings, such as audit trails, memory dumps, and so forth

As far as production and inventory control computer applications are concerned, the trend has been somewhat away from traditional reports, in favor of (unsolicited) exception reporting and (solicited) replies to inquiry, in message form. Communications-oriented systems equipped with random-access secondary storage devices, with the capability of inquiry through a remote terminal located in the production control office, are proving of considerable value to production and inventory control management. The information most frequently sought through inquiry is the status of a part number, location of a shop order and its progress, work load ahead of a productive facility, assembly-schedule performance, customer-order status, and shipping activity.

Comprehensive systems of inquiry designed primarily for top-management use are known as "management-information systems" (MIS). Such systems make any information in the *data base* (discussed below) immediately available to the authorized user to satisfy planned, as well as unplanned, requirements.

Management-information systems are characterized by a direct user-data relationship. The system is typically implemented by means of on-line random-access storage units containing the *data-base files,* remote terminals capable of two-way communication to provide direct entry for the user, plus a program to retrieve and structure the data into the format desired by the user. Such *customized reports* providing information to the user at the time he needs it in the form he needs it are attributes of a well-designed MIS. Such a system can also provide on demand successive layers of detail for the manager who wishes to trace a condition to its source.

While the concept of MIS grew out of the information needs of the top executive, it obviously has application on the operating-management level. The production control manager could well use an MIS covering his area of responsibility. Thus, a comprehensive MIS might consist of several such lower-level information subsystems which, along with sources of privileged information available only to top management, would constitute a pyramidlike system structure through the apex of which the executive would have access to the MIS files and programs at all levels.

Software. The term "software" covers all the programs through which the power of the computer hardware is enhanced (see also "Computer as a Concept" section above). Programs written to do the actual productive work (jobs) are known as "problem programs" "user programs," or "applications" and are outside of the scope of software, since they are not being supplied by the computer manufacturers. Software encompasses programs in the categories of the so-called *languages, control programs, service programs,* and *application programs.*

LANGUAGES: To grasp the concept of computer languages, one must keep in mind that the machine understands only its own *machine language,* i.e., instructions expressed in a *code* and format prespecified by the computer manufacturer. Originally computer programs were written by the programmer in this code, which can still be done. But this process is too laborious and error-prone because machine language is unnatural, difficult to remember, and quite complex. To overcome this problem, so-called higher-level languages have been developed that more closely resemble human forms of expression. Best-known examples are FORTRAN (Formula Translator) and COBOL (Common Business-oriented Language), that make the programmer's job much easier. Machines, however, cannot execute instructions written in this form. Therefore, each language actually consists of:

1. A *scheme* of expression (the language proper)
2. A *translator* program

The programmer writes, for example, in COBOL, and the various computer manufacturers supply translator programs, which are known sometimes as "compilers," that will convert the COBOL statements into machine language peculiar to the respective makes and models of computer machinery, which can then, and only then, execute it.

CONTROL PROGRAMS: A control program is a package of instructions that relieves the user of organizing and allocating the system's resources (memory, registers, secondary storage, and input-output units) for each new job. It automatically schedules and supervises the job flow through the system, controls the location and retrieval of data, etc., to assure the most efficient and continuous processing of jobs.

A control program consists of several subprograms or *routines* of which three are fundamental:

1. The supervisor

2. The scheduler

3. Input-output control

The supervisor controls the other two, as well as service programs (see below), language translators, and user programs.

The basic function of the scheduler is to communicate with the computer operator; and that of input-output control, to communicate with and control the peripheral devices.

SERVICE PROGRAMS: Programs in this category consist of:

1. *Housekeeping* and utility routines

2. *Application* programs

Housekeeping instructions prepare data and instructions for input, processing, and ouptut operations; maintain and update files, and transfer data between files.   Utility routines perform a variety of functions ranging from system testing or *diagnostics* to sort-merge operations.

APPLICATION PROGRAMS: Application programs are oriented toward jobs and user programs, but they are generalized to be useful to many different users, and typically are intended to assist with problems such as file organization, linkage of records, etc.   Often they are made up of *modules,* i.e., standard functions, calculations, etc., that would be used in a given type of application.   The user saves programming effort by selecting and incorporating pertinent modules into his program.

All the above programs are said to constitute the so-called *operating system* that is part and parcel of modern computers of medium to large scale.   The function of the operating system is to exploit the full resources of a data processing system by enabling the user to move a wide variety of work through his system with a minimum of manual effort.

Multiprogramming and Time Sharing.   Multiprogramming, or more precisely, multiprogram execution is a technique of processing several unrelated jobs in parallel.   Actually, as only one instruction is being executed at a time, the simultaneity consists of the central processor working, in turn, on segments of the various programs in some priority order and turning over control from one program to another every time a lower-speed operation such as input or output would cause the central processor to wait.

Only computers designed for multiprogramming are capable of it, because this mode of operation obviously requires a larger memory (to accommodate multiple programs and related data, as well as the operating system that is permanently occupying a portion of this memory), circuitry for *interrupt* functions, and enhanced capabilities in some of the peripheral units.   Without a relatively complex and sophisticated operating system, multiprogramming is inconceivable.

Time sharing differs from multiprogramming, although it is also a multiprogram execution technique, in that finite slices of time are preallocated to the various programs, *in rotation,* so that control is being transferred based on time elapsing rather than on the occurrence of a wait or external interrupt condition.   Time-sharing systems are characterized by multiple users working with the computer through remote terminals, simultaneously.   Each user is being provided *sustained access,* which means he is communicating with the system directly and without apparent time limitation.   Because of the difference between human speed and computer speed, it appears to the user that he has exclusive possession of the system, which is responding to his inputs very fast, although it is actually paying attention to him only periodically and servicing other users in the interim.

The time-sharing approach permits operation in the so-called *conversational mode,* man and machine "talking" to each other, back and forth, at a tempo set by the man.   While the individual user ponders or evaluates a given reply (message, report, image displayed) and is deciding what he will do next, the system is not idle, due to its other simultaneous users.

Computer hardware for time sharing must obviously be fast, have capacious memory, and be equipped with an internal electronic clock or *interval timer* to measure passage of time in very small increments.

An operating system including special time-sharing control programs is a necessity.   Obvious applications are primarily in the area of scientific or engineering computation, but the approach lends itself to a variety of applications including management-information systems and other inquiry systems, on-line data collection, production monitoring systems, direct numerical control, and others.

DATA BASE

Data Files.   The *data files* form the system foundation upon which the superstructure of applications is built; hence, these files are called, collectively, the "data base."

It is important to design the data files with care, so that all present and future needs are properly anticipated.   The convenience of programming later applications and the useful life of each application depend critically on the structure of the data files.   The role of the data base is in fact so fundamental that some designers implement the data base before even defining the applications which will use it.   While this is permissible, the preferred approach is to define the applications first, then design the data base to support them.

Assuming that the system applications have been defined, the information required for each application should be listed with the application description. Similarities in the data-base requirements of different applications should be sought.   Similarities cover both the actual data in the file and the sequence in which the applications process the file.   This study will yield tentative names and contents for the major files.   It is a good idea to design for future increases in the number of *records* (items) in each file and the number of *fields* (data) in each record.

There are three major choices which must be made in data-base and date-file design:

1. A large number of small files versus a small number of large files.   Favoring a large number of small files, each file can then be tailored to specific applications, with the most convenient key sequence.   There are minimal extraneous data to be read and written.   Sorting of files for different applications is minimized. On the other hand, a small number of large files use external storage more efficiently because keys and data are not repeated in several files.   The single location of each datum facilitates file maintenance, updating, and error correction.

2. Magnetic-tape storage versus direct-access storage.   The advantages of magnetic tape are low cost, ease of programming to update and reorganize files, and high speed for sequential record processing.   Direct-access storage is required, however, for on-line unscheduled processing and other applications requiring reference to any part of the file without an a priori schedule.   Direct access may be more economical in sequential processing where the proportion of records updated in a given file is low (called "low activity"), because all the records need not be passed through the computer in order to reach a few of them.   Tape and direct-access files may be used simultaneously by one system.   For example, in purchase-order generation, a tape vendor file may be used with requisition cards sorted in vendor-file sequence and a direct-access item file to generate purchase orders for any items, and an open-purchase-order

file keyed on purchase-order number can be created simultaneously on either a tape or direct-access storage device.

3. Fixed versus variable record lengths. The choice between fixed- or variable-length *logical records* is dictated by the nature of the job, but the designer can choose between processing fixed- or variable-length *physical records*. Fixed record lengths are preferred from the programming, main-memory-utilization, and file-housekeeping points of view. Sometimes the computer manufacturer's software for file management requires that the records be in fixed-record-length formats. A variable-length logical record may be broken into fixed-length physical record segments. Where a choice exists, the designer must balance the cost of variable-length record processing on his particular computer against the storage cost for extra keys, gaps, and unfilled records in fixed-length record segmentation.

PRODUCTION AND INVENTORY CONTROL SYSTEM FILES: The files of usual interest in production and inventory control applications are covered in four major categories:

1. Product and manufacturing specifications
2. Inventory control records
3. Records of production control decisions
4. Status of work in process

Different files within these categories are described below.

PRODUCT AND MANUFACTURING SPECIFICATIONS: Product-specification files generally contain the information required to issue production and testing orders plus the operating instructions required on the shop floor to carry out these orders. In addition, the specification files might serve as the only central depository for the current status of manufacturing specifications, reflecting latest engineering changes, as well as additions and deletions in the product line. For either function, or both, the files frequently contain, not the complete instruction in detail, but rather a reference to the current engineering-drawing number or operating-instruction sheet (routing), which is then maintained in a library external to the computer.

Generally, the product-specification record will be keyed in sequence on part number (material code) and contain fields for:

Part number and description
Standard lead time
Unit of measure
Source code (manufactured or purchased)
Order quantity (if not a calculated variable)
Order point (where applicable)
Bill of material, listing the standard units of each component required for one standard unit of this material
Cost accounting data
Manufacturing instructions; either the complete routing text or reference to the current drawing or instruction sheet

In practice, the product-specification file as defined above will usually consist of several separate record files, because they have traditionally been maintained separately by the departments responsible for their creation. A typical arrangement might be as follows:

1. *Part master file,* containing all the above data fields except the bill of material and routing data. Sometimes the inventory control records (defined below) are integrated with the part master records, the latter then forming the *header* of each inventory record.

2. *Product-structure file,* which defines the component-assembly relationships of the various end products. This file will be organized in terms of one of the various bill-of-material formats showing which component part numbers are used in the various assemblies and in what quantities they occur. Assembly-level codes and where-used information may be contained in this file, although the latter sometimes forms a separate where-used file.

3. *Manufacturing-process file,* also known as "routing" or "operations-record file." Each record in this file will describe the operations, and their sequence, prescribed for the manufacture of the part. Data on standards and tooling may also be contained in these records.

Inventory Control Records. The simplest inventory record shows only the on-hand balance which was current as of the latest update run for additions (receipts) and withdrawals (issues). These data are required for accounting purposes, but are generally inadequate for inventory control purposes. The next data to be added might be the amount on order or in process to become on-hand inventory at a future time and the amount already allocated to some future use. These quantities imply a budget, or projection, of future additions and withdrawals on the on-hand balance.

To be meaningful, these projections should be tied to a time frame; i.e., the date or time period of the projected addition or withdrawal should be provided.

These ideas suggest that an inventory record useful for inventory control purposes should provide an inventory projection showing planned additions and withdrawals out to the end of a planning horizon. If activities are planned to the nearest week, the file should project inventory status by week. The minimum length of the time horizon should be the interval equal to the product lead time.

Two file-organization schemes are possible, with the choice depending on the application needs and economies. The first is the "open order" organization, where each planned future transaction is loaded into the file and updating consists of changing transaction status as events occur. Initially, each transaction is in *planned* status. Then, updating changes the transaction status to *on order* for an addition or *allocated* for a withdrawal, and finally, to added or withdrawn when the planned action takes place.

The second technique is the "time-bucket" organization, where total additions, total withdrawals, and period-end inventories are projected for each future period and updating consists of recomputing the contents of the buckets as transactions come in.

Records of Production Control Decisions. As production control decisions are made, there is need to store this information in files where it can be retrieved or amended. The storage of planning decisions in inventory control files was discussed above. Depending on the application, other files may be called "work-center files," "schedule files," "open-shop-order" or "open-production-order files," and "machine-load files." In some shops, it is meaningful to distinguish between production planning, where the "when" and "how much" decisions are made, and production scheduling, where additional "what"-type decisions are made regarding the exact machines and labor to be used and the exact timing and sequencing of jobs are specified.

Status of Work in Process. The status of work in process is most easily stored in open-order files, which are essentially the same in function for purchase, shop, production, testing, and customer-shipment orders. The file record serves as a *satchel* or *bucket* for collecting data about the order as events occur at different times. Typically, the open-order record is created at the time that the order is released (placed). The file may be keyed on order-number sequence or part-number sequence and will cross-reference the abbreviated image of the same orders in the inventory control file. The file record is closed out in an accounting run after the last activity has been completed. Open-order files might contain any of the following data:

Order number
Part number (material code)
Image of the production-order paper work
Bill of materials, and actual lots of components allocated
Start dates; planned, scheduled, amended, actual
Actual finish dates and other milestone dates
Actual labor and material usage
Test results

Retrieval and Maintenance Considerations. Several of the files discussed may be printed out essentially verbatim to produce periodic reports bearing the same or similar names to those of the files. Thus, the inventory control file can be processed to give a stock status report showing opening balance, additions, withdrawals, closing balance, and projections updated for events since the last report. Work-center reports, schedule reports, and machine-load reports can come verbatim from the files of the same names. A production status report can be developed from the open-production-order file.

Some computer processing systems for production and inventory control require on-line updating of open-order and inventory control files for events as they occur, and provide on-line inquiry on the current status of these files. The need for on-line processing arises when there are a sufficient number of transactions within the smallest practical interval for batch updating, perhaps one day, so that without on-line updating, it would become necessary to keep a "real time" record of status with pencil and paper.

File maintenance deserves careful attention in system design, particularly in dynamic environments involving frequent changes in manufacturing specifications and frequent changes or upsets in production plans. The changeover from old to new specifications can lead to waste and confusion unless the timing of the change takes the current and projected stock of old components into account and each production order clearly indicates which specification applies to its lot of material. The maintenance of specification files must be provided for, both in data processing terms and in terms of the organization responsible for developing specifications. Where production plans are subject to change, it must be possible to amend open-order and inventory control files through a flexible set of change transactions which allow records to be added, deleted, or altered in the affected fields.

DATA COLLECTION AND DISSEMINATION

Modern data processing systems make it possible to convert large amounts of data into meaningful reports at an extremely high rate of speed. However, until information is collected and converted to machine-readable form, processing cannot begin. To reduce the interval between the time an event takes place on the shop floor and any resulting decision is made, automatic systems of data collection and dissemination are implemented.

These systems utilize reporting terminals located at strategic points throughout the manufacturing plant. The reporting stations transmit the data to a central output location. In an *off-line* system, the output device is either a card punch or a paper-tape punching unit. *On-line* systems have the capability of accepting the data via computer, directly, processing it, and communicating the appropriate feedback to the terminal or other monitoring location.

Data Collection Terminals. Terminals used in the manufacturing plant for collecting information vary in function and characteristics. For example, a typewriter can be linked to a computer, information typed and transmitted on-line, and the response data transmitted back.

However, to service the variety of applications requiring the use of in-plant terminals, consideration must be given to the environmental and human factors that exist in these locations. Thus a typewriter which is designed for an office environment and requires a certain degree of skill on the part of the operator is not well suited.

The terminals used for shop-floor reporting can have the following capabilities:

1. *Read a prepunched badge.* This plastic badge may consist of a laminated plastic material which when inserted in the terminal identifies the employee.

2. *Read a punched card.* A card may contain the prepunched information such as shop order or part number to be transmitted when inserted in the terminal.

3. *Record variable data* such as quantity produced, weights etc. Many devices are employed for this purpose, ranging from direct readout of machine-tool piece-count registers or weighing scales to so-called data cartridges and keyboard devices. The latter include dials, telephonelike slides, or conventional adding-machine keyboards.

4. *Receive printed messages.* This capability is normally restricted to on-line systems. Such a message could be a job assignment for an employee who has just transmitted the completion of a previous operation.

5. *Receive visually displayed messages.*

6. *Record time of day* for each transaction. This is accomplished by a digital time device which is contained in the receiving unit.

Applications for Data Collection and Dissemination. JOB REPORTING: A prepunched job card or labor ticket containing shop-order and part-number data will travel with the material from operation to operation. When this material and job card arrive in a department, the dispatcher assigns a job to the machine operator and locates the card in a card rack adjacent to the terminal. Upon completion of the operation, the employee assigned to this job inserts his badge which identifies him and keys in the operation number, machine number, and production count. This message is transmitted along with the time of day and provides all the data necessary for the following reports:

1. Labor-efficiency reports can be calculated by comparing the actual time per piece versus the job standard.

2. Payroll data can be calculated either for an incentive or hourly payroll

3. Job costing can be calculated by applying the appropriate overhead charges.

4. Job status can be maintained by classifying this data in shop-order sequence.

INSPECTION REPORTING: The job card which identifies the material being inspected is placed in the card reader. The number of pieces rejected and the reasons for rejection are entered into the manual entry. The man-number of the inspector is provided by the inspector's badge. A code indicating "reject," "scrap," or "rework" may also be entered by other manual entry. The output contains all necessary information to prepare reports for the number of pieces rejected, reason for rejection, inspector number, time, and date.

TOOL CONTROL REPORTING: Control of tool-crib activity is vital if schedules are to be met. To do so, it is necessary to record all tool issues and receipts. A tool-requisition card is issued with the manufacturing order. This card is used to report the withdrawal and return of the appropriate tool using a terminal located in the tool crib.

MATERIAL CONTROL: Material-requisition cards are received with the manufacturing order and used as a means of identifying the material withdrawn for a specific shop order. The amount of material may be entered manually. Requisitions of component parts and assemblies are handled in a similar manner. Receipts may be reported by the job ticket or material-requisition card which accompanies the material.

ATTENDANCE REPORTING: Attendance reporting is accomplished by having employees insert their badges in the terminal upon entering and leaving their work location. These data can be used to prepare absentee reports each morning showing employees in attendance in each department and pinpointing late arrivals and absentees.

DATA COLLECTION CONSIDERATIONS: Physical characteristics of data collection terminals must provide for reliable performance in the plant environment, where they will be exposed to dirt and other air contaminants, as well as fluctuating temperatures and humidity. In addition, built-in controls should be established to provide for ease of use by the average production worker and a sufficient amount of communication to inform the employee when an additional entry is required to complete a correct transaction.

Although many of the installed data collection systems operate in the off-line mode, a major consideration in the selection of the data collection system is the potential for its eventual growth to a *real-time* system and putting the terminals on-line to the computer. The objective of the real-time system is to give management the ability to receive information from the computer either upon demand or upon the occurrence of an exceptional event. For instance, foremen may require a listing of work queues for appropriate job assignment in their departments. By having the production workers record the job completion time in the on-line mode, the computer is able to keep track of the location and relative priority of all jobs in progress and can thus provide the foremen with this information.

These same data would be available to the sales department for purposes of answering job status inquiries which would be keyed into a terminal located in their department. It is in this real-time mode that the ultimate value of data collection and dissemination systems can be realized.

PRODUCTION AND INVENTORY CONTROL APPLICATIONS

Almost all production control functions can be performed by the computer, including forecasting, material planning, scheduling, loading, and dispatching. It is therefore important to do a thorough investigation into possible applications with a clear determination of costs versus benefits. This economic justification is considerably simplified if the benefits are defined in terms of basic production control objectives, which are:

To achieve the economic use of machines and manpower
To minimize the investment in inventory
To provide the desired degree of customer service
To keep clerical costs at a minimum
To provide management with useful information

The computer can assist in achieving these objectives, if the applications are properly designed and implemented.

Forecasting. It has been established that computer and management-science techniques are an invaluable tool in the preparation of a forecast. The various forecasting techniques have been covered in Chapter 8 of this handbook. The computer's role in forecasting for production control purposes is threefold:

1. Assistance in preparation of a dollar forecast
2. Conversion of a dollar forecast into a production forecast
3. Use of the production forecast in planning and control

The computer's ability to analyze masses of data using several alternatives is useful in forecasting from both historical data or market data. In the case of a forecast based on history, the computer can forecast usage of each item by screening out abnormal data, extending the history using rolling averages (usually exponentially smoothed or seasonally trended). Several software packages are available which contain the computer programs to perform this work. Analysis of market surveys or samples and the various factors affecting sales is also an area for computer application. In such instances, the production control or sales manager had best consult with an operations research practitioner, as the techniques are much more complicated than forecasting from historical data.

Where dollar forecasts are prepared (in contrast to forecasts by models or production units), the computer can convert the dollar forecast to units.

The primary uses of a production forecast by the computer include:

1. Materials planning
2. Revision of economic order quantities, order points, coverage quantities, etc.
3. Facilities planning
4. Manpower planning

Order Entry. The production control manager need not concern himself with the methods or procedures for sales-order processing or the mechanics of entering sales orders into the computer. However, he must concern himself with how the computer can answer the following questions:

1. Can production (inventories) satisfy the customer's requested shipping date?
2. If not, what production (inventory) steps must be taken?

Ideally, these questions should be answered *before* the shipping date is acknowledged. Many other applications are brought into play in answering the questions, including inventory control (availability of finished goods, subassemblies, etc.), loading and scheduling (facility and manpower availability), and materials planning (production-requirements determination and explosions).

Where shipments are made from finished-goods stocks, the computer can keep track of inventories and trigger replenishment orders on the production facilities.

In custom-made-product industries or job-shop production, the customer order should be processed against availability on a level-by-level basis. Thus, if assemblies are available, they are reserved by the computer for particular customers' orders. If assemblies are not available, a shop order (or schedule) for production is prepared and exploded to see if subassemblies are available. This level-by-level, net-availability calculation procedure is something that the computer can perform readily.

Materials Planning. Materials planning or requirements determination is one of the first and foremost computer applications. The materials planning application must normally be custom-designed to meet the company's policies, production processes, and procurement practices. Regardless of the data or technique used, the computer must answer two questions:

1. What to manufacture or purchase?
2. When is it needed?

There are four primary sources of data which can trigger a production need:

1. Forecast of model or unit usage for next month or next week based on a model or dollar forecast

2. Customer, engineering, and other known needs

3. An order point, which is a method of expressing forecast needs through the lead-time period

4. Internal usage such as production for stock, scrappage, etc.

Special techniques must be used to reflect requirements down through subsequent levels of subassemblies, fabrications, piece parts, purchased parts, or raw materials. These are referred to as "explosion techniques," and there are three basic methods:

1. *Bill-of-material or Level-by-level Explosion Technique.* In this system, the computer generally follows the engineering bills of material, *exploding* assemblies into subassemblies, subassemblies into parts, parts into raw material. Thus, through level-by-level techniques, excess stocks on higher levels are used up before components are ordered or scheduled for manufacturing.

This method takes more computer time, as the parts masters and bill-of-material files must be processed a level at a time.

2. *Stock-list or Quick-deck Explosion Technique.* In this system, the bills of material are organized in a complete stock list for each end assembly. One explosion is made to determine requirements at all levels—subassemblies, parts, and raw material. The advantage of this method is its speed and directness. The disadvantage is the excess stock at higher levels. Thus, excess stock is perpetuated instead of being applied against requirements. This method is used primarily in assembly operation or *four-wall* control systems where in-process inventories are not computer or stock-room controlled. It is also used to determine purchasing requirements under production "releasing" systems or where shipping schedules are released on a cumulative-requirements basis.

3. *Model-used-on (Where-used) Explosion Technique.* In special cases involving only a small number of end models, a where-used or "synthesis" method can be used. In this case, the quantity used on each different model is carried in the parts master and imploded directly against the model requirements.

In some production ordering systems, different triggering methods and techniques are used to apply to different segments of the inventories and production processes.

Inventory Control. Basic to all production control computer applications is inventory control—the maintenance of accurate, timely records of inventories for raw materials, purchased parts, work in process, and finished goods. In the inventory control application, it is important to remember that the computer will only process data—it will not provide any additional measures of control unless the controls are built into the system.

Control over receipts is achieved by keeping track of each open-purchase order on the computer, the posting of receipts against the open order, and the closing out of the order. If there are exceptions, the "record-accuracy program" should investigate, as described below.

Control over stock-room issues is achieved by the use of computer-prepared or preplanned requisitions which work as follows:

1. As schedules or shop orders are issued by the computer, requisitions are printed and used to withdraw stock.

2. The computer keeps track of each requisition and issues against it. If further material is needed, a manual requisition is drawn against the schedule and posted to the computer file of requisitions.

3. When the schedule or shop order is closed out, the quantities drawn can be compared with the quantities produced. Exceptions go to the "record-accuracy program."

The same type of control can be achieved in a four-wall-type or assembly-line operation by periodically comparing actual usage with exploded production. If significant unaccounted-for differences exist, they must be investigated.

Control over production reporting is attained in part by the comparison (above) of material drawn with material produced. Other control methods are mechanical, such as production meters, counters, or in-plant data-gathering equipment as discussed previously. Of course, the computer must keep track of actual production as against authorized production and report discrepancies for follow-up.

If all the controls are built into the system, the computer is keeping track of all material from the receiving dock to the shipping room and follows the material through the plant.

Computer record-accuracy programs are all-important to the success of the production control system. Normally, the computer makes many decisions based upon the stock status figures of on hand, on order, and requirements. These figures must be accurate. This requires the creation of a record-accuracy program. The purpose of this program is to investigate all exceptions which the computer discovers and to determine the *cause* of the error, such as unreported scrap, poorly trained employees, procedural falldowns, or other shortcomings in procedures. The second step in the program is to *correct the cause of the error* through procedural changes, training, supervision, and so forth. A discipline of accurate reporting is built up through this approach.

The cycle-count program would be part of the record-accuracy program. In this regard, the computer can select items to be counted and provide lists of outstanding paper such as shop orders or requisitions. All this will assist in reconciliation. The cycle count *must verify all status fields* in the computer file, including on hand, on order, and outstanding requisitions or requirements, because the fields are so interrelated that an error in one is almost always accompanied by a related error in another.

Another function of the record-accuracy program is the production control *system control group*. This group handles, audits, and controls all input to the computer. It also logs and distributes all computer reports, checks to see that all computer error lists have been handled properly and corrected, and forms the liaison between the factory and the data processing organization. It may also perform approval functions such as for unplanned material requisitions, and will handle emergency order processing which can't wait for the computer to act.

Loading, Scheduling, Dispatching, Expediting. In general, the computer can be of real value in plant or facility loading and scheduling. For assembly-production facilities, it can take master model schedules or releases and compute the plant-, departmental-, or machine-loads. It can also compute manpower-loads. Similarly, for shops, the computer can take customer orders or shop orders which they create and explode them into departmental, load-center, machine, or manpower requirements. Thus, load determination is a good computer application. It can also deduct the actual production from departmental- or machine-loads to determine the net-load and behind-schedule positions.

The computer, if it maintains a record of open-shop orders or schedules, can also prepare a priority for outstanding schedules and revise them to prepare hot lists. For example, it can determine which orders or schedules are needed for past-due customer orders and give these orders a high priority. The priority listing or hot lists can then be used by the foremen or dispatchers in determining what to run next.

Detailed scheduling is more difficult to program for a computer. The scheduler's job is one of determining what day to stage and start each work order or item scheduled for production, taking into account such factors as the capacity of the department, the backlog in the department, the priority of the orders, the mix of orders which individual load centers can handle, the shortage situation from feeding departments, etc.

There are many factors to be weighed in preparing a good schedule. These factors can possibly be defined, but the evaluation of all of them and the decision rules are difficult to state precisely, and therefore to program. In job shops, scheduling is a rather complex computer application for most departments or schedule centers. In assembly-type operations, the computer can do the scheduling job much more easily.

Dispatching is the assignment of specific work orders to individual operators and machines. Dispatching takes a knowledge of factory floor conditions, availability of operators, parts, tools, prints, etc. This is difficult to mechanize fully because the computer cannot easily *see* these floor conditions, and it is difficult to feed data on all these into the computer on a continuous basis.

The same difficulties are encountered in central-dispatching systems. Under central dispatching, an operator calls in and reports completed production. A person at the other end of the line picks out another work order and says "start this one." The computer can facilitate the dispatching job by providing the required scheduling and dispatching data, routing information, parts lists, tool requirements, etc.

Expediting does not lend itself readily to computer mechanization. Expediting is special action taken to speed up the normal flow or processing of an order. It consists of an objective review of the causes of shortages and the origination of action to correct the cause of shortages. This is difficult to do on a computer. On the other hand, hot lists can be computer-prepared for expediting action.

Rescheduling can be performed by the computer. When disruptions occur and present schedules are not meaningful, a properly designed computer system can recompute production requirements for materials planning applications and then create new schedules. The simplest approach is to back out the old orders or schedules and to feed in new forecasts or customer orders. It is important to build reschedule provisions into the original computer programs to avoid later special programming effort.

Management Inventory Reports. If the inventory control application is performed by the computer, a by-product is the preparation of management reports on inventory. Other reports which the computer should prepare include schedule-performance reports, factory-delay reports, shortage reports, excess and obsolete reports, excessive scrap or loss reports, and load and production reports.

Other reports also include customer service and vendor performance. Of course, an overall dollar report should be prepared, showing inventory turnover and purchase commitments by meaningful classes of inventory.

Purchasing. Purchasing should be considered as an integral part of the production control computer system. For assembly operations, explosions of monthly or weekly model schedules or releases must be extended down to purchased parts and raw materials in order to revise vendor shipping schedules. The expediting system must be extended back into purchasing.

Special computer applications for purchasing include maintenance of vendor-delivery and quality-performance statistics, vendor selection, automatic preparation of purchase orders, and follow-up on past-due deliveries.

Tool Control. There are three distinct computer applications for tool control:

1. Tool records
2. Tool utilization
3. Tool location

The first is the maintenance of records on each tool—when it was purchased, its cost, its usage to date. The second uses these basic data to determine when the tool should be repaired or replaced. The third keeps track (see "Data Collection," above) of issues and receipts by the tool crib of individual tools, as well as their condition.

Project Control. The computer can assist in controlling projects under the direction of production control. It can keep track of the budgeted expenditures and costs of each project. If it is a complicated project such as the phase-in of a new product, the *critical-path method* for project evaluation and control can be used effectively. This technique is an invaluable planning and control tool, as it pinpoints critical activities and *falldowns* in performance. Maintenance projects and research and development projects can also be computer-controlled.

Simulation Techniques. Simulation techniques should be used in all planning facets of production control systems. A simulation is a method of exploring the future and assisting in decision making by use of a symbolic model. A symbolic model is a mathematical expression of the relationships between the factors which have an effect on the decision. Very elementary production control models include:

1. Comparative inventory investment required if sales increase or decrease or if customer service is to be increased.

2. Manpower or facilities required for several different production levels

3. Optimum plant layout or flow of material based upon frequency and volume of material movement.

4. Warehouse- or facility-location studies

More sophisticated models result from the combination and integration of these simple models until the computer has a model of the entire plant and production processes to answer any and all questions concerning alternative courses of action which management might take, and the consequences of each. These complete models, however, take years to develop.

Applied Management Sciences. Operations research (OR), an aid to production control managers, is the application of scientific techniques to production problems. These techniques include linear programming, queuing theory, theory of games, dynamic programming, Monte Carlo techniques, and probability theory. The operations researcher generally tries to arrive at an optimum solution to the problem. Some applied operations research techniques in the area of production control include:

1. *Forecasting.* The uncertainties of forecasting can be identified and measured by OR through use of mathematical statistics and probability theory. In addition, future occurrences of specific events such as stock outs, machine breakdowns, and personnel absenteeism can be forecast using statistical methods, queuing theory, and dynamic programming. The simplest OR technique in this area is the computation of order points.

2. *Cost Analysis.* Cost determination can be improved through OR. Examples are least-cost scheduling, economic order quantities, product profitability, warehouse-size and location studies, make-or-buy decisions, and repair-or-replace decisions.

3. *Balancing of Resources and Facilities.* Production control *is* the balancing of demands with the resources and facilities available to fulfill the demand. OR offers a number of approaches, such as linear programming or queuing theory, to assist in the optimization of production and the preparation of plant load and schedules.

4. *Activity Sequencing.* Closely related to the balancing of resources is activity sequencing to aid in decisions as to what to produce, when to produce it, and in what sequence. Line balancing is a good example.

Two things are required for an effective OR effort—basic data and computational ability. The computer provides the latter. If properly designed, the basic production control files will contain most statistical data needed.

PRODUCTION AND INVENTORY CONTROL AS USER OF THE SYSTEM

Organization. In most organizations the computer and its associated personnel serve a number of departments besides production and inventory control. In this circumstance, computer operations and program development groups usually report to either general management or financial management. Computer *runs* serving the production planning functions must enjoy a high priority to meet their schedule of deadlines, just as accounting runs must meet their deadlines. The planning deadlines for production planning are typically more stringent, though, in that the information processing cycle is shorter. This is because, unlike the accounting report, a production planning report is part of a closed feedback control loop. Information lags, just like instrument and transmission lags in control theory, can seriously limit the performance of the system.

If, in developing data processing schedules, the need for a short cycle of operations is properly recognized, satisfactory service to production and inventory control can be provided even where computer operations do not report to a manufacturing executive. (It is interesting to note that the present-day *dedicated* process-control computers are usually controlled by the production organization.) As the dynamics of production control approach those of process control in the future, it can be expected that production and inventory control management will tend to support its own computer operations.

Two other organizational needs are recognized: one is for an inventory committee, and the second is for a standards committee. The inventory committee should set the policies toward which the planning function is oriented. Many of the powerful new computer planning aids will serve double duty by also serving as medium-range planning simulators, if the essential constants are inserted as adjustable parameters. The inventory committee can then commission appropriate one-time studies investigating the effects on inventories and work loads of changes in product mix, risk levels, risk based on profitability, pushback of reserve stocks to earlier manufacturing stages, lead-time allowances, and workload leveling policies.

The standards committee reviews standards, commissions studies for standards revision, and sets goals for modification of standards to increase profitability. As these powerful computer aids for the planning function are introduced, more and more of the decisions which actually affect the profit-and-loss statement of the company will depend on the values of standards for lead time, labor, equipment, and material usages.

Functions. The introduction of advanced computer aids in production and inventory control produces a subtle but important change in the function of this department. Its function now becomes one of management by exception. The routine decisions have been computerized, and planning personnel must devote more attention to review of computerized decisions, spotting exceptions which must be broken out for manual handling, and coordinating production work to make the actual results approximate the ideal represented by the plan. Each planning supervisor must thoroughly understand the computer routines and all the *assumptions* upon which their underlying models are based. Some of the new functions introduced by the computer system are:

1. Review of computer output for possible input errors, and malfunctions in the computer or programs.

2. Review of computer forecasts, order points, order quantities, customer-order entries, allocations, generated purchase orders, job orders, and shipping orders, and production schedules for situations which violate the assumptions upon which the computer procedures were based. For example, the planner may be aware of situations where the future cannot be projected from the past because of changes in forecast, the impact of competition, the likely disposition of a questionable lot of material, and the like.

3. Manual handling of unusual conditions, and obtaining additional information as required from the computer data base.

4. Manual entry of change transactions.

5. Primary interest in maintaining the quality of production standards and specifications in the computer system.

Responsibility. Production and inventory control continues to carry its traditional responsibility of maintaining the chain of supply from procurement through delivery to customers under the computerized system. Planning personnel are responsible for carrying out inventory and work-load smoothing policy while doing this. They continue to be responsible for the *when* and *how much* decisions, and initiate orders to make, move, and transform materials in the chain of supply. Under computerized operations, the planning department acquires a new responsibility for the quality, effectiveness, and documentation of computer programs which serve them. A successful system is critically dependent upon a close collaboration, mutual interest, and a full understanding between the persons who develop and run the computer programs and the production and inventory control management.

CONVERSION TO COMPUTER PROCESSING

There are many important steps which must be taken by many people in diverse organizational areas to convert successfully production control applications to computer processing. It is a team effort, requiring the close coordination of the data processing organization, production, engineering, sales, and purchasing. Therefore, the conversion effort (see Fig. 1) should be the responsibil-

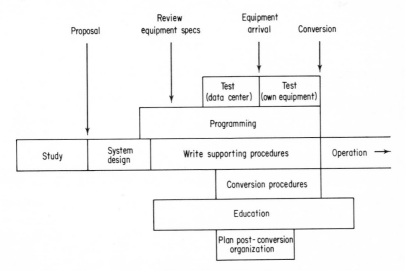

Fig. 1   System conversion phases.

ity of the production control manager himself and not delegated to systems and procedures personnel. The major phases of a conversion are as follows:

1. Economic study, preliminary system design, and proposal to management
2. Equipment selection and preparation of physical facilities
3. Detailed system design and testing including procedures, programming, and debugging
4. Preparation for conversion
5. Systems testing
6. Conversion
7. Follow-up

The production control manager should be concerned with all but the second phase.

System Design. Computerization, that is, the transfer of procedures to a machine, is an implementation concept which is difficult to discuss meaningfully in its own right, apart from the *system,* which is a set of interrelated, logically structured procedures and decision rules that can be consistently followed. Merely introducing a computer into a production and inventory control system that has not been soundly conceived in the first place cannot, by definition, transform it into a superior system. Contrary to common belief, formulation, or design, of a good system is rather difficult, whereas computerization is relatively easy.

System design occurs in two successive stages:

1. Preliminary system design through what is known as *"the study,"* leading to a proposal to management for commitment of resources to support the conversion project
2. System design implementation, following the approval of the proposal, in which the preliminary design is detailed and which results in "programming specs"

The study, typically carried out over a period of several months by a team of individuals appointed for this purpose, is essentially a process of review, intended to yield a fuller understanding of the problem and to indicate its solution. The system solution must take into account the marketing and manufacturing environment in which the company operates and should reflect the information needs of its production and inventory control functions.

The system designers should anticipate, and allow for, future growth, diversification, and competitive factors so that the system proves adequate in its future operational phase.

Recommended main objectives, or general systems criteria, are as follows:

1. Control by exception
2. Not primarily elimination of clerks, but elimination of clerical work by nonclerks (analysts, buyers, engineers, foremen)
3. Mechanization of routine decision making
4. Evaluation of information required for nonroutine decision making
5. A minimum of paper output
6. A high degree of information processing, i.e., output data that require little or no reinterpretation, analysis, accumulation, reconciliation, and re-recording
7. Speed in receiving, processing, and disseminating information so as not to lessen its usefulness
8. Provision for system expansion and refinement without fundamental resystemization and reprogramming

To assure a successful system design, the production control manager, with his staff, should be directly and actively involved in the effort.

The Conversion Preparation.   A plan for a system conversion should be prepared several months in advance.   Considerations which must be detailed in the plan are:

1. *Size and Makeup of the Conversion Team.*   Production supervision, engineering, purchasing, as well as production control and data processing systems personnel and others should participate in planning the conversion so that they feel they are part of the effort.   Also, they can contribute greatly to the plan.

2. *Phases of Installation by Application.*   If the various production control applications can be phased in on a step-by-step approach, the conversion program will be simplified.   This is not always possible to do as most applications are too integrated in nature.   If applications are phased in, the entire system should be designed to avoid the "one step forward, two steps backward" approach.

3. *Responsibilities,* manpower effort, interrelationships, and completion dates should be spelled out in the program.

4. *Recognition* should be given to the fact that production control personnel and plant supervision will be overworked during the conversion.   Therefore, plans should be made to ease the work load, or time the conversion during slack seasons.

If the conversion is complex, a critical-path diagram should be prepared and distributed to show each organizational area's responsibilities.   The month preceding and the month following the conversion should be controlled by a program expressed on a daily basis.

The conversion preparation should also include the buildup of new files, the procurement of new data, and an effort to verify or "clean up" all vital information.   For example, the new procedures may call for the creation of a computer file of open customer orders.   Rather than take an inventory of all paper work at conversion date, it is often desirable to build up the file during the months preceding the conversion.   This can be done using the new computer programs, or special computer programs.   Procurement of new fixed data can be done through special computer conversion programs.   For example, material class codes, new lead times, and other fixed data can be built up in cards or work tapes for the conversion date.   Most part-numbering systems have some organization which may be helpful in assigning codes or fixed fields.   Special computer programs using table look-up techniques can assign new data to parts.

A conversion is a good time to clean up old records.   Thus, if the on-hand balances are *inaccurate,* a physical inventory may be desirable.   If the bills of material are not *up to date,* a program for review and correction should be instituted.   If the standard cost data are inaccurate, a program to revise standards might be started.   Route sheets, stock lists, and other files should be critically examined for accuracy.   Many a computer system has failed because the basic files were not accurate—and this fact was not discovered until after the conversion.

Preparation for the conversion includes writing procedures on conversion programs such as an inventory of paper work to ascertain outstanding unfilled material requisitions.   Special forms may have to be designed, people trained, and the inventory supervised and controlled.   Special conversion programs may be required to post this data to the new files.

Systems Test.   Before the new system is installed, a complete systems test should be conducted, including:

1. *Clerical Procedures.*   All clerical procedures should be tested.   New source documents should be prepared on the floor using actual situations.   The flow of documents should be checked, especially for multipart forms.   The test should

include a run-through of input control procedures, feeding through the new key-punch procedures and into the new computer programs.

2. *Computer Procedures.* The computer system test is the responsibility of data processing and is designed to test the linkage between computer programs. It also tests that the operators have all information required to execute the programs.

3. *Data Processing Parallel Operation.* If at all possible, complete parallel operatons should be performed in the data processing department after a complete system testing. This is desirable because the production control personnel can continue to use the old system if major bugs are encountered in the new system. If parallel operations are not possible, provision should be made for continuing the old system if the new one doesn't work. The parallel operation is primarily the responsibility of the data processing organization, although the production control manager should review results.

Conversion. The conversion to new procedures, source documents, and reports must be carefully planned and controlled. Training sessions should be held to acquaint all personnel with the new forms and reports. During the conversion proper, a "fire fighting" group should be created to "spoon feed" the new system to the operating people. One person (usually a systems man or industrial engineer) should be assigned to each department. He must train the supervisors, show people how to fill out new forms, explain the first reports to supervisors, and put out all "fires" or resolve crises which arise within his area. A good communication system is essential to enable the "fire fighter" to obtain answers for the problems he doesn't know how to solve.

The production control desk should be set up well ahead of the conversion. Personnel should be trained, systems tests using actual source documents should be performed, and parallel operation made wherever possible. Data processing computer conversion problems should be handled with a small liaison team of one system man (normally the lead man), the data processing operations supervisor, and one production control man (normally the conversion leader). Fire fighters would report to the production control man. These three men should coordinate all activities.

Care must be taken to avoid informal discussions of problems at various levels. This will result in incorrect and misunderstood instructions. The resultant changes to programs, schedules, etc. will cause confusion and often failure.

The conversion itself should provide definite decision points for proceeding or "aborting" the conversion. If these are not carefully planned, including alternative procedures, the conversion can proceed beyond a point of no return and fail.

Follow-up. An essential part of the conversion is the follow-up which should take place for three to six months after the conversion. Specific points to be covered are as follows:

1. Are procedures working—are personnel having difficulties with new forms, reports, etc.?

2. Are the controls effective—or are too costly for the benefits achieved?

3. Were cost savings achieved?

4. Is the system doing everything that was called for in the original specification?

5. Are all users happy with the new system?

BIBLIOGRAPHY

Periodicals
Business Automation, 288 Park Ave. West, Elmhurst, Ill.
Computer Digest, 4th Floor, Book Building, Detroit, Mich.

Computers and Automation, 815 Washington St., Newtonville, Mass.
Control Engineering, 466 Lexington Ave., New York, N.Y.
Datamation, 1830 W. Olympic Blvd. Los Angeles, Calif.
Data Processing Magazine, 134 N. 13th St., Philadelphia, Pa.
Data Processor, Data Processing Division, International Business Machines Corp., White Plains, N.Y.
Systems Magazine, 200 Madison Ave., New York, N.Y.

Books

Bartee, Thomas C.: *Digital Computer Fundamentals,* 2d ed., McGraw-Hill Book Company, New York, 1966.
Bennett, William R., and James R. Davey: *Data Transmission,* McGraw-Hill Book Company, New York, 1965.
Chorafas, Dimitris N.: *Control Systems Functions and Programming Approaches,* Academic Press Inc., New York, 1965.
Cutter, Donald I.: *Introduction to Computer Programming,* Prentice-Hall, Inc., Englewood Cliffs, N.J., 1964.
D'Azzo, John J., and Constantine H. Houpis: *Computer and Control Engineering,* McGraw-Hill Book Company, New York, 1965.
Dearden, John: *Computers in Business Management,* Dow-Jones and Richard D. Irwin, Inc., Homewood, Ill., 1966.
Desmonde, William H.: *Real Time Data Processing Systems: Introductory Concepts,* Prentice-Hall, Inc., Englewood Cliffs, N.J., 1964.
Fisher, Peter F., and George F. Swindle: *Computer Programming Systems,* Holt, Rinehart and Winston, Inc., New York, 1964.
Flores, Ivan: *Computer Design,* Prentice-Hall, Inc., Englewood Cliffs, N.J., 1967.
————: *Computer Logic,* Prentice-Hall, Inc., Englewood Cliffs, N.J., 1961.
————: *Computer Programming,* Prentice-Hall, Inc., Englewood Cliffs, N.J., 1966.
Greene, James H.: *Production Control: Systems and Decisions,* Richard D. Irwin, Inc., Homewood, Ill., 1965.
Hellerman, Herbert: *Digital Computer System Principles,* McGraw-Hill Book Company, New York, 1967.
Horn, Jack: *Computer and Data Processing Dictionary and Guide,* Prentice-Hall, Inc., Englewood Cliffs, N.J., 1966.
Leeds, Herbert D., and Gerald M. Weinberg: *Computer Programming Fundamentals,* 2d ed., McGraw-Hill Book Company, New York, 1966.
McCormick, E. M.: *Digital Computer Primer,* McGraw-Hill Book Company, New York, 1959.
McCracken, Daniel: *Digital Computer Programming,* John Wiley & Sons, Inc., New York, 1957.
Martin, James: *Design of Real-Time Computer Systems,* Prentice-Hall, Inc., Englewood Cliffs, N.J., 1967.
Muth, J. F., and G. L. Thompson: *Industrial Scheduling,* Prentice-Hall, Inc., Englewood Cliffs, N. J., 1963.
Nathan, Robert, and Elizabeth Hanes: *Computer Programming Handbook,* Prentice-Hall, Inc., Englewood Cliffs, N.J., 1962.
Orlicky, Joseph: *The Successful Computer System,* McGraw-Hill Book Company, New York, 1969.
Popell, Steven D.: *Computer Time Sharing: Dynamic Information Handling for Business,* Prentice-Hall, Inc., Englewood Cliffs, N.J., 1966.
Savas, E. S.: *Computer Control of Industrial Processes,* McGraw-Hill Book Company, New York, 1965.
Schmidt, Richard N., and William E. Meyers: *Introduction to Computer Science and Data Processing,* Holt, Rinehart and Winston, Inc., New York, 1965.
Siders, R. A.: *Computer Graphics,* The Macmillan Company, New York, 1966.
Tocher, K. D.: *The Art of Simulation,* D. Van Nostrand Company, Inc., Princeton, N.J., 1963.

Chapter **24**

Information Transmission Systems

EDITOR:

Edward A. Fagyal, Sr. *Director, Systems and Procedures,*
McDonnell Douglas Corporation, St. Louis, Missouri

CONTRIBUTOR:

Walter H. Beers *Section Manager, Systems Analysis,*
McDonnell Aircraft Company, St. Louis, Missouri

R. E. Werner *Supervisor, Divisional Systems, McDonnell*
Aircraft Company, St. Louis, Missouri

M. A. Cepnik *Production Systems Planning Department,*
Chrysler Corporation, Highland Park, Michigan

CONTENTS

Management's needs for timely, accurate, and organized data have virtually exploded as the size and complexities of modern manufacturing processes continue to increase. In addition to having larger and more complex processes to control, today's management teams are faced with greater competition which necessitates increased control over costs, price, and product availability. In management's struggle for survival in this jungle of technology, they are demanding more and more information for planning and control purposes.

The characteristics of the production process will dictate the type, organization, and manner in which data should be gathered, accumulated, analyzed, and reported. The type of production-process characteristics which influence the information system design are:

1. *Value of Work in Process.* The total value of the work in process will largely determine the necessity for the information system's capability. The higher the value of the work in process, the greater the justification for accurate in-process information.

2. *Rate and Degree of Change of Work in Process.* The greater the rate and amount of change of work in process, the greater the need for timely in-process information.

3. *Complexity and Product-mix Fluctuations.* The degree of complexity and mix fluctuations will establish the need for control information. As the number of alternative actions available to management increases, the need for cost control information becomes greater.

Companies with operations in more than one location usually find that they must establish a communication system for efficient operation and management control. The communications link used most often utilizes existing telephone and telegraph facilities. This type of communication link is efficient, relatively low in cost, and can channel information from any number of remote sites to a central-processing point.

Specific benefits to be derived from the transmission of data are:

Reduction in time, effort, and expense in the converting of information to a form suitable for entry into a data processing system. This operation is accomplished by capturing source data at its origin.

Increase the performance of a system through the rapid movement of source data from point of origin to processing center. Large volumes of detailed information formerly delayed by distance, weather, and traffic conditions can be processed sooner than ever before.

Provides accessible and timely reports for management action and information.

These three objectives can be realized by using data communications to improve existing systems and open previously impractical application areas to the advantages of data processing. Companies which have operations predominantly centralized should also investigate the advantages of establishing an internal network for data collection and transmission. Distant operating facilities are by no means a requirement for cost justification of such a network.

FACILITIES FOR TRANSMISSION OF DATA

Facilities for the transmission of detailed data are available and widespread. To use the existing telephone and telegraph networks for information transmission, there must be a discipline established over all the data to be transmitted:

Data to be transmitted must conform to standards demanded by the system and the transmittal equipment used in the actual transmission of data.

Data transmission equipment requires processing codes and electrical signals which must be converted into signals acceptable to the circuits of the communication channels being used.

Input to a data transmission system normally is in the form of punched cards, use of a keyboard, punched paper tape, punched identification badges or tokens, and in some instances magnetic tape.

Information enters the system through an input terminal device, and from there the data normally go to a communications data set or modulator-demodulator before actually entering the communications network. A communications data set is basically a signal-conversion device. The conversion may require changes in speed and code structure as well as the insertion or deletion of control characters. The input terminal modifies the data to a form acceptable to the data set and the data set converts the signals to the form uesd by the circuit or channel network. At the central-processing point or receiving station, a similar data set reconverts the signals to a form acceptable to the data processing equipment.

The amount of discipline exercised over the data transmitted to the data processing system is of paramount importance because if inaccurate data are transmitted processing will not improve accuracy. Therefore, it is imperative that the data transmitted through the system be as accurate and valid as possible. This may be accomplished to a great degree by preparing and auditing input data prior to its transmission.

To the extent possible, manual entry of data should be eliminated. Punched cards or paper tape can be produced and checked prior to use. The punched card used for transmittal through card readers may be keypunched and verified before using. In a more sophisticated data processing system, the input card may be a direct output from a computer program. Such cards may then be used as "traveler" input cards and inserted into various input devices located at remote locations to record transactions or events as they occur.

TIMELINESS OF RESPONSE

The requirement for response time is a very important factor in any data transmission system. There are basically three types of response requirements, each having its direct affect on the cost and complexity of the system.

Real Time. Real-time systems require that a response to an input transaction be recorded, processed, and the result or output from the processing be available in time to affect the next transaction. The time allotted for this response varies with the application, but the patience of the customer is sometimes found to have been the governing factor. If the allowable response time is very short, direct, "on-line" communication between the originating point of transaction and the processing computer is essential. Requirements of a "real-time" communication system are discussed in more detail below.

Periodic Reporting. The scheduling of output reports on a fixed-time and fixed-date basis has been the most widely used approach to data processing. Periodic reporting permits the central-computer-processing operation to efficiently schedule its work and to gain the greatest utilization of hardware. The periodic reporting approach also provides the user with a specific date and time for the receipt of output reports or data. Periodic reporting does, however, restrict the flexibility of operating departments in that it is not always easy to change the scheduled output times. From a management and cost effectiveness point of view, periodic reports must be reviewed on a regular basis to determine that they are serving the purpose intended. If a thorough analysis is not performed, periodic reports have a tendency to be self-perpetuating.

Special Request. In many instances, printed output or decks of punched cards are required only upon request of a customer or under special operating conditions. Under these circumstances, a formal request may be prepared by the requesting party and submitted to the central-processing center requesting a specific output on a designated date and time. Special-request output routines are desirable in that output is produced only when absolutely necessary. There are, however, certain considerations that must be kept in mind. Special requests must be given special attention by the central data processing center to be scheduled within the normal framework of scheduled processing jobs. Blocks of processing time must be provided in the production schedule to permit acceptable turnaround time. Operating areas must also consider the data processing work load and schedules and provide sufficient lead time for efficient operations.

INFORMATION SYSTEMS: BATCH SYSTEMS

Batch processing is a technique used by most data processing installations. Data input documents such as daily employee job cards, cashed stock requisitions, and receiving reports are prepared in the course of the workday. These documents are then collected at a specific time each day and either carried or mailed to the computer center for processing. Normally, the first processing cycle is the key punching of information on the source documents into punched cards. Following key punching, the punched cards are submitted for computer processing based upon an established schedule. Computer processing takes place only after all source data for a specific job have been properly prepared and input-output control totals established as necessary.

It should be noted that one of the largest continuing costs of a batch system is the cost associated with the preparation of data for processing. All data to be processed must be converted to machine-readable form. Special devices are required for this data conversion, such as key punch machines which prepare punched cards, paper-tape punches, magnetic-ink character readers, optical scanners, tag perforators, etc.

The volume of data to be prepared should be scheduled so that a continuous flow is provided to avoid peak-load scheduling. Meeting with the demand for peak key-punch or data preparation loads can be very costly and often results in extended turnaround time before the input documents are submitted to the computer center.

The cost of data preparation increases proportionately with the requirement for accuracy. Key-punch operators should be trained carefully and their performance monitored on the basis of sample checks. However, many types of transactions require complete or nearly complete accuracy, and it is necessary to verify that each punched card (or transaction on paper tape) has been correctly prepared. The original process of preparing the punched card or paper tape is duplicated by another operator on a machine slightly modified (key-punch verifier), so that the characters "typed" by the key-punch operator are compared with the holes punched in the previously punched cards or paper tapes. The original cards or tapes are fed through the verifier without incident if the new characters punched by the operator match the holes already punched. If the information does not match, the verifier will stop and refuse to feed further, and will signal the operator that there is an error. This type of information-verification procedure affords some guarantee that information has been keypunched correctly, but almost doubles the cost of the original data preparation.

In addition to the key-punch verification of data, the accuracy of processed data can be further assured by the use of various checks and balances. Such procedures are batch totals, range checks, consistency checks, redundancy and "hash" totals.

Batch totals are the most universally used form of control in sequential processing applications. The principle is very simple in that the total number of documents or dollar balances entered must equal the total processed by the computer and printed on the output reports. As an example, when a bank processes checks, a clerk will total the dollar amount of each batch of checks before the information is processed by the computer. As the computer posts the checks, it totals the amounts and at the end of the processing compares the total posted to the original batch total. Systems can often be "surrounded" by batch totals to ensure the accuracy of the output documents.

Range checks utilize the fact that most business transactions follow patterns. For example, most gas bills for residential customers are expected to total less than $75. If the utility company's computer calculates a charge to a residential customer of $100 or more (allowing a safety factor), the computer could be instructed to reject it or call the fact to the operator's attention. A production storeroom on a production line may normally order no more than 10 of an item from inventory. If the computer discovers an order for more than 10, the request may be rejected. Range checks do not guard against error in detail, but they prevent extravagant errors ($1,000 instead of $10) that can result from key-punch or computer error.

The consistency check uses the principle of association between kinds of information. The computer can be programmed to recognize certain types of information. If the data processed do not contain special codes or significant digits, they are rejected. Applications using this technique could ensure that missile parts were not listed on airplane part lists.

The technique of redundancy can be used in the prevention of errors but requires the preparation of all input data twice. A popular method of checking is the use of "hash" totals. Hash totals are developed by adding groups of numbers together—they can be quantities, account numbers, or stock numbers. The group total is really meaningless (therefore, "hash"), but if any of the numbers in the group are changed (i.e., by a key-punch error) the hash total will be changed. A control clerk may prepare such a "hash" total for a group of numbers and submit it to the computer together with the input data for processing. The computer can be programmed to add up the data and determine if the result is the same as the "hash" total.

ON-LINE SYSTEMS

On-line systems require combined hardware and software capabilities to accumulate massive amounts of discrete or analog data, real-time analytical ability to determine significant trends or variances, "alarming" ability based upon prescribed criterion, inquiry capability, and periodic exception reporting ability.

The development of an on-line information system will normally take several phases. The first phase should be concerned with concentrating on the system's input for organization, accuracy, and source. This is, beyond any question, one of the most important areas of an on-line information system. Without complete, accurate, and correctly identified input data, the system will be worthless. The system's output during this initial stage can remain in batch mode as close to its original form as possible. This permits concentration of the system-group's resources on the extremely critical input area and minimizes the change to be experienced by the user organizations. Changing one facet at a time provides a very realistic and workable approach.

Phase two of the development process should be concerned with the storage of the data that has been gathered in phase one. The most flexible and universally accepted method of storage for dynamic data is in direct-access disk or drum devices. The advantage of having all data immediately accessible to the system lays the foundation for converting the system to an exception-reporting basis and provides the ability for random on-line inquiry. During phase two, the output from the system should be aligned with the concepts of real-time on-line operations.

On-line real-time systems originally were concerned with continuous processes found in the chemical and petroleum industries. The ability to monitor and control continuous processes by means of on-line real-time computer systems has proved extremely valuable for these dynamic processes. Computers now have the ability to record the vast amounts of data generated by these continuous processes, analyze the data, and take control actions on a real-time basis. Recently the principles developed in these systems engaged in controlling continuous processes have been applied to processes which have discrete-item products. Early indications are that these on-line real-time systems will prove as valuable for controlling discrete-item processes as they have for continuous processes. It should be apparent that continuous and discrete processes contain the same properties varying only in degree.

Output Capabilities. The on-line system should utilize one or all of the three following output techniques:

ALARM CAPABILITIES: The on-line system is capable of monitoring a manufacturing process through its input terminals and based upon decision criterion alarm responsible management through appropriate output devices. The system can communicate through Teletype networks with remote units located in responsible managements normal work area. *This output should generate action!*

EXCEPTION REPORTING: On-line systems should not be burdened with normal massive data reporting. The system has the ability to convert massive amounts of data into meaningful information and report only *significant* information to concerned management. The exception reporting can be achieved after the system's reliability has been proved and accepted by line management. A selling point in this area is that the usual manual system is currently operating on an exception basis because of necessity, and thus this concept is only formally recognizing what is actually being done in the present manual system.

INQUIRY CAPABILITY: Information systems which have the ability to handle on-line inquiries can make the system's supporting data available to all management who have a "need to know."

On-line inquiry capability will provide the system with a level of flexibility that will handle all random undefined or predictable output requirements.

EFFICIENCY OF OPERATIONS

Control. All information systems including data transmission must have built-in controls. Barometers of performance must be designed so that the overall efficiency of the operation can be determined. This can be accomplished in part by establishing sets of standards. Any deviation from these standards is brought to the attention of the group monitoring the system. The most successful systems have simple control features which are enforced. As an example, the transmission error factor can be determined by a simple computer count of error transmissions. During the checkout period of a new system, error transmission counts are made. Based on this count, a tentative standard is established. This standard can be adjusted as the system settles down, but when the usual error factor is 2 percent, those monitoring the system know that something is wrong in the hardware or transmission lines if this error factor jumps to 6 percent. Analysis of the cause of the error can lead to corrective action. This type of control is direct and simple, but effective.

Accuracy of Information. No data transmission system is perfect. Because of communication-line noise, interference, and momentary fading, there will always be some incidence of erroneous transmissions. Transmission errors can be reduced by error-checking routines within the hardware and through programming. In the event of a failure, the message can be retransmitted. Data transmission errors are only one of many types that can occur. Data preparation (keying) errors are likely, errors in reading or recording information in file storage devices are possible, errors in handling data within the computer itself occur, but not frequently. Automatic checks like those used to verify data transmission accuracy can help in finding and correcting some of these, but can never find them all. Successful real-time transmission systems require very careful preplanning and testing in coordination with the common carrier.

Timeliness. The timeliness of error detection is most important with data transmission systems so that prompt corrective action can be taken. Error detection, especially in data transmission, is important because the operator assumes that the computer received a valid message unless notified by an error message or signal light on the machine. If the message was received in error but not detected, that input record is lost. The system will no doubt print the messages received which cannot be processed because of some type of error. To go back to the source to determine what the message should have been is often impossible. Another reason error detection is important is that a given input terminal might transmit hundreds of messages each day. This data could be essential to the operation of the company and almost impossible to recreate.

Allocation of Resources. MONEY: As with any enterprise, money must be allocated to establish the system. Even though the system has great potential as a money-saving approach, it will be necessary to operate the old system while the new one is designed, developed, installed, and debugged. This means that the company must provide the money to support a system study, development of the system, acquisition of hardware, and its installation before any recovery can be made. The amount of funds required, of course, varies with the complexity of the system.

MEN: It should be noted that even though the transmission of data does not require manual pickup of source documents at various locations, manpower is still required to service the output devices even if the data transmission system is "on-line" with all data being placed directly on magnetic tape or disk. If the transmission system employs output card punches or paper tape, trained personnel must maintain the machines to see that supplies are in the machines and that output cards or rolls of tape are removed as required. If the company operates on more than one shift, these machines must be serviced whenever personnel are working. Many data transmission systems require 24-hour, 7-days-a-week support.

MATERIALS: The requirement for materials also varies with the application. All data transmission systems will require some cable and electrical wiring.

Input and output devices must be located near the point of transaction, and this usually requires that new electrical lines be run and that some type of cabling be installed to connect the device with existing communication facilities. Space for input and output devices is also an important consideration. Many times the installation of input and output devices requires that existing equipment be moved or that changes be made to existing facilities. This type of modification can be very costly unless planned in advance and monitored closely. Changes to existing facilities should not be charged to the cost of the system unless truly related.

APPLICATIONS

The previously used, common type of data transmission system utilized a number of remote input devices, such as card or tape readers, linked to an output card or tape punch via communications facilities. Output punched cards or paper tape were then processed by the computer on a scheduled time cycle. Processing output was usually in the form of tabulated reports which were hand-carried or mailed to operating personnel.

The advent of real-time data transmission systems offers a great deal more flexibility. The applications to which these on-line real-time systems have recently been applied cover most of the major functional areas in the manufacturing organization.

The initial application usually involves inventory control as the material control structure generally will serve as a common basis for all functions. This is true of all manufacturing processes which deal with material products.

The related function applications in addition to inventory control are:

1. *Time and Attendance.* This application captures the timekeeping transactions through on-line badge readers. It establishes the foundation for labor distribution applications and relating manpower costs to in-process inventory.

2. *Production Scheduling and Control.* This area deals with the scheduling of production through the manufacturing process. It is concerned with the planning responsibility of inventory control.

3. *Quality Control.* On-line real-time quality reporting brings into the system the quality level of production to correlate with the quantity data.

4. *Cost Analysis.* The final objective of the above applications is to reduce the manufacturing process to an "authorization minus actual equals variance" reporting basis. By converting material and manpower to dollars, the system has a real-time cost analysis control which can report significant variances against an established profit plan.

Such systems fall into these broad functional classes: inquiry systems, dispatching systems, and decision-making systems. Each class has a distinct capability, and therefore, a distinct set of applications.

Inquiry Systems. Inquiry systems are the simplest of the three and the most widely used. Probably the most widely observed example of inquiry systems in use are those installed in savings banks, where the important requirement for the system is that tellers must be able to obtain depositors' account balances. To provide tellers with the information, a relatively small random-access file storage device is on-line to the system. Inquiry terminals are provided to tellers and "communication systems" installed to interconnect them with the computer. The computer must also be provided with a suitable *executive program* so that it can interrupt processing in progress to answer inquiries. Simple inquiry systems such as the one described have applications in manufacturing and warehousing companies where the need to know inventory balances is critical to company operations. The cost of an inquiry system may cover a wide range.

Only through a detailed analysis of the application can estimated costs be determined.

Dispatching Systems. A dispatching real-time system has an active rather than passive function. The system responds to a demand by assigning responses to meet it, then reporting accordingly. Dispatching systems must be capable of performing a number of functions on the basis of demand made upon it. Most dispatching systems are used for some form of inventory control. Transactions must be recorded and the system must adjust the recorded balances, prepare the appropriate documents for the required items, and issue reorder documents automatically when the inventory levels become too low. To accomplish these tasks requires complex data processing systems using random-access devices and executive programs so that regularly scheduled computer jobs in processing can be interrupted to service the system. The cost to develop and support these systems is much greater than that of the inquiry system described above. Reliability of the system is extremely important because using organizations are heavily dependent upon the operation of the system. To ensure reliability, systems checks and balances must be incorporated, and in many cases, backup hardware installed so that the failure of any one device will not impair the system.

Decision-making Systems. The decision-making system performs much the same functions as the dispatching system, allocating resources to meet demands. The difference lies in the method employed. The dispatching system applies pre-established decision rules automatically. The decision-making system finds an optimum answer to every demand. To do this a linear-programming model may be employed, if the problem to be solved is perfectly understood. If not, a simulation model may be developed to provide a good (not necessarily the best) answer. These systems require extensive random-access storage devices and large computers. The computers required must be among the most rapid and versatile available and must be capable of solving complex sets of equations for efficiently performing what would otherwise be time-consuming simulations. They must deal with unexpected contingencies such as peak demands, failure of production facilities, and the like.

SYSTEMS STUDY CONSIDERATIONS

Problem Definition. Under no circumstances should action be taken toward the actual installation of an information transmission system until a thorough system study has been performed. Few organizations can afford multiple unrelated information transmission systems in different areas of the company. Systems studies must, therefore, be performed on a broad spectrum of applications. First, the personnel performing the study should be of the highest caliber. Affected members of management should agree at the outset on objectives of the study. At the conclusion of the systems study, management will be able to decide whether further investment in the system should be undertaken. If the conclusion is to proceed with the system, detailed system specifications are required.

Methodology. Whether the system under consideration is a new one or a modification of an existing one, flow charts graphically depicting the flow of information in each system should be prepared. These flow charts will pictorially illustrate the old and new system, showing how each document travels through the system and the action taken upon it by the operating areas.

Early in the design process, it is important to consider the procedures to be used by the personnel of the organization working with the computer system.

Normally, there are a number of clerical operations that are implied when the automated input and output records are designed. At the time they are designed, consideration must be given to the convenience and ease by which these documents can be prepared and used. Through analysis of flow charts, work simplification, decision tables, and other techniques described in Chapter 20 the proposed system can be readily analyzed. The development of a detailed systems work plan will pay for the effort expended by resulting in a system which will meet the objectives at the earliest possible date and at the lowest cost.

Data Integration. The success of the system will be governed to a great degree by the compatibility of input, output, and file data with other existing systems.

INPUTS TO THE SYSTEM: The major input documents should be defined, together with the points at which they originate and the mechanism required to transport the input information to the computer. Volumes, frequency of processing, and peak loads should be considered.

OUTPUTS OF THE SYSTEM: The required results of the processing should be defined, as well as the physical points to which the outputs must be delivered. The form of the output and its volume, frequency, and processing time allowed should be specified.

File Content and Organization. Each important file of information maintained by the computer must be described in detail. The number of digits and specific content of each automated file record and the number of records in each file must be specified.

The automated file-maintenance procedures must be specified together with expected frequencies of updating. Decisions as to whether sequential-processing or random-access methods are to be employed must be made at this time. Considerations influencing this decision are described elsewhere.

It is most important that standards for the design and control of automated input and output be established. The purpose of these standards is to ensure that all automated files of data originating in various segments of the organization will be compatible with each other and that each exact format is officially coordinated and established.

Controls over the files must be set up to assure that the system being developed will adequately screen the data input for validity, compatibility, and errors of omission, and that sufficient audit trails are provided. The system must also provide controls against intentional alteration of records and the possibility of accidental loss of master card-tape files or input records.

The effort expended to provide good documentation for the input and output and the establishment of adequate control will pay for itself many times.

It is obviously not economically desirable to develop a new system which is not compatible with other existing systems or lacks the necessary controls to ensure the validity of its output.

Report Formats and Data Retrieval. In the past, most data processing centers employed periodic reports. These reports were usually summarizations of past activity and reflected the happenings of the prior week, month, or quarter. Many reports were voluminous and difficult to analyze. Because of the volume of data to review, the technique of "exception" reporting has been widely accepted. This technique provides for the printing of information which fails to meet prescribed deviations. The result is improved reporting with emphasis placed on only those items which require attention.

Random-access devices have opened new avenues for data retrieval in that information on specific items may be obtained without searching an entire file. Direct-inquiry devices, such as typewriters and visual display units, may be connected to random-access files. Normally, computer processing can be interrupted by these inquiry terminals and specific records interrogated for data retrieval as required. It should be noted that interrogation can be for only one record at a time and that output formats normally are very restricted. Use of the inquiry terminals speeds the retrieval cycle for a specific piece of information from hours when processed under sequential-processing techniques, to seconds by the input-inquiry-terminal approach.

The cost justification for direct-access inquiry terminals must be analyzed carefully because the cost of data retrieval under this approach is normally greater than that of sequential processing. Another factor governing the use of random-access direct input-output devices is that the output report formats are restricted. A sequential-processing approach provides the capability of processing a number of programs, and the output reports can be the summarization or manipulation of several input files. Random-access inquiry systems normally provide for only simple calculations and limited referrals to other files. Reporting formats are restricted in that the format and the necessary programming steps to produce the report must be permanently stored in computer memory. The key factor in determining the method of information retrieval, whether it be a sequential-processing or random-access system, is the need for the information, what information is required, the frequency, the number of copies, and the controls necessary to ensure the validity of the report. These questions must be resolved before a decision can be made as to the method of data retrieval.

Periodicity and Cutoffs. It is important that firm input and output cutoff times be established for periodic file updating. Efficient batch-processing systems require scheduled input cutoff times so that the computer processing time can be accurately scheduled and the output reports released at a designated date and time. Complex systems require detailed schedules, which would include the cutoff time for input documents to be submitted to the computer center by operating personnel, cutoff periods on which all key punching must be completed, cutoff periods when computer processing must be finished, cutoff periods when the printers have completed these efforts, and a cutoff period when computer-center audit section completes their review of the output reports to ensure the validity of the data. Cutoff periods must be established on a realistic basis and once established closely adhered to.

IMPLEMENTATION

Pilot Installation and System Test. The approach to systems implementation utilizing a pilot installation concept is gaining broad acceptance. Even though the computer programs have undergone thorough testing, there are a number of other areas contributing to a successful operation which must be developed and tested. Personnel must be properly trained, new hardware checked out, and new procedures placed into effect. All these areas require constant monitoring by systems and operating personnel. A pilot installation allows the system to be placed in operation where every detail can be closely monitored and any deficiencies corrected as soon as possible. Also, only a small segment of the company is usually affected so that if troubles arise, manual steps can be taken to support the total system. Another advantage to the pilot approach is that it gets useful work into the computer at an earlier point, builds up confidence in the ability of the automated system to produce results, and builds up interest within the organization in its use.

Modular versus Total-systems Implementation. One of the most basic rules to be established with automated systems is to avoid moving too far too fast. One of the most common mistakes made with new automated installations has been overoptimism. Automated systems require human-developed logic which may involve decision rules, programming, clerical procedures, and many other important considerations.

An important factor in determining how fast you can install a sophisticated system will be based on the experience the company has with automated systems. If heavy experience is evidenced, larger steps may be taken with less risk; however, if this is a new field to the company, caution is the word. But whether the company has extensive automated systems background or is new to the field, a "phased" approach to implementation is normally "good business."

It is true that there may be extra costs involved in the phased approach. A portion of the total-systems design and programming may be reworked, since some of it was required to support intermediate systems which are subsequently superseded. But, on the other hand, through a phase approach the organization can avoid the potential economic and operational problems that would result if the company overextended itself. Total-systems implementations are very risky unless the system is small and has been thoroughly tested in parallel operation.

Parallel Operations. Usually the new automated system is expected to partly or wholly pay its way by replacing existing data-handling personnel and machines. However, these machines and personnel cannot be dispensed with until the new system is fully proved. It is expected that a number of unforeseen problems will arise, exceptional transactions may appear that were not anticipated, errors may be found in file records, and errors may be found in the computer programs. Therefore, it is usually necessary to plan for a period of "parallel operation" with the new system running at the same time as the old system and with the results of the two being compared. During this period, the full cost of both systems will be incurred. Parallel operations should be planned very carefully because if they last too long, excess expenditures may cause the entire program to be in jeopardy.

Cutover. Upon completion of each computer program, it must be tested thoroughly before being placed into operation. All individual parts of the program must be tested on specially prepared data which will simulate every condition the program was designed to handle with a relatively small amount of input. Precalculated answers must be obtained to determine that the program is operating as intended. During the time the data processing equipment and transmitting facilities are checked out, operating procedures can be tested for adequacy. Practice operations will not only serve to train personnel, but also reveal problems that may exist. Even though the system is satisfactorily solving test problems, and even though these test problems seem to be representative of conditions which will exist, there is no way to exactly duplicate the real flow of data.

The ideal way to cut over a system is to run the new system parallel with the old. As noted above, this may be expensive and requires feeding the same data to both systems and comparing the results. In most cases, it is too difficult and expensive to compare every input and output, but modifications to this principle can be made which will provide sufficient data for comparison. Complete cutover from the old to the new system should be made just as soon as the validity of the new system is established. A cutover schedule, which explains the procedures to be followed in detail, should be disseminated to all concerned with the implementation of the new system. Briefing sessions are helpful to assure understanding of cutover requirements.

MANAGEMENT CONSIDERATIONS

Plans and Programs.   Before completion of work on a data transmission system, an analysis of the company growth potential may be desirable.   If the system planned is to be limited to the installation of three or four input terminals in the same building, the analysis mentioned may not be warranted.   However, if the system contemplated is complex, that is, the installation of many remote input terminals linked to a computer many miles away, serious consideration should be given to the company's product and market plans.   It should be noted that a complex transmission system is not going to be operational in a few months.   Realistically speaking, a relatively long period of time will be required before the system is fully operational.   It must be determined that the need for the system will warrant the development costs involved and that the need will be present for an extended period of time.   Further, it must be determined that the system developed will provide capacity for anticipated increases in the volume of transactions.

Changes in product line may bring new factors into play.   The new system must be capable of responding to new situations.   It is very difficult, if not impossible, to foresee all the needs and requirements for a proposed data transmission system, but every facet of information available should be reviewed and analyzed.   Flexibility must be the key word for all data transmission systems.

The possibility of acquisition of new facilities may also play an important role in the systems plan.   The purpose, type, and location of a new facility must be considered in the data transmission plan.   The installation cost of communications facilities during construction is usually less than addition as an afterthought.   Also, without proper planning, it may be difficult, if not impossible, to interface the new requirements into an existing facility.   The number and type of input units and communications link must all be considered if the fully implemented system is to operate as intended.

Communications Requirement.   RESPONSE TIME: The time required to transmit a message and receive a reply varies greatly depending upon the type of communications facility in use.   Oversimplified, the time required really depends on how much the company is willing to spend and/or justify.   Wide microwave channels are capable of transmitting large volumes of data at high rates of speed but are very expensive.   Telegraph lines are inexpensive but relatively slow.   The decision on the type of communication facility must be based on a thorough analysis of the system requirements.   It is best to work with the communications common carrier to determine the facility which offers the most advantages for the application at the lowest cost.   In the case of existing telephone communications, several avenues are available.

There are broadband channels available using microwave or radio relay for high-speed transmission.   Such a network can normally carry approximately 5,100 characters per second.   Higher speeds are possible, but are dependent on the commercial availability of suitable channels and terminal equipment.

Voice grade channels provide for a line speed of approximately 250 to 300 characters per second.   Subvoice grade channels have a lower speed than voice grade.   Although there are no specific limits, subvoice grade channels are usually considered to be those within a range of 15 to 60 characters per second.

Telegraph grade channels have line speeds in the range of approximately 6 to 10 characters per second.   As can be seen, there are a number of communication channels available, each having advantages and disadvantages, and only through an analysis of the systems requirements can the proper selection be made.

DEGREE OF ACCURACY: Some of the factors that influence the efficiency of long-distance wires and cables are the distance involved, the ability of the copper or aluminum wire to carry the signal, interference from other circuits, and their electrical characteristics which cause distortion or loss of signals. Normally, the line quality supplied by the commercial carrier is satisfactory for most applications; however, it is possible to obtain lines of especially high quality at additional cost. These specially conditioned lines permit data transmission at lower error rates or higher rates of speed than would otherwise be possible. One possible disadvantage of these conditional lines is that alternative routes may not be readily available should they be required.

SYSTEM RELIABILITY: Data transmission systems require a high degree of systems integrity. Although all systems have error factors, these systems must be as error free as possible. Stringent control must be exercised because data transmitted normally is lost to further processing if errors are not corrected immediately. As an example, if an output device is malfunctioning but is not notifying the operator, many records may be lost to further processing because not enough valid data was recorded for reconstruction of the records.

Systems "downtime" must be kept to an absolute minimum. In the event input or output devices are inoperative at peak periods, operating personnel cannot transmit their required data. In the case of transmitting employee labor or attendance records, a great deal of additional cost can be incurred to recreate these records.

System reliability is usually so critical that "backup" hardware may be used to support the system. System switching to backup hardware must take place within time limitations dictated by the system. Backup hardware may be used only for a part of the system or for every systems component. Needless to say, backup hardware increases the operating cost of a data transmission system, but usually the risk of not providing support equipment is so great that the extra expense is justified.

Costs. The development of a new system or the modification of an existing one is an expensive operation. Highly trained personnel are required. Many man-months are required to develop the system, program the logic for the computer, and train operating personnel. A period of 6 to 12 months to install a new system is not unusual.

DEVELOPMENT: Development cost for a new or modified system can range from a few hundred dollars to hundreds of thousands. The systems development stage usually requires between three to nine months and will consist of a systems team of three to five systems analysts, operating department representatives, and vendor personnel. Interviewing management and recording, studying, and summarizing the data collected are a somewhat lengthy process. As a part of the systems development portion of the project, detailed systems specifications must be prepared. Inputs and outputs of the system must be clearly defined, master files described, computer program logic written, information flow charts prepared, and all special requirements peculiar to the system clearly stated. Standards for the system and operating procedures must be written. Failure to properly define the system and establish adequate controls is an invitation to disaster.

MAINTENANCE: From the day the system is first implemented until it is discontinued or superseded, the system requires constant maintenance. On some operational systems, the maintenance is relatively straightforward. If the programs are completely debugged, and all operating and clerical procedures have been worked out, the objective becomes one of maximizing efficiency. This is accomplished through careful planning, adherence to plans, and attention to detail. Other systems may require almost constant monitoring if they are critical to the daily operation of the company. Complex data transmission systems which carry data relative to payroll, stock balances, and the location of in-process parts must be monitored on a daily basis. Any deviation from the established standards must be analyzed immediately. Continuous monitoring is expensive but is one of the inescapable costs of any complex system.

DATA PROCESSING AND COMMUNICATION HARDWARE: Data transmission input devices are not usually expensive in themselves, but the support hardware can cause the overall system to be quite expensive per input terminal. Data transmission systems which utilize card or paper-tape input readers connected to an output card punch or tape are relatively simple and the cost within the reach of most organizations. Real-time systems utilizing dedicated data processing equipment and input-output devices are comparatively expensive. These systems require electronic data processing machines that have interrupt capability, other software program controls, and large high-speed memory. These systems also require a number of random-access file storage devices, as well as communication buffer terminals to handle the remote input-output terminals. The total cost of a real-time system, including its associated backup-equipment and transmission-line costs, may easily be twice as great as that of a sequential-processing system handling the same volume of work. Of course, the application may more than justify the additional cost.

COMMUNICATION LINES:

1. *Intraplant Communication Lines.* The cost of intraplant communication lines can range from almost nothing (where existing communication lines can be utilized) to thousands of dollars depending upon the number of input terminals and type of communication network. If at all possible, existing telephone communication facilities should be used because they offer flexibility and reasonable costs. Because of building-code requirements in many areas, most cable installations must be made in conduit, which is expensive. The requirements for this type of installation should be kept at a minimum. By using existing telephone company junction boxes located in the plant, conduit installations need be made only for "drop" lines and terminal hookup. With only the cost of installing new drop lines, the input terminals can be readily moved if facility changes are made. Flexibility is also important as far as cable installations are concerned. Careful analysis of cable requirements can result in avoidance of the expenditure of thousands of dollars on an inflexible intraplant communication network.

2. *Interplant Communication Lines.* Communication common carriers offer a great variety of services for data communication systems. These services include facilities for voice, data, printed messages, telemetry, and telephoto. Over 2,800 companies are recognized as communications common carriers. These companies can provide complete communication services to the subscriber including channels, modulating equipment, and the necessary terminating devices. Users may lease only the channels and provide purchased or leased terminal equipment for data transmissions. The cost of these services, of course, varies with the applications, but a wide range of services is available and through a thorough analysis the proper model can be selected at a reasonable cost.

Training. Data transmission systems, whose input and output terminals will be used by operating personnel throughout the company, require a very extensive program of orientation and training. It is desirable to use "live" training models of the terminals which are to be used, and to conduct carefully designed courses in their use at geographically convenient points. These courses should be given far enough ahead of time so that personnel will be fully trained by the time the system is operational. Even with detailed training sessions, "how-to-do-it" manuals should be prepared.   Personnel will not remember all that is discussed in the training classes.   Moreover, there will be a continuing flow of new personnel who did not attend the initial courses.   Therefore, complete procedures and manuals should be made conveniently available to systems users on a continuing basis.

TRAINERS AND TRAINING DEVICES: One of the most effective methods of training is to use a "live hands on" training device, i.e., install an input terminal and cable, connect it with a suitable output device, and allow personnel to make sample transmissions.   The "live" model may be no more than hooking up an input device to an output unit with 3 feet of cable, but its operating characteristics will be substantially the same as if it were miles away.   In fact, it is helpful in training if the operating personnel can see how the total system operates.   Nothing improves the chance of success more than to have the operating personnel understand the system and feel that they are a part of it.

Another effective training device for training large numbers of personnel is a motion picture describing the system and the use of the hardware.   Training films are effective because all personnel are presented the same information. Training lecturers often stress some points more than others, and if the same lecture must be given over and over by training personnel, there is a tendency to vary the presentation and be inconsistent in the presentation of the facts.   A recording of the training material used with slides or other visual aids can be very effective.

Training procedures and "how-to-do-it" manuals are absolute requirements. Personnel cannot be expected to retain all the information given at an orientation class.   The manuals and handbooks are a "must."

TRAINING TIME: The amount of training time, of course, varies with each application; but there are a few ground rules that will apply in almost all cases.   If at all possible, the personnel that are undergoing training should be taken away from the normal work area to a training classroom.   The purpose is twofold, in that by removing the people from their normal work area, they feel that their management has placed high priority on the project in that they could leave their work for a training class.   Second, in a formal classroom atmosphere, without the interruptions and distractions of the normal work area, it is much easier to gain their undivided attention.

It is also recommended that the systems analysts conduct the classes rather than the supervisor.   Individuals attending the classes will usually ask questions of the systems analysts that they wouldn't ask their supervisors.   The systems analyst is also in a better position to answer questions about the detailed operation of the system.   As to the length of time for each class, this too can vary, but normally, class periods should be kept down to one-hour sessions.   If possible, the classes should be small, not more than 15 or 20 trainees at each session. Training should take place on the same work shifts of the individuals being trained, and the training classes should be as close to the normal work areas as possible.

Following the formal training classes, on-the-job follow-up training is a must. When the system is implemented, systems personnel should be in the area at all times when the system is in use.   They should be circulating throughout the work area, assisting personnel and answering any questions that arise.   During these first few days and weeks, everything possible should be done to build confidence in the new system.   The systems analysts on the shop floor during this critical period can make the difference between success and failure.

Turnover Rate.   The turnover rate of the personnel required to operate the system is an important factor in the systems design.   Complex systems require trained personnel.   Training is expensive and time consuming.   If the turnover rate is high, the efficiency of the system is going to suffer materially. Systems which require large numbers of personnel to use data transmission input terminals must be kept simple. As an example, if input terminals are used to report employee attendance and labor hours, the terminals must be easy to use. The turnover rate in many manufacturing areas can be high depending on many factors, and the time provided for training may be only a few minutes for each employee. Under these conditions, the previously mentioned "how-to-do-it" booklets are important training tools. Reading the booklet and a few minutes of on-the-job training may be all the indoctrination that is given. Again, systems planning and monitoring are all-important if the system is to perform as intended.

OPERATIONAL CONSIDERATIONS

Terminal-selection Criteria. Data transmission terminal selections will be governed by many factors. At least three main considerations influence this selection. First, the cost of the terminal must be considered. Second, since this is usually the only portion of the system visible to the user, the terminal must be convenient and simple to use, and above all, it must be both rugged and reliable. A third determination that must be made is the type of communication network that will be required to support the system. Most data transmission systems now in operation use one of three basic communication channels. These line channels are called "simplex," "half-duplex," and "duplex."

Simplex circuits are similar to a one-way street in that they carry information in only one direction. A half-duplex circuit can carry information in either direction, but only in one direction at a time. A duplex circuit, also known as a "full duplex circuit," can carry information in both directions at the same time. A network can consist of any combination of these, according to the application requirements. In a half-duplex telephone circuit, reversing the flow of data requires a certain amount of time known as "turnaround time." In preliminary planning for the system, consideration must be given to the time required for answer-back signals that can occur before, during, and after each message as a response from the receiving station, indicating that it is ready to receive or that the last block of data was received correctly. In many instances, the time required for the answer back will affect the total throughput of the system.

Simplex, half-duplex, and duplex circuits are types of channels. The names indicate only the directional capability of the channel. The "grades" of channels are broad band, voice grade, subvoice grade, and telegraph. Circuits are graded on their basic line speed, expressed in characters per second, bits per second, or words per minute. The systems application will determine the type of channel configuration, but this area of channel selection is very important as it can greatly affect the continuing cost and performance of the overall system. Another important factor in the design of a data transmission system is the labor classification which will be operating the terminals. Management may find collective bargaining units very receptive to a presentation describing the nature of the equipment and its planned use.

PHYSICAL FEATURES: Unlike computers, which are usually placed in a controlled environment, remote input-output terminals must be installed in the office, stock room, or on the factory floor where the events take place. Under these conditions, terminals are subjected to all types of treatment and sometimes mistreatment. Personnel turn the wrong knobs, push the wrong buttons, and in general have little patience with hardware that does not function as expected. The selection of rugged hardware which can withstand large variances in temperatures, dusty conditions, and general abuse is most important. In most factory areas, fine dust is in the air and the terminals must be capable of operating within this environment.

An inoperative terminal may be important because it is the only one in the general vicinity. Personnel normally using the inoperative terminals must either prepare handwritten input documents or use alternate terminals which may be some distance from their normal work area.

One other consideration is that the terminal should be reasonably tamper-proof. If the terminal does not have some type of locking device on the maintenance access panel, operating personnel may have a tendency to attempt their own repairs. These efforts should be discouraged for several reasons, but especially because any attempt to repair terminals is potentially dangerous. All terminals are electrically operated and usually have some area within the mechanism that has high voltage. As a part of the training session, the procedure for requesting terminal repairs should be covered and personnel should be instructed that under no circumstances should they attempt the repair of any malfunctioning terminal.

VERSATILITY: The versatility of the input-output terminal is very important in that with proper selection of the devices, a number of systems can utilize the same terminal. As an example, a card reader located on the factory floor may be the input device for employee attendance recording, employee labor-hour reporting, and recording of movement of in-process parts. Such versatility allows the reader to be used throughout the work period instead of only at peak periods. It also reduces the training time required for new applications because most personnel are familiar with the hardware through other applications. Another factor to be considered is that if the same type of terminal is used for several applications, the cost of the overall system will usually be reduced. Many times, a new application may be added to the system by adding input units to the existing output device. If several types of terminals are used, there is a possibility that each type of terminal will require its own type of output device. Systems using several types and makes of hardware which are incompatible will cost more to install, rent, and maintain.

INPUT DEVICES: One of the basic elements of a data transmission system is the input-output device or terminal located at the point of transaction. There are a number of companies now offering input-output terminals, all having advantages and disadvantages. It is important that a thorough analysis be performed before a decision is made as to the specific selection of hardware. Once the company has completed the computer programming to support the system and incurred installation costs for the terminals, a change of hardware could be prohibitively costly. Another factor to be considered is that personnel trained to operate one type of terminal will have to undergo some retraining to use others. This also is expensive. The most common type of input devices are punched-card readers and punched-paper-tape readers. Visual displays, using a device similar to the cathode-ray tube, have provisions for data input. The light pen which has been used principally in graphics probably has general application also. Vendors offer a number of choices as to the number of characters their device can read per second, throughput rate, capacity, types of variable data-entry devices, and methods of operation. Paper-tape readers generally do not offer so large a selection, but several types are available. A variety of typewriter-type terminals are also available.

RELIABILITY: BACKUP-HARDWARE REQUIREMENTS: Even though most data transmission hardware on the market is reasonably reliable, it must be accepted that equipment malfunctions are going to take place and that provision must be taken to ensure that the system is not seriously affected by the loss of one piece of hardware. As an example, if several input terminals are connected to one output device in a subsystem and that output device malfunctions, the entire subsystem is affected. To prevent a system "breakdown," it is usually advisable to install a second output unit which can assume the role of the original piece of hardware. This may be expensive, but in many applications, downtime cannot be tolerated. The extra cost can usually be justified. If the system is carefully planned, the "backup" can be provided with a minimum of extra cost. This can be accomplished on systems which require several output units. Under these conditions, each output device services a series of input terminals. Two output devices are connected together so that in the event of a malfunction, a switch allows one device to service both sets of input terminals. Under this "backup" mode, the throughput of each input terminal is normally halved because one output device is handling twice as many input terminals, but the terminals are operative and messages are being received. Under this mode of operation, "backup" is provided and only a temporary drop in efficiency of the system occurs in event of output-device malfunction.

DATA CHECKS: Most input-output terminals use some type of data-checking feature. One of the most common is a "parity check," which is one or more digits or bits of information carried with a group of digits or bits which are dependent upon the remaining group in such a fashion that if an error occurs, it will be detected. Record-length checks are also common. The type and method of checking may differ, but all perform the same basic function of ensuring proper transmission of data, and if an error occurs, the record is identi-fied as an error transaction. Visual checks can be performed on punched cards. One of the simplest is that on some systems, all "good" transmission cards have a card punch in column 81. All that is required to check the validity of the transmission is to check for a punch in column 81.

Terminal Location. CONVENIENCE FACTORS: The convenience factor associated with the location of input-output terminals is most important. Convenient loca-tions for the terminals will encourage their use and reduce the time incurred traveling to and from the terminal to make transmissions.

It is generally accepted that terminals should be located so that they are within from 50 to 100 feet of the individual's work station. Time spent walking to the terminals is nonproductive and must be kept to a minimum. Another important factor in locating the terminals as near to the work station as feasible is to allow supervision to monitor the normal work and transmission of data.

Another factor to be considered is the height of the terminals so that they are accessible to all. Usually the terminals are installed so that the individual can stand in front of the terminal and make his transmission.

As mentioned, the terminals should be in the general work area, and if pos-sible, mounted along the aisles when used for employee attendance and labor-hour reporting. Pedestrian traffic flow is also an important factor. Once again, careful attention to the details can help to make a successful system.

ENVIRONMENTAL FACTORS: Air pollution is almost always a factor in factory areas. Dust, acid fumes, and metal chips are usually present, and the ter-minals must be able to operate under adverse conditions. Before making final selection of terminals, it is suggested that some be installed on an environ-mental-test basis for several weeks to determine how they perform under live conditions.

Temperature fluctuations are also important considerations, since some ter-minals have a high malfunction rate when the temperature exceeds 100 degrees Fahrenheit.

Humidity can be a factor, especially with card punches. Blank cards have a tendency to "swell" and cause card jams. These are important factors because they are ever present. In the event the hardware is not suitable, constant problems will arise leaving no solution ultimately except to make very costly changes.

OPTIMUM NUMBER OF TERMINALS: The number of terminals required in an information transmission system can best be determined by a thorough analysis of the applications which the system is to service. Many applications can be staggered throughout the work period, thus enabling a higher transmission-to-terminal ratio than can be obtained for a system that requires heavy usage in relatively short periods of time. The cost of additional terminals must be weighed against the expense of operator travel time to and from the terminal and time spent waiting to make a transmission. The complexity of setting up the device in preparation for making a transmission, as well as the transmission speed of the terminal, are two factors that are important in arriving at a decision as to the proper number of terminals for the system.

Throughput rate (the amount of information that can be sent through a system in a specified time) is one of the prime considerations in determining the type and quantity of the hardware needed for an information transmission system.

Terminal, receiver, line speed, length of message transmissions, operator proficiency, complexity of transactions, and quantity of variable data input can all affect the throughput of a system. While a terminal may be very fast in executing a transaction, it may not increase throughput if the line speed cannot accommodate all the active terminals that want to send data down the line. This problem could possibly be solved by increasing the number of lines, thus creating a lower-to-line ratio. However, this could result in the system becoming receiver-bound in that the receiver is unable to handle all the information coming across the line. The answer here could be to acquire additional or faster receivers. The important point to be noted is that the interrelation of the various hardware components of a system is significant in determining throughput.

Transaction time is a function of the hardware speed, terminal, receiver, line, and complexity of the transaction. Once an operator has passed the learning stage, the time that it takes him to make a transmission will be determined by the type and quantity of information that he is required to enter in the terminal. A fixed input as a badge or a card will require less time than a variable input such as a slideboard, typewriter, or cartridge. The travel time from work station to terminal and the return trip must also be a consideration in transaction time.

Peak transmission load is that period or periods when the highest volume of activity will be generated by the system. All potential applications must be carefully scrutinized from the standpoint of peak load times and how these peak times conform with applications already on the system. For existing systems, a continuous analysis of the peak periods must be maintained to ensure that the volume has not increased to a point where it could swamp the system.

Queue analysis, whether it is accomplished through the use of computer-generated statistics or by a visual review of terminals and receivers, is a valuable tool in determining the operating efficiency of an information transmission system. A queue analysis can indicate an improper assignment of operators to terminals, a need for switching of terminals to different lines, poor positioning of terminals, malfunctions in hardware, or the need for more or less hardware. Some type of queue analysis should be made on all information transmission systems periodically to ensure that the systems are continuing to operate as they were originally designed.

OUTPUT EQUIPMENT: In the past few years, numerous new types and models of output equipment have become available in the form of card and paper punches, view boxes, plotters, printers, and others to service information transmission systems. Each device has particular advantages, and the design and requirements of the system will determine what is needed. Before a decision is made as to type of output equipment, consideration should be given to the number of copies needed, distance of output equipment from receivers, response time necessary, maintenance requirements, cost, and multiple-application use. An important item in establishing remote output stations is the cost of operating personnel needed to staff the output stations. This cost should be weighed against savings in putting the data into machine-sensible form, transportation, and time for delivery of information under conventional methods. In some systems, the timing requirement is so critical that this alone will justify the establishment of multiple remote output locations.

CONCLUSIONS

Performance Surveillance. After a system has been installed and the initial performance checks have revealed that it is operating at a level of accuracy and efficiency that meets the standards as set out in the original design, there must be established routines for periodic reviews to determine that the high level of integrity is retained. Error routines, statistical data analysis and communication with operating areas can all play a part in detecting problems at an early date. It is very important that all problems are found as soon as possible so that corrective action can be initiated before service is impaired. Statistical data compiled on throughput can be a valuable tool in determining if a system is operating efficiently. Activity counts by time and transaction type can be recorded and a standard developed for comparison with daily volumes. As the daily activity rate varies, a deviation percentage is calculated. When this percentage figure begins to show that the deviation is increasing an analysis should be made to determine if there is a logical answer for the change. If not, immediate action should be taken to check out the individual components of the system. Error analysis routines can detect hardware and software failures and isolate the problem to the particular area. For example, operator difficulties become evident indicating new employees needing training or possible new conditions in the operating area the system is not recognizing and handling correctly. Changes can be incorporated before confidence is lost in the system.

Multiple use of terminals to accommodate more than one information transmission system on a single set of hardware can be very advantageous from a cost standpoint. In many instances, two or more completely different systems can use the same terminals without degrading service on either or any of them. When multiple use of terminals is possible, a lower average transaction cost can be attained which could be the deciding factor in determining whether an information transmission system is cost justifiable and should be installed. Before any additional uses are added to existing terminals, a thorough analysis of the new system should be made to see that the activity it generates does not conflict with existing systems using the hardware. Many times volume is not the significant factor in determining if a terminal can serve a multiple use. The time of peak loads of transactions and the area where the transaction will be made are two very important items in multiple use of terminals. If two or more systems are compatible except for certain periods in the daily work cycle, priorities for use of the terminals can be established.

Planning for Change. Every information transmission system developed will undergo change after it has been installed. Therefore, foresight in design to allow flexibility is one of the most important considerations when developing such a system. Change can take many forms, and in some instances, volume contraction can prove to be as serious as increased activity. A system which has been economical at a certain activity level might be an excessive and unwarranted expense should volume decrease significantly. Careful analysis should be given the individual components of a system to ensure that they are downward compatible. This is especially important in selection of receivers. The more usual type of change is an increase in activity, and here again, planning in the development stages can avert serious and expensive problems after a system has been operating. Installation costs for hardware and lines are an important cost segment of an information transmission system, and it would be rather shortsighted to install a system where the initial activity is the peak load that the system can handle. Reserve capacity built into the system at the start can prove to be a cost saving in the long run, as it avoids additional installation costs for hardware. Technological changes are also to be expected, and the availability of improved hardware should be reviewed from time to time and each system placed under continuous supervision to determine that it has not become obsolete.

Chapter **25**

Shop Data Collection Systems

EDITOR:

Eugene R. Marshall, P.E. *Department Chief, Planning Engineering and Standards Development, Western Electric Co., Inc., Indianapolis, Indiana*

CONTENTS

Data collection and transmission systems are used by each of us in all phases of our lives to gather the information we need to make our decisions. We may use informal systems such as relying on our memory, or we may record each transaction as it occurs and then enter the pertinent data into a formal bookkeeping system.

It may be possible for smaller businesses to be adequately administered by one individual. However, even these businesses require that the data for sales, purchases, material in process, and inventory records be recorded in some manner. As a company grows larger, the number of records, entries, and people involved in these systems increases. More time is then required to manually process these records. Furthermore, as the number of records and entries increases it generally becomes necessary to prepare intermediate reports or summaries in addition to reporting the totals for each category. As an example, although total sales may be the most important report for upper management, it is also necessary to summarize the output by product line, color, or some other factor for the intermediate-management level to use in planning production.

Small companies may be able to use a few clerks to manually process all the data for necessary manufacturing control. However, as companies increase in size, the clerical force required to process all data manually becomes unwieldy and the cost of the system becomes prohibitive.

It is possible to eliminate most of the duplicate formal and informal record keeping by designing a production information system to obtain the data directly from the shop in a form suitable for processing. Once the production information is collected and converted to a computer-analyzable form, reports can be generated consistent with the details required for any level of management. Checks and balances can then be built into the information system to find those areas where the input data may be in error. There are several advantages to having the data reduced to computer-analyzable form when they are received from the shop. The principal advantage is that all reports for the different levels of management can be made from the same data.

However, even in small manual data collection systems, the input data cannot generally be processed into usable information for use by the decision maker quickly enough to take corrective action at the required time. Intensive competition is causing management to take a very critical look at investment costs and services. Management in many companies has found that it is necessary to provide information to the decision maker more quickly than manual systems can operate. Computerized information systems are the only large-scale systems that can effectively provide feedback to management in time to take corrective action. Many companies are now manufacturing equipment to collect and transmit data. These firms are investing heavily in research and development to find ways of minimizing the cost of handling data as well as reducing system reaction time. As a result of this research effort, these companies have recently introduced many new types of equipment and systems, and many more developments in the field of information collection and transmittal can be expected in the future.

The following is an analysis and summary of the types of systems which are currently available for the collection of production data in a manufacturing plant and the systems design criteria which should be considered. One specific system cannot be recommended for general use, since each system must be chosen to fit the requirements of the manufacturing environment for which it is designed in addition to cost and noneconomic limitations imposed by management.

SYSTEMS DESIGN CRITERIA

The principal criteria which must be considered in the design of a system or evaluation of an existing system can be divided into several major categories. The criteria will be examined in the following order: What information is required to effectively manage the affairs of the company? When is the information required to be of value? How does the proposed system interface with the other systems required within the plant?

Reports: Who Needs What? Many hundreds of management reports can result from production data. A few examples of these reports are operator efficiency and payment; material usage and labor cost by part, assembly, order, and department; raw-material, in-process, and finished-goods investment; and status of production orders—on time, early, or late. The detail required in each of these reports is generally inversely related to the management level of the person using the information. The details which a first-line supervisor must have to effectively administer his area generally are not required by the next level of supervision. The first-line supervisor may need performance information daily by person while the second-line supervisor only has time to review a weekly summary of efficiency by product type for each of his major areas. Some form of exception reporting should also be used to bring trouble spots to the attention of first- and second-line supervision. The third-line supervisor should only receive weekly reports on the major areas of concern as well as exception reports on areas that are not within control limits.

Many members of management want to be put on distribution for most of the reports that are distributed to their subordinates. These extra reports generally increase the cost of operating the information system. They may also increase the reaction time of the system by adding a reprinting or reproduction step to produce the required number of copies of these reports. A general rule to use in designing an information system is that the total volume of data going to a manager should be less than the average volume that the supervisors reporting to him receive.

Timing: When Is the Information Required? Once it has been determined to whom the report must go, it is equally important to determine when each report must be received in order to be of value. A forecast showing a possible problem area is valueless if it is received after the problem has already occurred. Also, a daily report has little value to first-line supervision unless it is received near the start of the following day. These reports must also be available at a consistent time so that the supervisor can depend on receiving them. Once the reports can be expected at a specific time, they are more likely to be used by management. If these reports are not always on time, the supervisor must maintain a manual backup system. This increases the cost of the information system and reduces the supervisor's interest in maintaining it. Therefore, the time at which the report is received and the dependability of receiving the report are both important considerations in the design of a system.

This phase of the analysis may be one of the major factors in determining which type of data collection system must be installed. It may be very difficult to express in monetary terms the value of receiving a specific report. However, it is necessary to determine the relationship between the value of the report and the time that the report is received. Both the manner in which the data are collected and the computer equipment which will be used to process the information will be determined by these time-versus-cost factors. Data which must be keypunched onto cards in the tab room may require second- or third-shift key punching and the selection of an unfavorable cutoff time for the receipt of the last data to be processed. However, data that are received on punched cards, "marked-sensed" cards, or optically readable documents can be processed very quickly after the last information is received. Data received on punched paper tape and magnetic tape are generally ready to be processed by the computer system as soon as received.

The processing time of the reports is generally much greater on card-reading computers, since considerable time must be spent on peripheral equipment sorting the cards into the correct sequence for each different report. The time required for these sorting operations is much less on a tape-reading computer.

The error detection and correction routines built into the system also greatly affect the timing of all reports. Therefore, these routines are very important in the design of any data collection system. Some of the checks that can be built into the system which can automatically show out-of-control situations are too much or too little time reported, too low or high operator efficiency, too low or too high operation yield, and improper organization or operator identification. These possible errors must be clearly indicated at the earliest possible time on the reports. The procedure for correcting the errors should be positive enough for the supervisors to know which entries were corrected and the amount of the correction. Errors that are detected by the computer can be evaluated best by supervision if summarized at the end of the reports even if they are specially marked in the report.

Interface: How Will This System Fit in with the Others? The system that is installed to obtain production data will have an interface with other manual or computerized systems already in use at the plant. Some of these other systems include inventory measurement, production control, raw-material and purchased-parts ordering, and payroll. The complexity of the overall network of systems is generally related to the number and size of systems which are integrated. Before tying all the systems together, it may be better to operate the production information system independently for a period of time so that it can be debugged and refined without affecting any of the other systems. However, the production information system should be designed for future integration with the existing systems in the plant. By utilizing a step-by-step or modular design concept, it may take longer to complete an integrated plant or company information system. However, many of the individual parts of the system will be operative long before the system is completed. It is therefore necessary that all the data be collected in a format which is equally usable for all the component systems. This is extremely important whether a large system is installed in one step or in several stages.

DATA COLLECTION SYSTEMS

Manual Data Recording. All the manual systems described below are similar in that a pencil is the only tool which is used in the shop area to originate production reports. The earliest data collection systems found in industry fall into this category. This is also the most common method used in industry to enter data into the information systems.

MANUAL RECORDS: This is the oldest method of generating data for information systems and is still one of the most common ways to originate data for analysis on a computer. When this system is used to collect production information, some form of operator-performance record or summary sheet is used. All the information required by shop management for efficiency records and production and inventory control must be recorded on these sheets daily by the operator, time clerk, supervisor, or some other person in the shop area. This information must be collected and recorded daily even if the data are forwarded at less frequent intervals. This system requires that a summary of all production information be legibly printed in specific places on the production report. See Fig. 1 for an example of a production record designed for manual entries. These reports are then collected and sent to tabulating to have information extracted and keypunched into cards, paper tape, or transferred to magnetic tape. Manual data recording is practical for small shops or when the data are not needed quickly. The cost per entry is not great, but a great deal of keypunching effort is required to get the data in a form suitable for analysis.

PREPUNCHED INTERPRETED CARDS (PPIC): The use of prepunched interpreted cards to collect production information requires much less key-punching effort than the manual data system. These cards can be provided for all major production operations. They should contain all the information required for all the systems in which the data will be used. The operator only has to enter the variable information required: operator and organization identification, time charges, and production results. See Fig. 2 for an example of a card designed for this type of system.

For job shops, a sufficient number of these cards should be generated and sent out to the shop with the production order. This helps to reduce the time spent ordering, filing, and routing cards to the operator. The cards for items which are mass-produced should be stored in sufficient quantities on the production floor in predetermined storage locations. Then, each time a card is needed, someone must go to the files, obtain the card, and bring it to the person who will fill in the required information. The completed cards are then forwarded to tabulating to have the handwritten entries keypunched into the cards. This system is more suitable for use in large shops than the completely manual system,

OPERATOR'S PERFORMANCE RECORD

WEEK ENDING 8/14	DEPT. NO. 1423	CLOCK NO. 3102	OPER. GR. 24	CODE	NAME	Edward Myerson	
FILE DESC. O.S. NO.	965A	396R	311E			MACHINE	
FILE OR OPER. NO.	11	3	6			TROUBLE	
JOB GRADE	25	25	26				
O.S. CODE							
HOURS PER PART	.0179	.0167	.0179				
	21.8	10.1	7.8				

DATE	OUTPUT	HRS.	OUTPUT	HRS.	OUTPUT	HRS.	OUTPUT	HRS.	OUTPUT	HRS.	OUTPUT	HRS.
8/8	31,000	5	17,000	3								
8/9	14,650	2½	31,000	5								½
8/10					43,500	7¾						¼
8/11	44,000	7½										½
8/12	32,000	5¼	12,500	2½								¼
TOTAL	121,650	20¼	60,500	10½	43,500	7¾						1½

FILE DESC. O.S. NO.							
FILE OR OPER. NO.							
JOB GRADE							
O.S. CODE							
HOURS PER PART							

DATE	OUTPUT	HRS.	OUTPUT	HRS.	OUTPUT	HRS.	OUTPUT	HRS.	OUTPUT	HRS.	OUTPUT	HRS.
TOTAL												

REMARKS: (SEE REVERSE SIDE)   TOTAL HOURS [38½]   TOTAL POINTS [39.7]   % EFFICIENT [103]

Fig. 1 Operator's performance record.

since the key-punching time is greatly reduced. Because less key punching is required, the input is ready for processing much quicker than from manual records. In addition to the savings in total system cost and processing time, the use of prepunched interpreted cards greatly reduces the number of input errors.

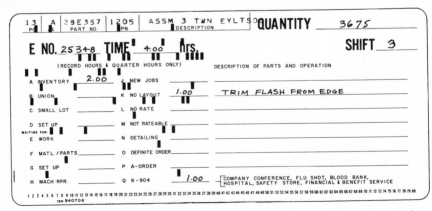

Fig. 2 Prepunched interpreted card. (*Courtesy of Western Electric Co., Inc.*)

MARK-SENSED CARDS: Relatively inexpensive equipment can be used to read entries made on tab cards by electrorecording pencils. The pencils are used to blacken in ovals printed on a tab card in positions corresponding to the 12 rows that are used to keypunch data into the card (Fig. 3). The cards are generated and distributed to the shop in the same manner as PPIC described above. The production information is then recorded by the operators on these cards by blackening the selected ovals completely with a special pencil. Each oval corresponds to a row on the card and uses an area three columns wide. The operator must be sure that there is sufficient marking material on the card for the processing unit to read. Equal care must be taken to keep all the marking in the oval and not smear any on the surface of the card, since these markings may cause the information on the card to be read incorrectly.

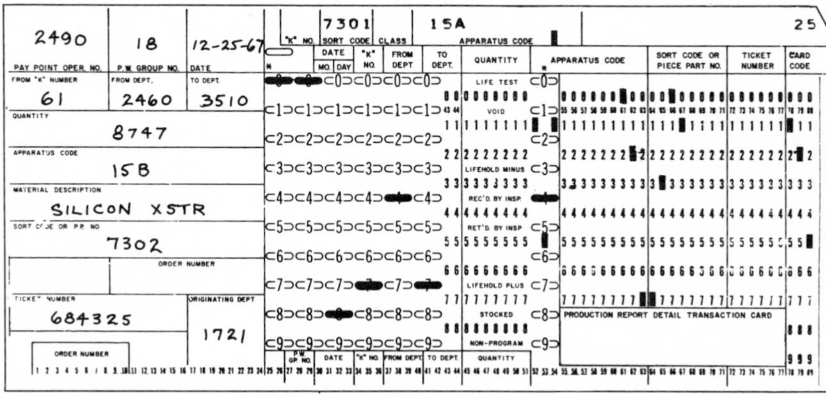

Fig. 3 Mark-sensed card. (*Courtesy of Western Electric Co., Inc.*)

These markings are read by an attachment that must be placed on a card reproducer. The information is then automatically punched into that card or another card. These punched cards can then be processed in the same manner as a key-punched card.

The marked card takes a little more time to complete than a PPIC, since in addition to blackening the ovals, the information is written on the card to allow errors detected by the sensing equipment to be corrected by the operator. However, the marked card does not require any key punching. Therefore, if the savings in key-punching time do not exceed the cost of marking the ovals and punching the cards on the reproducer, this method may be practical because of the reduction in time required to prepare the cards for analysis once they are received in the computer room. The information which may be placed in the marked card is limited to a total of one digit per column of prepunched data and one digit per three columns of marked data. However, with 80 card columns available, there is usually sufficient space available for most purposes. To economically justify a system using these cards, a fairly large number of cards must be used to offset the cost of the additional equipment. However, this system does not require as long a time interval for processing the reports as prepunched interpreted cards.

Mechanical Data Recording. Several mechanical devices may be used for the collection of production information. These devices are all simple to operate and cost from less than $5 to over $2,000 per unit. The units vary from simple, slow, versatile units to those which are quick and can operate only on a fixed format.

PORT-A-PUNCH CARDS: This type of system is extremely easy and inexpensive to install, since it requires a very low investment in mechanical equipment per operator, little training for the operator to learn how to use the cards, and no additional tab equipment. Port-A-Punch (PAP) cards appear very similar to electromarked cards except that some perforations are scored around the area where the holes would normally be keypunched (Fig. 4). The card is inserted into a plastic holder, and a pencillike stylus is used to punch out the prescored holes corresponding to the numbers or letters desired. In addition, the data are generally written on the card to provide a method of checking or troubleshooting the input. The cards are then immediately ready for processing by the computer, since no key punching is necessary.

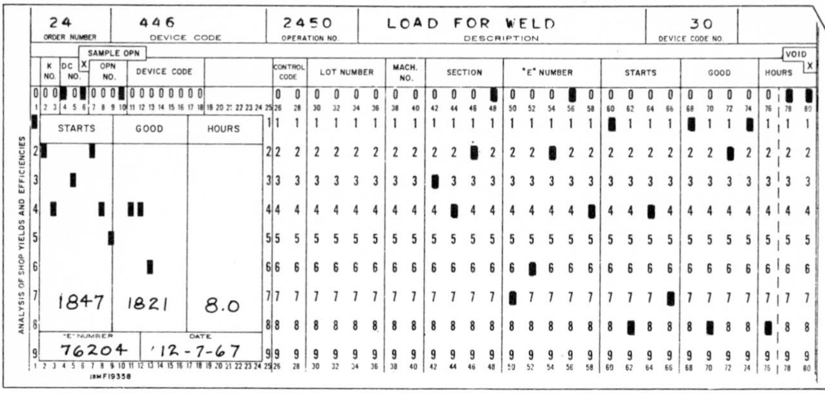

Fig. 4 Port-A-Punch card. (*Courtesy of Western Electric Co., Inc.*)

These cards can be designed, generated, stored, and distributed in exactly the same manner as prepunched interpreted cards. The principal differences between these systems are their costs. The cost per entry on a PAP card is somewhat higher than keypunching. However, if a large volume of cards is used daily, the cards can be used as soon as they arrive in the computer room without waiting to be keypunched.

When a report must be available at the start of the next working day, it may be less costly to use PAP cards than begin key punching on a second or third shift. When a lot of variable input is required, PAP cards may be more usable than mark-sensed cards because PAP cards require only two columns per variable entry. Two columns are required per prescored column to keep the strength of the card high enough to be handled. If these cards must be handled very often in processing, such as required with a card-reading computer, the data should be reproduced into standard tab cards to eliminate the possibility that some prescored holes will be knocked out by accident and incorrect data then processed.

The accuracy of the data may be increased by giving only a few operators in the shop the responsibility for collecting and punching the data into the cards for a specific group of operators. These persons are then in a position to review the validity of the data received from the operators. There must be a requirement for processing a fairly large number of these cards with little or no delay to justify the additional labor cost per entry of this system when compared to prepunched interpreted cards. However, this extra cost will generally assure that the reports can be issued at the beginning of the next workday.

MECHANICAL PUNCHES: Several mechanical devices (Fig. 5) which vary greatly in size and complexity are available for use in the shop to punch production data directly into standard tab cards. The simplest mechanical device that falls into this category has keys which the operator uses to manually punch a hole in the 0 to 12 rows of the card or skip a space in much the same manner as the key punches used in the tab room.

Fig. 5 Mechanical punch. (*Courtesy of International Business Machines Corp.*)

Other types of devices have several levers that are used to select the values which are to be punched into the card in the same manner as the levers are used on the devices which record the amount of the credit purchases at a gas station. The operator then pulls a handle to punch the indicated data into the card. If desired, the card can then be moved and more entries punched into it.

Several of these devices are also capable of printing the digit above the column at the same time as the hole is punched. However, these devices can generally punch only one hole in a column at a time, and many of them can punch only the numeric rows. These devices are generally used to add the variable information to prepunched interpreted cards.

Punches can be placed in strategic locations in the shop for use by groups of operators or by specific operators assigned the job of punching entries. The chief advantage gained from using mechanical punches is that the cards may be used as soon as they arrive in the computer room. The mechanical punches may be almost as inexpensive as key punching PPIC when all card handling is included. The purchase price of this type of equipment ranges from less than $100 per unit to over $1,000 per unit. Therefore, the number of entries per card and the number of cards which must be processed per day per station must be determined for each individual situation to determine which of these mechanical devices is the most economical to use.

MECHANICAL PRINTERS: The simple mechanical device that many service stations and department stores use to record credit purchases can also be used to collect production data (Fig. 6). Tickets can be imprinted with a combination of one or two plastic data cards containing the predetermined information while levers are used to record the variable input. The plastic data cards can provide up to 20 characters to identify the fixed production information while 7 digits of variable information can be recorded using the movable levers.

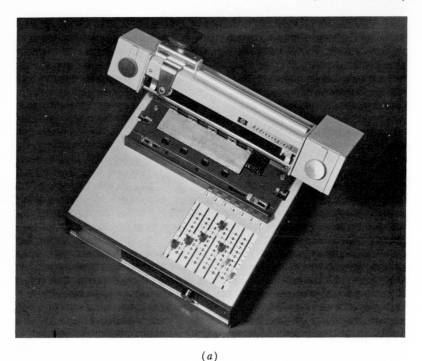

(a)

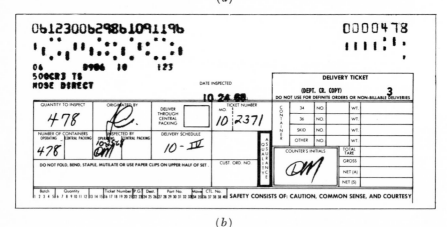

(b)

Fig. 6 (a) Addressograph data recorder; (b) Addressograph optically read card. (*Courtesy of Addressograph Multigraph Corp.*)

Several thousand different cards containing the fixed input information may be stored in rotating tab files in the same location as the recording devices. Tickets can be generated daily by a shop clerk from operator-performance records or by the operator at the completion of each job.   One pass through the printer is required for each card that must be used.   One card can show the operator and organization information and the hours worked recorded with the movable levers.   The product identification card can then be used while the movable levers are set to record the output.

Several copies of the ticket are generally made at one time.   The copy of the ticket is kept in the shop as a receipt, while the card is sent to the tab room to be read by an optical code scanner. The scanner transfers the data to punched paper tape or magnetic tape for further processing. If the optical code scanner is used only for this system, a large number of cards must be processed to bring the cost per card down to the level of the preceding systems.

One small disadvantage of this system is that the printed cards must be converted into a form that can be understood by the computer. However, the cards can be read and the data punched into the card very quickly using an optical code scanner. One of the advantages that this system has is that a copy of the data is kept by the originator as a receipt. The other advantages and disadvantages of this type of system are very similar to those for prepunched interpreted cards and mechanical punches.

Electromechanical Data Recording and Data Transmission. Many electromechanical devices are available which punch data into a tab card or paper tape from information entered on prepunched tab cards, identification cards, and/or variable information set on dials or levers. The principal difference between these devices and the mechanical units is that some of the information that is frequently used, such as part number, operator number, organization number, and cost center, from one or more input cards is taken from these cards and transferred to another card, punched paper tape, or magnetic tape. Only the variable entries must be entered by the operator on a keyboard or set of dials. Some of these devices can also transmit the data directly to a central collection area where the entries are recorded on punched paper or magnetic tape.

TYPEWRITERS: Typewriters which can generate punched paper tape or tab cards have been available for some time but have not gained general acceptance as an instrument to record production information. These typewriters (Fig. 7) can read punched cards or paper tape as well as record a great variety of variable data using an alphanumeric typewriter keyboard. The output of this type of machine is a typed document as well as punched paper tape, punched card, or magnetic tape.

Some form of output record must be used by the operator to record his

Fig. 7 Flexowriter automatic writing machine. (*Courtesy of Friden, Inc.*)

production information. This information can be typed onto a form while punched paper tape or tab cards are simultaneously generated. Punched cards can be used to type the part and operator information automatically with only the production quantity and hours worked typed in as variable information. The typed documents can then be kept by the shop while cards or tapes are forwarded to the tab room for processing. The system can also be used on-line to record the completion of each job. The typing units then transmit the information over telephone lines directly to a central data collection unit. The receiving unit can then record the data on punched paper tape or magnetic tape.

In addition to using these typewriter systems to generate cards that will be batch-processed, the systems can be designed to operate on-line as a transmitting typewriter. It is then possible for error messages, exception reports, and other information to be transmitted back to the shop. Considerable data must be processed before this type of system can be justified, since a substantial investment must be made in equipment. The principal benefit that is obtained by the use of these systems is the speed at which the data are available for analysis and feedback.

Fig. 8 Transaction recording unit. (*Courtesy of Radio Corporation of America.*)

TRANSACTION RECORDING UNITS: Many devices (Fig. 8) are currently available which can take selected data provided by the operator, arrange it in the desired format, and punch it all into a tab card or paper tape. Some of these devices can also transmit this information by wire to a receiving unit located in the tab room. These receiving units can record the data on punched paper tape, magnetic tape, or work on-line in a real-time system.

This type of equipment can often be set up to detect many types of input errors. This allows the operator to correct these errors before they get into the system. This equipment can be used by each individual operator when he completes his job or by a predesignated person in each area using the operator's performance records. For this type of system a file of prepunched and inter-preted master cards identifying the work performed must be available in the shop area. One of these prepunched cards must be inserted in the unit together with the operator identification card and variable information to record each entry.

The price of these units varies greatly as do their complexity and speed. Some nontransmitting units cost only several hundred dollars to purchase, while the simplest of the transmitting devices cost over one hundred dollars per month rental for each sending unit plus a substantial rental charge for each receiving unit. Each of these units is capable of processing large quantities of data. However, the number of punching or sending units required is a function of the peak load rather than the average load. With some on-line systems, it is possible to add a badge reader that can be used to clock people in and out of work. These badge-reading units work almost as fast as a standard time clock. By having the data from the clocking units feed into the production reporting system, the absence time can be automatically incorporated into all the reporting systems as well as used for attendance and payroll.

Telephone Transmission of Data. INTERPLANT DATA TRANSMISSION: Several data collection and transmission systems have been developed that use long-distance telephone circuits to reach a receiving unit or computer. These systems send

Fig. 9 Telephone data set. (*Courtesy of Western Electric Co., Inc.*)

information from a special card-reader attachment or keyboard (Fig. 9) at the sending end through commercial telephone lines to a receiving unit which punches paper tape or tab cards, records the information on magnetic tape, or places the information directly into the computer for processing. Variable information can be transmitted by depressing the desired numbers and symbols on the keyboard of the phone. Many companies use these units in sales offices to place their orders. Several airlines also use a similar system to coordinate all reservations through one master computer memory bank.

INTRAPLANT INDIVIDUAL UNITS: Many methods may be used to transmit the data by telephone to the recording unit. The simplest method is to have a push-button phone unit at every workplace and use it somewhat similar to an output counting device. At the start of each shift, the operator uses the input unit to identify himself and the job on which he is working. The operator then depresses one button to show the completion of a specific quantity of parts when the job is completed. Other push-button codes are used to indicate the start or stop of interruptions. The time is automatically recorded as each entry is made. All the information transmitted is charged against the last job entered. A new job code is entered only when the part or operation performed by the operator changes. The computer can then determine the production and delay times for each person and job, since all the output, start, and stop times are available.

This method of data collection can be used either as part of an on-line real-time system or in a data recording system with the information batch-processed. One of the chief advantages that this system has is the use of very low-cost data collection terminals. As a result, it may be practical to use one terminal for each operator in a large plant.

The disadvantage of the system is that operators will generally keep a duplicate set of records, since there is no permanent record generated at the terminal showing what has been transmitted. Whenever this type of transmitting unit is used, provision should be made for the operator to receive an audible feedback of the information transmitted. This type of system requires very little time and effort from the operator, even when a written record is kept of all transactions.

INTRAPLANT CARD-READING UNITS: A small number of card-reading telephones may be used in the shop by a group of operators in a manner similar to that of the electromechanical transmitting stations described above. These telephones use a prepunched plastic card to "dial" the predesignated job information into the recording unit. The variable information is then transmitted by depressing a series of dial buttons. The card-reading telephone (Fig. 10) is one of the

Fig. 10   Card-reading telephone.   (*Courtesy of Western Electric Co., Inc.*)

least-expensive data transmission terminals. Advantages and disadvantages of these units are very similar to those of the transaction recording units described above. However, some audio feedback system is required for these units to provide the operator an opportunity to verify the data transmitted. Also, the operator does not generally have the opportunity to verify what data have been transmitted by the unit. Other disadvantages and advantages of these units are similar to those of the electromechanical units previously described.

Central Control-room Recorders. Counting devices have been used for many years to tell the operator how many units have been produced by the machine he is operating. The operator then periodically reports his production and hours worked. The operator often fills out a lot card that is forwarded to production control after all the work on a specific operation is completed.

Fig. 11 Central control-room recorder. (*Courtesy of Telecontrol Corp.*)

There are several systems (Fig. 11) available that can transmit this information directly from the counter on the machine to a central control-room register. In addition to the number of units produced, these systems also provide a subtotal of units produced on the current shift, the total production time, total downtime, the number of units remaining to be produced, the identity of the employee performing the work, together with the part and operation identification. All this on-line, real-time information is then directly available for analysis by the person in the control room who is responsible for production planning. Therefore, when any rush jobs or emergencies arise, it is relatively easy to determine the status of every job in process and determine which job should be stopped to allow the new one to start.

These reporting systems generally provide communication from the control room to the operator and other support personnel as well as from the operator to the control room. Without leaving his machine, the operator can also signal the control center for assistance, material handlers, etc., as soon as the need occurs. This often prevents needless shutdowns of the machines. The control center can contact the appropriate person by phone, paging system, or lights on a control panel. When the operator completes a job he sends a signal to the control center. A record is kept of the downtime until the next job is set up. After the job is ready to run, a control center is told to start recording production for the specific part on that machine. Written reports can then be obtained from the information received by the control center. The method used to obtain the reports is dependent on the system installed. On the simpler systems, all information must be manually recorded on forms by someone in the control center so that the data can be keypunched.

Other more sophisticated systems use a small on-line, real-time computer to schedule and load the shop. The data are fed directly into this computer to analyze and summarize the production data and compare it to the remaining schedule. The computer then prints all the required documentation and reports as well as notifies the control room of all out-of-control conditions.

The central-control-center concept is most applicable to a job shop or any plant where it is important to keep a close control on the stage of completion of each part and all the machines in the shop.   One of the chief advantages of the system is the on-line, real-time knowledge of all jobs in process without the necessity for filling out and processing performance records.

Optical Character Reading.   One of the recent developments in the computerization of data manual from manual records is the optical character reader (OCR). Most of the current systems require that a specific typewritten font be used. Therefore, all the information required by the system must be printed on the forms using one of the fonts that can be read by the OCR equipment.   Some systems are capable of reading handwritten numbers or letters in combination with printed or type information.   However, the handwritten information must be a specific size and shape located in predesignated locations in the form (Fig. 12).

Fig. 12   Optical character reading.   (*Reprinted by permission of Educational Testing Service, Princeton, New Jersey.*)

The locations are indicated by lines that are not read by the optical character reader.

It is possible to print the general information on production forms and have the operators record only the variable information by neatly printing the values in the correct locations on the form with a pen or pencil.   If the OCR system cannot read handwritten information, the entries must be typed on the form with a special typewriter.   Typing is somewhat faster than key punching, but it is work that should be eliminated.

The use of OCR systems to collect data may be very practical when a large number of data collection points or work stations would be required to service a large work force, and the production information is not needed until after the end of the shift.   The processing time on peripheral equipment for the information on these forms is very low, since they can be read onto magnetic tape by OCR equipment almost as quickly as punched cards can be read onto tape by a computer. This system is very similar to other systems using tab cards and has the advantage of having a written record of all transactions available for audit if such a requirement must be met. The cost of the optical reading units is very high. Therefore, it may only be possible to justify the use of this type of equipment if it is already installed for use by some other system within the plant.

Pneumatic Tubes. The pneumatic tube which is frequently found in department stores for carrying cash and messages is also useful in the factory. It is especially useful in a factory when it is necessary to move production papers or small parts from one location to another.

The carrier of the system consists of a capsule which moves through a tube by a difference in air pressure. A centralized dispatcher is often used when a number of lines are used. One type of system eliminates the dispatcher by having a dialable device on the capsule which indicates the destination desired.

Companies should investigate applying the pneumatic tube when they have many production papers which must be moved frequently from one location to another. Tubes are often used between buildings as well as between departments within a building.

TelAutograph. The TelAutograph permits instant transmission of handwritten messages to selected unattended receivers any distance via telephone lines or microwave. A ballpoint pen writes directly on specially designed preprinted forms or plain roll paper with multiple copies available at both ends. No trained operators are needed. Machines turn off automatically. Desk-top units feature solid-state electronic and circuit boards for fast, easy maintenance.

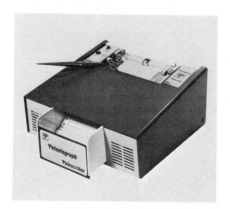 

Fig. 13 TelAutograph. (*Courtesy of TelAutograph Corp.*)

The sender writes his message with the attached pen (Fig. 13) on a flat horizontal surface. The message is conveyed to the receiver where an identical message is written automatically.

TelAutograph systems in business and industrial operations enable management to establish positive control over sales order, production reports, and inventory and purchasing areas.

SUMMARY

Collecting and processing data are essential in every efficient production control system.   Modern systems attempt to collect the information in the most usable form and process it as rapidly as possible.

Computer-based systems can be fed data which has been developed directly in card form.   More sophisticated systems are capable of feeding the information directly to the computer and function in a real-time mode.

There is probably no facet of production control which has developed as rapidly as shop data collection systems.

Techniques and Tools for Production and Inventory Control

Chapter **26**

Decision Making for Production and Inventory Control

COEDITORS:

Dr. Aaron Glickstein *Director of Advanced Systems, Food Fair Stores, Inc., Philadelphia, Pennsylvania*

R. Zwierzycki *Director of Data Processing, McHenry County College, Crystal Lake, Illinois*

CONTENTS

A key function of the business manager is decision making. Every manager is continuously faced with choices among various alternatives. It is characteristic of the business environment, due to its dynamic nature, that these decisions have to be made with imperfect information. Over the years there have been various degrees of interest in the techniques and tools which could aid the executive in gathering and quantifying information in the decision-making process.

Early efforts in the use of quantitative techniques for decision making were almost always oriented toward operational problems. One of the earliest attempts to quantify information and base decisions on facts rather than intuition was made by Frederick Winslow Taylor. In his book *Shop Management*,[1] first published in 1903, Taylor focused his attention on quantifying the means of measuring and evaluating labor productivity.

For example, he discussed a procedure to be used to establish the time required for hauling various materials. He presented the following formula for establishing a standard time for hauling material in a barrow:[1]

$$B = \left\{ p + \left[a + b + d + f + \frac{\text{distance hauled}}{100} (c + e) \right] \frac{27}{L} \right\} (1 + P)$$

where a = time filling a barrow for a given material
     b = time preparing to wheel
     c = time wheeling full barrow 100 feet
     d = time dumping and turning

e = time returning 100 feet with empty barrow
f = time dropping barrow and starting to shovel
p = time for loosening 1 cubic yard with pick
P = percentage of a day required to rest and for necessary delays
L = load of a barrow in cubic feet
B = time per cubic yard for picking, loading, and wheeling any given kind of earth to any given distance when the wheeler loads his own barrow

While this particular example may seem trite and unspectacular to us in this day of computers and sophisticated mathematical models, it does illustrate an important point. Even in one of the early reported examples there was the need for isolating and treating quantitatively all the variables involved in a given operating problem. Taylor recognized that to fill the barrow with different materials required different amounts of time. He recognized that in order to have a quantitative base on which to make a decision it is important to measure.

Another early example of work in quantitative decision making was the derivation of the *simple lot-size formula* by Ford Harris of the Westinghouse Corporation in 1915. While there are isolated illustrations of attempts to use quantitative methods in business decisions during the period preceding World War II, little headway was made until the early 1950s. It has been only in the last few years that our technology in computer data collection, storage, and retrieval and the development of quantitative operations research techniques have enabled the business community to base decisions on facts rather than intuition.

CHARACTERISTICS OF QUANTITATIVE DECISION MAKING

In this introduction to quantitative decision making we are considering an approach which places prime emphasis on quantification and quantitative analysis. Almost all approaches to quantitative decision making generally involve some common underlying characteristics including:

1. A well-defined objective
2. A mathematical and/or logical model
3. Optimization process

Objectives. The objective of most quantitative analysis is usually associated with either the improvement of the organization's profits or the reduction of its costs.

Models. The use of mathematical models is not new to the physical scientist. For example, most of us who have had a course in physics remember, even if we do not understand, Einstein's famous mathematical model $E = mc^2$, energy equals mass times the square of the speed of light.

The use of mathematical models in the field of business is, however, relatively new. Mathematical models may be classified either by the form they take or by the method of solution. If we are to classify models by the method of solution, we would specify those models which can be solved in *closed form* and those which can be solved by *simulation*. Closed-form models are those for which the state of the art is such that the equations can be solved mathematically. Simulation models, on the other hand, are those for which a solution is obtained by assuming certain values for some of the variables to obtain values for the variables of interest.

CLOSED MODEL:

Example   The following two equations can be solved for values of X and Y:

$$2X + Y = 10 \tag{1}$$
$$3X + 2Y = 5 \tag{2}$$

Multiplying Eq. (1) by 2 gives

$$4X + 2Y = 20$$

Subtracting Eq. (2) from Eq. (1) gives

$$X = 15$$

Substituting the value of X into Eq. (1) gives

$$2(15) + Y = 10$$
$$30 + Y = 10$$
$$Y = -20$$

This is an example of a model solvable in closed form.

ELEMENTARY SIMULATION:

Example   On the other hand, suppose that we have the following equation:

$$3X + Y = 10$$

It is impossible to solve this equation in closed form. We can, however, assume certain values of X to obtain the corresponding values of Y. For example, if $X = 2$, Y must equal 4; if $X = 4$, Y must equal -2. This is an example of an elementary solution through simulation.

Classifying models as to form, we would have "deterministic" models and "probabilistic" models. The difference here is whether there is a probability associated with the variables in the model or not. A simple example may be of assistance here also.

DETERMINISTIC MODEL:

Example   We are selling products A and B. Product A has a profit of \$1.00 per unit and B a profit of \$2.00 per unit. If we know that we will sell 50 of A and 100 of B, we can establish a "deterministic" model of the total profit as follows:

$$\text{Total profit} = 50 \text{ parts} \times \$1.00/\text{part} + 100 \text{ parts} \times \$2.00/\text{part}$$
$$= \$250$$

PROBABILISTIC MODEL:

Example   However, if we know only that we are going to sell 150 items and they will either all be A or all be B with probability $\frac{1}{3}$ and $\frac{2}{3}$, respectively, we can establish a "probabilistic" model as follows:

$$\text{Expected total profit} = (\tfrac{1}{3})(150)(\$1.00) + (\tfrac{2}{3})(150)(\$2.00)$$
$$= 50 + 200 = \$250$$

The answer is the same as before, but now it is *expected* profit. That is, if the probabilities are correct, repetition of the process a large number of times should result in an average profit near to \$250. (Note that on an individual run the profit will be either \$150 or \$300, it cannot be \$250.)

To achieve its full usefulness the model should capture the essence of the problem and be solvable. A model may be useful even if it can't be *solved* because it may place the important matters of a problem in the proper perspective. However, developing a model which leaves out a significant variable or relationship may well lead to more damaging results than if this approach were not used in the first place.

Optimization. Once a mathematical expression or model is obtained for a problem, the model is generally manipulated in an attempt to achieve an optimum solution. The best possible solution considering the variables, costs, and relationships in the model is desired. Optimization in the broadest sense will often apply in balancing the cost of seeking better and better solutions against the potential benefits of these better solutions.

EXPECTED VALUE AND UTILITY[2]

We are all familiar with some rather simple coin-tossing games. For example, suppose you were approached with the following proposal:

"Let us toss a coin. Every time a head appears you will win $2.00 and every time a tail appears you will lose $1.00."

Most of us would jump at the opportunity to participate in this game, assuming that we did not consider the person making the proposal to be a cheater. We would desire to play because without any statistical calculations we believe our expected winnings to be greater than the expected losses. Let us examine this game and see if our intuition has led us astray.

If the coin is honest, the probability of getting a head is equal to the probability of getting a tail. Since there are only two possible events, the probability of each occurring is equal to $\frac{1}{2}$. The expected winnings per toss are equal to $2.00 \times \frac{1}{2} = 1.00, and the expected losses per toss are equal to $0.50 (i.e., $1.00 \times \frac{1}{2}$). Therefore, this game provides potential net winnings of $0.50 (i.e., $1.00 - $0.50).

Therefore, the expected value is nothing more than a weighted average of the various possible value returns, where the assigned weights are the probabilities with which the possible outcomes are expected to occur. Expected value can therefore be defined as follows:

$$\text{Expected value} = P(E_1)V_1 + P(E_2)V_2 + \cdots P(E_n)V_n$$
$$= P(E)V$$

where $P(E_1)$ = probability of event E_1 occurring
V_1 = value of event E_1

Expected value is a criterion frequently used in quantitative decisions for making a choice between alternative courses of action. However, considerable care should be taken in using expected value as our decision criterion. The following example may serve to illustrate this point. Suppose we have four possible courses of action with the possible outcomes as shown in Table 1. Then

TABLE 1 Possible Outcomes of Four Games

Probability of occurrence	Gains and losses associated with course of action (negative values indicate loss)			
	1	2	3	4
0.2	−$1,000	−$10,000	−$100,000	−$1,000,000
0.5	2,000	2,000	20,000	2,000
0.3	333	6,333	36,333	666,333

the expected value of each course of action would be calculated as follows:

Course 1: Expected value = 0.2(−1,000) + 0.5(2,000) + 0.3(333) = $900
Course 2: Expected value = 0.2(−10,000) + 0.5(2,000) + 0.3(6,333) = $900
Course 3: Expected value = 0.2(−100,000) + 0.5(20,000) + 0.3(36,333) = $900
Course 4: Expected value = 0.2(−1,000,000) + 0.5(2,000) + 0.3(666,333)
                        = $900

From an expected value there does not appear to be any difference as to which course of action is chosen as all result in the same $900 expected gain. However, we might ask ourselves the question: "Can we afford to follow a course of action which in the long run has an expected value of $900 but which may result in a loss of $1,000,000?" Obviously some other criterion is required.

In situations such as the one described above, it may be possible to replace expected dollar values with "utilities." Utility is simply a way of representing the intrinsic value of money. For example, a company may evaluate a potential loss of $1,000,000 as quite different than just double the loss of $500,000 if the larger loss would result in bankruptcy. On the other hand, a very large gain may allow a further spectacular investment. It is possible that a small, consistent profit is more important than large profits one year followed by losses in the following year. It is the answers to questions of the preceding type which allows a firm to develop a utility function or determine some of the important characteristics of the utility function that it will use. Therefore, we shall refer to "utility" as the subjective value that a person or firm obtains from a particular return in a given situation involving risk.

Let us suppose that we have Mr. Playsafe, who is comfortably situated, has a good income, has some money in the stock market, and has lived through some minor stock-market adjustments. He is presented with the four possible courses of action shown in Table 1. Suppose they are presented to him as a new game. The game consists of a hat containing 10 chips. On two of these chips there is a "lemon," on five of the chips there is an "orange," and on three of the chips there is a "pineapple." The game can be played on any one of four tables depending on the types of stakes for which one wishes to play. Mr. Playsafe has to decide at which of these games he wishes to play. He quickly calculates that the expected gain of each game is $900. However, he realizes that he cannot afford a loss of $1,000,000 at Game 4 even though he would like to have the possible gain of $666,333. Having heard of "utility" theory, Mr. Playsafe sits down and develops his own utility function. See Table 2.

TABLE 2   Utility Function

Cash Certain	Utiles
−1,000,000	−100.000
−100,000	−6.000
−10,000	−0.600
−1,000	−0.070
+333	+0.018
+2,000	+0.090
+6,333	+0.250
+20,000	+1.000
+36,333	+1.700
+666,333	+20.00

Based on this utility function, Mr. Playsafe can now look at and evaluate each of the games based on his utility function. He therefore prepares Table 3,

TABLE 3 Four Games

Probability of occurrence	Utiles associated with each game			
	1	2	3	4
0.2	−0.070	−0.600	−6.000	−100.000
0.5	0.090	+0.090	+1.000	+0.090
0.3	0.018	+0.250	+1.700	+20.000

which shows the four games based on his utility function.   Now, the expected utility of each game would be calculated as follows:

Game 1: Expected utility = 0.2(−0.070) + 0.5(0.090) + 0.3(0.018) = +0.0364
Game 2: Expected utility = 0.2(−0.600) + 0.5(0.090) + 0.3(0.250) = +0.0000
Game 3: Expected utility = 0.2(−6.000) + 0.5(1.000) + 0.3(1.700) = −0.19
Game 4: Expected utility = 0.2(−100.000) + 0.5(0.090) + 0.3(20.000) =
$$-13.955$$

This is an example of four games where the expected dollar values are the same ($900), indicating *indifference*.   But on a utility scale Game 1 is a clear choice for Mr. Playsafe.   The particular utility function that Mr. Playsafe has illustrates risk avoidance.   That is, as the spread of the potential return grows, the underlying value (i.e., the utility) tends to decrease.

Suppose that we have Mr. Wheeler, a Texan wildcatter who is used to taking chances.   He has made and lost a fortune a number of times.   In fact, he has just brought in a number of wells that he has sold for a profit of $3 million. Mr. Wheeler is a risk taker, and he has the utility function shown in Table 4.

TABLE 4   Utility Function

Cash Certain	Utiles
−1,000,000	−30.000
−100,000	−3.500
−10,000	−0.500
−1,000	−0.000
+333	+0.005
+2,000	+0.008
+6,333	+0.500
+20,000	+0.750
+36,333	+1.000
+666,333	+50.000

Mr. Wheeler, therefore, sees each game as having the utility shown in Table 5.

TABLE 5   FOUR GAMES

Probability of occurrence	Utiles associated with each game			
	1	2	3	4
0.2	0.000	−0.500	−3.500	−30.000
0.5	+0.008	+0.008	+0.750	+0.008
0.3	+0.005	+0.500	+1.000	+50.000

The expected utility of each game can be calculated as follows:

Game 1: Expected utility $= 0.2(000) + 0.5(0.008) + 0.3(0.005) = 0.0055$
Game 2: Expected utility $= 0.2(-0.500) + 0.5(0.008) + 0.3(0.500) = 0.0540$
Game 3: Expected utility $= 0.2(-3.500) + 0.5(0.750) + 0.3(1.000) = -0.0250$
Game 4: Expected utility $= 0.2(-30.000) + 0.5(0.008) + 0.3(50.000) = 9.0040$

Therefore, Game 4 is a clear choice for Mr. Wheeler.

INVENTORY MODELS

Constant Known Demand. One of the simplest inventory models that can be considered is one with the following characteristics:
1. A single product
2. Constant known demand (i.e., demand equals 50 units per week)
3. No lead time (replenishment is available immediately)
4. No volume or quantity discounts
Under the above conditions, the only costs that must be considered in establishing our inventory are the purchasing costs and the inventory holding costs.

Let us assume that the cost of placing an order (typing, approving, transmission, payment, etc.) is equal to C_1 dollars. The annual demand is for D units of the product, and the number of units to order each time an order is placed is equal to Q. We are attempting to establish the optimum Q value.

The number of orders to be placed is equal to n and can be calculated by the following relation:

$$n = \frac{D}{Q} \tag{3}$$

The total purchasing cost is therefore equal to $(C_1)(D/Q)$.

To establish the inventory holding costs, it is necessary to determine the average inventory level. Assuming that we order only once a year, the graph of the inventory level over the course of a year is as shown in Fig. 1.

Since we have a constant known demand, our inventory is gradually and uniformly depleted. The average inventory is therefore $Q/2$. If we order six times per year, our order quantity is again Q. However, Q now assumes a value one-sixth as great as in the single-order case. The average inventory is still $Q/2$.

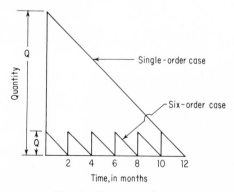

Fig. 1 Inventory chart.

Assume that the unit cost of each item equals C_2 dollars and the inventory carrying charge equals I percent. Then the cost of carrying inventory is given as follows:

$$\text{Inventory carrying cost} = C_2 I \frac{Q}{2}$$

The total is then:

$$\text{Total variable cost} = \frac{C_1 D}{Q} + C_2 I \frac{Q}{2}$$

The optimum order quantity (i.e., that Q which miminizes total cost) is then easily calculated by the use of calculus to be

$$Q = \sqrt{\frac{2 C_1 D}{C_2 I}}$$

Here again the general tactics of the profit-maximizing approach and a constructed model of the situation have been employed. Calculus was used for optimization on this particular case.

Shortage Cost. The previous model assumes that shortages are not allowed. The model can be altered to permit shortages. Assume that the shortage costs are equal to C_3 per unit short per unit time. The optimum lot size Q_1 is given by

$$Q_1 = \sqrt{\frac{2 C_1 D}{C_2 I}} \sqrt{\frac{C_3 + I C_2}{C_3}}$$

It can, therefore, be seen that if C_3 is large in relation to C_2, the economic order quantity approaches the Q which was developed for the no-shortage-allowed model.

Sensitivity Analysis. One of the most time consuming and difficult tasks in the development and use of inventory models is the establishment of the costs to be used in the model. It is therefore worthwhile to examine the sensitivity of the model to these factors.

Let us assume that our model involves the following values:

$D = 12,000$ units per year
$C_1 = \$3.50$
$C_2 = \$5.00$
$I = 18$ percent per year

The optimum order quantity is then given by

$$Q = \sqrt{\frac{(2)(3.50)(12,000)}{(5.00)(0.18)}} = 306 \text{ units}$$

Assume, however, that we have made some errors in establishing the cost figures. The values as used are as follows:

$D = 12,000$ units per year
$C_1 = \$4.20$ (20 percent overestimated)
$C_2 = \$5.00$
$I = 18$ percent per year

Based on our data the order quantity would have been calculated to be

$$Q = \sqrt{\frac{(2)(4.20)(12,000)}{(5.00)(0.18)}} = 334 \text{ units}$$

Therefore, an error of 20 percent in estimating the cost of placing an order results in only a 9.1 percent error in order quantity. This is a result of the square-root relationship.

Probabilistic Models. Forecasts are essential in formulating inventory policy. Every business uses a forecast of some kind in planning its buying and manufacturing program and in planning expansion and cutbacks. The forecast may be only the statement that next year will be like this year, or it may result from a long analysis of the economy, the industry, birth rates, etc., or it may be only the result of wishful thinking. The efficiency of the inventory policy will depend on the accuracy of the forecast and the knowledge of the market. There are forecasting methods which act as servomechanisms, i.e., new forecasts are regenerated, say, quarterly, as information on the market is gathered. Forecasts generally fall into two classes:

1. Continuous
2. One shot

Both classes of forecast, and indeed, any forecast, are probabilistic statements expressed with a degree of reliability.

There are many industries where there is an opportunity for making only a single buy decision due to the highly seasonal nature of the business. This occurs quite frequently in the retail industry in "high style" and "fad" items. If the buyer purchases too many of the items, he will have a loss due to obsolescence. On the other hand, if he buys too few of the items, he will have lost sales. It is possible to develop quantitative rules which prescribe optimum ordering quantities based on expected-profit considerations. The measure of effectiveness of the buying policy is the expected profitability of the last item, which is defined as the expected gain minus the expected loss. One should buy an amount such that the expected profitability on the last unit is positive.

The information required for this situation is:

1. Profit on each item sold
2. Loss on each item obtained and not sold
3. Expected probability of selling various quantities of the item

The expected profit on the Dth item can be written as

$$E_D = GP_D - L(1 - P_D)$$

where E_D = expected profit on Dth item
G = gain per unit sold
P_D = probability of selling Dth item
L = loss per unit not sold

Table 6 illustrates two cases. The first involves an item which becomes obsolete and therefore has a high unit loss associated with it. The second case involves an item which can be carried over to the following year. The loss is therefore equivalent to the inventory carrying cost. Examining Table 6, we see that the optimum policy for Case 1 involves the purchase of 1,145 units, while for Case 2 the optimum purchase quantity is 1,545 units.

The condition desired in this model is that E_D, the expected profitability, is not negative. That is, the last unit stocked should not produce a loss. Therefore, if we set $E_D = 0$ and solve for P_D, we have

$$GP_D - L(1 - P_D) = 0$$
$$P_D(G + L) = L$$
$$P_D = \frac{L}{G + L}$$

TABLE 6   Inventory Information

Case 1. Loss per unit = \$4.00; profit per unit = \$3.00

Demand, D	Probability of selling Dth unit, P_D	Expected profit on Dth unit, $P_D \times \$3.00$	Expected loss on Dth unit, $(1 - P_D)\$4.00$	Net profitability on Dth unit
400	0.98	\$2.94	\$0.08	\$ 2.86
600	0.95	2.85	0.20	2.65
800	0.88	2.64	0.48	2.14
1,000	0.76	2.28	0.96	1.32
1,100	0.63	1.89	1.48	0.41
1,145	0.57	1.72	1.72	0.00
1,200	0.50	1.50	2.00	−0.50
1,400	0.24	0.72	3.04	−2.32
1,600	0.12	0.36	3.52	−3.16
1,800	0.05	0.15	3.80	−3.65
2,000	0.02	0.06	3.92	−3.86
2,200	0.00	0.00	4.00	−4.00

Case 2. Inventory carrying cost = \$0.50; profit per unit = \$3.00

Demand, D	Probability of selling Dth unit, P_D	Expected profit on Dth unit, $P_D \times \$3.00$	Expected loss on Dth unit, $(1 - P_D)\$0.50$	Net profitability on Dth unit
400	0.98	\$2.94	\$0.01	\$ 2.93
600	0.95	2.85	0:03	2.82
800	0.88	2.64	0.06	2.58
1,000	0.76	2.28	0.12	2.16
1,200	0.50	1.50	0.25	1.25
1,400	0.24	0.72	0.38	0.34
1,500	0.16	0.48	0.42	0.60
1,545	0.143	0.43	0.43	0.00
1,600	0.12	0.36	0.44	−0.08
1,800	0.05	0.15	0.48	−0.33
2,000	0.02	0.06	0.49	−0.43
2,200	0.00	0.00	0.50	−0.50

Therefore one should buy the amount D whose probability of sale P_D is given by the expression above.

In the first of our illustrative examples, $G = \$3.00$, $L = \$4.00$, and

$$P_D = \frac{4.00}{4.00 + 3.00} = \frac{4}{7} = 0.572$$

i.e., one should buy D units, where $P_D = 0.572(1{,}145$ units). In the second example, $G = \$3.00$, $L = \$0.50$, and

$$P_D = \frac{0.50}{3.00 + 0.50} = \frac{1}{7} = 0.143$$

and one should buy 1,545 units, since the probability of selling 1,545 units or more is 0.143.

One can look backwards and ask for the probability of demand implied by a decision to purchase D units, to see if the decision was realistic. Note that analysis of this type does not try to replace good management and business judgment; it is part of an attempt to evaluate decisions in a quantitative manner.

Spare-parts Purchases. Another problem of interest in industry is that of spare parts or spare units purchased for major equipment. This is often not considered as an inventory problem, but as one affecting production operations only. It can, however, be defined in terms similar to inventory problems of the type discussed earlier.

As a typical problem of this type, consider that a company is contemplating purchase of some major equipment—a single large generator, for example. Certain spare assemblies can be purchased with the generator unit at large, direct savings. Should these assemblies be required at a later date, not only is the cost higher but delivery delays are such that large production losses result. The problem is then one of determining the number of spare units required so that the expected total loss is a minimum.

In this case the spare parts when ordered with the generator cost $500 each. The cost of generator downtime when a spare is not available is $10,000 per breakdown. A study of similar parts in 100 similar generators produces the data shown in Table 7.

TABLE 7   Spare-part Inventory

No. of spares required, n	No. of generators requiring n parts	Estimated prob. of occurrence of req. for n parts	Accumulated probability
0	90	0.90	0.900
1	5	0.05	0.950
2	2	0.02	0.970
3	1	0.01	0.980
4	1	0.01	0.990
5	1	0.01	1.00
6	0	0.00	1.00

$C_2 = \$10,000$
$C_1 = \$500$

One can prepare a "table of losses"; that is, calculate the expected loss if n spare units are purchased, for each value of n. The loss table must include two types of loss:

1. The loss incurred by spare units which are not used.
2. The loss incurred when spare units are not available

If no spare units are purchased, then the expected loss is only of type 2. If five or more spare units are purchased, then the losses are all of type 1.

In carrying out this calculation, it is assumed that if a spare part is not used, one loses the full purchase price. The losses for a set spare-parts program are given by the sum of the losses due to the shortage of parts, which can be written as $10,000 times the average number of parts short, and the losses due to the purchase of unnecessary equipment, which can be written as $500 times the average number of parts in excess supply. This can be written as shown in Table 8.

The first value in Table 8 ($S = 0$) is obtained by writing the probability that n units are not available and summing over all n, which gives the probability of downtime. This probability multiplied by the loss due to downtime gives the righthand column. When $S = 1$, the probability of being short 5 spare

TABLE 8   Loss Equation

No. of spares purchased	Loss equation	Loss in dollars
$S = 0$	$L_0 = 10,000(0.01 \times 5 + 0.01 \times 4 + 0.01 \times 3 + 0.02 \times 2 + 0.05 \times 1) =$	2,100
$S = 1$	$L_1 = 10,000(0.01 \times 4 + 0.01 \times 3 + 0.01 \times 2 + 0.02 \times 1) + (500 \times 1) =$	1,600
$S = 2$	$L_2 = 10,000(0.01 \times 3 + 0.01 \times 2 + 0.01 \times 1 + 500 \times 2) =$	1,600
$S = 3$	$L_3 = 10,000(0.01 \times 2 + 0.01 \times 1 + 500 \times 3) =$	1,800
$S = 4$	$L_4 = 10,000(0.01 \times 1) + 500(4) =$	2,100
$S = 5$	$L_5 = 500(5) =$	2,500
$S = 6$	$L_6 = 500(6) =$	3,000

units is zero, so this term vanishes. Since 1 unit is available, the probability of being short 4 units is equal to the probability of needing 5 units. Similarly, the probability of being short 3 units is equal to the probability of needing 4 units, etc. We must also include in the loss the cost of purchasing and storing a unit which is not required. In this case it is included in the last term of the loss equation (i.e., there is a loss of $500 for each unit available and not used). The other terms are derived by carrying out similar processes.

In this problem we find that the loss is a minimum when 1 or 2 spare units are purchased. We can obtain this result in another way, using the accumulated probabilities which are listed in the last column of the probability table (i.e., the probability that S or fewer spares are required). We write these as $P(r \leq S)$, which is the probability that the need r is less than or equal to S, the number of spare units available.

We note that

$$P(r \leq S - 1) \leq \frac{C_2 - C_1}{C_2} \leq P(r \leq S) \tag{4}$$

where C_1 = cost of an unused spare part
C_2 = cost of a breakdown

In this case $(C_2 - C_1)/C_2 = 0.950$ and from the probability table, if $S = 1$,

$$P(r \leq 0) \leq 0.950 \leq P(r \leq 1)$$

If $S = 2$,

$$P(r \leq 1) \leq 0.950 \leq P(r \leq 2)$$

Therefore 1 or 2 spare units are purchased.

Equation (4) allows one to evaluate the range of imputed costs of breakdown if n units are purchased. This is a useful technique if breakdown costs are unknown or difficult to evaluate. Let us assume that 3 spare units are purchased, then

$$P(r \leq 2) \leq \frac{C_2 - C_1}{C_2} \leq P(r \leq 3)$$

or

$$0.970 \leq \frac{C_2 - 500}{C_2} \leq 0.980$$

Solving on the left-hand and right-hand sides, one obtains minimum and maximum values of the imputed cost of a breakdown.

Minimum Cost   *Maximum Cost*

$\dfrac{C_2 - 500}{C_2} = 0.970$ $\dfrac{C_2 - 500}{C_2} = 0.98$

$C_2 = \$16,667$ $C_2 = \$25,000$

LINEAR PROGRAMMING

The general linear-programming problem involves the maximization or minimization of a linear function of several variables called an "objective function." The maximization or minimization of this linear function is subject to a series of linear inequalities called "constraints." Further, none of the variables may be negative.[3]

Mathematically the linear-programming problem can be stated as follows:

$$\text{Maximize } Z = \sum_{j=1}^{n+m} P_j X_j \qquad \text{for } P_j = 0 \text{ when } j \geq n$$

$$\text{Subject to } \sum_{j=1}^{n+m} a_{ij} X_j = C_i \qquad \text{for all } i = 1, \ldots, m$$

$$X_j \geq 0 \qquad (j = 1, \ldots, n+m)$$

Graphic Solution. The use of linear programming can perhaps be most easily illustrated with the following simple example involving a small firm which manufactures gidgets and widgets. The following characteristics may not be realistic from a manufacturing viewpoint, but they will serve the purpose of illustrating use of this powerful tool.

1. The firm has 200 hours of lathe capacity available per month.
2. The firm has 2,400 hours of manpower available per month.
3. Each gidget produced requires 5 hours of lathe time.
4. Each gidget produced requires 20 man-hours of labor.
5. Each widget produced requires 1 hour of lathe time.
6. Each widget produced requires 30 man-hours of labor.
7. The profit associated with each gidget sold is $70, and the profit associated with each widget is $50.

Given these data the firm is faced with the decision of what to do. Should the firm produce widgets or gidgets or perhaps some combination of both?

We can state this problem mathematically as follows:

Let
$\qquad X =$ number of gidgets to be manufactured
$\qquad Y =$ number of widgets to be manufactured

The lathe limitation can be expressed as

$$5X + Y \leq 200$$

The manpower limitation can be expressed as

$$20X + 30Y \leq 2,400$$

The object is to maximize profits. The objective function is

$$\text{Maximize profit} = 70X + 50Y$$

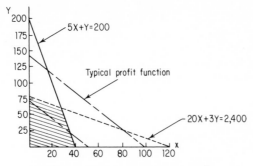

Fig. 2   Linear-programming graph.

Finally,

$$X \geq 0$$
$$Y \geq 0$$

The machinery (lathe) and labor limitations are shown in Fig. 2. The region shown below the solid line meets the machine (lathe) restriction, while the region shown below the dashed line meets the labor limitation and the shaded area meets both restrictions.

The profit function is shown by a series of parallel lines each having a slope of $-\frac{50}{70}$. The solution is to land on the highest of these profit lines which still falls in the shaded area. An examination of Fig. 2 shows that this occurs at

$$X = 27.7$$
$$Y = 61.5$$
$$\text{Profit} = \$5,014$$

A graphical solution becomes impractical as the number of variables increases. In most cases we find that most meaningful problems requiring linear programming are solved through the use of a computer. Most major computer manufacturers offer a linear-programming package with their computers.

A Linear-programming Production Scheduling Model. The following discussion covers the initial stages in the development of a model to handle a particular production scheduling problem. This model is set in the form of a linear program for several reasons:

1. Convenience
2. Relative ease in obtaining solutions to linear programs
3. To examine the structure of a model prior to certain detailed investigations (such as nonlinearities in costs)

The objective of this model and its potential use is cost minimization in an inventory management, production scheduling setting. More specifically the objective is to minimize the sum of:

1. Inventory holding costs
2. Production overtime-labor costs
3. Costs of changing the production labor force
4. Night-shift labor premiums
5. Interest on certain equipment investments

From this it can be seen that the variables of interest are:

1. Amount of a certain type of equipment
2. Labor-force level
3. Overtime

In addition, since several products are involved, there is the question of when to produce what types.

There are three general styles of products—A, B, and C (or men's shoes, women's shoes, and children's shoes). Further, each style of product can be made by three different, general production methods—X, Y, and Z (or Goodyear welt, Littleway lockstitch, and cement). Each of these methods involve somewhat different limiting factors.

We have, then, nine general combinations or types. There could be more, for example, men's shoes could be subdivided even further—all the way to the individual style, size and width variations if desired. This is not done because it seems that the nine combinations capture the essential nature of the problem. (This simplification is to be checked out with simulations at a later date.)

The reader will notice that this model answers only certain large-scale questions. Crucial detail questions such as, "Given that we are to produce men's welt shoes at such a rate for the next month, how much should we produce this week of $9\frac{1}{2}$ EE style X34821?" are left for a second stage which won't be covered here. Similarly, the lot-size question is omitted from the model for many reasons—one being that lot sizes are somewhat rigid due to their use in an incentive-wage structure.

The model is initially seen in monthly terms. Various constraints and relations employed in the model are as follows:

1. For each type of shoe and method of producing it, the initial inventory plus the accumulated production to any point in time must be greater than or equal to sales from the initial point to that same second point in time plus an additional period for delivery lags. Symbolically:

$$\sum_{i=1}^{j} S_{ik} \leq I_k + \sum_{i=1}^{j-1} P_{ik}$$

where S_{ik} = maximum reasonable demand for product k in period i
I_k = inventory of product k at the start of period 1
P_{ik} = production of product k to be scheduled for period i

This relation is of the material-balance type.

Note that with the nine general types of products (three styles times three methods) and a horizon of 24 periods, this simple relation expands to $9 \times 24 = 216$ constraints.

2. There is some semblance of proportionality between labor-hours expended and pairs of shoes produced:

$$\sum_{k} K_k P_{ik} = l_1 H_{i1} + l_2 H_{i2} + l_3 H_{i3}$$

where K_k = number of labor-hours required per pair of type k shoes
P_{ik} = number of pairs of type k shoes to be produced in month i
l_1 = regular-shift efficiency
l_2 = second-shift efficiency
l_3 = overtime efficiency
H_{i1} = regular man-hours in month i
H_{i2} = second-shift man-hours in month i
H_{i3} = overtime man-hours in month i

Here we would have one constraint for each time period or 24 constraints. The

K factors are determined from labor standards. The l factors are based on management estimates or a special study.

Notice that plant operating people are left with the task of adding or deleting hours in an optimal fashion.

3. The plant has the capacity to have roughly 500 men on the production floor at any one time as a result of the basic shop, machine placement, size, and routing. It is reasonable to have one man operate one or more machines but unreasonable to have more than one man operate one machine at any time.

Hence for a four-week, average month, we have a maximum regular-time labor of 500 men $\times$ 4 weeks $\times$ 40 man-hours per man per week = 80,000 man-hours. For each month we then have $H_{i1} \leq 80,000$. Similar considerations apply to second-shift and overtime operations.

In all, with a 24-period horizon a total of $3 \times 24 = 72$ constraints would result here.

4. Because of the equipment limits there are production bottlenecks which will hamper operations from time to time. A single regular shift cannot make over 2,000 pair of lockstitched shoes, or 900 pair of welt shoes, or 1,300 pair of cement shoes. Thus these considerations act as limits to the proportionalities set out in 2 above. This will be handled in two stages as follows:

$$P_{x1} \leq \frac{2{,}000 \times H_{i1} \times 20}{8 \times 500}$$

$$P_{x2} \leq \frac{2{,}000 \times H_{i2} \times 20}{8 \times 500}$$

$$P_{x0t} \leq \frac{2{,}000 \times H_{i3} \times 20}{8 \times 500}$$

$$P_{x1} \leq 2{,}000 \times 20$$

$$P_{x2} \leq 2{,}000 \times 20$$

$$P_{x0t} \leq 2{,}000 \times 20 \times \frac{20}{40}$$

based on a maximum of 20 hours overtime per week.

$$P_x = P_{x1} + P_{x2} + P_{x3}$$

where P_x = production of shoes of construction x
      P_{x1} = same production for the first shift

The first three relations indicate that there must be some operation in a shift to get some production from that shift. The next three relations cover the maximum amount of one type in each shift. Similar relations apply to the other general construction types.

5. Shoes are made on forms called "lasts." Several types of lasts are involved. Because of their role as slowly deteriorating catalysts, it is decided to include the number of lasts as a variable rather than as a strictly limiting factor.

The constraints are of the form

$$P_{ik} \leq a_k L_k$$

or
$$P_{ik} - a_k L_k \leq 0 \qquad \begin{cases} k = 1, 2, 3 \\ i = 1, \ldots, n \end{cases}$$

where a_k is a factor indicating the maximum number of pairs of type k shoes which could be produced in a month on L_k lasts.

These constraints are summarized below:

1. $\displaystyle\sum_{i=1}^{j} S_{ik} \leq I_k + \sum_{i=1}^{j-1} P_{ik}$ $\begin{cases} j = 1, \ldots, n \\ k = 1, \ldots, 9 \end{cases}$

2. $\displaystyle\sum_{k=1}^{9} K_k P_{ik} = l_1 H_{i1} + l_2 H_{i2} + l_3 H_{i3}$ $\{i = 1, \ldots, n$

3. $H_{i1} \leq 80,000$
   $H_{i2} \leq 80,000$ $\{i = 1, \ldots, n$
   $H_{i3} \leq 40,000$

4. $P_{i1} + P_{i2} + P_{i3} \leq \dfrac{2,000}{8} \times 20(H_{i1} + H_{i2}) + \dfrac{2,000}{4} \times 20 H_{i3}$

   $P_{i4} + P_{i5} + P_{i6} \leq \dfrac{900}{8} \times 20(H_{i1} + H_{i2}) + \dfrac{90}{4} \times 20 H_{i3}$

   $P_{i7} + P_{i8} + P_{i9} \leq \dfrac{1,300}{8} \times 20(H_{i1} + H_{i2}) + \dfrac{1,300}{4} \times 20 H_{i3}$

$$i = 1, \ldots, n$$

$$\sum_{k=1}^{3} P_{ik\alpha} \leq 40,000 \qquad \alpha = a, b$$

$$\sum_{k=1}^{3} P_{ik\alpha} \leq 20,000 \qquad \alpha = c$$

$$\sum_{k=4}^{6} P_{ik\alpha} \leq 40,000 \qquad \alpha = a, b$$

$$\sum_{k=4}^{6} P_{ik\alpha} \leq 20,000 \qquad \alpha = c$$

$$\sum_{k=1}^{9} P_{ik\alpha} \leq 40,000 \qquad \alpha = a, b$$

$$\sum_{k=7}^{9} P_{ik\alpha} \leq 20,000 \qquad \alpha = c$$

$$P_{ika} + P_{ikb} + P_{ikc} = P_{ik} \qquad k = 1, \ldots, 9$$

$$i = 1, \ldots, n \text{ in all above}$$

5. $P_{ik} \leq a_k L_k$ $\begin{cases} k = 1, \ldots, 9 \\ i = 1, \ldots, n \end{cases}$

For purposes of including the cost of changing employment levels, we shall also add the following relations:

6. $H_{i1} = H_{01} + \displaystyle\sum_{e=1}^{i} (H^+_{e1}) - \sum_{e=1}^{i} (H^-_{e1})$ $i = 1, \ldots, n$

   $H_{i2} = H_{02} + \displaystyle\sum_{e=1}^{i} (H^+_{e2}) - \sum_{e=1}^{i} (H^-_{e2})$ $i = 1, \ldots, n$

where S_{ik} = sales of type k in month i
$\quad I_k$ = initial inventory of type k
$\quad P_{ik}$ = production of type k in month i
$\quad K_k$ = man-hours required to produce a pair of type k shoes
l_1, l_2, l_3 = efficiency factors for first shift, second shift, and overtime
$\quad H_{i1}$ = first-shift man-hours in month i
$\quad H_{i2}$ = second-shift man-hours in month i
$\quad H_{i3}$ = overtime man-hours in month i
$\quad P_{ik}$ = production in month i of type k in shift α where $\alpha = a$ for the first shift; $\alpha = b$ for second; $\alpha = c$ for overtime
$\quad H_{01}$ = first-shift man-hours at the start
$\quad H_{02}$ = second-shift man-hours at the start
$\quad H_{e1}{}^+$ = man-hours added to first-shift operation in month 1
$\quad H_{e2}{}^-$ = man-hours deducted from first-shift operations in month 1
$\quad H_{e1}{}^+$ = man-hours added to second shift in month 1
$\quad H_{e2}{}^-$ = man-hours deducted from second shift in month 1
$\quad a_k$ = pairs per month per last, type k
$\quad L_k$ = number of type k lasts

It seems quite possible to simplify the constraints by performing various substitutions.

The objective function will now be developed. The significant cost elements are considered separately.

$$\text{Holding cost} = IC_1 \left[I_k + \sum_{i=1}^{j} (P_{ik} - S_{ik}) \right] \qquad j = 1, \ldots, n; k = 1, \ldots, 9$$

$$\text{Second-shift premium} = 0.10 C_2 \sum_{i=1}^{n} H_{i2}$$

$$\text{Overtime premium} = 0.50 C_2 \sum_{i=1}^{n} H_{i3}$$

$$\text{Lasts} = C_3 \sum_{k=1}^{9} (L_k - L_{k0})$$

$$\text{Changing employment} = C_4 \sum_{i=1}^{n} (H_{i1}{}^+ + H_{i2}{}^+) \tfrac{1}{160} + C_5 \sum_{i=1}^{n} (H_{i1}{}^- + H_{i2}{}^-) \tfrac{1}{160}$$

where I = monthly holding cost, percent
$\quad C_1$ = inventory value
$\quad C_2$ = average wage rate
$\quad C_3$ = "last" holding cost
$\quad C_4$ = cost of adding a man
$\quad C_5$ = cost of dropping a man

This general discussion serves to illustrate some of the considerations covered in the development of the model.

QUEUEING THEORY

Most of us are familiar with the lines of customers waiting for service at checkout counters in supermarkets or in front of tellers in banks. At one time or another, we may even have had the experience of getting into line in back of a "little old lady" clutching a large purse who, when she gets to the teller's window, starts pulling out rolls of pennies, unsigned checks, and generally slows down the progress of our line. While queueing theory will not tell us whether one should stay out of lines which contain "little old ladies," it will describe the behavior of systems involving service facilities. Queueing theory will help us to establish the optimum number of service facilities required under varying conditions. The use of queueing theory is not new. One of its earliest uses was by Erlang in the design of the Copenhagen telephone system. It has seen considerable use in the determination of optimum size of truck and railcar fleets, optimum number of checkout stands, optimum number of spare-part inventories, and optimum number of machine assignments to a repairman.

The Single-channel Service Station. The simplest illustration of a queueing problem is the one encountered in a job shop at a tool crib. Suppose you have a plant department serviced by a tool crib having one man giving out tools. The workers arrive at random at the tool crib. If the storekeeper is busy with one worker, the others form a line awaiting service. Further, assume that there is no priority—service is on a first-come, first-served basis. We will introduce the following notation:

Let λ = mean arrival rate
μ = mean service rate
$\rho = \lambda/\mu$
n = number in the system
$P_n(t)$ = probability of n units in the system at time t

If the arrival rate and the service rate both have Poisson distribution, the following relationships can be shown to hold true in steady state.[4]

1. The probability of n units in the system at time t is

$$P_n(t) = \rho^n(1 - \rho) \qquad \rho \le 1, n \ge 0$$

2. The average number of units being serviced or waiting for service:

$$L = \frac{\rho}{1 - \rho}$$

3. The average number of units waiting in line for service:

$$L_g = \frac{\rho^2}{1 - \rho}$$

4. The probability of having a queue:

$$P_{n>1} = \rho^2$$

5. The average length of nonempty queues:

$$L_a = \frac{1}{1 - \rho}$$

6. The average waiting time of an arrival:

$$W = \frac{\rho}{1 - \rho} \frac{1}{\mu}$$

7. The average waiting time of an arrival who waits:

$$W_a = \frac{1}{1 - \rho} \frac{1}{\mu}$$

8. The average time an arrival spends in the system:

$$T_s = \frac{1}{\mu - \lambda} = W_a$$

Let us assume that the storekeeper can service 25 requests per hour and that on the average 20 machinists per hour come to the tool crib looking for tools. Both arrival time and service rate have a Poisson distribution. Assume that the storekeeper is paid at the rate of $3.25 per hour and the machine operators at the rate of $3.65 per hour. The machine has a cost of $5.00 per hour. Therefore, every hour that a machine operator is idle has a cost of $5.00 + $3.65, or $8.65.

The expected nonproductive time for the machines and machine operators is the time spent in line by the machine operators.

The average number of units being serviced or waiting for service is

$$L = \frac{e}{1 - e} = \frac{\frac{20}{25}}{1 - \frac{20}{25}} = \frac{\frac{20}{25}}{\frac{.5}{25}} = \frac{0.8}{0.2} = 4$$

During an eight-hour day, the total cost of idle machine operators, machines, and storekeeper is

$$(4)(8)(8.65) + (8)(3.25) = \$302.80$$

The question can be raised if it is less expensive to build another toolroom and have one-half of the department go to the first toolroom and the other half go to the second toolroom. For the time being, let us disregard additional cost which might result from duplication of inventory.

With two tool cribs and assuming one-half of the department goes to each crib, the average number of calls would be reduced to 10.0 per hour. The average number of units being serviced or waiting for service at each tool crib is now

$$L = \frac{e}{1 - e} = \frac{\frac{10}{25}}{1 - \frac{10}{25}} = \frac{0.4}{0.6} = 0.67$$

During an eight-hour day, the total cost of idle machine operators, machines, and storekeepers is

$$(0.67)(8)(8.65) + (0.67)(8)(8.65) + (8)(3.25) + (8)(3.25) = \$144.73$$

Therefore, the total cost is reduced by $158.07 ($302.80 − $144.73) by adding another tool crib. This is true while at the same time the storekeeper's idle time has increased from 20 percent of the time to 60 percent of the time.

$$
\begin{aligned}
P_0(t) &= (1 - e)e^0 \\
&= (1 - \tfrac{20}{25})1 = \tfrac{5}{25} = \tfrac{1}{5} = 0.2 \\
&= (1 - e)e^0 \\
&= (1 - \tfrac{10}{25})1 = \tfrac{15}{25} = \tfrac{3}{5} = 0.6
\end{aligned}
$$

The next question to be raised is whether an additional tool crib is really the best answer. What would happen if we added another storekeeper to the existing tool crib? This question can be answered only by looking at the multi-service-facility model.

Multiservice Model. The notation used in the single-service station will be used in the multiservice model with the following addition:

Let k = number of service facilities

The behavior of the multiple-service queues can be given by the following ($K_u > \lambda$ must hold):[4]

1. The probability of zero units in the system service at time t is

$$P_0 = \frac{1}{\left[\sum_{n=0}^{k-1} \frac{1}{n!} \left(\frac{\lambda}{\mu} \right)^n \right] + \frac{1}{k!} \left(\frac{\lambda}{\mu} \right)^k \frac{k\mu}{k\mu - \lambda}}$$

2. The probability of n units in line waiting for service at time t is

$$P\{n \geq k\} = \sum_{n=k}^{\infty} P_n = \frac{\mu(\lambda/\mu)^k}{(k-1)!(k\mu - \lambda)} P_0$$

3. The average queue length is

$$L_g = \frac{\lambda\mu(\lambda/\mu)^k}{(k-1)!(k\mu - \lambda)^2} P_0$$

4. The average number of units being serviced or waiting for service is

$$L = \frac{\lambda\mu(\lambda/\mu)^k}{(k-1)!(k\mu - \lambda)^2} P_0 + \frac{\lambda}{\mu}$$

5. The average waiting time of an arrival is

$$W = \frac{\mu(\lambda/\mu)^k}{(k-1)!(k\mu - \lambda)^2} P_0$$

6. The average time an arrival spends in the system is

$$T_s = \frac{\mu(\lambda/\mu)^k}{(k-1)!(k\mu - \lambda)^2} P_0 + \frac{1}{\mu}$$

Using the same data as given in the single-service facility, we can now calculate the costs associated with using two storekeepers in the one tool crib. We are assuming that a single queue is formed and that this queue is serviced by whichever storekeeper is free.

The probability of zero units waiting in line at time t is

$$P_0 = \frac{1}{\frac{1}{0!} \left(\frac{20}{25} \right)^0 + \frac{1}{1!} \left(\frac{20}{25} \right)^1 + \frac{1}{2!} \left(\frac{20}{25} \right)^2 \frac{2(25)}{2(25) - 20}} = \frac{3}{7}$$

The average number of units in the system can be calculated as follows:

$$L = \frac{(20)(25)\left(\frac{20}{25} \right)^2}{(2-1)![(2)(25) - 20]^2} \left(\frac{3}{7} \right) + \frac{20}{25} = 0.952$$

Since on the average there are 0.952 units in the system, we can expect that during an eight-hour period the total waiting time will be 7.616 hours [(8)(0.952)]. Therefore the total cost of having two storekeepers in one toolroom can be given as follows:

$$\text{Total cost} = (7.616)(8.65) + (8)(3.25) = \$91.88$$

This example shows that it is more efficient to have both storekeepers at the same tool crib rather than opening a new tool crib for the second storekeeper. This is true because with both storekeepers at one location there is no line formed unless both storekeepers are busy at the same time.

Finite Number of Units Requiring Service. The two cases examined above (i.e., single-service facility and multiservice facility) are based on the assumption of a large group (approaching infinity) of persons requiring service. Another queueing problem arises when we have a finite number of units requiring service. Such situations arise frequently in the industrial environment—for example, an automatic screw machine department with a finite number of machines being serviced by one or more maintenance or setup men.

Suppose we have m machines each with a Poisson breakdown rate λ and a single repair man with a service rate μ. The steady-state probability of m machines not working is

$$P_m = \left\{ 1 + \frac{1}{1!}\left(\frac{\mu}{\lambda}\right)^1 + \cdots + \frac{1}{m!}\left(\frac{\mu}{\lambda}\right)^m \right\}^{-1}$$

And the probability of P_{m-k} machines not working is

$$P_{m-k} = \left(\frac{1}{k!}\right)\left(\frac{\mu}{\lambda}\right)^k P_m$$

The expected number of machines in the waiting line is

$$W = m - \frac{\lambda + \mu}{\lambda}(1 - P_0)$$

where P_0 equals the probability of the repairman being idle.

Suppose we have an automatic screw department with six machines and one repairman. The hourly cost per machine is $20.00 when it is not working and the hourly cost of the repairman is $4.00. Further:

$$\lambda = 2$$

$$\mu = 20$$

$$P_6 = \left\{ 1 + \frac{1}{1!}\left(\frac{20}{2}\right)^1 + \frac{1}{2!}\left(\frac{20}{2}\right)^2 + \frac{1}{3!}\left(\frac{20}{2}\right)^3 + \frac{1}{4!}\left(\frac{20}{2}\right)^4 + \frac{1}{5!}\left(\frac{20}{2}\right)^5 + \frac{1}{6!}\left(\frac{20}{2}\right)^6 \right\}^{-1}$$

$$P_6 = 0.000348$$

and the probability of P_0 units not working is

$$P_{6-6} = \left(\frac{1}{6!}\right)\left(\frac{20}{2}\right)^6 (0.000348)$$

$$P_0 = 0.4845$$

The expected number of machines in the waiting line is

$$W = 6 - \frac{2 + 20}{2}(1 - 0.4845) = 0.3295$$

The expected number of machines being serviced is

$$b = \sum_{n=1}^{m} {}_n P_n = W = 0.5159$$

The total cost per eight-hour day is then

$$\text{Total cost} = (8)(0.3295)(20.00) + 8(4.00) + 8(0.5159)(20.00)$$
$$= 52.72 + 32 + 82.59$$
$$= \$167.26$$

The question now arises whether the total cost would be reduced if there were additional maintenance men available to service these machines. This queueing problem will be examined next.[2]

Suppose that instead of only one serviceman we had r servicemen. Then the probability of n machines not running is

$$P_n = P_0 \left(\frac{\lambda}{\mu}\right)^n \left(\frac{m}{n}\right) \qquad \text{where } 0 \leq n < r$$

$$P_n = P_0 \left(\frac{\lambda}{\mu}\right)^n \left(\frac{m}{n}\right) \left(\frac{n!}{r!r^{n-r}}\right) \qquad \text{where } r \leq n \leq m$$

$$P_0 = 1 - \sum_{n=1}^{n=m} P_n$$

Let a = average number of machines working
  b = average number of machines being serviced
  L_g = average number of machines waiting in line

Then

$$m = a + b + L_g$$

$$b = \sum_{n=0}^{r-1} np_n + r \sum_{n=r}^{m} p_n$$

$$a = \frac{b\mu}{\lambda}$$

Suppose that we have the same situation as previously discussed except that r, the number of servicemen, is now increased to two. The following still holds true.

$$\lambda = 2$$
$$\mu = 20$$
$$m = 6$$

$$\text{Machine cost per hour} \quad = \$20.00$$
$$\text{Repairman cost per hour} = \$\ 4.00$$

The probability of one machine not working (requiring maintenance) is

$$P_1 = P_0 \left(\frac{2}{20}\right)^1 \left(\frac{6}{1}\right)$$

$$= P_0(0.1)^1 \frac{6!}{1!(6-1)!} = 0.6P_0$$

In a similar fashion the following values are calculated:

$$P_2 = 0.15P_0$$
$$P_3 = 0.03P_0$$
$$P_4 = 0.0045P_0$$
$$P_5 = 0.00045P_0$$
$$P_6 = 0.00002P_0$$

and $P_0 = 1 - (0.6P_0 + 0.15P_0 + 0.03P_0 + 0.0045P_0 + 0.00045P_0 + 0.00002P_0)$

$$P_0 + 0.78497P_0 = 1$$
$$P_0 = 0.5602$$
$$P_1 = 0.3361$$
$$P_2 = 0.0840$$
$$P_3 = 0.0168$$
$$P_4 = 0.0025$$
$$P_5 = 0.0003$$
$$P_6 = 0.00001$$

The average number of machines being serviced is

$$b = \sum_{n=0}^{n=1} nP_n + 2 \sum_{n=2}^{6} P_n$$
$$b = (1)(0.3361) + 2(0.0840 + 0.0168 + 0.0025 + 0.0003 + 0.0001)$$
$$= 0.54332$$
$$a = \frac{0.54332(20)}{2}$$
$$= 5.4320$$
$$L_g = 6 - 5.4332 - 0.5433 = 0.0235$$

The average number of machines not working is

$$b + L_g = 0.5668$$

The total cost is therefore

$$\text{Total cost} = (0.5668)(8)(20) + (2)(4)(8)$$
$$= 90.69 + 64$$
$$= \$154.69$$

Therefore, it is seen that in this case the total cost is reduced from $167.26 per day to $154.69 per day by adding one repairman. This holds true even though the average number of idle repairmen is 1.4567.

SIMULATION

"Simulation" has been defined in the Webster Dictionary as "to assume the appearance of, without the reality." A more formal definition has been given by R. Reed[5] as follows: "Simulation is the representation of reality through the use of a model or other device, which will react in the same manner as reality under a given set of conditions."

Simulation is not new; it has been used in the physical sciences for many years. For example, aeronautical engineers have tested properties of new airplane designs in wind tunnels, industrial engineers have used machine templates to investigate the most efficient machine layouts in plants, and army officers have engaged in war games to test strategic and tactical plans.

However, the use of simulation in the industrial environment has seen its greatest growth since the advent of the computer. The computer has enabled us to develop large-scale mathematical and logical models of various aspects of the business firm and to evaluate proposed changes in a relatively short period of time. Further, in recent years there has been a growth of special simulation languages such as SIMSCRIPT and GPSS which has simplified the task of developing the simulation model.

Types of Simulation Models.   Simulation models can be broken into the following two general classifications:

1. Time-independent models
2. Time-dependent models

Time-independent models are simulation models in which time does not play a part. The performance of the model depends solely on the number and nature of the events that affect the status of the system. For example, a company may develop a labor-contract model for the purpose of evaluating the cost of alternative wage rates and fringe-benefit packages. This model would include:

1. A file of the employee characteristics, such as age, seniority, hourly rate, number of dependents, date of employment, etc.

2. The mathematical-logical relationships between the employee characteristics and the salary and fringe-benefit packages.

The simulation would then consist of running the employee-characteristics file against the mathematical-logical-relationship model to evaluate the cost of a given wage rate and fringe-benefit package. The simulation is complete as soon as the entire employee file has been passed against the model. It is then possible to change any or all of the wage rates and fringe benefits, and run the employee file against the revised package to evaluate the cost of the alternative package. Note that neither the performance of the system nor the creation of events is a function of time.

Time-dependent models are those models whose performance is a function of time. The status of the model changes with time. For example, all queueing models are time dependent because inputs (i.e., customers, sales, etc.) continue to enter the waiting lines, and these inputs are a function of time. Similarly the service times for these inputs are time dependent.

Two approaches have been developed for simulating time-dependent models on the computer. The first of these is the "fixed-time-increment" procedure. Using this procedure a clock is simulated by the computer which records the instant of real time that has been reached in the system in order to maintain the correct time sequence of the events. This recorded time is called the "clock time." The developer of the model picks some uniform discrete interval of time (i.e., scan the system every minute, quarter of an hour, etc.) and the system is scanned or examined every unit of clock time to determine whether there are any events due to occur at that particular clock time.

The second approach is to use the "variable-time-increment" model. In this model, clock time is advanced by the amount necessary to cause the next most imminent event to take place. Events can occur at any desired point in clock time because time is advanced by variable increments rather than being divided into a sequence of uniform increments. When a given event has been executed, clock time is advanced to the time at which the next significant event is to occur. The intervening time periods when no changes occur in the system are skipped over.

The final decision concerning whether to use fixed- or variable-time-increment methods on a particular system depends on the nature of the system. However, it should be remembered that the efficiency of the fixed-time-increment method increases with the number of status variables and that the efficiency of the variable-time-increment model increases with the mean length of the events.

A Simple Simulation Model.   Most of us have at one time or another engaged in a game, either for fun or money, which involved the tossing of two 6-sided dice. If the dice are honest, we expect that each of the faces is equally likely to land face up. Therefore, the probability is equal to one-sixth of any of the values 1, 2, 3, 4, 5, or 6 occurring. Suppose that we know no statistics and are interested in finding out what probabilities are associated with throwing a 2, 3, 4, 5, 6, 7, 8, 9, 10, 11, or 12 when two dice are thrown simultaneously. One way of finding out is to take two dice and throw them a large number of times and keep track of the number of times each number occurs. However, suppose that we do not have the dice or are not certain that they are perfectly honest. We can simulate the throwing of the dice with the following simple experiment.

We will generate random numbers and have these random numbers associated with one of the six faces of the dice occurring. Table 9 gives the probability and cumulative probability of any one of the six faces occurring. We will

TABLE 9   Probabilities Associated with Dice

Face value	Probability of occurrence	Cumulative probability
1	0.166	0.166
2	0.166	0.332
3	0.166	0.498
4	0.166	0.664
5	0.166	0.830
6	0.166	0.996

therefore generate some random numbers and establish the relationship shown in Table 10. We can go to the computer or a table of random numbers and

TABLE 10   Random-number Relationships

Random Number Class Limits	Face Value Represented
000–166	1
167–332	2
333–498	3
499–664	4
665–830	5
831–996	6

generate or obtain the random numbers for our experiment. For example, Table 11 gives a set random numbers and their equivalent face values.

A summary of the simulation is given in Table 12. An examination of this table shows that the simulation does not agree precisely with the expected results. However, this variation is a result of the sampling error. If we generated thousands of numbers, our results would approach the expected values. This small example illustrates a simple simulation and indicates the need for running very large samples if our simulation is to reflect reality.

Simulation of a Queueing Problem. Users of railroad tank cars have to furnish their own cars as these are not supplied by the railroads. As a rule users lease these tank cars from leasing car companies. The question, therefore, arises as to how many cars a user should lease in order to ensure that cars are available when needed while at the same time ensuring that an excess of cars do not sit around idle and not in use. This is, therefore, a typical queueing problem. However, the distribution of cars shipped can vary by

TABLE 11   Simulation of Dice Experiment

Random no. first dice	Equivalent value	Random no. second dice	Equivalent value	Value of both dice
158	1	483	3	4
092	1	741	5	6
411	3	766	5	8
745	5	027	1	6
009	1	070	1	2
724	5	648	4	9
674	5	956	6	11
550	4	238	2	6
716	5	912	6	11
359	3	480	3	6
419	3	558	4	7
969	6	917	6	12
200	2	403	3	
458	3	932	6	
384	3	013	1	
019				
	4			
066	1	319		
179	2	627	4	6
493	3	484	3	6
837	6	730	5	11
705	5	887	6	11
068	1	198	2	3
124	2	407	3	5
597	4	093	1	5
467	3	222	2	5
543	4	296	2	6
041	1	014	1	2

the day of the week and the distributions of travel time and of cars shipped per day can assume some unusual forms. A simulation model of this system is developed since this queueing problem does not lend itself to a closed-form solution. The particular model is programmed for a computer and requires the

TABLE 12   Results of Simulation

Value obtained	Frequency	Probability	Theoretical probability
2	4	0.040	0.028
3	4	0.040	0.056
4	3	0.030	0.083
5	14	0.140	0.111
6	19	0.190	0.138
7	20	0.200	0.167
8	10	0.100	0.138
9	14	0.140	0.111
10	5	0.050	0.083
11	6	0.060	0.056
12	1	0.010	0.028
	100	1.000	0.999

following input:

1. *Card Type* 01: Specifying the number of days to be simulated and the number of cars to be used in the simulation.

2. *Card Type* 02: Specifying the number of departures for days 1, 2, 3, 4, 5, and 6 of the week and the upper class limits of the cumulative distribution.

3. *Card Type* 03: Specifying the number of days en route and the upper class limits of the cumulative distribution.

CARD TYPE 01:

Columns	Entry	Comments
1–2	Sequence no.	01
3–4	Plant no.	
5–7	Transient days	No. of days simulation is to be run for initialization purposes
8–10	Phase 2 days	No. of days to be simulated
11–13	Phase 3 days	These need be filled out only if a number of runs under same condition are desired
14–16	Phase 4 days	
17–19	Phase 5 days	
26–28	No. of cars	

CARD TYPE 02:

Columns	Entry	Comments
1–2	Sequence no.	All cards are numbered sequentially starting with 02
3–4	Day of the week	Monday = 01, Tuesday = 02, . . . Saturday = 06
5–6	No. of departures	
7–9	Upper limit of cum. prob.	Decimal place assumed between columns 8 and 9
10–11	No. of departures	
12–14	Upper limit of cum. prob.	

These are repeated to columns 79 permitting 14 classes per card. Multiple cards can be used.

CARD TYPE 03:

Column	Entry	Comments
1–2	Sequence no.	Continue sequential no. started with card type 02
3–4	08	
5–6	No. of trip days	
7–9	Upper limit of cum. prob.	
10–11	No. of trip days	
12–14	Upper limit of cum. prob.	

These are repeated to column 79 permitting 14 classes per card. Up to six cards can be used.

Using the car-usage simulator, simulations are run for the conditions shown in Tables 12 and 13. The computer system was used to simulate conditions

TABLE 13   Distribution of Cars Shipped per Day
(Days 1 through 6. None shipped on Day 7.)

No. of cars	Probability	Cumulative prob.
0	0.050	0.050
1	0.050	0.100
2	0.100	0.200
3	0.150	0.350
4	0.150	0.500
5	0.200	0.700
6	0.120	0.820
7	0.100	0.920
8	0.040	0.960
9	0.020	0.980
10	0.019	0.999

TABLE 14   Distribution of Travel Days

No. of days per trip	Probability	Cumulative probability
3	0.010	0.010
4	0.020	0.030
5	0.030	0.060
6	0.040	0.100
7	0.050	0.150
8	0.050	0.200
9	0.150	0.350
10	0.150	0.500
11	0.200	0.700
12	0.150	0.850
13	0.050	0.900
14	0.040	0.940
15	0.030	0.970
16	0.020	0.990
17	0.000	0.999

at a plant when 30, 40, or 50 cars were assigned to the plant. Each simulation duplicated 200 days of operation at the plant. This simulation took a total of four minutes of computer time.

The results of each simulation are given in two tables. The first table is the distribution of idle cars and the second table is the distribution of car shortages (see Tables 15 and 16). Tables 17 and 18 summarize the results of the three simulations. Given the results of this simulation, one can readily establish the number of cars one should have on lease. The criterion will be either (1) cost (i.e., comparing the cost of having cars idle versus the cost of being short of cars) or (2) a given level of service (i.e, the fleet should be of a given size to ensure that only a percentage X of the time will we be short of a car).

TABLE 15 Railroad Car Usage Simulation—Idle Cars

Plant No. 01   No. of cars assigned 040
Phase 03   No. of days in period covered 200
Total No. of trips departed during period 000746

Cars idle	Frequency	Cars idle	Frequency	Cars idle	Frequency	Cars idle	Frequency	Cars idle	Frequency
000	014	001	012	002	016	003	021	004	016
005	014	006	007	007	012	008	008	009	011
010	010	011	003	012	005	013	000	014	000
015	000	016	000	017	000	018	000	019	000
020	000	021	000	022	000	023	000	024	000
025	000	026	000	027	000	028	000	029	000
030	000	031	000	032	000	033	000	034	000
035	000	036	000	037	000	038	000	039	000
040	000								

TABLE 16 Railroad Car Usage Stimulation—Car Shortages

Plant No. 01   No. of cars assigned 040
Phase 03   No. of days in period covered 200
Total No. of trips departed during period 000746

Cars short	Frequency	Cars short	Frequency	Cars short	Frequency	Cars short	Frequency
01	009	11	000	21	000	31	000
02	007	12	000	21	000	32	000
03	003	13	000	23	000	33	000
04	002	14	000	24	000	34	000
05	002	15	000	25	000	35	000
06	000	16	000	26	000	36	000
07	000	17	000	27	000	37	000
08	000	18	000	28	000	38	000
09	000	19	000	29	000	39	000
10	000	20	000	30	000	40	000

TABLE 17 Frequency Distribution of Car Shortages

No. of cars short	Frequency of occurrence		
	30-car fleet	40-car fleet	50-car fleet
1	11	9	1
2	15	7	
3	11	3	
4	12	2	
5	5	2	
6	3		
7	1		
8			
9	1		

TABLE 18　Frequency Distribution of Idle Cars

No. of cars idle	Frequency of occurrence		
	30-car fleet	40-car fleet	50-car fleet
0	19	14	1
1	27	12	1
2	21	16	4
3	12	21	2
4	8	16	3
5	6	14	6
6	7	7	3
7	3	12	5
8	6	8	6
9	1	11	8
10	3	10	6
11	. . .	3	12
12	. . .	5	10
13	. . .	. . .	11
14	. . .	. . .	9
15	. . .	. . .	18
16	. . .	. . .	9
17	. . .	. . .	13
18	. . .	. . .	11
19	. . .	. . .	10
20	. . .	. . .	10
21	. . .	. . .	4
22	. . .	. . .	6
23	. . .	. . .	
24	. . .	. . .	1
25	. . .	. . .	
26	. . .	. . .	1
27	. . .	. . .	
28	. . .	. . .	1

This brief example serves to illustrate the type of problem that can be attacked through the use of simulation.

SUMMARY

In this chapter we have attempted to introduce to the reader some of the concepts of quantitative decision making. Some examples of the techniques available and their use in real-life situations are given. For the reader who is interested in more detailed study in some or all of these areas, the following bibliography should be of assistance.

REFERENCES

1. Frderick W. Taylor, *Scientific Management,* Harper & Brothers, Publishers, New York, 1947.
2. William Feller, *Probability Theory and Its Applications,* 2 ed., vol. 1, John Wiley & Sons, Inc., New York.
3. Ira Horowitz, *An Introduction to Quantitative Business Analysis,* McGraw-Hill Book Company, New York, 1965.
4. M. Sasieni, A. Yaspen, and L. Friedman, *Operations Research: Methods and Problems,* John Wiley & Sons, Inc., New York, 1963.
5. R. Reed, *Plant Layout,* Richard D. Irwin, Inc., Homewood, Ill., 1961.

BIBLIOGRAPHY

Beer, Staford: *Management Sciences,* Doubleday & Company, Inc., Garden City, N.Y., 1968.

Brown, R. G.: *Decision Rules for Inventory Management,* Holt, Rinehart and Winston, Inc., New York, 1967.

Buchan, J., and E. Koenigsberg: *Scientific Inventory Management,* Prentice-Hall, Inc., Englewood Cliffs, N.J., 1963.

Buffa, C.: *Production-Inventory Systems,* Richard D. Irwin, Inc., Homewood, Ill., 1968.

Buzzell, R. D.: *Mathematical Models and Marketing Management,* Harvard Business School, Division of Research, Boston, 1964.

Chorafas, D. N.: *Systems and Simulation,* Academic Press Inc., New York, 1965.

Churchman, C. W., R. L. Ackoff, and E. Arnoff: *Introduction to Operations Research,* John Wiley & Sons, Inc., New York, 1965.

Fabrycky, W. J., and J. Bank: *Procurement and Inventory Systems,* Reinhold Publishing Corporation, New York, 1967.

Hertz, D. B., and R. T. Edison: *Progress in Operations Research,* vol. 2, John Wiley & Sons, Inc., New York, 1964.

Horowitz, I.: *An Introduction to Quantitative Business Analysis,* McGraw-Hill Book Company, New York, 1965.

Naddor, E.: *Inventory Systems,* John Wiley & Sons, Inc., New York, 1966.

Saaty, T. L.: *Elements of Queueing Theory,* McGraw-Hill Book Company, New York, 1961.

Thompson, W.: *Operations Research Techniques,* Charles E. Merrill Books, Inc., Columbus, Ohio, 1967.

Chapter **27**

Descriptive Statistics

EDITOR:

Dr. Stephen D. Roberts *Assistant Professor, College of Engineering, Department of Industrial Engineering and Systems Engineering, University of Florida, Gainesville, Florida*

CONTENTS

Descriptive statistics as the name implies, deals with the collection, display, and characterization of information or data. Through descriptive statistics we attempt to collect and present statistical data in such a way that analysis of the data can be performed more clearly.

Personnel involved with production and inventory control are particularly interested in descriptive statistics for a number of reasons.

1. Descriptive statistics will improve the collection of information for management-information systems such as production planning, manpower utilization, inventory recording, and a host of other important information systems.

2. Descriptive statistics will aid in the presentation of data. The preparation of graphical and tabular displays can greatly improve the effective communication

of an important message to management. Descriptive statistical methods will enhance a report by concisely presenting the data simply and clearly so that the significance of the message is not clouded or concealed.

3. Descriptive statistics can reduce the uncertainty surrounding the data by describing the form of the information. Through this description, inferences can be made such as the need for more men in the screw machine department, the likelihood of work stoppage on the assembly line, the average performance in the milling department, and so forth.

COLLECTION OF INFORMATION

Description of the Data. *Data* are numerical information regarding some attribute of interest. Data can be either continuous or discrete. *Discrete data,* unlike continuous, may only assume certain values such as integers. *Continuous data,* on the other hand, may assume any value on a continuous scale. Continuous quantities are usually those describing measures of time, length, weight, temperature, and so forth. Examples of discrete data would be the number of parts in inventory, number of men in a department, and forecasted quantity of bearings. Usually, people in production and inventory control deal with discrete data. However, continuous-type information may sometimes be required.

Suppose one is interested in the amount of finished-stock inventory. This amount of inventory will probably be different each time it is measured. Hence the "amount of inventory" is called a "variable." The values of this variable are called "univariate data." This is because for each observation of inventory we obtain two numbers—parts and dollars. If more than two measurements are obtained for each observation, the data are referred to as "multivariate data."

When the quantity of all possible values of a variable is an exact quantity but not necessarily a known quantity, the data are said to have come from a "finite population." Other populations are called "infinite" if the number of possible values of the variable is infinite. Often very large populations are considered practically infinite and are so treated. Finite populations are most frequently encountered in production and inventory control, although very large populations, such as the number of parts in the shop, are usually treated as though this population were infinite, especially if one is interested in counting them.

Again, consider the amount of finished-stock inventory. One may go into the storage area and count the number of items for every product. However, this becomes prohibitively time consuming for most industrial situations. Consequently, we obtain a *sample* of the inventory or a part of the inventory population. This sample, of course, provides us with only a portion of the total *population.* Facts or characteristics about the total population are called "parameters." One such fact might be the percentage of products which exceed 1,000 units in inventory. One may estimate this percentage based on the proportion in the sample and make an inference to the total population. A value such as this calculated from a sample is called a "statistic" and is used to estimate a population parameter. The problem of inference constitutes a major portion of the field of statistics and is sometimes referrred to as "statistical inference."

An important type of sample which is extremely important for statistical studies is called a "random sample." In fact, most statistics are based in part on this type of sample. A sample is called a "random sample" if any unit in the population has an equal chance of being selected. This means that no unit or units have a greater probability of being taken into the sample than any other. For example, suppose we want a random sample of 10 numbers from the population of numbers 1 to 100. We may take this random sample any number of ways. One way is to use a random-number table, while another is to put all 100 numbers into a hat, shake it, and draw 10. In this way, the sampling is assured to be free of any bias or error caused by the method of obtaining the sample. Suppose a shop contains 100 work centers and one wants to know the average performance. By numbering the work centers (in any fashion), the above sampling procedure may be utilized to quickly obtain the performance simply from the sample. One should remember, however, that a haphazard choice does not qualify as a random sample.

It is randomness in the sample which allows inferences to be made from statistics to population parameters. The sample must not only be random but must also be representative. This means that one must be careful that the sample taken is in fact characteristic of the population. Hence the size of the sample must be large enough to adequately reveal the population characteristics. Sometimes special schemes such as stratification, proportionality, and so forth are used to ensure proper representation. These schemes form the foundation for sampling theory and statistical inference.

Methods of Data Collection. Any investigation regarding statistics must of necessity incorporate some way to gather data. There are many methods of obtaining information, varying from personal observations to elaborate punched-card systems. Fortunately for people involved in production and inventory control, most of their information requirements deal with factual occurrences such as back orders, standard times, due dates, and so forth, instead of subjective information about people. Consequently most of the information can be gathered from factual reports rather than by opinions, guesses, and so forth.

Important internal sources of data for production control include such reports as the production records, sales forecasts, routings, material supply schedules, budgets, scrap reports, etc. This information may be collected manually, by electronic data processing equipment, by card data processing equipment, by a key-sort system, and by many other methods. Most management-information systems provide means for collection and storage of data. Therefore familiarization with these modes of collection can greatly aid in obtaining information.

Frequently, external sources must be consulted. This is especially true in forecasting. In this case one might consult such publications as *Survey of Current Business*. Frequently, too, one might wish to sample what customers predict.

Thus the method of information collection is very critical to a statistical analysis. It must be performed with care and accuracy. To assure the required accuracy, categorizations and classes must be well defined and selected carefully. Understanding tabulation and graphical displays will aid in this collection.

DISPLAY OF DATA

After the collecting of data, it is helpful to display the data in some insightful fashion. This display can often reveal useful properties about data and imply important characteristics. One of the major reasons why the display is important is because it is a useful method presenting data which can be understood with a minimum of explanation—a fact greatly appreciated by management. In general, there are two methods of display: tabular and graphical.

Tabular Display. "Tabular display" refers to the establishment of tables which when presented in a given manner tend to emphasize some important aspect of the data. Tables may serve in a categorical sense aiding formal analysis or merely presenting historical data. Perhaps a more important table in descriptive statistics is the frequency table which illustrates the distributional form of the data. Thus the three tables of primary interest are the historical table, the research table, and the frequency table.

HISTORICAL TABLE: The *historical* or *reference table* is a means of collecting concise reference material. It generally takes the form illustrated by Table 1. This specific table illustrates the number of employees for each department for three separate years. The basic parts as indicated in Table 1 should be

TABLE 1   Number of Employees per Department for 1965–1967*

| Department | Year | | | Box head |
	1965	1966	1967	
Stock	3	4	5	
Plating	7	7	8	
Screw machine	8	9	10	
Milling	10	12	12	
Drilling	5	5	6	Field
Misc. parts	15	15	17	
Stores	5	5	6	
Assembly	20	22	23	
Warehousing	6	7	7	

Sub head — Column caption — Body caption

Row labels → Stub | Body

* The data indicates the average number of employees during the year.

SOURCE: Company records.

used as a guide in the preparation of such tables. It is important that emphasis be placed where most desired. People have a tendency to read from left to right and from top to bottom, so that the upper lefthand corner should be most prominent. In general, the arrangement should be easily understood and yet provide sufficient information to effectively communicate valuable information. Footnotes should provide additional explanation, and the information source should be acknowledged.

RESEARCH TABLE: The *research table*, sometimes called the "analytical" or "cross-reference table," provides an aid for more specific analysis of data. It is used mostly by statisticians to develop the analysis of an experimental design. An example of this kind of table is given by Table 2. This illustration attempts to present the effects of machine speeds, feeds, and material types on scrap rates. The problem is to illustrate the interrelationships between the variables. Since the table contains three variables, speed, feed, and material, it is sometimes called a "three-way table." For information such as this, more sophisticated statistical techniques are used for analysis. Techniques such as analysis of variance, regression, correlation, and others are frequently utilized. However, often just by presenting data in a tabular manner important results are indicated.

TABLE 2   Effects of Machine Speed, Feed,
and Material on Scrap Rates*

	Material					
	A		B		C	
	Feed		Feed		Feed	
Speed	0.005	0.010	0.005	0.010	0.005	0.010
200	0.05	0.06	0.04	0.08	0.08	0.02
250	0.04	0.07	0.05	0.07	0.06	0.03
300	0.02	0.06	0.07	0.07	0.05	0.03
350	0.01	0.05	0.09	0.08	0.06	0.04

* Speeds are in feet per minute while feeds are inches per revolution.
   Values of table are scrap rates.
   SOURCE: Scrap reports 15–34.

FREQUENCY TABLE: Of primary importance in descriptive statistics is the *frequency table*. This is described best with an illustration. Suppose one is interested in customer orders outstanding which are late. Table 3 presents the data as they are collected. There are 40 tardy orders. Obviously the data, as collected, are difficult to understand in their present form, so one would like to present them in a more usable and effective manner. In their original form the data are often referred to as "raw data." These raw data may be

TABLE 3   Tardiness of Orders (Days)

10	11	20	1	0
9	12	16	6	17
16	15	9	31	19
12	12	11	15	2
8	4	6	14	8
7	13	3	2	7
5	17	10	11	18
13	14	12	5	22

arranged into what is called an "array" merely by reorganizing the information so that the data are ordered. For this case, the data may be ordered according to the degree of tardiness as presented in Table 4. This is sometimes called a "frequency array," since the number of times or frequency of a particular number of days tardy is also presented as well as the days tardy.

However, reduction to a frequency array usually does not greatly improve the compactness of the presentation. This can be verified by examination of the table. Consequently it is often convenient to group the data into *classes* or groups of specified intervals. For this case it could be accomplished by using a *class size* of five. These grouped data are then tabulated in Table 5. Such a tabulation is called a "frequency distribution." A "class" refers to the designation of information within a given interval, while the interval itself is called a "class interval." For this case there are five classes each with an

TABLE 4   Frequency Array of Tardiness

Days tardy	Frequency	Days tardy	Frequency
0	1	11	3
1	1	12	4
2	2	13	2
3	1	14	2
4	1	15	2
5	2	16	2
6	2	17	2
7	2	18	1
8	2	19	1
9	2	20	1
10	2	22	1
		31	1

SOURCE: Table 3.

**TABLE 5   Frequency
Distribution of Tardiness**

Days Tardy	Number of Orders
0–4	6
5–9	10
10–14	13
15–19	8
Over 20	3
	40

SOURCE: Table 4.

interval of five. The boundaries of the classes, 0, 4, 5, 9, etc., are referred to as the "class limits."

One should note, however, that while this presentation does give a clear and concise picture of tardiness, it was achieved through some loss of information. This is illustrated by the fact that one cannot decipher from the table which orders are more than 19 days late. To obtain this information, one must refer back to the raw data.

Consequently the reduction of the data to a more concise form depends directly on the number of classes chosen. But this is not easy to determine and requires much insight. If there are too many classes, the resulting frequency distribution becomes bulky and the concentrations of the data are difficult to ascertain. But if there are too few classes, much of the information is concealed within the class intervals and the frequency distribution becomes so compact that an important pattern may be completely grouped within a class. A good rule of thumb states that the number of classes should range between 5 and 15. Obviously in some special situations 15 may be too few or 5 too many, but without any insight the rule has proved very useful.

Selection of the class interval and class limits is also difficult. The class limits should not be overlapping but should be exclusive. If, for example, the class limits were 0 to 5 for the first class and 5 to 10 for the second, an order having a tardiness of 5 could be placed in either the first or second class. If the class interval and limits are established before the data are collected, this consequence should be considered so that accurate data are obtained. In order to make the table easy to understand and construct, the class intervals should be equal. This was done in constructing the previous table and the reasons for this should be clear.

For discrete data it is not difficult to define class limits because the data can assume only certain values. Consequently the limits were defined as 0 to 4, 5 to 9, 10 to 14, and so forth, since this guaranteed that all data would be contained in mutually exclusive classes. However, this is difficult to do if the data are continuous in character. Suppose, for example, the tardiness were measured in half-days. A tardiness of 4.5 would not lie within the limits of any class boundary. Thus the class limits would have to be revised. To avoid this ambiguity one usually represents the class limits to one decimal point less than that of the data. For example, the class limits could be revised to the following: 0.00 to 4.54, 4.55 to 9.54, 9.55 to 14.54. Since the data are measured to only one decimal place, the new class limits will be nonoverlapping and the class intervals remain equal. Note that this may always be done, since any time data are collected they are to some extent made discrete and thus class limits may be constructed so that all information will fall within a class.

Hence it is important that there should not be any separation between classes. Often this is difficult to avoid without using too few classes. Therefore, it is sometimes convenient to utilize what is called "open-ended classes." This is in fact what the fifth class is in the table. An open-ended class has only one class limit. It is useful when part of the data appears far away from the major concentration of the information. In the tardiness example, the use of an open-ended class avoided the use of an empty class (25 to 29). Notice that open-ended classes can occur at the beginning of a frequency distribution as well as at the end. The disadvantage of such classes is that they cover an extremely large range and do not provide any magnitude information such as how many days over 20 are the orders late.

In addition to the class intervals, limits, size, and so forth, the *midpoints* of the classes are also important. The midpoint is merely the sum of the class limits divided by two or just the average of the class limits. The midpoint of the classes should be of such a magnitude that its value can actually be obtained. For continuous data this will present little problem. However, for discrete data the values of the data are restricted to a certain set of values. The midpoint is important since data within a class are often represented by their value and the data should tend to cluster about this point. Thus the use of the classes in the table appears satisfactory.

An important type of frequency table is called the "percent table." This table represents the proportion or percentage of data which may be found in a certain class. Thus it is merely the frequency table transformed to percentage data. An illustration of this for the tardiness example is given in Table 6. This table indicates, for example, that 25 percent of the orders are five to nine days late. If these 40 orders were a random sample of some larger population, we might use the percentage table to reflect the tardiness character of the population itself.

TABLE 6 Percent Table

Days Tardy	Percentage
0–4	15.0
5–9	25.0
10–14	32.5
15–19	20.0
Over 20	7.5
	100.0

SOURCE: Table 5.

TABLE 7   Cumulative Frequency Table

Days tardy	Cumulative no. of orders	Cumulative percent
0–4	6	15.0
5–9	16	40.0
10–14	29	72.5
15–19	37	92.5
Over 20	40	100.0

SOURCE: Table 5.

Sometimes it is even useful to collect cumulative data. For example, suppose we wanted the number of orders which were less than or equal to nine days late. Table 7 supplies this type of information. This is sometimes called a "less than" table. Note that this may also be presented in percentage form as indicated by Table 6. One may construct an equivalent "more than" cumulative table. The less-than table *begins* with zero, while the more-than table *ends* with zero. Often the *cumulative frequency table* (of the less-than type) is referred to as the "cumulative distribution," and represents an important concept in descriptive statistics.

Graphical Display. As with the tabular display, the graphical display is used to emphasize some particular aspect of the data but through a visual or pictorial media. Graphical presentations may be used to highlight certain significant facts and are often used in conjunction with tabular results. Management appreciates graphical displays which present, at a glance, simple and clearly significant points. Often graphical displays are used for presentation of information to a group of people where a large display can provide a persuasive exhibit. There are many types of graphical display, but among the most important are bar charts, line charts, pie charts, pictograms, histograms, and frequency polygons.

BAR CHARTS: The *bar chart* is one of the most popular of the graphical displays. It is simple to construct and easy to understand. The basic characteristic of the bar chart is that it is strictly one-dimensional. In other words, only the lengths of the bars vary. An example of a bar chart is given in Fig. 1. This

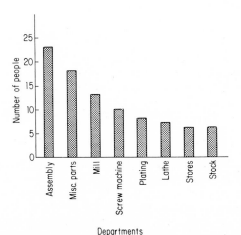

Fig. 1 Distribution of people during the year for plant departments. (*From Table 1.*)

presents the distribution of people during the year for the plant departments. Notice that the bars are separated for ease of identification, and normally the bars are ordered in increasing or decreasing order unless they are fixed by something such as time. The height of the bar represents the number of people. More specifically, this bar chart is called a "simple vertical bar chart" or "column chart." This chart may be turned on its side and would then be called a "simple horizontal bar chart." Gantt charts which are so popular in the field of scheduling are horizontal bar charts. The preference of vertical or horizontal will simply be a question of which makes the most effective presentation and which is simplest to construct.

In addition to the simple bar charts there exist a myriad of other bar charts. Among the most widely used are the component-part bar chart, the grouped bar chart, and the two-directional bar chart. These charts are illustrated in a horizontal fashion in Figs. 2, 3, and 4, respectively.

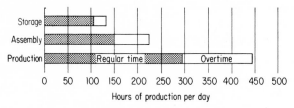

Fig. 2   Breakdown of production hours: component chart.   (*From timekeeping.*)

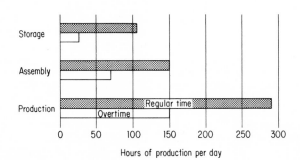

Fig. 3   Breakdown of production hours: grouped bar chart.   (*From Fig. 2.*)

The *component-part bar chart* is recognized because the bars themselves are composed of components. This type of chart permits a visual comparison of the contribution of regular and overtime to the total production-hours per day for each departmental group. However, all overtime components have different origins on the scale, and it is therefore difficult to compare the overtime among the departmental groups.

This disadvantage is overcome by the *grouped bar chart*. In this chart, both the overtime and regular time may be compared with each other and also with those of the other departmental groups. But this chart has a disadvantage which the component-part chart does not possess. Comparisons are difficult between the total production-hours for each departmental group when a total includes the sum of overtime and regular time.

When relative gains and losses are desired, the *two-directional chart* emphasizes the characteristics. The percent change in departmental performance for two years is presented. The departments are ranked from the most positive to the most negative so that analysis is simplified. Note that component-type bars may be used as well as grouped bars. These types of charts are extremely useful to indicate improvements or losses on the same chart around a common base of zero. In the example one is able to pinpoint which department's performance is deteriorating or improving.

In constructing bar charts, it is important that direct labeling as illustrated be used so that they are easily read. For the component-part or grouped charts, the bars should be shaded, cross-hatched, or colored so that each bar is distinct. Also the bars should be spaced, for ease in identification. Grouped bars of

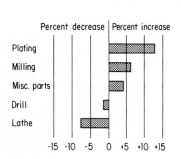

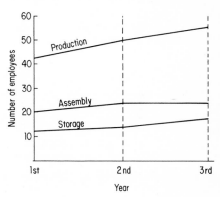

Fig. 4 Percent change in department performance for two years: two-directional chart. (*From performance records.*)

Fig. 5 Personnel requirements for departmental groups. (*From company records.*)

the grouped bar chart are, however, often side by side. The central theme in construction should be clarity and ease of presentation and identification.

LINE CHARTS: *Line charts* are particularly useful whenever the variable is a function of or depends upon time. Sales forecasts are examples of this type of need. Normally time is plotted on the horizontal axis while the quantity of interest is plotted on the vertical. Line charts may be *simple* or of the *component-part* type similar to bar charts. Figure 5 illustrates the simple line chart for the personnel requirements of three major departmental groups. These are assembly, production, and storage. The vertical axis could be of the same form as in Fig. 2 where the line segments connect components of the data thus forming a component-part line chart. The series of connecting lines is called a "curve" and represents the variable of interest as the time varies. The major advantage of such a chart is the ability to visualize the character of the data as it changes with respect to time.

PIE CHARTS: *Pie charts* or *circle charts* are used to portray components of a total. The pie chart is particularly eye-catching, but application is limited to component-type characteristics. An example of a pie chart is presented in Fig. 6. In constructing the pie chart a protractor is useful to obtain the desired proportions. Also it is desirable to arrange the sectors of the chart according to their magnitude. Colors can have a desirable effect in producing a more striking appearance. Pie-chart suitableness lies in its eye-catching appeal and it is therefore useful for public presentation. However, it lacks the accuracy of other charts.

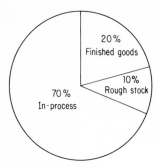

Fig. 6 Proportion of inventory. (*From inventory records.*)

1st Shift	🧍🧍🧍🧍🧍🧍🧍
2nd Shift	🧍🧍🧍
3rd Shift	🧍

Fig. 7 Number of employees per shift. Each symbol represents 10 employees. (*From company records.*)

PICTOGRAMS: Like the pie chart, the *pictogram* is used because of eye appeal and is particularly useful for a wide range of audiences. The pictogram is simply a bar chart constructed from symbols which serve the same purpose as the bars in the bar chart. A typical pictogram is shown in Fig. 7 denoting the number of employees for each shift. Note that in constructing such a chart the symbol has a numerical relationship with the data, and thus each symbol represents a certain segment of the data. For the case of Fig. 7, each symbol represents 10 employees. Sometimes the size of the symbol represents the data, and often fractional symbols are used. The pictogram should illustrate the data clearly and should not distract from the importance of the result. When constructing such a chart, avoid the pitfall of displaying too much information—thus confusing the viewer.

HISTOGRAMS: The *histogram* is a means of graphically illustrating a frequency distribution. In many ways it is similar to a vertical bar chart; however, it is two-dimensional in that both the width and height of the bars are variables. Consider the frequency distribution of Table 8, which depicts the distribution

TABLE 8 Frequency Distribution of Bar-stock Demand

Number of Bars Demanded	Frequency of Demand
30–34	1
35–39	4
40–44	13
45–49	26
50–54	50
55–59	39
60–64	20
65–69	5
70–74	2
	160

SOURCE: Company records.

of daily demand for stock over a period of 160 days. Figure 8 illustrates the histogram constructed from this frequency distribution using the class limits and frequency. The frequency for each class is represented by the height of the bar, while the width of the bar for each class is governed by the class limits. The bars are usually not separated, so the numbers on the horizontal axis form a practically continuous span.

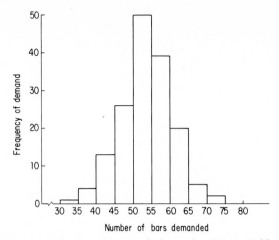

Fig. 8 Distribution of bar-stock demand. (*From Table 8.*)

It should be noted that a histogram cannot be constructed for distributions which have open-ended classes. One should also avoid using a histogram for distributions when classes are not equal. The histogram may be altered if classes are unequal, but closed by making the frequency within each interval proportional to the area of the bar for the class. For example, if one class interval is twice as wide as the rest, then the height of the bar for this particular class should be reduced by one-half. In general, however, one cannot use the histogram for cases involving open-ended classes, and care must be used if the class intervals are unequal.

FREQUENCY POLYGONS: The *frequency polygon* is an alternative method for graphically illustrating the frequency distribution and performs a function similar to that of the histogram. The frequency polygon for the data in Table 8 is shown in Fig. 9. The frequency polygon is formed by letting the midpoints of the classes assume the frequency of the class. Then these points are connected by a set of line segments thus forming a type of curve. One should

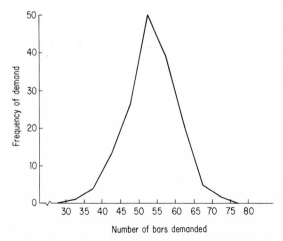

Fig. 9 Distribution of bar-stock demand. (*From Table 8.*)

note that the extra classes with zero frequency are artificially augmented to both ends of the distribution so that the curve will meet the horizontal axis on both ends, thus enclosing the frequency within the polygon.

As with the histogram, the frequency polygon cannot be constructed if one of the classes is open-ended. If the class intervals are unequal, the same adjustment must be made for the frequency polygon as has to be done for the histogram.

The choice of whether a frequency distribution is to be represented by a frequency polygon or histogram is merely a matter of personal preference. The only advantage of a frequency polygon is in comparing two or more distributions which are plotted on the same chart, but the histogram seems to be preferable when a discrete set of data is presented.

CUMULATIVE FREQUENCY REPRESENTATION: Like the frequency table, the frequency polygon or the histogram may be represented in cumulative form. For example, if the less-than distribution were to be graphed for Table 8, its cumulative frequency representation in polygon form would look like Fig. 10. Note that the vertical axis may be represented by frequency or by percentage.

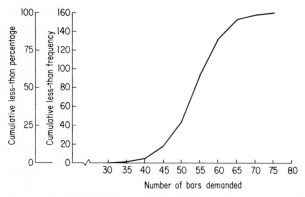

Fig. 10 Cumulative bar-stock demand. (*From Table 8.*)

Sometimes these types of curves are called "ogives." One should note that the ogive differs from the frequency polygon in that the cumulative frequency is plotted at the upper class limit (or between the upper limit of the class and the lower limit of the next class), so that the "less than" notion agrees with the graphed display.

Naturally a cumulative histogram could be constructed in the same manner in which Fig. 10 was developed. Cumulative representations tend to be S shaped, rising from zero at the lower left to the maximum at the upper right. These curves allow interpolation and are very similar to their continuous counterpart, the distribution functions. These are widely used in simulation studies, particularly those of the Monte Carlo variety.

MEASURES OF LOCATION

The frequency distribution has been found to be an important technique for describing the pattern of variation of some variable. The frequency table provides a tabular form of the distribution, while the frequency polgyon presents a graphical display. However, working directly with the frequency distribution is quite cumbersome, and one may wish to investigate the data by summarizing some of the more important characteristics or properties. This discussion is directed particularly to developing measures of the location or position of the distribution. Specifically, one wishes to know about what point the distribution or variable seems to be concentrated or clustered. Methods of measuring such a point are referred to as "measures of location." Sometimes they are called "measures of position," "measures of central tendency," and "measures of central values." In general, the measures of location tend to summarize the distribution in the sense that they characterize by a single value the location or position of the frequency distribution.

Mean. This first measure of location is called the "mean," or more accurately, the "arithmetic mean." This is the common "average" found in ordinary usage as illustrated, for example, by the batter's average, the average value of common stock, and the average shop performance. But since the term "average" has so many connotations, statisticians have chosen the term "arithmetic mean," or more briefly, "mean," to denote the sum of the values of a group of figures divided by the number of figures making up the sum. To define this more explicitly, consider n numbers whose values are $x_1, x_2, x_3, \ldots, x_n$. The mean is defined as follows:

$$\text{Mean} = \frac{x_1 + x_2 + \cdots + x_n}{n} = \frac{\sum_{i=1}^{n} x_i}{n}$$

where $\sum_{i=1}^{n} x_i = x_1 + x_2 + \cdots + x_n$.

To illustrate this computational method, suppose in a particular shop there are five screw machines whose production capabilities are as follows (in parts per hour): 255, 215, 157, 230, and 188. Using the above formula, the mean production capability of the screw machines is

$$\frac{255 + 215 + 157 + 230 + 188}{5} = \frac{1{,}045}{5} = 209$$

If the mean is calculated from the total population, it is denoted by the Greek letter μ (mu) and thus represents a population parameter. However, if the calculation is made for a sample, the mean is denoted by $\bar{x}$ (x bar) and is thus a statistic. For a particular population, μ is a constant; however, $\bar{x}$ for this same population is a variable, since the sample mean will depend on the values of the sample chosen. Hence for different samples from the same population, there will probably be a different mean.

MEAN OF THE FREQUENCY DISTRIBUTION: The mean may be computed from the frequency distribution as well as the raw data or data array. Consider the frequency distribution of Table 8 concerning the demand of bar stock. Obviously, one cannot work with the individual demands in this case, since they have been grouped into classes. Consequently one must make an assumption regarding the distribution. It is assumed, usually validly, that all frequencies located within each class may be represented by the midpoint. Hence, this emphasizes the necessity for selecting the classes and their midpoints with care. For most distributions found in production and inventory control, the errors introduced by this assumption tend to cancel themselves eventually. However, the formula for calculating the mean must be modified.

$$\text{Mean from a frequency distribution} = \frac{\sum\limits_{i=1}^{k} x_i f_i}{\sum\limits_{i=1}^{k} f_i} = \frac{\sum\limits_{i=1}^{k} x_i f_i}{N}$$

where $\sum\limits_{i=1}^{k} f_i = N$.

An illustration of this calculation for the mean bar-stock demand of Table 8 is given in Table 9. Since these are results from a sample (and this will always be the case unless it is indicated otherwise), one may assert that $\bar{x} = 8,490/160 = 53.0625$. Upon application of the previous formula. The table includes the general method for accomplishing the calculation. Of major importance are the columns containing x_i, f_i, and $x_i f_i$, since they form the basis of the calculation. The first four columns are taken from Table 8, while the last column is simply the product of the midpoints and frequencies.

TABLE 9   Calculation of Mean of Bar-stock Demand

Class	Bar demand	Midpoint, x_i	Frequency, f_i	$x_i f_i$
1	30–34	32	1	32
2	35–39	37	4	148
3	40–44	42	13	546
4	45–49	47	26	1,222
5	50–54	52	50	2,600
6	55–59	57	39	2,223
7	60–64	62	20	1,240
8	65–69	67	5	335
9	70–74	72	2	144
			$\sum\limits_{i=1}^{9} f_i = 160$	$\sum\limits_{i=1}^{9} x_i f_i = 8,490$

SOURCE: Table 8.

MEAN BASED ON CODED DATA: In spite of the fact that the mean is easy to calculate, one may further simplify the calculation through a *coding* procedure. It is especially useful for manual calculation and when the midpoints or class frequencies are themselves large numbers. In essence, the idea behind coding is merely to transform the data in such a way as to reduce computational effort to calculate the mean and transform the result back to original terms.

This may be accomplished by "ordering" each class according to an arbitrary scale so as to reduce the magnitude of the x_i values. In general, it appears most efficient to assign zero to that midpoint which seems closest to the probable mean. Then all midpoints below this "zero" are sequentially assigned positive values, while those midpoints above are sequentially assigned negative values. To understand this procedure, refer to Table 10. This table illustrates the computational procedure for coding the frequency distribution. The coded values are denoted by u_i. In this example, 52 is assigned the zero value, while succeeding values are positive and previous values become negative. It is important to note that the sum of the coded values (u_i) need not be zero and the choice of the zero location does not affect the result.

TABLE 10   Short-cut Tabulation of Mean Bar-stock Demand

Demand midpoints	Coded values, u_i	Frequency, f_i	$u_i f_i$
32	-4	1	-4
37	-3	4	-12
42	-2	13	-26
47	-1	26	-26
52	0	50	0
57	1	39	39
62	2	20	40
67	3	5	15
72	4	2	8
		$\displaystyle\sum_{i=1}^{9} f_i = \overline{160}$	$\displaystyle\sum_{i=1}^{9} f_i u_i = \overline{34}$

SOURCE: Table 8 or 9.

The formula for the mean based on coded values must again be modified. Letting c be the class interval and a the midpoint which is assigned the zero coded value, the mean is calculated by

$$\text{Mean based on coded values} = \left(\frac{\displaystyle\sum_{i=1}^{k} u_i f_i}{\Sigma f_i} \right) (c) + a$$

where k is again the number of classes. From Table 10, the mean based on coded values is calculated from the previous formula as

$$\bar{x} = \left(\frac{34}{160} \right) (5) + 52 = 53.0625$$

One should note that this value agrees with the result obtained from uncoded data, which in this case is five. The class interval c is easily obtained by subtracting two successive midpoints.

To verify that the results are independent of the location for the choice of the coded zero, Table 11 provides the tabulation when the zero is assigned 42. Note also that the sum of the coded values is not zero. Again, this mean

TABLE 11   Alternate Tabulation of Mean Bar-stock Demand

Demand midpoints	Coded values, u_i	Frequency, f_i	$u_i f_i$
32	-2	1	-2
37	-1	4	-4
42	0	13	0
47	1	26	26
52	2	50	100
57	3	39	117
62	4	20	80
67	5	5	25
72	6	2	12
		$\displaystyle\sum_{i=1}^{9} f_i = \overline{160}$	$\displaystyle\sum_{i=1}^{9} f_i u_i = \overline{354}$

SOURCE: Table 8 or 9.

agrees with the one calculated from Table 10, or

$$\bar{x} = \left(\frac{354}{160}\right)(5) + 42 = 53.0625$$

WEIGHTED MEAN: Suppose one wishes the average space utilization in all three storage areas—rough stock, in-process, and finish stock. The arithmetic average of the utilization in each of the three areas is inappropriate, since more than likely each store occupies a different area. Suppose the utilization in rough stock is 21 percent, in in-process 33 percent, and 47 percent in finish stock, and the area of rough stock is 700 square feet, in-process is 400 square feet, and finish stock occupies 1,050 square feet. Therefore the overall space-utilization mean for all stores is

$$\frac{(0.21)(700) + (0.33)(400) + (0.47)(1,050)}{700 + 400 + 1,050} = 0.359 \text{ or } 35.9\%$$

Thus by weighting each utilization with the proper area, a more representative mean is calculated. In this way the size of area is incorporated along with its utilization.

In general, suppose we have a set of n numbers $x_1, x_2, \ldots, x_n$ whose importance is reflected by the weights $w_1, w_2, \ldots, w_n$. Thus the "weighted mean" may be defined as

$$\text{Weighted mean} = \frac{\sum_{i=1}^{n} w_i x_i}{\sum_{i=1}^{n} w_i}$$

One should note that the method of calculating means for the frequency distribution employs the weighting concept, since the frequencies serve as weights.

Another application of the weighted mean utilizes the combination of several means. For example, suppose one knows the mean number of personnel in each of n departments. Letting $\bar{x}_1, \bar{x}_2, \ldots, \bar{x}_n$ be the mean number of people in each of the n departments, suppose the sizes of the departments are given by $m_1, m_2, \ldots, m_n$. Then the overall (sample) mean number of men in the n departments is given by

$$\bar{\bar{x}} = \frac{\sum_{i=1}^{n} m_i \bar{x}_i}{\sum_{i=1}^{n} m_i}$$

Hence one may use the above formula to calculate overall means which are in essence a form of the weighted means. Consequently overall means may be formulated from the means of several sets of data.

PROPERTIES OF THE MEAN: The following are among the most important characteristics of the mean:

1. The mean is a concept of general familiarity and is easily understood.

2. The mean always exists and therefore may be always calculated.

3. For a given set of values, only one mean may be calculated. Thus the mean is unique.

4. The mean is influenced by every value in the sample. If the data are

classified by a frequency distribution, then all midpoints and class frequencies affect the mean.

5. The unit measure of the mean is identical to the unit of measure describing the data, i.e., if the data are in units of demand, then the mean is described in units of demand.

6. The algebraic sum of the differences between the mean and the data is zero. Expressed mathematically,

$$\sum_{i=1}^{n} (x_i - \bar{x}) = 0$$

This property makes the short-cut method of calculation possible.

7. The sum of the squares of the differences between the mean and the data is a minimum. In other words, the sum of the squares of the differences between the data and any point other than the mean will produce a larger value. This property may be demonstrated by merely calculating the sum of the squared difference first about the mean and then about any other value. The interested reader may verify this for Table 9 utilizing the mean and any other values. This characteristic has a special significance in computing a measure of the variation called the "standard deviation," which is discussed later.

Median and Other Quartiles. In a series of ordered data (either increasing or decreasing) the *median* is the middle value or the value which divides the total frequency in half. If the n number in the ordered series is an odd number, then the median is merely the $(n + 1)/2$ value counting from either end. For example, consider the following ordered series composed of five numbers:

$$15 \quad 17 \quad 23 \quad 24 \quad 26$$

Since the number of values in the series is odd, the median is the $(5 + 1)/2$ or third number from either end. Thus the median of the above series is 23. If the n values of the ordered series are odd, then the median is the mean of the middle values. To illustrate this, consider the following ordered series composed of six numbers:

$$12 \quad 17 \quad 18 \quad 22 \quad 26 \quad 28$$

Since 18 and 22 are the middle two values, the median is $(18 + 22)/2 = 20$. Hence the median is a positional measure, since the values of the numbers in the series do not, in general, have a critical effect on the median. For example, one may change 12, 17, 26, and 28, and the value of the median would be unaffected as long as the order in the series is maintained.

MEDIAN OF THE FREQUENCY DISTRIBUTION: To determine the median of a frequency distribution, one must first determine the class which contains the median. Consider the data in Table 9. Since the total frequency is 160, the value which divides the frequencies in half is $N/2 = 160/2 = 80$, which by inspection of column 4 of Table 9 is contained in the fifth class. This class has class limits of 50 to 54. Since the first four classes have a total frequency of 44, the median is contained in the class having a frequency of 50, and this class is called the "median class." Because the value of 80 is 36 more than 44, the median may be interpolated within the fifth class or median class as being $\frac{36}{50}$ of the class interval beyond 50. Hence the median is located at $50 + \frac{36}{50} \times 5 = 53.6$. To interpolate within a class, it is assumed that the values within the class are evenly distributed between the class limits. The median may be expressed by the following formula:

$$\text{Median} = L + \left(\frac{N/2 - \Sigma f}{f_m}\right) (i)$$

where N = total number of frequencies in the frequency distribution
f_m = frequency in the median class
L = lower limit of the median class
i = class interval
Σf = sum of the frequencies below the median class

Upon application of this formula to the data in Table 9,

$$\text{Median} = 50 + \left(\frac{\frac{160}{2} - 44}{50}\right) (5) = 53.60$$

which is identical to the value obtained previously.

QUARTILES, DECILES, AND PERCENTILES: If the total frequency is divided into 4 equal proportions, the 3 values at the divisions are called "quartiles." If the frequency is divided into 10 equal proportions, the 9 dividers are referred to as "deciles." Likewise if the frequency is divided into 100 equal parts, the 99 dividers are called "percentiles." Note that the number of dividers is always one less than the number of parts. This is because both ends of the frequency are not counted.

The quartiles in general are determined in a manner similar to the median, and again interpolation is required when data come from the frequency distribution. To illustrate the general procedure, calculations for the quartiles will be presented. Suppose there exists an ordered array of 31 numbers. The first quartile would be the $(N + 1)/4$ number in the array or the eighth item. The second quartile is just the median or the $2(N + 1)/4$ number in the array. The third and last quartile is the $3(N + 1)/4$ number or the twenty-fourth item. By similar reasoning the first decile is the $(N + 1)/10$ number in the array, while the first percentile is the $(N + 1)/100$ number. Subsequent deciles and percentiles would be calculated in the manner similar to that for successive quartiles.

To calculate quartiles from the frequency distribution, one employs the procedure that was used to determine the median. Referring to Table 9, the first quartile must fall into the fourth class, since the $\frac{160}{4} = 40$ item is in that class if items are ordered. Because the first three classes have a total frequency of 18, the first quartile is the twenty-second item $(40 - 18 = 22)$ in the fourth class. Thus the first quartile may be calculated by interpolation as follows:

$$\text{First quartile} = 45 + \left(\tfrac{22}{26}\right)(5) = 49.23$$

The value of $\tfrac{22}{26}$ represents the fraction of the frequency in the fourth class which is below the first quartile. By adding this fraction of the class interval to the lower limit of the fourth class, the first quartile may be obtained.

The second quartile is the median, and as calculated previously, is equal to 53.60. The third quartile is the $3(160)/4 = 120$ item. Its value must be interpolated within the sixth class and may be calculated as follows:

$$\text{Third quartile} = 55 + \left(\tfrac{26}{39}\right)(5) = 58.33$$

Hence the three quartiles for the data in Table 9 are 49.23, 53.60, and 58.33. Note that calculation of the deciles and percentiles would utilize the same procedure. The interested reader may consult the references in the Bibliography at the end of this chapter for further detail concerning these calculations.

PROPERTIES OF THE MEDIAN: The following are among the most important characteristics of the median:

1. It is simple to calculate and will always exist for any set of data.

2. For any set of data, it is a unique value.

3. It is relatively unaffected by extremes in the data and is influenced by the position rather than by the actual value of each data value.

4. It can be calculated from a frequency distribution with open classes or unequal intervals (as long as the median doesn't fall in an open interval).

5. The sum of the absolute value of the differences between a set of values and the median is a minimum. The interested reader may verify this for a series of values.

Mode. The *mode*, which as a measure of location, is the value most frequently found in a set of data. Consequently it is often referred to as the most "probable" value in the set of data, since it occurs the most often. Many times, in everyday usage, the mode is the most "typical" value. For example, the typical grade received by a student is a C.

To demonstrate how to locate the mode in a data array, consider the following list of numbers:

$$9 \quad 11 \quad 10 \quad 8 \quad 12 \quad 10 \quad 9 \quad 13 \quad 9 \quad 7$$

The most frequently repeated number in this set is 9 and it is repeated three times. Thus 9 is the mode for this set of data.

MODE OF THE FREQUENCY DISTRIBUTION: The mode may also be determined from a frequency distribution by first noting which class has the highest frequency of occurrence. This class is commonly called the "modal class." If two adjacent classes have the highest (equal) frequency, then the mode is merely the boundary between the two classes.

To locate the mode within the modal class, the following formula may be used:

$$\text{Mode} = L_1 + \left(\frac{d_1}{d_1 + d_2}\right)(i)$$

where L_1 = lower class limit of the modal class

d_1 = difference between the frequencies in the modal class and the preceding class

d_2 = difference between the frequencies in the modal class and the succeeding class

i = size of the class interval

For example, the mode of the data given in Table 9 would be calculated as follows:

$$\text{Mode} = 50 + \left(\frac{24}{24 + 11}\right)(5) = 53.43$$

Hence calculation of the mode tends to move the mode away from the midpoint of the modal class toward that end which has a higher frequency.

PROPERTIES OF THE MODE: The following are among the most important characteristics of the mode:

1. It is extremely easy to calculate and enjoys a meaningful interpretation as a "typical" value.

2. It is unaffected by extremes in the data and may be computed from distributions involving open classes or classes having unequal class intervals.

3. It may not be unique in that the maximum frequency may be attained by more than one value. Also if all values have equal frequency, it does not exist at all.

Comparison of the Mean, Median, and Mode. For distribution whose general shape is perfectly symmetrical, the mean, median, and mode are identical (see Fig. 11). If the shape of the distribution is not symmetrical and the mass of the data tends to be concentrated toward the high numbers tailing off slowly with lower numbers, then the mean will have the lowest number followed by the median and then the mode. If the concentration of the data appears skewed toward lower values, then the mode will be the smallest number followed by the median and then the mean.

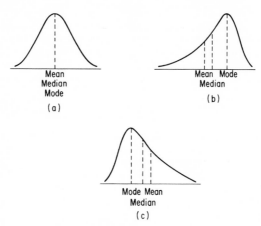

Fig. 11 Examples of symmetrical and skewed frequency distributions: (*a*) symmetrical; (*b*) skewed to left; (*c*) skewed to right.

For distributions which are moderately skewed, there exists an approximate relationship among the mean, median, and mode. These are roughly related as follows:

$$\text{Mode} = \text{mean} - 3 \ (\text{mean} - \text{median})$$

In general, the mean, median, and mode each measure the location of the frequency distribution. The mean represents the "average" or "center of gravity," while the median indicates a "central" or "middle" value and the mode indicates the most "typical" value. The question as to which should be used depends on the application and interpretation required of the results.

MEASURES OF VARIATION

It is a characteristic of frequency distributions and variables to contain *variation* or *variability*. Sometimes this variation is referred to as "dispersion." Measures such as the mean, median, and mode measure the position or central tendency; however, these measures do not adequately describe the degree of scatter often encountered.

Variation or dispersion in a frequency distribution is very important in decision making, especially in production and inventory control. Consider the demand of bar stock given in Table 8. Because of the variation in this demand, one cannot merely stock the average demand required (where average may be mean, median, mode, etc.) because the demand may be very high in certain periods and an "average" value of stock on hand will not suffice. This was illustrated by the frequency distribution of Table 8. Thus the degree of variation will determine the amount of safety stock carried for the bar stock. Consequently the variation in the frequency distribution can be very important, and in order to describe this characteristic one must determine measures which reflect this variation or dispersion.

Range. The simplest and most easily obtained measure of variation is the *range*. It is calculated as being the difference between the highest and lowest values in a group of data. For example, consider the following set of data:

$$15 \quad 5 \quad 17 \quad 18 \quad 9 \quad 13 \quad 15$$

The range for this example is merely 18 minus 5 or 13. Although easiest to calculate, the range is normally not a satisfactory method to measure variation. It reflects only the extremes in the data and does not account for the dispersion throughout the remaining data. Its main advantage is that it is simple to calculate and may be most useful when a rough, quick measure of the variation is required.

Interquartile and Interdecile Range. Sometimes it is common to eliminate extreme values when computing ranges. If the upper and lower quarters of the data are removed, the resulting range is called the "interquartile range." This measure reflects the range in which 50 percent of the data is contained. If one lets Q_1 be the first quartile and Q_3 the third, the interquartile range is simply the difference between Q_3 and Q_1 or $Q_3 - Q_1$. Calculation of the quartiles was discussed previously in the material describing measures of location.

If one calculates the first decile, D_1, and the ninth decile, D_9, then the *interdecile range* is merely $D_9 - D_1$. This range includes 80 percent of the values and consequently describes more of the data than the interquartile range.

Interquartile and interdecile ranges are better than simple ranges because they are location-based. This refers to the fact that their bases stem from the median and are thus related to some extent to a representation of the position or location of the data. Hence, in general, they reflect more of the dispersion of the data and are less subject to extremes. Also these interquartile and interdecile ranges are quickly obtained from frequency distributions even if there are open classes.

Average Deviation. In an effort to overcome the disadvantage of the range measure of variation, one might consider the deviation of individual values from some positional value such as the mean or median. This would allow all items in the data to influence the measure of variation. A method for accomplishing this scheme is to calculate the average of the absolute values of the deviations about the mean. This measure of variation is commonly referred to as the "average deviation." For lists of data, it may be expressed as follows:

$$\text{Average deviation} = \frac{\sum\limits_{i=1}^{n} |x_i - \bar{x}|}{n}$$

where $\bar{x}$ is the mean of the data under consideration.

Therefore for data which tend to be concentrated about the mean, the average deviation is low. As the dispersion or variation in the data becomes more pronounced, the average deviation *increases* to reflect this increased variability.

For data which are grouped into a frequency distribution, the deviations are calculated from the class midpoints. Thus for calculating the average deviation from a frequency distribution:

$$\text{Average deviation} = \frac{\sum\limits_{i=1}^{k} [|x_i - \bar{x}|f_i]}{N}$$

where x_i = midpoint of the ith class
$\quad f_i$ = class frequency
$\quad k$ = number of classes
$\quad N$ = total frequency

For the bar-stock example of Table 8, the computation of the average deviation is given in Table 12. The average deviation is shown to be:

$$\text{Average deviation of bar-stock demand} = \frac{879.7500}{160} = 5.498$$

TABLE 12   Calculation of Average Deviation of Bar Stock

Class	Midpoint, x_i	f_i	$|x_i - \bar{x}|^*$	$f_i |x_i - \bar{x}|$
1	32	1	21.0625	21.0625
2	37	4	16.0625	64.2500
3	42	13	11.0625	143.8125
4	47	26	6.0625	157.6250
5	52	50	1.0625	53.1250
6	57	39	3.9375	153.5625
7	62	20	8.9375	178.7500
8	67	5	13.9375	69.6875
9	72	2	18.9375	37.8750
		160		879.7500

* $\bar{x}$ = 53.0625.
SOURCE: Table 9.

It must possibly be preferable to sum the absolute deviations about the median rather than the mean since it is a minimum (see property 5 of the median); however, it has been common practice to use the mean. While the average deviation does represent an improvement as a measure of variation over the range, it is used very infrequently. The main reason for this is that more mathematically complex analysis cannot be performed because of the use of absolute values.

Variance and Standard Deviation. In an effort to eliminate the use of absolute values, one might simply square the deviations about the mean and find the average of the squared deviations. From property 7 of the mean, it should be recalled that the sum of the squared deviations from the mean is less than that about any other point in the distribution. But since squared measurements render the dimensions of that data meaningless, taking the square root of this average, squared deviations returns the measure of variation back to the dimensions of the original data. This measure of variation is referred to as the "standard deviation" and is defined as follows for a series of sample data:

$$\text{Standard deviation} = \sqrt{\frac{\sum\limits_{i=1}^{n} (x_i - \bar{x})^2}{n - 1}}$$

where $\bar{x}$ is the mean of the n data values. Note that the average value of the square deviations is found by dividing *by n − 1 instead of n*. This has been established from theoretical considerations and is principally because the standard deviation is calculated from a sample and not from the total population. If the total population were used one might divide by n; however, for most applications in production and inventory control the above formula will prove most suitable. The *variance* is simply the square of the standard deviation and may be found in a manner similar to that used for the standard deviation.

TABLE 13   Calculation of the Standard Deviation

Array

x_i	$(x_i - \bar{x})$*	$(x - \bar{x})^2$	x_i^2
6	−5	25	36
10	−1	1	100
11	0	0	121
11	0	0	121
13	2	4	169
15	4	16	225
66		46	772

$*\bar{x} = \dfrac{66}{6} = 11.$

Table 13 illustrates the calculation of the standard deviation of the following array:

$$6 \quad 10 \quad 11 \quad 11 \quad 13 \quad 15$$

From the table:

$$\text{Standard deviation} = \sqrt{\frac{46}{5}} = \sqrt{9.2} = 3.033$$

Frequently the above formula is awkward to use and is especially subject to rounding errors. An alternative formula, which gives identical results, is as follows:

$$\text{Standard deviation} = \sqrt{\frac{\Sigma x^2 - [(\Sigma x)^2/n]}{n - 1}}$$

To illustrate that the result is the same, refer again to the table for the basic calculations. The standard deviation is

$$\text{Standard deviation} = \sqrt{\frac{772 - [(66)^2/6]}{5}} = \sqrt{\frac{46}{5}} = 3.033$$

which is identical to the result obtained previously.

CALCULATION OF STANDARD DEVIATION FROM FREQUENCY DISTRIBUTION: To calculate the standard deviation from a frequency distribution, one simply regards the x_i observations as the class midpoints. Thus the formula becomes

$$\text{Standard deviation} = \sqrt{\frac{\sum\limits_{i=1}^{k} (x_i - \bar{x})^2 f_i}{N - 1}}$$

where k = number of classes
$\quad N$ = total frequency in the table
$\quad f_i$ = frequency within the ith class

While the previous formula serves to define the standard deviation as calculated from grouped data, it is extremely awkward to use in actual practice. Rather than calculate the standard deviation from the previous formula, one may use a short method of computation similar to that applied to the mean. Choosing a set of coded values u_i for the midpoints of the classes, the standard deviation may be calculated as follows:

$$\text{Standard deviation} = c \sqrt{\frac{N \sum\limits_{i=1}^{k} f_i u_i^2 - \left(\sum\limits_{i=1}^{k} f_i u_i\right)^2}{N(N - 1)}}$$

where c = class interval
$\quad f_i$ = frequency in class i
$\quad k$ = number of classes
$\quad N$ = total frequency in the distribution

Table 14 illustrates the computational scheme for computing the standard deviation using the short-cut method for the bar-stock example of Table 8. From

TABLE 14   Computation of Standard Deviation for Bar-stock Demand

Class interval	Midpoint, x_i	Frequency, f_i	Class deviation, u_i	$f_i u_i$	$f_i u_i^2$
30–34	32	1	−4	−4	16
35–39	37	4	−3	−12	36
40–44	42	13	−2	−26	53
45–49	47	26	−1	−26	26
50–54	52	50	0	0	0
55–59	57	39	1	39	39
60–64	62	20	2	40	80
65–69	67	5	3	15	45
70–74	72	2	4	20	32
		160		34	326

SOURCE: Table 8.

the data in Table 14, the standard deviation is calculated as

$$\text{Standard deviation} = 5 \sqrt{\frac{160(326) - (34)^2}{160(159)}} = 5 \sqrt{2.005}$$
$$= 7.08$$

SOME GENERAL ASPECTS OF STANDARD DEVIATION: The following are among the most important aspects of the standard deviation as a measure of variation:

1. For many of the distributions found in production and inventory control, one can say that about 68 percent of all values in a particular distribution do not deviate from the mean by more than 1 standard deviation; about 95 percent of the values do not deviate from the mean by more than 2 standard deviations; and about 99 percent of the values do not deviate from the mean by more than 3 standard deviations. In general, at the very worst, $1 - (1/k)$ of the values will not deviate from the mean by more than k standard deviations.

2. The standard deviation provides a measure of variability such that statistical tests regarding properties of the data can be analyzed. For example, one may wish to know if the production rates on two screw machines are statistically different.

3. The standard deviation provides a basis for inference regarding a population parameter. For example, one may calculate an interval in which he is almost sure the average bar-stock demand will lie.

4. Use of the standard deviation and variance establish the groundwork for more sophisticated statistical analysis of data such as regression analysis, correlation analysis, analysis of variance, etc.

Relative Measures of Variation. The previously discussed measures of variation deal with an absolute measure of variation in the sense that the magnitudes of the units are not considered. For example, suppose one is interested in the variation in departmental sizes. Suppose from historical records it is determined that department A has a standard deviation of 2.3 men, while that of department B has more variation than department A. However, the mean number of men in department A is 10, while that of B is 20. Since the magnitude of the means is not similar, this suggests the use of some relative measure of variation.

Perhaps the most popular of the relative measures is one which simply expresses the standard deviation as a percent of the mean. The measure called the "coefficient of variation" may be expressed as follows:

$$\text{Coefficient of variation} = \left(\frac{\text{standard deviation}}{\text{mean}}\right) 100$$

The advantage of a measure such as this is that variation is expressed as a percentage. Hence not only can variation involving different magnitudes be compared but the variation in data involving different units of measure such as time and distance may be compared also.

Another measure of relative variation is called the "coefficient of quartile deviation." This is especially useful for relative measures of variation involving open-end distributions. It is defined simply as the interquartile range as a percent of the sum of Q_1 and Q_3, as follows:

$$\text{Coefficient of quartile deviation} = \left(\frac{Q_3 - Q_1}{Q_3 + Q_1}\right) 100$$

This again reduces the variation to a percentage, making comparisons possible. The coefficient of quartile deviation is simply calculated through the use of quartiles as discussed earlier.

MEASURES OF THE SHAPE OF THE FREQUENCY DISTRIBUTION

While measures of variation and location indicate two of the most important characteristics of the frequency distribution, they do not indicate completely the shape of the frequency distribution. Although applications of measures of shape are found infrequently, they are important as a further description of the frequency distribution.

Skewness and Symmetry. The "skewness" in a distribution refers to the position of the concentration of the mass of the data with respect to the total distribution. In general, whenever the mean, median, and mode are not identical, skewness is present in the distribution. A distribution is said to be "symmetrical" if the shape of the distribution above the mean is a *reflection* of the distribution below the mean. Whenever symmetry is present, the mean, median, and mode of the distribution are identical. Figure 11*a* illustrates a symmetrical distribution.

A distribution such as that in Fig. 11*b* is said to be "skewed to the left" when there is a prominent "tail" to the left. In general for this type of skewness the mean will be exceeded by the median, which in turn will be exceeded by the mode. Figure 11*c* illustrates a "distribution skewed to the right" and the typical positions for the mean, median, and mode.

A measure of this skewness, called the "Pearsonian coefficient of skewness," is defined as follows:

$$\text{Coefficient of skewness} = \frac{3(\text{mean} - \text{median})}{\text{standard deviation}}$$

Whenever this measure is positive, the mean exceeds the median and the distribution is skewed to the right. If the coefficient is negative, the distribution is skewed to the left and the median exceeds the mean. Hence for perfectly symmetrical distribution, the mean, median, and mode are identical and the coefficient of skewness is zero.

Rather than use an empirical measure such as the coefficient of skewness, it has been more acceptable to use a measure referred to as α_3 (alpha three). It is defined as the average of the cubed deviations about the mean divided by the cube of the standard deviation. For list data, it is defined as follows:

$$\alpha_3 = \frac{\dfrac{1}{n} \displaystyle\sum_{i=1}^{n} (x_i - \bar{x})^3}{s^3}$$

where $\bar{x}$ is the mean of n observations whose standard deviation is s. For data in a frequency table, α_3 is defined to be

$$\alpha_3 = \frac{\dfrac{1}{N} \displaystyle\sum_{i=1}^{k} (x_i - \bar{x})^3 f_i}{s^3}$$

where f_i = frequency within the ith class
$\quad N$ = total frequency in the table
$\quad k$ = number of classes
$\quad s$ = standard deviation of the data

Using a short-cut method identical to that applied in calculating the mean and standard deviation, α_3 may be determined by coding the midpoints of the frequency table. Letting u_i be the coded value and c be the class interval, α_3 may be calculated from a frequency table as follows:

$$\alpha_3 = \frac{c^3}{s^3}\left[\frac{\displaystyle\sum_{i=1}^{k} u_i^3 f_i}{N} - 3\left(\frac{\displaystyle\sum_{i=1}^{k} u_i^2 f_i}{N} \right)\left(\frac{\displaystyle\sum_{i=1}^{k} u_i f_i}{N} \right) + 2\left(\frac{\displaystyle\sum_{i=1}^{k} u_i f_i}{N} \right)^3 \right]$$

It should be noted that this calculation requires little more data than that needed to calculate the standard deviation. The interested reader may verify that α_3 for the data in Table 8 (using Table 14) is

$$\alpha_3 = -0.098$$

This indicates that the bar-stock demand distribution is skewed to the left. The use of the previous formula for α_3 may be applied in the same manner in which the formula was used to calculate the standard deviation.

Kurtosis or Peakedness. "Kurtosis" refers to the peakedness of the distribution. A distribution possessing relatively flat tails but very peaked is called "leptokurtic." This type of shape is illustrated in Fig. 12a. Figure 12b indicates

(a)   (b)

Fig. 12 Illustrations of (a) leptokurtic and (b) platykurtic distributions.

a "platykurtic" distribution distinguished by very thin tails and a long broad hump.

A measure of this characteristic is referred to as α_4 (alpha four) and it may be computed as follows:

$$\alpha_4 = \frac{\dfrac{1}{N}\displaystyle\sum_{i=1}^{k}(x_i - \bar{x})^4 f_i}{s^2}$$

where the parameters are the same as those defined previously. Again one may utilize a short-cut form using a coding value u_i. Thus the formula becomes

$$\alpha_4 = \frac{c^4}{s^4}\left[\frac{\displaystyle\sum_{i=1}^{k}u_i^4 f_i}{N} - 4\left(\frac{\Sigma u_i^3 f_i}{N}\right)\left(\frac{\Sigma u_i f_i}{N}\right) + 6\left(\frac{\Sigma u_i^2 f_i}{N}\right)\left(\frac{\Sigma u_i f_i}{N}\right)^2 - 3\left(\frac{\Sigma u_i f_i}{N}\right)^4\right]$$

Again, development of the data is a simple extension to calculating the standard deviation and α_3. The interested reader may again verify $\alpha_4 = 3.24$.

In practice the bell-shaped curve or *normal curve* is often encountered. This curve possesses an α_4 equal to 3. In general, shape discussions are usually based on the normal curve. Thus for values of α_4 less than 3, the curves are platykurtic, and for values of α_4 greater than 3, the curves are leptokurtic. For the data of Table 8, the shape of the distribution would be considered slightly leptokurtic since $\alpha_4 = 3.24$ which is slightly greater than 3.

INTERPRETATION AND IMPLICATIONS

Statistical methods have been developed in this chapter to collect, display, and characterize data. The use of these tools depends directly on the specific application. Statistical techniques should be used merely to gain insight into the data and to present the data in such a way that important characteristics are emphasized. Never should one allow mathematical or statistical tools themselves to determine the results; they should be utilized to their fullest only in analyzing problems.

As an aid to decision making, the statistical techniques are invaluable. However, one should always be aware of the interpretation of such results. There is nothing sacred about the results obtained by statistical methods, and they should be scrutinized carefully for invalid assumptions and implications. Only by being familiar with the techniques can one validly judge the applicability. The explanation of descriptive statistics has been the subject of this chapter, and it is believed that they may usefully benefit anyone concerned with production and inventory control.

BIBLIOGRAPHY

Bowen, Earl L.: *Statistics with Applications in Management and Economics,* Richard D. Irwin, Inc., Homewood, Ill., 1960.

Freund, John E.: *Modern Elementary Statistics,* 2d ed., Prentice-Hall, Inc., Englewood Cliffs, N.J., 1965.

Griffin, John I.: *Statistics Methods and Applications,* Holt, Rinehart and Winston, Inc., New York, 1962.

Hanson, Kermit O.: *Managerial Statistics,* Prentice-Hall, Inc., Englewood Cliffs, N.J., 1955.

Neiswanger, William A.: *Elementary Statistical Methods,* The Macmillan Company, New York, 1956.

Neter, John, and William Wasserman: *Fundamental Statistics for Business and Economics,* 3d ed., Allyn and Bacon, Inc., Boston, 1966.

Tuttle, Alva M.: *Elementary Business and Economic Statistics,* McGraw-Hill Book Company, New York, 1957.

Chapter **28**

Statistical Theory

EDITOR:

Dr. Warren H. Thomas *Associate Professor, Department of Industrial Engineering, State University of New York at Buffalo, Buffalo, New York*

CONTENTS

The field of statistics is concerned with the analysis of data which exhibit a degree of variability and the drawing of appropriate conclusions as a result of this analysis. Measurements of nearly every type exhibit variability. Hence statistics has found a rightful role in many fields of endeavor—engineering, agriculture, economics, and physical, biological, and social sciences, to mention a few.

With respect to production and inventory control, variability enters at nearly every turn. The demand for a product is nearly always variable. The time required to process a product through a particular operation differs from piece to piece, the difference being greater for human-paced operations than for machine-paced ones. The number of pieces in a lot passing final inspection will differ from lot to lot. The lead time required to replenish inventory may not be the same every time an order is placed.

There are two basic problem types of concern in statistics: descriptive problems and inference problems. The former include the presentation of sets of observations in a manner in which they can be easily understood and interpreted. Interest usually includes determination of numerical values which describe the characteristics of the data. These descriptive measures are called "statistics." Often, in addition, visual interpretation is provided by representing the data graphically in frequency histograms.

Inference problems, on the other hand involve inductive generalization. The observations at hand frequently represent a *sample* from a larger whole usually referred to as a "population." The concern is not merely with providing a succinct description of the sample observations, but also with drawing conclusions about the population of which the observations are a sample; in other words, drawing inferences about the population.

Because confusion sometimes exists, a distinction between two terms is introduced at this point. First, from a set of sample observations, "statistics" can be calculated which characterize the sample. In like manner a population can be characterized by a set of descriptive measures. For the sake of distinction, these measures are known as "parameters." In practice these parameter values are not known. (Otherwise there is no problem.) A representative sample is taken from the population. The appropriate sample statistics can provide an estimate of population parameters of interest. The term "statistic" always refers to a sample characteristic; "parameter," to a population characteristic.

For example, management may wish to conduct a marketing survey to determine the average demand per family it might anticipate for a particular product within a specified geographic area. The average demand would be an unknown parameter. A representative sample of families would be taken from which an appropriate statistic would be calculated to provide an estimate of the unknown demand per family in the area.

The basic science underlying the field of statistics is *probability theory*. One must possess at least a rudimentary knowledge of the elements of this theory to comprehend sufficiently well the concepts of statistics.

These concepts are discussed in more depth below. First, a brief introduction to probability theory is provided. This is followed by a discussion of descriptive statistics, and then a somewhat more intensive consideration of inferential statistics is presented. At the end of the chapter is a glossary of symbols used, listed in the order of their first appearance.

ELEMENTS OF PROBABILITY THEORY

The purpose of this section is to provide an elementary foundation in probability theory sufficient to make meaningful the subsequent consideration of statistical methods. The treatment of probability is brief and is clearly oriented toward the particular use that will be made of it in this chapter. For a more in-depth coverage of probability, the reader is referred to one of the many good books available on the subject.[1]

Population. Inferential statistics is concerned with the drawing of conclusions about a population based on information contained in a sample from that population.

The *population* is the totality of all possible values of a particular characteristic for a specified group of objects.

The fact that a sample taken from the population contains observations which are not all identical is indicative of the fact that the population members differ one from another. Hence we concern ourselves with characterizing this variability in the population.

Random Variable. Assume that an experiment is to be run; e.g., a coin is to be flipped or a product is to be weighed. Let T denote the set of all possible outcomes of an experiment. In coin flipping only two outcomes are possible—heads or tails. In measuring the weight of a product a continuous range of weights would represent the set of possible outcomes. Note that this outcome need not be a numerical value as is illustrated by the flipping of a coin.

Let R represent the set of all possible real values from $-\infty$ to $+\infty$. A "random variable" is a numerically valued function which assigns to each point in T (1) a value in the set R and (2) a probability of occurrence. In the coin-flipping experiment a random variable might assign to a head the value 1 and to a tail 0. In the weighing of a product the set T and the set R are identical since the outcome is itself a real number. Consider, however, the weighing of 4 units. The set T in this case consists of all possible combinations of product weights. Several random variables can be defined. In one case the random variable might equal the average; in another, the maximum; or in a third case, the minimum. Hence three random variables have been defined on the same set T.

A practical interpretation of the concept of a random variable is that it represents the totality of possible numerical values that are characteristic of a population or that could be obtained in sampling from the population.

With the set R defined by the random variable there must be associated a probability distribution which represents the probabilities that the random variable takes on specific values (or values within specified intervals). A complete description of a random variable therefore includes both the specification of all possible numerical values that might be taken on by the variable and the probabilities that each of these values will occur.

Random variables can be conveniently divided into two classes—*discrete* and *continuous*. A discrete random variable is one which takes on one of a finite number of possible values, as in the coin-flipping example in which the random variable takes on only values of 0 or 1. A continuous random variable, on the other hand, can take on any of an infinite number of possible values within some interval. In the product-weighing example the random variable can conceptually take on any value between 0 and an upper limit on product weight. Hence it illustrates a continuous random variable.

It should be mentioned that in practice a discrete random variable may at times be handled as if it were continuous and vice versa. For example, the number of automobiles sold per week by a local automotive dealer is clearly a discrete variable, and should be considered as such. However, the number sold per week nationwide by a manufacturer, while still a discrete variable, could be reasonably considered a continuous one.

On the other hand, consider the weighing of a product in which a measuring device is capable of discriminating only to the nearest pound. The actual measurements, therefore, are discrete even though weight is intrinsically continuous.

Probability Distributions. Although there are several definitions for the term "probability," the "frequency" definition is the most common. It embodies the notion that as the number of times an experiment is rerun (trials) increases toward infinity, the probability of an occurrence of a certain value for the random variable equals the fraction of trials in which that value would occur.

It is convenient to discuss separately the probability distributions of discrete and continuous random variables. It should be emphasized, however, that the basic concepts are similar.

DISCRETE RANDOM VARIABLES: Let x_i denote a particular value which can be assumed by a discrete random variable. For example, roll two dice and define a random variable equal to the sum of the two faces. This variable takes on values

$$x_i = 2, 3, 4, \ldots, 12$$

Next let $p(x_i)$ represent the probability that the random variable takes on value x_i. This is known as the "probability distribution function" of x_i.

Assuming unbiased dice in which all face values are equally probable, the probability distribution function for the random variable equal to the sum of two faces is as shown in Table 1.

TABLE 1   Probability Distribution Function: Sum of Two Dice

x_i	2	3	4	5	6	7	8	9	10	11	12
$p(x_i)$	$\frac{1}{36}$	$\frac{2}{36}$	$\frac{3}{36}$	$\frac{4}{36}$	$\frac{5}{36}$	$\frac{6}{36}$	$\frac{5}{36}$	$\frac{4}{36}$	$\frac{3}{36}$	$\frac{2}{36}$	$\frac{1}{36}$

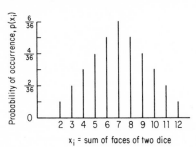

Fig. 1   Probability distribution function of discrete random variable.

This random variable is now completely defined. All values that it might take on are specified as are the probabilities that each of these might occur.

It is often convenient to describe the probability distribution functions graphically with a line on the x axis corresponding to the probability of occurrence of each value of x. Table 1 thus gives rise to Fig. 1.

Two properties which must be satisfied by every discrete random variable are:

The range of the probability function must be 0 to 1:

$$0 \le p(x_i) \le 1$$

and the sum of all probabilities is equal to 1:

$$\sum_{\text{all } x_i} p(x_i) = 1$$

The first property specifies that the probability of occurrence of any value x_i must be nonnegative and cannot exceed 1. The second property specifies that the sum of the probabilities over all values of x_i must equal 1. These are useful checks when attempting to enumerate all possible values of x_i and $p(x_i)$. Note that the random variable defined in Table 1 satisfies both of these requirements.

It is often of interest to have available the probability that a random variable takes on values less than or equal to a specified value. For this we define the "cumulative distribution function." Let $F(b)$ equal the probability that the random variable takes on values less than or equal to b. Hence

$$F(b) = \sum_{\text{all } x_i \leq b} p(x_i)$$

The cumulative distribution function for the random variable defined in Table

TABLE 2   Cumulative Distribution Function

x	2	3	4	5	6	7	8	9	10	11	12
$F(x)$	$\frac{1}{36}$	$\frac{3}{36}$	$\frac{6}{36}$	$\frac{10}{36}$	$\frac{15}{36}$	$\frac{21}{36}$	$\frac{26}{36}$	$\frac{30}{36}$	$\frac{33}{36}$	$\frac{35}{36}$	$\frac{36}{36}$

1 is listed in Table 2. Note that $F(b)$ is necessarily a nondecreasing function and that

$$F(+\infty) = \lim_{b \to +\infty} F(b) = 1$$

and

$$F(-\infty) = \lim_{b \to -\infty} F(b) = 0$$

A graphical interpretation is frequently useful and is shown for the example in Fig. 2. This is a "step function," since only discrete x_i values may occur.

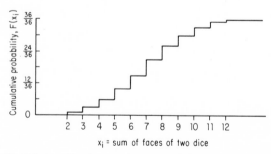

Fig. 2   Cumulative distribution function of discrete random variable.

The probability that the random variable takes on values less than or equal to 3.4, for example, is equal to $p(2) + p(3)$. Hence $F(b)$ is the same for all values of b from 3 to, but not including, 4.

CONTINUOUS RANDOM VARIABLES: A continuous random variable is one which may take on any value within a range of possible values. Therefore it conceptually may take any one of an infinite number of possible values in the range. It is meaningless to consider the probability of a particular value occurring. We therefore deal with the probability that the random variable takes on a value within some specified interval.

The probability that the random variable (RV) takes on values in the interval $[x_1, x_1 + dx]$ (see Fig. 3) is

$$Pr\{x_1 < \text{RV} < x_1 + dx\} = f(x_1)\, dx$$

where $f(x)$ is the "probability density function." $f(x)$ is most conveniently interpreted when plotted as in the figure. The area of the slice of height $f(x_1)$ and width dx corresponds to the probability of the random variable taking on values in that particular interval.

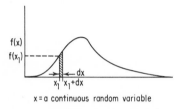

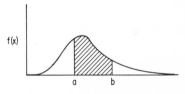

x = a continuous random variable   x = a continuous random variable

Fig. 3 Probability density function of a continuous random variable.

Fig. 4 Probability that $a < x < b$.

The probability that the random variable takes on a value between any two values a and b can be obtained by measuring the area under $f(x)$ from a to b as represented by the shaded portion in Fig. 4. This area can be found mathematically by integrating $f(x)$ from a to b.

$$Pr\{a < x < b\} = \int_a^b f(x)\, dx$$

For $f(x)$ to be a probability density function it must satisfy the conditions

$$f(x) \geq 0 \qquad \text{for all } x$$

and

$$\int_{-\infty}^{\infty} f(x)\, dx = 1$$

As with discrete random variables, it is frequently of interest to find the probability that the variable takes on a value less than or equal to a specific value, say, b. This can be found by

$$Pr\{x < b\} = \int_{-\infty}^b f(x)\, dx$$

This is defined as the "cumulative distribution function," $F(b)$.

Note that this is analogous to the discrete case discussed previously with the summation replaced by the integration operation. The probability that x falls between a and b can now be rewritten in terms of the difference in two values of the cumulative distribution function as

$$Pr\{a < x < b\} = Pr\{x < b\} - Pr\{x < a\}$$

$$= \int_{-\infty}^b f(x)\, dx - \int_{-\infty}^a f(x)\, dx = F(b) - F(a)$$

The cumulative distribution function can be evaluated for all possible values of x and plotted as shown in Fig. 5. This figure illustrates two basic properties. First, $f(x)$ must start at zero on the left-hand end since

$$F(-\infty) = \int_{-\infty}^{-\infty} f(x)\, dx = 0$$

and reach 1 on the right-hand side since

$$F(+\infty) = \int_{-\infty}^{+\infty} f(x)\, dx = 1$$

The density and cumulative functions can be directly related mathematically. We have already seen that

$$F(x) = \int_{-\infty}^{x} f(x)\, dx$$

It follows therefore that

$$\frac{d\,F(x)}{dx} = f(x)$$

Consider as a specific example the uniform distribution in which the probability density function is uniformly distributed in the interval 0 to a. The density function is shown in Fig. 6. Note that

$$f(x) = \begin{cases} 1/a & \text{for } 0 \le x \le a \\ 0 & \text{elsewhere} \end{cases}$$

which follows from the requirement that the area under the curve equal 1. It can be found by solving

$$\int_{0}^{a} K\, dx = 1$$

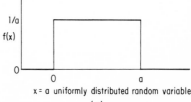

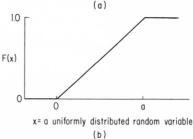

x = a uniformly distributed random variable

(a)

x = a uniformly distributed random variable

(b)

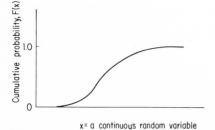

x = a continuous random variable

Fig. 5 Cumulative distribution function of continuous random variable.

Fig. 6 A uniformly distributed random variable: (a) probability density function; (b) cumulative distribution function.

for the constant K.

The cumulative distribution function is found by

$$F(x) = \int_0^x \frac{1}{a} \, dx = \frac{x}{a}$$

which is plotted also in Fig. 6.

Note that the slope of $F(x)$ at any point x corresponds to the height of $f(x)$ at that point. In this case the slope $F(x)$ is constant everywhere on the interval $(0,a)$ corresponding to the uniform density function in the interval.

Population Parameters. When considering the distribution of a random variable which describes the values taken on by members of a population, it is very convenient to have available several measures which characterize the population succinctly. These are the population parameters introduced earlier. There are two that are of particular interest in most applied work. These are the *mean* and *variance*.

MEAN: The mean provides an excellent measure of the central tendency of a random variable, i.e., a central-most value or the value about which the other values cluster, unless the distribution is highly skewed. If one were to plot the distribution on stiff cardboard and cut it out, the point at which its base would balance on a knife-edge would be the center of gravity. This center of gravity is the geometrical equivalent of the mean.

The "mean" of a random variable is defined as the *expected* value or average value of the variable. Because all values for the random variable do not occur with equal probability, each value entering this average must be weighted by the probability that it occurs.

Let x equal a value of the random variable and μ (mu) equal the mean of the random variable. (Note that we shall consistently use Greek letters to represent population parameters.) Further let $E(x)$ represent the expected value of x. Hence

$$\mu = E(x)$$

If x is a *discrete* variable,

$$\mu = E(x) = \sum_{\text{all } x_i} x_i p(x_i)$$

If it is a continuous variable, the summation is replaced by integration and $p(x_i)$ by $f(x) \, dx$.

$$\mu = E(x) = \int_{\text{all } x} x f(x) \, dx$$

Consider, for purpose of illustration, the discrete random variable previously defined as equal to the sum of the face of two rolled dice. Utilizing the values in Table 1, we obtain

$$\mu = \sum_{\text{all } x_i} x_i p(x_i) = 2(\tfrac{1}{36}) + 3(\tfrac{2}{36}) + \cdots + 12(\tfrac{1}{36}) = 7$$

Similarly we can illustrate the computations for a continuous random variable by finding the mean of the uniform distribution defined above in the section "Continuous Random Variables."

$$\mu = \int_{\text{all } x} x f(x) \, dx = \int_0^a x \frac{1}{a} \, dx = \frac{a}{2}$$

VARIANCE: Whereas the mean provides a measure of the central tendency of a random variable, the variance provides a measure of the degree of spread or dispersion of the variable about its mean. It corresponds in a geometrical sense to the moment of inertia useful when dealing with physical bodies.

The variance is defined as the expected or average squared deviation of the random variable from its mean. Conventionally the variance is denoted by σ^2 (sigma squared). Therefore we may write

$$\sigma^2 = E\{(x - \mu)^2\}$$

i.e., the expected squared deviation of the x's from their mean μ.

If x is a *discrete* variable,

$$\sigma^2 = E\{(x - \mu)^2\} = \sum_{\text{all } x_i} (x_i - \mu)^2 p(x_i)$$

If it is *continuous*,

$$\sigma^2 = E\{(x - \mu)^2\} = \int_{\text{all } x} (x - \mu)^2 f(x)\, dx$$

Note that because the variance is a squared measure, its units are squared units of the original variables. For example, if the units of the random variable are "days," the units of the variance would be days squared.

The positive square root of the variance is often of interest. It is known as the "standard deviation" and is represented by the symbol σ.

$$\sigma = \sqrt{\sigma^2}$$

The units of the standard deviation will, of course, be identical with those of the variable itself.

To illustrate computations, let us again consider the discrete random variable defined in Table 1.

$$\sigma^2 = \sum_{\text{all } x_i} (x_i - \mu)^2 p(x_i) = (2 - 7)^2(\tfrac{1}{36}) + (3 - 7)^2(\tfrac{2}{36}) + \cdots + (12 - 7)^2(\tfrac{1}{36})$$

$$= 5\tfrac{5}{6}$$

The variance of the continuous uniform distribution can be evaluated by

$$\sigma^2 = \int_{\text{all } x_i} (x - \mu)^2 f(x)\, dx = \int_0^a \left(x - \frac{a}{2}\right)^2 \frac{1}{a}\, dx = \frac{a^2}{12}$$

SOME FREQUENTLY ENCOUNTERED PROBABILITY DISTRIBUTIONS

Normal Distribution. The most common distribution encountered in statistical work is the *normal distribution*. A normally distributed random variable x is a continuous random variable whose probability density function $f(x)$ is given by

$$f(x) = \frac{1}{\sqrt{2\pi}\sigma} e^{-(x-\mu)^2/2\sigma^2}$$

where μ is the mean and σ the standard deviation. For convenience we shall occasionally use here the shorthand notation $N(\mu, \sigma^2)$ to represent a normally distributed random variable with mean μ and variance σ^2.

When graphed, the *density function* appears as shown in the upper portion of Fig. 7. It can be noted that the distribution is symmetrically centered about the mean μ. A useful interpretation of the standard deviation is possible inasmuch as σ equals the distance from the mean to the point of inflection. Further, about 68 percent of values lie between $\mu \pm \sigma$. Knowledge of μ and σ is sufficient to completely define the distribution. It is therefore referred to as a "two-parameter distribution."

The cumulative distribution function

$$F(x) = \int_{-\infty}^{x} f(x)\, dx$$

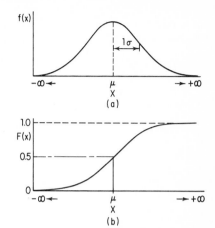

Fig. 7 Normally distributed random variable: (*a*) probability density function; (*b*) cumulative distribution function.

appears, when plotted, as depicted in the lower part of Fig. 7.

One needs to frequently evaluate the area under the density function to determine relevant probabilities. For example, given μ and σ, what is the probability that the random variable x exceeds b? Mathematically it is given by

$$Pr(x > b) = \int_{b}^{\infty} f(x)\, dx$$

which is equivalent to finding the shaded area of Fig. 8.

The normal density function is· unfortunately a function which cannot be easily evaluated. In practice the scheme is to use a table of the cumulative area. However, we would need a separate table for all combinations of μ and σ—clearly, an impossibility. Instead we use a table of the *standardized normal distribution* and use a simple transformation to relate it to the particular problem at hand. Let z represent the standardized normal variate.

$$z = \frac{x - \mu}{\sigma}$$

is the appropriate transformation relating the distribution of x to the z distribution.

The standardized normal variate has a mean of zero and a variance of one $[N(0, 1)]$. The density function

$$f(z) = \frac{1}{\sqrt{2\pi}}\, e^{-z^2/2}$$

Tables can be developed in many different ways. The one listed as Table A in the Appendix at the end of the chapter provides the probability that z takes on values greater than a particular value. Let z_a represent the value of z for which

$$Pr\{z > z_a\} = \int_{z_a}^{\infty} \frac{1}{\sqrt{2\pi}}\, e^{-z^2/2}\, dz = \alpha$$

Graphically this is equivalent to the shaded area in Fig. 9.

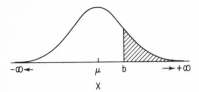

Fig. 8 Probability that $x > b$.

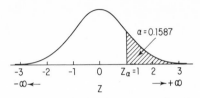

Fig. 9 Standardized normal distribution: probability that $z > z_\alpha$.

For example, the table shows that

$$Pr\{z > 1\} = 0.1587$$

and

$$Pr\{z > 1.645\} = 0.05$$

The probability is 0.1587 that z will take on a value greater than 1 and 0.05 that it will take on a value greater than 1.645.

Our interest is, however, not in z but in x which is $N(\mu, \sigma^2)$. Given b, a particular value in the distribution of μ, and recalling that $z = (x - \mu)/\sigma$,

$$Pr\{x > b\} = Pr\left\{z > \frac{b - \mu}{\sigma}\right\} = Pr\{z > z_\alpha\} = \alpha$$

This is represented graphically in Fig. 10. For example, given x which is $N(10,4)$, the probability that x will take on a value greater than 12 can be found as follows. Let

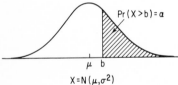

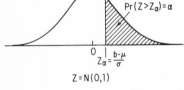

Fig. 10 Finding area under normal curve of interest.

$$z_\alpha = \frac{b - \mu}{\sigma} = \frac{12 - 10}{\sqrt{4}} = 1$$

Therefore

$$Pr\{x > 12\} = Pr\{z > 1\} = 0.1587$$

Instead of seeking the probability that x takes on a value greater than b, the problem might be to find b such that the probability that $x > b$ is equal to a given α.

For example, given x as $N(10,4)$, what is b for which

$$Pr\{x > b\} = 0.05$$

We solve this finding z_α corresponding to $\alpha = 0.05$. From the tables we found above $z_\alpha = 1.645$ satisfies this requirement; i.e.,

$$Pr\{z > 1.645\} = 0.05$$

Set

$$z_\alpha = \frac{b - \mu}{\sigma}$$

and solve for b.

$$1.645 = \frac{b - 10}{2}$$

from which we obtain

$$b = 13.29$$

Hence

$$Pr\{x > 13.29\} = 0.05$$

By utilizing the fact that the area under the entire curve from $-\infty$ to $+\infty$ equals 1, one can find

$$Pr\{x < b\} = 1 - Pr\{x > b\}$$

or

$$Pr\{z < z_\alpha\} = 1 - Pr\{z > z_\alpha\}$$

Again using the above example,

$$Pr\{x < 12\} = 1 - Pr\{x > 12\} = 1 - 0.1587 = 0.8413$$

Since the function is symmetric, tables contain entries only for the right-hand half (i.e., $z > 0$). Because of this symmetry and since the standardized normal has a zero mean,

$$Pr\{z < -z_\alpha\} = Pr\{z > +z_\alpha\}$$

as is shown in Fig. 11.

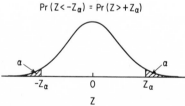

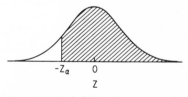

Fig. 11   Calculation of probabilities using symmetry of normal distribution.

Fig. 12   Probability that $z > -z_\alpha$.

Similarly the shaded area of Fig. 12 can be found by

$$Pr\{z > -z_\alpha\} = Pr\{z < +z_\alpha\} = 1 - Pr\{z > +z_\alpha\}$$

Consider the task of finding

$$Pr\{x > 8\}$$

given that x is $N(10,4)$. First find

$$z_\alpha = \frac{8 - 10}{2} = -1$$

$$Pr\{z_\alpha > -1\} = Pr\{z_\alpha < +1\} = 1 - Pr\{z_\alpha > +1\} = 1 - 0.1587 = 0.8413$$

The above can be combined to yield answers to questions of the form

$$Pr\{a < x < b\}$$

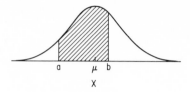

Fig. 13   Probability that $a < x < b$.

which is equivalent to the shaded area of Fig. 13. Reference to the figure shows that this can be evaluated by

$$Pr\{a < x < b\} = Pr\{x > a\} - Pr\{x > b\}$$

Given, as before, that x is $N(10,4)$, we find the probability that $8 < x < 12$ as follows:

$$Pr\{8 < x < 12\} = Pr\{x > 8\} - Pr\{x > 12\}$$
$$= Pr\{z > -1\} - Pr\{z > 1\}$$

A useful interpretation is possible using this result. Namely, the probability that a normally distributed variable takes on values within plus or minus 1 standard deviation ($\pm 1\sigma$) is 0.6826. Reference to Appendix Table A will show further that it takes on values within $\pm 2\sigma$ with probability 0.9544 and within $\pm 3\sigma$ with probability 0.9974. Although a normally distributed variable can theoretically take on any value, in practice we often assume that it takes on values only within $\pm 3\sigma$. The probability of an error is only 0.0013.

Binomial Distribution. If an experiment consists of n independent trials in which the outcome of each trial is either the occurrence or nonoccurrence of an event (such as defective or not defective in a quality control sample) and the probability of an occurrence is constant for each trial, the random variable equal to the number of occurrences is distributed according to the binomial distribution.

Let ρ = probability that event will occur on one trial

k = number of occurrences of the event in sample of size n

$\binom{n}{k}$ = number of ways k items can be selected from a sample of size n

$$= \frac{n!}{k!(n-k)!}$$

The probability distribution function is given by

$$p(k) = \binom{n}{k} \rho^k (1-\rho)^{n-k} \qquad \text{for } k = 0, 1, 2, \ldots, n$$

Because k takes on discrete values only, the binomial is a discrete distribution.

The binomial distribution has mean $n\rho$ and variance $n\rho(1-\rho)$.[2]

Poisson Distribution. When one is concerned with the occurrence of a relatively rare event and when the nonoccurrence of the event cannot be detected, the Poisson distribution often provides an accurate description of the probabilities of occurrence. Examples of its applicability might include the number of defects per unit, the number of customers arriving per hour to place a demand on an inventory system, or the daily number of breakdowns in a production line. In each case the nonoccurrence of the event (defect, customer, or breakdown) cannot be identified.

If we let

c = number of occurrences
λ = mean number of occurrences

the probability distribution function is defined by

$$p(c) = \frac{e^{-\lambda}\lambda^c}{c!} \qquad \text{for } c = 0, 1, 2, \ldots$$

The mean is λ, and interestingly, so is the variance. The Poisson is therefore a single parameter distribution whereas the binomial is a two-parameter (n, ρ) distribution as is the normal (μ, σ).

Like the binomial the Poisson is a discrete distribution inasmuch as c takes only discrete values.

DESCRIPTIVE STATISTICS

That portion of the field of statistics entitled "descriptive" is concerned with the presentation of sets of observations in such a manner that they can be easily understood and interpreted. This includes the graphical presentation of the data in the form of frequency histograms and polygons as well as the computation of certain descriptive measures.

It is important to emphasize that the concern in this discussion is solely with the characterization of a set of observations or data. The use of these data to draw conclusions or *inferences* about a larger population of which the data are but a sample is covered later in the chapter.

Frequency Histograms. Relevant aspects of probability theory have been discussed above. This theory provides a means of describing the variability (in terms of probability distributions and parameters) that is present in many measurements in which we might be interested. It assumes *complete* knowledge of the random variable representing the population of all possible values. Unfortunately we frequently do not have this complete knowledge although the variability of the data we obtain in practice clearly indicates that a population with variability is present. Hence our problems in practice are not with establishing whether or not variation is present, but rather with measuring it.

Frequency histograms provide a graphical device for observing the nature and degree of variation. It will be noted that they are analogous to the probability distributions plotted in Fig. 3.

Consider the following hypothetical situation. In order to design a production and inventory control system it is necessary to have quantitative information about the demand for a certain product. Weekly demand data collected for a period of 200 weeks are listed in Table 3.

There are many questions that might be asked. For example:

What is average weekly demand?

In what percentage of the weeks did the demand exceed 500 units?

What inventory level would satisfy the demand in 75 percent of the weeks?

It is difficult to formulate answers from the data as they are presented in the table. Therefore let us develop a "frequency table" in which the range of possible values (from 312 to 585 in this case) is divided into intervals or classes. The number of occurrences of observations in each class is then tabu-

TABLE 3   Weekly Demand—200 Weeks

438	438	427	433	391	471	411	468	469	474
491	413	500	337	384	453	489	375	454	484
502	523	489	450	454	510	349	472	514	546
384	467	524	343	447	463	438	472	428	415
485	404	393	437	475	445	513	430	406	484
420	456	390	422	451	431	450	435	412	404
508	481	412	407	477	432	383	457	510	484
470	474	499	472	479	443	448	485	432	478
454	535	465	535	434	569	425	375	424	396
385	474	469	475	424	443	469	494	418	521
443	420	479	532	457	381	421	460	369	395
413	396	585	525	390	483	529	508	425	476
419	395	427	391	457	537	321	472	479	489
420	535	453	479	438	395	468	466	461	495
508	491	322	466	454	376	440	436	409	371
439	440	493	520	453	370	467	444	454	367
453	398	476	490	475	463	389	463	473	503
455	312	415	568	440	526	421	448	439	529
457	519	473	453	441	479	474	390	363	482
480	519	342	463	460	475	444	400	496	437

lated.   The selection of the interval width and hence the number of intervals is arbitrary.   It is usually convenient to have from 10 to 25 intervals of equal width.   When choosing class intervals it is preferable to select them so that no result falls on the boundary.   If this is not convenient, make certain that it is explicitly understood in which of two adjacent classes a boundary value falls.

For the data, a class interval of 20 has been selected with class boundaries and the results of the tabulation of frequencies of occurrence in each of the classes as shown in Table 4.

These frequency data are often presented in a graphical form known as a "frequency histogram."   The class intervals form the horizontal axis, while the frequency of occurrence is plotted along the vertical axis.   For each class a

TABLE 4   Frequency Tabulation

Interval	Frequency of occurrence, f	Frequency in percent	Cumulative frequency, F	Cumulative percentage
301–320	1	0.5	1	0.5
321–340	3	1.5	4	2.5
341–360	4	2.0	8	4.5
361–380	8	4.0	16	8.0
381–400	19	9.5	35	17.5
401–420	16	8.0	51	25.5
421–440	30	15.0	81	40.5
441–460	30	15.0	111	55.5
461–480	42	21.0	153	76.5
481–500	19	9.5	172	86.0
501–520	12	6.0	184	92.0
521–540	12	6.0	196	98.0
541–560	1	0.5	197	98.5
561–580	2	1.0	199	99.5
581–600	1	0.5	200	100.0
	200	100.0		

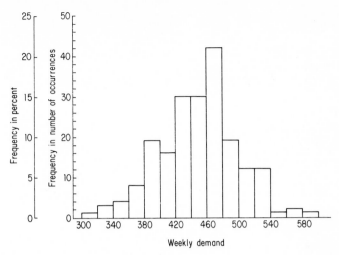

Fig. 14 Frequency histogram.

rectangle is drawn the height of which represents the frequency. Table 4 yields the histogram of Fig. 14.

Sometimes the frequency associated with a class interval is plotted as the point whose abscissa is the midpoint of the class. By connecting adjacent points, a "frequency polygon" is obtained as shown in Fig. 15. The frequency polygon is particularly useful when plotting discrete data where the class width equals the smallest increment of the variable. It is also useful when visually comparing several distributions.

Often one is interested in the percentage of occurrences for each class. If so, the ordinate scale is changed to show frequency in percent rather than in number of occurrences. Percent scales are shown on previous figures.

Since we often are interested in such questions as, "What percentage of weeks had a demand for 500 units or less?" we can develop a cumulative frequency

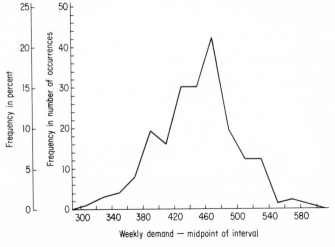

Fig. 15 Frequency polygon.

F by summing frequencies f of all classes equal to or less than the one of interest. These can be expressed as a number of occurrences, or as before, in percent. See the right-hand columns of Table 4 for the cumulative frequency of the example.

The cumulative frequency can be expressed graphically as is shown in the cumulative polygon in Fig. 16. The ordinate represents the percentage of time

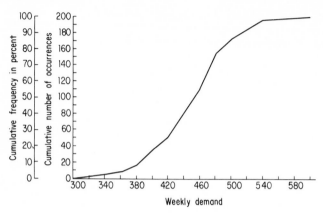

Fig. 16 Cumulative polygon.

that the demand is less than or equal to the corresponding abscissa value. The cumulative frequency is plotted on the ordinate at the right-hand end of the interval. Occasionally one will use the number of occurrences as the ordinate scale. The choice of scale is arbitrary.

From Fig. 16 (or Table 4) it can be seen that in approximately 86 percent of the weeks, the demand was for 500 or less units, from which it follows that in 14 percent of the weeks, the demand exceeded 500. Similarly an inventory level of slightly less than 480 units would have satisfied the demand in 75 percent of the weeks.

Measures of Central Tendency. Frequently we have need to supply a single number to describe the point about which a set of data observations cluster. In other words, what is the "middle" of a frequency distribution?

ARITHMETIC MEAN: There are several possible measures or statistics that might be used. By far the most common is the "arithmetic mean" or "average." The mean equals the sum of the observations divided by the number of observations. Let x_i represent the ith observation (as the demand in week i). If there are n observations, we wish to find the mean of $x_1, x_2, \ldots, x_n$. The mean $\bar{x}$ (x bar) is found by

$$\bar{x} = \frac{x_1 + x_2 + \cdots + x_n}{n}$$

which can be more succinctly written

$$\bar{x} = \frac{\sum_{i=1}^{n} x_i}{n}$$

Using the weekly demand data of Table 3, the mean weekly demand is found to be

$$\bar{x} = \frac{90,134}{200} = 450.7$$

MEDIAN AND MODE: Two other measures which are occasionally used to describe a distribution are the "median" and the "mode."

The median is the middle observation when they are arranged in order of magnitude. If the number of observations is an even number, the median is usually taken as the average of the two "middle" values. Because the median is a positional value, it is less affected by extreme values than the arithmetic mean.

The mode is the value of the observation which occurs most frequently if the variable is discrete or, if continuous, the class interval with the largest frequency of occurrence. The mode, like the median, is not severely affected by extreme values. For a normal distribution the mean, median, and mode are equal. For nonsymmetric distributions the median and mode may be better measures of central tendency than the mean. If the data of Table 3 are ordered it will be found that the median demand is 454 units while the mode occurs at a demand of 453 and 454 units (four occurrences each).

Measures of Variability. The use of a single measure of central tendency does not provide any information about the degree of variability of observations about the central value. For example, we might have two sets of observations, each with a mean of 100. However, in one set the individual values vary from 90 to 110, while in the other set all values lie between 99 and 101. It is important to have a measure which reflects the degree of dispersion or variability about the central value.

Accordingly, we often characterize a set of data by means of two statistics: one which provides a measure of central tendency and one which reflects the degree of variability.

RANGE: Several measures are possible candidates as variability indicators. The simplest is the *range*, which equals the largest value minus the smallest value.

$$\text{Range} = x_{max} - x_{min}$$

Since it depends on only two values, it is a fairly crude measure and is commonly used only with small samples.

VARIANCE AND STANDARD DEVIATION: The most common measure of dispersion is the variance or its square root, the standard deviation. As defined earlier, the "variance" is the average squared deviation from the mean.

Given a finite population which consists of n observations $x_1, x_2, \ldots, x_n$ whose mean is μ, the variance σ is given by[*]

$$\sigma^2 = \frac{\sum\limits_{i=1}^{n} (x_i - \mu)^2}{n}$$

The standard deviation σ is, of course, equal to the positive square root of the variance.

If one has a sample of n items and is interested in the variance *of the sample*, he is interested only in the values in that sample. For him the sample is a finite population whose mean μ can be found exactly by computing $\bar{x}$.

Therefore, if one wishes to know the variance of the sample itself, he should

[*] If one recognizes that each x_i occurs with frequency $1/n$, this expression can be made identical to that presented previously.

use

$$\sigma^2 = \frac{\sum_{i=1}^{n} (x_i - \bar{x})^2}{n}$$

However, we more frequently have a sample of n items from a larger population. In this case the sample mean $\bar{x}$ will nearly always be somewhat different than the true mean of the population μ. If one wishes to estimate the variance of the population from which the sample was drawn, he would use

$$\sigma^2 = \frac{\sum_{i=1}^{n} (x_i - \mu)^2}{n}$$

However, μ is nearly always unknown, thus necessitating the use of the sample mean $\bar{x}$ as an estimate of the population mean μ. However,

$$\sum_{i=1}^{n} (x_i - \bar{x})^2 < \sum_{i=1}^{n} (x_i - \mu)^2$$

since $\bar{x}$ is calculated from the same set of x_i observations. Accordingly the numerator will be slightly low. To compensate for this downward bias we use $n - 1$ instead of n as the denominator. We call this estimate s^2.

$$s^2 = \frac{\sum_{i=1}^{n} (x_i - \bar{x})^2}{n - 1}$$

Note very carefully the difference between σ^2 and s^2. The former is appropriate if our interest is in the variance of the sample data at hand only; the latter, if we wish to estimate the variance of the larger population from which the sample was obtained.

The denominators n or $n - 1$ are known as "degrees of freedom" when the expression is used to estimate a parameter of a larger population. The degrees of freedom represent the number of independent values in a computation. In the expression for s^2, $n - 1$ values can be selected independently. However, the nth must be selected such that the mean is $\bar{x}$. Hence we say there are $n - 1$ degrees of freedom. In σ^2, the mean μ is not computed from the data. All n x's may therefore be selected independently. Hence it has n degrees of freedom.

Computational Simplification: Because the computation of variances occurs very frequently in statistical work, it is worthwhile to seek a simpler computational form inasmuch as

$$\sum_{i=1}^{n} (x_i - \bar{x})^2$$

requires first the computation of $\bar{x}$ and then the determination of n deviations which are squared and summed.

Let us define SSx as the "sum of the squares" of the deviations of the x values from their mean.

$$SSx = \sum_{i=1}^{n} (x_i - \bar{x})^2$$

It can be shown that*

$$\sum_{i=1}^{n} (x_i - \bar{x})^2 = \sum_{i=1}^{n} x_i^2 - \frac{\left(\sum_{i=1}^{n} x_i\right)^2}{n}$$

Therefore, to compute the variance and standard deviation:

1. Compute

$$SSx = \sum_{i=1}^{n} x_i^2 - \frac{\left(\sum_{i=1}^{n} x_i\right)^2}{n}$$

2. Find

$$\sigma^2 = \frac{SSx}{n}$$

if interested in the variance of the sample itself, or

$$s^2 = \frac{SSx}{n-1}$$

if interested in estimating the variance of the population from which the sample was drawn.

3. Calculate the standard deviation:

$$\sigma = \sqrt{\sigma^2}$$

or

$$s = \sqrt{s^2}$$

For the demand example in Table 3, we can compute the sum of squares as follows:

$$\sum_{i=1}^{200} x_i = 90{,}135$$

$$\sum_{i=1}^{200} x_i^2 = 41{,}100{,}725$$

$$SSx = \sum_{i=1}^{200} x_i^2 - \frac{\left(\sum_{i=1}^{200} x_i\right)^2}{200}$$

$$= 41{,}100{,}725 - \frac{(90{,}135)^2}{200}$$

$$= 479{,}134$$

---

* $\Sigma(x_i - \bar{x})^2 = \Sigma(x_i^2 - 2x_i\bar{x} + \bar{x}^2) = \Sigma x_i^2 - 2\bar{x}\,\Sigma x_i + n\bar{x}^2$

Since

$$\bar{x} = \frac{\Sigma x_i}{n}$$

this reduces to

$$\Sigma x_i^2 - 2\left(\frac{\Sigma x_i}{n}\right)\Sigma x_i + n\left(\frac{\Sigma x_i}{n}\right)^2 = \sum_{i=1}^{n} x_i^2 - \frac{\left(\sum_{i=1}^{n} x_i\right)^2}{n} \qquad \text{QED}$$

The variance of the 200 observations is

$$\sigma^2 = \frac{SSx}{200} = \frac{479,134}{200} = 2,395.7$$

On the other hand, an estimate of the variance of the population of all possible demands is

$$s^2 = \frac{SSx}{200 - 1} = \frac{479,134}{199} = 2,407.7$$

Note that there is essentially no difference between the values of σ^2 and s^2 for this example. This illustrates the fact that the difference between n or $n - 1$ degrees of freedom is significant only for relatively small sample sizes.

The standard deviation s is found to be 49.1.

STATISTICAL INFERENCE

The primary role of statistics is to make use of the information contained in a sample to draw conclusions (make inferences) about the population from which the sample has been drawn. Inferential statistics takes two basic forms. The first is that of *tests of hypotheses* in which, on the basis of a sample from the population, one accepts or rejects the hypothesis as being plausible. The second is *estimation* in which a sample is drawn and statements are then made concerning the populations which might reasonably have yielded the sample.

Each is considered below. Since each requires the taking of a sample, the topic of sampling is first discussed.

Sampling. One is often faced in production and inventory control with the necessity to draw conclusions about a population but with the study restricted to only a portion of the population, i.e., a sample. There are a variety of reasons why sampling might be necessary or desirable.

1. Limitations of time, money, or personnel preclude examination of the entire population.

2. The entire population may not be available at the time the study must be made.

3. Precise information about a population is not necessary.

4. The examination of an item requires that it be destroyed.

PROBABILITY SAMPLING: Since an entire population is not examined, it is critical that inferences concerning it be based on a sample which is representative. "Probability sampling" refers to sampling schemes designed in such a way that the theory of probability can be used for the computation of expected values of an estimate and for its sampling variation. To use statistical tools for inferences, the sample needs to be a probability sample.

Although it might seem obvious that a sample needs to be representative of the population, examples of violations are not uncommon. Examples of violation of this principle would include the following:

The sample is restricted to the most accessible portion of the population such as the top of a container of items, the front of a file, or the top of a list.

In sampling from inventory records, the more active accounts or those with the highest dollar value are selected.

A plan uses only volunteers in studies in which an unpleasant or troublesome measurement process is required.

In taking a poll, an interviewer asks questions only of those who he thinks will be cooperative.

The units included are selected as being typical or average. This method, called "judgment" or "purposive selection," is sometimes useful but not as probability sampling.

In establishing a sampling plan it is necessary first to clearly define the population about which inferences are to be made and second to devise a scheme whereby each member of that population has a known probability of being selected. The nature of the population is a major determinant of the type of sample that should be taken.

SIMPLE RANDOM SAMPLING: A "simple random sample" is one which gives equal opportunity for each population member to be selected for inclusion in the sample.

There are several ways of selecting a simple random sample once the population has been explicitly defined. If the population consists of characteristics of small objects which can be physically mixed, mix the population thoroughly and select a sample of the desired size. However, in production and inventory control analyses the population of interest is not often of this type. Since the population cannot be mixed, the following procedure can be used:

1. Assign to each member of the population a unique identification number. Sometimes such a number already exists, as the case of employees each having a number.

2. Using a table of random digits (see Table 5) and starting at a random position within the table, select a random number of as many digits as necessary to include all possible population members.

3. If the random number equals the identification number of a population member which has not already been selected, select that member for inclusion in the sample.

4. If not, disregard the random number and select the next one from the table and continue with step 3.

5. Continue until the required sample size is obtained.

In practice samples are often selected without such an explicit randomization scheme. Although sufficient randomization *may* result, it is important to recognize that judgment or subjective methods in which an individual selects the members for inclusion in the sample do not tend to be devoid of personal bias.

SYSTEMATIC SAMPLING:[3] A sampling scheme which is sometimes useful if applied with care is "systematic sampling." As the name implies, the sampling is done according to a systematic procedure. To select a sample of n items from a population, randomly select a unit from the first k units and then select every kth unit thereafter. This would be useful, for example, in sampling from cards in a file drawer. By selecting a card every inch along the file, for example, a sample is obtained much more quickly than could be obtained with simple random sampling.

An important variation of systematic sampling is *cluster* sampling. The population is divided into k large sampling units each of which contains n original units. In cluster sampling one of the large sampling units is selected randomly. The n original units in it constitute the entire sample.

STRATIFIED RANDOM SAMPLING:[4] If the population is actually composed of non-homogeneous groups (e.g., seasons), "stratified" sampling is frequently used to ensure representativeness. Stratification requires that the population be divided into homogeneous groups or *strata*. Simple random samples are taken from within each stratum, the total sample being known as a "stratified sample." By stratification a more efficient sampling plan will result.

A stratified sample may be either proportional or disproportional. In a proportional plan the number of observations within each class are proportional to the size of the class in the population. For instance, if one wished to draw

TABLE 5   Table of Random Digits

2380	4072	3008	1403	1341	5417	0429	2183
1100	0011	0163	0876	3790	4854	5012	6793
3056	4643	0353	0324	8766	9682	9196	5561
3596	3171	6664	1438	8653	8974	5965	5347
7054	0858	1663	2252	8541	0973	8965	2839
0932	5976	7465	1000	8810	3864	3891	7094
2586	2239	156	0779	3270	2610	6227	7875
3300	1457	9042	1136	2379	5435	5360	2489
7794	6527	9013	5338	0907	7399	6226	0850
7761	6076	6604	4934	0167	6590	8035	8335
9340	7971	3762	0827	1103	9175	5124	2922
3617	3321	7369	4324	9618	8791	6179	6110
6654	2553	5427	9580	8636	5595	5847	4881
2305	0902	4666	9875	7255	4653	2628	6974
0891	7370	6201	0871	9413	8637	7107	4457
9978	5992	6144	2937	2324	7506	4124	3677
2205	4959	9903	4788	9595	4481	0526	5784
0642	2127	6986	2767	3726	7450	1164	6878
2687	4597	3392	8976	3333	9208	5249	4190
8033	2356	1841	9836	2445	6147	4872	1725
0236	5882	3172	6088	7979	3084	6690	3820
9055	9955	8230	9779	4607	9625	6288	6388
3216	1799	1854	4927	2873	2897	1521	8034
5440	0327	3002	5066	3378	4667	7600	5022
6444	3467	2802	5606	8420	0065	4607	5035
9523	1816	5194	4815	2139	9497	7735	8564
6365	1116	9403	6377	3633	4400	3697	3864
7140	8066	4131	2196	5990	6177	3149	0751
6259	0797	8446	3501	4987	8410	5582	0765
8551	4419	9560	7580	9443	8433	5610	8901
1088	6418	8721	4560	8866	2152	3119	8163
2864	3715	6513	5641	5227	589	6487	7956
2124	1140	7718	6047	6817	6473	7486	4725
5729	1844	9502	415	6974	8109	5881	3885
9655	2965	0890	8657	3933	5677	8664	4906
5471	8666	2756	8542	6441	1771	2653	7186
5998	1310	3875	1453	3846	9997	5363	2828
2228	7915	7436	3379	3349	9686	7969	9936
9139	5404	0172	2394	2820	5370	6836	8621
4480	9288	5408	8852	4436	6947	1760	3907

a sample of 200 from his company's inventory accounts and if 30 percent of these accounts could be classified as very active, 45 percent as moderately active, and 25 percent as slow moving, a proportional sampling scheme would be as follows:

$$
\begin{aligned}
\text{From the very active, sample } 200(0.30) \quad &= \quad 60 \\
\text{From the moderately active, sample } 200(0.45) &= \quad 90 \\
\text{From the slow moving, sample } 200(0.25) \quad &= \quad \underline{50} \\
\text{Total sample size} \quad &= \quad \overline{200}
\end{aligned}
$$

Sometimes there is a significant difference in variation from stratum to stratum. As will be discussed in some of the following material, the larger the degree of variability, the larger the sample size necessary to achieve an estimate of a specified precision. The total sample size can be reduced (on conversely precision increased for the same sample size) if larger proportions are drawn from strata with high variability and smaller proportions from those with low variability. Such a sample is known as a "disproportionate stratified sample." It should be noted that this term also includes procedures in which the same number of observations are taken in each stratum irrespective of its size. In any disproportionate plan, stratum means have to be weighted back to the population proportions for population estimates.

In proportional sampling each member of the population has an equal probability of being chosen, since the size of the sample from each stratum is proportional to the size of the stratum. Therefore, the arithmetic mean of the entire sample is an unbiased estimate of the population mean. However, such is not true in the case of disproportionate sampling. Proper weighting of each observation is required if serious bias is to be avoided.

SAMPLING DISTRIBUTIONS: Nearly all statistical testing procedures involve the taking of a sample of n items and the computation of some sample statistic (usually a function of the mean or standard deviation) upon which the test is based. It is necessary to have knowledge of the distribution of the statistic if many samples of the same size are drawn from the same population. This distribution, called the "sampling distribution," depicts the possible values that might be taken by the statistic and the probabilities associated with its taking them.

If samples of size n are drawn from a normal population with mean μ_x and standard deviation σ_x, sampling theory shows that the sample mean $\bar{x}$ is also normally distributed with mean

$$\mu_{\bar{x}} = \mu_x$$

and standard deviation

$$\sigma_{\bar{x}} = \frac{\sigma_x}{\sqrt{n}}$$

For example, consider a random variable x, which is normally distributed with

$$\mu_x = 20$$

$$\sigma_x = 3$$

The probability distribution function of x would appear when plotted as shown in Fig. 17a.

Now assume that many samples of size $n = 9$ are taken from this population. These would also follow a normal distribution with mean

$$\mu_{\bar{x}} = 20$$

but with standard deviation

$$\sigma_{\bar{x}} = \frac{\sigma_x}{\sqrt{n}} = \frac{3}{\sqrt{9}} = 1$$

as shown in Figure 17b. Note that as the sample size increases, $\sigma_{\bar{x}}$ decreases, thus yielding a smaller degree of dispersion of the sample means from their overall mean $\mu_{\bar{x}}$.

The sampling distribution provides the yardstick against which it is possible

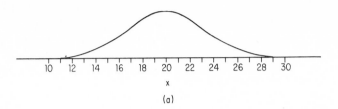

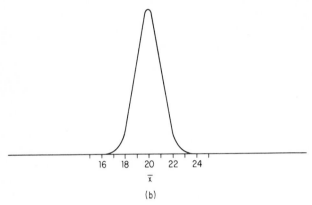

Fig. 17 Sampling distribution of $\bar{x}$: (a) density function of $\bar{x}$: $\mu_{\bar{x}} = 20$, $\sigma_{\bar{x}} = 3$; (b) density function of $\bar{x}$ for $n = 9$: $\mu_{\bar{x}} = 20$, $\sigma_{\bar{x}} = 1$.

to examine the reasonableness of concluding that a sample might or might not have come from a particular population.

The sampling distribution of other statistics is also of concern. Although these will be introduced as needed, it is important to realize that all sample statistics do not follow a normal distribution even though the parent population is normal.

CENTRAL-LIMIT THEOREM: The normal distribution occurs frequently in nature and hence is worthy of consideration for this reason. Its main importance comes, however, from the *central-limit theorem*. This theorem states that if samples of size n are drawn from any population of mean μ and finite variance σ^2 (not necessary normal), the distribution of sample means tends toward the normal distribution as n is increased. The mean of this distribution of $\bar{x}$'s is μ and the variance $\sigma_{\bar{x}}^2 = \sigma^2/n$. The only requirement for the central-limit theorem to hold is that the variance σ^2 be finite—the usual situation in applied problems. The approximation is quite good even for samples as small as four items.

Hence the central-limit theorem makes it possible to utilize the normal distribution for most tests in statistics. As long as conclusions are based on the means of samples, any errors introduced because of nonnormality are minimized.

Hypothesis Testing. The general purpose of hypothesis or significance testing is to examine the reasonableness of a statement (or hypothesis) specifying the parameters of a particular population (or populations). On the basis of a sample from the population, the hypothesis is either accepted or rejected.

For instance, a vendor states that he has been delivering orders with an average lead time of two weeks. On the basis of a sample of the orders placed with him, a conclusion can be made as to whether or not to accept his claim. In another case, there may be two assembly methods being considered for a product. On the basis of samples from each method, significance testing procedures can assist to determine whether the difference between production rates is actually significant or can be attributed merely to chance.

The general procedure which is followed in making such tests is as follows:

1. A population is specified.

2. Values are hypothesized for its unknown parameters of interest.

3. Rules are devised specifying what action is to be taken for all possible outcomes that might result when a sample is taken.

4. A sample size is determined and the sampling plan defined.

5. The sample is drawn and sample statistics of interest are calculated.

6. Based on the relationship of the sample statistics to the rules established in step 3, a decision is made as to whether to accept or reject the hypothesis stated in step 2.

RISKS OF WRONG CONCLUSIONS: If the hypothesis is *rejected*, the experimenter is concluding that there is sufficient evidence that the hypothesis is not tenable or reasonable. He may, for example, conclude that the lead time provided by a supplier is greater than two weeks. On the other hand, acceptance does *not* necessarily mean that the hypothesis is true, merely that there is not enough evidence to conclude it is false. In all statistical testing there is no test which will provide conclusively that something is true. To be sure, however, in practice we usually proceed as if the hypothesis is true if it is accepted. The company continues to do business with the vendor if it fails to find evidence that his lead time is different than two weeks, for example.

The fact that a hypothesis is accepted may be the result of one of two reasons. In the first case the hypothesis may be, in fact, true. On the other hand, there may be such a large degree of variability inherent in the data that any actual difference between the hypothesized parameters and the actual population parameters may be masked. Additional data (i.e., a larger sample) may enable one to remove some of the masking due to chance variation, thus possibly leading to rejection of the hypothesis where at first acceptance was the only possible conclusion. It is not possible to completely remove the effect of this inherent chance variation without the examination of the entire population. The problem would then, however, no longer be one of statistical inference, for complete information would be available.

Since conclusions are made on the basis of incomplete information, there is always some risk of reaching the wrong conclusion. In particular, we may conclude that a hypothesis is false when it is actually true, or conclude it is true when it is actually false. Although the possibilities of these risks are present whether or not statistical tests are used, the statistical approach provides a means for appraising and controlling them.

The first kind of risk, concluding a hypothesis false when it is actually true (often referred to as the "α error") forms the basis for the rule that specifies when a particular hypothesis should be accepted or rejected. The risk is determined by the probability that the experimenter is willing to accept that he will erroneously reject a hypothesis. The choice of this probability level depends upon the consequences of making an error of this type.

One might conclude that the α risk should always be made very small. However, for a given sample size doing so would increase the probability of committing an error of the second kind—concluding a hypothesis is true when actually it is false (frequently referred to as the "β error"). A carefully designed testing plan takes each of these risks into consideration by achieving a balancing of risks which is in accordance with the effects of actually committing either type of error.

The interpretation and control of these risks can best be understood in the context of a particular type of hypothesis testing—a hypothesis about the population mean when the population variance is known. This is presented in the following discussion. It is to be emphasized, however, that the general concepts apply to all hypothesis or significance testing although the details may differ. Indeed these concepts underlie nearly all statistical inference.

HYPOTHESES CONCERNING POPULATION MEANS: When testing a hypothesis about the population mean the particular test used depends on whether the population standard deviation is known in advance or must be estimated from the sample which is to be taken.

1. *Population Standard Deviation Is Known.* For purposes of illustration, consider a situation in which a population is known (or can be assumed) to be normally distributed with a standard deviation of 3. It is desired to examine the reasonableness of a statement that the population mean is 20. Following the general procedure discussed previously, a hypothesis is formed:

Hypothesis: $\qquad\qquad\qquad \mu_x = 20$

Also formed is an alternative hypothesis that states under what conditions the hypothesis is to be rejected. Which alternative hypothesis is appropriate depends entirely on the experimental situation. The choices are

$$\mu_x < 20$$
$$\mu_x > 20$$
$$\mu_x \neq 20$$

Let us assume that it is important that the hypothesis be rejected if there is evidence that the mean is either greater than or less than 20.

Next it is necessary to specify the magnitude of the α risk that is acceptable. If α is picked as 0.05, there is a probability of 0.05 that the hypothesis will be rejected when it is actually true. The test is to be made on the sample mean $\bar{x}$. If a sample of size 9 were drawn from the hypothesized population, the sampling distribution of $\bar{x}$ would appear as in Fig. 17b. It is reasonable for sample means to lie between 19 and 21. It is less likely, however, that they take on values as small as 17 or as large as 23. The probability, though, is *not* zero. It is necessary to define some point at which it is felt that a sample mean of such a value more than likely has come from some other population. The α level specifies this decision point.

We shall split the α risk evenly between the right and left tails because it is important that the hypothesis be rejected if μ_x is greater than or less than 20. We find the limits by

$$\mu_x \pm z_{\alpha/2}\sigma_{\bar{x}}$$

for which the probability is $\alpha = 0.05$ that a sample mean will fall outside these limits when $\mu_{\bar{x}} = \mu_x$ is actually 20. In this case these limits would be

$$20 \pm 1.96 \left(\frac{3}{\sqrt{9}}\right) = 20 \pm 1.96 = \begin{cases} 21.96 \\ 18.04 \end{cases}$$

A sample of size 9 would be drawn, and its mean $\bar{x}$ calculated. The hypothesis would be accepted if

$$18.04 \leq \bar{x} \leq 21.96$$

and rejected if not.

Note that the use of a smaller α (say, $\alpha = 0.01$) would establish wider limits because the z value from the standardized normal tables would be larger. The hypothesis would be accepted for a much wider range of $\bar{x}$. However, if the true mean is actually 22, for example, the probability of not detecting this is increased, i.e., the second kind of risk (β error).[5]

It is common practice to specify acceptance (or rejection) limits in a form which can be directly compared with a tabled value. In the case at hand, the sample statistic is

$$z_{obs} = \frac{(\bar{x} - \mu_0)}{\sigma_x} \sqrt{n}$$

where z_{obs} is read as the observed value of z and μ_0 is the hypothesized population mean.

The hypothesis is accepted if

$$-z_{\alpha/2} \leq z_{obs} \leq z_{\alpha/2}$$

where $z_{\alpha/2}$ is obtained directly from the standardized normal tables. If the alternative hypothesis is a one-tail rejection specification, accept the hypothesis if

$$z_{obs} \leq z_\alpha$$

when it is desired that rejection should occur if there is evidence that the population mean is larger than the hypothesized one. If the alternative hypothesis is the reverse, accept if

$$-z_\alpha \leq z_{obs}$$

All hypothesis tests follow a similar approach. From the sample, a statistic is calculated which is compared to critical values from an appropriate table. These are briefly described for several other common tests below.

2. *Population Standard Deviation Is Not Known.* In practice one does not usually have advance knowledge of the standard deviation of the hypothesized population and thus must obtain an estimate of it from the data. This estimate was previously defined:

$$s = \sqrt{\frac{SSx}{n-1}}$$

Sampling theory shows that

$$\frac{\bar{x} - \mu}{s/\sqrt{n}}$$

follows a t distribution. The t is a family of symmetric distributions each corresponding to a particular number of degrees of freedom (DF). It is somewhat flatter than the standardized normal for small degrees of freedom. As the degrees of freedom increase, it approaches the standardized normal. Various area values are tabulated for many different degrees of freedom and are given in Appendix Table B.

To conduct the test calculate

$$t_{obs} = \frac{x - \mu_0}{s/\sqrt{n}}$$

and compare with appropriate $t_{\alpha/2}$ or t_α for $n - 1$ degrees of freedom.

For example, test the hypothesis:

Hypothesis: $\mu = 10$
Alternative hypothesis: $\mu \neq 10$

$$\alpha = 0.01$$

using a sample of size 5. The hypothesis should be accepted if

$$-t_{0.005, 4\text{DF}} \leq t_{\text{obs}} \leq +t_{0.005, 4\text{DF}}$$

From Table B,

$$t_{0.005, 4\text{DF}} = 4.604$$

As a result of a sample of 5 items,

$$\bar{x} = 15$$

$$s = 3$$

from which

$$t_{\text{obs}} = \frac{15 - 10}{3/\sqrt{5}} = 3.73$$

Since $3.73 \leq 4.604$, the hypothesis is accepted, for there is not sufficient evidence to reject it.

TESTS FOR DIFFERENCES BETWEEN TWO POPULATION MEANS: Quite frequently it occurs that one wishes to compare the means of two populations. For example, is there a difference in the mean production rates for two machines, or between the demands in two marketing areas? A sample is drawn from each population and the sample means compared. The particular test depends on knowledge of the population standard deviations.

1. *Population Standard Deviations Are Known.* The most precise test is available if the population standard deviations are known. Denote one population as x, and the other as y. The first population is assumed to be $N(\mu_x, \sigma_x^2)$ and the other $N(\mu_y, \sigma_y^2)$. A sample of size n_x is taken from the first population from which the sample mean $\bar{x}$ is calculated. From the second population n_y observations are made from which $\bar{y}$ is calculated.

The hypothesis being tested is

Hypothesis: $\mu_x = \mu_y$

or equivalently,

Hypothesis: $\mu_x - \mu_y = 0$

To make test form

$$z_{\text{obs}} = \frac{(\bar{x} - \bar{y}) - (\mu_x - \mu_y)}{\sqrt{(\sigma_x^2/n_x) + (\sigma_y^2/n_y)}}$$

Since the hypothesis is $\mu_x - \mu_y = 0$ and since usually $\sigma_x = \sigma_y$ ($= \sigma$ for simplicity), this reduces to

$$z_{\text{obs}} = \frac{\bar{x} - \bar{y}}{\sigma \sqrt{(1/n_x) + (1/n_y)}}$$

This is compared with the appropriate value from the standardized normal tables.

2. *Population Standard Deviations Are Unknown But Assumed Equal.* If σ_x and σ_y are unknown but can be assumed equal, the test is made with the t distribution. Form

$$t_{\text{obs}} = \frac{\bar{x} - \bar{y}}{\sqrt{(SSx + SSy)/(n_x + n_y - 2)}\sqrt{(1/n_x) + (1/n_y)}}$$

which is compared with a critical value from the t distribution with $n_x + n_y - 2$ degrees of freedom.

If, however, there is reason to believe that the population variances may not be equal, a hypothesis of their equality should be tested. For details of hypotheses concerning variances and the test to be used for means if there is evidence that $\sigma_x^2 \neq \sigma_y^2$, consult any text on applied statistics.[6]

Estimation. In hypothesis or significance testing, a population is hypothesized to exist. A sample is drawn and sample statistics are computed. On the basis of these statistics the hypothesis is accepted as tenable or rejected. The question being answered is: "Might this sample have come from the particular population that has been hypothesized?"

In estimation an inference of essentially the reverse type is made. No prior statement is made concerning the population parameters. Instead a sample is drawn and the question to answer is: "What population(s) might this sample have come from?"

An estimator is a function of sample values that provides an estimate of a population parameter. There are two basic types of estimators—point estimates and interval estimates. Each is discussed below.

POINT ESTIMATION: A point estimate is a *single* value used to estimate the population parameter of interest. In each case a random sample is taken from the population of concern. A statistic is then calculated which provides an estimate of a corresponding population parameter. There are several estimators of common interest. These have been shown to provide quality estimates, a discussion of which, however, is beyond the scope of this chapter.[7]

Several of the following have been previously introduced.

1. To estimate the population mean μ, use the sample mean $\bar{x}$ computed by

$$\bar{x} = \frac{\displaystyle\sum_{i=1}^{n} x_i}{n}$$

2. When estimating the variance of a population σ^2, use

$$s^2 = \frac{SSx}{n - 1}$$

Recall that the variance of the sample *itself* is found by

$$\text{Var}(x) = \frac{SSx}{n}$$

This provides, however, a somewhat low estimate for the population variance—hence the loss of the degree of freedom in the denominator of s^2 to correct this downward bias.

3. When estimating the population proportion p of a binomial population, use

$$\hat{p} = \frac{k}{n}$$

where $\hat{p}$ = estimate of ρ
$\quad\ k$ = number of occurrences
$\quad\ n$ = sample size

A better estimate is provided by the average of estimates of r samples, each of size n:

$$\hat{p} = \frac{\hat{p}_1 + \hat{p}_2 + \cdots + \hat{p}_r}{r}$$

4. Similarly when sampling from a Poisson population, an estimate of λ, the mean number of occurrences, is provided directly by the number of occurrences c in the sample. A better estimate is provided, however, by the average of such estimates from r equal-size samples:

$$\hat{c} = \frac{c_1 + c_2 + \cdots + c_r}{r}$$

INTERVAL ESTIMATES: Estimation by point estimates does not permit the inclusion of information about the degree of variability associated with the variable used in the estimates. For example, a sample may yield a point estimate that the true production rate for a process is 50 units per minute. It may be important, however, to know whether the true value is between 49 and 51 or 40 and 60. To provide this type of information, *interval estimates* are employed.

An interval estimate, sometimes called a "confidence interval," is the specification of two values obtained from a single sample between which a parameter of interest is estimated to lie with a prescribed degree of confidence.

Let L = lower limit of the interval
$\quad\ U$ = upper limit

A $1 - \alpha$ confidence limit has a $1 - \alpha$ probability of including the true parameter in the interval $[L, U]$. In repeated samples $(1 - \alpha) \times 100$ percent of the intervals computed from sample values will include the parameter. Conversely, a proportion of the magnitude α will not include the true mean.

In the following material, procedures are described for establishing confidence limits for several parameters. Although the details may differ, every interval estimation follows the same general approach:

1. A sample is drawn from the population of interest.

2. A sample statistic is calculated from the sample.

3. Upper and lower limits are established for the appropriate population parameter.

A. *Confidence Interval for Population Mean:* If the population variance is known, the standardized normal (z) table is used. If it is unknown and hence must be estimated from the sample, the t distribution is used to establish the width of the interval.

1. *If Population Variance Is Known.* Assume that x is a random variable from a normally distributed population with mean μ (unknown) and standard deviation σ_x (known). As discussed in the section entitled "Sampling Distributions," the means of samples of size n will also be normally distributed with the same mean μ, but with standard deviation

$$\sigma_{\bar{x}} = \frac{\sigma_x}{\sqrt{n}}$$

To set $1 - \alpha$ confidence limits on the true mean μ, we take a sample and

compute its mean $\bar{x}_{obs}$ (where "obs" means
the "observed value"). Then the question
is asked: "What is the largest population
mean which might 'reasonably' have yielded
a sample mean of $\bar{x}$?" "Reasonable" is
dictated by the choice of the α level.

Since the concern is with a lower as well
as an upper limit, the α is split into $\alpha/2$ associated with the upper limit, and $\alpha/2$ with
the lower limit.

Referring to Fig. 18, the problem is to
determine the largest value of μ for which

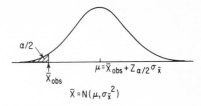

Fig. 18 Determination of upper limit
of confidence interval on population
mean μ.

$$Pr\{\bar{x} < \bar{x}_{obs}\} = Pr\left\{-z_{\alpha/2} < \frac{\bar{x}_{obs} - \mu}{\sigma_{\bar{x}}}\right\} = 0.025$$

where $z_{\alpha/2}$ is obtained from Appendix Table A.

Solving for μ at the point

$$-z_{\alpha/2} = \frac{\bar{x}_{obs} - \mu}{\sigma_{\bar{x}}}$$

yields

$$\mu = \bar{x}_{obs} + z_{\alpha/2}\sigma_{\bar{x}}$$

Hence the upper limit on μ is

$$\bar{x}_{obs} + z_{\alpha/2}\frac{\sigma_x}{\sqrt{n}}$$

In a similar fashion we can answer the question: "What is the smallest
population mean which might reasonably have yielded the sample mean $\bar{x}_{obs}$?"
Proceeding in a similar manner, the lower limit is

$$\bar{x}_{obs} - z_{\alpha/2}\frac{\sigma_x}{\sqrt{n}}$$

Therefore $(1-\alpha)$ confidence limits on the true mean, μ are given by

$$\bar{x}_{obs} \pm z_{\alpha/2}\frac{\sigma_x}{\sqrt{n}}$$

Consider, for example, a study to determine the average daily production
rate for a particular process. On the basis of past history, the daily production
is known to be approximately normally distributed with a standard deviation
of 4 units. The number of units produced on each of 10 randomly selected
days is found to be

$$98, 103, 106, 95, 98, 101, 102, 97, 94, 97$$

A 95 percent $(\alpha = 0.05)$ confidence interval on the true production rate is
desired. These data yield a mean production rate of 99.1. From Appendix
Table A,

$$z_{0.025} = 1.96$$

The limits are

$$99.1 \pm 1.96\frac{4}{\sqrt{10}} = 99.1 \pm 2.5$$

It is concluded, therefore, that the interval [96.6, 101.6] has a probability of 0.95 of including the true mean μ.

It is important to realize that it is still possible that the interval might not include the true value. This possibility has been controlled, however, by the selection of the α level. In this example the probability is only 0.05 that such might be true. If one wishes to decrease this probability (i.e., lower α), the interval that is obtained will be wider. In the above 99 percent confidence limits ($\alpha_{0.005} = 2.576$) would, for example, be [95.8, 102.4].

2. *If Population Variance Is Unknown.* Frequently it is reasonable to assume a normal population although knowledge of its variance is lacking. In such a case, it must be estimated from the same set of data to be used in estimating the population mean. Accordingly the t distribution is employed to establish the width of the interval.

To set the limits, take a sample of size n and compute $\bar{x}_{obs}$ and s^2. The $1 - \alpha$ confidence limits are given by

$$\bar{x}_{obs} \pm t_{\alpha/2, n-1DF} \frac{s}{\sqrt{n}}$$

For example, using the 10 observations of the previous example, 95 percent confidence limits are set as follows:

$$\bar{x}_{obs} = 99.1$$

$$s^2 = \frac{SSx}{9} = \frac{129}{9} = 14.33$$

$$s = 3.79$$

$$t_{0.025, 9DF} = 2.262$$

The limits are

$$99.1 \pm 2.262 \frac{3.79}{\sqrt{10}}$$

The interval [96.4, 101.8] has a probability of 0.95 of including the true population mean.

B. *Confidence Limits for Population Standard Deviation:* If one knows neither the mean nor standard deviation of a population, one of his interests may be the establishment of confidence limits on the standard deviation. Recall that a point estimate of the population variance is s^2. This is now used to establish the interval estimate. Distribution theory shows that if random sample of size n are drawn from a normal population with variance σ_x^2,

$$\frac{(n-1)s^2}{\sigma_x^2}$$

will have a chi-square (χ^2) distribution with $n - 1$ degrees of freedom. The chi square is a family of distributions with different distributions associated with different degrees of freedom. Several important points of each distribution are listed in Appendix Table C. These distributions are characteristically non-negative and nonsymmetric although they become more symmetric as the degrees of freedom increase. In practice, the normal distribution is used as an approximation when the degrees of freedom exceed 30.

The establishment of confidence limits from a sample of size n ($n \leq 30$) requires two points from χ^2 distribution for $n - 1$ degrees of freedom as shown

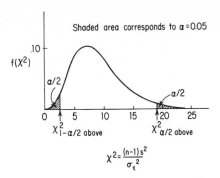

$$\chi^2 = \frac{(n-1)s^2}{\sigma_x^2}$$

Fig. 19   Density function of chi-square distribution: 9 degrees of freedom.

in Fig. 19.   The first is $\chi^2_{\alpha/2,n-1}$ which corresponds to the χ^2 value for which the probability is only $\alpha/2$ that a value greater than it will occur.   The other is the lower-tail critical value, $\chi^2_{1-\alpha/2,n-1}$, which is the point for which the probability of a χ^2 value less than it is $\alpha/2$, which is equivalent to the value for which the probability is $1 - \alpha/2$ that a value greater will occur.

The upper limit of the confidence interval is

$$s\sqrt{\frac{n-1}{\chi^2_{1-\alpha/2,n-1}}}$$

while the lower limit is

$$s\sqrt{\frac{n-1}{\chi^2_{\alpha/2,n-1}}}$$

where $s = \sqrt{SSx/(n-1)}$ is computed from the sample.

For illustration, consider the previous example in which, from a sample of size 10, an s of 3.79 was computed.   Let us establish 95 percent confidence limits on the true population standard deviation.   From Appendix Table C,

$$\chi^2_{0.025,9\text{DF}} = 19.023$$

and $$\chi^2_{0.975,9\text{DF}} = 2.700$$

Hence the upper limit is

$$s\sqrt{\frac{n-1}{\chi^2_{1-\alpha/2,n-1}}} = 3.79\sqrt{\frac{9}{2.700}} = 4.21$$

while the lower limit is

$$s\sqrt{\frac{n-1}{\chi^2_{\alpha/2,n-1}}} = 3.79\sqrt{\frac{9}{19.023}} = 2.61$$

The usual interpretation applies, i.e., the probability is 0.95 that the interval [2.62, 4.21] contains the true population standard deviation σ_x.

If one is interested in establishing confidence limits when the sample size exceeds 30, the chi-square distribution can be approximated by the normal distribution.[8]

The above constitute procedures for computing confidence limits for several frequently occurring estimation situations.   The notions can be and have been applied to the establishment of interval estimates for practically any other population parameter of interest.[9]

DETERMINATION OF SAMPLE SIZE: One often is interested in determining the size of a sample required to provide an estimate of a specified precision. Let us illustrate the concepts by considering a normal distribution with a standard deviation known to be 5. Assume that we wish to determine the sample size required to establish a 95 percent confidence of width ±0.5 unit (i.e., total interval of width 1 unit).

The population standard deviation σ_x is a constant which does not change throughout an experiment. However, a confidence interval is a function of

$$\sigma_{\bar{x}} = \frac{\sigma_x}{\sqrt{n}}$$

which can be made as small as possible by picking a sufficiently large n. Hence, for a given α and σ_x, one can obtain a confidence interval of any desired width by selecting the appropriate sample size.

Recalling the discussion of the confidence interval, we find the interval for the population mean by

$$\bar{x} \pm z_{\alpha/2} \frac{\sigma_x}{\sqrt{n}}$$

We wish, therefore, to find n such that

$$z_{\alpha/2} \frac{\sigma_x}{\sqrt{n}} = 0.5$$

where $z_{\alpha/2} = 1.96$ and $\sigma_x = 5$. Hence

$$n = \left(\frac{z_{\alpha/2}\sigma_x}{0.5}\right)^2 = \left(\frac{1.96 \times 5}{0.5}\right)^2 = 38.4$$

The actual sample size recommended would be 39, inasmuch as the width if $n = 38$ would be slightly larger than that required.

If σ^2 is unknown, the procedure is the same with the substitution of s^2 for σ^2 and $t_{\alpha/2,\text{DF}}$ for $z_{\alpha/2}$.

REGRESSION AND CORRELATION

Often it is of interest to examine the effects that some variables exert (or appear to exert) on others. The techniques of regression and correlation are useful in this examination.

In regression we wish to establish a relationship whereby the value of one variable can be predicted given knowledge of other variables. Let x represent an independent variable which can either be set to a desired value (as selling prices or advertising budgets) or else take values that can be observed but not controlled (as business indexes or competitive prices). This is used to predict a dependent or response variable y (as product demand).

In simple linear regression we seek to determine the coefficients a and b of the linear function

$$y = a + bx$$

where a is the y-axis intercept and b is the slope. Given a value of the independent variable x, a prediction can be made as to the value of the dependent variable. For example, we may wish to predict sales on the basis of knowledge of some general index of business activity.

Simple linear regression accomplishes the prediction with a single independent variable. Often, however, a better prediction can be achieved if several independent variables are considered simultaneously. This is the subject of multiple linear regression which is introduced later.

Correlation also is used to examine relationships. Instead of deriving a prediction equation, its objective is to provide a measure of the degree to which variables are associated. This measure is in the form of a correlation coefficient.

Simple Linear-regression Model. DEVELOPMENT OF REGRESSION EQUATIONS: Given a set of n data pairs in which values for the independent variable x and the dependent variable y are simultaneously measured for each of n observations, we wish to establish a linear relationship. Consider as an example the data of Table 6 in which for each of eight years a particular industry's domestic

TABLE 6 Domestic Sales versus Disposable Income

Disposable Income, x (in Billions of Dollars)	Domestic Sales, y (in Billions of Dollars)
181.6	0.435
206.1	0.621
226.1	0.819
236.7	0.879
250.4	0.933
254.8	0.970
274.0	1.070
284.0	1.180

SOURCE: B. E. Estes, *Sales Forecasting*, Special Report 16, American Management Association. From J. H. Greene, *Production Control: Systems and Decisions*, Richard D. Irwin, Inc., Homewood, Ill., 1965, p. 127.

sales are recorded along with the consumer disposable income. With an estimate of disposable income it should be possible to predict domestic sales for the industry. Disposable income in this case is the independent variable x, while domestic sales is the dependent variable y.

The first step in the analysis is to construct a *scatter diagram* of the sample data to provide a visual portrayal. The procedure is to plot for each value of x a point corresponding to the value of y. Hence there will be n data points, each representing an x, y pair of observations. Such a diagram is illustrated in Fig. 20 for the example.

It should be evident that an apparent linear relationship exists. The scatter diagram is particularly useful in the detection of nonlinear relationships. The techniques for linear regression fit a best-fitting straight line even though the relationship might actually be nonlinear. Hence visual examination of the relationships displayed by the data is desirable.

Given the n data points, we want to determine a straight line of the form $y = a + bx$ through these points. One method is to simply establish visually a line of reasonable fit. For some purposes such a scheme might be satisfactory. However, usually it is not. As dispersion of the points from the line increases, visual fitting becomes more difficult. Moreover a visual fitting is always subject to personal bias to some degree. Hence there is need for a quantitative method.

Underlying the method of linear regression is the existence of a true (although unknown) relationship between each x_i and y_i described by the model

$$y_i = \alpha + \beta x_i + \epsilon_i$$

where α is the true value of the y intercept and β is the true slope of the straight (or regression) line, describing the relationship.

If all data points lie on a straight line, one has the equation of a straight

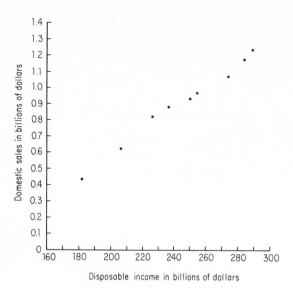

Fig. 20 Scatter diagram.

line, $y_i = \alpha + \beta x_i$. Inasmuch as all observations do not lie on such a line, an additional term must also be present. This term is defined as the *error;* ϵ_i identifies the error associated with the *i*th observation and enters the model in an additive manner:

$$y_i = \alpha + \beta x_i + \epsilon_i$$

Figure 21 shows how such a model assumes each y_i observation is comprised of two parts; the first $\alpha + \beta x_i$ being the point on the regression line corresponding to the particular x_i; and the second, the error (which would, if negative, cause the observation to fall below the line).

A basic assumption of regression is displayed by this model. Namely, all error is assumed associated with the dependent variable y, where the x variable is assumed to be an exact (no error) measurement.

Since the true regression coefficients α and β are not known, we wish to obtain estimates of them based on the information contained in the sample of n data points which have been generated by the true model. Let a be an *estimate* of the true intercept and b be an *estimate* of the true slope such that the line

$$y_i = a + bx_i$$

determined from the data produces an estimate of the true linear relationship

$$y_i = \alpha + \beta x_i$$

Denote the deviations of the observed y_i values from the corresponding point on a line drawn through the data points as e_i. Therefore each y_i can be related to its corresponding x_i by the model

$$y_i = a + bx_i + e_i$$

shown graphically by Fig. 22.

Note e_i is the error from any line $y = a + bx_i$ drawn through the data

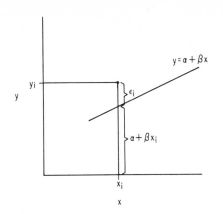

Fig. 21 Relationship of true regression line to observation.

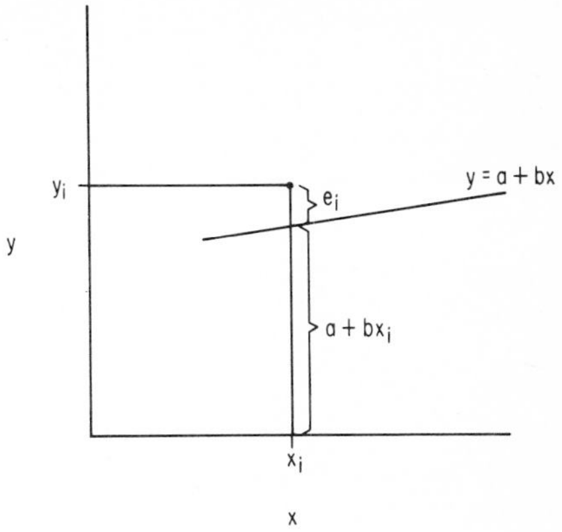

Fig. 22 Relationship of estimated regression line to observation.

points. The ϵ_i used above represents the deviation from the true (but unknown) regression line $y_i = \alpha + \beta x_i$.

Solving $y_i = a + bx_i + e_i$ for e_i yields

$$e_i = y_i - a - bx_i$$

The objective of the regression analysis is to find a and b such that some function of the error is minimized. The minimization of the sum of errors is unsatisfactory inasmuch as positive and negative errors cancel each other in the sum. Moreover, minimizing the sum of the absolute deviations, while theoretically satisfactory, is characterized by significant computational difficulties. However, if the errors are squared, the problem of cancellation in the sum is overcome while yielding a tractable computational problem. Hence the *method of least squares* determines the coefficients a and b of the best-fitting straight line such that the sum of the squares of the deviations of the observations from the line is a minimum.

We desire therefore to find a and b which minimize

$$Q = \sum_{i=1}^{n} e_i^2$$

$$= \sum_{i=1}^{n} (y_i - a - bx_i)^2$$

To minimize Q we take the partial derivatives of Q with respect to a and b and set them each equal to zero. We then solve for a and b.

$$\frac{\partial Q}{\partial a} = \frac{\partial}{\partial a} \sum_{i=1}^{n} (y_i - a - bx_i)^2$$

$$= \sum_{i=1}^{n} \frac{\partial}{\partial a} (y_i - a - bx_i)^2$$

$$= \sum_{i=1}^{n} 2(y_i - a - bx_i)(-1)$$

Setting $\partial Q/\partial a = 0$, we obtain

$$an + b \sum_{i=1}^{n} x_i = \sum_{i=1}^{n} y_i \tag{1}$$

$$\frac{\partial Q}{\partial b} = \sum_{i=1}^{n} 2(y_1 - a - bx_i)(-x_i)$$

$$= -2 \sum_{i=1}^{n} (x_i y_i - ax_i - bx_i^2)$$

which when equated to zero yields

$$a \sum_{i=1}^{n} x_i + b \sum_{i=1}^{n} x_i^2 = \sum_{i=1}^{n} x_i y_i \tag{2}$$

Equations (1) and (2) are known as the "least-squares normal equations." These two equations can be solved simultaneously to provide values of a and b which minimize Q. We obtain

$$b = \frac{\sum_{i=1}^{n} x_i y_i - \left[\left(\sum_{i=1}^{n} x_i \sum_{i=1}^{n} y_i \right)/n \right]}{\sum_{i=1}^{n} x_i^2 - \left[\left(\sum_{i=1}^{n} x_i \right)^2/n \right]}$$

and

$$a = \frac{\sum_{i=1}^{n} y_i}{n} - b \frac{\sum_{i=1}^{n} x_i}{n} = \bar{y} - b\bar{x}$$

Earlier in the chapter the sum of squares was defined:

$$SSx = \text{sum of squares of } x$$

$$= \sum_{i=1}^{n} (x_i - \bar{x})^2 = \sum_{i=1}^{n} x_i^2 - \frac{\left(\sum_{i=1}^{n} x_i \right)^2}{n}$$

and

$$SSy = \sum_{i=1}^{n} (y_i - \bar{y})^2 = \sum_{i=1}^{n} y_i^2 - \frac{\left(\sum_{i=1}^{n} y_i \right)^2}{n}$$

Let us now define

$$SPxy = \text{sum of products of } x \text{ and } y$$

$$= \sum_{i=1}^{n} (x_i - \bar{x})(y_i - \bar{y}) = \sum_{i=1}^{n} x_i y_i - \frac{\sum_{i=1}^{n} x_i \sum_{i=1}^{n} y_i}{n}$$

With this notation the equations for a and b can be more simply written as

$$b = \frac{SPxy}{SSx}$$

$$a = \bar{y} - b\bar{x}$$

TABLE 7   Details of Calculations

x	y	x^2	xy	y^2
181.6	0.435	32,978.56	78.9960	0.189225
206.1	0.621	42,477.21	127.9881	0.385641
226.1	0.819	51,121.21	185.1759	0.670761
236.7	0.879	56,026.89	208.0593	0.772641
250.4	0.933	62,700.16	233.6232	0.870489
254.8	0.970	64,923.04	247.1560	0.940900
274.0	1.070	75,076.00	293.1800	1.144900
284.0	1.180	80,656.00	335.1200	1.392400
1,913.7	6.907	465,959.07	1,709.2985	6.366957

Table 7 shows the calculations of the various sums and sums of squares and products required to compute a and b for the sample data.   This table yields

$$n = 8$$
$$\Sigma x = 1{,}913.7$$
$$\Sigma y = 6.907$$
$$\Sigma xy = 1{,}709.2985$$
$$\Sigma x^2 = 465{,}959.07$$
$$\Sigma y^2 = 6.366957$$

from which we can calculate

$$\bar{x} = 239.21$$
$$\bar{y} = 0.8634$$
$$SSx = 8{,}178.11$$
$$SSy = 0.403626$$
$$SPxy = 57.0578$$

The slope is found to be

$$b = \frac{SPxy}{SSx} = 0.00698$$

and the intercept

$$a = -0.8056 \text{ billion}$$

Our estimate of the population line of regression is

$$y = -0.8056 + 0.00698x$$

where y is domestic sales in billions of dollars and x is disposable income in billion dollars.   This best-fitting line is plotted on Fig. 23.

CONFIDENCE LIMITS AND SIGNIFICANCE TESTS ON SLOPE AND INTERCEPT.   The regression coefficients a and b calculated above are point estimates of the true parameters α and β, respectively.   Frequently one wishes to gain greater information about these estimates by computing confidence limits for the true values.

Several assumptions must be considered if meaningful confidence limits are to be established:

1. The true model is assumed to be

$$y_i = \alpha + \beta x_i + \epsilon_i$$

i.e., the relationship between x and y is linear.

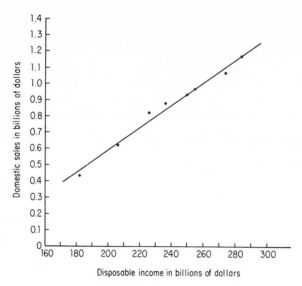

Fig. 23 Plot of best-fitting straight line.

2. The variance of y, although unknown, is assumed to be the same for all x. This variance is written as Var $(y|x)$, which is read as the "variance of y given x." Since it is assumed equal for all x, let

$$\text{Var } (y|x) = \sigma^2_{y|x}$$

3. The y values associated with a given x are assumed to be normally and independently distributed.

4. The measurements of the independent variable x are assumed to be exact, all error being associated with the dependent variable y. However, the assumption of the x's being exact quantities is not a critical one. Useful results can still be obtained from regression methods even though both x and y are random variables.

5. To obtain unbiased estimates, the sample is assumed to be random.

Let $\hat{y}_i = a + bx_i$
$\qquad$ = point on regression line corresponding to a given x_i

From before,

$$y_i = \text{observed } y \text{ value}$$
$$= \hat{y}_i + e_i$$

The confidence limits are based on an estimate of $\sigma^2_{y|x}$. We denote this estimate as $s^2_{y|x}$:

$$s^2_{y|x} = \frac{\sum\limits_{i=1}^{n} (y_i - \hat{y}_i)^2}{n - 2}$$

where $\sum\limits_{i=1}^{n} (y_i - \hat{y}_i)^2$ is the sum of squares of the deviations of the individual

y_i from the corresponding point on the regression line. Since $y_i - \hat{y}_i = e_i$,

$$\sum_{i=1}^{n} (y_i - \hat{y}_i)^2 = \sum_{i=1}^{n} e_i^2$$

which is defined as the sum of squares error or simply SSe. Therefore

$$s^2_{y|x} = \frac{SSe}{n - 2}$$

The $n - 2$ in the denominator reflects the fact that two degrees are lost because two regression coefficients have been computed from the data.

SSe can be more easily calculated by

$$SSe = SSy - \frac{[SPxy]^2}{SSx}$$

SSy is the sum of squares of deviations of the the y_i's from $\bar{y}$. This is a measure of total variability and is often called "total sum of squares." $[SPxy]^2/SSx$ is that portion of the total variability which can be accounted for by the regression relationship. SSe thus represents the unaccounted variability reflected by the deviations of the observed y values from the regression line.

For the example above, $SSe = 0.005534$ from which

$$s^2_{y|x} = \frac{SSe}{n - 2} = 0.0009223$$

ESTIMATION OF TRUE SLOPE: If a large number of random samples each with n data pairs were drawn from the same population, we would obtain many different values for the slope b. These would be normally distributed with mean β and variance σ_b^2. We estimate σ_b^2 which is unknown by

$$s_b^2 = \frac{s^2_{y|x}}{SSx}$$

s_b^2 can be used to establish confidence limits and test hypotheses about β.

$1 - \alpha$ confidence limits for the true slope can be established by

$$b \pm t_{\alpha/2, n-2\text{DF}} \times s_b$$

The t distribution is used inasmuch as we do not have prior knowledge of σ_b^2. For degrees of freedom, $n - 2$ is appropriate because the estimate of σ_b^2 is based on the sum of squares of deviations from the regression line for which two coefficients (a and b) were obtained from the data.

In the example,

$$s_{y|x} = \sqrt{s^2_{y|x}} = 0.03037$$

$$s_b = \frac{s_{y|x}}{\sqrt{SSX}} = \frac{0.03037}{\sqrt{8,178.11}} = 0.3358 \times 10^{-3}$$

0.95 confidence limits on β are found to be

$$0.00698 \pm 2.447(0.3358 \times 10^{-3}) = 0.00698 \pm 0.00082$$

We are 95 percent confident that the interval $[0.00616, 0.00730]$ contains the true slope β.

Often we wish to test the hypothesis that the true slope equals a particular value, β_0.

Hypothesis: $\beta = \beta_0$
Alternative hypothesis: $\beta \neq \beta_0$

To make the test, form

$$t_{obs} = \frac{b - \beta_0}{s_b}$$

and compare with $t_{\alpha/2, n-2\mathrm{DF}}$.

The usual objective is to determine whether there is evidence of a significant regression relationship. Accordingly we formulate the null hypothesis that the true slope is zero.

Hypothesis: $\beta = 0$
Alternative hypothesis: $\beta \neq 0$

Such a test for the example problem yields, with $\alpha = 0.05$,

$$t_{obs} = \frac{b - 0}{s_b} = \frac{0.00698}{0.3358 \times 10^{-3}} = 20.7$$

Since $t_{obs} > t_{0.025, 6\mathrm{DF}} = 2.447$, the hypothesis is rejected, thus permitting us to conclude that there is evidence of a significant relationship.

It should be clear that if the confidence interval for β does not contain zero, a test for significance of difference from zero will always yield the conclusion that such a difference may be present. Thus one of the tests is redundant.

ESTIMATION OF TRUE INTERCEPT: In like manner, a large number of samples, each of size n, drawn from the same population will yield many different values for the intercept a. These would be normally distributed with mean α and variance σ_a^2. The variance is estimated from the sample data by

$$s_a{}^2 = s^2{}_{y|x} \left(\frac{1}{n} + \frac{\bar{x}^2}{SSx} \right)$$

$1 - \alpha$ confidence limits for the true intercept α can be established by

$$a \pm t_{\alpha/2, n-2\mathrm{DF}} \times s_a$$

In the example,

$$s_a = s_{y|x} \sqrt{\frac{1}{n} + \frac{\bar{x}^2}{SSx}} = 0.08105$$

from which 0.95 confidence limits for α are found to be

$$-0.8056 \pm 2.447(0.08105) = -0.8056 \pm 0.1983$$
$$= [-1.0039, -0.6073]$$

While not frequently done, one can test the hypothesis that $\alpha = \alpha_0$ by forming

$$t_{obs} = \frac{a - \alpha_0}{s_a}$$

and comparing with the appropriate tabled t value for $n - 2\mathrm{DF}$.

PREDICTION LIMITS:

1. *Limits on Expected y for Specified x.* The coefficients of the regression line

$$y = a + bx$$

are determined from a set of n x, y data pairs. For a given x_i, the corresponding value of y on the regression line $\hat{y}_i$ is given by

$$\hat{y}_i = a + bx_i$$

If a second set of data were collected, different a and b coefficients would be obtained as was discussed previously. Using these new coefficients a different $\hat{y}_i$ would be obtained for a particular x_i. Subsequent samples would yield still different $\hat{y}_i$'s.

The magnitude of the difference is dependent on the magnitude of the errors present in the measurement of the y observations.

We often wish to establish confidence limits on $\hat{y}_i$ for a given x_i or, in other words, limits on the point on the true regression line corresponding to the x_i. The following interval has a $1 - \alpha$ probability of containing the true $\hat{y}_i$ corresponding to specified x_i.

$$a + bx_i \pm t_{\alpha/2, n-2DF} \times s_{y|x} \sqrt{\frac{1}{n} + \frac{(x_i - \bar{x})^2}{SSx}}$$

When these limits are plotted for various values of x_i, a confidence band results which represents limiting loci on the location of the true regression line. This is illustrated in Fig. 24 for the example problem. These limits are not parallel, since $(x_i - \bar{x})^2$ is small when x_i is near $\bar{x}$, but large when x_i differs widely from the mean. Hence the estimate of the true value of y_i is better when x_i is near $\bar{x}$.

2. *Limits on Individual y Observations.* The above discussion defines limits for average values of $y_i (\hat{y}_i)$ for a given x_i. However, because individual y_i observations deviate from their mean $\hat{y}_i$ (by ϵ_i), limits describing the anticipated range of individual y_i's will be wider than limits on $\hat{y}_i$. The limits

$$a + bx_i \pm t_{\alpha/2, n-2DF} \times s_{y|x} \sqrt{1 + \frac{1}{n} + \frac{(x_i - \bar{x})^2}{SSx}}$$

have probability equal to $1 - \alpha$ of including individual y_i observations. When applied to the example, these limits yield the outer limits of Fig. 24.

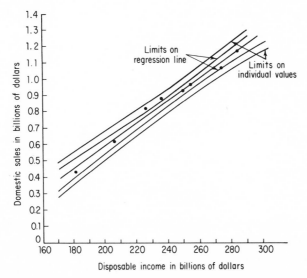

Fig. 24 Confidence band on true regression line and prediction interval for individual observations.

Correlation. In correlation the interest is in determining the *degree of relation-ship* between two variables rather than predicting one from the other. It differs theoretically from regression in the manner in which the observations are measured. In regression, the independent x is assumed measured without error whereas the dependent variable y is measured with error. In correlation both variables x and y are assumed to be measured with error, there being no differentiation between independent and dependent variables.

It should be clear by this time that a least-squares straight line can be fitted to any set of data whether or not the data really follow a linear relationship. We computed $s_{y|x}$ as a measure of dispersion of the data points from the regression line. The larger $s_{y|x}$, the poorer the fit, and vice versa. However, because s_{xy} is in the same units as the data, it is difficult to attach much meaning to it unless one is well acquainted with the data. Furthermore, it is impossible to compare relationships in which the units are not the same.

We therefore desire some measure which reflects the degree of joint behavior of two factors. This measure is the unitless *coefficient of correlation* r, computed by

$$r = \frac{SPxy}{\sqrt{SSx \times SSy}}$$

The correlation coefficient will lie in the range $-1 \leq r \leq +1$.

INTERPRETATION OF CORRELATION COEFFICIENT: The magnitude of $r(|r|)$ reflects the quality of the relationship. A high value indicates a good relationship, a low one a poor relationship. The sign of r specifies the direction. A plus means that y increases with increasing x, while a negative sign shows that y decreases with increasing x.

$|r| = 1$ would indicate a perfect fit, whereas $r = 0$ would result if there were no relationship whatsoever. Figure 25 provides graphical interpretation of the coefficient of correlation.

Although the assumption of error presence in the x measurement differs between correlation and regression, there is an important computational relationship which permits the correlation coefficient to provide further useful interpretation to the regression problem. From before,

$$SSe = SSy - \frac{[SPxy]^2}{SSx}$$

Since

$$r^2 = \frac{[SPxy]^2}{SSx \times SSy}$$

we obtain

$$SSe = SSy - SSy \times r^2$$
$$= SSy(1 - r^2)$$

When r^2 approaches 1, the deviation from the regression line (measured by SSe) approach zero. On the other hand, a poor fit is represented by an r^2 approaching 0 and SSe approaching SSy.

Therefore r^2 can be interpreted as representing the fraction of the total variability in y that is accounted for by x. r^2 is, for this reason, sometimes called the "coefficient of determination."

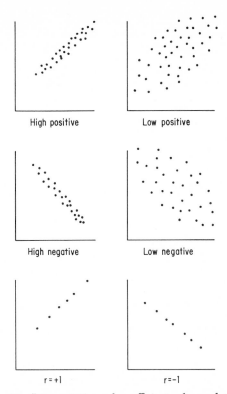

Fig. 25 Interpretation of coefficient of correlation.

SIGNIFICANCE TESTS FOR CORRELATION COEFFICIENT: Implicit in a correlation analysis is the existence of a true coefficient of correlation, ρ $(-1 \leq \rho \leq +1)$. The experimentally determined r is an estimate of ρ. One wishes therefore to draw inferences about ρ on the basis of r.

In particular, even though there is no correlation between x and y (i.e., $\rho = 0$), the experimentally determined r will nearly always be somewhat different than 0. Before concluding that $\rho \neq 0$, one should test the following hypothesis:

Hypothesis: $\rho = 0$
Alternative hypothesis: $\rho \neq 0$

Assuming x and y follow the bivariate normal distribution, we can compute as a test statistic

$$t_{obs} = \frac{|r|}{\sqrt{1-r^2}} \sqrt{n-2}$$

and compare with $t_{\alpha/2, n-2\mathrm{DF}}$. If hypothesis is accepted, we must conclude that we have insufficient evidence of a significant degree of correlation.

Multiple Regression. In previous material, equations were used to predict a dependent variable y using a single independent variable x. A regression equation of the form

$$y_i = a + bx_i$$

was developed.

Deviations of individual actual observation y_i from the predicted value thus computed are (by definition) attributed to the error term

$$e_i = y_i - \hat{y}_i$$

or

$$y_i = \hat{y}_i + e_i$$

The error term includes the effects of all other influences which affect y. The a and b coefficients are selected so as to minimize the sum of squares of the e_i's, but clearly they cannot eliminate the error.

Frequently the magnitude of the residual errors is sufficiently large so as to yield a prediction model of low precision and questionable usefulness. Even if a "reasonable" model has been developed, there may be interest in improving its predictive capabilities.

The precision of the prediction of the dependent variable y can be generally increased if it is based on more than one independent variable.

The predictive model if k independent variables are included becomes

$$y = a + b_1x_1 + b_2x_2 + \cdots + b_kx_k$$

Each of the additional x's accounts for some of the previously unaccounted-for variation unless x has no effect on y or is so highly correlated with another x in the equation that no new information is added. The error term would be reduced by a corresponding amount.

For purposes of illustration, consider two independent variables x_1 and x_2 used to develop a prediction equation. n data sets would be collected, each set of which could contain a y, x_1, x_2 reading. Each of these could be conceptually plotted as a point in a three-dimensional space with axes x_1, x_2, and y, thus yielding a collection of points scattered throughout the space. The problem then would be to determine the coefficients a, b_1, b_2 of the best-fitting plane

$$y = a + b_1x_1 + b_2x_2$$

passing through these points.

The determination of these coefficients follows a procedure analogous to that used for the sample-linear-model case. The ith point can be represented by

$$y_i = a + b_1x_{1i} + b_2x_{2i} + e_i$$

The error term is therefore

$$e_i = y_i - a - b_1x_{1i} - b_2x_{2i}$$

The problem is to find a, b_1, b_2 which minimize

$$\sum_{i=1}^{n} e_i^2$$

as before. These are found by setting to zero the partial derivative of the sum with respect to each of a, b_1, b_2. There will be three simultaneous normal equations in three unknowns which can be solved to determine the desired coefficients.

With more than two independent variables $(k > 2)$, the procedure is the same except that now we are finding the coefficients of hyperplanes in $k + 1$ dimensional space. The computational procedure is similar. However, the task of solving $k + 1$ normal equations in $k + 1$ unknowns becomes a problem of significant magnitude. For this reason nearly all multiple-regression analyses today rely on the use of digital computers for the necessary computations.[10]

MULTIPLE CORRELATION: In a manner analogous to the computation of the correlation coefficient r in the case of simple linear regression, a multiple-correlation coefficient R can be found when there is more than one independent variable. R^2 represents the amount of the variability in y which is accounted for by the set of independent variables. It is therefore a useful measure of the quality of the fit of the regression equation to the data. $R^2 = 1$ would represent a perfect fit (no residual error), whereas a low R^2 (near or equal to zero) would represent a very poor fit.

SELECTION OF PROPER MODEL: The usual goal in deriving a predictive model to be used for operational purposes is to obtain a model which includes only those factors which contribute significantly to the prediction. The selection of the factors to be included involves the balancing of two criteria. First, to make the equation useful for predictive purposes the model should include as many x's as possible so that reliable fitted values can be determined. Opposing this is the notion that because of the costs involved in obtaining information on a large number of x's, the equation should include as few x's as possible. The process of selecting a compromise between these extremes is often called "selecting the best regression equation."

An important characteristic of multiple regression is that the addition of new independent variables to the model can *never* decrease the quality of the prediction. If we let R_k^2 represent the correlation coefficient obtained with k independent variable and R_{k+r}^2 represent the coefficient when r additional independent variables are added,

$$R_{k+r}^2 \geq R_k^2$$

These are two possible causes for the addition of a new variable to have no effect on R^2 (and hence none on the prediction capabilities of the model). One cause might be that there does not exist a relationship between the dependent y and the new x. A second is that the new x may possess a significant correlation with y but may in addition be so highly correlated to one or more of the initial x's that it contributes nothing new.

The approach usually taken is to:

1. Initially select a set of independent variables which includes all variables which might conceivably possess predictive capability.

2. Determine the R^2 for this set. If its magnitude is unacceptable, search for additional factors and repeat this step.

3. Determine the subset of independent variables which is of minimal size but which does not significantly reduce the R^2 found in step 2. This subset selection is commonly done in one of three different ways:

   a. Examine *all possible subsets* and select that set which accomplishes the desired prediction with the minimum number of variables. If there are many variables, the number of problems examined is very large. In an effort to reduce wasted computational effort, a variation of this method considers only those subsets which the analyst thinks might be reasonable candidates for selection.

   b. The *backward-elimination* procedure starts with a model which includes all variables. The variable which contributes the least to the regression is identified and eliminated. The analysis proceeds with the reduced set and continues as long as variables can be removed without a significant reduction in the predictive capability of the model.

   c. The *forward-selection* process is the reverse of the above. The single independent variable most highly correlated with the dependent variable is selected first. Other variables are selected one at a time and inserted into the model until a satisfactory regression equation is obtained.

It is important to note that these procedures may not necessarily yield the same selection of variables for inclusion in the final regression equation. However, in many cases in practice they do yield the same results.[11]

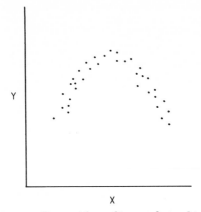

Fig. 26 Data with nonlinear relationship.

HIGHER-ORDER MODELS: Assume that the data from a simple, two-variable (x, y) regression study yielded, when plotted, Fig. 26. Although it is possible to determine the coefficients of the equation of the best-fitting straight line

$$y = a + bx$$

it should be obvious that such an equation would be a poor predictive device since there is clear evidence of a second-order relationship. A more appropriate model would be

$$y = a + b_1x_1 + b_2x_1{}^2$$

If we let

$$x_2 = x_1{}^2$$

the model becomes

$$y = a + b_1x_1 + b_2x_2$$

The procedures of multiple regression can then be to determine a, b_1 and b_2.

In like manner, one can include the effect due to the interaction of two variables, say, x_i and x_j, by creating a third variable x_k where

$$x_k = x_ix_j$$

By making the appropriate transformations it is possible to examine practically any type of relationship. For example assume one wished to find the coefficients of

$$y = \alpha + b_1x_1 + b_2 \ln x_1 + b_3x_3 + b_4x_1x_3{}^2 + b_5(x_1 - x_3)$$

Let $x_2 = \ln x_1$
$\quad x_4 = x_1 x_3{}^2$
$\quad x_5 = x_1 - x_3$

The proper transformation can sometimes be determined through a theoretical analysis of the relationships. Often, however, it can be determined only by visual examination of the plotted data and by comparison of the quality of the fit resulting from several candidate transformations if more than one seems reasonable.

Correlation and Causation. It is important to realize that the presence of a significant level of correlation does not necessarily imply causation. For example, a significant correlation between demand for automobiles and the demand for refrigerators does not mean that one type of demand causes the other. More than likely they are entirely disassociated yet appear to be related since they both might be similarly affected by a third factor, such as general business activity.

On the other hand, the presence of a significant level of correlation may be due entirely to chance, as, for example, a significant correlation between rainfall in New York and sales of television sets in Indiana.

The determination of causation cannot be made without an analysis of the theoretical relationships between the factors. Similarly, distinguishing between chance and a third-factor relationship if no direct causation is present can be accomplished only through a study of the possible theoretical relationships.

The absence of causation would mean that one cannot cause one variable to change by adjusting the other. However, this does not necessarily imply that one is not useful for predicting the other. For example, one could not affect the demand for automobiles by changing the demand for refrigerators (by advertising, price reductions, etc.). However, if a relationship exists, knowledge of the demand for refrigerators can quite reasonably be used to predict demand for automobiles. Therefore, if both are related to some third factor, a valid prediction of one, given the other, is possible.

On the other hand, if the significant correlation is deemed due solely to chance, one factor could not be validly used to predict the other.

GLOSSARY OF SYMBOLS

x_i or x	Particular value assumed by a random variable; also independent variable in regression
$p(x_i)$	Probability density function of discrete random variable
$F(x)$	Cumulative distribution function (discrete or continuous)
$f(x)$	Probability density function of continuous random variable
μ or μ_x	Population mean
σ^2	Population variance
σ or σ_x	Population standard deviation
z	Variate from standardized normal distribution
z_α	Particular value of z for which probability of $z > z_\alpha$ is α
n	Sample size
ρ	True population proportion for binomial distribution; also true population correlation coefficient
k	Number of occurrences of an event in sample of size n
c	Number of occurrences in Poisson distribution
λ	Mean number of occurrences in Poisson distribution

$\bar{x}$ Arithmetic mean or average of sample values

s^2 Unbiased estimate of a population variance computed from a sample

SSx Sum of squares of deviations of x values from their mean

$\mu_{\bar{x}}$ Mean of population of sample means

$\sigma_{\bar{x}}$ Standard deviation of population of sample means

α Probability of rejection of true hypothesis—risk of error of first kind (sometimes used as a probability measure); also y intercept of true regression line

β Probability of accepting a false hypothesis when an alternative hypothesized value is true; also slope of true regression line

z_{obs} Statistic computed from observed sample which is compared with a value from the standardized normal tables

DF   Degrees of freedom

μ_0 Hypothesized value of a population mean that is being tested

$t_{\alpha,n-1\text{DF}}$ Value from the t distribution with $n-1$ degrees of freedom for which the probability of $t > t_{\alpha,n-1\text{DF}}$ is α when the hypothesis is true

t_{obs} Statistic computed from a sample which is compared with a value from the appropriate t distribution

$\hat{p}$ Sample statistic used to estimate true population proportion ρ

$\hat{c}$ Sample statistic used to estimate true mean number of occurrences in a Poisson distribution

$\chi^2_{\alpha,n-1\text{DF}}$ Value from the chi-square distribution with $n-1$ degrees of freedom for which the probability of $\chi^2 > \chi^2_{\alpha,n-1\text{DF}}$ is α

y Dependent variable in regression

a y-axis intercept of the best-fitting regression line

b Slope of the best-fitting regression line

ϵ_i Deviation of the ith observation from the true regression line

e_i Deviation of the ith observation from the best-fitting regression line

Q Sum of e_i^2

$SPxy$ Sum of products of x and y deviations from their means

$\sigma^2_{y|x}$ True variance of ϵ_i for a given x

$\hat{y}_i$ Point on best-fitting regression line corresponding to a given x_i

$s^2_{y|x}$ Estimate of $\sigma^2_{y|x}$

SSe Sum of squares error (equivalent to Q)

σ_b^2 True variance of sample slopes (b)

s_b^2 Estimate of σ_b^2 based on sample observations

σ_a^2 True variance of sample intercepts

s_a^2 Estimate of σ_a^2 computed from sample

r Coefficient of correlation computed from sample

r^2 Coefficient of determination

R Multiple-correlation coefficient

REFERENCES

1. H. O. Brunk, *An Introduction to Mathematical Statistics*, Prentice-Hall, Inc., Englewood Cliffs, N.J., 1960; A. M. Mood, *Introduction to the Theory of Statistics*, McGraw-Hill Book Company, New York, 1950; E. Parzen, *Modern Probability Theory and Its Applications*, John Wiley & Sons, Inc., New York, 1960.
2. B. Ostle, *Statistics in Research*, The Iowa State University Press, Ames, Iowa, 1963.
3. For details on the use of systematic sampling, see W. G. Cochran, *Sampling Techniques*, 2d ed., John Wiley & Sons, Inc., New York, 1963.
4. For further details on stratified sampling, as well as on the design and interpretation of other special-purpose sampling precedures, see Y. Chou, *Applied Business and Economic Statistics*, Holt, Rinehart and Winston, Inc., New York, 1963;

Cochran, *op. cit.;* or W. E. Deming, *Sample Design in Business Research,* John Wiley & Sons, Inc., New York, 1960.

5. For further discussion of this point, see A. H. Bowker and G. J. Lieberman, *Engineering Statistics,* Prentice-Hall, Inc., Englewood Cliffs, N.J., 1959; A. J. Duncan, *Quality Control and Industrial Statistics,* rev. ed., Richard D. Irwin, Inc., Homewood, Ill., 1959; Ostle, *op. cit.;* or other texts on applied statistics.

6. Bowker and Lieberman, *op. cit.;* W. J. Dixon and F. J. Massey, *Introduction to Statistical Analysis,* 2d ed., McGraw-Hill Book Company, New York, 1957; Duncan, *op. cit.;* W. A. Neiswanger, *Elementary Statistical Methods,* rev. ed., The Macmillan Company, New York, 1956; Ostle, *op. cit.;* and R. L. Wine, *Statistics for Scientists and Engineers,* Prentice-Hall, Inc., Englewood Cliffs, N.J., 1964.

7. For further theoretical considerations, see K. A. Brownlee, *Statistical Theory and Methodology in Science and Engineering,* 2d ed., John Wiley & Sons, Inc., New York, 1965; or Ostle, *op. cit.*

8. Duncan, *op. cit.,* provides details of the approximation procedure.

9. For details of these other procedures, consult any of a number of excellent statistical texts; e.g., Dixon and Massey, *op cit.;* Duncan, *op. cit.;* and Ostle, *op. cit.*

10. For discussion of the mathematical bases of the multiple-regression models, see N. R. Draper and H. Smith, *Applied Regression Analysis,* John Wiley & Sons, Inc., New York, 1966; N. L. Johnson and F. C. Leone, *Statistics and Experimental Design in Engineering and the Physical Sciences,* vol. 1, John Wiley & Sons, Inc., New York, 1964; or Ostle, *op. cit.*

11. An excellent detailed description and evaluation of these methods and several variations are included in Draper and Smith, *op. cit.,* chap. 6.

APPENDIX

TABLE A   Normal Distribution: This Table Gives the Area, α, under the Standard Normal Curve from z_α to $+\infty$

z_α	.00	.01	.02	.03	.04	.05	.06	.07	.08	.09
0.0	.5000	.4960	.4920	.4880	.4840	.4801	.4761	.4721	.4681	.4641
0.1	.4602	.4562	.4522	.4483	.4443	.4404	.4364	.4325	.4286	.4247
0.2	.4207	.4168	.4129	.4090	.4052	.4013	.3974	.3936	.3897	.3859
0.3	.3821	.3783	.3745	.3707	.3669	.3632	.3594	.3557	.3520	.3483
0.4	.3446	.3409	.3372	.3336	.3300	.3264	.3228	.3192	.3156	.3121
0.5	.3085	.3050	.3015	.2981	.2946	.2912	.2877	.2843	.2810	.2776
0.6	.2743	.2709	.2676	.2643	.2611	.2578	.2546	.2514	.2483	.2451
0.7	.2420	.2389	.2358	.2327	.2296	.2266	.2236	.2206	.2177	.2148
0.8	.2119	.2090	.2061	.2033	.2005	.1977	.1949	.1922	.1894	.1867
0.9	.1841	.1814	.1788	.1762	.1736	.1711	.1685	.1660	.1635	.1611
1.0	.1587	.1562	.1539	.1515	.1492	.1469	.1446	.1423	.1401	.1379
1.1	.1357	.1335	.1314	.1292	.1271	.1251	.1230	.1210	.1190	.1170
1.2	.1151	.1131	.1112	.1093	.1075	.1056	.1038	.1020	.1003	.0985
1.3	.0968	.0951	.0934	.0918	.0901	.0885	.0869	.0853	.0838	.0823
1.4	.0808	.0793	.0778	.0764	.0749	.0735	.0721	.0708	.0694	.0681
1.5	.0668	.0655	.0643	.0630	.0618	.0606	.0594	.0582	.0571	.0559
1.6	.0548	.0537	.0526	.0516	.0505	.0495	.0485	.0475	.0465	.0455
1.7	.0446	.0436	.0427	.0418	.0409	.0401	.0392	.0384	.0375	.0367
1.8	.0359	.0351	.0344	.0336	.0329	.0322	.0314	.0307	.0301	.0294
1.9	.0287	.0281	.0274	.0268	.0262	.0256	.0250	.0244	.0239	.0233
2.0	.0228	.0222	.0217	.0212	.0207	.0202	.0197	.0192	.0188	.0183
2.1	.0179	.0174	.0170	.0166	.0162	.0158	.0154	.0150	.0146	.0143
2.2	.0139	.0136	.0132	.0129	.0125	.0122	.0119	.0116	.0113	.0110
2.3	.0107	.0104	.0102	.00990	.00964	.00939	.00914	.00889	.00866	.00842
2.4	.00820	.00798	.00776	.00755	.00734	.00714	.00695	.00676	.00657	.00639
2.5	.00621	.00604	.00587	.00570	.00554	.00539	.00523	.00508	.00494	.00480
2.6	.00466	.00453	.00440	.00427	.00415	.00402	.00391	.00379	.00368	.00357
2.7	.00347	.00336	.00326	.00317	.00307	.00298	.00289	.00280	.00272	.00264
2.8	.00256	.00248	.00240	.00233	.00226	.00219	.00212	.00205	.00199	.00193
2.9	.00187	.00181	.00175	.00169	.00164	.00159	.00154	.00149	.00144	.00139

z_α	.0	.1	.2	.3	.4	.5	.6	.7	.8	.9
3	.00135	$.0^3968$	$.0^3687$	$.0^3483$	$.0^3337$	$.0^3233$	$.0^3159$	$.0^3108$	$.0^4723$	$.0^4481$
4	$.0^4317$	$.0^4207$	$.0^4133$	$.0^5854$	$.0^5541$	$.0^5340$	$.0^5211$	$.0^5130$	$.0^6793$	$.0^6479$
5	$.0^6287$	$.0^6170$	$.0^7996$	$.0^7579$	$.0^7333$	$.0^7190$	$.0^7107$	$.0^8599$	$.0^8332$	$.0^8182$
6	$.0^9987$	$.0^9530$	$.0^9282$	$.0^9149$	$.0^{10}777$	$.0^{10}402$	$.0^{10}206$	$.0^{10}104$	$.0^{11}523$	$.0^{11}260$

SOURCE: Reproduced by consent of publisher from Frederick E. Croxton, *Elementary Statistics with Applications in Medicine*, Prentice-Hall, Inc., Englewood Cliffs, N.J., 1953, p. 323.

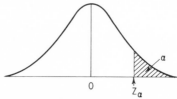

TABLE B   t Distribution: This Table Gives Specified Value of t_α for d Degrees of Freedom and a One-tail Area of α

d	\multicolumn{10}{c}{Value of α}
	0.40	0.30	0.20	0.10	0.05	0.025	0.01	0.005	0.001	0.0005
1	0.325	0.727	1.376	3.078	6.314	12.71	31.82	63.66	318.3	636.6
2	0.289	0.617	1.061	1.886	2.920	4.303	6.965	9.925	22.33	31.60
3	0.277	0.584	0.978	1.638	2.353	3.182	4.541	5.841	10.22	12.94
4	0.271	0.569	0.941	1.533	2.132	2.776	3.747	4.604	7.173	8.610
5	0.267	0.559	0.920	1.476	2.015	2.571	3.365	4.032	5.893	6.859
6	0.265	0.553	0.906	1.440	1.943	2.447	3.143	3.707	5.208	5.959
7	0.263	0.549	0.896	1.415	1.895	2.365	2.998	3.499	4.785	5.405
8	0.262	0.546	0.889	1.397	1.860	2.306	2.896	3.355	4.501	5.041
9	0.261	0.543	0.883	1.383	1.833	2.262	2.821	3.250	4.297	4.781
10	0.260	0.542	0.879	1.372	1.812	2.228	2.764	3.169	4.144	4.587
11	0.260	0.540	0.876	1.363	1.796	2.201	2.718	3.106	4.025	4.437
12	0.259	0.539	0.873	1.356	1.782	2.179	2.681	3.055	3.930	4.318
13	0.259	0.538	0.870	1.350	1.771	2.160	2.650	3.012	3.852	4.221
14	0.258	0.537	0.868	1.345	1.761	2.145	2.624	2.977	3.787	4.140
15	0.258	0.536	0.866	1.341	1.753	2.131	2.602	2.947	3.733	4.073
16	0.258	0.535	0.865	1.337	1.746	2.120	2.583	2.921	3.686	4.015
17	0.257	0.534	0.863	1.333	1.740	2.110	2.567	2.898	3.646	3.965
18	0.257	0.534	0.862	1.330	1.734	2.101	2.552	2.878	3.611	3.922
19	0.257	0.533	0.861	1.328	1.729	2.093	2.539	2.861	3.579	3.883
20	0.257	0.533	0.860	1.325	1.725	2.086	2.528	2.845	3.552	3.850
21	0.257	0.532	0.859	1.323	1.721	2.080	2.518	2.831	3.527	3.819
22	0.256	0.532	0.858	1.321	1.717	2.074	2.508	2.819	3.505	3.792
23	0.256	0.532	0.858	1.319	1.714	2.069	2.500	2.807	3.485	3.767
24	0.256	0.531	0.857	1.318	1.711	2.064	2.492	2.797	3.467	3.745
25	0.256	0.531	0.856	1.316	1.708	2.060	2.485	2.787	3.450	3.725
26	0.256	0.531	0.856	1.315	1.706	2.056	2.479	2.779	3.435	3.707
27	0.256	0.531	0.855	1.314	1.703	2.052	2.473	2.771	3.421	3.690
28	0.256	0.530	0.855	1.313	1.701	2.048	2.467	2.763	3.408	3.674
29	0.256	0.530	0.854	1.311	1.699	2.045	2.462	2.756	3.396	3.659
30	0.256	0.530	0.854	1.310	1.697	2.042	2.457	2.750	3.385	3.646
40	0.255	0.529	0.851	1.303	1.684	2.021	2.423	2.704	3.307	3.551
50	0.255	0.528	0.849	1.298	1.676	2.009	2.403	2.678	3.262	3.495
60	0.254	0.527	0.848	1.296	1.671	2.000	2.390	2.660	3.232	3.460
80	0.254	0.527	0.846	1.292	1.664	1.990	2.374	2.639	3.195	3.415
100	0.254	0.526	0.845	1.290	1.660	1.984	2.365	2.626	3.174	3.389
200	0.254	0.525	0.843	1.286	1.653	1.972	2.345	2.601	3.131	3.339
500	0.253	0.525	0.842	1.283	1.648	1.965	2.334	2.586	3.106	3.310
∞	0.253	0.524	0.842	1.282	1.645	1.960	2.326	2.576	3.090	3.291

SOURCE: Reproduced from A. Hald, *Statistical Tables and Formulas*, John Wiley & Sons, Inc., New York, 1952, p. 39, by consent of publisher.

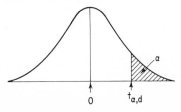

TABLE C   Chi-square Distribution: This Table Gives Specified Value of χ_α^2 for d

d	Value of α									
	0.995	0.99	0.98	0.975	0.95	0.90	0.80	0.75	0.70	0.50
1	$.0^4393$	$.0^3157$	$.0^3628$	$.0^3982$	.00393	.0158	.0642	.102	.148	.455
2	.0100	.0201	.0404	.0506	.103	.211	.446	.575	.713	1.386
3	.0717	.115	.185	.216	.352	.584	1.005	1.213	1.424	2.366
4	.207	.297	.429	.484	.711	1.064	1.649	1.923	2.195	3.357
5	.412	.554	.752	.831	1.145	1.610	2.343	2.675	3.000	4.351
6	.676	.872	1.134	1.237	1.635	2.204	3.070	3.455	3.828	5.348
7	.989	1.239	1.564	1.690	2.167	2.833	3.822	4.255	4.671	6.346
8	1.344	1.646	2.032	2.180	2.733	3.490	4.594	5.071	5.527	7.344
9	1.735	2.088	2.532	2.700	3.325	4.168	5.380	5.899	6.393	8.343
10	2.156	2.558	3.059	3.247	3.940	4.865	6.179	6.737	7.267	9.342
11	2.603	3.053	3.609	3.816	4.575	5.578	6.989	7.584	8.148	10.341
12	3.074	3.571	4.178	4.404	5.226	6.304	7.807	8.438	9.034	11.340
13	3.565	4.107	4.765	5.009	5.892	7.042	8.634	9.299	9.926	12.340
14	4.075	4.660	5.368	5.629	6.571	7.790	9.467	10.165	10.821	13.339
15	4.601	5.229	5.985	6.262	7.261	8.547	10.307	11.036	11.721	14.339
16	5.142	5.812	6.614	6.908	7.962	9.312	11.152	11.912	12.624	15.338
17	5.697	6.408	7.255	7.564	8.672	10.085	12.002	12.792	13.531	16.338
18	6.265	7.015	7.906	8.231	9.390	10.865	12.857	13.675	14.440	17.338
19	6.844	7.633	8.567	8.907	10.117	11.651	13.716	14.562	15.352	18.338
20	7.434	8.260	9.237	9.591	10.851	12.443	14.578	15.452	16.266	19.337
21	8.034	8.897	9.915	10.283	11.591	13.240	15.445	16.344	17.182	20.337
22	8.643	9.542	10.600	10.982	12.338	14.041	16.314	17.240	18.101	21.337
23	9.260	10.196	11.293	11.688	13.091	14.848	17.187	18.137	19.021	22.337
24	9.886	10.856	11.992	12.401	13.848	15.659	18.062	19.037	19.943	23.337
25	10.520	11.524	12.697	13.120	14.611	16.473	18.940	19.939	20.867	24.337
26	11.160	12.198	13.409	13.844	15.379	17.292	19.820	20.843	21.792	25.336
27	11.808	12.879	14.125	14.573	16.151	18.114	20.703	21.749	22.719	26.336
28	12.461	13.565	14.847	15.308	16.928	18.939	21.588	22.657	23.647	27.336
29	13.121	14.256	15.574	16.047	17.708	19.768	22.475	23.567	24.577	28.336
30	13.787	14.953	16.306	16.791	18.493	20.599	23.364	24.478	25.508	29.336

SOURCE: Reproduced by consent of publisher from Frederick E. Croxton, *Elementary Statis* 328–329.

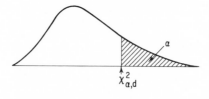

$$\chi_{a,d}^2$$

Degrees of Freedom and a Tail Area of α

Value of α

0.30	0.25	0.20	0.10	0.05	0.025	0.02	0.01	0.005	0.001
1.074	1.323	1.642	2.706	3.841	5.024	5.412	6.635	7.879	10.827
2.408	2.773	3.219	4.605	5.991	7.378	7.824	9.210	10.597	13.815
3.665	4.108	4.642	6.251	7.815	9.348	9.837	11.345	12.838	16.268
4.878	5.385	5.989	7.779	9.488	11.143	11.668	13.277	14.860	18.465
6.064	6.626	7.289	9.236	11.070	12.832	13.388	15.086	16.750	20.517
7.231	7.841	8.558	10.645	12.592	14.449	15.033	16.812	18.548	22.457
8.383	9.037	9.803	12.017	14.067	16.013	16.622	18.475	20.278	24.322
9.524	10.219	11.030	13.362	15.507	17.535	18.168	20.090	21.955	26.125
10.656	11.389	12.242	14.684	16.919	19.023	19.679	21.666	23.589	27.877
11.781	12.549	13.442	15.987	18.307	20.483	21.161	23.209	25.188	29.588
12.899	13.701	14.631	17.275	19.675	21.920	22.618	24.725	26.757	31.264
14.011	14.845	15.812	18.549	21.026	23.337	24.054	26.217	28.300	32.909
15.119	15.984	16.985	19.812	22.362	24.736	25.472	27.688	29.819	34.528
16.222	17.117	18.151	21.064	23.685	26.119	26.873	29.141	31.319	36.123
17.322	18.245	19.311	22.307	24.996	27.488	28.259	30.578	32.801	37.697
18.418	19.369	20.465	23.542	26.296	28.845	29.633	32.000	34.267	39.252
19.511	20.489	21.615	24.769	27.587	30.191	30.995	33.409	35.718	40.790
20.601	21.605	22.760	25.989	28.869	31.526	32.346	34.805	37.156	42.312
21.689	22.718	23.900	27.204	30.144	32.852	33.687	36.191	38.582	43.820
22.775	23.828	25.038	28.412	31.410	34.170	35.020	37.566	39.997	45.315
23.858	24.935	26.171	29.615	32.671	35.479	36.343	38.932	41.401	46.797
24.939	26.039	27.301	30.813	33.924	36.781	37.659	40.289	42.796	48.268
26.018	27.141	28.429	32.007	35.172	38.076	38.968	41.638	44.181	49.728
27.096	28.241	29.553	33.196	36.415	39.364	40.270	42.980	45.558	51.179
28.172	29.339	30.675	34.382	37.652	40.646	41.566	44.314	46.928	52.620
29.246	30.434	31.795	35.563	38.885	41.923	42.856	45.642	48.290	54.052
30.319	31.528	32.912	36.741	40.113	43.194	44.140	46.963	49.645	55.476
31.391	32.620	34.027	37.916	41.337	44.461	45.419	48.278	50.993	56.893
32.461	33.711	35.139	39.087	42.557	45.722	46.693	49.588	52.336	58.302
33.530	34.800	36.250	40.256	43.773	46.979	47.962	50.892	53.672	59.703

tics with Applications in Medicine, Prentice-Hall, Inc., Englewood Cliffs, N.J., 1953, pp.

Chapter **29**

Nomographs

EDITOR:

Hawley W. Merrihew *Senior Consultant, Management Sciences Division, H. B. Maynard & Co., Inc., Pittsburgh, Pennsylvania*

CONTENTS

A nomograph is a chart used to illustrate grapically the relationship between variables. The word "nomograph" is derived from the Greek word *nomos* which means law or custom, to which has been added the word "graph," meaning to write. The relationships or laws may be derived from either empirical data or mathematical equations.

TYPES OF NOMOGRAPHS

There are three general nomograph forms of interest to production and inventory control personnel:
1. Concurrency charts
2. Z or N charts
3. Parallel line alignment charts

Figure 1 illustrates the *concurrency chart* with the data plotted on cartesian coordinates. A family of straight lines is used to show the relationships among the three variables, X, Y, and T. Thus for $T = T_1$, the value Y can be obtained for any value of X by merely using the straight line OA as a reference. From the value of $X(a)$ project a line vertically to the T_1 reference line (b) and then horizontally to determine the value of $Y(c)$.

Figure 2 illustrates a Z or N *chart*, so-called because of its shape. The value of Y is obtained by laying a straightedge across the axes as indicated. For a given set of values of $X(a)$ and $T(b)$, a value of $Y(c)$ may be determined.

Figure 3 illustrates an *alignment chart*. The axes are parallel and the value of $Y(c)$ is obtained by laying a straightedge across the axes as indicated and reading off the value for Y for any given values of $X(a)$ and $T(b)$.

In each example given above, the equation indicated is a *product* form. We are not limited to this form as will be shown. Equations that include addition, division, and exponent operations may be handled.

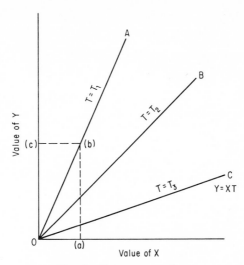

Fig. 1   Concurrency chart.

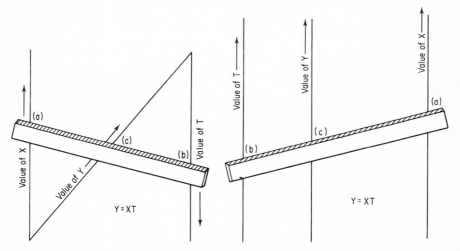

Fig. 2   Z or N chart.   **Fig. 3**   Parallel line alignment chart.

For each of the three types of nomographs, an example will be presented.

Construction of Concurrency Charts.   Figure 4 illustrates a concurrency chart representing the cost of storing material for various storage costs and number of units.   The equation for this chart is

$$C = KN \tag{1}$$

where C = total cost of storage for one year
  K = cost to store one unit for one year
  N = number of units to be stored

The equation is plotted for three values of K, and the three lines shown on the chart are for the different values of K.   The horizontal axis represents

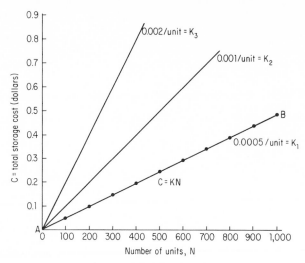

Fig. 4 Concurrency chart.

the number of units to be stored, and the vertical axis represents the total cost of storage. To determine the cost, project a vertical line from the number of units to be stored to the appropriate line for K and then move horizontally to the vertical-cost axis to determine the answer.

The steps in constructing a concurrency chart are as follows:

1. Set up the independent variable N and the dependent variable C on axes at right angles to each other.

2. Determine the range over which the variables are to be plotted:

N from 0 to 1,000 units

C from 0 to 0.9 dollars

3. Subdivide the axes and plot the variables. Label the axes.

4. For each value of the parameter K plot a separate line. This is most easily accomplished by setting up a table and computing N and C for values of K_1. For example:

C	N	K_1
0.05	100	0.0005
0.1	200	0.0005
0.15	300	0.0005
0.20	400	0.0005
0.25	500	0.0005
0.30	600	0.0005
0.35	700	0.0005
0.40	800	0.0005

Now from the table plot the line for $K_1 = 0.0005$ per unit. This is the line AB. Repeat this procedure for each value of K—in this case, for $K_2 = 0.001$ per unit and $K_3 = 0.002$ per unit.

Construction of the Z or N Chart. The equation $C = KN$ has been replotted in Fig. 5 to illustrate the Z or N form of nomograph. Notice that the value of C is plotted on the lefthand side of the chart and increases upward, whereas

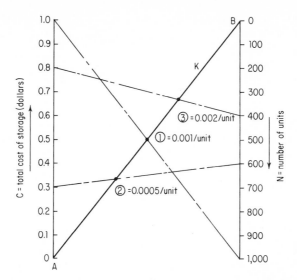

Fig. 5 Z chart for $C = KN$ (illustrating principle of duality).

the number of units, N, is plotted on the righthand side and decreases downward. The cost to store one unit for a year, K, is plotted on the diagonal line AB, and each line from Fig. 4 now becomes a point on Fig. 5. (The points created on Fig. 5 representing each line on Fig. 4 are indicated by the circled numerals, 1, 2, and 3.)

A completed version of the Z chart for Eq. (1) is illustrated in Fig. 6. Compare the compactness of the Z chart with the concurrency chart for presenting many values of K.

The translation of the points to lines and lines to points is based upon the principle of duality where a *line* on the concurrency chart is translated as a

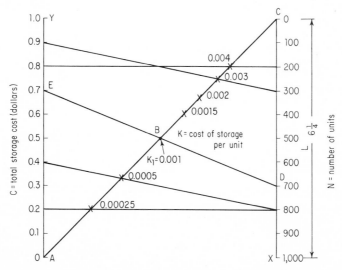

Fig. 6 Z or N chart for $C = KN$.

point on the Z chart. The basis for the relationship between variables in the Z chart can be seen from the following reasoning illustrated in Fig. 6.

The triangles ABE and DBC are similar.

$$\frac{AE}{DC} = \frac{AB}{BC} \tag{2}$$

Let $AE = C_1 m_y$
$DC = N_1 m_x$

where m_y and m_x are called "scale factors" and relate the functions N_1 and C_1 to the line lengths AE and DC. If we substitute these values into Eq. (2), we obtain the following:

$$\frac{AB}{BC} = \frac{C_1}{N_1}\frac{m_y}{m_x} = K_1\frac{m_y}{m_x}$$

and
$$C_1 = K_1 N_1$$

In Fig. 6 note that AE is the length of the line needed to represent the cost C_1, and DC is the length of the line needed to represent the number of units N_1. The position of K_1 on the line AC indicates the ratio AB/BC representing the ratio of C_1 to N_1. The scale factors merely adjust the variables to fit the length of the line.

SCALE FACTORS: The length of the line CX in the figure is $6\frac{1}{4}$ inches and is calibrated from 0 to 1,000 units, thus the *modulus* or scale factor for this line is $\frac{6.25}{1,000}$ or 0.00625 inch per unit. When the scale factor is multiplied by the value of the total number of units N_1, the length of the line CX is the resultant, hence,

$$CX = N_1 m_x$$

Substituting values for N_1 and m_x yields

$$CX = 1,000(0.00625) = 6.25 \text{ inches}$$

Scale factors, or moduli, are always developed during the construction of a nomograph. Basically the scale factor relates the physical length of the line to the function that it represents.

The relationship between the function N and the length of line L in Fig 6 is illustrated in Table 1. Note that $L = CX$ when $N = 1,000$, where N is the number of units and L is the length of the line.

TABLE 1   Relationship between N and L

Value of N	0	100	200	300	400	500	600	700	800	900	1000
Value of L	0	0.625	1.25	1.875	2.5	3.125	3.75	4.375	5.0	5.625	6.25

The equation $C = KN$ can also be plotted as an alignment chart. The method for developing this plot requires additional derivation and will be shown in a subsequent section.

Construction of Alignment Charts. Alignment charts appear in two basic forms in this chapter: the addition chart and the multiplication chart. Examples of their construction will be deferred until the handling of empirical data has been developed.

CONVERTING EMPIRICAL DATA TO A NOMOGRAPH

Because the relationships used in constructing nomographs are often derived from empirical data, it is necessary to review the means by which such data can be converted to a suitable form. There are two basic methods that will be described: first, a means for converting data into a nomograph by graphical means without deriving an equation for the relationship between the variables, and second, a method of curve fitting where an equation is derived to fit the data.

Types of Equations. As shown in Table 2, there are several ways of modifying equations so that they may be described by straight lines. The first column shows the original equation and the second column shows how this data can be transformed to the straight-line form. The objective is to find a representative equation for the data which will convert the data to a straight-line form permitting the construction of a nomograph.

TABLE 2   Nomograph Equations

Equation	Original equation	Straight-line form
1	$y = ax + b$	$y = ax + b$
2	$y = bx^a$	$\log y = a \log x + \log b$
3	$y = bx^a + c$	$\log(y - c) = a \log x + \log b$
4	$y = a + bx + cx^2$	$\dfrac{y - y_1}{x - x_1} = b + cx + cx_1$
5	$y = \dfrac{x}{ax + b}$	$\dfrac{1}{y} = \dfrac{a}{x} + b$

Equation 1: The first equation represents the straight line and can be used directly to form a nomograph without change.

The straight-line equation, $y = ax + b$, is of the same form as the equation $C = KN$ used in developing the concurrency and Z charts above. The relationship can be seen as follows:

Let $y = C =$ the dependent variable
   $K = a =$ a constant representing the slope of the line
   $x = N =$ the independent variable
   $b = 0 =$ the point where the straight line intercepts the y axis

Equation 2: The second equation in the table is of exponential form which may be converted to a straight-line form by taking the logarithms of both sides.

Equation 3: The third equation in the table is shifted to a logarithmic form, as illustrated.

Equation 4: The fourth equation is shifted to a straight-line form by selecting a point $x_1 y_1$ on the curve and then using these values to obtain the straight-line relationship as follows.

$$y_1 = a + bx_1 + cx_1{}^2 \tag{3}$$

Subtract Eq. (3) from the original equation and rearrange it

$$\frac{y - y_1}{x - x_1} = b + cx + cx_1 \tag{4}$$

Plotting the term on the left versus x yields a straight line where $b + cx_1$ is the y intercept and c is the slope.

Equation 5: The factors in the last equation in the table are merely rearranged to provide a straight-line form.

Fitting Curve to Data. The steps in handling empirical data by the curve-fitting routine are as follows:

1. Plot the data and relate to a known equation such as given in the table.
2. Convert the equation to a straight-line form and evaluate the constants.
3. Construct an appropriate nomograph.

To construct a nomograph from empirical data, we must create a straight-line equation for the data and therefore have to determine the constants in the equation. The equation of a straight line is $y = ax + b$ where x and y are the variables, and a and b are the constants representing the slope of the line and the intercept with the vertical axis. Four ways to evaluate the constants are outlined below:

1. Graphical method
2. Selected-point method
3. Method of averages
4. Least-squares method

The graphical and selected-points methods are the least accurate, whereas the methods of averages and least squares are the most accurate.

To illustrate the procedure for these various methods, let us utilize the data in Table 3, obtained from an analysis of the time required to run stainless steel

TABLE 3   Stainless-steel Reduction Table

Number of pounds	Reduction in thousandths of an inch			
	10	20	30	40
	Time required			
25	1.0	2.0	3.0	4.0
50	1.5	3.0	4.5	6.0
100	2.5	5.0	7.5	10.0
150	3.8	7.0	10.5	13.5
200	5.0	9.0	14.0	18.0
300	7.0	13.0	19.0	25.0

through a rolling mill. The rolling mill reduces the thickness of the steel by the amount indicated as "reduction in thousandths of an inch." The data were obtained with a fixed starting width for the stainless steel. For each value of weight there are four time values given, one for each reduction figure. We shall use these data to illustrate the four methods for determining the constants of a straight-line equation so that a nomograph can be constructed.

Graphical Method. CONCURRENCY CHART: The data presented in the table are plotted in Fig. 7 and provide a series of straight lines forming a concurrency chart. The vertical axis is time T, in hours; the horizontal axis is the weight W, in pounds of material to be reduced. Each line represents the relationship between the weight of material and time for a given reduction.

Since the plot is a series of straight lines, the relationship between the

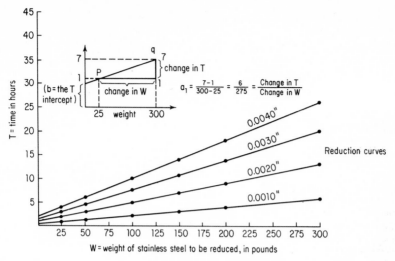

Fig. 7 Production of stainless steel.

variables is obviously of the type $y = ax + b$. Let the equation for the rolling time be

$$T = aW + b \qquad (5)$$

where T = time to roll in hours
$\quad\ \ W$ = weight of material in pounds
$\quad\ \ a$ = slope of the curve
$\quad\ \ b$ = T intercept

To obtain the constants, refer to the insert in Fig. 7 illustrating the basic terms a and b of Eq. (5).

$$a_1 = \frac{7-1}{300-25} = \frac{6}{275} \qquad \text{(for ten-thousandths of an inch reduction)}$$

The value of W in the denominator of the equation ranges from 300 down to 25 as the value of T in the numerator ranges from 7 down to 1. Thus from the graph we have the change in T for a given change in W. The same operation is repeated for the other three lines:

$$a_2 = \frac{13-2}{300-25} = \frac{11}{275}$$

$$a_3 = \frac{19-3}{300-25} = \frac{16}{275}$$

$$a_4 = \frac{25-4}{300-25} = \frac{21}{275}$$

The intercepts with the vertical axis are read from the figure as follows $(W = 0)$:

$$b_1 = 0.5$$
$$b_2 = 1.0$$
$$b_3 = 1.5$$
$$b_4 = 2.0$$

Inserting this information in Eq. (5), the equations for the four lines on the chart are

$$T_1 = \tfrac{6}{275}W + 0.5 \qquad \text{(ten-thousandths)} \tag{6}$$
$$T_2 = \tfrac{11}{275}W + 1.0 \qquad \text{(twenty-thousandths)} \tag{7}$$
$$T_3 = \tfrac{16}{275}W + 1.5 \qquad \text{(thirty-thousandths)} \tag{8}$$
$$T_4 = \tfrac{21}{275}W + 2.0 \qquad \text{(forty-thousandths)} \tag{9}$$

Based upon Eq. (6) through (9) we can extrapolate to determine equations which will represent the behavior of weight versus time for reductions of fifty- and sixty-thousandths. The equations for the fifty- and sixty-thousandths of an inch reduction are

$$T_5 = \tfrac{26}{275}W + 2.5 \tag{10}$$
$$T_6 = \tfrac{31}{275}W + 3.0 \tag{11}$$

Equations (10) and (11) are derived by noting that the change in a for each ten-thousandths of an inch reduction is $\tfrac{5}{275}$, and the change in b is 0.5. These can be derived by inspecting Eq. (6), through (9). For example, the difference in a between Eqs. (6) and (7) is $\tfrac{5}{275}$, and the difference in b is 0.5. Using the observed changes, the constants in Eq. (9) can be modified to develop Eq. (10). Hence:

Constant from Eq. (9) + difference = constant for Eq. (10)

$$\tfrac{21}{275} + \tfrac{5}{275} = \tfrac{26}{275} = a_5 \qquad \text{for Eq. (10)}$$
and
$$2.0 + .5 = 2.5 = b_5 \qquad \text{for Eq. (10)}$$

From Eqs. (10) and (11), additional lines can be plotted on the concurrency chart.

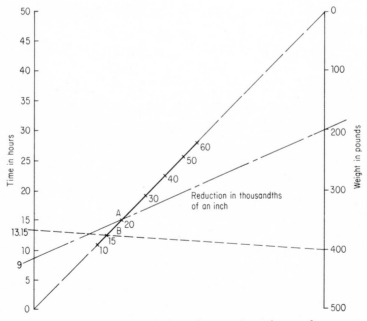

Fig. 8   Z nomograph for reduction of stainless steel.

Z OR N CHART: From the data provided and the equations developed, we can also lay out a Z chart for the time-versus-weight relationship. Figure 8 illustrates a Z chart for the reduction formula. The left axis is calibrated from 0 to 50 hours, and the right axis is calibrated from 0 to 500 pounds. The diagonal may be calibrated for ten-, twenty-, thirty-, and forty-thousandths of an inch reduction by plotting any convenient data shown in Table 3. For example, point A and twenty-thousandths was determined by selecting 200 pounds from the left-hand column and 9 hours which appears under the column headed by 20. These two values are plotted on their respective axes of the chart and connected by a line. The intercept of this line with the diagonal is point A for twenty-thousandths of an inch reduction. This point may be rechecked by selecting any other two values in the columns of the table.

For Eqs. (6) through (9) we have numerical values from the table of data. For Eqs. (10), (11), and (12) we can solve for values for T by inserting values for W within the range of 0 to 500 pounds. This will give us numerical values for calibrating the diagonal scale. The equations can also be used to interpolate and determine T and W for intermediate values of reduction. The equation for a reduction of fifteen-thousandths is

$$T_7 = \frac{8.5}{275} W + 0.75 \tag{12}$$

For example, how much time is required to reduce 400 pounds of stainless steel by fifteen-thousandths? The value is obtained as follows:

$$T = \frac{8.5}{275}(400) + 0.75$$
$$= 13.15 \text{ hours}$$

This set of values, 400 pounds and 13.15 hours, can be used for plotting the fifteen-thousandths reduction point on the diagonal as illustrated by point B on the chart.

The values for the constants derived in the example can be obtained by other means, but this method is called the "graphic method" because the values are read from the graph of the data. The graphical method of curve fitting can be summarized in the following steps:

1. Plot the data in straight-line format.
2. Pick two points, p and q, on the graph of the straight line and form a triangle to obtain the slope of the curve. (In the example, to find a_1 we used the points $W_p = 25$, $T_p = 1$, and $W_q = 300$, $T_q = 7$.)
3. Determine the T intercept by *letting* $W = 0$ and reading the value of T from the graph.
4. Form the equation for each value of slope (in the example, for each value of reduction.)

Selected-point Method. The second method of determining the values of the constants and setting up the equations is the method of *selected points*. First select two points on the graph, say, $W_p = 25$, $T_p = 1$, and $W_q = 300$, $T_q = 7$ (for this example the ten-thousandths of an inch reduction line is used). Insert these values in Eq. (5) as follows:

$$T = aW + b \tag{5}$$
$$7 = a300 + b \tag{5a}$$
and
$$1 = a25 + b \tag{5b}$$

Solve the equations simultaneously for a and b as follows: Subtract Eq. (5b) from Eq. (5a) to obtain:

$$6 = 275a$$

Solve for a:

$$a = \frac{6}{275}$$

Substitute the value of a in Eq. (5b) to obtain:

$$1 = \left(\frac{6}{275}\right)(25) + b$$

Solve for b:

$$b = 1 - \frac{6}{275}(25)$$
$$= \frac{5}{11}$$

Next insert these values of a and b in Eq. (5) to obtain the first equation of the group:

$$T = aW + b$$
$$= \frac{6}{275} W + \frac{5}{11}$$

Note that the value of the constant b differs slightly from the values read from the graph. This is due to the inherent error in reading a graph.

In summary, the method of selected points is a two-step approach:
1. Take two points from the data and insert in the equation for a line.
2. Use the points and solve the simultaneous equations for the constants.

Method of Averages. The third technique is the *method of averages*. In this case the straight line derived is the one with the algebraic sum of the observed and calculated values equal to zero. Expressed mathematically,

$$\sum_{i=1}^{n} (y - ax - b) = 0 \tag{13}$$

where y is the observed value and (ax + b) is the calculated value. In the case of our example, Eq. (13) would read

$$\sum_{i=1}^{3} (T - aW - b) = 0$$

where T is the observed value and $a_i W + b_i$ is the calculated value. The data from our example for ten-thousandths of an inch reduction are displayed in Table 4.

We wish to form a pair of simultaneous equations so we can determine the constants a and b for the equation of a straight line. The six points represent the data points used to plot the graph. To accomplish this we shall take the sum of the first three terms from Table 4 and form one equation; then take the sum of the second three terms to form a second equation. The two developed equations are

$$5 = a175 + b$$

and

$$15.8 = a650 + b$$

TABLE 4   Methods of Averages

T	W	$T = aW + b$
1	25	$1\ \ = a25 + b$
1.5	50	$1.5 = a50 + b$
2.5	100	$2.5 = a100 + b$
3.8	150	$3.8 = a150 + b$
5.0	200	$5.0 = a200 + b$
7.0	300	$7.0 = a300 + b$

When these equations are solved simultaneously for a and b they yield the following: $a = 6.2/275$ and $b = 1.1$. When the values are inserted in the general equation it becomes

$$T = \left(\frac{6.2}{275}\right) W + 1.1 \tag{14}$$

Equations for producing lines and points for reduction of twenty-, thirty-, and forty-thousandths of an inch are determined in the same way. After the equations are developed, the concurrency or Z chart can be produced as discussed previously. The method of averages is similar to the graphical technique of drawing a line through a series of plotted points such that the line appears to be located at a place that is in the center of the plotted data.

Least-squares Method. Another method of fitting a straight line to data is the *least-squares* technique where the algebraic sum of the squares of the observed and calculated values is a minimum. Hence

$$\sum_{i=1}^{n} (T - aW - b)^2 = \text{minimum} \tag{15}$$

The calculated value is T and the observed value is $aW + b$. For this to be true, the first derivative of Eq. (15) with respect to a and b must be set equal to zero. Thus,

$$\frac{d}{da} \sum_{i=1}^{n} (T - aW - b)^2 = \sum_{i=1}^{n} 2(-WT + aW^2 + bW) = 0$$

$$\frac{d}{db} \sum_{i=1}^{n} (T - aW - b)^2 = \sum_{i=1}^{n} 2(-T + aW + b) = 0$$

or

$$\sum_{i=1}^{n} (-WT + aW^2 + bW) = 0 \tag{16}$$

$$\sum_{i=1}^{n} (-T + aW + b) = 0 \tag{17}$$

Solving Eqs. (16) and (17) simultaneously will give the values of a and b necessary to meet the conditions for least squares. Table 5 has been constructed to determine the various terms required to solve these equations, for the line representing ten-thousandths of an inch reduction. Substituting these total

TABLE 5   Least-squares Table

T	W	W^2	WT
1	25	625	25
1.5	50	2,500	75
2.5	100	10,000	250
3.8	150	22,500	570
5.0	200	40,000	1,000
7.0	300	90,000	2,100
Total 20.8	825	165,625	4,020

values in Eqs. (16) and (17) yields the following values for a and b:

$$-4{,}020 + a(165{,}625) + b(825) = 0$$
$$-20.8 + a(825) + b = 0$$
$$a = 0.025$$
$$b = -0.2$$

The equation for the first straight line (ten-thousandths of an inch reduction) is

$$T = 0.025W - 0.2$$

It is interesting to compare the results by the four methods:

$$T = 0.025W - 0.2 \qquad \text{(by least squares)}$$
$$T = 0.023W + 1.1 \qquad \text{(by method of averages)}$$
$$T = 0.022W + 0.5 \qquad \text{(by method of selected points)}$$
$$T = 0.022W + 0.5 \qquad \text{(by the graphical method)}$$

The constants developed for each of the straight lines are similar but differ owing to the different techniques of development.

Any of the four methods for determining the constants of a straight-line equation may be used; however, the choice depends upon the accuracy required. For example, the graphical method and method of selected points can be used with data accurate to two places, whereas the methods of averages and least squares should be used with more accurate data (e.g., three places).

Fitting Nonlinear Curves.   If the curve representing the data is nonlinear and a means for converting the data into a straight-line representation cannot be found, we can make the conversion directly from the curve of the data. For example, the curve line shown in Fig. 9 represents the rolling time for a special metal alloy, being a reduced ten-thousandths of an inch (0.02 to 0.01). The data can be converted to a suitable form by drawing the line AB. The line extends from the beginning of the curve to the end and forms a chord. From each point that is known on the curve extend a horizontal line, ST, parallel to the axis such that it will intercept the chord. Where the horizontal line intercepts the chord extend a vertical line, TU, up to the line CB. Line CB represents a modification of the layout of line AD such that a straight-line relation exists between weight of the metal to be reduced and the rolling time. Line AD is linear, whereas line CB is logarithmic, and when the data are plotted using axes CB and AC a straight line results. A nomograph can now be constructed from the data plotted using axes AC and CB and using any of the techniques outlined previously.

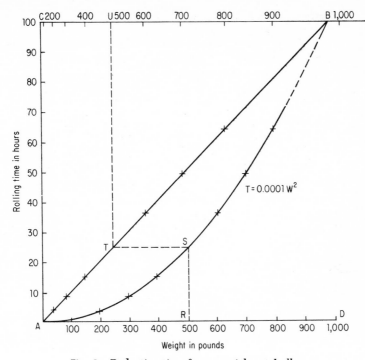

Fig. 9 Reduction time for a special metal alloy.

Actually this curve has an equation that can be translated to a straight-line format. The equation of the curve is

$$T = 0.0001 W^2 \tag{18}$$

Equation (18) is of the form $y = ax^b$ where $a = 0.0001$ and $b = 2$. The equation of this curve can be expressed in logarithmic form as follows:

$$\log T = \log (0.0001) + 2 \log W \tag{19}$$

Let $U = \log T$
$\quad V = \log W$
$\quad K = \log (0.0001)$
$\quad C = 2$
$\quad U = CV + K$

Set up a table and from the data determine the values for the terms of Eq. (19). This is illustrated in Table 6 for ten-thousandths of an inch. Equation (19) for ten-tousandths of an inch reduction has been plotted in Fig. 10. The graph is plotted on log paper, but instead of the log value the actual values of the variables are used. If other values of reduction are desired, similar lines can be drawn with other values of slope. By plotting several lines as shown, a concurrency chart is constructed and from this a Z chart can be made.

Steps for Handling Empirical Data. In summary, the steps required are:

1. Plot the data and attempt to identify the type of equation that the curve represents. From these facts plot the data in straight-line form. Either use the straight-line equation or translate the data to straight-line form by using a chord drawn on the curve.

TABLE 6   Rolling Time for Special Metal Alloy

T, hours	W, pounds	U log T	CV 2 log W	K log (0.0001)
9	300	0.954	4.954	6.000–10
16	400	1.204	5.204	6.000–10
25	500	1.398	5.398	6.000–10
36	600	1.556	5.556	6.000–10
49	700	1.690	5.690	6.000–10
64	800	1.808	5.808	6.000–10
81	900	1.910	5.910	6.000–10
100	1,000	2.000	6.000	6.000–10

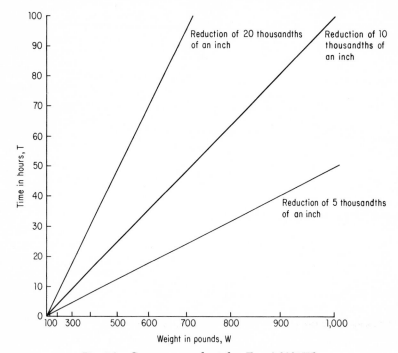

Fig. 10   Concurrency chart for $T = 0.0001W^2$.

2. From the straight-line plot, a concurrency chart or a Z chart can be constructed.

ADDITION CHARTS: ALIGNMENT CHARTS

From this point on, we shall relate the basic charts to their equations and derive analytical relationships required for constructing the charts.

An addition chart or alignment chart is illustrated in Fig. 11, which is based upon the equation:

$$X = Y + Z \tag{20}$$

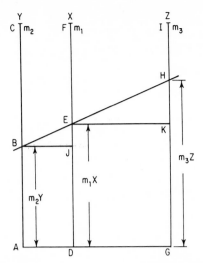

Fig. 11   Addition chart for equation of the form $X = Y + Z$.

The name of the nomograph is obviously derived from the *addition* that is performed in obtaining the resultant X.

In the nomograph let the following relationship exist for the three vertical axes:

$$DF = m_1X$$
$$AC = m_2Y$$
$$GI = m_3Z$$

where m_1, m_2, and m_3 are the scale factors or moduli relating the length of the lines to the functions X, Y, and Z, respectively.   The moduli m_2 and m_3 are chosen for convenience, but m_1 must satisfy the equation:

$$m_1X = m_2Y + m_3Z \qquad (21)$$

The following illustrates how m_1 is obtained: The triangles BJE and EKH in Fig. 11 are similar:

$$BJ = AD \qquad \text{and} \qquad EK = DG$$

Therefore,

$$\frac{AD}{EJ} = \frac{DG}{HK}$$

but
$$EJ = DE - AB$$
and
$$HK = GH - DE$$

Hence,

$$\frac{AD}{DE - AB} = \frac{DG}{GH - DE}$$

The line drawn between BEH represents a solution of the equation and permits us to say:

$$DE = m_1X$$
$$AB = m_2Y$$
$$GH = m_3Z$$

Therefore,

$$\frac{AD}{m_1X - m_2Y} = \frac{DG}{m_3Z - m_1X}$$

rearranging yields

$$m_1X = \frac{m_2Y}{1 + \dfrac{AD}{GD}} + \frac{m_3Z}{1 + \dfrac{DG}{AD}}$$

Let

$$\frac{m_2}{m_3} = \frac{AD}{DG}$$

then

$$m_1X = \frac{m_2 + m_3}{m_2 + m_3} Y + \frac{m_2 + m_3}{m_2 + m_3} Z$$

If we let

$$m_1 = \frac{m_2 m_3}{m_2 + m_3}$$

the equation reduces to

$$X = Y + Z$$

To set up this type of chart, the steps are as follows:
1. Choose m_2 and m_3 for convenience in plotting.
2. Make $m_1 = m_2 m_3 / (m_2 + m_3)$.
3. Space the center line X in accordance with the relationship

$$\frac{m_2}{m_3} = \frac{AD}{DG}$$

4. Graduate the scales in accordance with the relationship of the following equations:

$$DE = m_1X$$
$$AB = m_2Y$$
$$GH = m_3Z$$

Example   Consider the equation

$$C_T = C_S + C_I$$

where C_T = total cost
$\quad C_S$ = annual cost of setups
$\quad C_I$ = annual cost of holding inventory

Refer to Fig. 12 where the lines for C_I and C_S are drawn 8 inches long and 6 inches apart.   The ranges of the variables are as follows:

C_T from \$40,000 to \$600,000 per annum (range = \$560,000)
C_S from \$20,000 to \$100,000 per annum (range = \$80,000)
C_I from \$20,000 to \$500,000 per annum (range = \$480,000)

The scale is 8 inches long and the range of variation C_I is \$80,000;   therefore the modulus m_S is determined as follows:

$$m_S = \frac{8}{80,000} = \frac{1}{10,000}$$

The scale is 8 inches long and the range of variation for C_I is \$480,000; therefore the

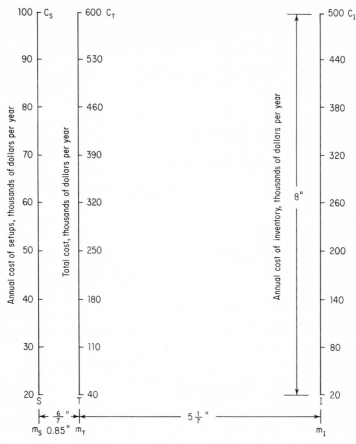

Fig. 12 Example of an addition chart.

modulus m_I is determined as follows:

$$m_I = \frac{8}{480,000} = \frac{1}{60,000}$$

Thus:

$$m_T = \frac{\left(\frac{1}{10,000}\right)\left(\frac{1}{60,000}\right)}{\left(\frac{1}{10,000} + \frac{1}{60,000}\right)}$$

$$m_T = \frac{1}{70,000}$$

Space the center line in the proportion of

$$\frac{m_S}{m_I} = \frac{\frac{1}{10,000}}{\frac{1}{60,000}} = \frac{ST}{TI} = \frac{6}{1}$$

Therefore $ST = 6TI$
but $ST + TI = 6$
Hence $ST = \frac{6}{7}$
and $TI = 5\frac{1}{7}$ inch

Place the center scale and graduate all scales to complete the chart.

Addition charts, for more than two terms in the right-hand side of the equation, are constructed merely by an extension of the basic principle.

Example   Consider the equation with three terms on the right-hand side: the right-hand side:

$$f(s) = f(t) + f(u) + f(v)$$

Let the example equation be

$$s = 5t + 3u + 2v$$

where $f(s) = 5$
$\quad\quad f(t) = 5t$
$\quad\quad f(u) = 3u$
$\quad\quad f(v) = 2v$

Let the range of the variables be
s varies from 30 to 132
t varies from 1 to 5 (5 to 25 for $5t$)
u varies from 3 to 9 (9 to 27 for $3u$)
v varies from 8 to 40 (16 to 80 for $2v$)

Refer to Fig. 13 where this example is illustrated.   For convenience let the length of each variable line be 4 inches and place the $f(t)$ and $f(u)$ scales 2 inches apart.

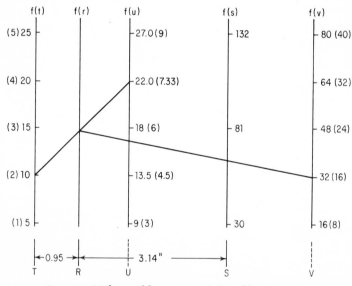

Fig. 13   Multivariable version of the addition chart.

To simplify the approach and so that we can use the equations developed for an addition with only three variables, let $r = 5t + 3u$; hence we construct a chart for $f(t)$, $f(u)$, and $f(r)$ where:

$$m_t = \frac{4}{25 - 5} = \frac{4}{20} = \frac{1}{5}$$

$$m_u = \frac{4}{27 - 9} = \frac{4}{18} = \frac{2}{9}$$

$$m_r = \frac{\frac{1}{5}(\frac{2}{9})}{\frac{1}{5} + \frac{2}{9}} = \frac{2}{19}$$

Place the scale for $f(r)$ between the $f(t)$ and $f(u)$ scales such that $TR/RU = \frac{1}{5} \div \frac{2}{9} = \frac{9}{10}$. But $TR + RU = TU = 2$ inches and $RU = \frac{10}{9} TR$, thus $TR = 0.95$ inch. Place $f(r)$ scale 0.95 inch to the right of the $f(t)$ scale.

Calibrate the $f(t)$ and $f(u)$ scales as shown. $f(r)$ is merely a pivot line and need not be calibrated. Next use the $f(r)$ line and the $f(v)$ lines to represent independent variables, and $f(s)$ is the line for the resultant. The scale factors for $f(s)$ and $f(v)$ are determined as follows: Choose a 4-inch line for $f(v)$, then

$$m_v = \frac{4}{80 - 16} = \frac{1}{16}$$

m_r was determined earlier as $\frac{2}{19}$; therefore,

$$m_s = \frac{\frac{2}{19}(\frac{1}{16})}{\frac{2}{19} + \frac{1}{16}} = \frac{2}{51}$$

Now $RS/SV = \frac{2}{19} \div \frac{1}{16} = 0.421$. Let us place the $f(r)$ and $f(v)$ scales 5 inches apart; then $RS + SV = 5$ inches and $RS = 3.14$ inches.

Calibrate the scales and the chart is complete. Although the $f(r)$ line is not calibrated, two lines are drawn on the chart to show how the computations are carried out using the $f(r)$ lines as a pivot. Multivariable charts are simply an extension of the basic addition chart and are constructed using the principles developed for the basic addition chart.

MULTIPLICATION CHARTS

A multiplication chart is, as its name implies, a nomograph designed for handling equations of the following type:

$$f(x) = f(y)f(z) \tag{22}$$

We have previously described the N or Z chart as applicable to handling multiplicative formulas. We shall now develop a more general approach for developing parallel line charts for multiplication. Equations such as Eq. (22) can be handled by placing them in logarithmic form such as

$$\log f(x) = \log f(y) + \log f(z)$$

and treating them as addition charts. By way of example consider the equation

$$N = \frac{4}{3}\left(\frac{P}{M}\right)E \tag{23}$$

where N = number of pieces of equipment
  E = equipment hours to make the part
  P = number of persons working on the job
  M = man-hours to make the part
  $\frac{4}{3}$ = constant reflecting machine utilization
To construct a chart let $P/M = Z$. Then

$$N = \frac{4}{3}ZE$$

which becomes the following when placed in logarithmic form:

$$\log N = \log \frac{4}{3} + \log Z + \log E$$

and can be handled by the method of the addition chart. A chart for this equation is illustrated in Fig. 14.

Example The procedure for the design of this chart is as follows:
  1. Choose a suitable range of variables:
E varies from 1 to 100

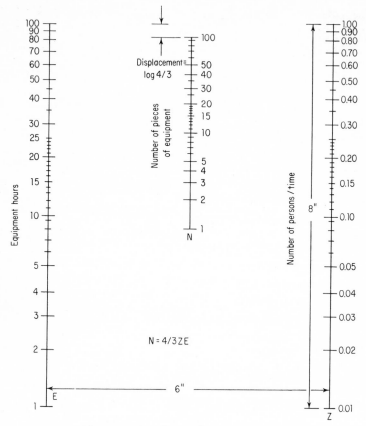

Fig. 14 Alignment chart for number of pieces of equipment.

Z varies from 0.01 to 1.0
N varies from 1 to 100

2. Select convenient lengths for the axes representing E and Z, say, 8 inches, and space them 6 inches apart.

3. Determine the scale factors:

$$\text{Scale factor} = \frac{\text{length of axis}}{\text{range of variable}}$$

$$m_n = \frac{8}{\log 100 - \log 1} = \frac{8}{2} = 4$$

$$m_z = \frac{8}{\log 1 - \log 0.01} = \frac{8}{2} = 4$$

4. Placement of the axes is determined as follows:

$$\frac{m_n}{m_z} = \frac{4}{4} = 1 = \frac{EN}{NZ}$$

Thus $EN = NZ$ and line for N is placed midway between the E and Z lines. Calibrate the scales using a log scale and displace the N scale by the amount of the constant multiplier, that is, $\log \frac{4}{3}$.

A second version of the chart appears in Fig. 15. Here the equation is plotted as a concurrency chart with the reciprocal of Z plotted on the lefthand

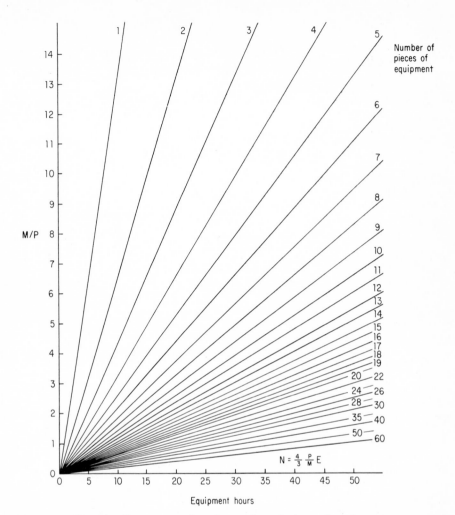

Fig. 15 Concurrency chart for number of pieces of equipment.

axis. The horizontal axis is equipment-hours and each slanted line plotted represents the number of pieces of equipment.

Now utilizing the concurrency chart as a source, we can plot a Z chart for the same equation. This is illustrated in Fig. 16. The reciprocal of Z is plotted on the left-hand scale, the equipment-hours in the right-hand scale, and the number of pieces of equipment along the diagonal. The left axis increases from bottom to top, whereas the right axis increases from top to bottom.

In summary, then, multiplicative equations can be handled by taking the logarithm of both sides of the original equation and handling the resulting straight-line equation as a form of addition chart, concurrency chart, or Z chart.

If the equation is of the form

$$f(x) = f(y)/f(z) \qquad (24)$$

it can be handled again by taking the logarithm of both sides of the equation

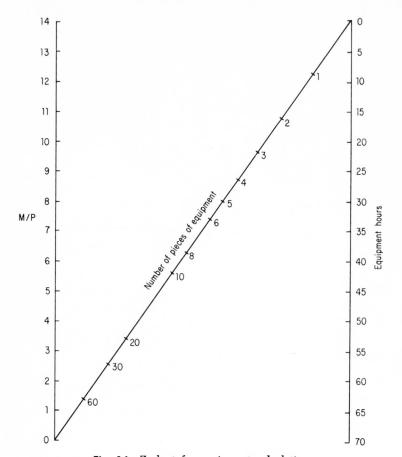

Fig. 16 Z chart for equipment calculation.

and making up a nomograph of the addition type. However, the function $f(z)$ must be plotted as a decreasing function owing to the negative sign which precedes its logarithm. For example,

$$\log f(x) = \log f(y) - \log f(z) \tag{25}$$

Log $f(z)$ must be plotted so it increases in value in a direction that is opposite to $\log f(x)$ and $\log f(y)$.

Figure 17 illustrates for comparative purposes the addition chart and the Z chart set up for handling an equation of the type represented by Eq. (24) and (25).

Figure 17a illustrates the addition-chart version of the multiplicative equation; note that all functions increase in value from bottom to top.

Figure 17b illustrates the setup for Eq. (25) where the $f(z)$ axis increases in a direction opposite to the $\log f(x)$ and $\log f(y)$.

Figure 17c illustrates the layout of a multiplicative formula with the direction of increasing amounts indicated by the arrows.

Figure 17d illustrates the Z-chart version of Eq. (24). Note that $f(z)$ is set to increase in the opposite direction to that of Fig. 17c.

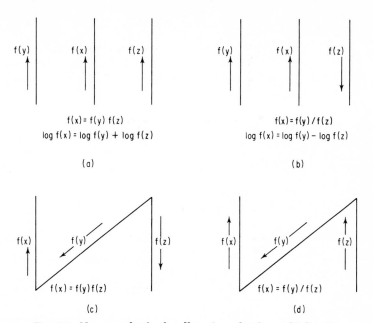

Fig. 17 Nomographs for handling formulas for multiplication.

PROPORTIONAL CHARTS

We are frequently faced with handling equations that consist of more complex arrangements of functions, for example, the optimal lot-size equation:

$$Q_0 = \sqrt{\frac{2RC_p}{C_i}} \qquad (26)$$

where Q_0 = optimal lot size
R = annual requirement
C_p = cost of preparing an order
C_i = cost of holding an item per year

The formula could be placed in logarithmic form and set up as an addition chart; however, we shall develop another type of nomograph for handing Eq. (26). It is called a "proportional chart" because it is used for treating equations of the following type:

$$f(x) = \frac{f(u)f(v)}{f(w)} \qquad (27)$$

The proportional chart for the optimal lot-size formula is illustrated in Fig. 18. Equation (26) has been arranged as follows:

$$Q_0{}^2 = \frac{2RC_p}{C_i} \qquad (26)$$

Referring to the figure we have made the following assumptions:

$$AB = m_q f(Q_0)$$
$$CD = m_r f(R)$$
$$DF = m_i f(C_i)$$
$$AE = m_p f(C_p)$$

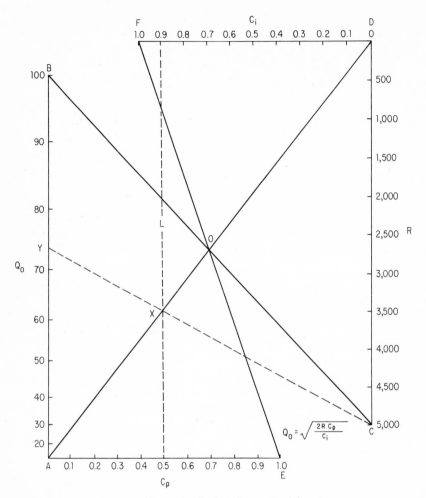

Fig. 18 Proportional chart for optimal lot size.

Triangles AOB and DOC are similar, so we can say

$$\frac{AB}{CD} = \frac{AO}{OD}$$

and because triangles FOD and AOE are also similar,

$$\frac{AE}{DF} = \frac{AO}{OD}$$

Hence

$$\frac{AB}{CD} = \frac{AE}{DF}$$

Therefore by replacement

$$\frac{m_q f(Q_0)}{m_r f(R)} = \frac{m_p f(C_p)}{m_i f(C_i)}$$

and

$$\frac{m_q}{m_r} = \frac{m_p}{m_i}$$

Example The chart is referred to as a "proportional chart" because the equation is in the form of a proportion. To set up the chart, proceed as follows:

1. Choose the range of the variables:

C_i, the cost of handling, varies from 0 to 1

C_p, cost of preparation, varies from 0 to 1

R, annual requirements, varies 0 to 5,000

Q_0^2, economic lot size squared, varies from 0 to 10,000

2. Set the length of the axes at some convenient value:

$$AE = DF = 5 \text{ inches}$$
$$AB = CD = 8 \text{ inches}$$

3. Determine the three moduli in accordance with the range of the variables and then compute the fourth. The modulus is determined by using the formula:

$$m = \frac{\text{length of line}}{\text{number of units}}$$

For example,

$$m_r = \frac{CD}{R}$$
$$= \frac{8}{5,000}$$

This is the effective modulus. In this case the constant 2 of Eq. (26) has been included. That is, the actual modulus is

$$m_{ra} = \frac{CD}{ZR} = \frac{8}{10,000} = \frac{4}{5,000}$$

so

$$m_r = m_{ra} \times 2$$
$$= \frac{4}{5,000} \times 2$$
$$= \frac{8}{5,000}$$

and

$$CD = m_{ra} \times 2R$$
$$= \frac{4 \times 2 \times 5,000}{5,000}$$
$$= 8 \text{ inches}$$

In other words the effective modulus is $\frac{8}{5,000}$ owing to the presence of the constant 2 in Eq. (26).

$$m_p = \frac{AE}{C_p} = \frac{5}{1}$$
$$m_i = \frac{DF}{C_i} = \frac{5}{1}$$

4. Calibrate the scales, and the chart is complete. Length of the C_i scale is 5 inches. Subdivide the line DF into 10 parts as shown in the figure. Similarly AE is subdivided into 10 parts and labeled C_p. Line DC is 8 inches long and represents $2r$ (rather than r). Subdivide DC into 10 parts and calibrate for range of r.

5. The AB scale is calibrated for Q_0 rather than Q_0^2, thus yielding the optimal lot size. Actually AB is calibrated to run from 0 to 10,000; however, to relate the proportional-chart scale AB to Q_0 instead of Q_0^2 we must take the square root of each term on AB. Subdivide AB into 10 parts (steps of 1,000 units each) and list values on line AB equal to the square root of the terms as listed in Table 7. After the scale is calibrated for Q_0, remove the subdivision and retain only the markers for Q_0.

6. Reading from the chart is accomplished by placing a straightedge vertically between the values of C_i and C_p as indicated by the dotted line L in the figure. This is drawn between $C_p = 0.5$ and $C_i = 0.9$, and crosses line AD at point X.

If the value of R is 5,000, then a second line CXY is drawn to pass from the point

TABLE 7

Q_0	$Q_0{}^2$
20	400
30	900
40	1,600
50	2,500
60	3,600
70	4,900
80	6,400
90	8,100
100	10,000

C through the point X terminating on the Q_0 axis at 74.5, the value desired. Note that

$$Q_0 = \sqrt{\frac{(2)(5000)(0.5)}{0.9}}$$
$$= \sqrt{5,555}$$
$$= 74.5$$

Any values could have been chosen to set up the dotted lines for solution as long as they obeyed the equation.

The obvious drawback of plotting the optimal lot size on the proportional-chart form is that the square root of the $Q_0{}^2$ term is required and the scale becomes non-linear and rather limited in range.

Equipment Equation in Proportional Form. To further illustrate the proportional chart, we shall show how Eq. (23) with its chart can be replotted as a proportional chart. This is illustrated in Fig. 19; in this case we have not combined N and M in a single variable. The design of the chart is accomplished as follows:

1. The basic equation is

$$N = \frac{4}{3}\left(\frac{P}{M}\right) E \tag{23}$$

2. The range of variables are
N varies from 0 to 100
P varies from 0 to 300
M varies from 0 to 300
E varies from 0 to 75

3. Select convenient lengths for the axes:

$$AC = DE = 8 \text{ inches}$$
$$AB = DF = 6 \text{ inches}$$

4. Set up scale factors:

$m_p = \frac{6}{300}$
$m_m = \frac{6}{300}$ modulus for man-time
$m_n = \left(\frac{8}{75}\right)\left(\frac{4}{3}\right) = \frac{8}{100}$ effective modulus for equipment-hours

$$m_e = \left(\frac{m_p}{m_m}\right) m_h$$

$$m_e = \frac{8}{100}$$

5. Draw the lines and calibrate the scales. Note that the effective modulus for equipment-hours occurs owing to the multiplier $\frac{4}{3}$.

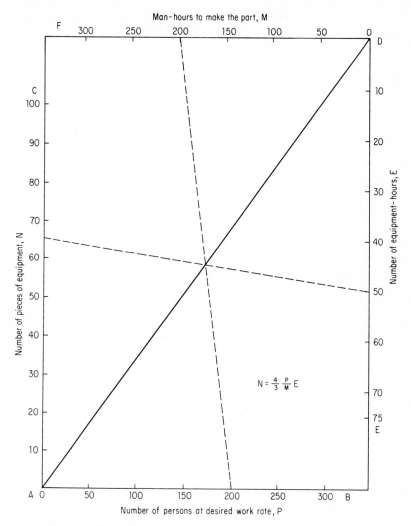

Fig. 19 Proportional chart for number of pieces of equipment.

CIRCULAR NOMOGRAPH

Another arrangement of a chart to handle the multiplicative formula is the circular nomograph. For example, a formula such as

$$f(x) = f(y)f(z)$$

is easily placed in circular form. However, circular charts are ideally suited to equations that involve trigonometric functions. A basic circular nomograph is illustrated in Fig. 20. One obvious advantage of a circular chart is that plotting data on the circumference of a circle allows information to be presented more compactly than in the straight-line version.

The circular nomograph illustrated in the figure is set up with $f(x)$ plotted along the diameter, $f(y)$ plotted around the upper half of the circumference, and $f(z)$ plotted around the lower half of the circumference. The points x, y, and z on the chart must relate through the equation

$$f(x) = f(y)f(z) \tag{27}$$

This can be shown to occur under the following conditions: Triangles AED and CDB are similar, and ABC is a right triangle. Therefore

$$\frac{DB}{\sin \alpha} = \frac{DC}{\sin (90 - \beta)} = \frac{DC}{\cos \beta}$$

$$DC = \left(\frac{DB}{\sin \alpha}\right) \cos \beta$$

and

$$\frac{DC}{\sin \beta} = \frac{AD}{\sin (90 - \alpha)} = \frac{AD}{\cos \alpha}$$

$$DC = \left(\frac{AD}{\cos \alpha}\right) \sin \beta$$

thus

$$DC = \frac{DB \cos \beta}{\sin \alpha} = \frac{AD \sin \beta}{\cos \alpha}$$

hence

$$\frac{DB}{AD} = \tan \alpha \tan \beta \left(\text{because } \tan \theta = \frac{\sin \theta}{\cos \theta}\right)$$

Let

$$m_x f(x) = \frac{DB}{AD}$$

$$m_y f(y) = \tan \alpha$$

$$m_z f(z) = \tan \beta$$

then

$$m_x f(x) = m_y f(y) m_z f(z)$$

or

$$\left(\frac{m_x}{m_y m_z}\right) f(x) = f(y)f(z) \tag{28}$$

Let $m_x = m_y m_z$ and Eq. (28) reduces to

$$f(x) = f(y)f(z)$$

Example As a practical example we shall make a circular nomograph (Fig. 21) from the equation:

$$P = FR$$

where P = number of persons required to do a piece of work
   F = factor that relates the number of persons to the rate of doing work
   R = rate of doing work

The design of the chart proceeds as follows:
 1. The range for variables is
P varies from 0 to 2,000
R varies from 0 to 50
F varies from 0 to 40
 2. Select the scale factors and the diameter of the circle. Let P run along the diameter of the circle, and F and R run around the circumference of the circle. The diameter of the circle is 3 inches. Refer to the figure where the basic setup and terms are given.
 First determine the scale factor for the diameter. From the derivation we know that

$$m_p P = \frac{AB}{CA}$$

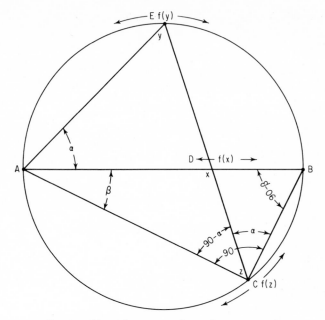

Fig. 20   Basic derivation of circular nomograph.

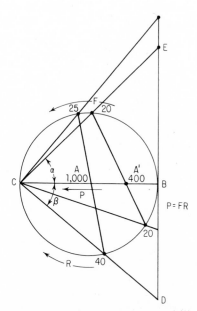

Fig. 21   Circular nomograph for determining number of persons.

But $CA = D - AB$ (D is the diameter).   Therefore

$$m_p P = \frac{AB}{3 - AB}$$

Assume the midrange value for P is 1,000, that is, $P = 1,000$ will occur at $AB = 1.5$ inches.   Thus

$$P = 1,000 \qquad \text{when } AB = 1.5 \text{ inches}$$

and

$$m_p 1,000 = \frac{1.5}{3 - 1.5}$$

$$m_p = \tfrac{1}{1,000}$$

Next select m_s and m_f:

$$m_s = \tfrac{1}{50}$$
$$m_f = \tfrac{1}{20}$$

Although m_s and m_f must yield a product of $\tfrac{1}{1,000}$, their values may be selected over a wide range of combinations.

$$m_p = m_s m_f = (\tfrac{1}{50})(\tfrac{1}{20}) = \tfrac{1}{1,000}$$

3. Calibrate the scales and the chart is complete. At $P = 1,000$, let $f(R) = 40$ and $f(F) = 25$. Now

$$\tan \alpha = m_f f(F) = (\tfrac{1}{20})25 = \tfrac{5}{4}$$
$$\tan \beta = m_R f(R) = (\tfrac{1}{50})40 = \tfrac{4}{5}$$
$$\frac{AB}{3 - AB} = \left(\frac{1}{1,000}\right)(1,000)$$

and

$$AB = 1.5 \text{ inches}$$

These points have been plotted on the figure. Choose a second point, say $P = 400$, and place these points on the nomograph. For $P = 400$, let $R = 20$ and $F = 20$, then

$$\tan \alpha = m_f f(F) = (\tfrac{1}{20})20 = 1$$
$$\tan \beta = m_R f(R) = (\tfrac{1}{50})20 = \tfrac{2}{5}$$
$$\frac{A'B}{3 - A'B} = \left(\frac{1}{1,000}\right)(400)$$

and

$$A'B = 0.86 \text{ inch}$$

The angles can be laid out by using the value of the tangent rather than finding the angle and setting it up with a compass. The line DBE was used for this purpose in the figure. To complete the calibration of the scales a table of values should be made and then carefully translated to the chart.

CALIBRATION OF SCALES

Scales for alignment charts and nomographs must be carefully prepared and should not have adjacent strokes closer than $\tfrac{1}{20}$ inch. Always use as large a scale as possible and make clear, sharp lines. To produce scales of various sizes and uniformity with minimum chance for error, the following techniques are suggested:

Prepare a table of the length and functional value of each variable that is being plotted. For example, for the equation

$$y = x + 10$$

with x ranging from 0 to 40 over a 5-inch scale, first determine the scale factor

$$m_y = \frac{5}{50 - 10} = \frac{1}{10}$$

then set up the scale equation

$$L = \tfrac{1}{10}(x + 10)$$

and prepare a table of values to be plotted. Refer to Table 8 where these data have been listed. From these data carefully set up and graduate the scales as shown below.

If the scale to be graduated is nonlinear, the process of graduating the scale can be carried out with the use of special rulers or printed scales. However, there are several simple methods using ordinary supplies that can be used to calibrate the scales. For example, Fig. 22 illustrates one basic mechanism. Lay out a vertical scale, such as line AB, 10 inches long, and graduate it with the aid of a log table. That is, read the logarithm of a number and place the number on the line AB in proportion to its logarithm. Log $2 = .3010$; therefore, place the unit 2 at a distance of 3.01 inches from the bottom of the scale. In this way form a single cycle, from 1 to 10, on the line AB. Draw a second line at right angles to AB and graduate it linearly in 1-inch steps from 10 to 1 as represented by line AC. Complete the triangle ABC by drawing

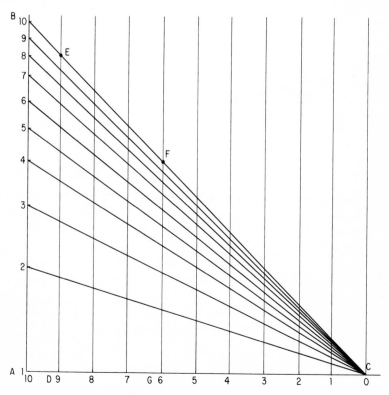

Fig. 22 Chart for laying out nonlinear scales.

TABLE 8   Calibration Table

y	L (inches)	x
10	1	0
20	2	10
30	3	20
40	4	30
50	5	40

```
Y
0    10    20    30    40    50
└────┴─────┴─────┴─────┴─────┘
0     1     2     3     4     5
              L (inches)
```

a line between A and C. Draw a series of vertical lines such as DE every inch along the chart. These vertical lines intersect the line BC at the value of 10 for each line length. Thus for a 9-inch scale the value of 10 is plotted at the point E. Similar triangles are formed for other numerical values on the line AB and the resultant is a chart that can be ued for calibrating scales of 10 inches or less.

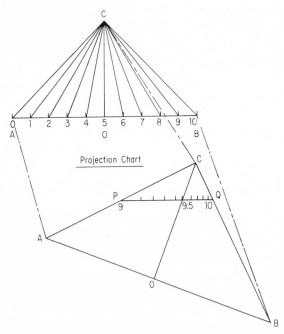

Fig. 23 Subdividing a scale with a projection chart. The top figure illustrates the projection chart for calibrating a nonlinear scale. Here the scale is subdivided into 10 equal parts and $OA = OB = OC$. In the bottom figure the line PQ is to be subdivided into 10 parts between 9 and 10. A point is given for 9.5 which is not centrally located. The projection chart is placed over the line PQ as shown, and adjusted until AC passes through PQ at 9. The projection chart is pivoted until OC passes through 9.5, and CB passes through 10. The line PQ can be subdivided between 9 and 10 in accordance with the points of intersection of the projection pattern and the line PQ.

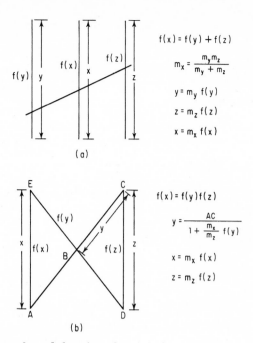

$$f(x) = f(y) + f(z)$$

$$m_x = \frac{m_y m_z}{m_y + m_z}$$

$$y = m_y f(y)$$

$$z = m_z f(z)$$

$$x = m_x f(x)$$

(a)

$$f(x) = f(y) f(z)$$

$$y = \frac{AC}{1 + \dfrac{m_x}{m_z} f(y)}$$

$$x = m_x f(x)$$

$$z = m_z f(z)$$

(b)

Fig. 24 Nomographs and their formulas: (a) alignment chart; (b) Z or N chart.

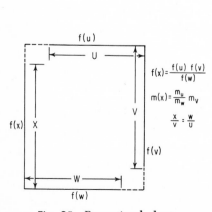

$$f(x) = \frac{f(u) \, f(v)}{f(w)}$$

$$m(x) = \frac{m_u}{m_w} m_v$$

$$\frac{x}{v} = \frac{w}{u}$$

Fig. 25 Proportional chart.

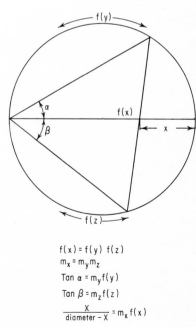

$$f(x) = f(y) \, f(z)$$
$$m_x = m_y m_z$$
$$\text{Tan } \alpha = m_y f(y)$$
$$\text{Tan } \beta = m_z f(z)$$
$$\frac{X}{\text{diameter} - X} = m_x f(x)$$

Fig. 26 Basic equations for circular chart.

The similar triangles ABC and DEC are related as follows:

$$\frac{AB}{AC} = \frac{DE}{DC}$$

The line DE is calibrated logarithmically (1 to 10) over a length of 9 inches. Similarly FG is calibrated logarithmically over a length of 6 inches. The chart can be extended to greater lengths as required.

To subdivide nonlinear scales one can use the projection method. This method is illustrated by the drawings in Fig. 23. The top figure illustrates the *projection chart* for calibrating a nonlinear scale. Here the scale is subdivided into 10 equal parts and $OA = OB = OC$. In the bottom figure the line PQ is to be subdivided into 10 parts between 9 and 10. A point is given for 9.5 which is not centrally located. The projection chart is placed over the line PQ as shown, and adjusted until AC passes through PQ at 9. The project chart is pivoted until OC passes through 9.5, and CB passes through 10. The line PQ can be subdivided between 9 and 10 in accordance with the points of intersection of the projection pattern and the line PQ.

SUMMARY

Nomographs developed in this chapter are summarized in Figs. 24, 25, and 26. Each figure contains the basic nomograph and the equations required for setting up scale factors. Nomographs are suited to computations that are frequently repeated and to the examination of the behavior of related variables. Nomographs provide a simple method for making calculations that are relatively free of errors, and require that the user have little knowledge of mathematics.

BIBLIOGRAPHY

Adams, D. P.: *Nomograph*, Shoe String Press, Hamden, Conn., 1964.

Allcock, H. J., and J. R. Jones: *The Nomogram*, 5th ed., Pitman Publishing Corporation, New York, 1963.

Chemical Processing (periodical); *Nomographs*, Chemical Publishing Company, Inc., New York, 1960.

Crowhurst, N. H.: *Graphical Calculators and Their Design*, Hayden Publishing Company, New York, 1965.

Davis, D. S.: *Nomography and Empirical Equations*, 2d ed., Reinhold Publishing Corporation, New York, 1962.

Epstein, L. I.: *Nomography*, John Wiley & Sons, Inc., New York, 1958.

Giet, Armand: *Abacs or Nomographs*, Philosophical Library, Quakertown, 1956.

Johnson, Lee H.: *Nomography and Empirical Equations*, John Wiley & Sons, Inc., New York, 1952.

Kharbanda, O. P.: *Nomograms for Chemical Engineers*, Academic Press, Inc., New York, 1958.

Kuong, J. F.: *Applied Nomography*, vol. 1, Gulf Publishing Company, Houston, 1965.

Levens, A. S.: *Nomography*, John Wiley & Sons, Inc., New York, 1959.

Lytel, A. H.: *Handbook of Electronic Charts and Nomographs*, Howard W. Sams & Co., Inc., Indianapolis, 1961.

Moffett, D. W.: *Charts and Nomographs for Electronic Technicians and Engineers*, Gernsback Publications, Inc., New York, 1965.

Otto, E.: *Nomography*, The Macmillan Company, New York, 1963.

Peters, R. L.: *Materials Data Nomographs*, Reinhold Publishing Corporation, New York, 1965.

Section Eight

APICS-*Factory* Report

Average number of components per finished product:

0–1	2–10	11–20	21–50	Over 50
9%	25%	13%	13%	40%

Average number of operations per order:

1–4	5–10	11–20	Over 20
13%	42%	21%	24%

Total employment at your plant and what percent of this works full time on production and inventory control?

Range of total employment	Percent	Average percent in P&IC	1961 average percent
1–99	6	5.5	5.5
100–199	12	3.2	3.7
200–299	11	3.1	3.4
300–399	9	3.4	3.6
400–499	6	3.3	3.3
500–599	8	2.8	4.5
600–699	6	2.7	3.8
700–799	2	1.9	3.4
800–899	4	3.0	2.8
900–999	3	4.2	3.3
1,000–1,499	12	2.8	3.5
1,500–1,999	8	3.1	3.5
2,000–4,999	8	3.1	
5,000 and above	5	4.5	
Total	100	Weighted average = 3.3%	

How many full-time employees in production and inventory control and what percent is this of total employment?

Range of P&IC employment	Percent	Average percent of total employment
1–2	7	2.2
3–4	12	2.1
5–6	11	2.1
7–8	8	2.5
9–10	7	3.2
11–12	5	2.3
13–14	4	4.4
15–16	6	2.6
17–18	2	3.0
19–20	3	2.8
21–26	4	3.1
27–35	8	4.0
36–50	8	3.0
51–70	5	4.7
71–100	3	4.5
101–200	3	7.2
201 and above	4	7.0
Total	100	Weighted average = 3.3%

9. How do current inventory levels compare with:

Category	Percent last year			Percent five years ago		
	Higher	Same	Lower	Higher	Same	Lower
Raw materials......	52	23	25	71	7	22
In process.........	56	24	20	73	10	17
Finished goods......	48	22	30	69	8	23
Total inventory.....	59	20	21	72	8	20

10. How does current, *actual* lead time compare with those of a year ago?

Higher	Same	Lower
53%	25%	22%

11. Estimate average ratio of total in-plant lead time (shop order to completion) to actual setup and running time:

   a. Respondents who appeared to have answered by *ratio* of total lead time to setup and running time:

Less than 2:1	2:1 through 4:1	5:1 through 10:1	11:1 through 19:1	20:1 and Above
25%	42%	20%	7%	6%

   b. Respondents who appeared to have answered by percentages of setup and running time to total lead time:

Less than 30%	30% to 50%	51% to 75%	76% to 99%
39%	30%	13%	18%

   c. Thirty-three percent had no response indicating that this question was badly misunderstood. The validity of this particular answer is questionable.

Conclusion. The fact that only a minority has been educated in courses aimed at industrial management, coupled with the majority having started in some other field, may explain the strong compulsion for continued education—42 percent of the replies indicate that advanced courses have been taken. The need for even further education ranks as the second most beneficial area for more effectiveness as shown later in Question 49.

Of universal interest to the practitioner responsible for the operation of his department is the number of people required to perform the tasks. Logically, the quantity depends on the size of the company and the type of manufacturing operation. A semiprocess-type plant may require very few while a job shop with many different products may require more. However, the average of 3.3 percent of employment comes through consistently. The 1961 average was 3.5 percent. Because of increasing management emphasis in the area of production and inventory control, this decrease if significant may be accounted for through the gains achieved in data processing.

ORGANIZATION AND SCOPE OF RESPONSIBILITY

To establish the extent to which the production and inventory control department is responsible for various functions such as determining levels of production and inventories, scheduling, loading, calculating lead times, and resolving make-or-buy decisions, Questions 12 through 20 were asked.

The influence of engineering and purchasing is most evident, and in a substantial (30 percent) number of APICS survey companies, production and inventory control is primarily responsible for contacting customers on delivery promises. The sales department is only a surprisingly 6 percent higher.

12. What function is primarily responsible for:

Function	Percent P & IC		Percent engineering		Percent other	
	1966	1961	1966	1961	1966	1961
Release of new products to factory for production	66	50	16	24	18	26
Authorization of tooling for new products	18	18	43	24	39	58
Setting levels of production	79	77	2	- -	19	23

13. What function is primarily responsible for determination of inventory levels?

Function	Percent P & IC		Percent other (1966)
	1966	1961	
Finished goods	74	70	26 (9% = sales and marketing)
Work in process	89	88	11
Production materials	84	81	16
Supplies	62		26 (7% = mfg. and supply store)

14. What function is primarily responsible for customer contact on delivery promises?

Function	Percent
	0 10 20 30 40
Sales	
Production and inventory control	
Customer service	
Purchasing	
Contract administrator	
Activity not performed here	
Other	

15. What function is primarily responsible for the following action?

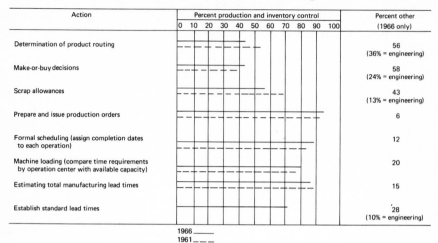

Action	Percent production and inventory control 0 10 20 30 40 50 60 70 80 90 100	Percent other (1966 only)
Determination of product routing		56 (36% = engineering)
Make-or-buy decisions		58 (24% = engineering)
Scrap allowances		43 (13% = engineering)
Prepare and issue production orders		6
Formal scheduling (assign completion dates to each operation)		12
Machine loading (compare time requirements by operation center with available capacity)		20
Estimating total manufacturing lead times		15
Establish standard lead times		28 (10% = engineering)

1966 _____
1961 _ _ _

16. What function is primarily responsible for control of raw-materials inventories?

Action	Percent Production and Inventory Control 0 10 20 30 40 50 60 70 80 90 100	Percent Purchasing 0 10 20	Percent other (1966)
Record keeping			13
Place purchase requisitions			10
Determine order quantity			9
Determine item inventory level			9
Determine inventory reserves			10

1966 _____
1961 _ _ _

17. Evaluate the "interface" and cooperation between production and inventory control and tangent functions:

Poor ——————   Marginal ....   Good — — —

Department	Percent of respondents 0 10 20 30 40 50 60 70 80 90 100
Production	
Purchasing	
Sales	
Systems and procedures	
Industrial engineering	
Plant management	

18. Is materials management (the organizational grouping of all functions related to production materials—purchasing, production control, materials handling, etc.) used at your plant?

Yes	No
32%	68%

If so, have specific, significant improvements resulted?

Yes	No	Not Indicated
59%	4%	37%

19. At your plant, to whom does production control report?

Title	Percent of respondents
	0 10 20 30
Plant manager	
Production or mfg. manager	
General manager	
Materials manager	
V.P. manufacturing	
Other	

20. In turn, which of the following report to production control?

Function	Percent replying "yes"
	0 10 20 30 40 50 60 70 80 90 100
Scheduling	
Production planning	
Dispatching	
Finished-goods inventory	
Stores	
Receiving	
Materials handling and movement	
Shipping	
Traffic	
Documentation	
Purchasing	
Other	

Conclusion. Question 18 concerning materials management indicates that the organizational concept of materials management has been installed in 32 percent of the companies represented. The 1961 survey did not ask a similar question. It will be of interest to see the results from the next survey to find the extent of the trend to this relatively new approach. The fact that only 4 percent of those who were using it felt that no improvements resulted is to some degree offset by the large 37 percent who did not care to comment one way or the other.

Production and inventory control by its own definition must establish communications with other company activities in order to fulfill its mission of good customer service, efficient manufacturing operation, and minimum dollar investment. The fact that these relationships are not yet what they should be is reflected in Question 17. The cooperation with manufacturing is rated high but frictions are evident with sales and systems. This may not be surprising for sales where there is apt to be little understanding of manufacturing problems and great enthusiasm for deliveries. However, it was an ominous note in the survey to find the similar low rating for the systems group.

The tremendous need for production and inventory control people to improve their performance (see Question 48) coupled with the realization that improvements need to come from computers and improved techniques (see Question 49) mean an increasing need for the system function. The improvement of the relationship appears to be a paramount requirement if the desired improvement is to come.

METHODS, TECHNIQUES, AND DATA PROCESSING

The following questions show that the "scientific approach" has a long way to go to replace old-fashioned judgment, intuition, and executive opinion. And when the results of the latter are forecasts from the sales department, 86 percent of them are further "adjusted" before being used! Techniques such as exponential smoothing, simulation, linear programming, PERT, and the familiar EOQ calculation, although becoming more popular, appear to be more a subject for discussion at APICS meetings than applied to control production and inventory. Questions 21 through 36 reflect their low rate of acceptance as well as pointing out the effect of data processing equipment on production and inventory control operations.

21. What types of estimating does your plant use for sales forecast (if more than one, please indicate which time period(s) are used for each type)?

Type	Use for sales forecast		5 years		Annual		Moving 12 months		Moving 3 months		Quarterly		Monthly	
Sales manager's estimate	53	67	18	14	41	58	11	11	11	14	16	27	15	25
Executive opinion	44	33	15	14	22	30	5	4	4	7	8	9	8	11
Marketing analysis	27	26	18	13	24	23	8	5	7	6	8	8	8	8
Expected share of market	22	29	15	14	25	27	5	4	3	2	7	6	5	5
Correlation with economic indicators	21	13	9	7	12	13	3	2	3	2	4	5	4	3
Trend and cycle analysis	24	15	7	6	10	11	6	5	6	4	6	5	7	7
Charts with control limits	11	8	3	4	6	4	3	2	3	4	4	2	5	5
Adjusted by latest sales information	47	30	5	5	13	19	7	6	10	8	15	15	22	20
Exponential smoothing	14	7	1	1	3	5	4	4	5	3	2	3	6	4
Other	7		1		3		2		2		1		3	

Percent in left-hand columns — 1966
Percent in right-hand columns — 1961

22. Are sales department forecasts used for planning purposes without adjustments or interpretation by production planning department or others?

Yes   No

14%   86% (1961 = 80%)

If so, are forecasts jointly developed?

Yes   No

55% (1961 = 35%)   45%

23. How do you estimate inventory carrying costs?

Fixed percent of total manufacturing costs	37%
Allocated space, handling, and utility costs	19%
Measurable associated costs plus factor for theft and obsolescence	17%
Not estimated	19%
Other	8%
Total	100%

24. At your plant, which methods are used for what?

Method	Used to determine production output (not shipments)		Used to determine levels of inventory					
			Finished goods		In-process		Raw materials	
Executive opinion _ _ _ _ _ _ _ _	36	38	31	31	15	18	20	21
Overall financial consideration _ _ _	25	34	34	38	20	26	29	36
Level of employment (i.e., to offset seasonal fluctuations) _ _ _ _ _	32	35	22	24	16	18	6	10
Plant load reflected by inventory control system or customer order _	56	17	36	15	42	16	31	15
Optimum inventory calculations _ _	17	14	27	14	17	11	25	15
Inventory turnover ratios _ _ _ _	16	18	28	26	17	18	24	23
Linear programming _ _ _ _ _ _	4	5	2	3	2	4	1	3
Shop simulation _ _ _ _ _ _ _ _	4		1		3		1	
Other _ _ _ _ _ _ _ _ _ _ _ _	4	8	4	6	4	4	4	6

Percent left-hand columns — 1966
Percent right-hand columns — 1961

25. What factors determine the size and timing of production orders?

Method	Percent used to determine quantity						Percent used to determine timing					
	0	10	20	30	40	50	0	10	20	30	40	50
Available men and machine capacity _ _ _ _ _												
Judgement or opinion _ _ _ _ _ _ _ _ _ _ _ _ _												
Reorder point _ _ _ _ _ _ _ _ _ _ _ _ _ _ _												
Exploded requirement _ _ _ _ _ _ _ _ _ _ _ _												
EOQ formula _ _ _ _ _ _ _ _ _ _ _ _ _ _ _												
Two-bin system and standard lot size _ _ _ _ _												
Other _ _ _ _ _ _ _ _ _ _ _ _ _ _ _ _ _												

26. How are delivery promises made to customers by your plant (more than one method could be used)?

By quotation of standard delivery time — 45%

Based on the inventory status of finished goods, work in process, and raw materials — 50%

Based on machine time available for each product — 24%

Other — 18%

27. Estimate what percent of your customers expect delivery of your product in less than published lead times:

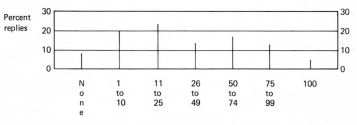

Percent of customers

28. Do you have a system for keeping customers advised of delays that could affect deliveries?

Yes   No

81%   19% (1961 = 17%)

If so, is it operating satisfactorily?

Yes   No

75%   25% (1961 = 20%)

29. In your planning, do you use straight-line scheduling (complete one operation before start of next) or overlapping scheduling (start of second operation before completion of first)?

Straight-line   Overlapping

45%   55%

30. Is the time element in your detail scheduling and machine loading based on (more than one element could be used):

1966 ————
1961 — — —

31. Does your plant do:

	Yes	No	Not indicated
Dispatching by foremen	26%	43%	31%
Dispatching by dispatchers in factory who report to production control	35%	43%	22%
Centralized dispatching with communications between the plant and the dispatching center	48%	27%	25%

32. Is in-process job status and progress reported via:

50%   A separate paper-work system

25%   The payroll job tickets

13%   Mechanical or electronic production monitoring equipment timekeeper station

12%   Other

100%   Total

33. How are inventory reserves (safety stock) set?

70%   Plain judgment, taking into account abnormal use, delivery delays, etc. during lead time

30%   Mathematical formula based on probability distribution

34. Is there a person or department whose major responsibility is operations research methods and techniques?

	Percent yes	Percent no	Percent not indicated
In your plant?	* 22	68	10
In your parent company?	35	43	22
If so, have significant improvements resulted?	48	52	- - -

*In 1961, 23 percent replied "yes"

35. Is your plant using any of the following techniques to plan or control production or inventories?

36. What method do you use to process data in the following application areas?

Type of Information	Manual system		Desk calculator	Control boards		Edge-notched cards		Punch-card (tab.) equip.		Stored program computer		Do not process	
Order entry	51	. .	5	5	. .	1	. .	24	. .	27	. .	2	. .
Customer's delivery	53	58	5	10	7	1	2	16	27	23	10	5	4
Production orders:													
Quantity and timing	61	66	9	12	8	1	1	13	15	24	11	2	1
Preparation	69	67	7	3	3	1	2	11	15	17	8	1	2
Detail schedules for mfg.	58	69	6	12	11	1	1	10	11	13	5	3	7
Follow-up reporting	57	68	3	8	7	1	1	11	14	14	5	3	4
Inventory records:													
Finished	40	56	4	2	1	1	1	22	34	27	15	1	1
Work in process	44	59	4	3	3	2	3	15	24	21	9	4	5
Raw materials	50	67	5	1	1	1	1	14	23	20	10	2	1
Machine loading	45	. .	4	9	. .	1	. .	8	. .	11	. .	11	. .
Average of the above	53		5	7		1		14		20		3	

Percent in left-hand columns — 1966
Percent in right-hand columns — 1961

Question	Percent yes	Percent no	Percent not indicated	Percent no 1961
37. Is there an organization chart for your department?_ _ _ _ _ _ _	69	13	18	21
38. Is there an adequate job description for every position?_ _ _ _ _ _	60	22	18	27
39. Do you have training methods or programs for each of the positions in your department?_ _ _ _ _ _ _ _ _ _ _ _	36	45	19	51
40. Do you have a procedure manual that describes how to perform each of the tasks in your department?_ _ _ _ _ _ _ _ _	33	47	20	61
If so, is the manual up to date?_ _ _ _ _ _ _ _ _ _ _ _ _	51	49	–	–
Is the manual adequate?_ _ _ _ _ _ _ _ _ _ _ _ _ _ _	57	43	–	–
41. Do you have an internal education program on the functions and operations of your department?_ _ _ _ _ _ _ _ _ _ _	33	49	18	71
42. Are company production and inventory policies and objectives in written form?_ _ _ _ _ _ _ _ _ _ _ _ _ _ _ _ _	33	49	18	–
If so, are they current?_ _ _ _ _ _ _ _ _ _ _ _ _ _ _ _	80	20	–	–
43. Do you usually understand what is expected of you?_ _ _ _ _ _	74	6	20	–

Conclusion. Statistics, mathematical calculations, and operations research techniques are making inroads in the field of managing production and inventories, but there seems to be a considerable gap between the theory and the practice of running plant operations. Only 22 percent indicated that their plants had an operations research department (about the same as in 1961), and 52 percent of these felt that it had *not* resulted in any significant improvement. Since 1961, companies using the EOQ calculation to control production have increased from 28 to 31 percent, and similarly, to control inventories, from 38 to 49 percent.

It is important to recognize that these techniques do not apply to all companies, yet some questions clearly point out the fact that big improvements are possible in many plants. For example, 70 percent of the practitioners replying indicated that they use only plain judgment in setting inventory reserves. And in the area of inventory management—where real strides have been made in the practical application of scientific techniques—there still appear to be many who are not aware of these techniques. For example, many experts in this area feel that some form of requirement explosion is the proper way to control the inventory of components that go into an assembled product. Yet 90 percent of the answering companies make an assembled product and only 27 percent use a requirement explosion for the timing of production orders and 42 percent use reorder point. A surprising 30 percent still use judgment. Perhaps this is why so many of these companies feel that better education (see Question 49) of their production and inventory control personnel is essential to better management.

The processing of information is evolving in an expected manner—the use of the computer has grown considerably since 1961 with a corresponding decline in punched-card tabulating equipment. The great potential for growth is evidenced by the fact that the majority of companies still use a manual system for most operations.

OPERATION OF THE DEPARTMENT AND MEASURING ITS EFFECTIVENESS

Concerning the operation of the department, two general impressions appear in Questions 37 through 44: (1) the procedures, policies, job descriptions, and organization charts have not been formalized into written format, and (2) a sizable number of respondents did not care to reply to most of these questions—indicating an apparent lack of importance to their particular operation.

Questions 45 through 50 cover the popularity of various means of measuring performance and suggestions for improved effectiveness.

44. How are openings in your department usually filled?

		Percent frequency				
	Total	100	80–99	60–79	50–59	Less than 50
Promote within.....	33	13	35	18	22	12
Outside hire........	29	5	10	6	29	50
Both..............	38					
Total...........	100					

45. Does your plant measure performance against delivery promises according to:

	Yes	No	Not indicated
Items delivered as promised.............................	45%	19%	36%
Age of past-due items in number of days or weeks..........	38%	19%	43%
Quantities delivered as promised........................	26%	26%	48%
Dollars delivered as promised..........................	25%	27%	48%
Other..	37%	48%	85%

46. Does your plant measure the effectiveness of your management of *inventories* according to:

	Yes	No	Not indicated	1961 yes
Inventory turnover.............................	58%	11%	31%	86%
Dollar investment.............................	56%	9%	35%	89%
Quantities or dollars of obsolete items...........	35%	20%	45%	60%
Quantities or dollars of surplus items............	28%	25%	47%	56%
Return on investment in inventories..............	24%	24%	52%	41%
Other...	5%	6%	89%	

47. Does your plant measure the effectiveness of your management of *production* according to:

	Yes	No	Not indicated	1961 yes
Comparison of actual with planned production.....	63 %	9 %	28 %	90 %
Overtime of hourly production workers...........	37 %	16 %	47 %	75 %
Machine utilization ratio......................	24 %	23 %	53 %	39 %
Other...	9 %	5 %	86 %	

48. Do you feel your plant's production and inventory control is as good as it should be?

Yes	No	Not Indicated
7%	75%	18%

49. What would most assist production and inventory control to become effective?

Improved techniques	53%
Better education and training of P&IC personnel	48%
More accurate and dependable forecasts	45%
Computers	36%
Improved basic information (bills of material, routings, etc.)	31%
Greater management support	30%
Other	8%

50. Do you feel the importance and impact of production and inventory control is properly appreciated at your plant?

Yes	No	Not Indicated
43%	34%	23%

Conclusion. While the means of measuring performance are varied both in type and in popularity, a very significant 75 percent of the replies indicated their plant's production and inventory control is not as good as it should be. Only 7 percent were satisfied with their performance.

This dissatisfaction may be the key to the rapid growth of APICS—the society attracting people facing similar problems, with the mutual desire to improve their operations.

The trend reflected in Questions 46 and 47 could be interpreted as a lack of confidence in several widely known yardsticks of performance, i.e., inventory turnover, dollar investment, return on investment, etc. Barometers that fail to consider the conflicting objectives of good service, minimum investment, and efficient operation give distorted figures of actual performance. For example, a high inventory turnover is certainly not a desirable achievement if customer service and manufacturing costs go out of control. And in a tight labor market, the amout of overtime hours can become a meaningless measurement of good production control effort. Unfortunately, the survey failed to indicate a performance measurement that is widely accepted by the practitioners.

Question 49 lists the areas where the respondents felt that improvement must come from. Interestingly, at the top of the list is improved techniques followed closely by better internal education and improved forecasts. This appears to once again highlight a dilemma of today's manager of production and inventory control—he recognizes that many procedures are outdated, not producing satisfactory results, and yet he is unable to implement successfully most of the newer, scientific techniques.

Thirty percent did feel that greater management support was needed and only 43 percent felt that management recognized the importance of production and inventory control.

SUMMARY

The publication of the survey in its entirety disseminates a considerable amount of information, gathered from a large sample of American industry. One is always curious about what the "other guy" is doing and how an individual operation compares with the many. While this is the intent, it is important to draw only cautious conclusions from such comparisons. What the majority of companies may or may not be doing does not necessarily mean it is correct. Second, techniques have to be applied judiciously and certainly do not apply universally.

When used as a perspective and digested with judgment, the survey can serve as a valuable educational vehicle.

The 1966 data is a picture of the time. With the dynamic field of production and inventory management, it is not surprising to find the progress made since 1961. A survey taken in a corresponding length of time beyond 1966 will, undoubtedly, reflect even greater progress. The aspect with the greatest potential appears to be the conversion of theory into practice—the 1966 gap between the two is obviously large. The next APICS survey will be largely measuring the success of the practitioners in bridging this gap between the available scientific techniques and effective operating performance.

Index